W9-AEW-043
WITHDRAWN
L. R. COLLEGE LIBRARY

STRUCTURE OF MOLECULES

STRUCTURE OF MOLECULES AND THE CHEMICAL BOND

Written by

Y. K. SYRKIN and M. E. DYATKINA

Translated and revised by

M. A. PARTRIDGE and D. O. JORDAN

LONDON

BUTTERWORTHS SCIENTIFIC PUBLICATIONS

1950

BUTTERWORTHS PUBLICATIONS LTD
BELL YARD · TEMPLE BAR · LONDON, W.C.2

BUTTERWORTH & CO (AFRICA) LTD · DURBAN

BUTTERWORTH & CO (AUSTRALIA) LTD · SYDNEY
MELBOURNE · BRISBANE · WELLINGTON · AUCKLAND

BUTTERWORTH & CO (CANADA) LTD · TORONTO

U.S.A. edition published by
INTERSCIENCE PUBLISHERS INC.
250 FIFTH AVENUE, NEW YORK I, N.Y

First edition in English April 1950
Reprinted May 1953
Oct. 1958

Set in Monotype Baskerville type
First printed in Great Britain by Love & Malcomson Ltd., Redhill, Surrey
Reprinted in Great Britain by Lowe & Brydone (Printers) Ltd., London

PREFACE

DURING the past twenty five years our knowledge of the structure and properties of atoms and molecules has been increased considerably by the progress made in both the theoretical and experimental methods of approach to the problems involved. The introduction of wave mechanics has permitted the development of theories of atomic and molecular structure which have placed on a theoretical basis such fundamental concepts as the spatial configuration of atomic orbitals, the nature and directional characteristics of bonds between atoms in molecules and the mechanism of chemical reactions. However, calculations of bond strengths and distances and of activation energies are possible only with the simplest systems and perhaps the greatest contribution of wave mechanics to chemistry up to the present has been the introduction of ideas which, by general application to the experimental data for complex molecules, has increased considerably our understanding of the structure of such molecules and the reactions which they undergo. Therefore it is necessary that in any treatise on molecular structure, the theoretical and the experimental aspects of the problem should be considered side by side. This is what the authors have attempted in this book. In the early chapters the wave mechanics of simple atoms and molecules are discussed ; all the mathematical derivations are collected in the last three chapters of the book apart from the Heitler-London treatment of the homopolar bond, which the authors consider should be familiar to all who desire to understand the present position regarding the theory of the chemical bond and which is presented in a form such that the necessary approximations and simplifications may be appreciated readily. The later chapters are confined to a survey of the experimental data relevant to a study of molecular structure and to the theoretical conclusions which may be drawn therefrom.

The translation is based on the Russian edition published in 1946 and during the course of the translation it became evident that some revision of the original text was desirable. Such revision has been made only where it is apparent that advances in the subject, made since the publication of the original work, have extended or necessitated a modification of the views put forward by the authors. We feel that it is desirable to state which parts of the original text have been so revised. In Chapter 2, the expanded form of the periodic table has been included along with the Mendeléef form and the section on the synthesis of new elements rewritten. In Chapter 5, the section on *cyclo*-octatetrene has been rewritten. Chapter 7, dealing with molecular orbitals, has been almost entirely rewritten and we wish to acknowledge our indebtedness to the published work of Professor C. A. COULSON which was of great assistance to us. In Chapters 8 and 9, recent data collected by Dr A. G. GAYDON has been incorporated and the discussion extended or rewritten where necessary to conform with the new data. The sections on the hydrogen bond in Chapter 12 have been revised and extended. Chapter 15, on the boron hydrides, has been almost entirely rewritten and the structures proposed by Dr K. S. PITZER given in addition to those put forward by the authors. In making these modifications, which we hope will have improved the value of the book, we have always attempted to conform as far as possible with the authors' general method of treatment, as indicated in the original work. *Figure 5* was reproduced from *Physical Review* by permission of Professor H. E. WHITE and *Figure 25* was reproduced from *Quarterly Reviews* by permission of Professor C. A. COULSON and of the Council of the Chemical Society, London.

We wish to acknowledge our thanks to Mr G. STANLEY SMITH for the loan of his copy of the Russian text, to the Commonwealth Fund for a Fellowship to one of us (D. O. J.) during part of the tenure of which the translation was largely carried out and to Mr D. R. REXWORTHY and the editorial staff of Butterworths Scientific Publications for their most helpful cooperation.

November 1949

MONICA A. PARTRIDGE
University of Nottingham

D. O. JORDAN
Princeton University, N.J.
University of Nottingham

CONTENTS

PAGE

PREFACE v

1 THE HYDROGEN ATOM
- Rutherford-Bohr theory of atomic structure 1
- Matter as wave motion 3
- The wave equation 4
- The Schrödinger wave equation 6
- Solution of the wave equation for the hydrogen atom 9

2 PERIODIC CLASSIFICATION OF THE ELEMENTS
- The problem of atoms containing many electrons 16
- Pauli's exclusion principle and electron orbitals 17
- Distribution of electrons in atoms 19
- Periodicity of properties 36

3 THE HOMOPOLAR (COVALENT) BOND
- Development of ideas on the chemical bond 43
- The hydrogen molecule ion, H_2^+ 45
- The hydrogen molecule, H_2 55
- The Pauli principle 61
- Calculation of the bond energy and interatomic distance for the hydrogen molecule 65

4 SATURATION AND DIRECTION OF VALENCY BONDS
- Saturation of valencies. Localized bonds 68
- Directional covalency 72
- Hybridization of bond orbitals 74
- σ- and π- bonds 76

5 RESONANCE OF VALENCY STRUCTURES
- Benzene 81
- Conjugated systems 84
- Naphthalene 86
- Other aromatic hydrocarbons 91
- Free radicals 95

6 RESONANCE OF COVALENT AND IONIC STATES
- The ionic (heteropolar) bond 100
- Bonds of intermediate type 104
- Valency structures of the elements 107
- Alternating polarity of atoms in valence bond structures 126

PAGE

7 METHOD OF MOLECULAR ORBITALS
Molecular orbitals of diatomic molecules 129
Distribution of electrons in homonuclear diatomic molecules: 133
Distribution of electrons in heteronuclear diatomic molecules 136
The three electron bond 138
Molecular orbitals of some simple polyatomic molecules 139
Comparison of the electron pair and molecular orbital treatments 141

8 SPECTRA OF DIATOMIC MOLECULES
General characteristics of molecular spectra 143
Potential energy curves 146
Results of spectrographic measurements 149
Ortho and para hydrogen 158

9 VIBRATIONAL FREQUENCIES AND INTERATOMIC DISTANCES IN POLYATOMIC MOLECULES
Raman, Mandelstam and Landsberg effect 163
Characteristic frequencies 167
Interatomic distances 179
Covalent radii 189

10 DIPOLE MOMENTS
Dielectric polarization 193
Refraction of inorganic and organic compounds 197
Dipole moments and the ionic character of bonds 204
Dipole moments of hydrocarbon molecules 211
Dipole moments of aliphatic compounds 214
Dipole moments of aromatic compounds 219
Dipole moments and molecular structure 235

11 BOND ENERGIES
Additivity of bond energies in organic compounds 237
Deviations from the additivity rule 243
Bond energies in inorganic compounds 255

12 INTERMOLECULAR ATTRACTION
Van der Waal's forces 262
Molecular compounds involving van der Waal's forces 269
Molecular compounds involving chemical bonds 269
The hydrogen bond 273
Intramolecular hydrogen bonds 282
Internal rotation 286

13 THE CHEMICAL BOND IN CRYSTALS
Crystal structure of the elements 294
Molecular crystals 308
Coordination lattices 312
Ionic crystals 315
Interionic distances in crystals 319

		PAGE
	Halogen compounds	324
	Hydrides, oxides, hydroxides and the anions of the oxyacids	329
	Silicates	334
	Sulphides and some other compounds	339
14	COMPLEX COMPOUNDS	
	Valency states of atoms involving *d* electrons	343
	Magnetic criterion of bond type	349
	Metallic carbonyls	358
	Nitrosyl and nitro compounds	366
	Cyanides	369
	Halogen compounds	379
	Ammino compounds and salt hydrates	383
	Inner coordination compounds	389
	Conclusions	393
15	STRUCTURE OF THE BORON HYDRIDES	
	Diborane B_2H_6	395
	Higher boron hydrides	399
16	SOLUTION OF THE THREE ELECTRON PROBLEM USING SLATER'S METHOD	
	Reaction of atoms with molecules	408
	Slater's method	409
	Energy of activation	429
17	THE POLYELECTRON PROBLEM AND RESONANCE ENERGY	
	The four electron problem	434
	Evaluation of integrals of secular equation	436
	Calculation of energies for molecules of butadiene, benzene and fulvene	439
	Calculation of resonance energy by the molecular orbital method	447
	Comparison of calculated and experimental values of resonance energy	449
	Colour of chemical compounds	450
18	MATHEMATICAL APPENDIX	
	Solution of the Schrödinger equation for the hydrogen atom	452
	Directional covalency	458
	Hybrid electron functions	461
	Vibrational and rotational states	466
	The Clausius-Mosotti equation	469
	The Langevin-Debye equation	472
	Dipole moments of bonds	474
	Deformation, orientation and dispersion effects	478
	Energy states of an electron gas	482
	AUTHOR INDEX	487
	SUBJECT INDEX	491
	FORMULA INDEX	500

1

THE HYDROGEN ATOM

RUTHERFORD-BOHR THEORY OF ATOMIC STRUCTURE

THE progress in atomic physics that occurred at the end of the nineteenth and at the beginning of the twentieth centuries led to the conclusion that the atom is not an indivisible unit, but consists of a positively charged nucleus, having dimensions of the order of 10^{-12} to 10^{-13} cm, in which is concentrated the greater portion of the mass of the atom, and electrons which are particles possessing unit negative charge e, equal to $4{\cdot}779 \times 10^{-10}$ e.s.u and a mass of $9{\cdot}1 \times 10^{-28}$ gm. The atoms of the various elements differ from one another in mass, in the magnitude of the nuclear charge and, since the atom is electrically neutral, in the number of electrons. The suggestion that the positive charge on the nucleus, expressed as an integral multiple of the unit charge e, represented the atomic number was first made by VAN DEN BROEK. The importance of this suggestion was quickly realized and the first experimental evidence in its favour was given by MOSELY's investigation of the x-ray spectra of the elements ; it was directly tested by GEIGER and MARSDEN and later and more accurately, by CHADWICK, using RUTHERFORD's law for the scattering of α-particles by thin metal foils.

The nuclear theory of atomic structure, put forward by Rutherford, regarded the electrons as moving in orbits round the nucleus. The dynamical theory of this system was developed by BOHR, who found it necessary to supplement classical mechanics by the quantum mechanics of PLANCK. According to classical theory, a system consisting of an electron moving in a circular orbit round a nucleus, to which it is attracted according to Coulomb's law, would lose energy, with the result that the electron would approach and finally collide with the nucleus. Thus on the basis of classical theory, the Rutherford atom would only be stable for about 10^{-11} seconds, after which time the electron would have fallen into the nucleus.

The experimental foundation of the quantum theory of atomic structure as put forward by Bohr, lies in the stability of the atom and in the existence of discrete energy levels and the ability of the atom to absorb and emit energy only in quanta, as demonstrated by the discontinuous nature of atomic spectra and by the critical potential measurements of FRANCK and HERTZ. Bohr postulated that the atom could only exist in a limited number of orbits or stationary states, which were defined by the quantum condition that the angular momentum mvr can assume only certain limited values which are given by the expression

$$mvr = nh/2\pi \qquad \ldots.(1.1)$$

where m is the mass and v the angular velocity of the electron, r is the radius of the orbit, h is Planck's constant equal to $6{\cdot}6 \times 10^{-27}$ erg sec and n is a positive integer. The rotation of the electron in the closed orbits does not involve the loss of energy and for these selected orbits, to account for the stability of the atom, the inward coulombic attractive force is equated to the outward centrifugal force

$$e^2/r^2 = mv^2/r \qquad \ldots.(1.2)$$

From equations 1.1 and 1.2 we have the following expression for the radius of the permitted orbits

$$r = n^2h^2/4\pi^2e^2m \qquad \ldots.(1.3)$$

Thus r is proportional to n^2 and the radius a of the first orbit, $n = 1$, is given by

$$a = h^2/4\pi^2e^2m = 0{\cdot}528 \times 10^{-8}\ cm \qquad \ldots.(1{\cdot}4)$$

The radius of the second orbit, $n = 2$ will be $4a$, the radius of the third orbit, $n = 3$ will be $9a$ *etc.*

The potential energy V of the system is the work done in bringing the electron from infinity to a distance r from the nucleus, thus

$$V = \int_{\infty}^{r} \frac{e^2}{r^2}\, dr = -\frac{e^2}{r} \qquad \ldots.(1{\cdot}5)$$

The kinetic energy T of the atom will be

$$T = mv^2/2 \qquad \ldots.(1.6)$$

which in combination with equation 1.2 gives

$$T = e^2/2r \qquad \ldots.(1.7)$$

Thus the total energy of the atom is given by

$$E = V + T = -e^2/2r = -2\pi^2e^4m/n^2h^2 \qquad \ldots.(1.8)$$

On passing from an outer orbit with energy E_2 to an inner orbit with energy E_1 an electron will emit a quantum of radiation with energy

$$E_2 - E_1 = h\nu = 2\pi^2e^4m\ (1/n_1^2 - 1/n_2^2)/h^2 \qquad \ldots.(1.9)$$

where ν is the frequency of the emitted radiation. We may therefore write

$$1/\lambda = \bar{\nu} = R_H\ (1/n_1^2 - 1/n_2^2) \qquad \ldots.(1.10)$$

where $R_H = 2\pi^2e^4m/h^3c$ and is known as the Rydberg constant, c is the velocity and λ the wavelength of light, and ν is termed the wave number.

The success of the Bohr theory lay in the fact that formulae 1.9 and 1.10 were in excellent agreement with experimental data. Thus, for example, the theoretical value of the Rydberg constant is 109677·76 cm^{-1}, compared with the experimental value of 109678·18 cm^{-1}.

The application of the quantum theory to the hydrogen atom leads to the introduction of the quantum number n, on the value of which the energy of the atom depends. The treatment of Bohr was developed by SOMMERFELD to account for the fine structure of the lines in the spectrum of hydrogen and other elements. As a result of this treatment, the electrons were considered to be rotating in elliptical as well as circular orbits, which could be oriented with respect to each other in a magnetic field. In place of the single quantum number used in the Bohr treatment, the atom was defined in terms of three quantum numbers, n, l and m, where n is now termed the principal quantum number, l the azimuthal quantum number which determines the value of the angular momentum, and m defines the orientation of the orbit relative to the direction of a magnetic field.

The theory of Bohr and Sommerfeld has been applied extensively to atomic spectra with considerable success, but it has proved of little use when applied to molecules and the problem of the chemical bond ; attempts by PAULI[1] and NIESSEN[2] to apply the theory to the simplest molecular system *i.e.* the hydrogen molecule ion were unsuccessful. This stable molecule, which has a bond energy of 61 kcal/gm mol, was shown on the basis of the Bohr-Sommerfeld theory to be unstable. More recently, defects have become apparent in the application of this theory to atomic spectra.

The weakness of the Bohr treatment lies in the attempt to combine quantum and classical theories and in particular in the attempt to apply the laws obeyed by macroparticles to the very small particles that occur in atoms. Instead the quantum condition of discrete energy levels should be derived directly from a general theory ; such a theory has been produced on the basis of wave and quantum mechanics through the work of DE BROGLIE, SCHRÖDINGER, HEISENBERG and DIRAC.

MATTER AS WAVE MOTION

The development of wave mechanics has been made possible through the introduction by de Broglie of a new principle dealing with the wave character of matter. The basis of this principle is the recognition that different interpretations are appropriate to different kinds of measurements ; thus atoms and electrons which have hitherto been regarded as discrete particles are considered to possess a dual character, in the sense that they may possess both corpuscular and wave properties. A duality of a similar kind had been revealed earlier in studies on the propagation of light.

The theory of the propagation of light has passed through several stages during its development. Newton first conceived light as consisting of a collection of corpuscles obeying the laws of mechanics, but studies of such phenomena as reflection, dispersion, refraction, interference and diffraction led to rejection of this theory in favour of the electromagnetic wave theory of light. This concept assumes that radiation consists of a wave motion with electric and magnetic vectors at right angles to each other and to the direction of the wave, and that matter contains particles which are electrical in character and in which electrical dipoles are produced by the passage of the wave. Other phenomena, however, which were first investigated at the beginning of the twentieth century and which were associated with the absorption and emission of light by matter, were found to be incompatible with a wave theory. Examples of such phenomena are the photoelectric and Compton effects which can be explained only by assuming that radiation consists of a stream of particles or light quanta, photons, the energy of each quantum being $h\nu$ where h is Planck's constant and ν is the frequency of the radiation.

A survey of all the available experimental data thus shows that some phenomena, such as diffraction and interference, can only be explained on the basis of the electromagnetic wave theory, whereas other phenomena, the most important being the photoelectric effect, require a corpuscular theory of light. Although this duality was recognized for phenomena associated with the propagation and absorption of light, it was not until de Broglie put forward his views, that electrons and other atomic particles, the corpuscular nature of which was supported by a considerable amount of physical and chemical experimental evidence, were considered also to possess wave properties.

De Broglie suggested that with every moving particle there is associated a wave motion of wavelength λ, which is related to the mass m and velocity v of the particle by the relation

$$\lambda = h/mv \qquad \ldots .(1.11)$$

Experimental evidence was obtained by DAVISSON and GERMER in 1927 and later by THOMSON which supported the de Broglie relationship. These authors showed that crystals diffracted a beam of electrons in exactly the

Table I. Comparison of Values for Interatomic Distances

Substance	Interatomic distance A	
	X-ray diffraction	*Electron diffraction*
Aluminium	4·063	4·035
Gold	4·06	3·99–4·20
Platinum	3·91	3·89
Lead	4·92	4·99
Iron	2·87	2·85
Silver	4·08	4·11
Copper	3·60	3·66
Tin	2·86	2·86

same way as a beam of x-rays is diffracted and, furthermore, that a comparison of lattice distances, calculated from electron diffraction data assuming equation 1.11 with values obtained by x-ray diffraction, showed excellent agreement (*Table I*). These data clearly indicate the wave character of electrons as well as confirm the correctness of the de Broglie relationship. More recent experiments by ESTERMAN and STERN have shown that this relationship also applies to the diffraction of α-particles (helium ions, He^{++}) the mass of which is 7,360 times that of the electron. Thus it would appear that the de Broglie relationship is applicable to all particles, but it is seen in *Table II* that the wavelengths for particles with large masses are extremely small and for a particle of mass 1 gm the de Broglie wavelength is $6{\cdot}6 \times 10^{-27}$ cm which would require for its experimental determination a diffraction grating with rulings 10^{-27} cm apart, whereas in crystals the distance between the atoms is of the order of 10^{-8} cm. It is thus evident that the wave properties of large particles are never observed. It is therefore necessary to formulate a mechanics of particles in such a way as to conform with the wave properties of atomic particles and at the same time to be applicable to large particles, being converted into classical mechanics in the process.

Table II. Wavelengths Associated with Various Particles Calculated from the de Broglie Equation

Particle	*Mass gm*	*Velocity cm/sec*	*de Broglie wavelength cm*
Slow electron	9×10^{-28}	1	7·27
Slow electron	9×10^{-28}	100	0·0727
Electron accelerated by potential of 1 volt	9×10^{-28}	$5{\cdot}94 \times 10^{7}$	$1{\cdot}22 \times 10^{-7}$
Electron accelerated by potential of 100 volt	9×10^{-28}	$5{\cdot}94 \times 10^{8}$	$1{\cdot}22 \times 10^{-8}$
α-Particle accelerated by potential of 100 volt	$6{\cdot}6 \times 10^{-24}$	$6{\cdot}94 \times 10^{6}$	$1{\cdot}43 \times 10^{-10}$
α-Particle from radium	$6{\cdot}6 \times 10^{-24}$	$1{\cdot}51 \times 10^{9}$	$6{\cdot}56 \times 10^{-13}$
Particle of 1 gm moving at velocity 1 cm/sec	1	1	$6{\cdot}6 \times 10^{-27}$
Tennis ball	46	2,500	$5{\cdot}71 \times 10^{-32}$

THE WAVE EQUATION

The idea of a wave may be illustrated by considering a stretched string or the surface of a liquid : if any part of the string is displaced, then a wave is propagated along the string and the string vibrates ; similarly if a stone is dropped into water, water waves will travel outwards radially from the centre of the disturbance. All wave motions have two important properties in common : the disturbance travels through the medium without giving to the medium as a whole any permanent displacement, and energy is transferred from one point to another. Thus if at a given point there is a fluctuating particle, then this fluctuation is passed on from one particle to another, so producing the wave.

In order to study the laws of wave propagation it is necessary to consider not only the disturbing force, but also the restoring force which tends to return the oscillator to its original position. The simplest kind of wave is that in which the restoring force is directly proportional to the displacement,

$$F = -k\psi \qquad \ldots.(1.12)$$

and is termed the harmonic wave. In equation 1.12, ψ is the displacement and k the proportionality constant which is numerically equal to $-F$ for unit displacement. The negative sign indicates that the restoring force opposes the displacing force.

According to Newton's laws of motion

$$md^2\psi/dt^2 = F \qquad \ldots.(1.13)$$

where m is the mass of the particle being displaced. It follows from equations 1.12 and 1.13 that

$$md^2\psi/dt^2 = -k\psi \qquad \ldots.(1.14)$$

In a harmonic wave the wave profile is a sine or cosine curve, thus we may write

$$\psi = a \sin \omega t \qquad \ldots.(1.15)$$

where ω is the angular velocity, t is the time and a is a constant. From equation 1.15 we obtain

$$d\psi/dt = a\omega \cos \omega t \qquad \ldots.(1.16)$$

and

$$d^2\psi/dt^2 = -a\omega^2 \sin \omega t \qquad \ldots.(1.17)$$

From relationships 1.14, 1.15 and 1.17 it follows that

$$md^2\psi/dt^2 = -ma\omega^2 \sin \omega t = -k\psi = -ka \sin \omega t \qquad \ldots.(1.18)$$

and hence

$$\omega = (k/m)^{\frac{1}{2}} \qquad \ldots.(1.19)$$

When equation 1.19 is substituted in formula 1.15 the expression obtained

$$\psi = a \sin (k/m)^{\frac{1}{2}}\, t \qquad \ldots.(1.20)$$

must satisfy the condition for harmonic motion.

In a similar manner we have the solution for the cosine curve that

$$\psi = b \cos \omega t \qquad \ldots.(1.21)$$

The linear combination of the solutions 1.15 and 1.21 given above will also be a solution of equation 1.14. This is an example of the principle of superposition, which states that when all the relevant equations are linear we may superpose any number of individual solutions to form new functions which are themselves also solutions. The use of this principle is fundamental in the wave mechanical treatment of molecules and it will be discussed later. The linear combination here is

$$\psi = a \sin \omega t + b \cos \omega t \qquad \ldots.(1.22)$$

which, on differentiation with respect to t, gives

$$d^2\psi/dt^2 = -\omega^2 (a \sin \omega t + b \cos \omega t)$$

Substitution for ω from equation 1.19 and combining with 1.22 gives

$$md^2\psi/dt^2 = -k\psi \qquad \ldots.(1.14)$$

This solution may be written in the alternative form $\psi = A \exp (i\omega t)$ or $\psi = B \exp (-i\omega t)$ or in the general form

$$\psi = A \exp (i\omega t) + B \exp (-i\omega t) \qquad \ldots.(1.23)$$

That this is so may be shown by following the same steps as employed in the solution of equation 1.15. The introduction of this form of solution, involving the unit of imaginaries $i = \sqrt{-1}$, is in certain circumstances more convenient.

In a general harmonic wave the displacement ψ is not necessarily zero when $t = 0$, as indicated by equations 1.15 and 1.21. Thus the general solution will be

$$\psi = a \cos (\omega t - \phi) \qquad \ldots .(1.24)$$

where ϕ is a constant. When $t = \phi/\omega$, $\cos (\omega t - \phi)$ will be unity and ψ will have a maximum value equal to a. This maximum value of the displacement is termed the amplitude. Since ω is the angular velocity, the frequency ν will be given by $\nu = \omega/2\pi$. The reciprocal of the frequency, $\Gamma = 1/v$ is termed the period of the wave. If the velocity of propagation of the wave is c, then a point situated a distance $\lambda = c\,\Gamma$ from the initial displacement will vibrate in the same phase. The distance λ is termed the wavelength.

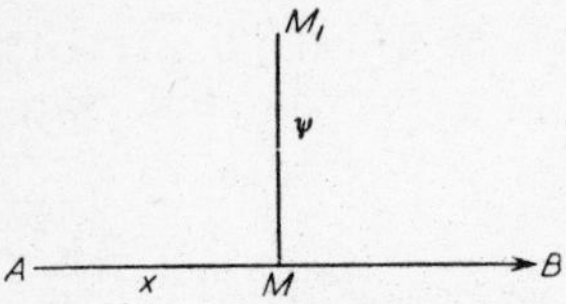

Figure 1. *Propagation of a wave*

In order to obtain the equation of wave motion let us consider a lateral vibration with amplitude a which is transmitted from A in the direction B (*Figure 1*). A point M, situated a distance x from A, will after a period of time t, be at M_1. The distance $MM_1 = \psi$. If the time taken for the wave to travel from A to M is τ, then the time of oscillation of the point M is $t - \tau$ and the equation for the wave becomes

$$\psi = a \sin 2\pi\nu\,(t - \tau) \qquad \ldots .(1.25)$$

but $\tau = x/c$, hence

$$\psi = a \sin 2\pi\,(\nu t - \nu x/c) = a \sin 2\pi\,(\nu t - x/\lambda) \qquad \ldots .(1.26)$$

which on differentiation gives

$$\partial^2\psi/\partial x^2 = -\,4\pi^2\psi/\lambda^2\,,\ \partial^2\psi/\partial t^2 = -\,4\pi^2\nu^2\psi \qquad \ldots .(1.27)$$

and

$$\partial^2\psi/\partial x^2 = (1/c^2)\,\partial^2\psi/\partial t^2 \qquad \ldots .(1.28)$$

It is possible to generalize equations 1.27 and 1.28 to deal with plane waves in three dimensions. We then obtain

$$\frac{\partial^2\psi}{\partial x^2} + \frac{\partial^2\psi}{\partial y^2} + \frac{\partial^2\psi}{\partial z^2} = \nabla^2\psi = \frac{1}{c^2}\,\frac{\partial^2\psi}{\partial t^2} \qquad \ldots .(1.29)$$

and

$$\frac{\partial^2\psi}{\partial x^2} + \frac{\partial^2\psi}{\partial y^2} + \frac{\partial^2\psi}{\partial z^2} = \nabla^2\psi = -\,\frac{4\pi^2}{\lambda^2}\psi \qquad \ldots .(1.30)$$

This is the equation of wave motion. ∇^2 (read as ' del squared ') is the Laplacian operator and represents

$$\frac{\partial^2}{\partial x^2} + \frac{\partial^2}{\partial y^2} + \frac{\partial^2}{\partial z^2}$$

THE SCHRÖDINGER WAVE EQUATION

The wave mechanical treatment of atoms may be carried out in various ways, differing in mathematical complexity, but leading to the same general conclusions. We shall employ the methods of Schrödinger, not because they are superior to the treatments of Heisenberg and Dirac, but because of their relative mathematical simplicity.

The basis of wave mechanics is the wave equation of Schrödinger which can be obtained by the combination of the de Broglie relationship

$$\lambda = h/mv \qquad \ldots .(1.11)$$

with the equation of wave motion 1.30. The velocity v in equation 1.11 is first expressed in terms of the total energy E and the potential energy V Thus the kinetic energy is given by

$$T = E - V = mv^2/2 \qquad \ldots.(1.31)$$

whence it follows that

$$v = \sqrt{\frac{2}{m}(E - V)} \qquad \ldots.(1.32)$$

which on substitution in relationship 1.11 gives

$$\lambda = \frac{h}{\sqrt{2m(E - V)}} \qquad \ldots.(1.33)$$

Substitution of this expression for λ in the equation of wave motion 1.30 then gives the Schrödinger wave equation

$$\frac{\partial^2\psi}{\partial x^2} + \frac{\partial^2\psi}{\partial y^2} + \frac{\partial^2\psi}{\partial z^2} + \frac{8\pi^2 m}{h^2}(E - V)\psi = 0 \qquad \ldots.(1.34)$$

The steps leading to equation 1.34 must not be regarded as a rigorous derivation of the Schrödinger equation, since we have employed an equation of classical mechanics to obtain a wave mechanical expression from which the quantum condition of discrete energy levels may be devised.

In the equation of wave motion 1.30 the quantity ψ referred to the amplitude of a wave ; no such simple idea can be attached to ψ in the Schrödinger wave equation 1.34, however, and before proceeding further we must consider the physical significance of this quantity. The wave equation may be applied to the hydrogen atom by substituting the approximate value of the potential energy V in equation 1.34 ; the hydrogen atom consists of one electron with a charge $-e$, rotating about a proton with a charge $+e$ and thus the potential energy of the system is given by $V = -e^2/r$ where r is the distance between the electron and the proton. The Schrödinger equation for hydrogen is therefore

$$\nabla^2\psi + \frac{8\pi^2 m}{h^2}\left(E + \frac{e^2}{r}\right)\psi = 0 \qquad \ldots.(1.35)$$

The solution of this equation gives ψ as a function of r. Thus, in general, ψ will be a function of the coordinates of the space in which the electron moves, but we still cannot assign any particular physical significance to ψ. However, an analogy is found in optics where the intensity of a beam of light, which may be defined as the number of photons crossing unit area in unit time, is proportional to the square of the electric vector. In a similar way we may regard ψ^2 as a measure of the intensity of the electron wave or alternatively we may regard $\psi^2 d\tau$, where $d\tau$ is the element of volume $dxdydz$, as indicating the probability that the electron will be situated in the element of volume $d\tau$, *i.e.* that the coordinates of the electron lie between x and $x + dx$, y and $y + dy$ and z and $z + dz$. It would be more correct to write $\psi\psi^*$ or $|\psi^2|$ in place of ψ^2, where ψ^* represents the complex conjugate of ψ. This is due to the fact that ψ may be partly imaginary. Thus, if we have $\psi = a + ib$ where $i = \sqrt{-1}$, then ψ^* is $a - ib$. The product $\psi\psi^* = (a + ib)(a - ib) = a^2 + b^2$ is real. On the other hand, $\psi^2 = (a + ib) = a^2 + 2iab - b^2$ is still imaginary because of the term $2iab$. In the treatment given here we shall confine ourselves to instances where ψ is real, and $\psi\psi^* = \psi^2$.

This interpretation of ψ gives a different picture of the electron rotating about the nucleus compared with that of the Bohr theory. The electron is clearly not localized and may be found in any element of volume around the nucleus according to the varying probability of the different positions. If the probability of finding the electron in a certain position in space is one in ten, then in its motion about the nucleus the electron will exist in that position for one tenth of a given period of time ; for the remaining nine tenths of the time it will be found in other positions. We may alternatively consider the electron as ‘ smeared ’ over the whole of space in an uninterrupted cloud. Then if the probability of locating the electron in a given element of volume is one in ten this indicates that there is present in this volume one tenth of the electron cloud and therefore one tenth of the total electronic charge. Thus the charge is proportional to the density of the electron cloud at any particular point.

It is possible to show that the attempt to localize the electron, as in the orbit of the Bohr theory, encounters insurmountable difficulties. In order to locate the electron orbit it is essential that at least two points on the path of the electron be fixed, thus it may be considered necessary to ‘ illuminate ’ the atom with light, which will have a wavelength of the same order of magnitude as the dimension of the orbit *i.e.* 10^{-8} cm. Taking the velocity of light as 3×10^{10} cm sec^{-1}, the energy of one quantum is $E = Nh\nu =$ 285,000 kcal/gm atom. The ionization potential of hydrogen, however, is only 312 kcal/gm atom and hence, on illumination, the atom receives 913 times as much energy as is necessary to produce ionization and therefore instead of ‘ seeing ’ the electron and locating its position the electron is expelled from the atom.

This illustration may be regarded as an example of Heisenberg’s Uncertainty Principle, which can be stated in the following form : ‘ The more accurately the velocity of an electron is defined, the less certainly is its position known and, conversely, the more accurate the definition of the position of an electron, the less precise is the value of its velocity ’. Expressed mathematically this becomes

$$\Delta v \geqslant k/\Delta x \qquad \ldots.(1.36)$$

in which the velocity has a value between v and $v + \Delta v$, and the position of the electron is between x and $x + \Delta x$. The proportionality constant k is found to be equal to h/m and hence

$$\Delta x \Delta v \geqslant h/m \qquad \ldots.(1.37)$$

This principle enables us to make an appreciation of the relationship which exists between wave mechanics and classical mechanics. The right hand side of equation 1.37 is inversely proportional to m and hence for a very heavy particle h/m is very small, which makes it possible for the product $\Delta x \Delta v$ also to be very small. Under such circumstances it is therefore possible that both Δx and Δv may be small and hence both the velocity and the position of the particle may be known with certainty. This applies in classical mechanics. When, however, m is very small as for atomic particles, h/m is large and thus either Δx or Δv but not both may be small and hence the position and the velocity cannot at the same time both be known with certainty. This is true for the mechanics of very small particles *i.e.* wave mechanics.

The physical interpretation of ψ^2 given above carries with it the important restriction that the summation of the probabilities of finding the electron at a particular point over the whole of space must be unity. Although ψ^2 is only proportional to the probability of locating the electron in a particular position it can be made the absolute probability in the following manner. For any solution ψ of the wave equation we may obtain other solutions by multiplying ψ by a constant c. Thus $c\psi$ is a solution, if ψ is a solution. This constant may now be fixed in order to make ψ^2 the absolute probability. The total probability of finding the electron somewhere in space will then be unity *i.e.*

$$\iiint \psi_{(x,y,z)} \psi_{(x,y,z)} \, dxdydz = \int \psi^2 d\tau = 1 \qquad \ldots.(1.38)$$

This process is termed normalization to unity.

The Schrödinger equation is of such a form that the solutions ψ have significance only for certain values of E, a result which is analogous to that obtained with the equation for the vibration of a stretched string where only those vibrations are possible which have a whole number of semi-waves placed along the string. Thus the wavelength is fixed by the relationship $\lambda/2 = L/n$ where λ is the wavelength, L the length of the string and $n = 1, 2, 3$ *etc.* In the Schrödinger equation, for each value of E there occur one or more values of ψ which are the solutions of the equation and as with the stretched string, it is found that these values of E are integral multiples of the lowest value. Thus the quantum nature of energy which was assumed in the Bohr theory appears in wave mechanics as the natural result of the solution of a mathematical problem. Schrödinger appreciated this advantage of wave mechanics over Bohr's quantum mechanics and has stated[3]

> In this respect I wish to point out, first for the simplest case of the hydrogen atom, that the usual rules of quantum mechanics may be replaced by another postulate in which there is no mention of whole numbers. The introduction of quantisation then follows naturally as, for instance, in the solution of the problem of a vibrating string when the number of nodes must be a whole number. The new conception may be generalised and touches I believe, very deeply, the true nature of quantum laws.

SOLUTION OF THE WAVE EQUATION FOR THE HYDROGEN ATOM

The solution of the Schrödinger equation for the hydrogen atom given in Chapter 18 leads to the conclusion that the energy of the atom may only have certain values which are given by an expression identical with that derived by the methods of Bohr. The theoretical calculation of the Rydberg constant follows in exactly the same way as in the Bohr treatment. The various values of E obtained from these solutions give the possible energy levels (*eigen* values) corresponding to the various permitted states of the atom. For each state there exists also the appropriate wave function (*eigen* function) describing the behaviour of the electron in the atom. With a knowledge of these functions it is possible to determine the probability of finding the electron at different points in space and thus to imagine the existence of an electron cloud around the nucleus corresponding to the most probable positions of the electron for a particular atomic state. When the atom possesses the minimum possible energy it is in its ground state; higher values of the energy correspond to the possible excited states of the atom.

The Schrödinger equation shows that the state of the electron in the hydrogen atom is expressed in terms of three quantum numbers *n*, *l*, and *m* which correspond to the three degrees of freedom of movement in space. The quantum number *n*, termed the principal quantum number, may have any positive integral value which determines the energy of the electron. For a given value of *n*, the azimuthal quantum number *l* may have any integral value between *o* and $n - 1$. For a given value of *l* the third quantum number, the magnetic quantum number *m* may have any integral value from $+ l$ to $- l$, *i.e.* $+ l, + l - 1, + l - 2, \ldots\ldots + 2, + 1, 0, - 1, - 2, \ldots\ldots, - l$; the total number of such values being $2l + 1$.

In wave mechanics the quantum numbers *n*, *l* and *m*, are obtained directly from the theory. In the Bohr treatment, on the other hand, the value of *l* was associated with the magnitude of the minor axis of the elliptical orbit, and hence the lowest possible value of *l* was 1, since when *l* is zero the ellipse degenerates into a straight line and the electron during its motion would pass through the nucleus. Before the introduction of wave mechanics and the theoretical proof that *l* may have the value zero, it had been necessary to modify the Bohr theory, by putting $l = 0$ in order to conform with spectroscopic evidence.

The physical interpretation of the quantum numbers *n*, *l* and *m*, whereby they are connected with the axes of the elliptical orbits and their orientation in space, is now no longer tenable and it is only possible to say that the principal quantum number *n* is related according to equation 1.8 with the total energy of the atom in a particular state, and the quantum numbers *l* and *m* are related to the angular momentum. The angular momentum is given by $\{ l (l + 1) \}^{\frac{1}{2}} h/2\pi$ and its component in the direction of the *z* axis by $mh/2\pi$; these expressions correspond to $lh/2\pi$ and $mh/2\pi$ respectively, given by the Bohr theory.

When $n = 1$ we have shown above that *l* can only have the value zero. If $n = 2$ then *l* may have two values, either zero or 1. The electronic states for which $l = 0$ are termed *s* states whatever the value of *n*, and for $l = 1$ they are termed *p* states. When $l = 0$, *m* may only have the value zero; but when $l = 1$, *m* may have one of three values: $+ 1, 0, - 1$. It thus transpires that for the value $n = 2$ there exist one *s* state and three *p* states. When the principal quantum number $n = 3$, the possible states are as follows: one with $l = 0$ (*s* state), three with $l = 1$ (*p* states, *m* having the values $+ 1, 0, - 1$) and five when $l = 2$ (corresponding to the values of m: $+ 2, + 1, 0, - 1, - 2$ and termed the *d* states). We thus have nine states for the value of $n = 3$.

When $n = 4$, in addition to the above states for $l = 0$, 1 and 2, there are seven states when $l = 3$ (corresponding to the values of m: $+ 3, + 2, + 1, 0, - 1, - 2, - 3$) termed *f* states.

From the above examples it is clear that it is a simple matter to determine the total number of possible electronic states for any value of *n*, there being *n* values of *l* and $(2l + 1)$

Table III. Electronic States of the Hydrogen Atom

n	*l*	*m*
1	0	0
2	0	0
	1	+ 1, 0, − 1
3	0	0
	1	+ 1, 0, − 1
	2	+ 2, + 1, 0, − 1, − 2
4	0	0
	1	+ 1, 0, − 1
	2	+ 2, + 1, 0, − 1, − 2
	3	+ 3, + 2, + 1, 0, − 1, − 2, − 3

values of m for each value of l. *Table III* shows the states of the hydrogen atom between $n = 1$ and $n = 4$. These may be expressed in the form

$$\sum_{l=0}^{l=n-1} (2l + 1) = n^2 \qquad \ldots.(1.39)$$

It will be shown in Chapter 2, when the building up of the periodic system of the elements is discussed, that the quantity n^2 is of great importance.

As already pointed out, the energy of the hydrogen atom in any

Table IV. Complete Wave Functions of the Hydrogen Atom

n	l	m	*State*	*Wave function*
1	0	0	1s	$\psi_{100} = \frac{1}{\sqrt{\pi a^3}} e^{-\frac{r}{a}}$
2	0	0	2s	$\psi_{200} = \frac{1}{4\sqrt{2\pi a^3}} \left(2 - \frac{r}{a}\right) e^{-\frac{\ }{2a}}$
2	1	0	2p	$\psi_{210} = \frac{1}{4\sqrt{2\pi a^3}} \frac{r}{a} e^{-\frac{r}{2a}} \cos\theta$
2	1	±1	2p	$\psi_{211} = \frac{1}{4\sqrt{2\pi a^3}} \frac{r}{a} e^{-\frac{r}{2a}} \sin\theta\cos\phi$ $\psi_{211} = \frac{1}{4\sqrt{2\pi a^3}} \frac{r}{a} e^{-\frac{r}{2a}} \sin\theta\sin\phi$
3	0	0	3s	$\psi_{300} = \frac{1}{81\sqrt{3\pi a^3}} \left(27 - 18\frac{r}{a} + 2\frac{r^2}{a^2}\right) e^{-}$
3	1	0	3p	$\psi_{310} = \frac{\sqrt{2}}{81\sqrt{\pi a^3}} \left(6 - \frac{r}{a}\right) \frac{r}{a} e^{-\frac{r}{3a}} \cos\theta$
3	1	±1	3p	$\psi_{311} = \frac{\sqrt{2}}{81\sqrt{\pi a^3}} \left(6 - \frac{r}{a}\right) \frac{r}{a} e^{-\frac{r}{3a}} \sin\theta\cos\phi$ $\psi_{311} = \frac{\sqrt{2}}{81\sqrt{\pi a^3}} \left(6 - \frac{r}{a}\right) \frac{r}{a} e^{-\frac{r}{3a}} \sin\theta\sin\phi$
3	2	0	3d	$\psi_{320} = \frac{1}{81\sqrt{6\pi a^3}} \frac{r^2}{a^2} e^{-\frac{r}{3a}} (3\cos^2\theta - 1)$
3	2	±1	3d	$\psi_{321} = \frac{\sqrt{2}}{81\sqrt{\pi a^3}} \frac{r^2}{a^2} e^{-\frac{r}{3a}} \sin\theta\cos\theta\cos\phi$ $\psi_{321} = \frac{\sqrt{2}}{81\sqrt{\pi a^3}} \frac{r^2}{a^2} e^{-\frac{r}{3a}} \sin\theta\cos\theta\sin\phi$
3	2	±2	3d	$\psi_{322} = \frac{1}{81\sqrt{2\pi a^3}} \frac{r^2}{a^2} e^{-\frac{r}{3a}} \sin^2\theta\cos^2\phi$ $\psi_{322} = \frac{1}{81\sqrt{2\pi a^3}} \frac{r^2}{a^2} e^{-\frac{r}{3a}} \sin^2\theta\sin^2\phi$

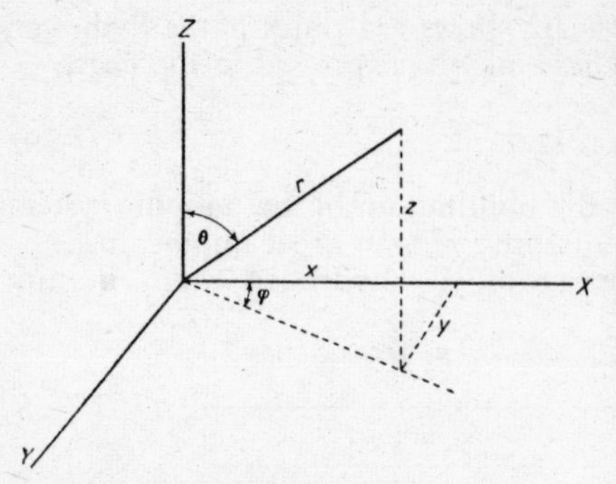

Figure 2. Relationship between spherical coordinates r, θ and φ and Cartesian co-ordinates, x, y and z

particular electronic state depends only on the value of the principal quantum number n and not on l and m. When $n = 2$ there are four possible states, one for $l = 0$ and three for $l = 1$ (see *Table III* and equation 1.39); the energies of these four states are all equal although their wave functions differ. Such an instance where several different states, each corresponding to a solution of the Schrödinger equation, exist for the same energy value, is an example o degeneracy. Thus the state of the hydrogen atom when $n = 2$ is four-fold degenerate. The idea of degeneracy plays an important part in wave mechanics particularly in the application to the chemical bond.

The solutions of the Schrödinger equation for the first three energy levels of the hydrogen atom are given in *Table IV*. The wave functions are expressed in terms of the spherical coordinates, r, the distance of the electron from the nucleus and the angles θ and ϕ. The relationship between spherical and Cartesian coordinates is seen in *Figure 2*.

For the ground state of the hydrogen atom, $n = 1$, $l = 0$, the function ψ is dependent only on the distance r from the nucleus and not on the angles θ and ϕ; the function ψ_{100} is given in *Figure 3* (upper curve) as a function of r. It follows therefore since the probability of locating the electron in a spherical shell between r and $r + dr$ will be

$$D(r)dr = \psi^2_{100} \times 4\pi r^2 dr = (4r^2/a^3) \exp(-2r/a).\,dr \quad \ldots.(1.40)$$

that the atom of hydrogen is spherically symmetrical and that the probability of finding the electron at any particular distance from the nucleus is the same regardless of the direction chosen.

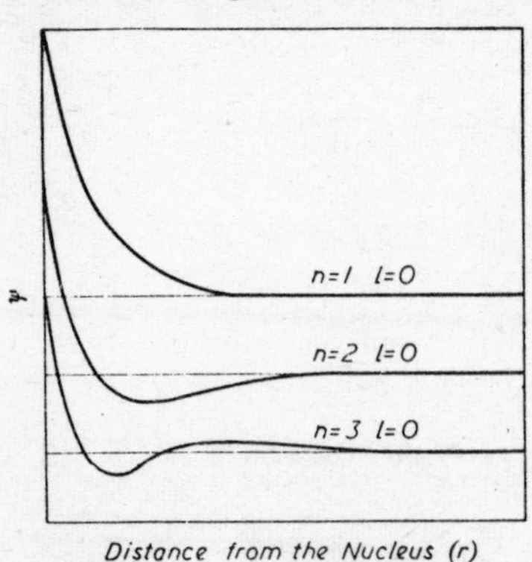

Figure 3. Variation of the functions ψ_{100}, ψ_{200}, and ψ_{300} with r

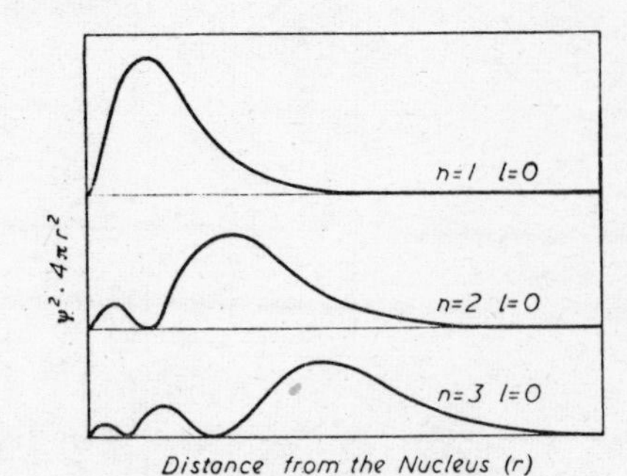

Figure 4. Radial distribution function (D) for the 1s, 2s and 3s states of the hydrogen atom

If we plot the function $D(r) = \psi^2_{100} \times 4\pi r^2$ against r (*Figure 4*, upper curve) we see that the probability of finding the electron at a distance r

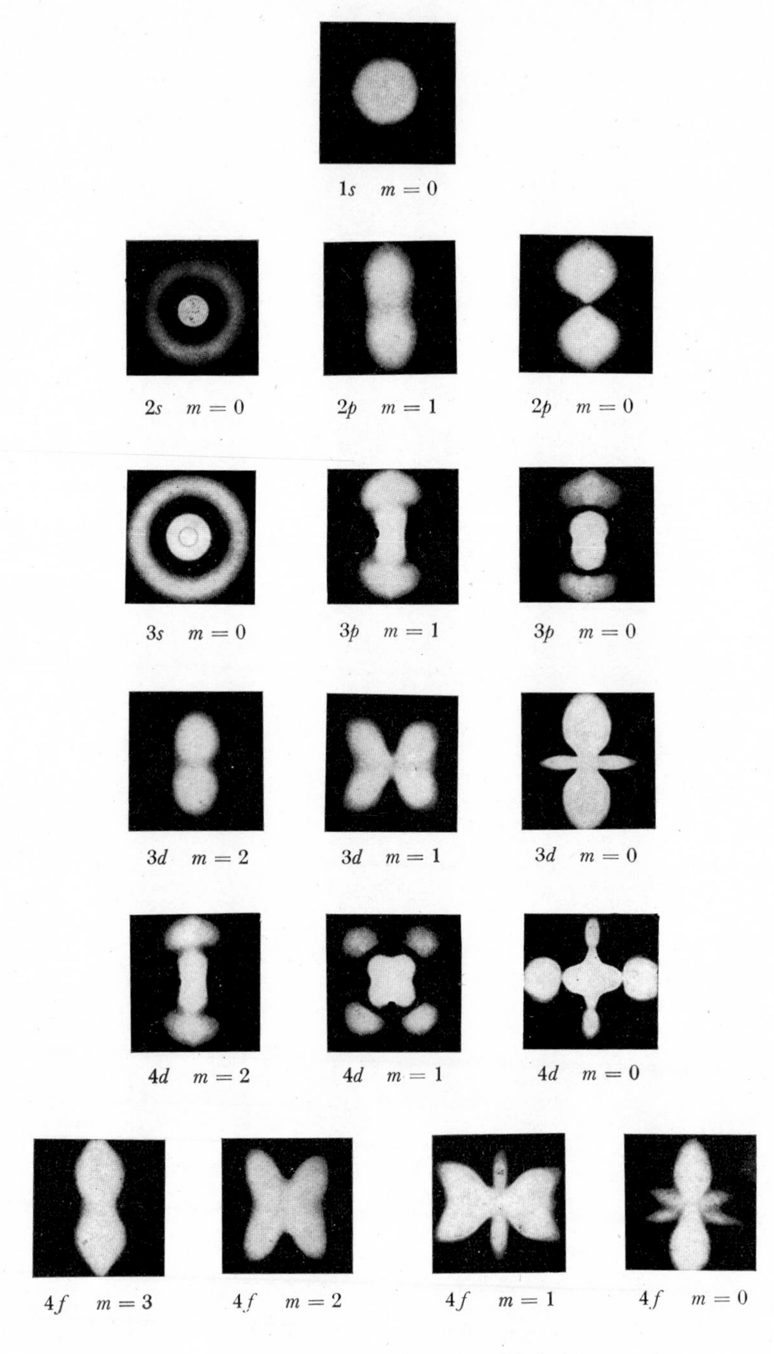

Figure 5. Electron cloud for various states of the hydrogen atom[4]

from the nucleus is small at small distances, due to the factor r^2, and also at very large distances, due to the exponential term, and that there is a maximum value at intermediate distances. The value of r at this maximum value of $D(r)$ represents the most probable distance of the electron from the nucleus and may be obtained by differentiating equation 1.40 and equating to zero. Whence

$$\frac{dD(r)}{dr} = \frac{8}{a^3} r \exp\left(-\frac{2r}{a}\right) - \frac{8}{a^4} r^2 \exp\left(-\frac{2r}{a}\right) = 0 \quad \ldots.(1.41)$$

which reduces to

$$r = a \quad \ldots.(1.42)$$

It may also be shown (Chapter 18) that

$$a = h^2/4\pi^2 me^2 = 0{\cdot}528 \text{ Å} \quad \ldots.(1.43)$$

Thus the maximum density of the electron cloud is found to occur at a distance from the nucleus exactly equal to the normal Bohr orbit (see equation 1.4).

In spite of this agreement between the Bohr theory and the wave mechanical treatment as to the magnitude of the electron orbit in the ground state of the hydrogen atom, it is important to appreciate the very great differences which exist between the two theories. In the Bohr theory the electron may be found only at a fixed distance, *i.e.* 0·528 Å, from the nucleus ; in the wave mechanical treatment on the other hand the electron may exist at any distance from the nucleus but the most probable position is at 0·528 Å. Thus the hydrogen atom in its ground state may be regarded as a nucleus surrounded by a continuous electronic cloud having the form of a sphere (*Figure 5*) the probability of finding the electron in a certain spherical layer increasing with the distance from the nucleus up to 0·528 Å and then decreasing. At 1 Å the density of the electron cloud is very small.

For the excited states of the atom of hydrogen, different types of electron clouds occur. When $n = 2$, l may be 0 or 1. If the first, when $n = 2$, $l = 0$, $m = 0$ *i.e.* in the 2*s* state, the function ψ_{200} again depends only on the value of r (*Table IV*) and the electron cloud possesses spherical symmetry. The plot of function ψ_{200} against r is, however, very different from that of ψ_{100} (*Figure 3*) in that the value of ψ_{200} becomes zero at a finite value of r as well as when r is zero and infinity, whereas ψ_{100} is zero only when r is zero or infinity. This behaviour is reflected in the plot of the probability function $D(r)$ against r (*Figure 4*) since, when $\psi = 0$, $D(r) = 0$. The distribution of the electronic cloud for the 2*s* electrons of the hydrogen atom may be imagined in the following manner. The density of the cloud increases as the distance from the nucleus increases, passes through a low maximum and falls to zero ; the density then increases again as r increases and passes through a second higher maximum, the position of which corresponds to the radius of the second Bohr orbit and finally approaches zero as r tends to infinity. The complete electron cloud thus has the appearance of a sphere surrounded by a second spherical shell as shown in *Figure 5*.

When $l = 1$ ($n = 2, 3, 4$ *etc*) the wave functions depend not only on the distance of the electron from the nucleus but also upon the direction ; thus ψ is dependent upon r, θ and ϕ (see *Table IV*). The physical picture of these p states is somewhat more complex than that of the s states. In the Bohr-Sommerfeld theory orbits with the same value of n but different

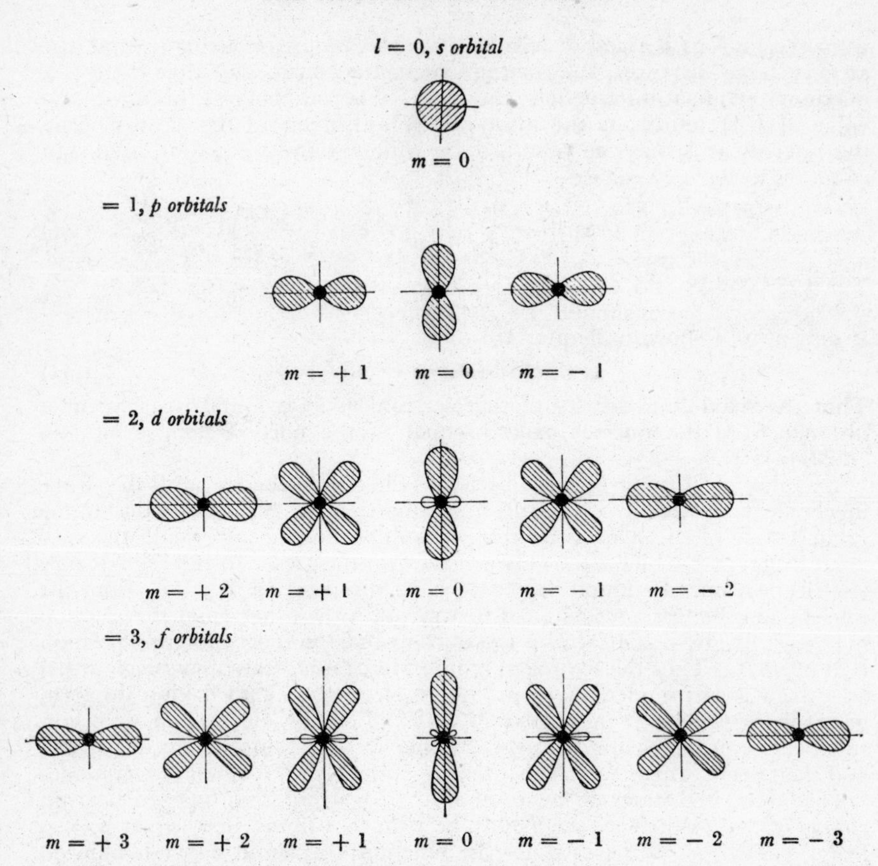

Figure 6. Angular distribution functions for different electronic states of the hydrogen atom

values of l were distinguishable by their different eccentricities, and the ratio l/n represented the ratio of the minor to the major axis of the ellipse. This picture is no longer tenable for the wave mechanical treatment and when the wave functions are shown graphically it is found that when $l = 1$, the electronic cloud has a form resembling an elongated figure eight (*Figures 5* and *6*). In place of the spherical symmetry of the electron clouds associated with the s electrons, there exists for the p electrons a maximum density in a particular direction which will be shown later to play an important part in the formation of directed valency bonds.

Wave functions which have the same value of l but different values of m describe electronic states having the same angular momentum as well as the same total energy, but in which the orbits are differently oriented in space. In the old quantum theory, the orbits were considered to be oriented at different angles to an arbitrarily fixed axis, but according to wave mechanics the three electronic clouds of the three p states are elongated figures of eight which are perpendicular to one another.

When the principal quantum number has the value three, the $3s$ electrons will also possess spherical symmetry (*Table IV*), but the ψ_{300} function becomes zero at two intermediate values between zero and infinity (*Figure 3*). The electron cloud thus consists of an inner sphere and two outer spherical shells (*Figures 4* and *5*) and the last maximum (*Figure 4*) coincides with the third Bohr orbit. The electronic clouds for the $3p$ electrons ($n = 3$, $l = 1$) are the same as those described above for the $2p$ state. When $n = 3$ and $l = 2$, there appear for the first time the *d* states; these five states correspond to the values for m of $+2$, $+1$, 0, -1, -2. For $m = \pm 2$ the electronic clouds have the form of an elongated figure eight (*Figures 5* and *6*) and when $m = \pm 1$ or 0 the electronic clouds have the more complex shapes shown in *Figure 6*.

REFERENCES

[1] PAULI, W. *Ann. Phys. Lpz.* 68 (1922) 177
[2] NIESSEN, K. F. *Dissertation* Utrecht, 1922
[3] SCHRÖDINGER, E. *Ann. Phys. Lpz.* 79 (1926) 361
[4] WHITE, H. E. *Phys. Rev.* 37 (1931) 1416

2

PERIODIC CLASSIFICATION OF THE ELEMENTS

THE PROBLEM OF ATOMS CONTAINING MANY ELECTRONS

OUR present knowledge of the structure of atoms which has been developed through quantum and wave mechanics permits an explanation of the periodic law, which forms the basis of the periodic table of MENDELÉEFF. The formulation of this law was a very important step in the development of chemical theory and by means of the periodic classification of the elements, Mendeléeff succeeded in removing several apparent anomalies which existed at that time. Of the sixty four elements known to Mendeléeff, considerably less than the total number were included in the table. Several of the atomic weights accepted at that time were altered in order to permit the elements to fit into the classification: *e.g.* uranium was corrected from 120 to 240, and the oxide given the formula UO_3 in place of U_2O_3 which had been suggested by PÉLIGOT; the atomic weight of beryllium was changed from 13·5 to 9, indium from 75·6 to 113, thorium from 116 to 232 and cerium from 92 to 138. The atomic weights of platinum, osmium, iridium, gold, titanium, lanthanum, yttrium and erbium were also changed. Furthermore in order to arrange the elements in order of their chemical behaviour it was necessary in several cases to change the previously accepted order based on atomic weight. These changes were nearly all subsequently proved to be correct and only in a few cases such as iodine, tellurium, cobalt and nickel was the original Mendeléeff classification found to be incorrect.

Several early attempts were made to put the periodic classification on a theoretical basis but without success. The periodicity of the elements occurs after 8 and sometimes after 18 elements, forming the short and long periods of the table, and if an attempt is made to correlate this periodicity with some function of the element *e.g.* the valency, no simple general relationship is found to exist.

The discovery of the rare gases of the atmosphere by RAYLEIGH and RAMSEY following Rayleigh's observation that the nitrogen obtained from air is heavier than that obtained by chemical decomposition, resulted in the completion of the groups of the periodic table by the formation of a zero group, the introduction of which did not necessitate any rearrangement of the remainder of the elements. The zero group was placed between the most electronegative non-metals and the most electropositive metals; thus neon came between fluorine and sodium, argon between chlorine and potassium, krypton between bromine and rubidium and xenon between iodine and caesium. The importance of the introduction of the zero group lay in the fact that each period, whether short or long, terminated with an element having zero valency, thus suggesting a completion of some stage in the structure of the atom.

A further advance in the understanding of the periodic law arose from the discovery by MOSELEY that the atomic number is more fundamental than the atomic weight in determining the position of a particular element in the periodic classification. The considerable amount of evidence on which the periodic table was built made it clear that this sequence of the elements is not a coincidence but must be founded on some natural law, yet the solution of this problem was not ultimately reached until the introduction of quantum mechanics.

In the previous chapter it has been shown that a satisfactory description of the structure of the hydrogen atom may be obtained by means of wave mechanics. The problem considered was a comparatively simple one, since in the atom of hydrogen there is only one electron, which results in a simple expression for the potential energy *viz* $-e^2/r$ and in this case Schrödinger's equation may be solved exactly. In other atoms there is not one, but several electrons and if the behaviour of each electron in a polyelectron atom did not depend upon the presence of the others *i.e.* if its behaviour were determined only by its attraction to the nucleus, then the Schrödinger equation for that atom could be divided into several equations for a hydrogen atom, depending on the number of electrons, in which the expressions for the charge on the nucleus e would be replaced by Ze, where Z is the atomic number. However, in addition to the attraction to the nucleus, the electrons mutually interact, repelling each other according to Coulomb's law. The mutual repulsion energy is e^2/r_{ik}, where r_{ik} is the distance between the two electrons. The potential energy term for a polyelectron atom will consist therefore, of a series of terms of the type $-Ze^2/r_1$ where r_1 is the distance of the electron from the nucleus, representing the attraction energy between the electron and the nucleus, and a series of terms of the type e^2/r_{ik} representing the repulsion energy between various pairs of electrons. The complexity of the resultant potential energy term adds greatly to the difficulty of producing an exact solution of Schrödinger's equation for the polyelectron atom. However, without actually solving the complete equation, it is possible to obtain valuable information concerning the distribution and behaviour of the electrons by using the solutions for the hydrogen atom.

If we neglect the interaction of the electrons with each other we may consider any atom as being ' hydrogen like '. It is obviously impossible by this means to obtain any correct data for energy levels of the atom considered, but nevertheless it is possible to form a qualitative picture of the atomic system and to arrive at a theoretical explanation of the periodic law. Proof as to the validity of the deductions made is forthcoming from spectroscopic data and from the chemical behaviour of the elements.

PAULI'S EXCLUSION PRINCIPLE AND ELECTRON ORBITALS

The possible states of the electron in the hydrogen atom have already been described in *Table III*, and the same states are permissible in hydrogen-like atoms. The fundamental question now arises as to how the various electrons in a polyelectron atom are distributed throughout these positions. It will be clear from our knowledge of the elements that certain restrictions, limiting the number of possible electronic states, will have to be introduced. The three quantum numbers, n, l, and m, which we have so far discussed are, however, insufficient for a complete description of the behaviour of an electron. It would appear that in addition to these quantities, an electron possesses an angular momentum, with which is associated a magnetic moment, given by the expression $\sqrt{s(s+1)}.\ h/2\pi$. This property of the electron, generally referred to as electron spin, was introduced by UHLENBECK and GOUDSCHMIDT[1] in order to explain the multiple splitting of spectral lines. The factor s in the above expression is termed the spin quantum number and can only have the values $\pm 1/2$.

The fact that the phenomena of electron spin is not derived from the Schrödinger equation is a weakness of this treatment. The relativistic quantum mechanics of Dirac, however, which has been developed up to the present only for a single particle, does lead to a description of the particle in terms of four quantum numbers, one of which determines the spin.

The two values of the spin quantum number may be regarded as corresponding to the two possible orientations of the spin angular momentum with respect to the orbital angular momentum. The resultant angular momentum is described in terms of a quantum number j, which has the values $l \pm s$, and the corresponding values of the angular momentum are given by $\sqrt{j(j+1)}.\ h/2\pi$. If any two electrons in an atom have the same value of the spin quantum number it is considered that the electron spins are orientated in a parallel manner, this behaviour we shall denote by two arrows pointing in the same direction ($\uparrow\uparrow$). If, however, the two electrons have different values, *viz* $s = +1/2$ and $s = -1/2$ then the spins are antiparallel, which we shall represent by two arrows pointing in the opposite directions ($\downarrow\uparrow$).

Having defined the four quantum numbers n, l, m and s which describe the electron, we may now return to the problem of the possible electronic states of a polyelectron atom. These are defined by the Pauli exclusion principle, which states that no two electrons in the same atom can possess

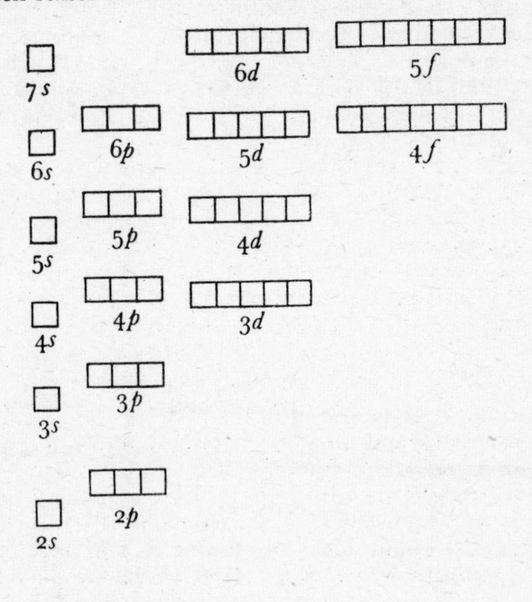

Figure 7. Approximate stability sequence of atomic orbitals

the same values of the four quantum numbers. Thus if two electrons in an atom have identical values of n, l and m it must follow that their spins are antiparallel. Electronic states corresponding to definite values of n, l and m are termed orbitals. Each orbital will thus accommodate, according to the Pauli principle, two electrons with antiparallel spins. The term orbital has arisen from the Bohr theory and it must be remembered that its use does not imply a fixed electronic orbit as conceived in the original theory, but a particular probability distribution in space, as defined by wave mechanics.

The periodic classification of the elements is derived directly on the basis of Pauli's principle. In the formulation of the periodic system it is necessary to explain the order in which the electrons assume their various states, *i.e.* into which orbital the electron falls when we pass from an atom with atomic number Z to the succeeding atom with atomic number $Z + 1$. Each electron will occupy the state possessing minimum energy, and as has been shown for the case of the hydrogen atom, the energy is dependent only on the principal quantum number n as given by equation 1.8. In polyelectron atoms the dependence of energy on quantum number is, however, more complicated, being determined not only by the principal quantum number n, but also by l. As a general rule an s orbital ($l = 0$) is more stable than a p orbital ($l = 1$), which in turn is more stable than a d orbital ($l = 2$).

For the higher quantum numbers the relationship between the energy values of the orbitals is more complicated (see *Figure 7*). Thus for example, the $4s$ orbital ($n = 4, l = 0$) is more stable than the $3d$ orbital ($n = 3, l = 2$). This complexity does not permit a construction of the electronic distribution of the elements on the basis only of the analogy to a hydrogen like atom and it is necessary for each element to use the spectroscopic data to determine the electronic states. The sequence of the distribution thus obtained can, with only a few exceptions, be expressed by the data given in *Figure 7*.

DISTRIBUTION OF ELECTRONS IN ATOMS

The values which may be given to the four quantum numbers are as follows:

1 $n = 1, 2, 3, 4, \ldots\ldots$

2 $l = 0, 1, 2, 3 \ldots\ldots n - 1$ corresponding to the s, p, d, f, ... states respectively

3 to each value of l there are $2l + 1$ values of the magnetic quantum number m which has values from $+l$ to $-l$

4 to each value of n, l and m there are two values of s, $+1/2$ and $-1/2$.

These restrictions on the values of the various quantum numbers represent, together with the Pauli exclusion principle, the basis of the periodic classification.

When $n = 1$, $l = 0$ and $m = 0$, s may have the values $\pm 1/2$; it therefore follows that the first orbital, *i.e.* when $n = 1$, can accommodate no more than two electrons. If a third electron was introduced into this orbital, it would also have the values $n = 1$, $l = 0$, $m = 0$ and either $s = +1/2$ or $-1/2$ and thus would correspond exactly to the state of one of the electrons already contained within the orbital, its entry is thus prohibited by the Pauli principle. These deductions are in direct agreement with the periodic classification of the elements in which the first two elements, *viz* hydrogen and helium, complete the first period. The electronic formula of the hydrogen in its ground state will therefore be,

H $1s$

and of helium He $1s^2$

The figure on the left gives the value of the principal quantum number, the letter represents the value of l and the superscript the number of electrons associated with a particular value of l for that atom.

When $n = 2$, l can have the values 0 and 1 and hence both s and p orbitals are permissible. If $l = 0$, then $m = 0$ and this orbital may contain two electrons having the values of $s + 1/2$ and $- 1/2$. When $l = 1$, three values of m are permissible, *viz* $+ 1, 0, - 1$ and to each of these orbitals there may be ascribed the values $s = \pm 1/2$. Thus when the principal quantum number has the value 2, there exist one s and three p orbitals which may contain 2 and 6 electrons respectively, *i.e.* eight in all. These four orbitals permit the construction of the second period of the Mendeléeff table containing eight elements.

When $n = 3$, by following the same arguments as given in the preceding paragraph, it is seen that there will be one s and three p orbitals, together with five d orbitals for the case where $l = 2$ when m has the five values $+ 2, + 1, 0, - 1, - 2$. Since each orbital can accommodate, according to the Pauli principle, not more than two electrons with opposite spins, it follows that where the principal quantum number has the value 3, the complete shell can accommodate $2 + 6 + 10 = 18$ electrons.

In general, for a particular value of the principal quantum number, there cannot be more than two s, six p, ten d and fourteen f electrons and the total possible number of electrons for a given value of n is therefore equal to $2n^2$. Thus the introduction of the concept of spin leads to the doubling of the number of possible electronic states (equation 1.39). The possible distribution of electrons for a hydrogen like atom is shown in *Table V* and it is seen that the series 2, 8, 18, 32, . . . which has arisen from the application of the Pauli principle is in agreement with the numbers of elements occurring in the periodic table of Mendeléeff. The electron shells with values for the principal quantum number 1, 2, 3, 4, *etc* are often referred to as the K, L, M, N, *etc* shells.

Let us consider the derivation of the electron configuration of the elements from lithium to neon which constitute the second period of Mendeléeff's classification. The distribution of the electrons in the ground positions of the atoms is given below. In the atom of lithium, the first two electrons occupy the $1s$ position, the third electron according to the Pauli principle must fall into the electron shell having the main quantum number equal to two. The electron accordingly occupies the position of minimum energy within this shell, which is the $2s$ orbital.

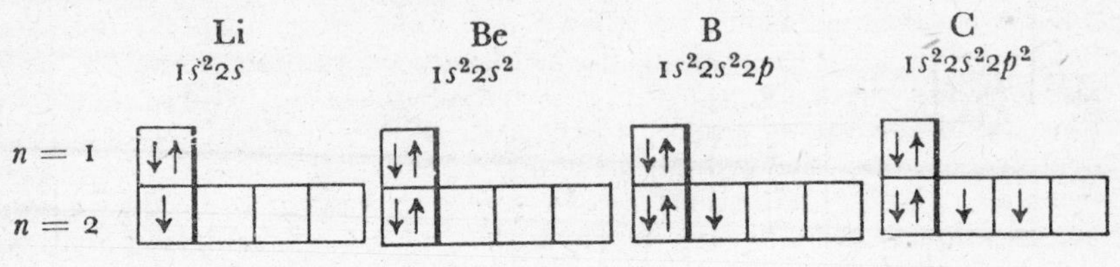

Table V. Distribution of Electrons for Hydrogen-like Atoms

	K	*L*		*M*			*N*			
h	1	2		3			4			
l	0	0	1	0	1	2	0	1	2	3
m	0	0	+1 0 −1	0	+1 0 −1	+2 +1 0 −1 −2	0	+1 0 −1	+2 +1 0 −1 −2	+3 +2 +1 0 −1 −2 −3
Orientation of spin	↓↑	↓↑	↓↑ ↓↑ ↓↑	↓↑	↓↑ ↓↑ ↓↑	↓↑ ↓↑ ↓↑ ↓↑ ↓↑	↓↑	↓↑ ↓↑ ↓↑	↓↑ ↓↑ ↓↑ ↓↑ ↓↑	↓↑ ↓↑ ↓↑ ↓↑ ↓↑ ↓↑ ↓↑
Electronic level	$1s^2$	$2s^2$	$2p^6$	$3s^2$	$3p^6$	$3d^{10}$	$4s^2$	$4p^6$	$4d^{10}$	$4f^{14}$
Number of electrons in shell	2	8		18			32			

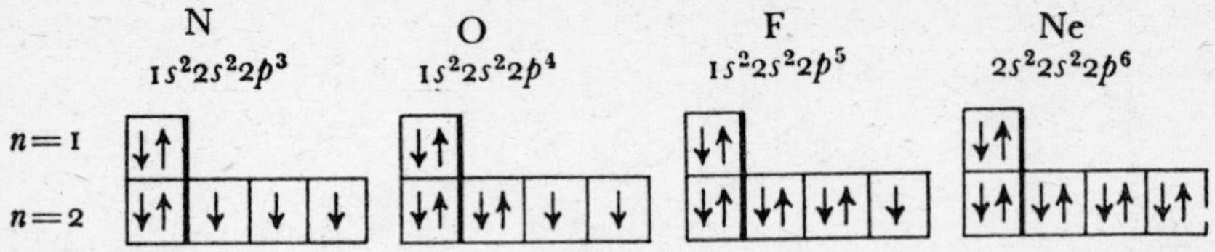

	N	O	F	Ne
	$1s^2 2s^2 2p^3$	$1s^2 2s^2 2p^4$	$1s^2 2s^2 2p^5$	$2s^2 2s^2 2p^6$
$n = 1$	↓↑	↓↑	↓↑	↓↑
$n = 2$	↓↑ ǀ ↓ ǀ ↓ ǀ ↓	↓↑ ǀ ↓↑ ǀ ↓ ǀ ↓	↓↑ ǀ ↓↑ ǀ ↓↑ ǀ ↓	↓↑ ǀ ↓↑ ǀ ↓↑ ǀ ↓↑

In the atom of beryllium the fourth electron completes the $2s$ orbital and thus with boron the fifth electron must enter a $2p$ orbital. The additional electrons of carbon and nitrogen each occupy a $2p$ orbital as shown in the diagrams above. Once the three $2p$ orbitals contain an electron each, the introduction of further electrons, as in the atoms of oxygen, fluorine and neon, bring about the completion of these orbitals. With neon the electronic shell $n = 2$ is completed since all the possible eight electron positions are filled and in accordance with this, the second period of the periodic classification contains eight elements.

The eighth element of the second period, neon, possesses several chemical peculiarities when compared with the other elements of this series. The total spin angular momentum will be zero, since the spins of the separate electrons in each orbital are antiparallel, and furthermore, the total angular momentum will be zero. Experimental observation of the properties of neon makes it possible to relate the completion of an electronic shell with chemical inactivity.

In the elements of the second period the following numbers of unpaired electrons occur :

Li	Be	B	C	N	O	F	Ne
1	0	1	2	3	2	1	0

These numbers of unpaired electrons are significant since they indicate the number of electrons which may be accommodated in that shell through compound formation. Thus these numbers indicate the valency of the element. Both hydrogen and lithium possess a single unpaired electron and are accordingly monovalent ; helium and neon in which no unpaired electrons occur have zero valency. Oxygen having two unpaired electrons is divalent ; nitrogen with three, trivalent ; fluorine with one monovalent and carbon with two may, under certain circumstances, be divalent

However, for beryllium, boron and carbon there appears to be no relationship between the chemically observed valency and the number of unpaired electrons. Beryllium is always divalent, boron trivalent and in the majority of its compounds carbon is tetravalent. It might have been supposed that the case of beryllium was analogous with that of helium, since both elements have a completed s orbital, but beryllium as distinct from helium has, along with the $2s$ orbital, three $2p$ orbitals. The excitation of an electron in an helium atom from the $1s$ to the $2s$ state requires the absorption of a considerable amount of energy (460 kcals). In the atom of beryllium, however, owing to the comparatively insignificant difference in the energies of the $2s$ and $2p$ states (62 kcals) unpairing of the electrons is possible. Thus beryllium may be regarded as possessing either the unexcited (ground) state or an excited state having the electronic formula :

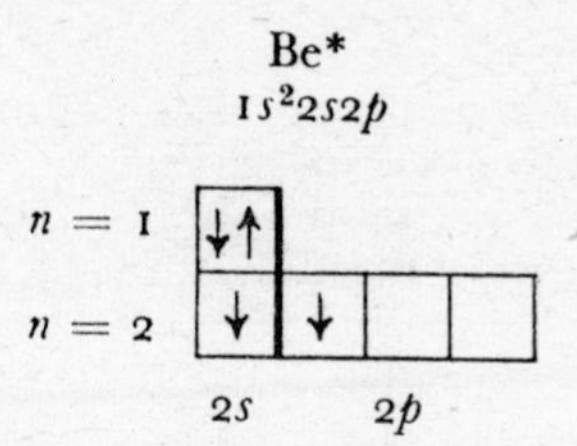

the asterisk* denoting an excited state of the atom. In this state the atom of beryllium has two unpaired electrons and hence is divalent. The energies of excitation of beryllium and other elements in that group of the periodic table are known from spectroscopic measurements and are given in *Table VI*. As is to be expected the excitation energy decreases with increasing atomic number.

Table VI. Excitation Energies of Group II Elements

Element	*Electron transition*	*Energy kcals*
Be	$2s^2 \rightarrow 2s\,2p$	62
Mg	$3s^2 \rightarrow 3s\,3p$	62
Ca	$4s^2 \rightarrow 4s\,4p$	43
Sr	$5s^2 \rightarrow 5s\,5p$	41
Ba	$6s^2 \rightarrow 6s\,5d$	36

In exactly the same way for the atoms of boron and carbon one of the 2*s* electrons may be transferred to a vacant 2*p* orbital so that the electronic configurations will be :

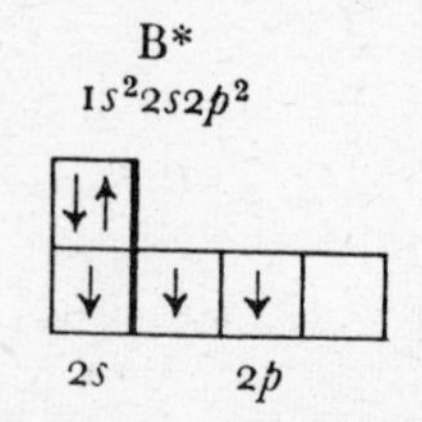

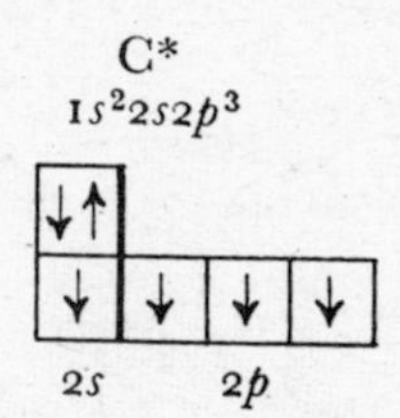

The excited atom of boron has three unpaired electrons and is consequently trivalent and the excited atom of carbon has four unpaired electrons and is tetravalent. Thus the numbers of unpaired electrons in the atoms of the second period may now be written as

Li	Be*	B*	C*	N	O	F	Ne
1	2	3	4	3	2	1	0

and this order follows exactly the valencies of these elements.

For the atoms of nitrogen, oxygen and fluorine, such excitation processes would not change the number of unpaired electrons since in the atoms of these elements there are no vacant 2*p* orbitals. In order to increase the valency of nitrogen a transfer of a 2*s* electron to a 3*s* state would be necessary. Such a transition however, would involve too great an amount of energy for the resulting state to be of significance in determining the valency of nitrogen. Thus nitrogen cannot be five covalent, and in those compounds where nitrogen may be considered as being pentavalent there is in fact one electrovalent bond together with four covalent bonds, as in NH_4^+ and the nitro group. These compounds will be considered later. Thus the ability of an element to enter into chemical combination may be lacking in atoms in an unexcited state, but may be present as the result of excitation or ionization, either process involving the expenditure of energy.

The distribution of electrons in the *p* orbitals given above is not immediately apparent. For example, it would be possible for the two *p* electrons of carbon to be placed in one 2*p* orbital, or the three *p* electrons of nitrogen to be placed not in three different orbitals but in two, *viz*

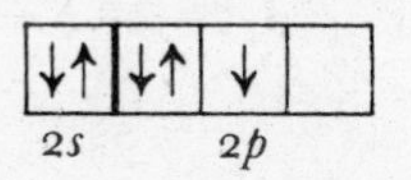

The accepted distribution of the *p* electrons is based on spectroscopic data, which leads to the following rule : for a given value of *l*, electrons are distributed in such a way that the number of unpaired electrons with parallel spins is a maximum, and hence the total spin angular momentum is also a maximum. This rule, known as Hund's law[2], depends on the fact that states with a maximum number of electrons with parallel spins is the most probable arrangement on the basis of energy consideration. Thus for the atom of nitrogen the state with three unpaired *p* electrons is more probable than the state with only one unpaired *p* electron since an excitation energy of 55 kcals is required to convert the former into the latter state. Similarly for the atom of oxygen, the state with two unpaired electrons

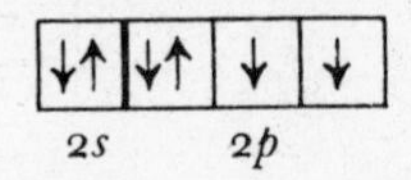

is more stable by 45 kcals than the state with no unpaired electrons

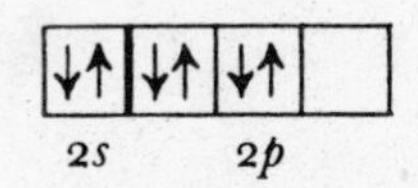

and for carbon the energy difference between the two states

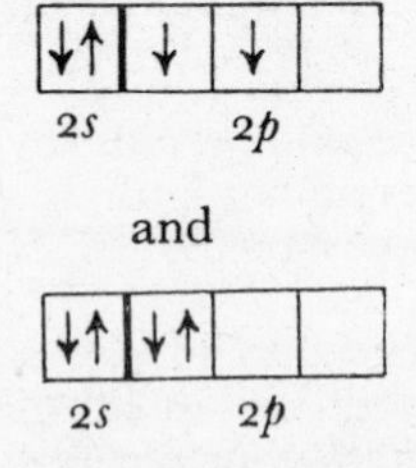

is 29 kcals. The spectral terms for these states are as follows[3]: for nitrogen $^4S_{3/2}$ and ^2D, for oxygen $^3P_2$ and $^1D_2$ and for carbon $^3P_0$ and $^1D_2$.

Sodium, the element following neon, possesses similar chemical properties to lithium ; this is understandable on the basis of the electronic formulae of these atoms since after the completion of the second electronic shell with neon, the next electron can occupy only the 3*s* orbital.

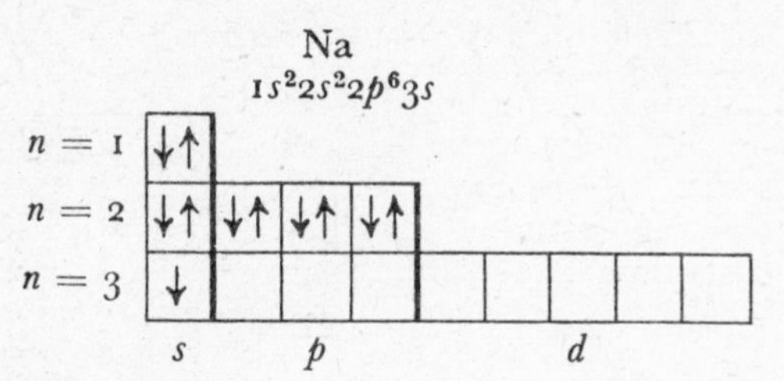

The process of the completion of the electronic shell is repeated as for the second period elements and is shown by the electronic formulae :

		3s	3p		
Mg	$1s^2\ 2s^2\ 2p^6\ 3s^2$	↓↑			
Al	$1s^2\ 2s^2\ 2p^6\ 3s^2\ 3p$	↓↑	↓		
Si	$1s^2\ 2s^2\ 2p^6\ 3s^2\ 3p^2$	↓↑	↓	↓	
P	$1s^2\ 2s^2\ 2p^6\ 3s^2\ 3p^3$	↓↑	↓	↓	↓
S	$1s^2\ 2s^2\ 2p^6\ 3s^2\ 3p^4$	↓↑	↓↑	↓	↓
Cl	$1s^2\ 2s^2\ 2p^6\ 3s^2\ 3p^5$	↓↑	↓↑	↓↑	↓
Ar	$1s^2\ 2s^2\ 2p^6\ 3s^2\ 3p^6$	↓↑	↓↑	↓↑	↓↑

The number of unpaired electrons in the unexcited states of the atoms of the third period are the same as in the second period :

Na	Mg	Al	Si	P	S	Cl	Ar
1	0	1	2	3	2	1	0

and considering the excitation from the $3s$ to the $3p$ state :

Na	Mg*	Al*	Si*	P	S	Cl	Ar
1	2	3	4	3	2	1	0

and thus the fundamental valencies of these elements are the same as the corresponding elements of the second period. The behaviour of the elements in the various groups is, however, not entirely analogous as the difference in energy between the $3p$ and $4s$ states is less than that between the $2p$ and $2s$ states, and elements of the third period, much more readily than those of the second period, are transferred to an excited state with a corresponding increase in the valency. In addition, in the third period there exist the $3d$ states comprising five orbitals which permit, by electronic excitation, an increase of valency. These views are exemplified in the behaviour of fluorine and chlorine. Fluorine is always monovalent, whereas chlorine gives a series of compounds with oxygen *e.g.* Cl_2O, Cl_2O_3, ClO_2, *etc*, which clearly involve a variable valency, which can only occur by the excitation of $3p$ electrons to $3d$ and $4s$ states. Similarly oxygen is divalent, whereas sulphur possesses a variable valency. These differences in behaviour can be explained only in terms of energy relationships. If electronic excitation, involving the unpairing and increase in the number of unpaired electrons, requires an expenditure of energy which can be accounted for from a knowledge of bond energies, then a variable valency is possible. If on the other hand the endothermic electronic excitation energy is greater than the exothermic combination of the atoms, then that particular element will possess only a single valency state. Thus the very high electronic excitation energy of helium, 460 kcals, prevents it from being a reactive element.

In the atom of argon, only the $3s$ and $3p$ orbitals are occupied, but in this electronic shell there exist also the five $3d$ orbitals. The energy of the $3d$ states, however, is considerably greater than that of the $3p$ and is in fact greater than that of the $4s$ orbital. It is this fact which results in the inert character of argon and makes it comparable with neon. The electrons of the two succeeding elements potassium and calcium thus occupy the $4s$ orbital which, as indicated above, is more stable in the case of these elements than the $3d$ orbitals. Thus a fourth period is commenced. The occupation of the $3d$ orbitals commences only with the next element, scandium, atomic number 21, in which the $3d$ state has a lower energy level than the $4p$ state. The energy relationships of the $3p$, $3d$ and $4s$ states are known empirically from the spectroscopic data ; a theoretical attempt to deal with this problem has been made by FERMI[4] who has pictured the atom as an electron cloud existing in the field of the nucleus. On passing from one atom to the next, the new electron occupies the energy level having the lowest energy, a fact in accordance with Pauli's principle. This approach leads to the prediction that the formation of *s*, *p*, *d* and *f* states will start at the first, fifth, twenty-first and fifty-fifth elements. Experiment shows that the *s* electron appears first with hydrogen, atomic number 1, the *p* electron with boron, atomic number 5, the *d* electron with scandium, atomic number 21 and the *f* electron with cerium, atomic number 58.

The electronic configuration of the atom of scandium is :

Sc

$$1s^2 2s^2 2p^6 3s^2 3p^6 3d 4s^2$$

	s	*p*			*d*				
$n = 3$	↓↑	↓↑	↓↑	↓↑	↓				
$n = 4$	↓↑								

From scandium to vanadium, atomic number 23, there occurs a further filling of the $3d$ orbitals and hence the electronic formula of vanadium is

$$\text{V} \quad 1s^2\ 2s^2\ 2p^6\ 3s^2\ 3p^6\ 3d^3\ 4s^2$$

With the next element, chromium, however, it appears that for the first time in the construction of the periodic classification an element does not retain the electronic configuration of the previous atom. Thus in the atom of chromium there is only one $4s$ electron and five $3d$, in place of the two $4s$ and four $3d$ electrons which might have been expected. The electronic formula for chromium is therefore

$$\text{Cr} \quad 1s^2\ 2s^2\ 2p^6\ 3s^2\ 3p^6\ 3d^5\ 4s$$

and it must be assumed that this configuration is more stable *i.e.* has a lower energy value than the predicted formula

$$\text{Cr} \quad 1s^2\ 2s^2\ 2p^6\ 3s^2\ 3p^6\ 3d^4\ 4s^2$$

In the next element, manganese, the 4*s* orbital is completely filled and it has the formula

$$\text{Mn} \quad 1s^2\ 2s^2\ 2p^6\ 3s^2\ 3p^6\ 3d^5\ 4s^2$$

With the elements iron, cobalt and nickel the 3*d* orbital continues to fill up and finally, with copper in which one 4*s* electron transfers to the 3*d* state, the filling of the 3*d* orbitals is completed

$$\text{Fe} \quad 1s^2\ 2s^2\ 2p^6\ 3s^2\ 3p^6\ 3d^6\ 4s^2$$
$$\text{Co} \quad 1s^2\ 2s^2\ 2p^6\ 3s^2\ 3p^6\ 3d^7\ 4s^2$$
$$\text{Ni} \quad 1s^2\ 2s^2\ 2p^6\ 3s^2\ 3p^6\ 3d^8\ 4s^2$$
$$\text{Cu} \quad 1s^2\ 2s^2\ 2p^6\ 3s^2\ 3p^6\ 3d^{10}\ 4s$$

After copper, the next element zinc, fills the one free place in the 4*s* orbital and the succeeding six elements, from gallium to krypton, fill the 4*p* orbital, and the period ends with the following configuration for krypton

$$\text{Kr} \quad 1s^2\ 2s^2\ 2p^6\ 3s^2\ 3p^6\ 3d^{10}\ 4s^2\ 4p^6$$

The fourth period, as has been shown above, begins with the filling of an *s* orbital, which is in agreement with the chemical similarity of potassium and calcium with sodium and magnesium respectively. After this orbital has been completed, however, the elements which follow show new properties, such as a variable valency. The reason for this behaviour is that the 3*d* orbitals are being filled and the difference in energy of the 3*d*, 4*s* and 4*p* states is small so that electronic excitation, producing an increased valency, may easily occur. It is difficult with elements such as chromium, manganese, iron, cobalt and nickel to determine the value of the unexcited valency although it is possible to determine the number of unpaired electrons. The valency may be more or less than the number of unpaired electrons and the position is complicated by the tendency to form electrovalent or ionic bonds in addition to covalent bonds.

After the completion of the 4*s* and 4*p* states with krypton, a fifth period commences. As in the fourth period the 5*s* orbital is more stable than the 4*d* or 4*f* states and is filled by the elements rubidium and strontium. The occupation of the 4*d* orbitals commences with the next element, yttrium and continues normally for the next element. With niobium however, the spectroscopic data show that one 5*s* electron has also been transferred to the 4*d* state, and a single electron occurs in the 5*s* orbital up to the element rhodium, atomic number 45. In the next element, palladium, the remaining 5*s* electron is also transferred to the 4*s* state, which is thereby completely filled with ten electrons

$$\text{Pd} \quad 1s^2\ 2s^2\ 2p^6\ 3s^2\ 3p^6\ 3d^{10}\ 4s^2\ 4p^6\ 4d^{10}$$

The remaining elements of the fifth group, beginning with silver and ending with xenon fill the 5*s* and 5*p* orbitals. The 4*f* orbitals which remain unfilled in the fifth period are filled in the sixth period after caesium and barium which occupy the 6*s* orbital and lanthanum which has the electronic formula

$$\text{La} \quad 1s^2\ 2s^2\ 2p^6\ 3s^2\ 3p^6\ 3d^{10}\ 4s^2\ 4p^6\ 4d^{10}\ 5s^2\ 5p^6\ 5d\ 6s^2$$

Fourteen electrons are distributed in the seven 4*f* orbitals and form the lanthanons, or rare earths. These elements possess a common outer

Table VII. Electron Configuration of Atoms in their Normal States

Element	*Atomic Number*	*K*	*L*		*M*			*N*				*O*				*P*			*Q*
		1*s*	2*s*	2*p*	3*s*	3*p*	3*d*	4*s*	4*p*	4*d*	4*f*	5*s*	5*p*	5*d*	5*f*	6*s*	6*p*	6*d*	7*s*
H	1	1																	
He	2	2																	
Li	3	2	1																
Be	4	2	2																
B	5	2	2	1															
C	6	2	2	2															
N	7	2	2	3															
O	8	2	2	4															
F	9	2	2	5															
Ne	10	2	2	6															
Na	11	2	2	6	1														
Mg	12	2	2	6	2														
Al	13	2	2	6	2	1													
Si	14	2	2	6	2	2													
P	15	2	2	6	2	3													
S	16	2	2	6	2	4													
Cl	17	2	2	6	2	5													
Ar	18	2	2	6	2	6													
K	19	2	2	6	2	6		1											
Ca	20	2	2	6	2	6		2											
Sc	21	2	2	6	2	6	1	2											
Ti	22	2	2	6	2	6	2	2											
V	23	2	2	6	2	6	3	2											
Cr	24	2	2	6	2	6	5	1											
Mn	25	2	2	6	2	6	5	2											
Fe	26	2	2	6	2	6	6	2											
Co	27	2	2	6	2	6	7	2											
Ni	28	2	2	6	2	6	8	2											
Cu	29	2	2	6	2	6	10	1											
Zn	30	2	2	6	2	6	10	2											
Ga	31	2	2	6	2	6	10	2	1										
Ge	32	2	2	6	2	6	10	2	2										
As	33	2	2	6	2	6	10	2	3										
Se	34	2	2	6	2	6	10	2	4										
Br	35	2	2	6	2	6	10	2	5										
Kr	36	2	2	6	2	6	10	2	6										
Rb	37	2	2	6	2	6	10	2	6			1							
Sr	38	2	2	6	2	6	10	2	6			2							
Y	39	2	2	6	2	6	10	2	6	1		2							
Zr	40	2	2	6	2	6	10	2	6	2		2							
Nb	41	2	2	6	2	6	10	2	6	4		1							
Mo	42	2	2	6	2	6	10	2	6	5		1							
Tc	43	2	2	6	2	6	10	2	6	6		1							
Ru	44	2	2	6	2	6	10	2	6	7		1							
Rh	45	2	2	6	2	6	10	2	6	8		1							
Pd	46	2	2	6	2	6	10	2	6	10									
Ag	47	2	2	6	2	6	10	2	6	10		1							
Cd	48	2	2	6	2	6	10	2	6	10		2							

Table VII. Electron Configuration of Atoms in their Normal States—continued

Element	*Atomic Number*	*K*	*L*		*M*			*N*				*O*				*P*			*Q*
		1*s*	2*s*	2*p*	3*s*	3*p*	3*d*	4*s*	4*p*	4*d*	4*f*	5*s*	5*p*	5*d*	5*f*	6*s*	6*p*	6*d*	7*s*
In	49	2	2	6	2	6	10	2	6	10		2	1						
Sn	50	2	2	6	2	6	10	2	6	10		2	2						
Sb	51	2	2	6	2	6	10	2	6	10		2	3						
Te	52	2	2	6	2	6	10	2	6	10		2	4						
I	53	2	2	6	2	6	10	2	6	10		2	5						
Xe	54	2	2	6	2	6	10	2	6	10		2	6						
Cs	55	2	2	6	2	6	10	2	2	10		2	6			1			
Ba	56	2	2	6	2	6	10	2	6	10		2	6			2			
La	57	2	2	6	2	6	10	2	6	10		2	6	1		2			
Ce	58	2	2	6	2	6	10	2	6	10	1	2	6	1		2			
Pr	59	2	2	6	2	6	10	2	6	10	2	2	6	1		2			
Nd	60	2	2	6	2	6	10	2	6	10	3	2	6	1		2			
Pm	61	2	2	6	2	6	10	2	6	10	4	2	6	1		2			
Sm	62	2	2	6	2	6	10	2	6	10	5	2	6	1		2			
Eu	63	2	2	6	2	6	10	2	6	10	6	2	6	1		2			
Gd	64	2	2	6	2	6	10	2	6	10	7	2	6	1		2			
Tb	65	2	2	6	2	6	10	2	6	10	8	2	6	1		2			
Ds	66	2	2	6	2	6	10	2	6	10	9	2	6	1		2			
Ho	67	2	2	6	2	6	10	2	6	10	10	2	6	1		2			
Er	68	2	2	6	2	6	10	2	6	10	11	2	6	1		2			
Tm	69	2	2	6	2	6	10	2	6	10	12	2	6	1		2			
Yb	70	2	2	6	2	6	10	2	6	10	13	2	6	1		2			
Lu	71	2	2	6	2	6	10	2	6	10	14	2	6	1		2			
Hf	72	2	2	6	2	6	10	2	6	10	14	2	6	2		2			
Ta	73	2	2	6	2	6	10	2	6	10	14	2	6	3		2			
W	74	2	2	6	2	6	10	2	6	10	14	2	6	4		2			
Re	75	2	2	6	2	6	10	2	6	10	14	2	6	5		2			
Os	76	2	2	6	2	6	10	2	6	10	14	2	6	6		2			
Ir	77	2	2	6	2	6	10	2	6	10	14	2	6	9					
Pt	78	2	2	6	2	6	10	2	6	10	14	2	6	9		1			
Au	79	2	2	6	2	6	10	2	6	10	14	2	6	10		1			
Hg	80	2	2	6	2	6	10	2	6	10	14	2	6	10		2			
Tl	81	2	2	6	2	6	10	2	6	10	14	2	6	10		2	1		
Pb	82	2	2	6	2	6	10	2	6	10	14	2	6	10		2	2		
Bi	83	2	2	6	2	6	10	2	6	10	14	2	6	10		2	3		
Po	84	2	2	6	2	6	10	2	6	10	14	2	6	10		2	4		
Ar	85	2	2	6	2	6	10	2	6	10	14	2	6	10		2	5		
Rn	86	2	2	6	2	6	10	2	6	10	14	2	6	10		2	6		
Fr	87	2	2	6	2	6	10	2	6	10	14	2	6	10		2	6		1
Ra	88	2	2	6	2	6	10	2	6	10	14	2	6	10		2	6		2
Ac	89	2	2	6	2	6	10	2	6	10	14	2	6	10		2	6	1	2
Th	90	2	2	6	2	6	10	2	6	10	14	2	6	10	1	2	6	1	2
Pa	91	2	2	6	2	6	10	2	6	10	14	2	6	10	2	2	6	1	2
U	92	2	2	6	2	6	10	2	6	10	14	2	6	10	3	2	6	1	2
Np	93	2	2	6	2	6	10	2	6	10	14	2	6	10	4	2	6	1	2
Pu	94	2	2	6	2	6	10	2	6	10	14	2	6	10	5	2	6	1	2
Am	95	2	2	6	2	6	10	2	6	10	14	2	6	10	6	2	6	1	2
Cm	96	2	2	6	2	6	10	2	6	10	14	2	6	10	7	2	6	1	2

electronic structure, the arrangement being $5s^2\ 5p^6\ 5d\ 6s^2$ and differ only in the number of deep-lying $4f$ electrons. The similarity of chemical behaviour of these elements is thus understandable since chemical behaviour is determined, in general, by the outer electrons.

After the completion of the $4f$ state, the $5d$ orbitals continue to be filled, the first element in this series being hafnium with the electronic formula

$$\text{Hf}\quad 1s^2\ 2s^2\ 2p^6\ 3s^2\ 3p^6\ 3d^{10}\ 4s^2\ 4p^6\ 4d^{10}\ 4f^{14}\ 5s^2\ 5p^6\ 5d^2\ 6s^2$$

This formula permits the conclusion to be made that this element, atomic number 72, is not a lanthanon, but is an analogue of zirconium. In this way the quantum theory has limited the number of lanthanons to fourteen elements, for which there was no previous criterion, and indicated the correct place of the element hafnium, similar to the way in which Mendeléeff predicted correctly the positions of gallium, germanium and scandium.

The electronic configuration of all atoms is shown in *Table VII* and the periodicity of the elements in *Tables VIII* and *IX*. *Table VIII* is based on that of Mendeléeff but whereas the division of the elements into groups and subgroups was originally empirical, it is now shown to be based on the electronic structure of the atom. Under each subgroup there is given the distribution of the outer electrons. On the right hand side of the table is given the electronic configuration of the penultimate shell and the main quantum number of the outermost electrons. The superscript given to each symbol refers to the electronic configuration of the completed inner shells which are given beneath the table. The division into the subgroups A and B is based on the fact that the penultimate electron shells of the elements in these groups contain the configuration $s^2\ p^6$ and $s^2\ p^6\ d^{10}$ respectively. The lanthanons and actinons, in which the $4f$ and $5f$ orbitals respectively are filled, are not shown on the table.

The absence of inner completed electronic shells where $n = 1$ leads to certain differences in the properties of hydrogen and helium compared with other elements having a similar configuration of the outer electrons and these two elements have therefore been placed in a separate part of the table. Helium cannot be grouped with the alkaline earth metals, although their electronic configuration, s^2, is identical; chemically, helium is an inert gas, but since the remainder of the members of this group possess six p electrons in the outermost shell, a different classification is required. In a similar way the electronic configuration of hydrogen is identical with that of the alkali metals, the s electron of the hydrogen atom is, however, bound more strongly than in the alkali metals and furthermore, the chemical behaviour of hydrogen is not very similar to that of lithium or sodium and it is therefore placed in a separate group.

To illustrate the use of the table, let us consider the configuration of tungsten. It has an atomic number of 74, the superscript 5 indicates that the structure of the inner complete shell is

$$1s^2\ 2s^2\ 2p^6\ 3s^2\ 3p^6\ 3d^{10}\ 4s^2\ 4p^6\ 4d^{10}\ 4f^{14}$$

The penultimate electronic shell, as indicated at the right hand side of the table is $5s^2\ 5p^6$ and in the outermost shell there are present four $5d$ and two $6s$ electrons, the $5d$ electrons being unpaired. The number of unpaired electrons in the ground state of the atom is determined experimentally from spectroscopic data in the following way. If the multiplet splitting is denoted by M, then the multiplicity is given by $M = 2S + 1$, where S

is the resultant spin vector equal to Σs. Thus when $M = 1$ (singlet state) it follows that S is zero and hence all the spins must be paired; when $M = 2$ (doublet state), $S = 1/2$, indicating the existence of one unpaired electron; when $M = 3$ (triplet state), $S = 1$ and there will be two unpaired electrons, each with the value $s = +1/2$. Thus in general the number of free unpaired electrons is given by $(M - 1)$.

The expanded form of the periodic table shown in *Table IX* has several advantages over the original form and is based much more closely on the electronic distribution obtained from spectral data and the Pauli principle (see *Table V*) than is the Mendeléeff form. It is not now generally considered that the chemical similarity of elements containing the same number of electrons in *p* and *d* orbitals is such as to justify their classification as subgroups of the same periodic group. The transition group of elements, whose chemical behaviour is closely determined by the presence of an incomplete *d* shell of electrons, have therefore been removed from the subgroups and placed between the main groups II and III. The only serious objection to this form of table lies in the inclusion of the copper and zinc groups within the transition group. If we regard a transition element as one with an incomplete, but not empty, *d* shell then those elements together with palladium are not transitional. It is convenient, however, to include them in the transition group as representing the limiting stage to be attained by the completion of the *d* shell. What similarity exists between the copper and zinc groups and the alkali and alkaline earth metals respectively, may be attributed to the similarity of the electronic configuration of the *s* orbital, but the influence of the completed shell of *d* electrons on the properties of these elements (*e.g.* the ionization potential) is sufficiently marked not to justify their inclusion as subgroups of groups I and II.

Until very recently only ninety-two elements were recognized and the periodic classification ended with the element uranium. In 1940 McMillan and Abelson[5] showed that bombardment of uranium with neutrons led to the production of an isotope of a new element, neptunium, of atomic number 93. This isotope Np^{239}, which has a half life period of 2·3 days, is the decay product of U^{239} formed by the neutron bombardment of U^{238}. The chemical behaviour of this element showed that it was closely related in its properties to uranium and dissimilar from rhenium. These data were the first convincing evidence that it was the 5*f* shell that was being filled and not the 6*d*. These elements thus form a group named the actinons, analogous to the lanthanons. A second isotope of neptunium, Np^{237}, was obtained by bombarding uranium with fast neutrons, the reaction taking place being U^{238} $(n, 2n)$ $U^{237} \xrightarrow{\bar{\beta}} Np^{237}$. The importance of this isotope lies in the fact that it has the very long half life period of $2{\cdot}25 \times 10^6$ years, and that it has been prepared in weighable quantities. The second transuranium element to be prepared was plutonium[6], Pu^{238}_{94} having a half life period of 50 years, the reactions being U^{238} $(d, 2n)$ $Np^{238} \xrightarrow{\bar{\beta}} Pu^{238}$. Chemical studies show it to have properties very similar to uranium and neptunium but the lower oxidation states are more stable. Americium, atomic number 95, was the fourth transuranium element obtained. The reactions taking place on the bombardment of U^{238} by high energy helium ions are U^{238} (α, n) $Pu^{241} \xrightarrow{\bar{\beta}} Am^{241}$. The third element to be

Table VIII. The Periodic Classificat

Periodic group		I		II		III		IV		V			VI		
Sub group		*A*	*B*	*A*	*B*	*A*	*B*	*A*	*B*	*A*	*B₁*	*B₂*	*A*	*B₁*	*B₂*
Number of outer electrons		1		2		3		4		5			6		
Distribution of outer electrons	*p*									↓			↓		
								↓		↓			↓		
						↓		↓		↓			↓↑		
	s	↓	↓	↓↑	↓↑	↓↑	↓↑	↓↑	↓↑	↓↑	↓↑	↓	↓↑	↓↑	↓
	d														↓
												↓		↓	↓
											↓	↓		↓	↓
									↓		↓	↓		↓	↓
							↓		↓		↓	↓		↓	↓
Number of unpaired electrons		1		0		1		2		3		5	2	4	6
		Li $_{3}$		Be $_{4}$		B $_{5}$		C $_{6}$		N $_{7}$			O $_{8}$		
		Na $^{1}_{11}$		Mg $^{1}_{12}$		Al $^{1}_{13}$		Si $^{1}_{14}$		P $^{1}_{15}$			S $^{1}_{16}$		
		K $^{2}_{19}$		Ca $^{2}_{20}$			Sc $^{2}_{21}$		Ti $^{2}_{22}$		V $^{2}_{23}$				Cr
			Cu $^{2}_{29}$		Zn $^{2}_{30}$	Ga $^{2}_{31}$		Ge $^{2}_{32}$		As $^{2}_{33}$			Se $^{2}_{34}$		
		Rb $^{3}_{37}$		Sr $^{3}_{38}$			Y $^{3}_{39}$		Zr $^{3}_{40}$			Nb $^{3}_{41}$			Mo
			Ag $^{3}_{47}$		Cd $^{3}_{48}$	In $^{3}_{49}$		Sn $^{3}_{50}$		Sb $^{3}_{51}$			Te $^{3}_{52}$		
		Cs $^{4}_{55}$		Ba $^{4}_{56}$			La $^{4}_{57}$		Hf $^{5}_{72}$		Ta $^{5}_{73}$			W $^{5}_{74}$	
			Au $^{5}_{79}$		Hg $^{5}_{80}$	Tl $^{5}_{81}$		Pb $^{5}_{82}$		Bi $^{5}_{83}$			Po $^{5}_{84}$		
		Fr $^{6}_{87}$		Ra $^{6}_{88}$			Ac $^{6}_{89}$								

Electron configuration of inner shells (indicated by superscript)

[1] $1s^2$ [2] $1s^2 2s^2 2p^6$ [3] $1s^2 2s^2 2p^6 3s^2 3p^6 3d^{10}$ [4] $1s^2 2s^2 2p^6 3s^2 3p^6 3d^{10} 4s^2 4$

of the Elements (Mendeléeff)

VII			VIII								O	—	—
A	B_1	B_2	B_1	B_2	C_1	C_2	C_3	D_1	D_2	D_3		—	—
7			8		9			10			8	1	2
↓											↓↑		
↓↑											↓↑		
↓↑											↓↑		
↓↑	↓↑	↓	↓↑	↓	↓↑	↓		↓↑	↓		↓↑	↓	↓↑
	↓	↓	↓	↓	↓	↓	↓	↓	↓	↓↑			
	↓	↓	↓	↓	↓	↓	↓↑	↓	↓↑	↓↑			
	↓	↓	↓	↓	↓	↓↑	↓↑	↓↑	↓↑	↓↑			
	↓	↓	↓	↓↑	↓↑	↓↑	↓↑	↓↑	↓↑	↓↑			
	↓	↓↑	↓↑	↓↑	↓↑	↓↑	↓↑	↓↑	↓↑	↓↑			
1	5		4		3		1	2		0			

A	B_1	B_2	B_1	B_2	C_1	C_2	C_3	D_1	D_2	D_3	O	—	—	*Configuration of penultimate shell*	*Principal quantum number of outer electrons*
												H_{1}	He_{2}	—	1
F_{9}											Ne_{10}			s^2	2
Cl^{1}_{17}											Ar^{1}_{18}			s^2p^6	3
	Mn^{2}_{25}		Fe^{2}_{26}		Co^{2}_{27}			Ni^{2}_{28}							4
Br^{2}_{35}											Kr^{2}_{36}			$s^2p^6d^{10}$	
		Tc^{3}_{43}		Ru^{3}_{44}		Rh^{3}_{45}				Pd^{3}_{46}				s^2p^6	5
I^{3}_{53}											Xe^{3}_{54}			$s^2p^6d^{10}$	
	Re^{5}_{75}		Os^{5}_{76}				Ir^{5}_{77}		Pt^{5}_{78}					s^2p^6	6
At^{5}_{85}											Rn^{5}_{86}			$f^{14}s^2p^6d^{10}$	
														s^2p^6	7

$s^2 2s^2 2p^6 3s^2 3p^6 3d^{10} 4s^2 4p^6 4d^{10} 4f^{14}$

6 $1s^2 2s^2 2p^6 3s^2 3p^6 3d^{10} 4s^2 4p^6 4d^{10} 4f^{14} 5s^2 5p^6 5d^{10}$

Table IX Periodic Classific

Periodic group		I	II	*Transition group*													
Distribution of outer electrons	*p*																
	s	↓	↓↑	↓↑	↓↑	↓↑	↓	↓↑	↓	↓↑	↓	↓↑	↓	↓↑	↓		↓
	d			↓	↓	↓	↓	↓	↓	↓	↓↑	↓↑	↓↑	↓↑	↓↑	↓↑	↓
					↓	↓	↓	↓	↓	↓	↓	↓	↓↑	↓↑	↓↑	↓↑	↓
						↓	↓	↓	↓	↓	↓	↓	↓	↓	↓↑	↓↑	↓
							↓	↓	↓	↓	↓	↓	↓	↓	↓	↓↑	
									↓	↓	↓	↓	↓	↓	↓	↓	
Number of unpaired electrons		1	0	1	2	3	5	4	6	5	5	4	4	3	3	1	
Principle quantum number of outer electrons	1																
	2	Li	Be														
	3	Na	Mg														
	4	K	Ca	Sc	Ti	V			Cr	Mn		Fe		Co			
	5	Rb	Sr	Y	Zr		Nb		Mo		Tc		Ru		Rh		
	6	Cs	Ba	La	Hf	Ta		W		Re		Os				Ir	
	7	Fr	Ra	Ac													
Lanthanons				Ce	Pr	Nd	Pm	Sm	Eu	Gd	Tb	Dy	Ho	Er	Tm	Yb	
Actinons				Th	Pa	U	Np	Pu	Am	Cm							

PERIODIC CLASSIFICATION OF THE ELEMENTS

Elements (expanded form)

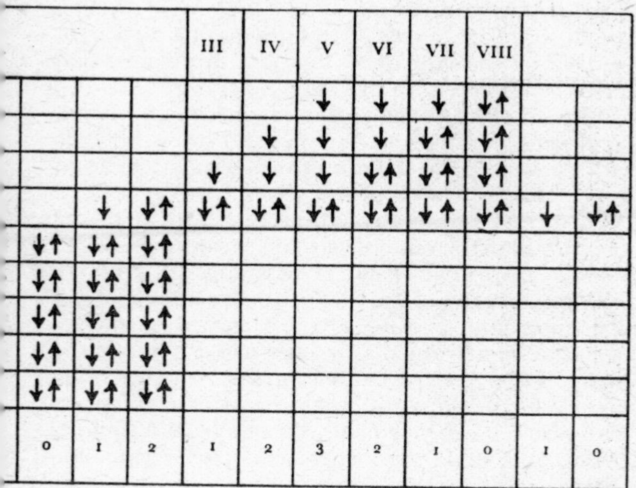

			III	IV	V	VI	VII	VIII			*Configurations of inner shells*
					↓	↓	↓	↓↑			
				↓	↓	↓	↓↑	↓↑			
			↓	↓	↓	↓↑	↓↑	↓↑			
	↓	↓↑	↓↑	↓↑	↓↑	↓↑	↓↑	↓↑	↓	↓↑	
↓↑	↓↑	↓↑									
↓↑	↓↑	↓↑									
↓↑	↓↑	↓↑									
↓↑	↓↑	↓↑									
↓↑	↓↑	↓↑									
0	1	2	1	2	3	2	1	0	1	0	
									H	He	
			B	C	N	O	F	Ne			$1s^2$
			Al	Si	P	S	Cl	A			$1s^2 2s^2 2p^6$
	Cu	Zn									$1s^2 2s^2 2p^6 3s^2 3p^6$
			Ga	Ge	As	Se	Br	Kr			$1s^2 2s^2 2p^6 3s^2 3p^6 3d^{10} 4s^2$
Pd	Ag	Cd									$1s^2 2s^2 2p^6 3s^2 3p^6 3d^{10} 4s^2 4p^6$
			In	Sn	Sb	Te	I	Xe			$1s^2 2s^2 2p^6 3s^2 3p^6 3d^{10} 4s^2 4p^6 4d^{10} 5s^2$
	Au	Hg									$1s^2 2s^2 2p^6 3s^2 3p^6 3d^{10} 4s^2 4p^6 4d^{10} 5s^2 5p^6$
			Tl	Pb	Bi	Po	At	Rn			$1s^2 2s^2 2p^6 3s^2 3p^6 3d^{10} 4s^2 4p^6 4d^{10} 4f^{14} 5s^2 5p^6 5d^{10} 6s^2$
											$1s^2 2s^2 2p^6 3s^2 3p^6 3d^{10} 4s^2 4p^6 4d^{10} 4f^{14} 5s^2 5p^6 5d^{10} 6s^2 6p^6$

prepared was curium, which was identified in the product of the bombardment of Pu^{239} with helium ions, the reaction being Pu^{239} (α, n) Cm^{242}. Both americium and curium form triply charged positive ions in solution and are carried quantitatively by the lanthanon fluorides in precipitation reactions and are separated from them with difficulty.

Of the synthetic transuranium elements only plutonium has been found naturally; it exists in very small quantities (1 part in 10^{14}) in pitchblende and carnotite in which it is produced by the absorption of neutrons from various sources by the uranium isotope U^{238} in the ore.

The problem of the structure of the atom may be regarded as falling into two parts: the configuration of the outer electronic shells, upon which the chemical behaviour of the elements largely depends and the structure of the nucleus in which the greater part of the mass of the atom is centred. In view of the very large number of isotopes of the elements which are known to exist, it cannot but be significant that in only four cases does the order of the atomic weights differ from the order of the elements when arranged with increasing value of nuclear charge, *i.e.* atomic number. Many more exceptions to this might be imagined; thus there exist isotopes of argon, chlorine, calcium and potassium whose isotopic weights are respectively 36, 37, 40 and 41, and if these isotopes were to predominate in the naturally occurring elements, the order of atomic weights would be different from that which actually exists and which is identical with the order of these elements in terms of their atomic number. Any theory of the structure of the nucleus must therefore ultimately explain why there exists an approximate relationship between the mass m, in hydrogen units, and the nuclear charge Z, in electronic units, given by:

$$m/Z = 1/2 \text{ to } 1/2{\cdot}6$$

PERIODICITY OF PROPERTIES

Quantum mechanics has shown that periodicity is conditioned by the repetition of the configurations of outer electrons and it is natural that only those properties which are concerned with the structure of the outer electrons of the atoms should reveal periodicity. Thus it is found that ionization potentials, ionic dimensions, polarisation *etc* when considered as a function of atomic number give a curve similar to the atomic volume curve. Other

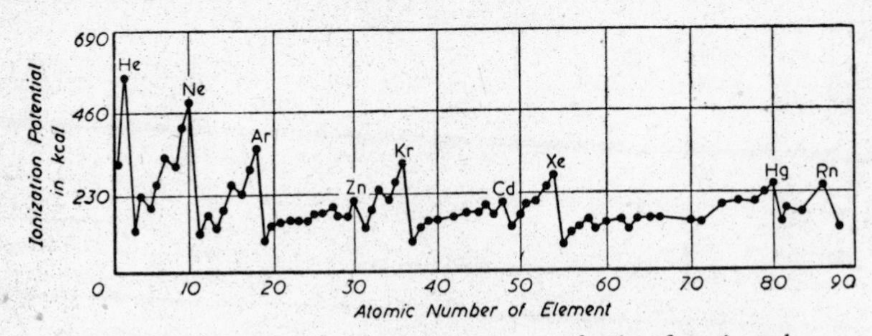

Figure 8 Ionization potentials of the elements as a function of atomic number

phenomena, such as the heat capacities of monatomic gases, which are not influenced by the outer shells of electrons, show no periodic properties.

A study of properties which show periodicity is therefore most important, and leads to a better understanding of the observed chemical periodicity; such deductions that may be made, however, are at the moment only qualitative.

Ionization potentials— The ionization potential represents the energy necessary to remove an electron from the atom. This energy we shall designate as I_1 and is generally termed the first ionization potential. The second ionization potential, I_2, represents the energy required to remove an electron from the singly charged positive ion. The first ionization potentials of the atoms are given in *Table X* and are also represented in *Figure 8*. where the periodicity is evident. The variation of the ionization potential with atomic number reveals a series of important generalizations, which will be discussed in some detail because of the importance of ionization potentials in several chemical processes, such as the tendency for a given element to form ionic compounds.

Table X. First Ionization Potentials (kcals)

																H	He
																312	563·8
Li	Be											B	C	N	O	F	Ne
123·5	213·8											190·1	258·3	333·4	312·2	(414·7)	494·4
Na	Mg											Al	Si	P	S	Cl	Ar
117·7	175·3											137·3	186·6	253·4	237·5	298·6	361·5
K	Ca	Se	Ti	V	Cr	Mn	Fe	Co	Ni	Cu	Zn	Ga	Ge	As	Se	Br	Kr
99·5	140·3	154·0	156·9	155·7	155·3	170·5	180·4	195·8	175·3	176·9	215·6	137·5	186·4	241·9	223·5	(265)	321·2
Rb	Sr	Y	Zr		Mo		Ru	Rh	Pd	Ag	Cd	In	Sn	Sb	Te	I	Xe
95·8	130·6	150	159·4		165·9		(177)	177·4	191·2	173·7	206·4	132·7	168·2	192·4	206·4	241·9	278·3
Cs	Ba	La			W		Os		Pt	Au	Hg	Tl	Pb	Bi			Rn
89·2	119·6	128·8			186·6		200·4		204·6	211·7	239·1	139·8	170	167·0			246·5
	Ra																
	121·0																

Consider the series of elements in the first and second groups shown in *Table X*:

Li	Na	K	Rb	Cs
123·5	117·7	99·5	95·8	89·2

Be	Mg	Ca	Sr	Ba
213·8	175·3	140·3	130·6	119·6

The energy involved in liberating an electron from an atom of an alkaline earth metal is greater than that required in the case of the corresponding alkali metal; thus we may conclude that an unpaired *s* electron is removed from an atom much more easily than a paired one. This indicates that the pairing of two electrons in an *s* orbital increases the attraction energy between an *s* electron and the atom.

Considering the elements of the second and third groups:

Be	Mg	Zn	Cd	Hg
213·8	175·3	215·6	206·4	239·1

B	Al	Ga	In	Tl
190·1	137·3	137·5	132·7	139·8

it is seen that a *p* electron is more easily removed from the atom than one of a pair of *s* electrons. The comparison of gallium, indium and thallium with respectively zinc, cadmium and mercury rather than with calcium, strontium and barium is necessary in view of the electronic configurations :

$$\begin{array}{ll} \text{Ga} & 1s^2\,2s^2\,2p^6\,3s^2\,3p^6\,3d^{10}\,4s^2\,4p^1 \\ \text{Zn} & 1s^2\,2s^2\,2p^6\,3s^2\,3p^6\,3d^{10}\,4s^2 \\ \text{Ca} & 1s^2\,2s^2\,2p^6\,3s^2\,3p^6\qquad\;\; 4s^2 \end{array}$$

The inner shells of gallium and zinc are identical, whereas those of gallium and calcium are not (see below).

There appears to be a considerable difference between atoms containing *d* electrons when compared with those which do not, *e.g.*

K	Rb	Cs	
99·5	95·8	89·2	($s^2\,p^6\,s$)
Cu	Ag	Au	
176·9	173·7	211·7	($s^2\,p^6\,d^{10}\,s$)
Ca	Sr	Ba	
140·3	130·6	119·6	($s^2\,p^6\,s^2$)
Zn	Cd	Hg	
215·6	206·4	239·1	($s^2\,p^6\,d^{10}\,s^2$)

The presence of a completed *d* shell markedly raises the ionization potential of the element. The explanation of this phenomenon is related to the theory of the homopolar bond ; the additional mutual interaction of the *s* and *d* electrons evidently increases the strength of the attraction energy between the *s* electron and the atom.

In the case of the fourth and fifth groups, it is worthy of note that the ionization potentials of the elements in the fourth group, possessing three unpaired electrons, N, P, As *etc*, are greater than the neighbouring elements of the fifth group, where only two of the *p* electrons are unpaired. The ionization potentials of the halogens lie between the corresponding elements in groups six and eight. In every case the inert gas, having a completely filled series of *s* and *p* orbitals has the greatest ionization potential.

The dissimilar sequence of ionization potentials within a particular period (see *Figure 8*) is closely linked with the electronic character of the outer shell of electrons, whether it contains *s*, *p*, *d* or *f* electrons, and the number of unpaired electrons within each shell.

The variation of the ionization potential in the groups of elements is also of significance. As a general rule the ionization potential decreases as the group is descended, *i.e.* as the atomic number increases and the difference in the first and second periods is considerable, *e.g.*

$$\begin{aligned} I_N - I_P &= 80 \text{ kcals} \\ I_O - I_S &= 74{\cdot}7 \text{ kcals} \\ I_C - I_{Si} &= 71{\cdot}7 \text{ kcals} \end{aligned}$$

The decrease is less, however, between elements of the second and third periods :

$$\begin{aligned} I_P - I_{As} &= 11.5 \text{ kcals} \\ I_S - I_{Se} &= 14 \text{ kcals} \\ I_{Si} - I_{Ge} &= 0{\cdot}2 \text{ kcals} \end{aligned}$$

This marked difference is possibly connected with the fact that in germanium, arsenic and selenium, a shell of *d* electrons is present. Comparison of the various different ionization potentials, *Table XI*, indicates a marked difference in ionization energy between electrons of different main quantum number. In this table the values given are relative to the ionization potential of hydrogen (312 kcals). In the atom of lithium the relative ionization energy of the outer 2*s* electron is 0·4 units, whereas the second electron, which is a 1*s* electron requires an amount of energy fourteen times as great, thus indicating that the electrons with quantum number $n = 1$, are held much more firmly to the atom. In the case of beryllium, the successive relative ionization potentials are 0·7, 1·34, 11·3 and 16. Here there is a marked difference in value between the second and first electronic shells. The same behaviour is observed with other elements, and in *Table XI* the change of main quantum number is indicated by the thick line.

Table XI. Ionization Potentials relative to that of Hydrogen

Element	*Atomic Number*	*Configuration of outer electrons*	I_1	I_2	I_3	I	I_5	I_6	I_7	I_8
H	1	s	1·00							
He	2	s^2	1·84	4·00						
Li	3	s	0·4	5·9	9·0					
Be	4	s^2	0·7	1·34	11·3	16·0				
B	5	s^2p	0·61	1·85	2·8	19·3	25			
C	6	s^2p^2	0·83	1·79	3·52	4·74	24·0	36·0		
N	7	s^2p^3	1·07	2·18	3·49	5·43	7·19	40·5	49·0	
O	8	s^2p^4	1·00	2·58	4·04	5·69	8·07	10·14	54·5	64
F	9	s^2p^5	(1·33)	2·57	4·62	6·40	7·56	11·0	13·6	70
Ne	10	s^2p^6	1·58	3·02	4·67					
Na	11	s	0·38	3·5	5·24					
Mg	12	s^2	0·56	1·10	5·89					
Al	13	s^2p	0·44	1·38	2·09	9·0				
Si	14	s^2p^2	0·60	1·20	2·46	3·32	12·47			
P	15	s^2p^3	0·80	1·46	2·22	3·53	4·78			
S	16	s^2p^4	0·76	1·72	2·58	3·48	4·93	6·47		
Cl	17	s^2p^5	0·96	1·73	2·93	3·50	5·00	(6·8)	8·0	
Ar	18	s^2p^6	1·16	2·05	3·01	12·6				
K	19	s	0·32	2·34	3·47					
Ca	20	s^2	0·45	0·87	3·76					
Sc	21	s^2d	0·49	0·95	1·82	5·33				
Ti	22	s^2d^2	0·50	1·00	2·03	3·17	7·07			
V	23	s^2d^3	0·50	1·04	1·95	3·59	5·05	9·05		
Cr	24	sd^5	0·50	1·23	(2·0)	(3·7)	(5·4)			
Mn	25	s^2d^5	0·50	1·16	(2·4)	(3·72)	(5·6)			

Electron affinity— The electron affinity, which is a characteristic property of an atom in a similar way to the ionization potential, represents the energy required to combine an atom and a free electron with the formation of a negative ion. Until relatively recently, values were calculated from the lattice energies of ionic crystals by the Born-Haber cycle. During the last ten years, however, the electron affinity of the halogen atoms has been determined experimentally[7] and in *Table XII* the values of IONOV and DUKELSKI[7] are given together with the value for oxygen determined by VIER and MAYER[8]. These experimental values are in good agreement with the values calculated from lattice energies and from experimental heats of dissociation of the alkali metal halides. Calculated values of the electron affinity for several different atoms are given in *Table XIII*.

Table XII. Experimental Values of Electron Affinity

Atom	Energy kcals	Atom	Energy kcals
F	95	I	76
Cl	86	O	71
Br	84		

Table XIII. Calculated Values of Electron Affinity

Atom	Energy kcals	Reference	Atom	Energy kcals	Reference	Atom	Energy kcals	Reference
H	16·4	9	Li	12	10	Na	5	11
			Be	−14	12	Mg	−21	12
			B	3	11	Al	2	11
			C	21	11	Si	14	12
			N	−17	11	P	5	12
						S	48	12
			F	94	10	Cl	85	12
He	0	10	Ne	−28	12	Ar	−23	12
Cu	23	11	Ag	26	11	Au	56	11
						Hg	42	12

The electron affinity of mercury according to the experimental data of SIMON and SEWARD[13] is close to 35 kcals, in reasonable agreement with the calculated value. The energy required to give two electrons to oxygen as calculated from the lattice energy of oxides is between − 157 and − 175 kcals, and for sulphur the energy of the reaction $S \rightarrow S^{2-}$ is between − 71 and − 80 kcals. As is shown clearly in *Tables XII* and *XIII* only the halogens possess a high positive affinity for the electron; with oxygen the affinity for a single electron is less than in the case of the halogens, but the affinity for a second electron is negative. It may be concluded from these data that the tendency to form a complete electronic shell similar to an inert gas is not marked except for the halogens. The transition of N to N^{3-} would require 550 kcals[11]. In general therefore with atoms having three unpaired electrons the tendency towards taking up even a single electron is small and the electron affinity is close to zero; with atoms possessing two and one unpaired electrons, the electron affinity may be considerable but with the inert gases the electron affinity has a negative value.

The small affinities of lithium and sodium are of little importance, but copper, silver and gold, with completed *d* shells, possess marked electron affinity and whereas the alkaline earth metals, with completed *s* levels, have negative electron affinities, mercury, with a completed *d* and *s* level, has a high positive electron affinity.

Electronegativity— The comparison of atoms according to their electropositive or electronegative character *i.e.* their tendency to form positive or negative ions has played an important part in the development of chemical theory, and is in many ways more important than comparisons of electron affinity and ionization potential.

Consider two atoms A and B and let the electron of atom A be removed.

This process requires an amount of energy I_A equivalent to the ionization potential of A. If this electron is now transferred to B there will be a release of energy F_B, the electron affinity of B. The overall loss of energy in the transfer of the electron from A to B will be equal to $I_A - F_B$. If we carry out the reverse process, removing the electron from B and transferring it to A the loss of energy will be $I_B - F_A$. If both these quantities are equal ***i.e.***

$$I_A - F_B = I_B - F_A \text{ or } I_A + F_A = I_B + F_B$$

then the transference of the electron from A to B with the formation of A^+ and B^- demands the same amount of energy as the formation of A^- and B^+ and both atoms may be regarded as being equally electronegative.

If, however,

$$I_A - F_B > I_B - F_A \text{ then } I_A + F_A > I_B + F_B$$

and it is more difficult to remove the electron from A and transfer it to B, than to transfer the electron from B to A. Thus the electronegativity of A is more than that of B. MULLIKAN[14] has suggested that the values of I and F for each atom may be used to calculate the electronegativity and values calculated in this way are given in *Table XIV*.

Table XIV. Electronegativity of Elements according to Mullikan

Element	Electronegativity kcals	
	uncorrected value	*corrected value*
F	510	586
Cl	385	452
Br	349	418
I	318	382
H	328·4	328·4
Li	135	135

The lower values given in the second column of *Table XIV* are due to the fact that the ionization potential (considering iodine) represents the energy involved in removing from the atom of iodine one of its paired p electrons, since the iodine ion according to the rule of Hund will have the following configuration :

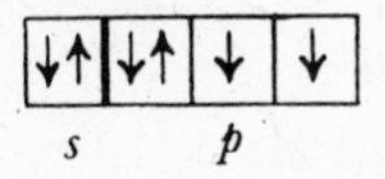

According to Mullikan, for the formation of an ionic bond interest lies not so much in the normal ion which could take part in two covalent bonds, but in an ion of the following structure :

↓↑	↓↑	↓↑	

s p

containing no unpaired electrons. This type of ion will be produced by removing from the atom the single unpaired electron, which will require more energy than the ionization potential leading to the normal ion, the difference between the two ionization potentials being equal to the excitation energy between the above two states. Mullikan introduced corrections to allow for this and the corrected values are given in the third column of *Table XIV*. The corrected values show the halogens more electronegative than hydrogen in agreement with their chemical behaviour. It is noteworthy, however, that the electronegativity value of hydrogen lies much nearer to the halogens than to the alkali metals.

The electropositive character of the metals is determined by the fact that their ionization potentials are not great and their electron affinities are close to zero. The gradual variation of the electronegativity values of the metals is due to the progression of their ionization potentials, the electronegativity falling in the case of the alkali metals from lithium to caesium. Mullikan has attempted to calculate the electronegativities of polyvalent atoms but the values obtained can only be regarded as approximate, as the higher ionization potentials and the electron affinities, where several electrons are involved, are not known exactly.

REFERENCES

[1] UHLENBECK, G. E. and GOUDSMIT, S. *Naturwiss.* 13 (1925) 953
— — *Nature, Lond.* 11 (1926) 264
[2] HUND, F. *Linienspektren und periodisches System der Elemente* Berlin, 1927
WHITE, H. E. *Introduction to Atomic Spectra* New York, 1934
[3] BACHER, R. F. and GOUDSMIT, S. *Atomic Energy States as Derived from the Analyses of Optical Spectra* New York, 1932
[4] FERMI, E. *Z. Physik* 48 (1928) 73
[5] MCMILLAN, E. M. and ABELSON, P. H. *Phys. Rev.* 57 (1940) 1185
[6] SEABORG, G. T., MCMILLAN, E. M., KENNEDY, J. W. and WAHL, A. C. *ibid* 69 (1946) 366
SEABORG, G. T., WAHL, A. C. and KENNEDY, J. W. *ibid* 69 (1946) 367
[7] IONOV, N. I. and DUKELSKI, V. M. *J. exp. theor. Phys. U.S.S.R.* 10 (1940) 1248
MCCALLUM, K. J. and MAYER, J. E. *J. chem. Phys.* 11 (1943) 56
SUTTON, P. P. and MAYER, J. E. *ibid* 3 (1935) 20
GLOCKLER, G. and CALVIN, M. *ibid* 4 (1936) 492
BUCHDAHL, R. *ibid* 9 (1941) 146
[8] VIER, D. T. and MAYER, J. E. *ibid* 12 (1944) 28
[9] HYLLERAAS, E. A. *Z. Physik* 65 (1930) 209
KAZARNOWSKI, J. *ibid* 38 (1926) 12
[10] WU, T. *Phil. Mag.* 22 (1936) 837
[11] HELMANN, H. and MAMOTENKO, M. *J. exp. theor. Phys. U.S.S.R.* 8 (1938) 24
[12] GLOCKLER, G. *Phys. Rev.* 46 (1934) 111
[13] SIMON, J. H. and SEWARD, R. P. *J. chem. Phys.* 6 (1938) 790
[14] MULLIKAN, R. S. *ibid* 2 (1934) 782

3

THE HOMOPOLAR (COVALENT) BOND

DEVELOPMENT OF IDEAS ON THE CHEMICAL BOND

THE fundamental problem of chemistry, which may be briefly stated as the explanation of the combination of atoms to form molecules, has been the subject of speculation for a considerable time, and by the beginning of the nineteenth century a relationship between chemical reactivity and electrostatic charges on the atoms was contemplated. The investigation of the electrolysis of water, of aqueous solutions and of fused alkalis formed the basis for the electrostatic theory of valency developed by BERZELIUS in 1812. This theory, which assumed that the force between atoms in molecules was entirely electrostatic in character was found to be entirely satisfactory for a large number of inorganic compounds. The success of this theory was, however, shortlived. The development of organic chemistry, leading to the isolation of a large number of compounds whose properties were very different from the inorganic salts, led to the rejection of the electrostatic theory as a general theory of valency. The nature of the problem may be indicated by reference to the C–H and C–Cl bonds. In acetic acid it is possible to replace electropositive hydrogen by electronegative chlorine leaving the compound more or less unchanged in its general properties, apart from an increase in acid strength. According to the Berzelius theory these bonds would be represented by $C^- H^+$ and $C^+ Cl^-$ respectively and it was argued that if this were correct, the replacement of a negative by a positive carbon atom would be expected to alter considerably the properties of the compound. Similarly with methane and carbon tetrachloride, whose formulae according to the Berzelius theory would be :

$$\begin{array}{ccc} & H^+ & \\ H^+ & C^{4-} & H^+ \\ & H^+ & \end{array} \qquad\qquad \begin{array}{ccc} & Cl^- & \\ Cl^- & C^{4+} & Cl^- \\ & Cl^- & \end{array}$$

Again the very great change in the polarity of the carbon atom was regarded either as impossible, or at least liable to produce a much greater change in the relative reactivity of these compounds than was observed.

The systematic investigation of a large number of organic compounds led to the formulation, largely by VAN'T HOFF and LE BEL, of a structural theory of valency which permitted an adequate description of organic compounds and which is still of considerable application at the present day. The ideas of this theory were very simple, ascribing to hydrogen, oxygen, nitrogen and carbon valencies of one, two, three and four respectively. In contrast to the theory of Berzelius which had attempted to explain the nature of the force acting between atoms in compounds, the theory developed from the study of organic compounds made no attempt to explain the nature of the bonding forces. The structural theory has been developed in recent years and modified considerably by the introduction of such ideas as double bonds, partial valency and the resonance of valency structures, but the basis of the idea remains unchanged.

An extension of the structural theory of valency was made by WERNER in the field of inorganic chemistry at about the same time as the development of structural organic chemistry. In order to explain the structure and formation of complex inorganic compounds in which the number of atoms or radicles surrounding a central atom did not correspond to its normal valency as given in the periodic classification, it was necessary to introduce the idea of the coordinate link. The nature of the forces involved in this link, however, remained as obscure as the nature of the bond in organic compounds.

The development of atomic theory at the end of the nineteenth and at the beginning of the twentieth centuries and in particular the knowledge that atoms consist of positively charged nuclei and negatively charged electrons led to a revival of the electrostatic theory of Berzelius by KOSSEL in 1916. The periodic system of the elements may be regarded as consisting of two parts, the inert gases and all other elements. The group of inert gases is characterised by a complete lack of chemical reactivity and Kossel considered that the criterion of this inert nature was a complete octet of electrons. Considering the atoms situated on either side of an inert gas *e.g.* neon, sodium has an extra electron compared with neon whereas the other element, fluorine has one less than neon. By the transfer of an electron from sodium to fluorine leading to the formation of two ions, Na^+ and F^-, both atoms have obtained the stable inert gas structure of neon. The electrostatic attraction between the two ions Na^+ and F^- then leads to the formation of the ionic crystal of sodium fluoride. If the total energy involved in the three processes : $Na = Na^+ + e$; $F + e = F^-$; $Na^+ + F^- = NaF$ (crystal), is positive then the formation of the ionic compound will occur.*

In the formation of binary salts of the type NaF, the electronic charges, as suggested by Kossel, do play an important part. It will be shown later, however, that electrostatic forces do not provide a complete explanation of the stability of ionic compounds and the energy of gaseous sodium chloride, for example, is a little greater than the value calculated on the basis of Kossel's theory. Nevertheless the electrostatic theory may be regarded as a fair approximation for a large number of inorganic ionic compounds.

In the same way as the theory of Berzelius failed to explain the nature of the valency forces in organic compounds, so Kossel's theory failed to account not only for the valency forces in organic compounds, but also in simple molecules such as H_2, O_2, N_2, CO *etc*. The first attempt to explain the formation of such covalent or homopolar compounds was made by LEWIS in 1916 and consisted of a correlation of the classical structural theory of organic chemistry and the newer data concerning the structure of the atom. According to Lewis the covalent bond consisted of the interaction of two electrons, one being donated by each atom. The evidence for this speculation lay in the observation that of the very large number of molecules known at that time, all but a few exceptions contained an even number of electrons. The few exceptions were extremely reactive molecules, *e.g.* NO, which readily formed compounds containing an even number of electrons, *e.g.* NOCl. The theory of Lewis as modified by LANGMUIR was

* The position of chemical equilibrium is characterized by a minimum value of the Gibbs free energy G. $\Delta G = \Delta H - T\Delta S$, where H is the heat content, S the entropy and T the absolute temperature. In the case of the formation of molecules from atoms, ΔS is always negative, because, as statistical mechanics show, the entropy of a diatomic molecule is less than the sum of the entropy of the individual atoms since the randomness has been reduced. Therefore $- T\Delta S$ will always be positive. Thus the more exothermic the reaction, *i.e.* the greater $- \Delta H$, the greater the shift of equilibrium in favour of the formation of the diatomic molecule.

a considerable contribution to valency theory, but this theory together with that of Kossel must be regarded as an approximation, which although giving a qualitative picture of the chemical bond and which describes in certain cases the nature of the molecule, fails to explain completely the nature of the forces involved in the chemical bond. A solution to this problem has only come as a result of the application of quantum mechanics.

THE HYDROGEN MOLECULE ION, H_2^+

In the atom, electrons move in the field of a single nucleus whereas in a molecule, the electrons exist in a field due to several nuclei and wave mechanics show that the latter state may be more favourable on the basis of energy considerations. Let us consider the simplest molecule *viz* the hydrogen molecule ion H_2^+, formed by the combination of a hydrogen atom and a proton. In this molecule a single electron exists in the field of two nuclei. The existence of this molecule has been demonstrated spectroscopically and the heat of formation of the molecule from a hydrogen atom and a proton is 61 kcals/gm mol. ; the distance between the nuclei is 1·06Å. The ion is, however, very reactive and the energy liberated in the reaction $H_2^+ + e = H_2$ is 354 kcals and it has therefore, a very limited existence. The problem of the structure of the hydrogen molecule ion is one which can only be dealt with adequately from the point of view of wave mechanics ; attempts to apply the Bohr method to the motion of a single electron round two nuclei were completely unsuccessful.

The formation of the hydrogen molecule ion may be conceived in the following way. Let an atom of hydrogen (proton *a* together with an electron) and a proton *b* exist initially at a great distance apart:

a •   *b*

In this position the electron evidently belongs to the nucleus *a*, because it exists for by far the greater part of its time in the field of this nucleus and the probability of locating the electron very far from nucleus *a* is very small, *e.g.* even if the distance between the nuclei is reduced to 5×10^{-7} cm the electron will be found near the nucleus *b* only 1 in 10^{12} years. Thus it may be concluded that in this initial state, the energy of the system is practically equal to the sum of the energies of the proton and the atom of hydrogen. However, as the proton *b* approaches the atom *a*, the probability of the transfer of the electron from *a* to *b* increases, and it may be calculated, that when the distance between the nuclei is 2×10^{-8} cm (2 Å) the transfer will occur once every 10^{-14} secs.

As the nuclei approach, the idea that the electron belongs to one particular nucleus loses meaning and once the H_2^+ molecule has been formed it is physically impossible to show whether the molecule has been formed from atom *a* and nucleus *b* or from atom *b* and nucleus *a*. It will, however, be convenient to picture three possible configurations of the electron in the system of two nuclei :

1 The electron may be regarded as being attached to nucleus *a*, and nucleus *b* is denuded
2 The electron is regarded as being attached to nucleus *b* and *a* is denuded
3 The transitional state when the electron is attached to both nuclei simultaneously; this may be represented physically as an electronic cloud between the two nuclei.

The resulting identity of states *a* and *b* and the production of the intermediate state results in the formation of a chemical bond.

The first conclusion which may be drawn from this elementary introduction is that a chemical bond between two atoms is only possible when the atoms or molecules concerned have approached as close as approximately 10^{-8} cm., since only at such distances is the probability of electronic transfer sufficiently great to produce bonding. The interaction energies fall off rapidly as the distance between the nuclei increases and from the point of view of chemical reaction, a distance between nuclei of 10^{-7} cm may be regarded as infinite.

It will be clear from the above discussion that the delocalization of the electron plays an important part in the theory of the chemical bond. In place of the fixed orbits of Bohr, quantum mechanics leads to a statistically probable description of the state of the electron when it exists both in the field of a single or of several nuclei.

In order to simplify somewhat the following treatment, use will be made of the atomic units of HARTREE[1] which result in a simpler form of the Schrödinger equation. The Bohr radius, $a = h^2/4\pi^2me^2 = 0{\cdot}528$Å is taken as the unit of length, the unit of charge is regarded as the charge on the electron, $e = 4{\cdot}799 \times 10^{-10}$ e.s.u and the unit of mass is taken as the mass of the electron, which is $9{\cdot}1 \times 10^{-28}$ gm. Energy is expressed in terms of the charge and the Bohr orbit, $E = e^2/a$. This value, which represents twice the value for the energy of the atom of hydrogen in its ground state, $E_H = e^2/2a$, is taken as the unit of energy and is equal to 27·08 ev = 624 kcals/gm mol.

Employing these units the Schrödinger equation 1.34 becomes

$$\nabla^2\psi + 2(E - V)\psi = 0 \qquad \ldots.(3{\cdot}1)$$

The repulsion energy between the electron and the nucleus will be $-1/r$, where r is the distance from the electron to the nucleus in units of the Bohr radius.

In the molecule H_2^+, r_a and r_b represent the distances between the electron and the nuclei *a* and *b*, and *R* is the distance between the nuclei (see *Figure 9*). The potential energy *V* will be the sum of the various charge interaction terms, *i.e.* interaction between the electron and nucleus *a*, $(-1/r_a)$; interaction between the electron and nucleus *b*, $(-1/r_b)$; and the mutual interaction of the two nuclei $(+1/R)$.

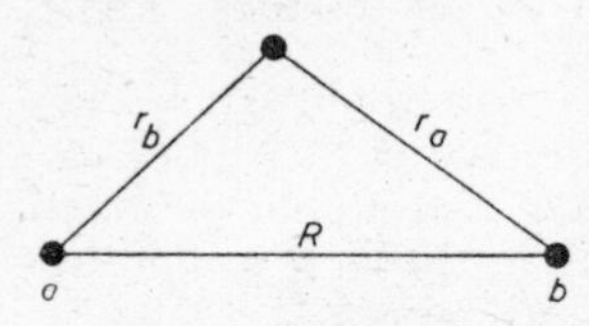

Figure 9. Coordinates for the hydrogen molecule ion

The total potential energy is thus given by

$$V = -1/r_a - 1/r_b + 1/R \qquad \ldots.(3{\cdot}2)$$

and the Schrödinger equation for the H_2^+ molecule becomes

$$\nabla^2\psi + 2(E + 1/r_a + 1/r_b - 1/R)\psi = 0 \qquad \ldots.(3{\cdot}3)$$

This equation describes the state of the electron for a particular value of *R*; variation of the value of the internuclear distance gives different values for the energy of the system. When *R* is large, the interaction energy is zero but as the atom and the proton approach each other, the electron attracts both nuclei and the potential energy is decreased, *i.e.* an exothermic process has taken place. The decrease of energy, however, has a limit, becuase as the nuclei approach each other, their mutual repulsion reduces the attraction due to the electron and ultimately at very small distances, is greater than the attraction energy. Thus a stable equilibrium state, where the energy is a minimum, will exist at a particular value of R which is found by experiment to be 1·06 Å.

For the hydrogen molecule ion it is possible to solve the Schrödinger equation and calculate the energy of formation of the molecule. The solution is only approximate, however, and the value for the energy cannot be regarded as exact, but the solution does permit a picture of the forces involved in a chemical bond to be obtained. As pointed out above, when the distance between the nuclei is great, the system may be considered as an atom a and a separate nucleus b. The Schrödinger equation then has the form

$$\nabla^2\psi_a + 2(E + 1/r_a)\psi_a = 0 \qquad \ldots.(3.4)$$

which is identical with the equation for the hydrogen atom. The wave function ψ_a refers to the electron in the field of the nucleus a. The solution of this equation in atomic units (see *Table IV*) will be

$$\psi_a = \{\exp(-r_a)\}/\sqrt{\pi} \qquad \ldots.(3.5)$$

This solution is only approximate as the electron is also attracted towards the nucleus b, which thus exerts upon the electron a 'perturbing' action. The term perturbation has been borrowed from planetary mechanics. If it be imagined that the movement of the earth round the sun has been calculated considering only the presence of those two bodies, then this calculation would only be approximate since other planets, *e.g.* Mars, exert some influence on the path followed by the earth. This influence is termed perturbation and the resultant orbit is a perturbed orbit.

In the problem of the hydrogen molecule ion the perturbation is represented by the existence of an additional energy of interaction, that of the electron with the second nucleus, which will have the value $1/r_b$. Owing to the distance between the nuclei, the perturbation is small and would appear to be fully accounted for in equation 3.4 and its solution 3.5. But the electron may be located at b, in which case the system would consist of a nucleus a and an atom b. In this way the function ψ_a is, by itself, insufficient for the description of the state of the electron, and there is an additional solution ψ_b referring to the electron in the field of the nucleus b. Each of the functions ψ_a and ψ_b corresponds to the same value for the energy of the system since in each case the system consists of an atom of hydrogen and a proton.

Since we have two functions corresponding to a single value for the energy, the linear combination of these functions will also be a solution *i.e.*

$$\psi = c_1\psi_a + c_2\psi_b \qquad \ldots.(3.6)$$

where c_1 and c_2 are certain coefficients.

It must be appreciated that this solution is approximate, since it is a combination of the functions ψ_a and ψ_b. Such a solution will be correct only when R is great and the perturbation produced by the second nucleus is small. If the distance between the nuclei is decreased, perturbation becomes important, but for the moment the solution in terms of the equation 3.6 only will be considered. The coefficients c_1 and c_2 are chosen so that the energy of the molecule is a minimum. This means that of all the approximate functions of the form of 3.6 the best possible approximate solution will be chosen. This process is termed the variation method.

The Schrödinger equation,

$$\nabla^2\psi + 2(E - V)\psi = 0 \qquad \ldots.(3.1)$$

may be rewritten in the form :

$$(-\nabla^2/2 + V)\psi = E\psi \qquad \ldots.(3.7)$$

or replacing $(-\nabla^2/2 + V)$ by the Hamiltonian operator $\mathcal{H}$:

$$\mathcal{H}\psi = E\psi \qquad \ldots.(3.8)$$

Since this condensed form of the Schrödinger equation will frequently be referred to in the following discussion, it will be convenient to make a digression here to discuss briefly the properties of operators.

An operator is an abbreviated expression representing a particular mathematical operation. Operators are used even in elementary mathematics although that particular term is rarely used in that connection ; thus a^3 is written for the successive multiplication of a by a and again by a. In the same way the symbols ln and sin are operators. The calculation of the differential coefficient d/dx is also a specific mathematical operation. Let this operation be represented by the operator D such that the action of the operator on a function *e.g.* x^2, is represented by Dx^2, the function being written on the right hand side of the operator *viz*

$$Dx^2 = \frac{d}{dx}\,x^2 = 2x$$

In a process of multiplication the actual order in which the multipliers are written down is of no importance, *e.g.* $\psi E\psi = E\psi^2$, but when the process of differentiation is considered there is a significant difference whether the function is to the right or to the left of the operator D. Thus xDx is not equal to Dx^2 :

$$xDx = x\left(\frac{d}{dx}x\right) = x\,;\; Dx^2 = \frac{d}{dx}\,x^2 = 2x$$

Thus a multiplier on the left hand side of the operator indicates that x is multiplied by the function which appears as the result of the action of the operator D on x, whereas a multiplier on the right hand side of the operator indicates that the functions are first multiplied together and the operator then acts on the product.

In equation 3.8 the operator $\mathcal{H}$ is given by :

$$\mathcal{H} = -\nabla^2/2 + V = -\frac{1}{2}\frac{\partial^2}{\partial x^2} - \frac{1}{2}\frac{\partial^2}{\partial y^2} - \frac{1}{2}\frac{\partial^2}{\partial z^2} + V \qquad \ldots.(3.9)$$

and its action on a function placed on the right hand side of $\mathcal{H}$ involves the determination of the second differential coefficient for each coordinate, followed by division by 2, a reversal of sign and the addition to the resultant expression of the function V. The expression $E\psi$ in equation 3.8 means simply that E is multiplied by the function ψ, since E is not an operator.

From equation 3.8 an expression for the energy of the H_2^+ molecule may be determined. Let both sides of equation 3.8 be multiplied by ψ and integrated over configuration space

$$\int\psi\mathcal{H}\psi d\tau = \int\psi E\psi d\tau \qquad \ldots.(3.10)$$

The right hand side may be rewritten as $E\int\psi^2 d\tau$, but no such simplification can be made with the left hand side. Thus from 3.10 it follows that

$$E = \frac{\int \psi \mathcal{H} \psi d\tau}{\int \psi^2 d\tau} \qquad \ldots .(3.11)$$

Since the function ψ in equation 3.11 cannot be determined, the approximate solution for the case of the H_2^+ molecule *viz*

$$\psi = c_1\psi_a + c_2\psi_b \qquad \ldots .(3.6)$$

must be used. The variation method consists of choosing a function ψ such that the minimum value of the energy is obtained. The use of equation 3.6 can only lead to an approximate value for E, since it is based on solutions which are true only when the distance between the nuclei is large. Exact quantitative results therefore must not be expected; the value of the method lies in the information obtained concerning the nature of the chemical bond.

For the hydrogen molecule ion the Hamiltonian operator has the form

$$\mathcal{H} = -\nabla^2/2 - 1/r_a - 1/r_b + 1/R \qquad \ldots .(3.12)$$

and thus the problem becomes that of obtaining the minimum value of the expression

$$E = \frac{\int \psi\,(-\nabla^2/2 - 1/r_a - 1/r_b + 1/R)\,\psi d\tau}{\int \psi^2 d\tau} \qquad \ldots .(3.13)$$

Substituting for ψ from equation 3.6 we obtain,

$$E = \frac{\int (c_1\psi_a + c_2\psi_b)\,(-\nabla^2/2 - 1/r_a - 1/r_b + 1/R)\,(c_1\psi_a + c_2\psi_a)\,d\tau}{\int (c_1\psi_a + c_2\psi_b)^2 d\tau} \qquad \ldots .(3.14)$$

and since c_1 and c_2 are constants independent of E,

$$E = \frac{c_1^2 \int \psi_a \mathcal{H} \psi_a d\tau + c_1c_2 \int \psi_b \mathcal{H} \psi_a d\tau + c_1c_2 \int \psi_a \mathcal{H} \psi_b d\tau + c_2^2 \int \psi_b \mathcal{H} \psi_b d\tau}{c_1^2 \int \psi_a^2 d\tau + 2c_1c_2 \int \psi_a\psi_b d\tau + c_2^2 \int \psi_b^2 d\tau} \qquad \ldots .(3.15)$$

This expression may be simplified in view of the fact that in the particular case being considered there is no distinction between the two nuclei *a* and *b* and hence

$$\int \psi_a \mathcal{H} \psi_b d\tau = \int \psi_b \mathcal{H} \psi_a d\tau \qquad \ldots .(3.16)$$

The expression 3.16 may be proved as follows. The left hand side of equation 3.16 on substitution for $\mathcal{H}$ becomes :

$$\int \psi_a \left(-\frac{\nabla^2}{2}\psi_b - \frac{1}{r_a}\psi_b - \frac{1}{r_b}\psi_b + \frac{1}{R}\psi_b \right) d\tau \qquad \ldots .(3.17)$$

but from the solution for the atom *b*,

$$-\nabla^2\psi_b/2 - \psi_b/r_b = E_b\psi_b \qquad \ldots .(3.18)$$

which on substitution in 3.17 gives

$$\int \psi_a E_b \psi_b d\tau - \int \frac{\psi_a\psi_b}{r_a} d\tau + \int \frac{\psi_a\psi_b}{R} d\tau \qquad \ldots .(3.19)$$

Similarly the right hand side of equation 3.16 is given by

$$\int \psi_b \left(-\frac{\nabla^2}{2}\psi_a - \frac{1}{r_a}\psi_a - \frac{1}{r_b}\psi_a + \frac{1}{R}\psi_a \right) d\tau$$

$$= \int \psi_b E_a \psi_a d\tau - \int \frac{\psi_a \psi_b}{r_b} d\tau + \int \frac{\psi_a \psi_b}{R} d\tau \quad \ldots .(3.20)$$

and since $E_a = E_b$ equation 3.16 is correct. The functions ψ_a and ψ_b are solutions of Schrödinger's equation for the separate atoms and may be normalized to unity, *i.e.*

$$\int \psi_a^2 d\tau = 1 \text{ and } \int \psi_b^2 d\tau = 1 \quad \ldots .(3.21)$$

Equations 3.16 and 3.21 permit 3.15 to be rewritten in the form

$$E = \frac{c_1^2 \int \psi_a \mathcal{H} \psi_a d\tau + 2c_1c_2 \int \psi_a \mathcal{H} \psi_b d\tau + c_2^2 \int \psi_b \mathcal{H} \psi_b d\tau}{c_1^2 + 2c_1c_2 \int \psi_a \psi_b d\tau + c_2^2} \quad \ldots (3.22)$$

Let

$$\mathcal{H}_{aa} = \int \psi_a \mathcal{H} \psi_a d\tau \qquad \mathcal{H}_{ab} = \int \psi_a \mathcal{H} \psi_b d\tau$$

$$\mathcal{H}_{bb} = \int \psi_b \mathcal{H} \psi_b d\tau \qquad S_{ab} = \int \psi_a \psi_b d\tau \quad \ldots .(3.23)$$

Then equation 3.22 becomes :

$$E = \frac{c_1^2 \mathcal{H}_{aa} + 2c_1c_2\mathcal{H}_{ab} + c_2^2\mathcal{H}_{bb}}{c_1^2 + c_2^2 + 2c_1c_2S_{ab}} \quad \ldots .(3.24)$$

In order to obtain the minimum value of E, 3.24 is differentiated with respect to c_1 and c_2 and the derivatives $\frac{\partial E}{\partial c_1}$ and $\frac{\partial E}{\partial c_2}$ equated to zero. Thus :

$$\left.\begin{aligned} \frac{\partial E}{\partial c_1} &= \frac{(2c_1\mathcal{H}_{aa} + 2c_2\mathcal{H}_{ab})(c_1^2 + c_2^2 + 2c_1c_2S_{ab}) - (2c_1 + 2c_2S_{ab})(c_1^2\mathcal{H}_{aa} + 2c_1c_2\mathcal{H}_{ab} + c_2^2\mathcal{H}_{bb})}{(c_1^2 + c_2^2 + 2c_1c_2S_{ab})^2} \\ \frac{\partial E}{\partial c_2} &= \frac{(2c_1\mathcal{H}_{ab} + 2c_2\mathcal{H}_{bb})(c_1^2 + c_2^2 + 2c_1c_2S_{ab}) - (2c_2 + 2c_1S_{ab})(c_1^2\mathcal{H}_{aa} + 2c_1c_2\mathcal{H}_{ab} + c_2^2\mathcal{H}_{bb})}{(c_1^2 + c_2^2 + 2c_1c_2S_{ab})^2} \end{aligned}\right\} \quad \ldots .(3.25)$$

or,

$$\left.\begin{aligned} &(2c_1\mathcal{H}_{aa} + 2c_2\mathcal{H}_{ab}) - (2c_1 + 2c_2S_{ab}) \frac{(c_1^2\mathcal{H}_{aa} + 2c_1c_2\mathcal{H}_{ab} + c_2^2\mathcal{H}_{bb})}{c_1^2 + c_2^2 + 2c_1c_2S_{ab}} = 0 \\ &\text{and} \\ &(2c_1\mathcal{H}_{ab} + 2c_2\mathcal{H}_{bb}) - (2c_2 + 2c_1S_{ab}) \frac{(c_1^2\mathcal{H}_{aa} + 2c_1c_2\mathcal{H}_{ab} + c_2^2\mathcal{H}_{bb})}{c_1^2 + c_2^2 + 2c_1c_2S_{ab}} = 0 \end{aligned}\right\} \quad \ldots .(3.26)$$

On combining with equation 3.24, 3.26 may be written as :

$$(2c_1\mathcal{H}_{aa} + 2c_2\mathcal{H}_{ab}) - (2c_1 + 2c_2S_{ab})E = 0 \quad \ldots .(3.27)$$

$$(2c_1\mathcal{H}_{ab} + 2c_2\mathcal{H}_{bb}) - (2c_2 + 2c_1S_{ab})E = 0$$

and we obtain two equations of the first order with two unknowns, c_1 and c_2, which may be written in the form :

$$c_1(\mathcal{H}_{aa} - E) + c_2(\mathcal{H}_{ab} - ES_{ab}) = 0 \quad \ldots .(3.28)$$

and

$$c_1(\mathcal{H}_{ab} - ES_{ab}) + c_2(\mathcal{H}_{bb} - E) = 0 \quad \ldots .(3.29)$$

The equations 3.28 and 3.29 are a pair of simultaneous equations of the form :

$$\left.\begin{aligned} 5x - 3y = 0 \\ 6x - 4y = 0 \end{aligned}\right\} \qquad \ldots.(3\cdot30)$$

It is evident that $x = 0$ and $y = 0$ are solutions of equation 3.30, but the question arises, are other solutions possible ? From the first equation it is evident that $x/y = 3/5$ and from the second that $x/y = 2/3$. Thus since the ratio x/y derived from the two equations is different, it is evident that the pair of equations 3.30 have no non-trivial solutions *i.e.* no solutions other than $x = 0, y = 0$. For the more general system

$$\left.\begin{aligned} ax + by = 0 \\ cx + dy = 0 \end{aligned}\right\} \qquad \ldots.(3\cdot31)$$

it follows that

$$-b/a = -d/c \text{ or } bc = ad \qquad \ldots.(3\cdot32)$$

In such a case there exists a definite relationship x/y which satisfies the equations other than the solution $x = 0, y = 0$. Equation 3.32 may be written as a determinant constructed from the coefficients of equation 3.31, thus :

$$\begin{vmatrix} a & b \\ c & d \end{vmatrix} = 0 \qquad \ldots. (3\cdot33)$$

The solutions of equations 3.28 and 3.29 in which $c_1 = 0$ and $c_2 = 0$ are clearly of no interest to the present problems ; other solutions will exist if

$$\begin{vmatrix} \mathcal{H}_{aa} - E & \mathcal{H}_{ab} - ES_{ab} \\ \mathcal{H}_{ab} - ES_{ab} & \mathcal{H}_{bb} - E \end{vmatrix} = 0 \qquad \ldots.(3\cdot34)$$

or

$$(\mathcal{H}_{aa} - E)(\mathcal{H}_{bb} - E) - (\mathcal{H}_{ab} - ES_{ab})^2 = 0 \qquad \ldots.(3\cdot35)$$

Such an equation is generally referred to as a secular equation. From this equation it is possible to determine E. This is the best solution obtainable commencing from a function of the type 3.6, although it must be pointed out that the choice of a more complex function, leading to a better approximation, might be made.

In the case of the hydrogen molecule ion both atoms, with nuclei a or b, are identical and hence

$$\mathcal{H}_{aa} = \mathcal{H}_{bb} \qquad \ldots.(3\cdot36)$$

and thus equation 3.35 simplifies to

$$(\mathcal{H}_{aa} - E)^2 = (\mathcal{H}_{ab} - ES_{ab})^2 \qquad \ldots.(3\cdot37)$$

and so for the energy E, two expressions are obtained :

$$E_1 = \frac{\mathcal{H}_{aa} + \mathcal{H}_{ab}}{1 + S_{ab}} \qquad \ldots.(3\cdot38)$$

and

$$E_2 = \frac{\mathcal{H}_{aa} - \mathcal{H}_{ab}}{1 - S_{ab}} \qquad \ldots.(3\cdot39)$$

From 3.28 it follows that,

$$\frac{c_1}{c_2} = -\frac{\mathcal{H}_{ab} - ES_{ab}}{\mathcal{H}_{aa} - E} \qquad \ldots.(3\cdot40)$$

and by substituting the values obtained for E in equation 3.38 and 3.39 into 3.40 it is found that $c_1/c_2 = \pm 1$, *i.e.*

$$c_1 = +c_2 \quad \text{or} \quad c_1 = -c_2 \qquad \ldots (3.41)$$

Thus the two different functions which exist, corresponding to the two energy values E_1 and E_2, are :

$$\psi_1 = c_1(\psi_a + \psi_b) \qquad \ldots (3.42)$$

and

$$\psi_2 = c_1(\psi_a - \psi_b) \qquad \ldots (3.43)$$

and these functions represent solutions of the wave equation for the hydrogen molecule ion given in equation 3.3.

Absolute values for the coefficients c_1 and c_2 may be found from the normalization equations :

$$\int \psi_1^2 d\tau = c_1^2 \int (\psi_a + \psi_b)^2 d\tau = c_1^2 \left\{ \int \psi_a^2 d\tau + 2\int \psi_a\psi_b d\tau + \int \psi_b^2 d\tau \right\} = 1$$

which from equations 3.21 and 3.23 simplify to

$$c_1^2(2 + 2S_{ab}) = 1 \qquad \ldots (3.44)$$

and consequently for ψ_1,

$$c_1 = c_2 = \frac{1}{\sqrt{2 + 2S_{ab}}} \qquad \ldots (3.45)$$

and for ψ_2,

$$c_1 = -c_2 = \frac{1}{\sqrt{2 - 2S_{ab}}} \qquad \ldots (3.46)$$

The following expressions are thus finally obtained for ψ_1 and ψ_2 :

$$\psi_1 = (\psi_a + \psi_b)/(2 + 2S_{ab})^{\frac{1}{2}} \qquad \ldots (3.47)$$

and

$$\psi_2 = (\psi_a - \psi_b)/(2 - 2S_{ab})^{\frac{1}{2}} \qquad \ldots (3.48)$$

where ψ_a and ψ_b are solutions for the hydrogen atom,

$$\psi_a = \{\exp(-r_a)\}/\sqrt{\pi}$$
$$\psi_b = \{\exp(-r_b)\}/\sqrt{\pi} \qquad \ldots (3.5)$$

The fact that two expressions for the energy have been obtained and two wave functions ψ_1 and ψ_2 is not fortuitous, but is most important from the physical representation of the chemical bond as we shall see later.

We shall now calculate the values of the integrals $\mathcal{H}_{aa}$, $\mathcal{H}_{bb}$, $\mathcal{H}_{ab}$ and S_{ab}. By definition,

$$\mathcal{H}_{aa} = \int \psi_a(-\nabla^2/2 - 1/r_a - 1/r_b + 1/R)\psi_a d\tau \qquad \ldots (3.49)$$

in which ψ_a is the solution of the equation for the hydrogen atom *viz*,

$$(-\nabla^2/2 - 1/r_a)\psi_a = E_a\psi_a \qquad \ldots (3.4)$$

where E_a is the energy of the hydrogen atom. By substituting equation 3.4 in 3.49 we have,

$$\mathcal{H}_{aa} = E_a - \int (\psi_a^2/r_b) d\tau + 1/R = E_a + C + 1/R \qquad \ldots (3.50)$$

where

$$C = -\int (\psi_a^2/r_b) d\tau \qquad \ldots (3.51)$$

In this expression, $\psi_a^2 d\tau$, as has been shown, represents the probability of locating the electron in the element of space $d\tau$; this probability is proportional to the density of the electron cloud at any given point, and C may be regarded as representing the energy of the interaction of the electron cloud with the second nucleus and thus represents the Coulomb energy of attraction.

The integral $\mathscr{H}_{aa}$, thus represents the energy of the hydrogen atom together with the Coulombic interaction of the electron of hydrogen atom a with nucleus b and of the nuclei with each other, $1/R$. In the same way,

$$\mathscr{H}_{bb} = E_b - \int (\psi_b^2/r_a) d\tau + 1/R = E_b + C + 1/R \quad \text{....(3.52)}$$

and since both nuclei are identical,

$$\mathscr{H}_{aa} = \mathscr{H}_{bb} \quad \text{....(3.36)}$$

By definition,

$$\mathscr{H}_{ab} = \int \psi_a(-\nabla^2/2 - 1/r_a - 1/r_b + 1/R)\psi_b d\tau \quad \text{....(3.53)}$$

which on combination with equation 3.4 *viz*,

$$(-\nabla^2/2 - 1/r_b)\psi_b = E_b\psi_b \quad \text{....(3.4)}$$

leads to

$$\mathscr{H}_{ab} = E_a \int \psi_a\psi_b d\tau - \int (\psi_a\psi_b/r_a) d\tau + 1/R \int \psi_a\psi_b d\tau \quad \text{....(3.54)}$$

$$= E_a S_{ab} + I + S_{ab}/R$$

An integral of the type, $I = -\int (\psi_a\psi_b/r_a) d\tau$, termed a resonance or exchange integral, is met here for the first time and represents the energy of interaction of the electron cloud with one of the nuclei. S_{ab} is generally referred to as a non-orthogonal integral.

Substitution of equations 3.50 and 3.54 in 3.38 and 3.39 gives

$$E_1 = E_a + \frac{1}{R} + \frac{C + I}{1 + S_{ab}} \quad \text{....(3.55)}$$

$$E_2 = E_a + \frac{1}{R} + \frac{C - I}{1 - S_{ab}} \quad \text{....(3.56)}$$

It is possible to show that the integrals C, I and S_{ab}, which have been introduced into the formula for the energy, may be expressed in terms of the distance between the nuclei as follows:

$$C = -\frac{1}{R} + \left(\frac{1+R}{R}\right) \exp(-2R) \quad \text{....(3.57)}$$

$$I = -(1 + R)\exp(-R) \quad \text{....(3.58)}$$

$$S_{ab} = (1 + R + R^2/3)\exp(-R) \quad \text{....(3.59)}$$

Like E_a, the integrals C and I are negative, and so when the state of the system is such as can be described by ψ_1 as in equation 3.47, an additional stabilization of the system occurs, the energy of the molecule being lower than that of a system consisting of a separate atom of hydrogen and a proton by the quantity $\frac{C + I}{1 + S_{ab}}$. This energy term with positive sign represents the bond energy, which is released on the formation of the molecule.

By the use of equations 3.55, 3.57, 3.58 and 3.59 it is now possible to determine the energy of the bond in the hydrogen molecule ion as a function of the internuclear distance R; this is shown in *Figure 10*. It will be noticed that the energy passes through a minimum, the position of which corresponds to the ground state of the stable molecule. The calculated value of the bond energy is 41 kcals and for the internuclear distance, 1·32 Å. The agreement with the experimental values of 61 kcals and 1·06 Å is not good, but the discrepancy is due to the fact that the atomic functions ψ_a and ψ_b, have been employed in order to describe the molecule. In spite of its approximate nature, the above treatment is of considerable value in that it serves to introduce an important physical concept. The fact that the electron may be located in a position where it is equally under the influence of both nuclei emphasizes the fact that the two atoms, as described by the functions ψ_a and ψ_b, do not exist separately but are superimposed. The particular function describing this state of the molecule will now be discussed in more detail.

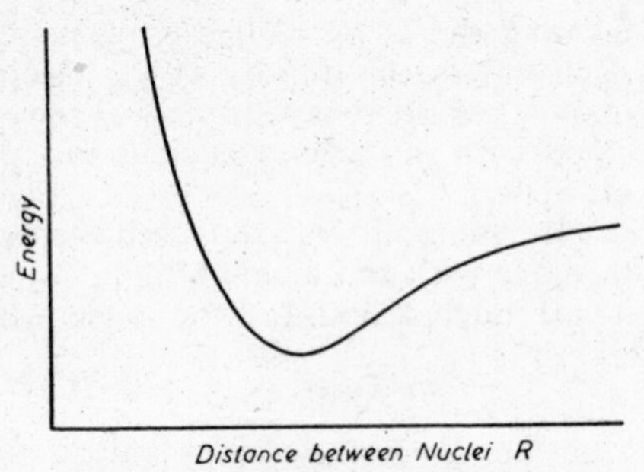

Figure 10. Energy curve for the hydrogen molecule ion

The function describing the case where bonding occurs has the form :

$$\psi_1 = (\psi_a + \psi_b)/(2 + 2S_{ab})^{\frac{1}{2}} \qquad \ldots.(3.47)$$

and substituting for ψ_a and ψ_b from equation 3.5 we obtain

$$\psi_1 = \{\exp(-r_a) + \exp(-r_b)\}/\{\pi(2 + 2S_{ab})\}^{\frac{1}{2}} \qquad \ldots.(3.60)$$

The square of this function which determines the density of the electronic cloud at any point is

$$\psi_1^2 = (\psi_a^2 + 2\psi_a\psi_b + \psi_b^2)/(2 + 2S_{ab})$$
$$= \{\exp(-r_a) + \exp(-r_b) + 2\exp(-r_a - r_b)\}/\pi(2 + 2S_{ab}) \qquad \ldots.(3.61)$$

It is evident from equation 3.61 that we can consider the total electronic cloud as made up of three parts. The first two of these *viz,*

$$\psi_a^2 = \{\exp(-2r_a)\}/\pi \quad \text{and} \quad \psi_b^2 = \{\exp(-2r_b)\}/\pi$$

represent spherical clouds corresponding to the electron being at one or other of the nuclei. The third term,

$$2\psi_a\psi_b = \{2\exp(-r_a - r_b)\}/\pi$$

corresponds to an ellipsoidal cloud.* The resulting electron cloud is shown diagrammatically in *Figure 11*. The upper curve shows the value of the function ψ_1^2 along the line joining the nuclei and the lower diagram gives the contours of equal electron density.

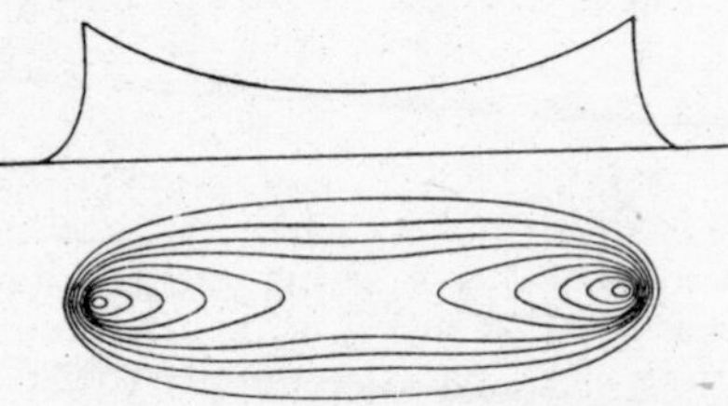

Figure 11. Electron distribution function for the hydrogen molecule ion

The electron cloud shows a lower

* For the electron cloud, $\psi_a^2 = \{\exp(-2r_a)\}/\pi$ levels of equal density are determined by the equation $\exp(-2r_a) =$ constant, or $r_a =$ constant, *i.e.* the levels of equal density appear as concentric spheres with the nucleus as centre. In the case of the cloud $2\psi_a\psi_b = \{2\exp(-r_a - r_b)\}/\pi$, levels of equal density will be given by $\exp(-r_a - rb) =$ constant or $r_a + r_b =$ constant. This equation corresponds to an ellipsoid with centres at the nuclei a and b.

density in the region between the nuclei. The emergence of the chemical bond may be regarded as due to the fact that the superposition or resonance of the two states given by ψ_a and ψ_b leads to three structures, represented by ψ_a^2, ψ_b^2 and the transitional structure, $\psi_a\psi_b$.

An analogous phenomenon appears in optics. If φ represents the amplitude of a vibration, then the intensity of this vibration is φ^2. If two amplitudes are added together, *i.e.* when the two waves interfere :

$$\varphi = \varphi_1 \pm \varphi_2 \quad \ldots.(3.62)$$

and the intensity of the resulting vibration is

$$\varphi^2 = (\varphi_1 \pm \varphi_2)^2 = \varphi_1^2 + \varphi_2^2 \pm 2\varphi_1\varphi_2 \quad \ldots.(3.63)$$

Thus this problem also does not resolve itself simply into the sum of the two intensities, but may be greater or less than $(\varphi_1^2 + \varphi_2^2)$ by the quantity $2\varphi_1\varphi_2$.

The relative contributions of the individual structures to the resulting electronic cloud is termed the weight of that structure. These quantities represent the ratio of that part of the electron cloud corresponding to a given structure to the total electron cloud and are generally expressed as a fraction or a percentage. From equation 3.61 it follows that these contributions are for the first structure, $\psi_a^2/\psi_1^2(2 + 2S_{ab})$; for the second structure, $\psi_b^2/\psi_1^2(2 + 2S_{ab})$ and for the third or transitional structure, $2\psi_a\psi_b/\psi_1^2(2 + 2S_{ab})$. Integration of these functions throughout space and normalization leads to the value for the first and second structures being, $1/(2 + 2S_{ab})$ and that for the transitional structure being, $S_{ab}/(1 + S_{ab})$. If the value of S_{ab} for the equilibrium position of the H_2^+ molecule is now substituted, the following structural weights are obtained : for the first and second structures 31 per cent each, for the transitional structure 38 per cent.

It must be realised that, in view of the assumptions made, these calculations are only approximate, but nevertheless this treatment of the H_2^+ molecule makes an understanding of the nature of the chemical bond possible. A more exact solution would lead to more complex functions in view of the fact that the electron cloud is really continuous and the division of the cloud into three parts is a considerable simplification. The more exact solutions of HYLLERAAS and JAFFÉ[2] show almost exact agreement with experiment for values of the bond energy and internuclear distance.

THE HYDROGEN MOLECULE, H_2

In the hydrogen molecule two electrons exist in the field of two nuclei and attempts to solve the Schrödinger equation for this case have proved unsuccessful. An approximate method similar to that given above for the simpler case of the hydrogen molecule ion may, however, be solved. This was first carried out by HEITLER and LONDON[3] in 1927.

Previously we have only considered the application of the Schrödinger equation to problems involving a single electron. In the case of several electrons, the wave function depends upon the coordinates of all the particles, $(x_1\, y_1\, z_1 \ldots\ldots x_i\, y_i\, z_i \ldots\ldots x_n\, y_n\, z_n)$ where i is the number of the electron which can have any value from 1 to n, where n is the number of electrons.

Thus the Schrödinger equation for the case of n electrons will be

$$\sum_{i=1}^{n}\left(\frac{\partial^2\psi}{\partial x_i^2}+\frac{\partial^2\psi}{\partial y_i^2}+\frac{\partial^2\psi}{\partial z_i^2}\right)+2(E-V)\psi=0 \qquad \ldots.(3.64)$$

where V represents the sum of all the potential energy terms for all the particles. Equation 3.64 may be more briefly written as

$$\sum_{i=1}^{n}\nabla_i^2\psi+2(E-V)\psi=0 \qquad \ldots.(3.65)$$

In this case $\psi^2 dx_1 dy_1 dz_1 \ldots\ldots dx_n dy_n dz_n$ will represent the probability of the first electron being located between x_1 and x_1+dx_1, y_1 and y_1+dy_1, z_1 and z_1+dz_1 and of the second electron between x_2 and x_2+dx_2, y_2 and y_2+dy_2, z_2 and z_2+dz_2 *etc.*

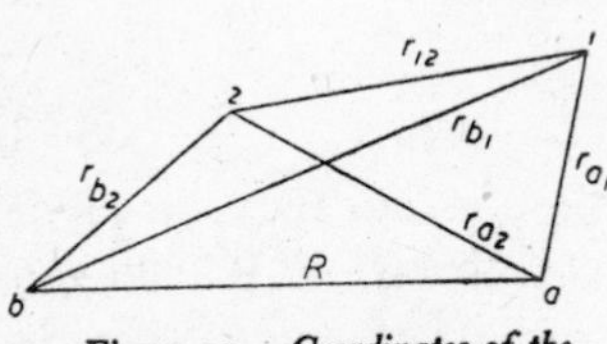

Figure 12. Coordinates of the hydrogen molecule

For the molecule of hydrogen there are two nuclei, a and b and two electrons, *1* and *2* (see *Figure 12*) and we shall define :

r_{a_1} = distance between the first electron and the nucleus a
r_{a_2} = ,, ,, ,, second ,, ,, ,, ,, a
r_{b_1} = ,, ,, ,, first ,, ,, ,, ,, b
r_{b_2} = ,, ,, ,, second ,, ,, ,, ,, b
R_{ab} = the distance between the nuclei a and b
r_{12} = the distance between the two electrons.

The potential energy term will consist of the various energies of interaction of the electrons with the nuclei, of the nuclei with each other and of the electrons with each other. Thus in atomic units the potential energy is given by,

$$V=-1/r_{a_1}-1/r_{a_2}-1/r_{b_1}-1/r_{b_2}+1/R+1/r_{12} \qquad \ldots.(3.66)$$

and the Schrödinger equation for the hydrogen molecule becomes :

$$\nabla_1^2\psi+\nabla_2^2\psi+2(E+1/r_{a_1}+1/r_{a_2}+1/r_{b_1}+1/r_{b_2}-1/R-1/r_{12})\psi=0 \qquad \ldots.(3.67)$$

where as before,

$$\nabla_1^2=\frac{\partial^2}{\partial x_1^2}+\frac{\partial^2}{\partial y_1^2}+\frac{\partial^2}{\partial z_2^2} \qquad \ldots.(3.68)$$

Putting equation 3.67 in the operator form, we have

$$\mathscr{H}\psi=E\psi \qquad \ldots.(3.69)$$

where

$$\mathscr{H}=-\nabla_1^2/2-\nabla_2^2/2-1/r_{a_1}-1/r_{a_2}-1/r_{b_1}-1/r_{b_2}+1/R+1/r_{12} \qquad \ldots.(3.70)$$

The treatment which we shall employ here is similar to that used for the hydrogen molecule ion. The two atoms will be considered as being initially a sufficient distance apart to prevent interaction. Under these conditions the atoms may be considered separately and electron 1 will be at nucleus a and electron 2 at nucleus b. The total energy of the system will be the sum of the energies of the two atoms *i.e.* $2E_0$. The state of the system is described by the expression

$$\psi_1=\psi_a(1)\psi_b(2)=\{\exp(-r_{a_1}-r_{b_2})\}/\sqrt{\pi} \qquad \ldots.(3.71)$$

in which $\psi_a(1)$ indicates that the first electron is located at nucleus a, and $\psi_b(2)$ shows that the second electron is located at nucleus b. $\psi_a^2(1)dx_1dy_1dz_1$ represents the probability of finding the first electron, belonging to nucleus a, in an element of volume $dx_1dy_1dz_1$ and $\psi_b^2(2)\, dx_2dy_2dz_2$ represents similarly the probability of finding the second electron, belonging to the nucleus b in an element of volume $dx_2dy_2dz_2$. When the nuclei are a considerable distance apart, we may assume that these probabilities are independent of each other and the probability of finding the first electron in the volume element $dx_1dy_1dz_1$ and the second electron in the volume element $dx_2dy_2dz_2$ simultaneously, will be equal to the product of the individual probabilities :

$$\psi_1^2 d\tau = \psi_a^2(1)\psi_b^2(2)dx_1dy_1dz_1\, dx_2dy_2dz_2 \qquad \ldots.(3{\cdot}72)$$

and

$$\psi_1 = \psi_a(1)\psi_b(2) \qquad \ldots.(3{\cdot}71)$$

The probability of the transference of an electron from one nucleus to the other will increase as the nuclei approach each other and from the point of view of wave mechanics it is incorrect to locate the first electron at nucleus a and the second electron at nucleus b. The two electrons are indistinguishable and it is impossible to regard one electron as located at a certain nucleus. Therefore in addition to equation 3·71 we must consider a second expression in which the electrons have been transposed,

$$\psi_2 = \psi_a(2)\psi_b(1) \qquad \ldots.(3{\cdot}73)$$

The two functions ψ_1 and ψ_2 both correspond to the same energy value, so that the system is two-fold degenerate. Hence the linear combination of 3·71 and 3·73 will be a solution,

$$\psi = c_1\psi_1 + c_2\psi_2 = c_1\psi_a(1)\psi_b(2) + c_2\psi_b(1)\psi_a(2) \qquad \ldots.(3{\cdot}74)$$

The solution now follows the same procedure as in the case of the H_2^+ molecule, and consists in the evaluation of the coefficients c_1 and c_2 for which the expression

$$E = \frac{\int \psi\mathscr{H}\psi d\tau}{\int \psi^2 d\tau} \qquad \ldots.(3{\cdot}11)$$

is a minimum. In polyelectronic problems integration must be carried out for all the coordinates of all the particles, and $dx_1dy_1dz_1dx_2dy_2dz_2$ is normally written $d\tau_1 d\tau_2$.

Substituting equation 3·74 in 3·11 gives

$$E = \frac{\int\left\{c_1\psi_a(1)\psi_b(2) + c_2\psi_b(1)\psi_a(2)\right\}\mathscr{H}\left\{c_1\psi_a(1)\psi_b(2) + c_2\psi_b(1)\psi_a(2)\right\}d\tau_1 d\tau_2}{\int\left\{c_1\psi_a(1)\psi_b(2) + c_2\psi_b(1)\psi_a(2)\right\}^2 d\tau_1 d\tau_2} \qquad \ldots.(3{\cdot}75)$$

Simplification and normalization, since ψ_a and ψ_b are solutions for the hydrogen atom *viz*

$$\int \psi_a^2 d\tau = 1 \quad \text{and} \quad \int \psi_b^2 d\tau = 1 \qquad \ldots.(3{\cdot}21)$$

leads to

$$E = \frac{c_1^2\mathscr{H}_{11} + c_2^2\mathscr{H}_{22} + 2c_1c_2\mathscr{H}_{12}}{c_1^2 + c_2^2 + 2c_1c_2S_{12}} \qquad \ldots.(3{\cdot}76)$$

in which

$$\begin{aligned} \mathcal{H}_{11} &= \int \psi_a(1)\psi_b(2)\mathcal{H}\psi_a(1)\psi_b(2)d\tau_1 d\tau_2 \\ \mathcal{H}_{22} &= \int \psi_b(1)\psi_a(2)\mathcal{H}\psi_b(1)\psi_a(2)d\tau_1 d\tau_2 \\ \mathcal{H}_{12} &= \int \psi_a(1)\psi_b(2)\mathcal{H}\psi_a(2)\psi_b(1)d\tau_1 d\tau_2 \\ S_{12} &= \int \psi_a(1)\psi_b(1)\psi_a(2)\psi_b(2)d\tau_1 d\tau_2 \end{aligned} \qquad \ldots(3{\cdot}77)$$

Differentiating 3.76 with respect to c_1 and c_2 and equating to zero gives

$$\frac{\partial E}{\partial c_1} = \frac{(2c_1\mathcal{H}_{11}+2c_2\mathcal{H}_{12})(c_1^2+c_2^2+2c_1c_2S_{12})-(2c_1+2c_2S_{12})(c_1^2\mathcal{H}_{11}+c_2^2\mathcal{H}_{22}+2c_1c_2\mathcal{H}_{12})}{(c_1^2+c_2^2+2c_1c_2S_{12})^2}=0$$

$$\frac{\partial E}{\partial c_2} = \frac{(2c_2\mathcal{H}_{22}+2c_1\mathcal{H}_{12})(c_1^2+c_2^2+2c_1c_2S_{12})-(2c_2+2c_1S_{12})(c_1^2\mathcal{H}_{11}+c_2^2\mathcal{H}_{22}+2c_1c_2\mathcal{H}_{12})}{(c_1^2+c_2^2+2c_1c_2S_{12})^2}=0 \qquad \ldots(3{\cdot}78)$$

and following the method of simplication employed in the case of equations 3.25 to 3.27 we have :

$$\left.\begin{aligned} c_1(\mathcal{H}_{11}-E)+c_2(\mathcal{H}_{12}-ES_{12}) &= 0 \\ c_1(\mathcal{H}_{12}-ES_{12})+c_2(\mathcal{H}_{22}-E) &= 0 \end{aligned}\right\} \qquad \ldots(3{\cdot}79)$$

From which it follows that :

$$\begin{vmatrix} \mathcal{H}_{11}-E & \mathcal{H}_{12}-ES_{12} \\ \mathcal{H}_{12}-ES_{12} & \mathcal{H}_{22}-E \end{vmatrix} = 0 \qquad \ldots(3{\cdot}80)$$

and hence

$$(\mathcal{H}_{11}-E)(\mathcal{H}_{22}-E)-(\mathcal{H}_{12}-ES_{12})^2=0 \qquad \ldots(3{\cdot}81)$$

and

$$(\mathcal{H}_{11}-E)^2=(\mathcal{H}_{12}-ES_{12})^2 \qquad \ldots(3{\cdot}82)$$

since, as before, it may be shown that

$$\mathcal{H}_{11}=\mathcal{H}_{22} \qquad \ldots(3{\cdot}83)$$

From equation 3.82 we obtain two expressions for the energy *viz,*

$$E_1=(\mathcal{H}_{11}+\mathcal{H}_{12})/(1+S_{12}) \qquad \ldots(3{\cdot}84)$$

and

$$E_2=(\mathcal{H}_{11}-\mathcal{H}_{12})/(1-S_{12}) \qquad \ldots(3{\cdot}85)$$

We will now consider the meanings of the integrals $\mathcal{H}_{11}$, $\mathcal{H}_{12}$ and S_{12}. We have,

$$\mathcal{H}_{11}=\int\psi_a(1)\psi_b(2)\left\{-\frac{\nabla_1^2}{2}-\frac{\nabla_2^2}{2}-\frac{1}{r_{a_1}}-\frac{1}{r_{b_1}}-\frac{1}{r_{a_2}}-\frac{1}{r_{b_2}}+\frac{1}{R}+\frac{1}{r_{12}}\right\}\psi_a(1)\psi_b(2)d\tau_1 d\tau_2 \qquad \ldots(3{\cdot}86)$$

The wave functions ψ_a and ψ_b are solutions of the Schrödinger equation for the hydrogen atom, *i.e.*

$$\left.\begin{aligned} \left(-\frac{\nabla_1^2}{2}-\frac{1}{r_{a_1}}\right)\psi_a(1) &= E_o\psi_a(1) \\ \left(-\frac{\nabla_2^2}{2}-\frac{1}{r_{b_2}}\right)\psi_b(2) &= E_o\psi_b(2) \end{aligned}\right\} \qquad \ldots(3{\cdot}4)$$

where E_o is the energy of the hydrogen atom in its ground state. Introducing the relationships 3.4 into 3.86 we obtain,

$$\mathscr{H}_{11} = 2E_o + \int \left\{ -\frac{1}{r_{b_1}} - \frac{1}{r_{a_2}} + \frac{1}{r_{12}} + \frac{1}{R} \right\} \psi_a^2(1)\psi_b^2(2)d\tau_1 d\tau_2 = 2E_o + C \quad \ldots.(3.87)$$

The term C is the Coulombic integral representing the interaction energy of the electrons with the nuclei and also the interaction energy between the electrons and the nuclei themselves. The integral $\int \frac{\psi_a^2(1)}{r_{b_1}} d\tau_1$ represents the attraction of electron 1, *i.e.* the electron originally located with nucleus a, for nucleus b and similarly $\int \frac{\psi_b^2(2)}{r_{a_2}} d\tau_2$ is the attraction of the electron of atom b for the nucleus a. The term $1/R$ represents the energy of repulsion of the nuclei and $\int \psi_a^2(1)\psi_b^2(2)d\tau_1 d\tau_2/r_{12}$ the mutual repulsion energy of the electrons.

In exactly the same way it may be shown that

$$\mathscr{H}_{22} = \mathscr{H}_{11} = 2E_o + C \quad \ldots.(3.88)$$

The integral $\mathscr{H}_{12}$ is, however, the most interesting to the present study. By definition,

$$\mathscr{H}_{12} = \int \psi_a(1)\psi_b(2) \left\{ -\frac{\nabla_1^2}{2} - \frac{\nabla_2^2}{2} - \frac{1}{r_{a_1}} - \frac{1}{r_{b_1}} - \frac{1}{r_{a_2}} - \frac{1}{r_{b_2}} + \frac{1}{R} + \frac{1}{r_{12}} \right\} \psi_b(1)\psi_a(2)d\tau_1 d\tau_2$$

$$= 2E_o \int \psi_a(1)\psi_b(1)\psi_a(2)\psi_b(2)d\tau_1 d\tau_2 + \int \left\{ -\frac{1}{r_{a_1}} - \frac{1}{r_{b_2}} + \frac{1}{R} + \frac{1}{r_{12}} \right\} \times$$

$$\times \psi_a(1)\psi_b(1)\psi_a(2)\psi_b(2)d\tau_1 d\tau_2$$

$$= 2E_o S_{12} + A \quad \ldots.(3.89)$$

The integral A in 3.89 represents a new type of expression with no analogue in classical mechanics and only an approximate physical picture of its significance may be made. It may be regarded as the energy developed as a result of the exchange of positions by the electrons as represented by the expression

$$\psi_a(1)\psi_b(1)\psi_a(2)\psi_b(2)$$

Furthermore by definition from equations 3.77 and 3.23,

$$S_{12} = \int \psi_a(1)\psi_b(1)\psi_a(2)\psi_b(2)d\tau_1 d\tau_2$$

$$= \int \psi_a(1)\psi_b(1)d\tau_1 \int \psi_a(2)\psi_b(2)d\tau_2$$

$$= S_{ab}^2 \quad \ldots.(3.90)$$

By the substitution of equations 3.87 and 3.89 into 3.84 and 3.85 we obtain the following expressions for the energy of the hydrogen molecule,

$$E_1 = 2E_o + (C + A)/(1 + S_{12}) \quad \ldots.(3.91)$$

$$E_2 = 2E_o + (C - A)/(1 - S_{12}) \quad \ldots.(3.92)$$

Evaluation of the integrals C and A shows that both have negative values and that the value of the exchange integral A exceeds considerably that of the Coulombic integral C. E_1 is thus less than the sum of the energy of the two free, non-interacting hydrogen atoms, $2E_o$ and thus corresponds to the case where the atoms are mutually attracted and form a stable hydrogen molecule. In the second solution, since A is larger than C, E_2 will be greater than $2E_o$ and thus the energy of the system will have increased as a result of the electron exchange. Such a case can only lead to the repulsion of the atoms.

Substitution of equations 3.87, 3.89, and 3.91 in 3.79 shows that when bonding occurs,

$$c_1/c_2 = 1 \quad \text{or} \quad c_1 = c_2 \qquad \ldots.(3.93)$$

and the substitution of 3.92 in 3.79 leads to the relationship

$$c_1/c_2 = -1 \quad \text{or} \quad c_1 = -c_2 \qquad \ldots.(3.94)$$

Thus we have two possible functions representing two states of the hydrogen molecule *viz*

$$\psi_I = c_1 \{ \psi_a(1)\psi_b(2) + \psi_b(1)\psi_a(2) \} \qquad \ldots.(3.95)$$

and

$$\psi_{II} = c_1 \{ \psi_a(1)\psi_b(2) - \psi_b(1)\psi_a(2) \} \qquad \ldots.(3.96)$$

or introducing the values of ψ for the hydrogen atom in its ground state,

$$\psi_I = \{ \exp(-r_{a_1} - r_{b_2}) + \exp(-r_{b_1} - r_a) \} / \{\pi(2 + 2S_{12})^{\frac{1}{2}}\} \qquad \ldots.(3.97)$$

and

$$\psi_{II} = \{ \exp(-r_{a_1} - r_{b_2}) - \exp(-r_{b_1} - r_{a_2}) \} / \{\pi(2 - 2S_{12})^{\frac{1}{2}}\} \qquad \ldots.(3.98)$$

where the terms $1/\{\pi(2 \pm 2S_{12})^{\frac{1}{2}}\}$ are obtained by normalization in the same way as was shown in equation 3.44. On squaring ψ_I and ψ_{II} we obtain expressions for density of the electron cloud :

$$\begin{aligned}\psi_I^2 &= \{ \psi_a^2(1)\psi_b^2(2) + \psi_b^2(1)\psi_a^2(2) + 2\psi_a(1)\psi_b(2)\psi_a(2)\psi_b(1)\} / (2 + 2S_{12}) \\ &= \{ \exp(-2[r_{a_1} + r_{b_2}]) + \exp(-2[r_{b_1} + r_{a_2}]) \} / \{(2 + 2S_{12})\pi^2\} + \\ &+ \{2 \exp(-[r_{a_1} + r_{b_2} + r_{a_2} + r_{b_1}])\} / \{(2 + 2S_{12})\pi^2\} \qquad \ldots.(3.99)\end{aligned}$$

$$\begin{aligned}\psi_{II}^2 &= \{\psi_a^2(1)\psi_b^2(2) + \psi_b^2(1)\psi_a^2(2) - 2\psi_a(1)\psi_b(2)\psi_a(2)\psi_b(1)\} / (2 - 2S_{12}) \\ &= \{ \exp(-2[r_{a_1} + r_{b_2}]) + \exp(-2[r_{b_1} + r_{a_2}]) \} / \{(2 - 2S_{12})\pi^2\} - \\ &- \{ 2 \exp(-[r_{a_1} + r_{b_2} + r_{a_2} + r_{b_1}])\} / \{(2 - 2S_{12})\pi^2\} \qquad \ldots.(3.100)\end{aligned}$$

The first and second terms of equations 3.99 and 3.100 represent the spherical electron clouds, corresponding to the presence of the electrons at the nuclei whilst the third term describes the exchange cloud, which is elliptical in shape. This we shall term the transitional structure as for the hydrogen molecule ion.

In the hydrogen molecule the contribution of the first structure to the final state of the molecule is $\psi_a^2(1)\psi_b^2(2)/\psi_I^2(2 + 2S_{12})$, similarly the contribution of the second structure is $\psi_b^2(1)\psi_a^2(2)/\psi_I^2(2 + 2S_{12})$ and of the transitional structure $2\psi_a(1)\psi_b(2)\psi_a(2)\psi_b(1)/\psi_I^2(2 + 2S_{12})$. Integration of these functions throughout space and normalization to unity leads to the expressions $1/(2 + 2S_{12})$ for the first and second structures and $S_{12}/(1+S_{12})$ for the transitional structures.

At the equilibrium position, $S_{12} = 0{\cdot}56$ and hence the structural weights of the first and second structures is 32 per cent and of the transitional structure 36 per cent.

The electron cloud where a chemical bond is formed is shown in *Figure 13*; *Figure 14* shows the corresponding case where repulsion occurs. In the latter if we consider the electrons to be equidistant from both nuclei (*i.e.* when $r_{a_1} = r_{b_1}$ and $r_{a_2} = r_{b_2}$) it is found on substitution in equation 3.100 that the probability of such a configuration is zero and hence the electrons are never in these positions. This fact is indicated in *Figure 14*.

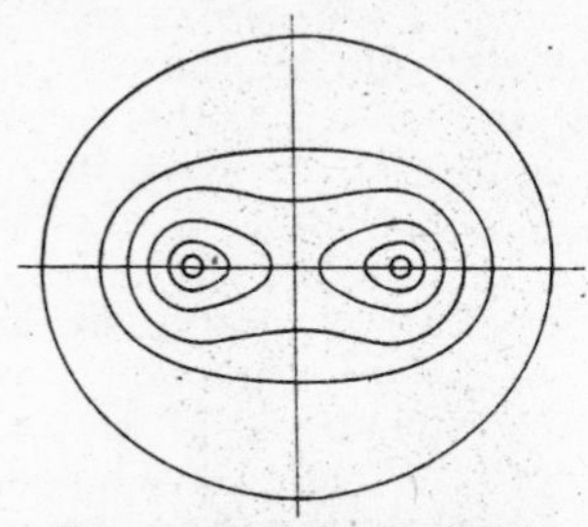

Figure 13. Electron distribution for the hydrogen molecule when bonding occurs

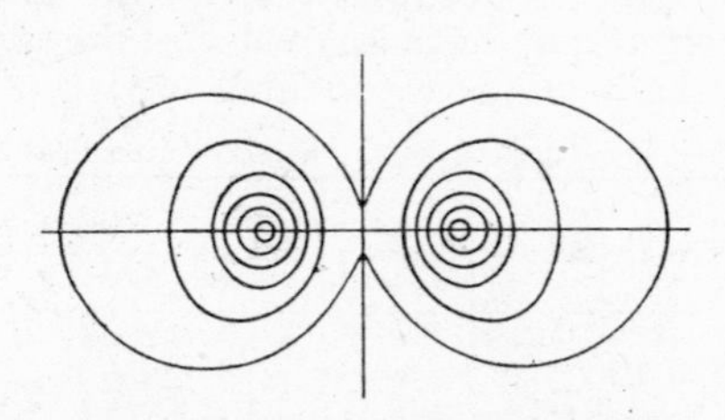

Figure 14. Electron distribution for the hydrogen molecule when repulsion occurs

THE PAULI PRINCIPLE

In the above treatment of the hydrogen molecule ion and the hydrogen molecule, the effect of electronic spin has been excluded, but the complete wave function of an electron must include not only the orbital motion, with which we have been concerned so far, but also a contribution for the spin. With single atoms it was possible to introduce a fourth quantum number s in addition to the three quantum numbers n, l and m in order to account for the spin of the electron, and for polyelectronic molecules it is possible to proceed in an analogous manner. The complete wave function of an electron is considered to be the product of the orbital wave function, *i.e.* the wave function that we have been considering so far, and a wave function representing the orientation of the spin axis of the electron.

If ψ represents the orbital wave function of an atom for a given value of the quantum numbers n, l and m, then the spin wave function may be represented by two functions α and β whose values are determined by the following conditions:

$$\alpha^2(+\tfrac{1}{2}) = 1\ ,\ \alpha^2(-\tfrac{1}{2}) = 0\ ,\ \beta^2(+\tfrac{1}{2}) = 0\ ,\ \beta^2(-\tfrac{1}{2}) = 1 \qquad \ldots.(3.101)$$

These conditions mean that the wave function α refers to the state of the electron in which the spin quantum number s, has the value $+ {}^1/_2$, and in consequence the probability of it having the value $- {}^1/_2$ is zero. Similarly the function β describes those states corresponding to a value for s of $- {}^1/_2$ and consequently the probability of it having the value $+ {}^1/_2$ is zero. The complete wave function of the electron is then represented by

$$\Phi = \psi\alpha \quad \text{or} \quad \Phi = \psi\beta \qquad \ldots.(3.102)$$

For two electrons, the complete wave function of the first electron will be $\psi_a(1)\alpha(1)$ which denotes that the first electron is attached to the nucleus a and the solution is given by

$$\psi_a(1) = \{\exp(-r_{a_1})\}/\sqrt{\pi} \qquad \ldots.(3.5)$$

and that the spin wave function corresponds to $s = +1/2$. The function of the second electron is $\psi_b(2)\beta(2)$, which means that the second electron is attached to nucleus b, its orbital wave function is ψ_b and the spin wave function corresponds to $s = -1/2$. The complete wave function of the two electron system is then given by,

$$\Phi = \psi_a(1)\psi_b(2)\alpha(1)\beta(2) \qquad \ldots.(3.103)$$

The function given in equation 3.103 is, however, a special case in which the spins of electrons 1 and 2 are antiparallel. In the general case each electron may have any value of the spin quantum number, so that in place of the two wave functions $\psi_a(1)\psi_b(2)$ and $\psi_a(2)\psi_b(1)$, representing the exchange of the electrons between the two nuclei, we shall have eight complete wave functions (*Table XV*). All eight wave functions correspond to the same value of the energy, differing only in the arrangement of the electrons.

Table XV. Complete Wave Functions for the Two Electron Problem

Complete wave function	Electron 1 at nucleus	Electron 2 at nucleus	Quantum number of Electron 1	Quantum number of Electron 2	Orientation of spin
$\psi_a(1)\psi_b(2)\alpha(1)\alpha(2)$	a	b	$+\frac{1}{2}$	$+\frac{1}{2}$	↓ ↓
$\psi_a(1)\psi_b(2)\beta(1)\beta(2)$	a	b	$-\frac{1}{2}$	$-\frac{1}{2}$	↑ ↑
$\psi_a(1)\psi_b(2)\alpha(1)\beta(2)$	a	b	$+\frac{1}{2}$	$-\frac{1}{2}$	↓ ↑
$\psi_a(1)\psi_b(2)\beta(1)\alpha(2)$	a	b	$-\frac{1}{2}$	$+\frac{1}{2}$	↑ ↓
$\psi_b(1)\psi_a(2)\alpha(1)\alpha(2)$	b	a	$+\frac{1}{2}$	$+\frac{1}{2}$	↓ ↓
$\psi_b(1)\psi_a(2)\beta(1)\beta(2)$	b	a	$-\frac{1}{2}$	$-\frac{1}{2}$	↑ ↑
$\psi_b(1)\psi_a(2)\alpha(1)\beta(2)$	b	a	$+\frac{1}{2}$	$-\frac{1}{2}$	↓ ↑
$\psi_b(1)\psi_a(2)\beta(1)\alpha(2)$	b	a	$-\frac{1}{2}$	$+\frac{1}{2}$	↑ ↓

In view of the fact that the electrons are indistinguishable, we have employed in place of the separate functions $\psi_a(1)\psi_b(2)$ and $\psi_b(1)\psi_a(2)$, linear combinations of the form :

$$\psi = c_1\psi_a(1)\psi_b(2) + c_2\psi_b(1)\psi_a(2) \qquad \ldots.(3.74)$$

and a similar procedure must be employed in the case of the functions given in *Table XV*. Without further information it is not possible to state which of the possible linear combinations are significant. Such information is given, however, by the Pauli principle. It is essential to select the combination which includes only those states permitted by the Pauli principle. In order to do this it is necessary to understand symmetric and antisymmetric wave functions.

Wave functions are termed symmetric if they remain unchanged on transposition of the electrons. This process may best be explained by taking an example. The function

$$\psi_I = \psi_a(1)\psi_b(2) + \psi_b(1)\psi_a(2) \qquad \ldots.(3.95)$$

is symmetric because on transposition of the electrons we obtain

$$\psi_I' = \psi_a(2)\psi_b(1) + \psi_b(2)\psi_a(1) \qquad \ldots.(3.104)$$

which is identical with equation 3.95 *i.e.* $\psi_I = \psi_I'$ and the function ψ_I remains unchanged on the rearrangement of the electrons. An antisymmetric wave function reverses its sign in the transposition of electrons *e.g.* the function

$$\psi_{II} = \psi_a(1)\psi_b(2) - \psi_b(1)\psi_a(2) \qquad \ldots.(3.96)$$

on rearrangement of electrons becomes

$$\psi'_{II} = \psi_a(2)\psi_b(1) - \psi_b(2)\psi_a(1) \qquad \ldots.(3{\cdot}105)$$

and

$$\psi'_{II} = -\psi_{II}$$

The square of the wave function gives the density of the electron cloud, and when two electrons, *e.g.* electrons i and k, exchange places, in view of their identity, there is clearly no change in the density distribution and therefore

$$\psi^2(x_1 \ldots. x_i \ldots. x_k) = \psi^2(x_1 \ldots.. x_k \ldots.. x_i) \qquad \ldots.(3{\cdot}106)$$

and ψ^2 will always be symmetric. In a similar way it is clear that the square of the symmetric (3·95) and antisymmetric (3·96) wave functions for the hydrogen molecule are symmetric. Thus

$$\psi_I^2 = \psi_a^2(1)\psi_b^2(2) + \psi_b^2(1)\psi_a^2(2) + 2\psi_a(1)\psi_b(2)\psi_a(2)\psi_b(1)$$

$$\psi_I'^2 = \psi_b^2(1)\psi_a^2(2) + \psi_a^2(1)\psi_b^2(2) + 2\psi_b(1)\psi_a(2)\psi_b(2)\psi_a(1)$$

and hence

$$\psi_I^2 = \psi_I'^2$$

also

$$\psi_{II}^2 = \psi_a^2(1)\psi_b^2(2) + \psi_b^2(1)\psi_a^2(2) - 2\psi_a(1)\psi_b(2)\psi_a(2)\psi_b(1)$$

$$\psi_{II}'^2 = \psi_b^2(1)\psi_a^2(2) + \psi_a^2(1)\psi_b^2(2) - 2\psi_b(1)\psi_a(2)\psi_b(2)\psi_a(1)$$

and hence

$$\psi_{II}^2 = \psi_{II}'^2$$

Thus the orbital wave functions may be either symmetric or antisymmetric and both types of function are important for describing the state of a molecule.

The complete wave function is different, however, and it will appear that only an antisymmetric complete function, which reverses its sign on transposition of the electrons, is acceptable on the basis of Pauli's principle, which states in wave mechanical terms: 'Only that complete wave function may be selected which does not permit the two electrons to exist in the same state'. Let us consider a symmetrical complete wave function and assume that the two electrons have the same values of the quantum numbers n, l, m and s; when the electrons are interchanged the wave function will be identical with the original. Thus by the use of a symmetric function it is possible to describe an electronic state which is not permitted by the Pauli principle. It may therefore be concluded that the complete wave function cannot be symmetric.

Now let us consider an antisymmetric complete wave function which is also prohibited by Pauli's principle. Again it is assumed that there are two electrons having the same values of n, l, m and s. Transposition of the electrons should not alter the function since both electrons are in identical states, but since the function is antisymmetric, the sign must be reversed; these two statements can be compatible only when the function is zero. Thus when the complete wave function is antisymmetric it becomes zero when in disagreement with Pauli's principle. Thus not all the linear combinations of the functions in *Table XV* are possible, but only those which lead to a complete wave function which is antisymmetric. For example consider the linear combination

$$\psi_a(1)\psi_b(2)\alpha(1)\alpha(2)+\psi_b(1)\psi_a(2)\alpha(1)\alpha(2) = \{\psi_a(1)\psi_b(2)+\psi_a(2)\psi_b(1)\}\alpha(1)\alpha(2) \quad \ldots.(3.107)$$

By reversing the positions of the electrons we obtain

$$\{\psi_b(1)\psi_a(2) + \psi_b(2)\psi_a(1)\}\ \alpha(1)\alpha(2)$$

i.e. the same function, and consequently it is symmetric and must be rejected. Examination of the functions in *Table XV* lead to the following four possible antisymmetric linear combinations :

$$\psi_a(1)\psi_b(2)\alpha(1)\beta(2) + \psi_b(1)\psi_a(2)\alpha(1)\beta(2) - \psi_a(1)\psi_b(2)\beta(1)\alpha(2) - \\ - \psi_b(1)\psi_a(2)\beta(1)\alpha(2) \\ = \{\psi_a(1)\psi_b(2) + \psi_b(1)\psi_a(2)\}\{\alpha(1)\beta(2) - \beta(1)\alpha(2)\} \quad \ldots.(3.108)$$

$$\psi_a(1)\psi_b(2)\alpha(1)\beta(2) - \psi_b(1)\psi_a(2)\alpha(1)\beta(2) + \psi_a(1)\psi_b(2)\beta(1)\alpha(2) - \\ - \psi_b(1)\psi_a(2)\beta(1)\alpha(2) \\ = \{\psi_a(1)\psi_b(2) - \psi_b(1)\psi_a(2)\}\{\alpha(1)\beta(2) + \beta(1)\alpha(2)\} \quad \ldots.(3.109)$$

$$\psi_a(1)\psi_b(2)\alpha(1)\alpha(2) - \psi_b(1)\psi_a(2)\alpha(1)\alpha(2) \\ = \{\psi_a(1)\psi_b(2) - \psi_b(1)\psi_a(2)\}\ \alpha(1)\alpha(2) \quad \ldots.(3.110)$$

$$\psi_a(1)\psi_b(2)\beta(1)\beta(2) - \psi_b(1)\psi_a(2)\beta(1)\beta(2) \\ = \{\psi_a(1)\psi_b(2) - \psi_b(1)\psi_a(2)\}\ \beta(1)\beta(2) \quad \ldots.(3.111)$$

These functions comprise the linear combination of the wave functions which we have already discussed, together with terms representing the spin wave functions. It has been shown in the last section that the formation of the chemical bond is described by the symmetric wave function

$$\psi_I = \psi_a(1)\psi_b(2) + \psi_b(1)\psi_a(2) \quad \ldots.(3.95)$$

and in order to make the complete wave function antisymmetric it is necessary to combine function 3.95 with an antisymmetric spin wave function since the product of an antisymmetric and a symmetric function will be an antisymmetric function. The only possible antisymmetric spin wave function is

$$\sigma_1 = \alpha(1)\beta(2) - \beta(1)\alpha(2) \quad \ldots.(3.112)$$

The product of equations 3.95 and 3.112 leads to 3.108

It will be seen from *Table XV* that equation 3.112 describes the state of the two electron molecule in which the electron spins are orientated in opposite directions, and the total spin angular momentum will therefore be zero, *i.e.*

$$\Sigma s = (+\tfrac{1}{2}) + (-\tfrac{1}{2}) = 0 \quad \ldots.(3.113)$$

Thus we may conclude that for a bond to be formed the spins of the participating electrons must be antiparallel and the two electrons will then be located in one orbital.

If the orbital wave function is antisymmetric

$$\psi_{II} = \psi_a(1)\psi_b(2) - \psi_b(1)\psi_a(2) \quad \ldots.(3.96)$$

then in order that the resultant complete wave function be antisymmetric, the spin wave function must be symmetric. The three such functions are :—

$$\sigma_2 = \alpha(1)\alpha(2) \qquad \ldots.(3.114)$$

$$\sigma_3 = \alpha(1)\beta(2) + \beta(1)\alpha(2) \qquad \ldots.(3.115)$$

$$\sigma_4 = \beta(1)\beta(2) \qquad \ldots.(3.116)$$

where $\sigma_2 = \alpha(1)\alpha(2)$, $\Sigma s = (+\tfrac{1}{2}) + (+\tfrac{1}{2}) = +1$, $\sigma_3 = \alpha(1)\beta(2) + \beta(1)\alpha(2)$, $\Sigma s = (+\tfrac{1}{2}) + (-\tfrac{1}{2}) = 0$ and $\sigma_4 = \beta(1)\beta(2)$, $\Sigma s = (-\tfrac{1}{2}) + (-\tfrac{1}{2}) = -1$.

Thus on the basis of the above conclusions we see that for the hydrogen molecule there are four possible complete wave functions :

$$\{\psi_a(1)\psi_b(2) + \psi_b(1)\psi_a(2)\}\{\alpha(1)\beta(2) - \beta(1)\alpha(2)\} \qquad \Sigma s = 0 \qquad \ldots.(3.108)$$

$$\{\psi_a(1)\psi_b(2) - \psi_b(1)\psi_a(2)\}\{\alpha(1)\alpha(2)\} \qquad \Sigma s = +1 \qquad \ldots.(3.96) \text{ and } (3.114)$$

$$\{\psi_a(1)\psi_b(2) - \psi_b(1)\psi_a(2)\}\{\alpha(1)\beta(2) + \beta(1)\alpha(2)\} \qquad \Sigma s = 0 \qquad \ldots.(3.96) \text{ and } (3.115)$$

$$\{\psi_a(1)\psi_b(2) - \psi_b(1)\psi_a(2)\}\{\beta(1)\beta(2)\} \qquad \Sigma s = -1 \qquad \ldots.(3.96) \text{ and } (3.116)$$

It follows, therefore, that there is only one state of the hydrogen molecule with a symmetric orbital wave function, which as we have seen leads to bond formation. On the other hand there are three states with antisymmetric orbit wave functions, which lead to repulsion. The stable form is termed a singlet and the repulsion form a triplet state. On a collision between two atoms of hydrogen, the probability that a molecule will result is therefore 1 : 4.

CALCULATION OF THE BOND ENERGY AND INTERATOMIC DISTANCE FOR THE HYDROGEN MOLECULE

Having calculated the values of the integrals C and A (equations 3.91 and 3.92), it is possible to determine the energy of the molecule as a function of the internuclear distance. The curves obtained are shown in *Figure 15*. The upper curve gives the repulsion energy of atoms with electrons of parallel spins, the next lower curve represents the Coulombic energy, the third the energy of the molecule according to equation 3.91 and the lowest curve represents the experimentally determined value.

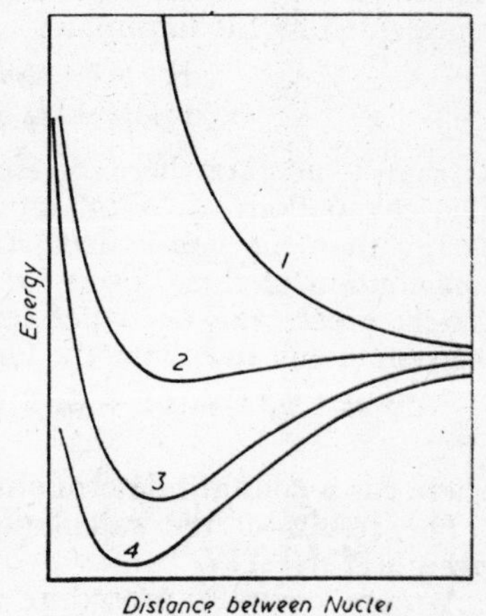

Figure 15. Energy curves for the hydrogen molecule

The Coulombic energy clearly is not very large ; the curve passes through a shallow minimum, which although representing attraction of the atoms, gives an energy value which is too small to explain the stability of the molecule. Inclusion of the exchange energy (third curve) gives a much more satisfactory explanation of the strength of the chemical bond and shows that only 14 per cent of the total bond energy can be regarded as Coulombic in nature. The calculated value of the bond energy is 72·3 kcals and of the interatomic distance is 1·64 atomic units = 0·86 Å.

The experimental value for the dissociation energy of the hydrogen molecule into unexcited atoms is 103·2 kcals. To this value must be added the zero point energy (see Chapter 8) equal to 6·2 kcals; when the molecule dissociates into atoms the whole energy of the bond is not used up, but 6·2 kcals less, since the molecule in its ground vibrational state possesses this amount of energy. Thus the actual experimental value for the bond energy of the hydrogen molecule is 109·4 kcals. The experimental value of the internuclear distance is 0·74 Å. The discrepancy between the calculated and experimental values is explained by the fact that in the treatment employed, we proceeded from atomic functions which were correct only when the nuclei were at an infinite distance apart and applied them to the state where the internuclear distance is of the order of 10^{-8} cm.

Several authors have attempted to improve on the approximate method of Heitler and London. WANG[4] made use of the functions ψ_a and ψ_b, but altered the effective charge on the nucleus by using the expression

$$\psi_a = \{\exp(-Zr_a)Z^{3/2}/\sqrt{\pi}\} \qquad \ldots(3.117)$$

and obtained the value of Z, when E had a minimum value. ROSEN[5] attempted to include the polarising effect of the second nucleus on the electron cloud of the first atom and in place of a spherical 1*s* electron cloud he employed a cloud elongated in the direction of the second nucleus. This may be represented as the partial combination of the 2*p* with the 1*s* state, *e.g.*

$$\psi_a = \psi_{1s_a} + \eta\psi_{2p_a} \qquad \ldots(3.118)$$

where η is a coefficient.

WEINBAUM[6] introduced a further development; along with the uncharged states corresponding to the functions $\psi_a(1)\psi_b(2)$ and $\psi_b(1)\psi_a(2)$ it is possible that there exist also those states where both electrons are located simultaneously in one or other of the nuclei. These ionic states may be represented by the formulae :

$H^- H^+$ (*both electrons on nucleus a*)

$H^+ H^-$ (*both electrons on nucleus b*)

To these ionic states there correspond the functions $\psi_a(1)\psi_a(2)$ and $\psi_b(1)\psi_b(2)$. The calculations of Weinbaum show that the ionic states are of higher energy than the non-ionized states and are therefore less probable. The contribution of these forms to the final state of the molecule is approximately 4 per cent, *i.e.* 2 per cent from each form. The wave function of the system will thus have the form

$$\psi = \{\psi_a(1)\psi_b(2) + \psi_a(2)\psi_b(1)\} + c\{\psi_a(1)\psi_a(2) + \psi_b(1)\psi_b(2)\} \qquad \ldots(3.119)$$

where c is a constant determining the contribution of the ionic form.

The results of the calculations of Wang, Rosen and Weinbaum are given in *Table XVI*.

A more complex procedure was introduced by JAMES and COOLIDGE[7]. One of the chief reasons for the incorrect value obtained by the earlier methods is that the wave function does not take into account the mutual repulsion of the electrons. It is true that the Hamiltonian operator (equation 3.70) includes a term for the interaction of electrons but allowance should also be made in the wave function for the system. Incorporating this effect it was possible, as shown in *Table XVI*, to achieve almost exact agreement with the experimental values.

Table XVI. Bond Energy (E) and internuclear distance (R) for hydrogen molecule

Author	E kcals	R Å	Z	η	C
Heitler and London, Sigiura[8]	72·3	0·86	1	0	0
Wang	86·6	0·78	1·17	0	0
Rosen	77·2	0·80	1	0·1	0
Rosen	92·6	0·77	1·17	0·1	0
Weinbaum	73·9	0·81	1	0	0·158
Weinbaum	92·2	0·77	1·19	0	0·256
Weinbaum	94·5	0·77	1·19	0·7	0·175
James and Coolidge	108·8	0·74	—	—	—
Experimental values	109·4	0·74	—	—	—

The Heitler-London method, although approximate, has the advantage that a physical picture of the nature of the chemical bond may easily be obtained. The bond is formed by two electrons, one from each atom with opposite spin and owing to the transfer of the electrons, two states arise, which on superposition yield a transitional cloud, which serves to bond the atoms together. Such a bond is termed the homopolar or covalent bond. This physical picture of the bond is clearly the basis of the electron pair bond of Lewis.

REFERENCES

[1] HARTREE, D. R. *Proc. Camb. phil. Soc.* 24 (1928) 89
[2] HYLLERAAS, E. A. *Z. Phys.* 71 (1931) 739
JAFFÉ, G. *ibid* 87 (1934) 535
TELLER, E. *ibid* 61 (1930) 458
FINKELSTEIN, B. N. and HOROWITZ, G. E. *ibid* 48 (1928) 118
DICKINSON, B. N. *J. chem. Phys.* 1 (1933) 317
GUILLEMIN, V. and ZENER, C. *Proc. nat. Acad. Sci. Wash.* 15 (1929) 314
BURRAU, Ø. *Kgl. Danske. Videnskab. Selskab. Math.-fys. Medd.* 7 (1927) 1
[3] HEITLER, W. and LONDON, F. *Z. Phys.* 44 (1927) 455
[4] WANG, S. C. *Phys. Rev.* 21 (1928) 579
[5] ROSEN, N. *ibid* 38 (1931) 2099
[6] WEINBAUM, S. *J. chem. Phys.* 1 (1933) 593
[7] JAMES, H. M. and COOLIDGE, A. S. *ibid* 1 (1933) 825
[8] SIGIURA, V. *Z. Phys.* 45 (1927) 484

4

SATURATION AND DIRECTION OF VALENCY BONDS

SATURATION OF VALENCIES. LOCALIZED BONDS

IN CONSIDERING the saturation of valencies it will be convenient to follow the method of Heitler and London and consider the interaction of helium and hydrogen. The helium atom possesses two electrons in a completed 1*s* orbital. Let these electrons be designated 1 and 2, in agreement with the Pauli principle the spins of these electrons will be opposite. The electron of the hydrogen atom is represented by the number 3. The system being considered is thus represented by:

$$\text{He}\underset{1}{\downarrow}\ \underset{2}{\uparrow} \qquad \underset{3}{\uparrow}\text{H}$$

The possibilities of the exchange of the hydrogen electron with either of the helium electrons is restricted in the first place by the Pauli principle. The exchange of electrons 1 and 3 results in the appearance of two electrons with parallel spins existing in one orbital which is not permitted by the exclusion principle. There remains in consequence only the possibility of the exchange of electrons 2 and 3, which because they have parallel spins, will, as has been shown in the last chapter, lead not to bond formation but to mutual repulsion. Thus no molecule HeH is formed.

Following a similar argument, Heitler and London also considered the possibility of the interaction of two atoms of helium. Let the two nuclei be denoted by the letters *a* and *b* and the electrons numbered 1 to 4. The system to be considered is thus represented by:

$$\overset{a}{\underset{1}{\downarrow}\ \underset{2}{\uparrow}} \qquad \overset{b}{\underset{3}{\downarrow}\ \underset{4}{\uparrow}}$$

The formation of a bond can only occur by the transposition of two electrons having opposite spins, *e.g.* 1 and 4. Such an exchange, however, is forbidden by the Pauli principle, since electron 4 would enter into an orbital along with electron 2 having the same direction of spin. This inability for an exchange of electrons to occur explains both the monatomic nature of helium and its chemical inertness. In general, all atoms containing only orbitals with two paired electrons will be chemically inert; only when an orbital contains a single unpaired electron can bond formation occur.

A theoretical basis has thus been obtained for the hypothesis, put forward earlier, giving the relationship between the valency of atoms and the number of unpaired electrons. Each unpaired electron can take part in the formation of one bond and thus chemical properties are determined not simply by the number of outer electrons possessed by an atom, but by the number of unpaired electrons. The presence of completed shells of electrons leads, on the formation of molecules, to the partial weakening of the bond; this is illustrated by a comparison of the hydrogen molecule with the diatomic molecules formed by the alkali metals. As with hydrogen, the bond in these molecules is formed by *s* electrons located in the outer orbit; the difference lies in the fact that the hydrogen molecule possesses no inner shell of electrons. Thus lithium, apart from the outer 2*s* electrons, has two more deeply located 1*s* electrons, and the two saturated shells of the two atoms in the lithium molecule repel each other, with the result that the bonding due to the electron cloud of the outer 2*s* electrons is considerably weakened. The dissociation energies and interatomic distances at equilibrium[1] are given in *Table XVII*, and it will be noticed that all the molecules of the alkali metals have much lower dissociation energies than has the hydrogen molecule, and much larger interatomic distances. In the hydrogen molecule the interatomic distance is 0·74 Å whereas in the lithium molecule it is 3·5 times greater (2·67 Å) and the dissociation energy is almost one quarter (26 kcals as compared with 103·2 kcals). As the number of complete electronic shells is increased on proceeding from lithium to caesium, so the dissociation energy decreases and the internuclear distance increases.

Table XVII. Dissociation Energies and Interatomic Distances in the Diatomic Molecules of Hydrogen and the Alkali Metals

Molecule	Dissociation energy kcals	Interatomic distance Å
H_2	103·2	0·74
Li_2	26·0	2·67
Na_2	17·0	3·08
K_2	12·0	3·92
Rb_2	11·0	—
Cs_2	10·0	—

The quantum states of the two electrons forming a chemical bond determine the three quantum numbers of the orbital within which they are contained. Such an orbital is termed a molecular orbital and the fact that any attempt at interaction by a third electron leads to repulsion is the cause of valency saturation, which is a characteristic property of covalency.

Attraction by Coulomb forces does not lead to valency saturation. If a positive ion is attracted by a negative ion, that does not prevent it from being attracted to other negative ions. Thus with electrostatic attraction it is not the normal valency which is characteristic, but the number of surrounding ions. In the crystal lattice of sodium chloride, each chloride ion is surrounded by six sodium ions and in the caesium chloride lattice eight caesium ions surround one ion of chlorine. The numbers 6 and 8 bear no relationship to the number of unpaired electrons.

The interaction of two unbonded electrons may be shown to lead invariably to repulsion[2]. When two electrons situated in different hydrogen atoms come together, their spins can couple in four different ways, as shown in Chapter 3. One of these, when $\Sigma s = 0$, corresponds to a symmetric orbital wave function and bonding occurs with the formation of a hydrogen molecule; in the other three cases, when $\Sigma s = +1, 0, -1$, the orbital wave function is antisymmetric and repulsion occurs. Since all four types of coupling have equal probability, it follows that one fourth of the encounters between hydrogen atoms will lead to the formation of molecules in the singlet state and in the other three-fourths to the triplet state and repulsion of the atom. Similar conditions will prevail when two electrons, each situated in a different hydrogen molecule, approach each other. At any instant the probability of finding the electron pair in the singlet state compared with a triplet state will be in the ratio 1 : 3. Thus the average interaction energy E, of two non-bonded hydrogen atoms in different hydrogen molecules will be given by,

$$E = \tfrac{1}{4}E_1 + \tfrac{3}{4}E_2 \qquad \ldots.(4{\cdot}1)$$

where E_1 is the energy of the singlet state and E_2 that of the triplet state. If the integrals S_{12} are assumed to be negligibly small, then the values of E_1 and E_2 as given by equations 3.91 and 3.92 will be :

$$E_1 = 2E_0 + C + A \qquad \ldots.(4{\cdot}2)$$
$$E_2 = 2E_0 + C - A \qquad \ldots.(4{\cdot}3)$$

where C is the Coulombic energy, A the exchange energy and E_0 the energy of the hydrogen atom. From equations 4.1, 4.2 and 4.3 we obtain

$$E = 2E_0 + \frac{C + A}{4} + \frac{3(C - A)}{4} = 2E_0 + C - \frac{A}{2} \qquad \ldots.(4{\cdot}4)$$

Since the numerical value of A is very much greater than C, $A/2$ will be greater than C and since both are negative the resultant value of E will be greater than $2E_0$; thus there will be a repulsion between two atoms not connected by a covalent bond. This argument is valid only if the two hydrogen molecules are some distance apart. If the distance between the molecules becomes approximately equal to the internuclear distance within the molecules there is no evidence for considering the system *abcd* (*Figure 16*) as consisting of the molecules *ab* and *cd* rather than of the molecules *ac* and *bd*. This particular case must be considered as a system in which four electrons exist in the field of four nuclei. In such a system formula 4.4 does not apply.

```
H————H
a    b
:    :
c    d
H————H
```

Figure 16. The system of four atoms of hydrogen

In contrast to the hypothetical molecule H_4, real molecules present examples of localized bonds in a very large number of cases. The molecule of ethane, for example, can have only one structural formula :

```
H       H
 \     /
H—C—C—H
 /     \
H       H
```

Any other arrangement, *e.g.*

```
H       H
 \     /
H—C=C—H

H———————H
```

whilst not conflicting with the valencies of the atoms, is nevertheless improbable. The interatomic distance in the C—H bond is 1·09 Å, whereas the distance between the two hydrogen atoms of two CH_3 groups is found to be 2·02 Å (this is the distance between the two hydrogen atoms joined by a link in the second formula). The exchange energy in such a system will be negligible as it diminishes rapidly with an increase of interatomic distance ; in the hydrogen molecule this is 0·74 Å. The energy of the first structure is, therefore, so very much greater than that of the second that the contribution of the latter is negligible. It is on the basis of this argument that a molecule may be considered as a collection of atoms joined by localized bonds.

This conception of the chemical bond has been considerably extended by SLATER[3] and by PAULING[4] and yields results of great importance in chemistry. The essential postulate in this treatment, which has become known as either ' the method of localized pairs ' or ' the method of directed valence bond ', is that the energy of the molecule consists of the following components : (*1*) the total Coulombic energy, (*2*) the sum of the exchange energies of the various separate links and (*3*) the repulsion energy of the unbonded electrons. Let us apply this treatment to the simple triatomic molecule *abc*,

$$\underset{\uparrow\downarrow}{a\text{——}b}\underset{\uparrow\downarrow}{\text{——}c}$$

Atoms *a* and *c* have a single electron each, but atom *b* has two valency electrons and the complete molecule contains two bonds, *ab* and *bc*. The electrostatic attraction and repulsion of all the electrons and nuclei enter into the Coulombic energy term. The exchange energy of the links *ab* and *bc* will be :

$$A_{ab} + A_{bc}$$

In addition, there will be the repulsion of the three pairs of electrons not used in a particular bond, *i* the electrons of atoms *a* and *c*, *ii* the electron of atom *a* and the electron of atom *b*, not paired with it, *iii* the electron of atom *c* and the electron of atom *b*, not paired with it. These repulsion energies will be :

$$-\frac{A'_{ac}}{2}-\frac{A'_{ab}}{2}-\frac{A'_{bc}}{2}$$

where A' represents the exchange integral in the case of unpaired electrons. The interaction of the two unpaired electrons of atom *b* have already been accounted for in the energy of the atom. A_{ab} will not be equal to A'_{ab} as can be seen by reference to *Figure 17*. Since it has been supposed that atom *b* has two unpaired electrons, it follows that these must be *p* electrons. The electron clouds of these two *p* electrons will appear as two figure eights oriented at right angles. The atoms *a* and *c* will then place themselves so that there is the greatest possible superposition of electron clouds (*a* and *c* are assumed to have a single *s* electron each, these are represented as circles in *Figure 17*) and it will be seen that the interaction of the unlinked electrons, *viz* circle *a* with vertical figure eight and circle *c* with horizontal figure eight, will be very small.

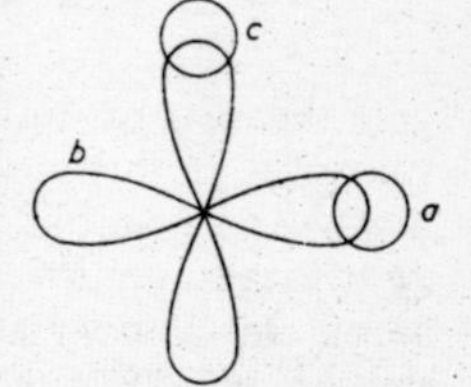

Figure 17. Electron distribution for a triatomic molecule a b c

The total energy of the molecule therefore will be :

$$E = C + A_{ab} + A_{bc} - \frac{A'_{ab}}{2} - \frac{A'_{bc}}{2} - \frac{A'_{ac}}{2} \qquad \ldots.(4.5)$$

and thus in its general form, the energy of a polyelectron molecule will be,

$$E = C + \Sigma A_{ik} - \tfrac{1}{2}\Sigma A'_{ik} \qquad \ldots.(4.6)$$

where A_{ik} represents the exchange energy of electron pairs forming a covalent bond and A'_{ik} represents the exchange energy of nonbonding pairs of electrons.

Quantitative data relevant to the determination of the energy of molecules will be discussed later.

DIRECTIONAL COVALENCY

Experimental data indicate that valency bonds are localized in a particular direction in space and the idea, first put forward by VAN'T HOFF, that the four valencies of the carbon atom are directed towards the four corners of a tetrahedron has been supported by recent physical measurements which permit the determination of valency angles.

The suggestion was put forward by PAULING[4] that the direction of a bond will correspond to that in which the electron clouds of the two electrons forming the bond overlap to the greatest possible extent and the electrons will therefore exist most probably between the two nuclei. The greater the overlap of the individual orbits the greater will be the density of the charge between the nuclei and hence the stronger the bond. It was shown in Chapter 1, that the fundamental difference between the *s* and *p* orbitals was that the former was dependent only on *r*, the distance of the electron from the nucleus, whereas the latter was dependent also on the angles θ and ϕ. In general therefore, *s* orbitals are spherically symmetrical and consequently there is no directional property of the valency. With *p* electrons, however, there are three possible orbitals, p_x, p_y and p_z, consisting of figure eights directed at right angles to each other and it follows therefore, that when an atom forms bonds involving *p* orbitals, the angle between the bonds should be 90° (see Chapter 18).

In the oxygen atom there are two unpaired *p* electrons,

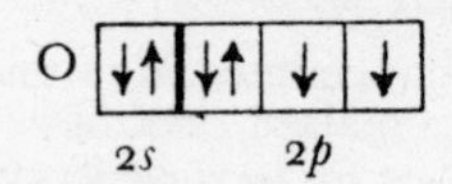

and the two orbitals of the valency electrons will be at 90° to each other. Compound formation with two hydrogen atoms will occur through the maximum possible overlapping of the hydrogen 1*s* orbitals with the oxygen 2*p* orbitals, say the $2p_x$ and $2p_y$. This will result in the oxygen atoms lying along the *x* and *y* axes, and hence the angle between the two O—H bonds should be 90°. Experimental data, based on spectroscopic and dipole moment measurements, show that the molecule has a triangular structure

```
  O
 / \
H   H
```

and that the angle between the bonds is slightly greater than 90°. The reason for the discrepancy will be discussed later.

In the nitrogen atom there are three unpaired *p* electrons and thus the angles between the three N—H bonds in ammonia should be 90°. Experimental data show that the angle is rather more than this, being 108°, but nevertheless the general structure of the molecule is that of a triangular pyramid and the flat model,

```
H   H
 \ /
  N
  |
  H
```

is in disagreement with experiment. The experimental data for oxygen, nitrogen and other atoms are summarized in *Table XVIII*.

Table XVIII. Observed Valency Angles

Molecule	*Bond angle*	*Experimental value*	*Experimental method*
H_2O (*gas*)	H—O—H	105°	*spectroscopic*
F_2O (*gas*)	F—O—F	100°	*electron diffraction*
Cl_2O (*gas*)	Cl—O—Cl	115°	" "
$(CH_3)_2O$ (*gas*)	C—O—C	111°	" "
CH_2—CH_2 O O CH_2—CH_2	C—O—C	110°	" "
CH—CH ‖ ‖ CH CH O	C—O—C	107°	" "
H_2S (*gas*)	H—S—H	92°	*spectroscopic*
S_8 (*crystal*)	S—S—S	106°	*X-ray*
S_8 (*gas*)	S—S—S	100°	*electron diffraction*
BaS_3 (*crystal*)	S—S—S	103°	*X-ray*
$K_2S_3O_8$ (*crystal*)	S—S—S	103°	"
CH—CH ‖ ‖ CH CH S	C—S—C	91°	*electron diffraction*
SCl_2 (*gas*)	Cl—S—Cl	103°	" "
H_2Se (*gas*)	H—Se—H	90° (*approx*)	*spectroscopic*
Se (*crystal*)	Se—Se—Se	105°	*X-ray*
Te (*crystal*)	Te—Te—Te	102°	"
NH_3 (*gas*)	H—N—H	108°	*spectroscopic*
$N(CH_3)_3$ (*gas*)	C—N—C	108°	*electron diffraction*
PH_3 (*gas*)	H—P—H	93°	*spectroscopic*
P (*crystal*)	P—P—P	99°	*X-ray*
$P(CH_3)_3$ (*gas*)	C—P—C	100°	*electron diffraction*
PF_3 (*gas*)	F—P—F	104°	" "
$PFCl_2$ (*gas*)	Cl—P—Cl	102°	" "
PCl_3 (*gas*)	Cl—P—Cl	101°	" "
PBr_3 (*gas*)	Br—P—Br	100°	" "
PI_3 (*gas*)	I—P—I	98°	" "
As (*crystal*)	As—As—As	97°	" "
$As(CH_3)_3$ (*gas*)	C—As—C	96°	" "
$AsCl_3$ (*gas*)	Cl—As—Cl	103°	" "
$AsBr_3$ (*gas*)	Br—As—Br	100°	" "
AsI_3 (*gas*)	I—As—I	100°	" "
Sb (*crystal*)	Sb—Sb—Sb	96°	*X-ray*
$SbCl_3$ (*gas*)	Cl—Sb—Cl	104°	*electron diffraction*
$SbBr_3$ (*gas*)	Br—Sb—Br	96°	" "
SbI_3 (*gas*)	I—Sb—I	98°	" "
Bi (*crystal*)	Bi—Bi—Bi	94°	*X-ray*

The experimental error in the determination of valency angles is probably not more than 5 per cent and the discrepancies between the observed and theoretical angle may in certain cases be due to experimental error. However, since all the valency angles are greater than 90° a more significant explanation must be given. In the water molecule the valency angle is 105°, thus exceeding the theoretical value by 15°. This discrepancy is brought about in two ways. First, there exists a repulsion between the two hydrogen atoms by virtue of the interaction of non-bonding electrons and secondly, as a result of resonance with the ionic states

both atoms of hydrogen possess positive charges thus producing a Coulombic repulsion. In support of the latter explanation examination of the data in *Table XVIII* shows that in a series of compounds in which the contribution from the ionic forms decreases along the series, there is a corresponding decrease in the magnitude of the valency angle *e.g.* H_2O, H_2S, H_2Se ; NH_3, PH_3 ; PF_3, PCl_3, PBr_3, PI_3.

HYBRIDIZATION OF BOND ORBITALS

The carbon atom in its ground state has two unpaired p electrons :

C	↓↑	↓	↓	
	2s	2p		

As with the oxygen atom it might be expected that the two p electrons were used in bond formation thus leading to a valency of two. Since carbon is normally tetravalent, however, the carbon atom must be in an excited state with one of the s electrons transferred to the vacant p orbital. This excitation requires an energy of 80 kcals[5] which must be compensated for when valency bonds are formed. The resulting tetravalent carbon atom has one s and three p orbitals and it might be supposed that three of these should be oriented at right angles to one another and that the fourth should have no directional properties. It has long been known, however, that the four bonds of carbon are exactly equivalent and are directed towards the four corners of a tetrahedron (*Table XIX*). This is explained by the formation of four sp^3 hybrid bonds in place of the single s and three p bonds. The states of the electrons are then described by the linear combination of the orbital wave functions, *viz*

$$\psi = a\psi_s + b\psi_{p_x} + c\psi_{p_y} + d\psi_{p_z}$$

It is found that a bond involving

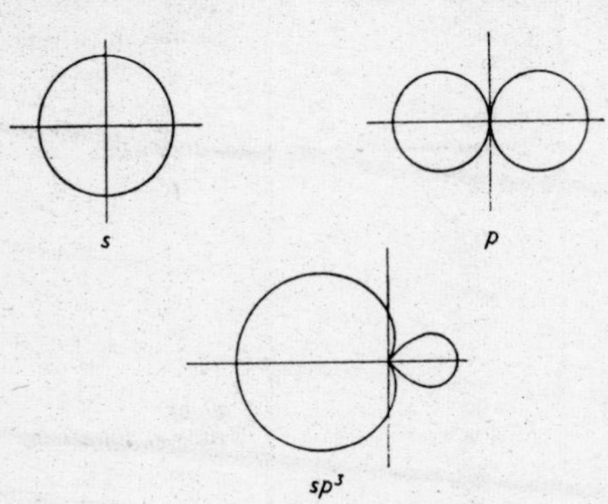

Figure 18. The s, p and tetrahedral hybrid sp³ orbitals

an orbital formed by the linear combination of *s* and *p* orbitals, taken with certain values of the numerical coefficients *a*, *b*, *c*, and *d*, has a bond strength greater than an *s* or *p* orbital alone (for greater detail see chapter 18). The reason for this increased bond strength is seen in *Figure 18* where the hybrid sp^3 orbital is seen to be concentrated more in one direction, compared with a *p* orbital, and in consequence enables overlapping of bond orbitals to occur to a greater extent.

When carbon is linked with four neighbouring atoms, the four valencies are directed towards the corners of a regular tetrahedron. Such a configuration is favourable for several reasons. Firstly, the hybrid sp^3 tetrahedral orbitals permit greater overlapping of orbitals and hence a greater bond energy than *s* or *p* orbitals. Secondly, when a reacting atom X approaches the carbon atom, in addition to the maximum overlapping of the bonding orbitals, the extent of the overlapping of the orbital of the electron of X with non-bonding electrons of the carbon atom is a minimum and finally the mutual repulsion of the X atoms is a minimum. The electron diffraction data shown in *Table XIX* shows that the valency angle of carbon is either equal to or very close to the tetrahedral angle. Hybridization of orbitals leading to a tetrahedral configuration occurs in exactly the same way with silicon, germanium, and tin.

Table XIX. Observed Valency Angles of some Carbon Compounds (by electron diffraction)

Molecule	*Valency angle*	*Experimental value*
CH_4	H—C—H	109° 28′
$CH_3—CH_3$	H—C—H	109° 28′
$CH_3—CH_2—CH_3$	C—C—C	111° 30′ ± 3°
$(CH_3)_2CH—CH_3$	C—C—C	111° 30′ ± 3°
$(CH_3)_4C$	C—C—C	109° 28′
$(CH_3)_3CCl$	C—C—C	111° 30′ ± 2°
$(CH_3)_3CBr$	C—C—C	111° 30′ ± 2°
C_2H_5Cl	C—C—Cl	111° 30′ ± 2°
C_2H_5Br	C—C—Br	109° ± 2°
$(CH_3)_2CHCl$	C—C—Cl	109° ± 3°
$(CH_3)_2CHBr$	C—C—Br	109° 30′ ± 3°
CH_3CCl_3	C—C—Cl	109° ± 2°
CH_2F_2	F—C—F	110° ± 1°
CH_2Cl_2	Cl—C—Cl	112° ± 2°
CH_2FCl	F—C—Cl	110° ± 2°
$CHCl_3$	Cl—C—Cl	112° ± 2°
CH_2Br_2	Br—C—Br	112° ± 2°
$CHBr_3$	Br—C—Br	111° ± 2°
$C_6H_{12}N_4$*	N—C—N	110° ± 2°
$SiHCl_3$	Cl—Si—Cl	110° ± 2°
$SiHBr_3$	Br—Si—Br	110° ± 2°

* Hexamethylenetetramine

Similar behaviour is found with other atoms. Boron in the trivalent state has one *s* and two *p* electrons and hybridization leads to the formation of three equivalent hybrid sp^2 orbitals lying in the same plane and with a valency angle of 120°. Experimental data[6] for $B(CH_3)_3$ are in agreement with this prediction. Beryllium and mercury in the excited state necessary for bond formation, have one *s* and one *p* electron which form two hybrid *sp* bonds at an angle of 180° to each other.

Comparison of the elements of the third and fifth groups, both having three unpaired electrons leads to an explanation of their stereochemistry. Boron has one *s* and two *p* electrons and thus forms three planar sp^2 hybrid bonds, whereas nitrogen possesses three *p* electrons which form bonds at right angles to each other. The comparison is similar between elements of the sixth group and beryllium, in the former case the unpaired electrons are *p* electrons thus forming two bonds at 90°, whilst beryllium with one *s* and one *p* electron forms two linear *sp* hybrid bonds.

σ- AND π- BONDS

The existence of multiple bonds between atoms has been known for some considerable time. Thus with the nitrogen molecule each atom uses fully its three valency bonds and the link is therefore a triple one. Such a bond was represented by Lewis as three pairs of dots to correspond to the three pairs of bonding *p* electrons,

N ⠿ N

Such a simple representation cannot be correct as the three *p* orbitals of each nitrogen atom will be approximately at right angles to the other two. One pair of electrons will give maximum overlapping along the line of centres and such a link is termed a σ bond. The remaining orbitals will exist in two directions perpendicular to the line of centres and mutually at right angles. Overlapping will also occur between pairs of these orbitals, forming two supplementary bonds, termed π bonds. The arrangement of bonds in the nitrogen molecule, which contains one σ and two π bonds is shown in *Figure 19*. The electrons forming a π bond are termed π electrons. With these bonds there is no directional property in the same sense that it exists in the examples considered in the previous section. The bond occurs when two *p* orbitals from different atoms are parallel, since such a configuration permits the maximum possible overlap. As the angle between the orbitals increases, the exchange energy decreases rapidly and is a minimum when the orbitals are perpendicular to each other.

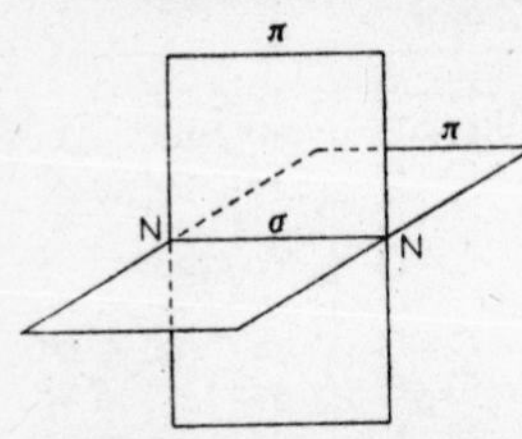

Figure 19. Arrangement of bonds in the nitrogen molecule

Two atoms, having one *s* electron each, on molecule formation give a σ bond *e.g.* H_2 and Li_2 ; an *s* electron of one atom and a *p* electron or hybridized electron of another atom also give a σ bond, as in such links as H—Cl, O—H, N—H and C—H ; in H_2O there are two, in NH_3 three, and in CH_4, four σ bonds. If two atoms form multiple bonds, then only one of these will be a σ bond and the remainder π bonds.

In order to study the application of the concept of σ and π bonds we shall consider first the double bond between the two carbon atoms in ethylene. In this molecule each carbon atom is surrounded by three atoms, two hydrogen and one carbon, with these it forms three σ bonds using up three of its valency electrons in doing so. The remaining unpaired electron cannot form a second σ bond between the carbon atoms as this would cause four electrons to be in the same quantum state, a condition which is forbidden by the Pauli principle. Thus the remaining electron pair forms a π bond. The maximum bonding energy of a π bond is only attained when two *p* orbitals are parallel to each other and hence the π bond in ethylene is considered to be formed from 'pure', *i.e.* non-hybridized *p* orbitals, in contrast to the σ bonds which are formed between hybridized orbitals. In ethylene therefore the three σ bonds of each carbon atom are formed by three sp^2 hybrid orbitals similar to those existing in boron. The three bonds will be in one plane and will be at an angle of 120° to each other. The direction of the π bond formed by the remaining *p* orbitals of the carbon atoms will be perpendicular to this plane and will be equally above and below the plane of the σ bonds. All six atoms of the ethylene molecule lie in one plane, since only under these conditions is the maximum energy of the π bond attained; the bond arrangement is shown diagrammatically in *Figure 20*. In a similar way, the double bond in such groups as C=O and C=N is also composed of one σ and one π bond.

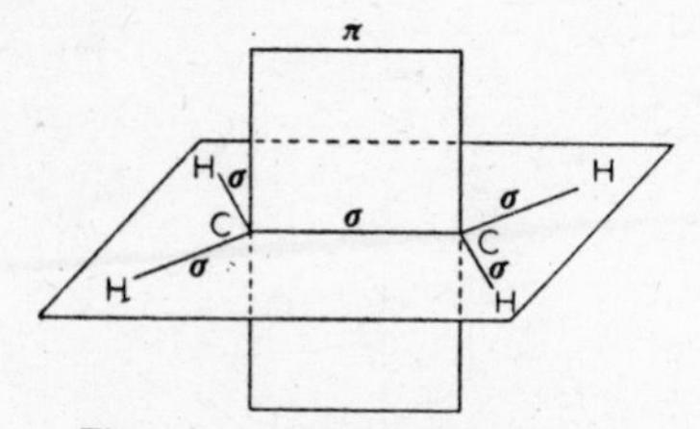

Figure 20. Arrangement of bonds in the ethylene molecule

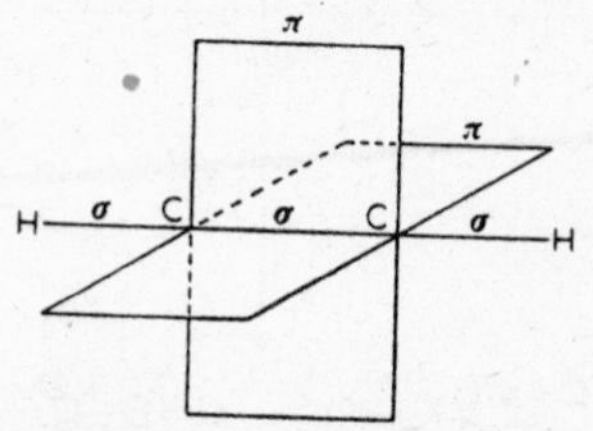

Figure 21. Arrangement of bonds in the acetylene molecule

The triple bond in acetylene, like that in nitrogen, is composed of one σ and two π bonds and here also the π bonds are formed between electrons in non-hybridized p states. The σ electrons, two to each carbon atom, are located in sp hybrid orbitals, formed by the linear combination of one s and one p wave function, as in beryllium, and the molecule is therefore linear. The arrangement of bonds is shown diagrammatically in *Figure 21*. In a similar way the triple bond in the nitrile group C≡N is composed also of one σ and two π bonds.

The planar configuration of ethylene and the linear structure of acetylene are supported by experimental data. In *Table XX* are given the values obtained by electron diffraction measurements for the valency angle of a series of carbon compounds containing double bonds. It will be seen that the values are all close to 120°.

We thus conclude from the foregoing discussion that carbon may exist in three different valency states:

1 four σ bonds, directed to the corners of a tetrahedron

2 three σ bonds in one plane at an angle of 120° to each other and one π bond perpendicular to the plane of the σ bonds

3 two σ bonds lying in a straight line and two π bonds perpendicular to the σ bonds and mutually at right angles.

The stereochemistry of the carbon compounds is determined entirely by the number of surrounding atoms. When there are four neighbours, the structure is always tetrahedral, when three it is planar and when two, linear.

In classical stereochemistry the molecule of ethylene was represented as two tetrahedra with a common side. This view is now shown to be erroneous since it suggests that the two bonds forming the double bond are identical, whereas, as we have seen, such a link actually consists of a σ and a π bond. In a similar way a triple bond, as in acetylene, was represented as two tetrahedra with a common face. Not only is this incorrect in view of the fact that the bonds actually consist of one σ and two π bonds, but it also predicts incorrect chemical behaviour. The addition reaction in which an acetylenic compound is transformed to an ethylenic compound, is represented on the classical model as a change from two tetrahedra with a common face to two tetrahedra with a common edge.

Table XX. Valency Angle of Carbon Compounds containing Double Bonds

Molecule	*Valency angle*	*Experimental value*	*Configuration*
$(CH_3)_2C=C(CH_3)_2$	C=C—C	124°	C C C=C C C
$(CH_3)_2C=CH_2$	C=C—C	124°	C C=C C
$COCl_2$	O=C—Cl	117°	Cl C=O Cl
$CSCl_2$	S=C—Cl	116°	Cl C=S Cl
CH_3CHO	C—C=O	122°	H CH_3—C O
HCOOH	O—C=O	125°	O—H —C O
HCOONa	O—C=O	124°	O^- —C O
NH_2CH_2COOH	O—C=O	122°	O—H —C O
COOH | $2H_2O$ COOH	O—C=O	124°	O—H —C O

Such a process would always lead to the formation of the *cis* isomer, whereas it is known that treatment of acetylenedicarboxylic acid HOOCC≡CCOOH with bromine gives dibromomaleic and dibromofumaric acids, the *cis* and *trans* forms respectively. The formation of the dibromofumaric acid is more favoured from energy considerations, since the molecule is stabilized by the formation of two hydrogen bonds with the bromine atoms (for hydrogen bond formation between the hydrogen of a carboxyl group and a bromine atom, see Chapter 12).

```
                                        O
                                        ‖
COOH                        Br          C
 |                   .....    \       /   \
 C                  H           C          O
 ⫴        →         |           ‖          |
 C                  O           C          H
 |                    \       /   \   .....
COOH                    C           Br
                        ‖
                        O
```

The structure of allene, $CH_2{=}C{=}CH_2$, is represented diagrammatically in *Figure 22*, the σ bonds of the middle carbon atom are linear, as in acetylene and the two π bonds with the two other carbon atoms are mutually perpendicular.

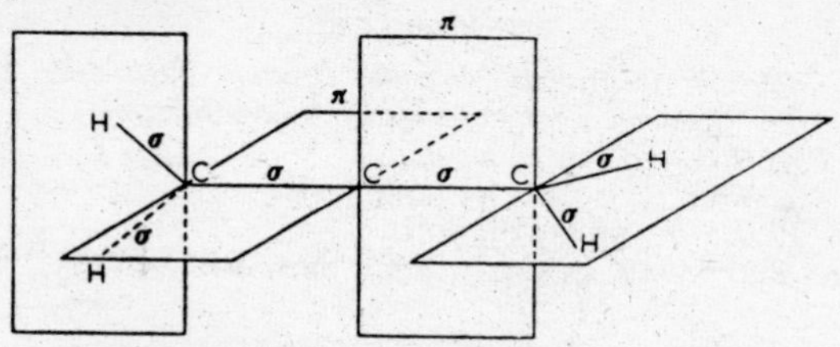

Figure 22. Arrangement of bonds in the allene molecule

The molecules $CH_2{=}C{=}O$ and $O{=}C{=}O$ (*Figures 23* and *24*) have analogous structures ; the absence of any dipole moment in carbon dioxide confirms the linear configuration.

It will be appreciated that the angles of 120° and 180° that exist between

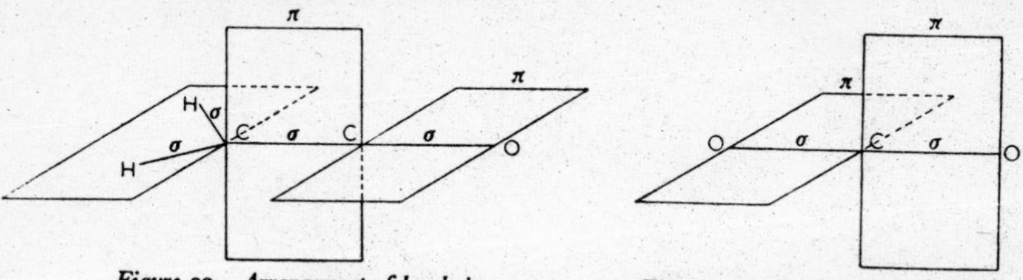

Figure 23. Arrangement of bonds in $CH_2{=}C{=}O$

Figure 24. Arrangement of bonds in the carbon dioxide molecule

the valency bonds of carbon forming a double and triple bond respectively must now be regarded as the normal valency angles. Hitherto the classical theory had postulated that the normal valency angle was 109° 28′, the tetrahedral angle ; any marked divergence from this angle, as occurred in the ethylenic and acetylenic compounds, was assumed to be accompanied by a strain in the molecule. This theory was applied by BAEYER to the problem of the stability of ring systems with considerable success. The wave mechanical treatment, however, shows that there is no strain involved in the formation of double and triple bonds and that valency angles of 109° 28′, 120° and 180° are normal for the valency states σ^4, $\sigma^3\pi$ and $\sigma^2\pi^2$ respectively. The decrease in the stability of ring systems in which the actual valency angles deviate considerably from the theoretical values for the particular valency state of the constituent atom, may be attributed entirely to the decrease in the extent of the overlapping of bonding orbitals. Thus a σ bond is strongest when the atoms lie in the direction of the original p or hybrid bonds, since maximum overlapping occurs in this direction. Similarly π bonds have their maximum energy when the p orbitals forming the π bond lie parallel to each other; as the angle between the orbitals is increased, so the strength of the π bond decreases. The reactivity of ethylenic and acetylenic compounds, *e.g.* the ease of hydrogenation and halogenation, is explained by the fact that a π bond is less strong than a σ bond and less energy is used in rupturing a π bond than is subsequently gained in forming the σ bond, *e.g.* C—H. The most stable state of a molecule is therefore that in which the number of σ bonds is a maximum and the greater the deviation from that state by the formation of π bonds the greater the reactivity of the resulting substance.

REFERENCES

[1] HERZBERG, G. *Molecular Spectra and Molecular Structure* New York, 1939
[2] PENNEY, W. G. *The Quantum Theory of Valency* London, 1935
[3] SLATER, J. C. *Phys. Rev.* 38 (1931) 1109
[4] PAULING, L. C. *J. Amer. chem. Soc.* 53 (1931) 1367
[5] UFFORD, C. W. *Phys. Rev.* 53 (1938) 568
[6] LEVY, H. A. and BROCKWAY, L. O. *J. Amer. chem. Soc.* 59 (1937) 2085

5

RESONANCE OF VALENCY STRUCTURES

BENZENE

KNOWLEDGE regarding the localization of valency bonds in molecules appears unsatisfactory in a number of cases, of which that of benzene is one of the most important. In the benzene molecule each carbon atom forms three σ bonds, one with a hydrogen atom and one with each of the two neighbouring carbon atoms; the bonds are arranged in one plane at an angle of 120° to each other. The six σ bonds between carbon atoms lie in the same plane and form a regular hexagon. Perpendicular to the plane of the ring are the orbitals of the remaining p electrons of the carbon atoms, which form figures of eight with the loops lying above and below the plane of the ring. Overlapping of these orbitals leads to the formation of π bonds and it is possible to imagine two particular configurations, with π bonds existing between carbon atoms 1—2, 3—4, 5—6 and 2—3, 4—5, 6—1:

According to the classical structural theory, the molecule should be described by one of these formulae. Such an assumption, however, is not in conformity with the properties of an electron taking part in bond formation. In the case of the hydrogen molecule, we have seen in Chapter 3 that according to the Heitler-London theory there are two possible electronic configurations: first, when electron *1* is located at nucleus *a* and electron *2* at nucleus *b*, and secondly, when electron *1* is at nucleus *b* and electron *2* is at nucleus *a*. There is no justification for assuming that only one of these two possible configurations exists since it is impossible to assign the electron to a particular nucleus so long as there exists a second nucleus where the presence of the electron is equally advantageous. Both states are equally probable and the superposition of these states leads, as has been shown, to a decrease in energy and the formation of the molecule.

Following a similar argument for the molecule of benzene, it is impossible to prefer one of the two valency forms to the other since the electron of the first carbon atom may equally well be exchanged with that of the second carbon atom as with that of the sixth. Consequently both forms exist in the molecule and when these are superimposed there arises the transitional structure which possesses a lower energy th n either of the original states and is therefore more stable. Unfortunately it is impossible to represent this transitional structure with the use of the conventional valency nomenclature and it was to overcome this difficulty that the idea of the resonance of valency structures was introduced by SLATER[1] and PAULING[2]. The actual state of a benzene molecule is that in which the densities of the electron clouds between all the pairs of carbon atoms is the same. Such an arrangement cannot be represented in a formula by the conventional symbols of structural theory. Thus recourse is made to two possible formulae, neither of which independently represents the actual state of the molecule, but only extreme states, in which the *p* electrons are represented as being located at certain nuclei. The molecule is then described as a resonance hybrid of these forms.

It is important to stress the difference between resonance and tautomerism. The concept of resonance has been introduced to describe the delocalization of electrons ; in all the different forms of the molecule as represented by valence bond structures, among which resonance is said to occur, the configuration of the nuclei is the same. In tautomerism, on the other hand, the atoms are arranged in different ways and tautomeric changes, in which one form is changed into the other, occur as the result of chemical reactions. The tautomeric forms are in fact different chemical entities and in theory and frequently in practice, each can be isolated.

For benzene we have considered so far only the Kekulé structures in which the π bonds are formed between neighbouring atoms ; such forms represent the greatest possible interaction of the electron clouds, since the distance between neighbouring carbon atoms is only 1·4 Å, and will thus contribute more than other possible structures to the resultant state of the molecule. But it is necessary to consider all possible valency structures among which there is resonance and thus for benzene the three Dewar forms must be considered :

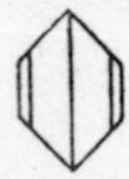

In these structures one of the π bonds occurs between atoms in the *para* position. Since the exchange energy decreases very rapidly with increase in distance between the nuclei, it follows that the energy of the *para* π bond will be small. The energy of each of the three Dewar structures is thus greater than that of the two Kekulé forms and hence their contribution to the final state of the atom is less. Nevertheless it is necessary when considering the benzene molecule, to consider these three possible forms along with the structures of Kekulé.

Resonance occurs wherever one molecule can be represented by two or more valence bond structures. In general the resulting molecule is the more stable, the greater the number of possible structures. Where a molecule can be represented by two structures, the extent of the resonance between these two forms is determined by the relative energies of the two structures. If they are of equal energy, then their contribution to the final state of the molecule will be equal and the resonance will be a maximum ; if, however, one form has a higher energy than the other, then the former will contribute less to the final state of the molecule and resonance will be less. In the extreme case where the energy of one form is so high that its contribution to the state of the molecule is insignificant, resonance does not occur. Although there is an arbitrary element introduced into the concept of resonance by the choice of the various structures amongst which resonance occurs, it is generally a simple matter to distinguish the most probable forms. Only those states which have the same value for the total spin of the valency electrons can be considered. Thus in benzene for example, the total spin in each of the five structures discussed above, is zero.

It may be shown by quantum mechanics that the number of independent or canonical structures amongst which resonance can occur is given by,

$$\frac{n\,!}{\frac{n}{2}\,!\left(\frac{n}{2}+1\right)!}$$

where n is the number of non-localized electrons. In benzene, besides the electrons forming the σ bonds, which are localized, there are six π electrons and thus the number of canonical structures is :

$$\frac{1.2.3.4.5.6}{1.2.3.\ 1.2.3.4}=5$$

The five structures are the two Kekulé and the three Dewar forms. It is possible, however, to construct other structures of benzene *e.g.* by joining atoms in the *meta* position with a π bond or by making all three π bonds of the Dewar type :

These and other similar structures are not independent and for the case when the atoms are arranged in a ring only those structures for which the bonds do not cross need be considered ; all the other forms can be represented by resonance contributions of these structures[3, 4, 5].

If the benzene nucleus were to be regarded as consisting of a system of three single and three double bonds between carbon atoms, the heat of formation of benzene would be the sum of the heats of formation of three C=C bonds, three C—C bonds and six C—H bonds. As we have shown, however, the benzene nucleus cannot be regarded as a system containing localized double bonds since each bond between carbon atoms is neither single nor double, but has an intermediate character, and the value for the heat of formation of the benzene nucleus is found to be approximately 39 kcals/gm mol. greater than that calculated assuming localization of the double bonds[6]. This energy, which stabilizes the molecule, is termed the resonance energy. Similar results are obtained from data for the heats of hydrogenation. It is this resonance energy which gives to benzene its aromatic properties. From a thermodynamic viewpoint unsaturation of a compound is due to the relative instability of a double bond compared with two single bonds ; the resonance energy, by reducing this instability, gives the molecule a degree of stability approaching that of a saturated hydrocarbon. The distance between neighbouring atoms of carbon in a molecule of benzene is 1·40 Å, a value which is between that in saturated hydrocarbons (1·54 Å) and that in ethylene (1·32 Å).

The identity of all the carbon bonds in benzene are to some extent supported by the experimental results of LEVINE and COLE[7]. It is well known that one molecule of benzene reacts with three molecules of ozone to give the triozonide which on decomposition yields three molecules of glyoxal :

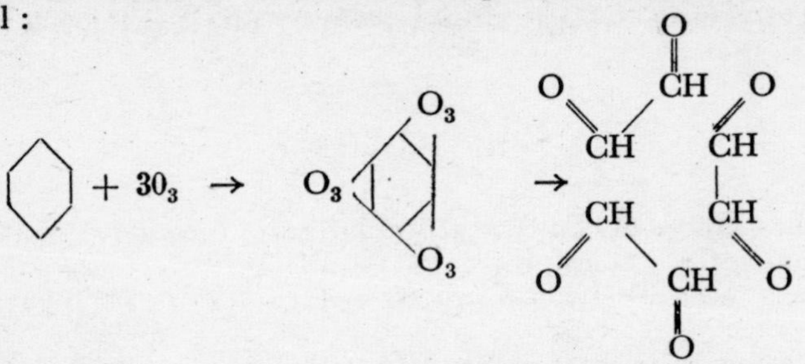

$$\text{C}_6\text{H}_6 + 3\text{O}_3 \rightarrow \text{C}_6\text{H}_6(\text{O}_3)_3 \rightarrow 3\,\text{O}{=}\text{CH}{-}\text{CH}{=}\text{O}$$

Localization of the bonds in *o*-xylene would yield the following two forms :

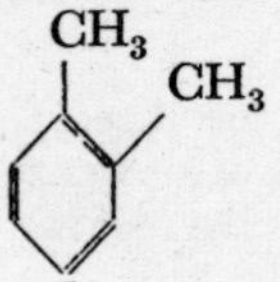

CH_3 CH_3 *I* CH_3 CH_3 *II*

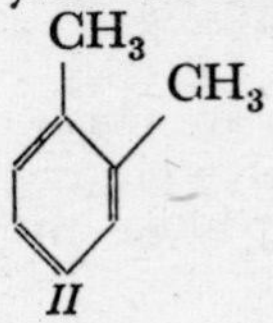

Ozonization of the form *I* would yield two molecules of methylglyoxal and one of glyoxal,

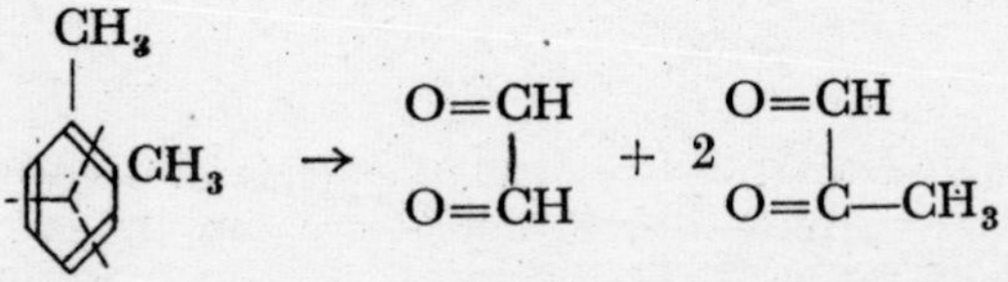

$$\text{I} \rightarrow \begin{matrix}\text{O}{=}\text{CH}\\ |\\ \text{O}{=}\text{CH}\end{matrix} + 2\begin{matrix}\text{O}{=}\text{CH}\\ |\\ \text{O}{=}\text{C}{-}\text{CH}_3\end{matrix}$$

whereas ozonization of the form *II* leads to the production of diacetyl and two molecules of glyoxal,

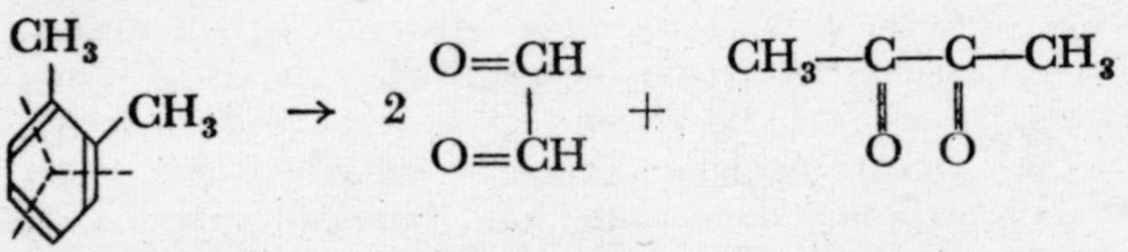

$$\text{II} \rightarrow 2\begin{matrix}\text{O}{=}\text{CH}\\ |\\ \text{O}{=}\text{CH}\end{matrix} + \text{CH}_3{-}\underset{\text{O}}{\underset{\|}{\text{C}}}{-}\underset{\text{O}}{\underset{\|}{\text{C}}}{-}\text{CH}_3$$

Levine and Cole established experimentally that all three products were formed. The significance of this work, however, must not be exaggerated since it does not prove unambiguously that the bonds between the carbon atoms are all identical ; an equally valid argument could be based on the assumption of the existence of two isomers having the Kekulé structures.

The reactivity of benzene towards substituting reagents is linked with the fact that in the course of substitution, not only is resonance of the benzene ring structure preserved, but the possibility of resonance structures involving the substituting groups may occur. This problem will be discussed later.

CONJUGATED SYSTEMS

The partial delocalization of π bonds and the resulting resonance of the molecule permit an explanation to be made of the properties of non-cyclic compounds containing conjugated double bonds *e.g.* butadiene. The configuration of the butadiene molecule has been shown by electron diffraction to be

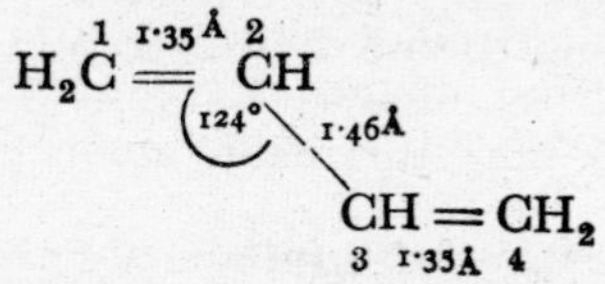

$$\begin{array}{l} \overset{1}{}\;\overset{1{\cdot}35\,\text{Å}}{}\;\overset{2}{} \\ H_2C = CH \\ \quad (124^\circ) \searrow 1{\cdot}46\,\text{Å} \\ \qquad\quad CH = CH_2 \\ \qquad\quad \underset{3}{}\; 1{\cdot}33\,\text{Å}\; \underset{4}{} \end{array}$$

The distance between the central two carbon atoms, 1·46 Å, is smaller than that between a normal single bond, 1·54 Å. This observation suggests that the bond between carbon atoms *2* and *3* possesses some double bond character. The distances between atoms *1* and *2*, and *3* and *4* is, in both cases, 1·35 Å which cannot be considered significantly different from the value of the C=C bond in ethylene, 1·32 Å. The heat of formation of butadiene, however, is somewhat higher than the value obtained by the addition of the bond energies of two C=C bonds, one C—C bond and six C—H bonds. This evidence shows that the molecule is stabilized by resonance between two or more structures.

The anomalous behaviour of butadiene on halogenation has been recognized for some time. It would be expected that the addition of bromine across one of the double bonds would produce only the molecule $CH_2Br{\cdot}CHBr{\cdot}CH{=}CH_2$. However, in addition to the 1,2-dibromo, compound there is a considerable yield of the 1,4-dibromo compound $CH_2Br{-}CH{=}CH{-}CH_2Br$, which contains a double bond in the 2,3 position. In order to explain this behaviour, THIELE proposed a theory of partial valencies. In this theory the second link in a double bond does not fully neutralize the affinity of the two carbon atoms so that they are left with a 'residual affinity'. In a system of alternate double and single bonds, the residual affinities of the inner atoms combine across the single bonds whilst those of the outer atoms remain free to attract other atoms. Thiele's formula for butadiene was therefore

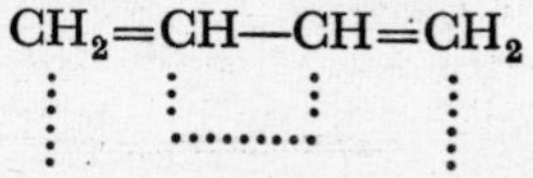

$$CH_2{=}CH{-}CH{=}CH_2$$

(with dotted lines below each carbon; those from the two inner carbons joined by a dotted line)

where the dotted lines represent the partial valencies. The nature of the partial valencies remained obscure until the development of the wave mechanical theory of valency which explains the behaviour in the following way. The π bonds between carbon atoms *1* and *2*, and *3* and *4* are not considered to be completely localized and as in benzene, electron exchange between atoms *2* and *3* and *1* and *4* is possible. Thus we may write two structures for butadiene

$$CH_2{=}CH{-}CH{=}CH_2$$

I

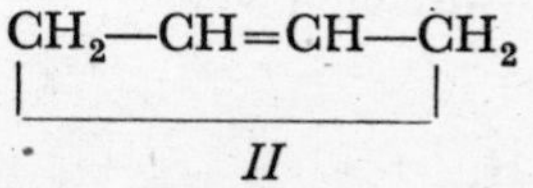

$$CH_2{-}CH{=}CH{-}CH_2$$

(with the end carbons joined by a line below)

II

The second structure will have a higher energy than the first because of the much reduced interaction between the electrons of atoms *1* and *4*, and therefore contributes less to the final state of the butadiene molecule than the first structure, nevertheless resonance between the two structures does result in a small increased stability of the molecule. The carbon atoms *1* and *4* are incompletely saturated since in the second structure the bonding between them is very weak (the distance is 2·8 Å in the *cis* and 3·5 Å in the *trans* configuration). This nonsaturation of atoms *1* and *4* explains their reactivity.

cyclo-Butadiene has not been isolated, presumably because thede formation of the valency angles from 120° to 90° produces a greater loss of stability than can be overcome by the resonance of the resulting molecule.

cyclo-Octatraene does not possess aromatic properties,

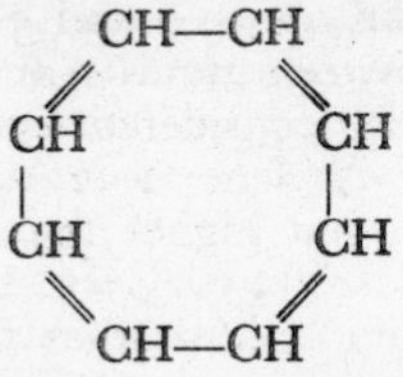

```
         CH—CH
        /     \
      CH       CH
      |        |
      CH       CH
        \     /
         CH—CH
```

and recent x-ray studies[8] have shown that the molecule is not flat and that the bond lengths in the molecule are not equal, being 1·34 Å for the double bond and 1·54 Å for the single bond, values which are almost identical with those for bonds in aliphatic compounds. It has therefore been concluded that in agreement with the thermochemical data, the molecule is not stabilized by resonance.

NAPHTHALENE

The characteristic chemical properties of naphthalene which have to be explained may be enumerated as follows :

a The reactions of naphthalene show it to be less aromatic *i.e.* more unsaturated than benzene. Thus naphthalene is more easily oxidized and reduced, and substitution reactions occur much more readily, particularly in the α–position, than in benzene.

b Hydrogenation takes place more readily with naphthalene than with benzene. This fact is well illustrated by the reaction of dihydro-benzene with naphthalene resulting in the oxidation of the dihydro-benzene to benzene, the formation of dihydronaphthalene and the liberation of energy in the form of heat,

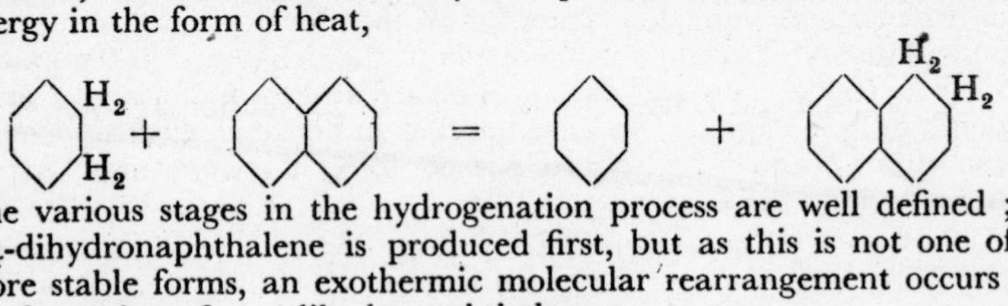

$$\text{(dihydrobenzene, } H_2, H_2) + \text{(naphthalene)} = \text{(benzene)} + \text{(dihydronaphthalene, } H_2, H_2)$$

c The various stages in the hydrogenation process are well defined ; the 1,4-dihydronaphthalene is produced first, but as this is not one of the more stable forms, an exothermic molecular rearrangement occurs with the formation of 1, 2-dihydronaphthalene :

$$\text{(naphthalene)} + H_2 \rightarrow \text{(1,4-dihydronaphthalene, } H_2, H_2) \rightarrow \text{(1,2-dihydronaphthalene, } H_2, H_2)$$

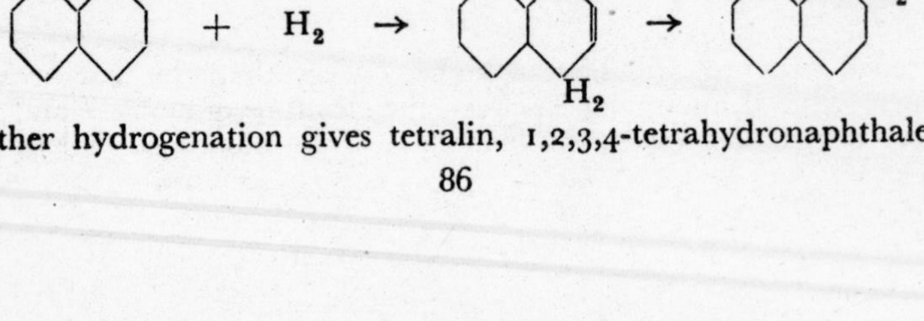

Further hydrogenation gives tetralin, 1,2,3,4-tetrahydronaphthalene, a process which takes place easily and rapidly. The hydrogenation of the second ring to produce decalin, takes place less easily and more slowly.

d The substitution reactions of naphthalene, even in the case of the formation of monosubstituted derivatives, are complex. Substitution in the α-position is most common, *e.g.* in sulphonation and nitration, but a complicating factor is introduced by changes in the relative magnitude of the energy of activation for substitution reactions in the α- and β-positions with variation of temperature. Thus at high temperatures the energy of activation for the sulphonation reaction producing β-naphthalene sulphonic acid is lower than that for the α-derivative. The equilibrium mixture for the β-derivative is therefore formed first and this form predominates in the product. At lower temperatures (80° C), the energy of activation of the reaction forming the α-derivative is less than for the β-derivative and hence α-naphthalene sulphonic acid predominates in the reaction product.

e There are indications of inequality in the properties of the various bonds. Thus although the 1,2-disubstitution products are well known, no 2,3-disubstitution products have as yet been isolated.

f The formation of molecular compounds occurs more readily with naphthalene than with benzene ; this may be attributed to the greater unsaturation of naphthalene compared with benzene.

It is not possible at the present time to give an exhaustive explanation of all the properties of naphthalene and its derivatives. However, the application of quantum mechanics does enable certain empirical rules to be explained theoretically. In order to do this there is no need to reject the Erlenmeyer formula for naphthalene, but only to consider the additional properties due to the resonance in the two six membered rings.

Naphthalene contains 10 electrons capable of forming π bonds and therefore the number of structures which contribute to the final state of the molecule is :

$$\frac{10!}{5!\ 6!} = 42$$

The arrangement of the valency bonds in the various canonical structures is determined by the same rule as for benzene. The atoms are distributed symmetrically in a circle and joined by all possible ways without the crossing of the valence bonds[4, 5, 6]. The full number of independent structures, corresponding to the total number of canonical structures, is then obtained.

If the naphthalene rings are numbered in the customary manner and are rearranged in the same order in a circle *viz,*

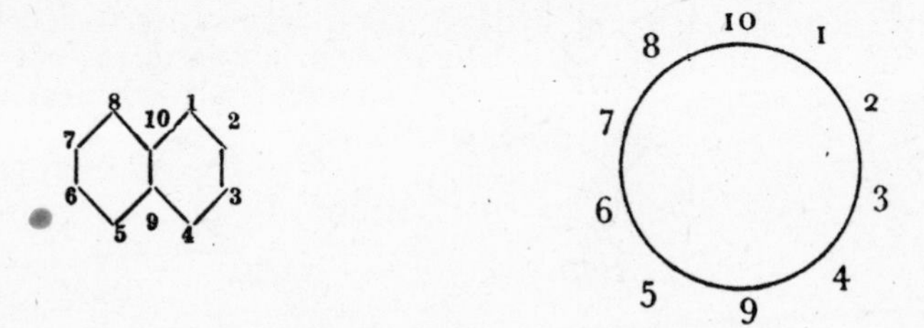

then by uniting the atoms in the manner shown in the diagram we obtain

Table XXI. Canonical Structure of Naphthalene

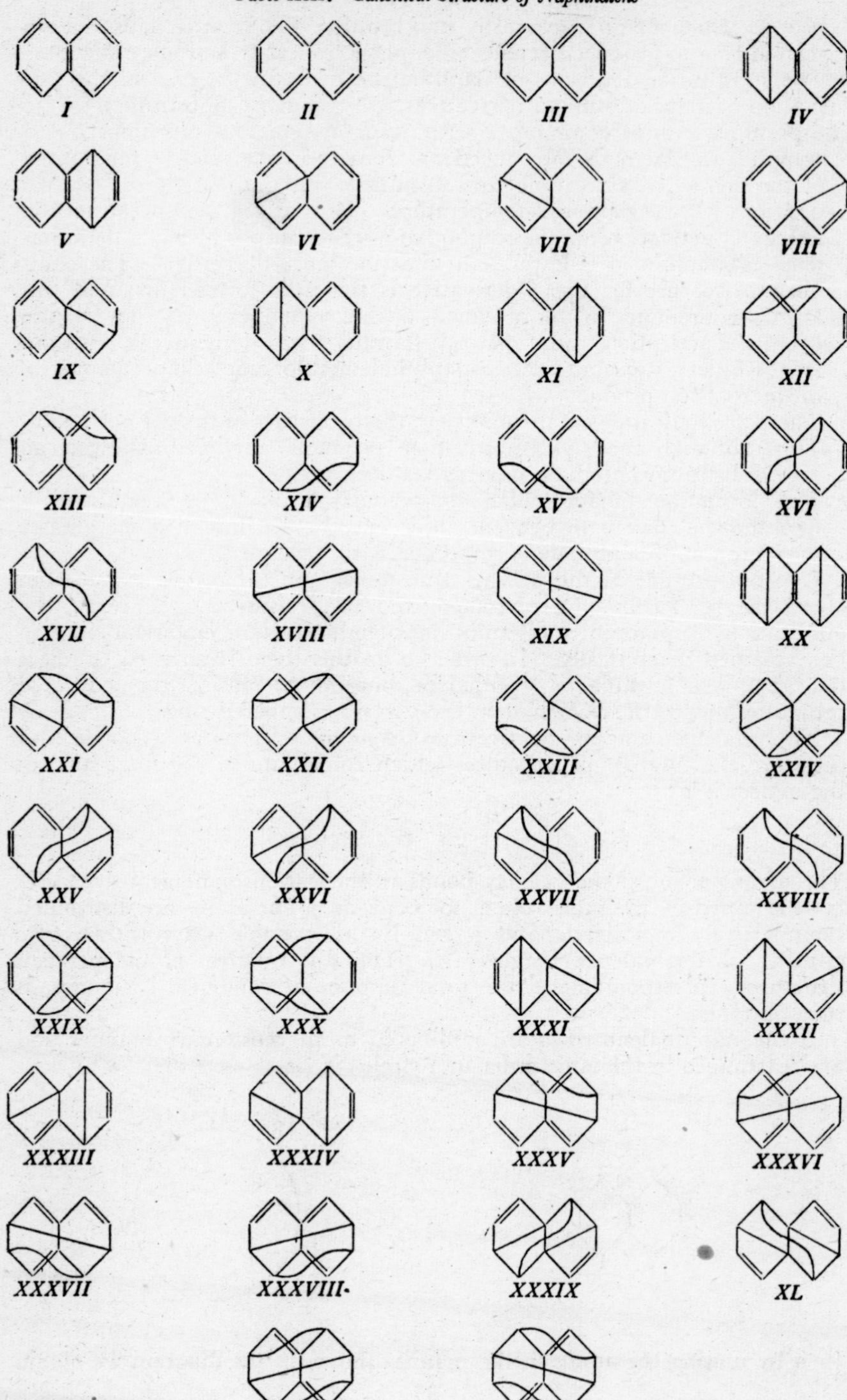

the original Erlenmeyer formula. In a similar way it is possible to work out

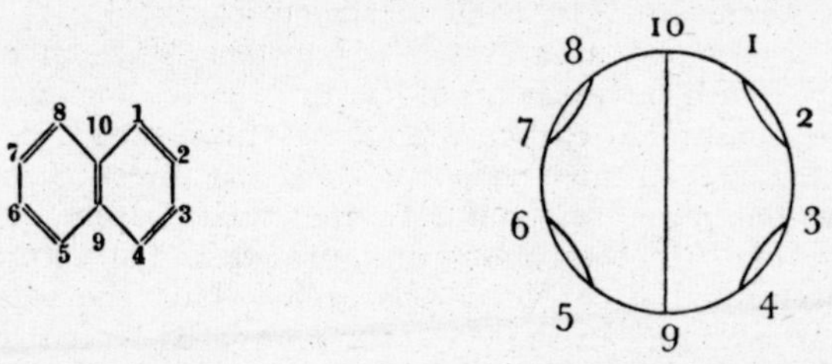

all the remaining structures and all 42 canonical structures are given in *Table XXI.* Although in this table there are formulae with intersecting valency bonds, if the formulae are drawn out in the circular form it is found that no intersections occur, *e.g.* in structure *XLII* the bonds are between atoms 1—10, 2—8, 3—7, 4—6, and 5—9 and when represented in the circular form we have :

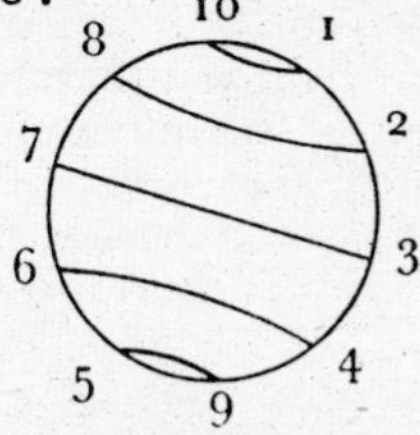

Let us consider the first three structures (*I, II* and *III* in *Table XXI*) in which the π bonds are only between neighbouring carbon atoms. These structures which may be referred to as the Kekulé structures, will contribute more to the final state of the molecule than other forms because of the greater energy of the π bonds. Since these three structures will contribute equally to the resultant molecule, the 1—2 bond possesses two thirds double bond character, whereas the 2—3 bond possesses only one third double bond character. Thus the lack of equality of the bonds in naphthalene is explained. Furthermore, SHERMAN has shown that the symmetrical structure *I* makes a greater contribution to the resultant molecule than do the structures *II* and *III*. This will cause a further increase of the double bond character of the 1—2 bond and a reduction of the double bond character of the 2—3 bond.

Let us now consider those formulae containing four π bonds between adjacent carbon atoms and one elongated π bond (structures *IV* to *XIX* in *Table XXI*). Of these structures eight are of the Dewar type where the distance between the carbon atoms is 2·8 Å (structures *IV* to *XI*), four contain a bond between carbon atoms 3·61 Å apart (structures *XII* to *XV*), two contain a bond between carbon atoms 3·65 Å apart (structures *XVI* and *XVII*) and there are two with a distance of 5 Å between the carbon atoms (structures *XVIII* and *XIX*). The strength of the π bonds decreases considerably with the increase of distance and when this becomes as much as 5 Å (as in structures *XVIII* and *XIX*) the resulting bond contributes very little energy to the stability of the molecule.

In each of the structures *XX* to *XXXVIII*, there are three normal π bonds between neighbouring carbon atoms and two between carbon atoms at greater distances, whereas in structures *XXXIX* to *XLII* there are two normal and three long π bonds. The contribution of these structures to the molecule is small and therefore we may regard only the first nineteen structures as significant. In each of structures *IV*, *V*, *X*, *XI*, *XVI* and *XVII* there occurs two unsaturated α positions, since in each case two α positions are joined by a π bond of length $\geqslant 2{\cdot}8$ Å and such a bond is so weak that the constituent carbon atoms may be regarded as being almost trivalent in character in those valence bond structures. Structures *XII* to *XV* each have one α and one β unsaturated carbon atom, structures *VI* to *IX* each have one β carbon atom unsaturated and structures *XVIII* and *XIX* two unsaturated β carbon atoms each. Thus the valency of the α position is not saturated in sixteen cases, compared with twelve for the β position. This conception of the relative unsaturated valency of the α and β positions leads to an explanation of the fact that substitution occurs more easily in the α than in the β position. A more detailed calculation[10], taking into consideration all the forty two structures, shows that the quantum weights of the nonsaturated α and β positions in naphthalene are in the ratio 2 : 1.

The behaviour of naphthalene on hydrogenation may now be explained. The addition of two atoms of hydrogen occurs at the α positions of one ring leading to the formation of 1,4-dihydronaphthalene. Since the α positions are the least saturated, the energy of activation for the reaction with hydrogen at these positions will be less than at any other positions and hence it would be expected that the 1,4 compound would be obtained first. This molecule,

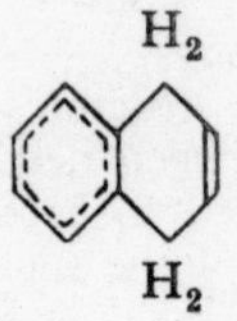

possesses a fixed double bond in the 2—3 position which cannot participate in the resonance of the molecule since the 1 and 4 carbon atoms are fully saturated, each taking part in four σ bonds. Although the formation of 1:4-dihydronaphthalene takes place more rapidly than hydrogenation in other positions, this does not necessarily infer that the 1,4-disubstituted molecule is the most stable modification and 1,2-dihydronaphthalene is found to be more stable than the 1,4-compound by virtue of the resonance that can occur in the partially hydrogenated ring :

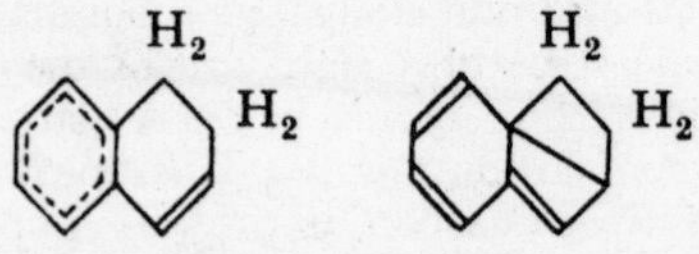

Therefore the rearrangement of the dihydrogenated naphthalene from the 1,4-compound to the 1,2-compound is thermodynamically favourable and does in fact occur.

Complete hydrogenation of one ring occurs first, since only by so doing can the resonance of the second ring be preserved. If the four hydrogen atoms were distributed throughout both rings, *e.g.* two in each, the remaining double bonds would either become localized or the number of effective structures would be reduced. It is particularly interesting to note that when two molecules of 1,4-dihydronaphthalene react together, one molecule of naphthalene and one of tetralin are produced, the reaction being accompanied by the liberation of energy ($\Delta H = -30$ kcals/gm mol). The reason for this behaviour is that although the total number of single and double bonds remain the same, we have replaced two molecules in which resonance only occurs in one ring in each molecule, by a molecule of naphthalene which is greatly stabilized by resonance, and one molecule in which resonance occurs in one ring :

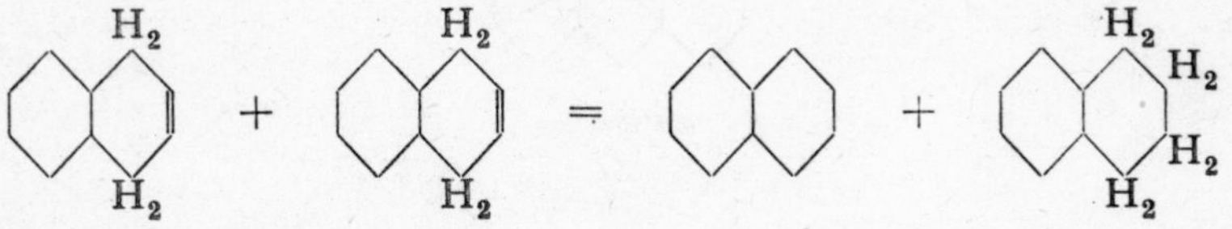

H_2 H_2 + H_2 H_2 = + H_2 H_2 H_2 H_2

Hence the reaction may be regarded as a transfer from a benzene resonating system to a naphthalene and a benzene resonating system, with a corresponding increase in stability.

OTHER AROMATIC HYDROCARBONS

Certain other aromatic hydrocarbons will now be considered briefly. Anthracene is less aromatic than naphthalene. There are fourteen electrons available for the formation of π bonds and so the full number of canonical structures will be $\frac{14!}{7!\,8!} = 429$. The most significant structures, however, are the following. Four Kekulé structures (*I* to *IV*)

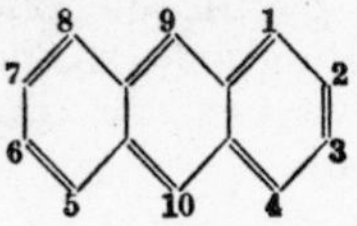

8 9 1 7 2 6 3 5 10 4

I  *II*  *III*

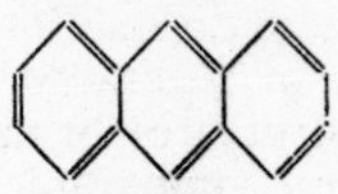

IV

and fourteen Dewar type structures *V* to *XI*

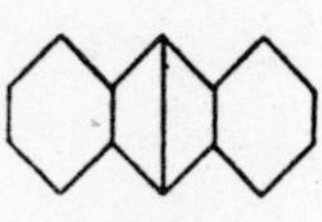

four structures
V

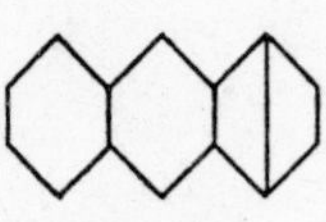

three structures
VI

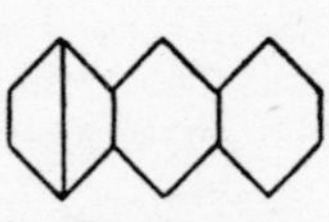

three structures
VII

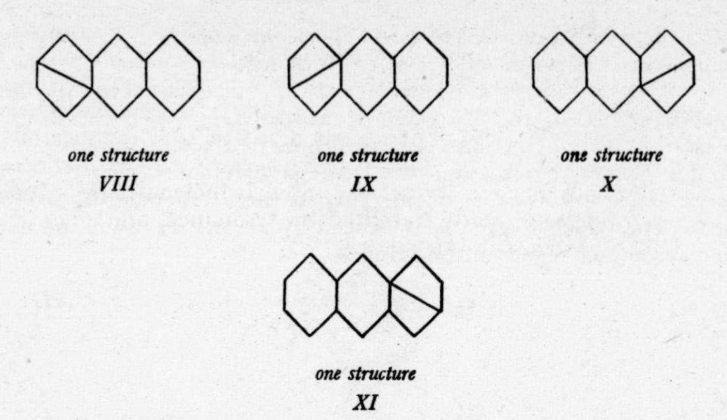

one structure *VIII* *one structure* *IX* *one structure* *X*

one structure *XI*

With the aid of these structures we may obtain an approximate evaluation of the relative unsaturation of the various atoms. This is shown in *XII* where the figures represent the number of valence bond structures in which a particular carbon atom is involved in a Dewar type bond

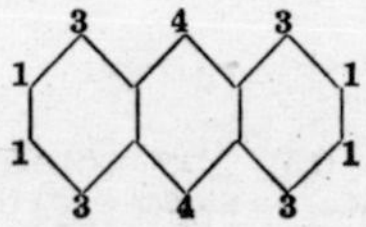

3 4 3
1 1
1 1
3 4 3

XII

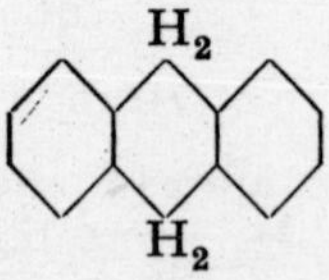

H_2

H_2

XIII

The 9 and 10 positions are the most unsaturated and hydrogenation leads to the formation of 9, 10-dihydroanthracene. Not only is the energy of activation for the hydrogenation reaction reduced by the increased unsaturation of the 9 and 10 carbon atoms, but the resulting molecule possesses considerable resonance energy by virtue of the two benzene rings and represents the most stable isomer of dihydroanthracene.

The higher reactivity of anthracene compared with naphthalene, as shown by the greater ease of hydrogenation, is directly related to the fact that the Dewar structures containing one long π bond contribute more to the final state of the molecule in anthracene than in naphthalene. Thus taking the Kekulé and Dewar structures for naphthalene *I* to *XI*, *Table XXI*, the relative unsaturation figures, comparable with those given in *XII* are :

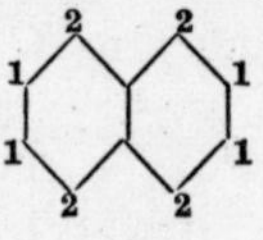

2 2
1 1
1 1
2 2

XIV

Naphthacene (*XV*) has five Kekulé structures and Dewar structures with one long π bond play an even greater part in the reactivity of the molecule than in anthracene. This applies to even a greater degree

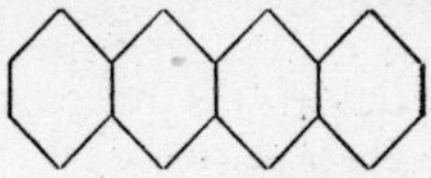

XV

XVI

to 2, 3, 6, 7-dibenzanthracene (pentacene, *XVI*) in which the addition of hydrogen atoms in the *para* positions in the central ring does not prevent resonance in the two adjacent naphthalene ring systems, *XVII*.

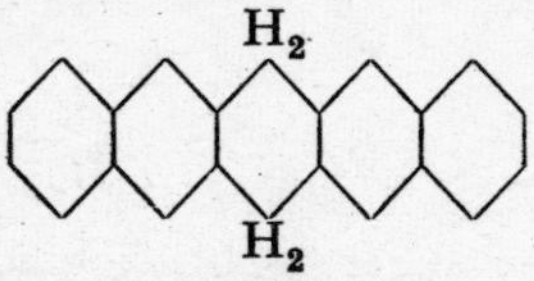

H_2

H_2

XVII

For the hydrocarbons so far considered, which consist of benzene rings connected linearly, the number of Kekulé structures is one more than the number of rings. Thus in benzene it is two, naphthalene three, anthracene four, naphthacene five and dibenzanthracene six. The number of structures with elongated π bonds, however, increases considerably as the number of benzene rings in the molecule is increased and it is this fact that is responsible for the gradual increase in reactivity with the size of the molecule.

A non-linear arrangement of three benzene rings occurs in phenanthrene (*XVIII*)

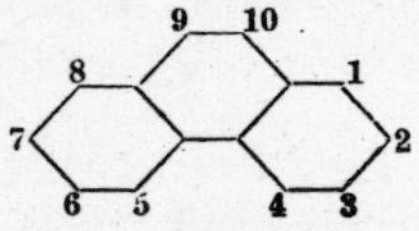

9 10 8 1 7 2 6 5 4 3

XVIII

In this molecule five Kekulé structures occur :

XIX  *XX* 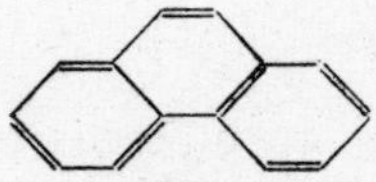 *XXI*

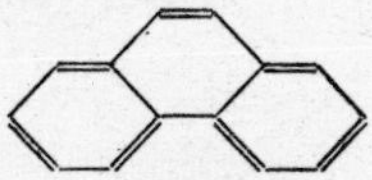

XXII 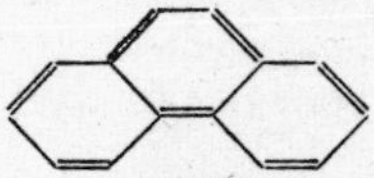 *XXIII*

It will be noticed that in four of the five structures the link between carbon atoms 9 and 10 is double; these atoms are therefore the most reactive. Hydrogenation produces 9, 10-dihydrophenanthrene *XXIV*. This com-

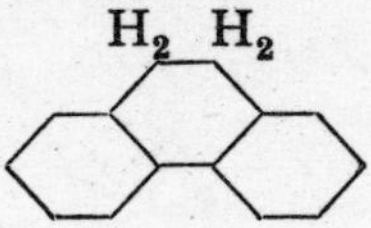

H_2 H_2

H_2 H_2 H_2 H_2

XXIV 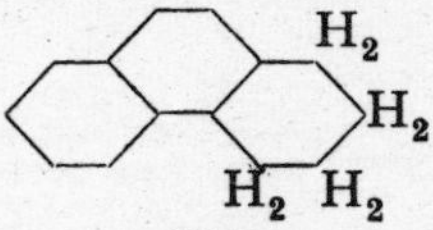 *XXV*

pound is also the most stable of the various possible dihydro derivatives, since the resonance of the adjacent benzene rings is unaffected. Further hydrogenation gives 1, 2, 3, 4-tetrahydrophenanthrene *XXV*; the formation of this molecule evidently involves the migration of the hydrogen atoms at the 9, 10 positions into the side ring. It is clear that this tetrahydrophenanthrene is more stable than any other configuration since it does not interfere with the resonance of the remaining naphthalene ring. If there were no migration and for example, the 1, 2, 9, 10-tetrahydrophenanthrene *XXVI* were obtained, the resonance

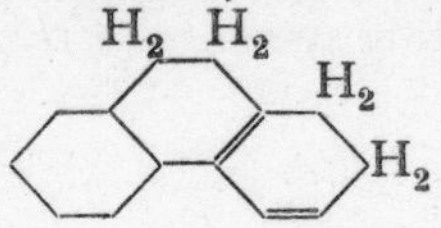

XXVI 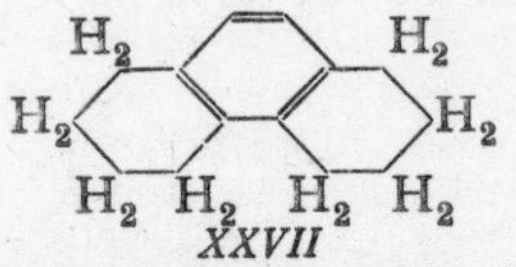 *XXVII*

energy, which is the same as for 2-phenylbutadiene, would be less by about 30 kcals, than that of the 1, 2, 3, 4-tetrahydrophenanthrene, *XXV*. Further hydrogenation produces octahydrophenanthrene (octanthrene *XXVII*) in which the central benzene ring still possesses non-localized bonds and its resonance therefore stabilizes the molecule.

Until relatively recent times there has been a controversy concerning the validity of one or other of the formulae for the hydrocarbons described above. Thus structures for naphthalene have been proposed by ERLENMEYER, SCHERRER, HARRIES and WILLSTÄTTER, BAMBERG and others. However it is now clear that such arguments are pointless since all such formulae represent possible structures which contribute to the ultimate state of the molecule. What is of importance, as we have seen, is the weight of the various contributions, since it is this which determines the chemical reactivity of the molecule.

In addition to the Kekulé and Dewar structures in the separate benzene rings, diphenyl possesses additional structures with π bonds between the rings

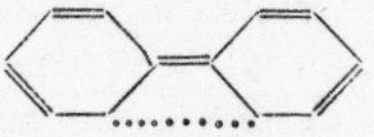

XXVIII 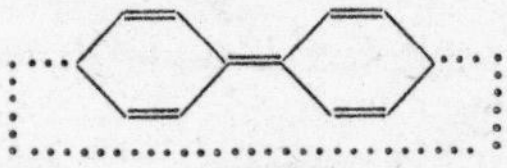 *XXIX*

Such structures are only possible if both rings lie in one plane, when the figures of eight of all the π electrons are parallel. x-ray data suggests that this is so[11], but it has not been confirmed by more recent electron diffraction measurements[12].

Hydrocarbons of the type

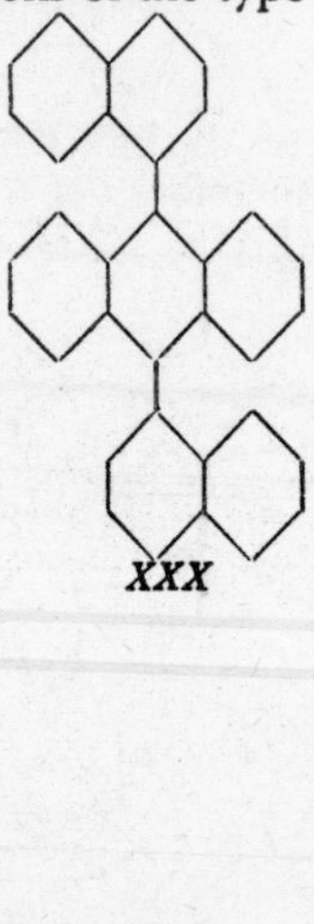

XXX 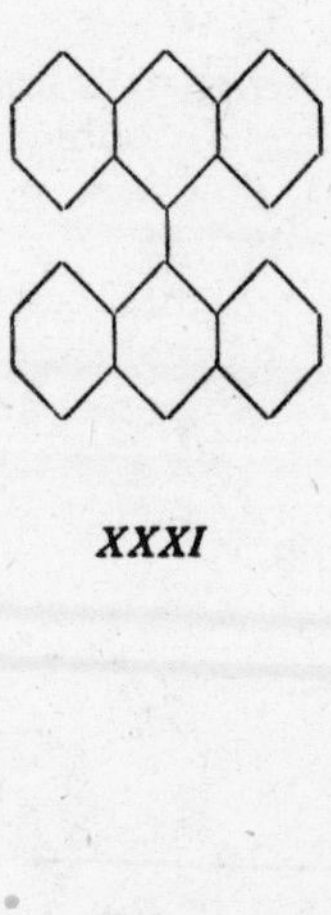 *XXXI*

may also apparently have resonance structures of the same type as diphenyl, but owing to steric hindrance due to repulsion between the hydrogen atoms, the various ring systems cannot lie in the same plane. For this reason contributions to the resonance of the molecule from structures of the diphenyl type cannot occur[13].

FREE RADICALS

The discovery of triphenylmethyl by GOMBERG in 1900 was most unexpected. It had been anticipated that hexaphenylethane would be a stable, unreactive compound, but Gomberg found that it could be isolated only by treating triphenylmethyl bromide with silver powder in the complete absence of air. Solutions of hexaphenylethane reacted rapidly with several reagents *e.g.* oxygen, iodine and nitric oxide and the conclusion that the hexaphenylethane dissociated into triphenylmethyl radicals was confirmed by molecular weight determinations. Since the tetravalency of carbon had at that time been fully established it is not surprising therefore, that the idea of trivalent carbon was difficult to accept. However, other free radicals were discovered and it became established that in addition to trivalent carbon they could involve divalent nitrogen, and monovalent oxygen and sulphur. The common characteristic of all free radicals is the existence in the molecule of one unpaired electron, this causes the well known paramagnetic properties of all monoradicals.

The formation of free radicals cannot be explained on the basis of classical valency theory; the stability of these molecules may however, be adequately explained by the quantum theory of valency. Ethane does not under normal circumstances dissociate into two methyl radicals. The reaction

$$H_3C—CH_3 \longrightarrow 2\dot{C}H_3$$

only takes place with the absorption of 82·6 kcals *i.e.* it is strongly endothermic (the dot over the carbon atom represents the unpaired electron). This fact is not surprising since it is a stable single bond between two carbon atoms which is being broken. In order to explain how the dissociation energy required to break a molecule into free radicals may be lowered we shall consider first the molecule of dibenzyl. On dissociation, two free radicals are obtained :

$$C_6H_5CH_2—CH_2C_6H_5 \longrightarrow 2C_6H_5\dot{C}H_2$$

and in each of these a trivalent carbon occurs. However, it is clear that the unsaturated carbon atom need not necessarily be that of the CH_2 group, *I*, but may also be that of the *para* and *ortho* carbon atoms of the benzene ring, *II*, *III* and *IV*

$—\dot{C}H_2$ $=CH_2$ $=CH_2$ $=CH_2$

I *II* *III* *IV*

Thus in the free radical several valency bond structures are possible in addition to the normal resonance structures of benzene which are still present in *I*, and resonance amongst all these states will lead to an increase in the stability of the free radical. Consequently, for the dissociation of dibenzyl less energy is required than for the dissociation of ethane because of the stabilization of the resulting free radicals by resonance. Thus in the molecule of dibenzyl, the link between the two CH_2 groups is weaker than in ethane and the bond between the phenyl carbon atom and the CH_2 group should be stronger in view of its partial double bond character. The x-ray data confirms this conclusion by showing that the $CH_2—CH_2$ distance is 1·58 Å as compared with 1·54 Å in ethane and the $C_6H_5—CH_2$ distance is 1·47 Å. An increase in an interatomic distance represents a weakening, and a decrease a strengthening, of the bond.

The dissociation of hexaphenylethane leads to the formation of two triphenylmethyl radicals. With the central carbon atom in the trivalent state eight Kekulé structures are possible ; the nine carbon atoms in the *ortho* and *para* positions in the three rings may also be in a trivalent state and thus in all, 36 valence bond structures are possible for the free radical. As a result of the resonance among these structures there is a gain in energy of the free radical by 50 kcals, with the result that the dissociation energy of hexaphenylethane is as low as 11–12 kcals.

In the hexaphenylethane molecule the valence bonds of the two ethane carbon atoms are tetrahedral, but during the dissociation this configuration is replaced by the planar configuration which is present in the free radical. The planar structure may, however, be slightly distorted owing to the repulsion of the *ortho* hydrogen atoms of the benzene rings.

When hexa-diphenylethane $[(C_6H_5—C_6H_5)_3\,C—C\,(C_6H_5—C_6H_5)_3]$ dissociates into two tri-diphenylmethyl radicals, each radical contains nineteen carbon atoms which may exist in the trivalent state : the central carbon atom and the *ortho* and *para* atoms of each ring. A very large number of valence bond structures is therefore possible with this radical, giving to it a considerable stability, thus explaining the great ease with which hexa-diphenylethane dissociates into free radicals.

Table XXII. Degree of Dissociation into Free Radicals

Free radical formed	*Dissociation per cent*	*Temperature °C*	*Concentration mols/l*
Triphenylmethyl	2·8	20	0·03
Diphenylyl-p-*tolylmethyl*	5	25	0·1
(p-*diphenylyl*)-*diphenylmethyl*	12·8—14·1	25	0·036
(m-*diphenylyl*)-*diphenylmethyl*	11·4—12·0	25	0·036
Diphenyl-o-tolylmethyl	25	25	0·1
Diphenyl-β-naphthylmethyl	6	25	0·1
Diphenyl-a-naphthylmethyl	27	25	0·1
Phenyl-di-(p-*diphenylyl*)*methyl*	18	25	0·1
Tri-(p-*diphenylyl*)*methyl*	26	25	0·0125
Tri-(m-*diphenylyl*)*methyl*	60	25	0·025
Di-β-naphthylphenylmethyl	13	25	0·1
Tri-β-naphthylmethyl	{80	25	0·062
	53	25	0·0125
a-naphthyl-(p-*diphenylyl*)-*phenylmethyl*	54	54	0·01

In *Table XXII* the degrees of dissociation of a series of substances are given. The extent of dissociation is dependent on the temperature, concentration and on other conditions.

The formation of a free radical possessing only one carbon atom which can exist in the trivalent state *e.g.* the formation of a methyl radical from ethane, does not take place to any great extent at normal temperatures. This is due to the fact that since the free radical is not stabilized by resonance, it can only be formed by a strongly endothermic reaction. Those molecules which readily dissociate to form free radicals do so because the dissociation energy has been reduced by the increased stability of the resulting free radicals, due to resonance among several valence bond structures. If in the free radical the single unpaired electron is localized at one carbon atom, as in $\cdot CH_3$, then such a free radical is extremely reactive, but if the unpaired electron is shared among several carbon atoms *e.g.* in tri-diphenylmethyl, where nineteen different positions are possible, the reactivity is decreased. As is to be expected in a molecule possessing an unpaired electron, the electron affinity of free radicals is high, that of triphenylmethyl being 48 ± 5 kcals[14].

Following the same general argument used above to explain the dissociation of various arylethanes, an understanding may be obtained for the relative stability of free radicals compared with free atoms, *e.g.* nitrogen and oxygen, containing unpaired electrons. Tetraphenylhydrazine dissociates to some extent into two molecules of diphenyl nitrogen :

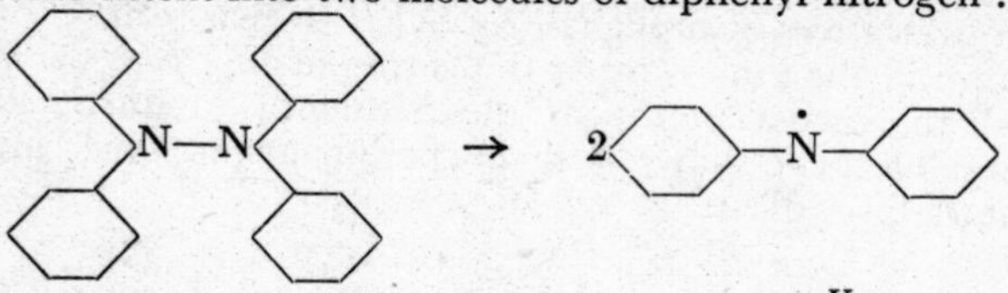

N—N → 2 —N—

V

The unpaired electron, however, is shared with six carbon atoms, since resonance amongst the seven structures represented by *V*, *VI*, *VII* and *VIII* occurs.

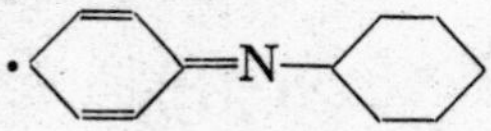

=N—

two structures
VI

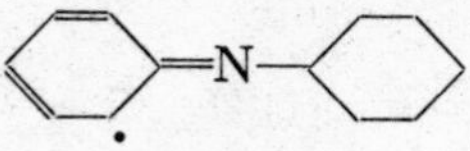

=N—

two structures
VII

=N—

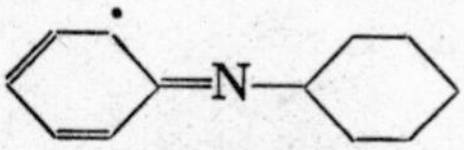

two structures
VIII

Thus the nitrogen atom cannot be regarded as divalent since if the contribution of the structures *V* to *VIII* is equivalent, the proportion of divalent character is only one seventh. Similar reasoning applies to free radicals containing oxygen, *e.g.* the 9-methoxy-10-phenanthroxy radical *IX*.

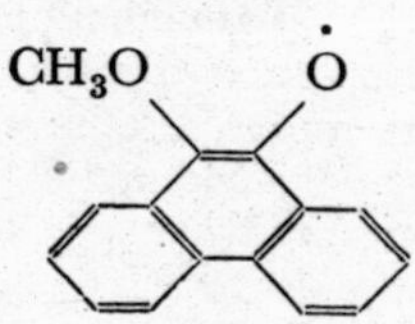

CH_3O O

IX

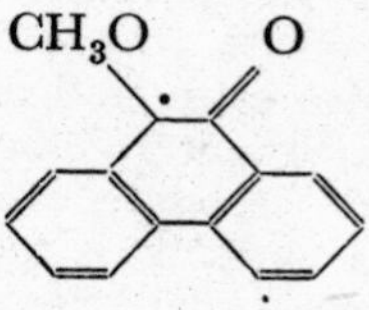

CH_3O O

X

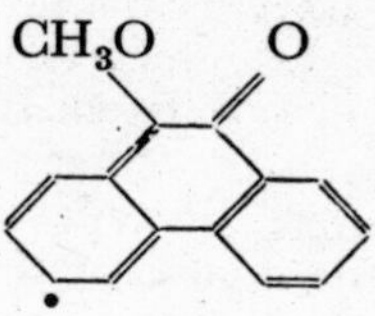

CH_3O O

XI

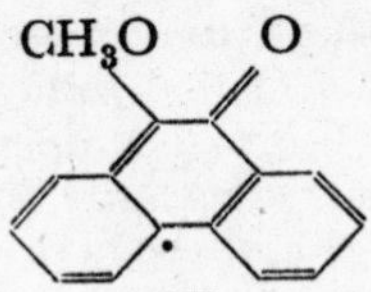

CH_3O O CH_3O O CH_3O O

XII 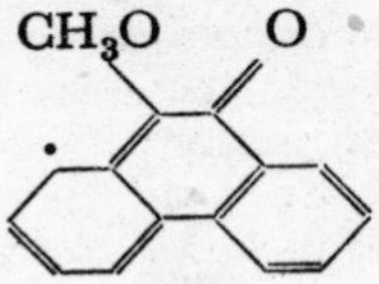 *XIII* 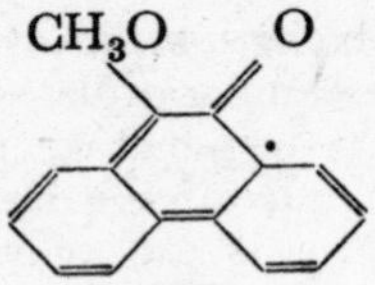 *XIV*

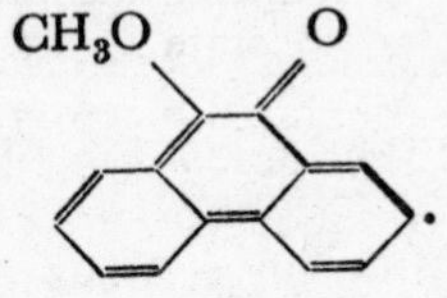

CH_3O O CH_3O O

XV 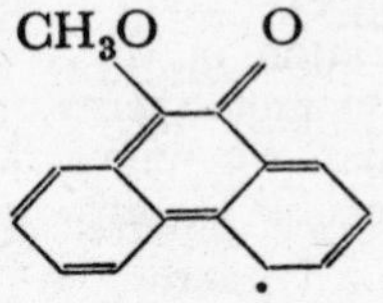 *XVI*

In this molecule the possibility of resonance with structures containing trivalent carbon stabilizes the molecule and reduces the reactivity of the free radical.

BI-RADICALS

Molecules containing two trivalent carbon atoms occur in compounds such as the *meta* derivatives of diphenyl, *e.g.* *XVII*, which cannot form a quinonoid structure in the same way as the corresponding *para* derivative *XVIII* in which all the carbon atoms are quadrivalent. Magnetic studies of the dimeric form of *XVII* shows it to be paramagnetic thus confirming the existence of the bi-radical.

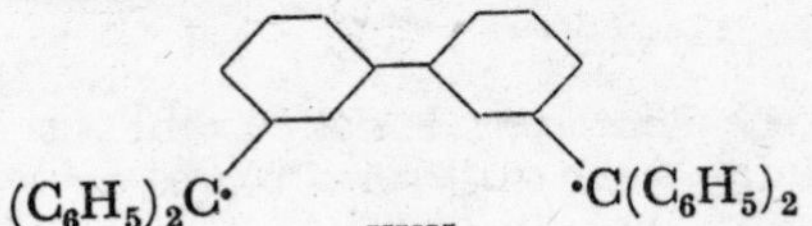

$(C_6H_5)_2C\cdot$ $\cdot C(C_6H_5)_2$

XVII

$(C_6H_5)_2C=$ $=C(C_6H_5)_2$

XVIII

The case of CHICHIBABIN's hydrocarbon $(C_6H_5)_2{\cdot}C{\cdot}C_6H_4{-}C_6H_4{\cdot}C{\cdot}(C_6H_5)_2$ is somewhat more complicated. This hydrocarbon is deeply coloured and readily reacts with oxygen and for these reasons the suggestion was made that it may exist in the form of the bi-radical *XIX*,

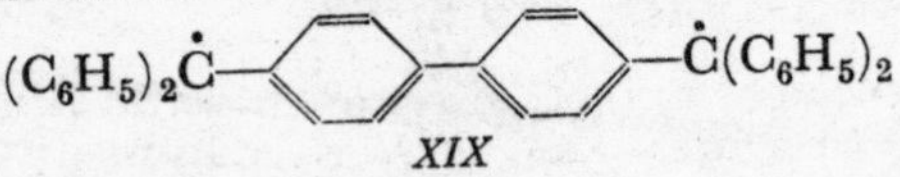

$(C_6H_5)_2\dot{C}-$ $-\dot{C}(C_6H_5)_2$

XIX

rather than in the quinonoid form *XVIII*.

The latter structure *XIX* represents the molecule in a triplet (paramagnetic) state, whereas the former *XVIII* represents a singlet (diamagnetic) state. These two states cannot resonate with each other, since the total spin moment is different in the two cases, and one state represents the ground state and the other an excited state of the molecule. Magnetic studies show that Chichibabin's hydrocarbon is diamagnetic and hence it follows that the ground state of the molecule is the singlet state *XVIII* and that the energy of excitation to the triplet state *XIX*, must be large enough to prevent the number of excited molecules in equilibrium with the ground state being significant at the temperature of the magnetic measurements. If the number of benzene rings is increased, as in *XX*,

$(C_6H_5)_2C$= ⟨ ⟩ = ⟨ ⟩ = ⟨ ⟩ =$C(C_6H_5)_2$

XX

the energy of excitation to the triplet state is reduced and at equilibrium the concentration of the triplet (paramagnetic) state is sufficient to be detected by magnetic measurements.

If the coplanar configuration of the two central benzene rings in *XVIII* is made impossible by introducing substituent groups into the *ortho* positions, as in *XXI*

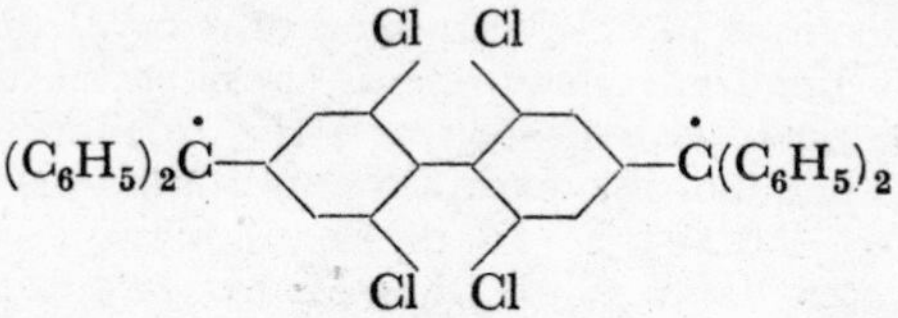

Cl Cl

$(C_6H_5)_2\dot{C}$— ⟨ ⟩ — ⟨ ⟩ —$\dot{C}(C_6H_5)_2$

Cl Cl

XXI

the quinonoid structure becomes impossible, and the molecule in the ground state is a true bi-radical.

REFERENCES

[1] SLATER, J. C. *Phys. Rev.* 37 (1931) 489
[2] PAULING, L. C. *Proc. nat. Acad. Sci. Wash.* 18 (1932) 293
— *J. chem. Phys.* 1 (1933) 362
[3] PAULING, L. C. *The Nature of the Chemical Bond* Cornell, 1939
[4] RUMER, Y. *Nachr. Ges. Wiss. Göttingen Math-physik.* (1932) 337
[5] EYRING, H., WALTER, J. and KIMBALL, G. E. *Quantum Chemistry* New York, 1944
[6] PAULING, L. C. and SHERMAN, J. *J. chem. Phys.* 1 (1933) 606
[7] LEVINE, A. A. and COLE, A. G. *J. Amer. chem. Soc.* 54 (1932) 338
WIBAUT, J. L. and HAAYMAN, P. W. *Nature, Lond.* 144 (1933) 290
— — *Rec. trav. chim. Pays-Bas* 60 (1941) 842
[8] KAUFMAN, H. S., FANKUCHEN, I. and MARK, H. *ibid* 161 (1948) 165
[9] PROSEN, E. J., JOHNSON, W. H. and ROSSINI, F. D. *J. Amer. chem. Soc.* 69 (1947) 2068
[10] SYRKIN, J. K. and DYATKINA, M. E. *J. gen. Chem. U.R.S.S.* 11 (1941) 626
[11] DHAR, J. *Indian J. Phys.* 7 (1932) 43
[12] KARLE, I. L. and BROCKWAY, L. O. *J. Amer. chem. Soc.* 66 (1944) 1974
[13] JONES, R. N. *ibid* 63 (1941) 1658
[14] SWIFT, E. *ibid* 60 (1938) 1403

6

RESONANCE OF COVALENT AND IONIC STATES

THE IONIC (HETEROPOLAR) BOND

IN CHAPTER 3 the covalent bond has been discussed and the question now arises whether this is the only possible type of bond between atoms. Let us consider the gaseous molecule of sodium chloride. The sodium and chlorine atoms each have one unpaired electron, $3s$ in sodium and $3p$ in chlorine, so that in principle the formation of a covalent bond is possible. The calculation of bond energies presents considerable difficulties even in a simple molecule such as hydrogen and the calculation for more complicated molecules is impossible except by an approximate method such as that introduced by PAULING[1]. In this method, it is assumed that the energy of the covalent bond A—B, is equal to one half of the sum of the bond energies of the homopolar molecules A—A and B—B, *i.e.*

$$E_{A-B} = \tfrac{1}{2}\,(E_{A-A} + E_{B-B}) \qquad \ldots.(6.1)$$

The bond A—A, *e.g.* Na—Na in the molecule Na_2, and the bond B—B, *e.g.* Cl—Cl in Cl_2 are formed by the interaction of two electrons from different atoms, both electrons participating in the formation of the bond to the same degree. According to the method of Pauling, one half of the energy of the bond is apportioned to each electron, and each electron of the atoms A and B contribute the same energy to the molecule AB, as to the molecules AA and BB.

A theoretical proof of this method of calculating bond energies cannot be made and its validity can only be tested by its application to specific cases where calculated and observed values of the bond energies may be compared. A convenient series of molecules for this purpose is the inter-halogen compounds, since because of the similarity of the properties of the halogen atoms, the bonds will be largely covalent. For a similar reason, molecules formed between alkali metal atoms may also be considered. The energies of the bonds in the molecules BrCl, ICl, IBr and NaK are shown in *Table XXIII.* The values of the bond energies of Cl_2, Br_2, I_2, Na_2 and K_2 used in deriving the calculated value were 57, 45, 35, 17 and 12 kcals respectively. The agreement between the calculated and experimental values is good and we may therefore conclude that for bonds which are highly covalent in character, the method of Pauling gives satisfactory results.

Table XXIII. Calculation of Bond Energies (Pauling)

Molecule	*E calc. kcals*	*E observed kcals*
BrCl	51	52
ICl	46	49
IBr	40	42
NaK	14·5	14·5

If this method of calculation is now applied to molecules such as NaCl, LiF and KBr, we find considerable discrepancies between the calculated and experimental values. Thus for sodium chloride the bond energy of the covalent bond will be :

$$\tfrac{1}{2}\,(E_{Na_2} + E_{Cl_2}) = \tfrac{1}{2}\,(17 + 57) = 37 \text{ kcals}$$

a value in very poor agreement with the experimental value of 98 kcals obtained from spectroscopic data. It is therefore concluded that the bond in the sodium chloride molecule is not covalent.

The bond energy may also be calculated on the assumption that the molecule is ionic and that the bond energy is due entirely to the electrostatic interaction of the ions. The energy value E which is to be calculated is that of the formation of the ionic molecule Na^+Cl^- from atoms, *i.e.*

$$Na + Cl \rightarrow Na^+Cl^-_{gas} + E$$

The transformation of a sodium atom into a sodium ion requires the absorption of an amount of energy I, equal to the ionization potential, *i.e.*

$$Na_{gas} \rightarrow Na^+ + e - I$$

where $I = 118$ kcals. The electron is acquired by the chlorine atom and an amount of energy equivalent to the electron affinity of chlorine is liberated, *i.e.*

$$Cl + e \rightarrow Cl^- + F$$

where $F = 86$ kcals.

The Coulombic attraction of two ions of opposite unit charge situated a distance r apart is given by :

$$E_1 = - e^2/r \qquad \ldots.(6.2)$$

It will be assumed that the ions are non-distorted ; the problem of polarization will be discussed later. In addition to the attraction between the ions there will be a repulsion caused by the completed electronic shells of the sodium and chloride ions. The transfer of paired electrons, as we have seen in Chapter 3, leads to a repulsion energy. Exact calculation of this energy is difficult but it may be done by an approximate method. The error involved does not significantly affect the result, as the repulsion energy is small in comparison with the energy of attraction. In Chapter 3 it was shown that the exchange energy of repulsion decreased exponentially with the distance between the atoms :

$$E_2 = A \exp(- ar) \qquad \ldots.(6.3)$$

where A and a are constants. It is possible to replace this function by a simpler one by assuming that the energy of repulsion, since it falls off very rapidly with increase of distance, is inversely proportional to a high power of r, *i.e.*

$$E_2 = B/r^n \qquad \ldots.(6.4)$$

The error involved in making this approximation amounts to only a few kcals for the sodium chloride molecule. This is negligible for our present purpose. The total energy of interaction of the ions is then given by,

$$E' = E_1 + E_2 = - e^2/r + B/r^n \qquad \ldots.(6.5)$$

Since the molecule formed is stable, it follows that at a particular value of r, E' will be a minimum. Hence we may write :

$$\frac{dE'}{dr} = \frac{e^2}{r_0^2} - \frac{nB}{r_0^{n+1}} = 0 \qquad \ldots.(6.6)$$

where r_0 represents the interatomic distance at equilibrium.

From equation 6.6 it follows that

$$\frac{e^2}{r_0^2} = \frac{nB}{r_0^{n+1}} \qquad \ldots.(6.7)$$

and hence,

$$B = e^2 r_0^{n-1}/n \qquad \ldots.(6.8)$$

Substitution of this value of B in equation 6.5 gives :

$$E' = -\frac{e^2}{r_0}\left(1 - \frac{1}{n}\right) \qquad \ldots .(6.9)$$

and hence the bond energy of the ionic molecule Na^+Cl^- is given by,

$$E = -I + F + \frac{e^2}{r_0}\left(1 - \frac{1}{n}\right) \qquad \ldots .(6.10)$$

The value of n in equation 6.10 is approximately 9, and calculation of E gives the value as 85 kcals. This value is much closer to the experimental value of 98 kcals than was the value obtained assuming that the bond was covalent. Values for a series of alkali halide molecules are given in *Table XXIV* and it is seen that in every case the bond energy, calculated for an ionic type of bond, is much closer to the observed value than that calculated on the assumption of a covalent bond. This conclusion is also supported indirectly by the values of the interatomic distances of these molecules, all of which are larger than would be expected if the molecules were covalent. All the interatomic distances given in *Table XXIV* are above 2·5 Å and there is no known instance of a homopolar bond having an energy of the order of 80 to 100 kcals at such a distance.

It is thus apparent that there are two different types of bond, the homopolar or covalent and the ionic. In the former the main contribution to the bond energy is due to the quantum mechanical exchange phenomena and in the latter to Coulomb attraction between the ions. In molecules such as H_2, N_2, Cl_2, Na_2, IBr and NaK the bond may be regarded as covalent, but in molecules formed from atoms of widely differing electronegativity, *e.g.* LiCl, NaCl, NaBr, KI, the bond is almost entirely ionic. Caesium fluoride presents a special case however, since the electron affinity of fluorine (95 kcals) is greater than the ionization potential of caesium (89 kcals) so that in the change of caesium and fluorine atoms into ions, a small liberation of energy, amounting to 6 kcals, occurs.

Table XXIV. Bond Energies of Alkali Halides

Molecule	*Internuclear distance* Å	*Bond Energy kcals*		
		Covalent bond according to Pauling's equation	*Ionic bond according to equation 6.10*	*Experimental value*
NaCl	2·51	37	85	98
NaBr	2·64	31	77	88
NaI	2·90	26	59	73
KCl	2·79	34	92	104
KBr	2·94	28	85	91
KI	3·23	24	68	77
RbCl	2·89	34	91	101
RbBr	3·06	28	84	91
RbI	3·26	23	70	76
CsCl	3·06	33	93	103
CsBr	3·14	27	89	93
CsI	3·41	23	73	82

Apart from the difference in the bond energy, other criteria, both direct and indirect, exist between the two different types of bond. Ionic molecules in the solid state form an ionic crystal lattice which is characteristic for the particular molecule. In such a lattice, each ion is surrounded by ions of opposite charge at equal distances from the central ion and individual molecules cease to exist. The number of ions packed round the central ion is limited by the size of the ions, the attraction and repulsion energies between the ions and other factors. The links of the central ion with its nearest neighbours are all of the same strength and the number of such nearest neighbours is not controlled in any way by the valency of the central atom. Covalent substances in the solid state form molecular lattices, formed by packing the molecules together to produce the most stable structure. The forces holding the molecules together in the crystal lattice are van der Waal's forces, which are weak and diminish rapidly with distance from the molecule. When an ionic compound passes from the solid to the gaseous state, ionic bonds are broken and the heat of sublimation of ionic crystals is therefore very high ; for salts of the sodium chloride type the value is between 50 and 60 kcals. For molecular compounds, the heat of sublimation is much lower, about 10 kcals, because the forces being overcome are very much weaker. For the same reason ionic compounds melt at high temperatures whereas typical simple homopolar substances, such as H_2, Cl_2 and N_2, are gaseous at room temperature.

The dissociation of gaseous molecules into ions and the process of electrolytic dissociation in water also frequently suggest the ionic character of a bond. Each case must, however, be examined carefully as exceptions occur. Thus although hydrogen chloride dissolves in water to form hydrogen and chloride ions, it is not an ionic molecule ; owing to the affinity of the water molecule for a proton (180 kcals), a chemical reaction takes place between a molecule of hydrogen chloride and a molecule of water with the formation of hydrogen H_3O^+ and chloride Cl^- ions. In the same way it is not always correct to determine the nature of a chemical bond by the products of dissociation of the gaseous molecules, *i.e.* whether it dissociates into atoms or ions. Instances are known where at distances of 2 to 3 Å, the energy of the heteropolar bond is greater than that of the covalent bond and the link is primarily ionic, but that at greater distances the electrostatic interaction is small and does not compensate for the difference between the ionization potential and electron affinity of the two atoms ; because of this possibility, an ionic molecule may dissociate into atoms.

The nature of the bond in a molecule will determine whether or not there is a permanent electric dipole moment. An electric dipole exists wherever the centres of gravity of the positive and negative charges in a molecule are at different points. The magnitude of this dipole is measured in terms of the dipole moment μ defined by

$$\mu = er \qquad \ldots .(6.11)$$

where e represents the charge, positive and negative, on the two parts of the molecule and r is the distance between the centres of charge. In a true covalent molecule the dipole moment is zero ; polarization of a covalent molecule occurs, however, whenever it is placed in an electric field, but the resulting dipole is induced and is not a permanent property of the molecule in the absence of an applied field. On the other hand, an ionic molecule is strongly polar ; in the limiting case, the positive and negative charges are focused at the centres of the ions. Under these conditions, the dipole moment will have a value of 9 to 12 × 10^{-18} e.s.u, since the electronic charge is approximately 4·8 × 10^{-10} e.s.u and the interionic distance

Table XXV. Dipole Moments of Ionic Molecules

Molecule	10^{-18} e.s.u	*Molecule*	10^{-18} e.s.u
KCl	8·0	RbBr	10
KBr	9·07	CsCl	10
KI	9·24	CsI	10·2

between 2 and 3 Å. This value is in agreement with the experimental data (*Table XXV*) determined by the molecular beam method.

BONDS OF INTERMEDIATE TYPE

In a very large number of compounds the chemical bond cannot be considered as purely ionic or purely covalent; the dipole moments of such bonds are greater than zero but considerably less than the values given in *Table XXV*. Typical examples of such bonds are HF, HCl, HBr, HI, NH, OH, CCl *etc.* If the experimental values for the bond energies of the hydrogen halides are compared with those calculated by the Pauling's method it is found (*Table XXVI*) that for HI the calculated value is greater than the experimental. Such a result is clearly impossible since, because of resonance which was not taken into account in the calculation, the experimental value should always be the greater. A similar result occurs with the hydrides of the alkali metals. In order to overcome this difficulty Pauling suggested that the geometric mean of the covalent bond energies should be taken:

Table XXVI. Bond Energies of Hydrogen Halides

Molecule	*E calc.* (*kcals*)	*E observed* (*kcals*)
HF	84	147
HCl	80	102
HBr	74	83
HI	69	63

$$E_{A-B} = (E_{A-A} \times E_{B-B})^{\frac{1}{2}} \quad \ldots (6.12)$$

in place of the arithmetic mean (equation 6.1). The calculated value of the bond energy of hydrogen iodide then becomes 60 kcals, *i.e.* below the experimental value; in a similar way satisfactory values for the hydrides of the alkali metals are obtained. Although the calculated values are, in general, more acceptable in these particular cases, the difference between values calculated by the two methods are not significantly different. In the series of compounds HF, HCl, HBr and HI the divergence between calculated and observed values is least with HI and greatest with HF and Pauling considers that the magnitude of the difference between the two values is a measure of the deviation of the bond from true covalency.

The idea that a link, such as that which occurs in hydrogen chloride, is of an intermediate type is not new; FAJANS, LEWIS and SIDGWICK all considered that there existed an uninterrupted change of bond type from a pure covalent bond on the one hand to a pure ionic bond on the other. Such an intermediate type of bond may be considered as an ionic bond which has been polarized, *i.e.* the electron cloud of the anion has been displaced towards the cation by electrostatic attraction, and the suggestion has been made that the bond could be described in terms of electrostatic theory. In a nonpolarized anion the centre of gravity of the negative charge is coincident with the nucleus; the field due to the cation, however, produces a displacement of this negative charge in the direction of the cation thus inducing in the anion a dipole moment acting in the reverse direction to the original dipole. The resulting dipole moment of the molecule is thus less than that given, by the product *er*.

The magnitude of the dipole moment m induced by a field of unit strength is termed the polarizability α of the molecule ·

$$m = \alpha F \quad \ldots (6.13)$$

where F is the electric field. Attempts to calculate the induced polarization using equation 6.13 and thus to calculate the energy and dipole moment of the bond have, in general, failed owing to the use of the molar refractivity R to calculate α. The relationship between α and R is given by the Lorentz-Lorenz equation :

$$R = \frac{4}{3}\,\pi \mathcal{N}\alpha = \frac{n^2 - 1}{n^2 + 2} \cdot \frac{M}{d} \qquad \ldots .(6.14)$$

where M the molecular weight, $\mathcal{N}$ the Avagadro number, n the refractive index and d the specific gravity. The inaccuracy of this assumption has been demonstrated by DEBYE[2] in the following way. In the hydrogen chloride molecule the internuclear distance is 1·27 Å and if the bond were entirely ionic in character, the dipole moment would be :

$$\mu = er = 4{\cdot}8 \times 10^{-10} \times 1{\cdot}27 \times 10^{-8} = 6{\cdot}06 \times 10^{-18} \text{ e.s.u}$$

as compared with the experimental value of $1{\cdot}03 \times 10^{-18}$ e.s.u
The field due to the proton is given by

$$F = e/r^2 \qquad \ldots .(6.15)$$

and this induces in the chloride ion a moment acting in the reverse direction :

$$m = \alpha F = \alpha e/r^2 \qquad \ldots .(6.16)$$

and the total moment is then given by,

$$\mu = er - m = er(1 - \alpha/r^3) \qquad \ldots .(6.17)$$

The refractivity of the chloride ion is $R = 8{\cdot}45$ cc and hence by equation 6.14, $\alpha = 3{\cdot}22 \times 10^{-24}$ cc. Substitution of this value of α in equation 6.17 and putting $r = 1{\cdot}27 \times 10^{-8}$ cc gives :

$$\mu = 6{\cdot}06 \times 10^{-18}\,(1 - 1{\cdot}63) = -\,3{\cdot}8 \times 10^{-18} \text{ e.s.u}$$

The calculated moment thus considerably exceeds the experimental value and furthermore represents the dipole as acting in the opposite direction: the chlorine is represented as positive and the hydrogen negative. This result is clearly incorrect and Debye has shown that the error is due to the fact that the Lorentz-Lorenz equation is not valid at the small distances considered owing to the non-uniform character of the field. If the internuclear distances were of the order of 5 Å, this type of calculation would be permissible. Attempts have been made to calculate the polarizability in a non-uniform electric field by the methods of wave mechanics[3], but have not yet been successful in producing a theory of the intermediate type of bond.

A different approach to this problem has been made by Pauling[1, 4]. If each of two atoms forming a bond have a single valency electron, it is theoretically possible for either a covalent or an ionic bond to be formed. In the first case the electrons are localized and both electrons move in the field of both nuclei, in the second case an electron is transferred from one atom to the other and both electrons move in the field of one nucleus. If the energy of one type of bond is very much greater than that of the other, then that form which has the higher energy will determine the nature of the bond and in the extreme case, the bond will be either entirely ionic or entirely covalent. However, when the energies of the two bond types are closer together, but not necessarily equal, both forms will contribute to the final state of the molecule and the bond will be a resonance hybrid of the covalent and ionic forms, the molecule being stabilized by the resonance energy. There is no difference between the resonance described here and that discussed in connection with the structure of benzene, which happens to be a particular case, in that the two Kekulé structures are both covalent and have the same energy. When the two forms possess different energies, that with the greater energy is the more probable and contributes more to the final state of the molecule. Even in molecules such as sodium chloride there is present, in addition to the ionic bond, a covalent bond, although its energy is so small that it is generally ignored. The resonance between the two forms, however, may be the explanation of the fact that the experimental values of the bond energy are greater than the values calculated on the assumption of an ionic bond for molecules of the sodium chloride type (*Table XXIV*).

The resonance between the covalent and ionic bond structures of a molecule produces, by the superposition of the electron clouds of the ionic bond and of the covalent bond, a transitional electron cloud. This is discussed below in terms of wave mechanics. The electron cloud of the bond, however, will of course be continuous and the splitting into component parts, which this method of treatment has incurred, is the direct result of the attempt to describe a complex chemical bond in terms of two simpler types of bonds which may be represented by classical structural symbols.

If the covalent state of the molecule is described by the function ψ_c and the ionic state by ψ_i, then the intermediate state of the molecule may be described by the linear combination of these two wave functions :

$$\psi = c_1\psi_c + c_2\psi_i \qquad \ldots.(6.18)$$

where the coefficients c_1 and c_2 determine the contribution of the two states to the molecule and the ratio c_1/c_2 will be such as to make the bond energy a maximum for the particular set of molecular parameters (*e.g.* the relative electronegativities of the participating molecules) pertaining to this molecule. The wave function for the covalent bond (see Chapter 3) is given by

$$\psi_c = \psi_a(1)\psi_b(2) + \psi_b(1)\psi_a(2) \qquad \ldots.(6.19)$$

and that for the ionic bond by

$$\psi_i = \psi_a(1)\psi_a(2) \qquad \ldots.(6.20)$$

which infers that both electrons are located at nucleus *a* (*a* refers to the nucleus of atom A and *b* to the nucleus of atom B). Substitution of equations 6.19 and 6.20 in 6.18 gives the wave function of the molecule :

$$\psi = c_1\psi_c + c_2\psi_i = c_1\{\psi_a(1)\psi_b(2) + \psi_b(1)\psi_a(2)\} + c_2\psi_a(1)\psi_a(2) \qquad \ldots.(6.21)$$

The expression for the electron cloud of the molecule will be obtained by squaring the expression 6.21, *viz*,

$$\psi^2 = c_1^2\{\psi_a^2(1)\psi_b^2(2) + \psi_b^2(1)\psi_a^2(2) + 2\psi_a(1)\psi_b(1)\psi_a(2)\psi_b(2)\} + + c_2^2\psi_a^2(1)\psi_a^2(2) + 2c_1c_2\{\psi_a^2(1)\psi_a(2)\psi_b(2) + \psi_a^2(2)\psi_a(1)\psi_b(1)\} \qquad \ldots.(6.22)$$

This expression is composed of three parts, first the terms representing the electron cloud in a covalent molecule (equation 3.99) :

$$\psi_a^2(1)\psi_b^2(2) + \psi_b^2(1)\psi_a^2(2) + 2\psi_a(1)\psi_b(1)\psi_a(2)\psi_b(2) \qquad \ldots.(6.22a)$$

secondly, the term representing the electron cloud when both electrons are located at nucleus *a*, *i.e.* an ionic structure :

$$\psi_a^2(1)\psi_a^2(2) \qquad \ldots.(6.22b)$$

and thirdly, the transitional electron cloud :

$$\psi_a^2(1)\psi_a(2)\psi_b(2) + \psi_a^2(2)\psi_a(1)\psi_b(1) \qquad \ldots.(6.22c)$$

In the transitional structure one electron is located at the nucleus, ($\psi_a^2(1)$), and the second electron gives an elliptical cloud $\psi_a\psi_b$ (see equation 3.61 *et seq*). The latter term is identical with that obtained for the hydrogen molecule ion and we may therefore conclude that the transitional electron cloud represents a state in which one electron is located at one atom, whilst the second electron forms a single electron bond. The second term in equation 6.22c occurs as a result of the exchange of the positions of the electrons. Only one nucleus appears in expression 6.22c *viz a* ; this refers to the more electronegative of the atoms forming the bond. The complete electron cloud of the diatomic molecule may thus be conceived as elliptical in shape with the maximum density not occurring midway between the nuclei as in a true covalent bond, but nearer to one atom than the other. The greater the ionic character of the bond, the greater is the shift of the position of maximum density towards the more electronegative atom.

In the above discussion we have considered that the bond between two atoms A and B may be described as a resonance hybrid of the covalent A—B and ionic A^- B^+ structures. Theoretically we should also consider the alternative ionic structure A^+ B^- and resonance between the three structures would further increase the energy of the bond. In general, however, the second ionic state is so improbable as to contribute little stability to the molecule. Thus for example, it will be appreciated readily that the state Na^- Cl^+ or H^- Cl^+ are most improbable and do not play a part in determining the behaviour of the molecules. The contribution of such states to the resonance of the molecule is, therefore, in general neglected.

VALENCY STRUCTURES OF THE ELEMENTS

In order to apply the resonance theory of the transitional type of bond it is necessary to reconsider the electronic states of the atoms of the elements and to consider the valence bond structures of certain of their compounds, which may make an appreciable contribution to the state of the molecule.

The number of covalent bonds which a given atom can make is determined by the number of unpaired electrons. The loss or gain of an electron converts a neutral atom into a positive or negative ion and we shall consider two types of ions :

a Ions having no unpaired electrons. Ions of this type generally possess an inert gas electronic structure, *e.g.* H^-, Li^+, Be^{2+}, O^{2-}, F^-, Na^+, Mg^{2+}, S^{2-}, Cl^- *etc.* The interaction of such ions generally leads to ionic compounds since in the absence of unpaired electrons covalent bonds cannot be formed.

b Ions containing unpaired electrons, *e.g.* O^-, N^-, C^+, C^-, B^+, B^- *etc.* The role of such ions in molecules is extremely important since they may take part in both ionic and covalent bond formation and it is most significant that the number of covalent bonds made by such ions may be greater than in the original neutral atom. The formation of the ion from the neutral molecule will be accompanied by the loss of energy ; nevertheless this will be compensated for by the resulting Coulombic interaction, by the formation of covalent bonds, and by the possibility of resonance between the ionic and covalent structures.

In the following discussion, the terms mono– di– and trivalent will be used to denote the presence of one, two or three unpaired electrons respectively. Defined in this way the valency represents the maximum number of covalent bonds in which a particular element can partake. The number of elementary charges on an ion will be termed the ' chargeability '. Thus there are, for example, singly, doubly, and triply charged positive and negative ions.

Such a definition of terms is necessary in order to avoid confusion of meaning. For example, reference is often made to the trivalent ion of aluminium. If by this it is meant that the aluminium ion is forming three covalent bonds, then the statement is correct and the aluminium ion is trivalent ; but if, however, the statement is meant to denote the fact that aluminium has lost three electrons, then it is a triply charged ion and not trivalent since its electronic configuration will be that of an inert gas and it will have no unpaired electrons. The correct description of aluminium in this case is that it is a triply charged, zerovalent ion. The necessity for this careful definition of valency will become apparent in the following discussion, where it will often be necessary to refer simultaneously to the charge and covalency of an ion.

We shall now discuss the ionic states of various atoms :

Hydrogen $1s$—In addition to the homopolar monovalent state $1s$, two ionic forms of hydrogen are possible, H^+ and H^-. The former corresponds to the positive singly charged and zerovalent ion. The latter is formed when an electron is acquired by a hydrogen atom and occupies the second position in the $1s$ orbital. The negative hydrogen ion therefore possesses a helium like $1s^2$ shell and is therefore zerovalent. The reaction between a hydrogen atom and an electron is exothermic, ΔH being $-16{\cdot}4$ kcals. The hydrogen ion, H^-, occurs in the ionic states of certain hydrides, thus in lithium hydride, for example, resonance occurs between the states Li–H and $Li^+ H^-$.

Helium $1s^2$—The two electrons are paired in the $1s^2$ shell and as a consequence helium is zerovalent. The loss of one electron converts helium into a monovalent, singly charged positive ion He^+, with a single electron in the $1s$ orbit. The ionization potential is, however, very high, being 564 kcals, and neither the formation of a covalent bond nor electrostatic interaction with a negative ion would compensate for such a loss of energy. The maximum energies of these two types of bonds is approximately 100 kcals and 200 kcals respectively. An additional electron would have to be accommodated in the $2s$ orbital, and hence the formation of the monovalent negative ion He^- ($1s^2 2s$) is strongly endothermic.

Lithium $1s^2 2s$—The neutral atom is monovalent and on the loss of one electron the zerovalent singly charged positive ion Li^+ is formed. The formation of a negative ion Li^- is theoretically possible, this would have the electronic configuration $1s^2 2s^2$ and would thus be zerovalent. Such an ion could only be of importance in compounds with more electropositive substances *e.g.* LiCs, but in molecules such as lithium hydride the contribution to the resonance of the molecule of the form $Li^- H^+$ may be considered as negligible.

Beryllium $1s^22s^2$—The atom of beryllium forms two positive ionic states, the monovalent singly charged Be^+ $1s^22s$ and the zerovalent, doubly charged Be^{2+} $1s^2$. The ionization potential in the latter is very much greater than in the former and therefore the singly charged ion must play a large part in the compounds of beryllium. In $BeCl_2$, in addition to the covalent structure

$$Cl - Be - Cl$$

formed by beryllium in the $1s^22s2p$ state, two ionic forms are possible involving the monovalent singly charged ion :

$$Cl^- \ Be^+—Cl \quad \text{and} \quad Cl—Be^+ \ Cl^-$$

and one ionic form involving the doubly charged zerovalent ion :

$$Cl^- \ Be^{2+}Cl^-$$

The contribution of this form to the resonance of the molecule, however, will be small.

The singly charged negative ion of beryllium may be either mono or trivalent : Be^- $1s^22s^22p$ or Be^- $1s^22s2p^2$ respectively.

Boron $1s^22s^22p$— On the loss of one electron boron may form a zerovalent $1s^22s^2$ or divalent $1s^22s2p$ singly charged positive ion. The formation of the divalent ion requires not only the energy necessary to expel the electron, the ionization potential, but also the excitation energy necessary to transfer one $1s$ electron, to a $2p$ state *viz* $1s^22s^2 \rightarrow 1s^22s2p$ (compare with the corresponding excitation of the monovalent neutral atom to the trivalent state, discussed in Chapter 2). The doubly charged positive ion of boron, B^{2+} $1s^22s$ is monovalent and the triply charged positive ion B^{3+} is zerovalent and in view of the high ionization potential involved, is unlikely to make an appreciable contribution to the structure of boron compounds.

Boron trichloride will be a resonance hybrid of the following structures

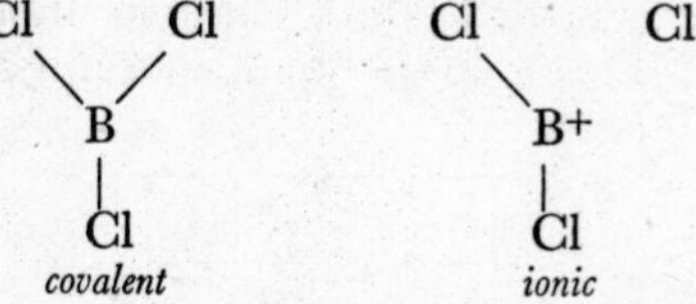

covalent *ionic*

There will be three ionic structures, since the ionic bond can occur in each of the three boron-chlorine links, and the negative charge is therefore not located on any one chlorine atom but shared equally among all three. The existence of the three equivalent structures amongst which resonance occurs increases the stability of the molecule compared with the case where the negative charge is located at one atom.

The contribution of the forms

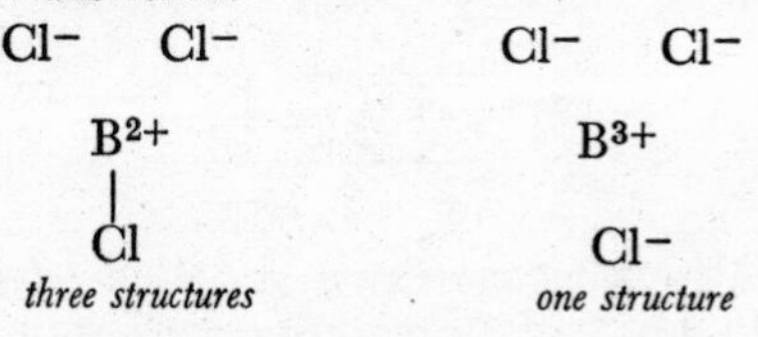

three structures *one structure*

will be very small.

When boron gains an electron it becomes a carbon-like tetravalent ion $1s^22s2p^3$ with a single negative charge. As in carbon the four valencies are directed towards the corners of a tetrahedron. This electronic structure occurs in hydrofluoroboric acid $[H^+ (BF_4)^-]$, in which the BF_4^- ion exists as a resonance hybrid of the following valence bond structures

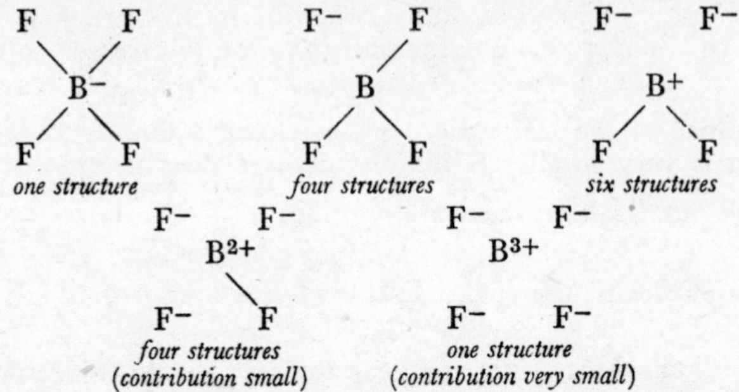

Esters of boric acid, $B(OC_2H_5)_3$ dissolve in ethyl alcohol forming an acid. The reaction which takes place may be represented as follows :

$$B(OC_2H_5)_3 + 2C_2H_5OH \rightleftharpoons B^-(OC_2H_5)_4 + C_2H_5OH_2^+$$

The structure of the negative ion

$$\left[\begin{array}{ccc} C_2H_5O & & OC_2H_5 \\ & B^- & \\ C_2H_5O & & OC_2H_5 \end{array}\right]^-$$

may be represented by a similar series of structures to those given above for BF_4 and as in that case, the negative charge is not localized in the boron atom but shared with the oxygen atoms.

The problem of the structure of the boron hydrides will be considered in Chapter 15.

Oxygen $1s^2 2s^2 2p^4$—The neutral atom has two unpaired p electrons and is therefore divalent. The gain of an electron gives a singly charged monovalent negative ion,

O^-	↓↑	↓↑	↓↑	↓
	2s	2p		

and the loss of an electron yields a singly charged trivalent positive ion,

O^+	↓↑	↓	↓	↓
	2s	2p		

In the positive ion it will be noticed that a monovalent configuration is possible:

O^+	↓↑	↓↑	↓	
	2s	2p		

but in the ion, as in the molecule, that state is preferred which gives the maximum possible number of unpaired electrons. Both of these singly charged ions occur in molecules containing oxygen. The doubly charged negative ion, having a neon electronic configuration, is zerovalent ; its formation, however, is highly endothermic.

Four structures exist for the molecule of water :

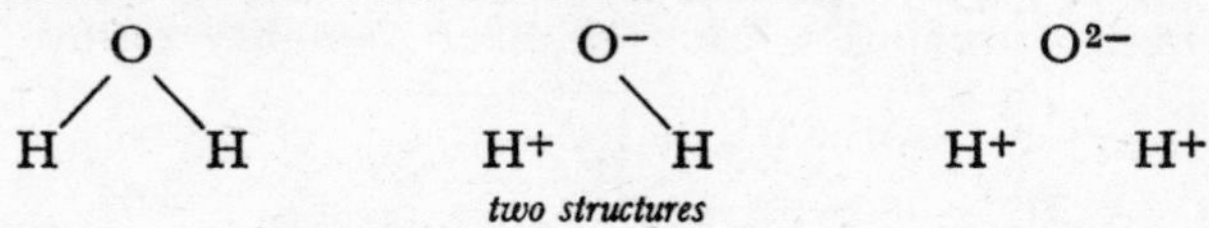

two structures

the importance of the last structure containing a doubly charged negative oxygen ion is very small. Similar structures exist in organic compounds containing oxygen *e.g.*

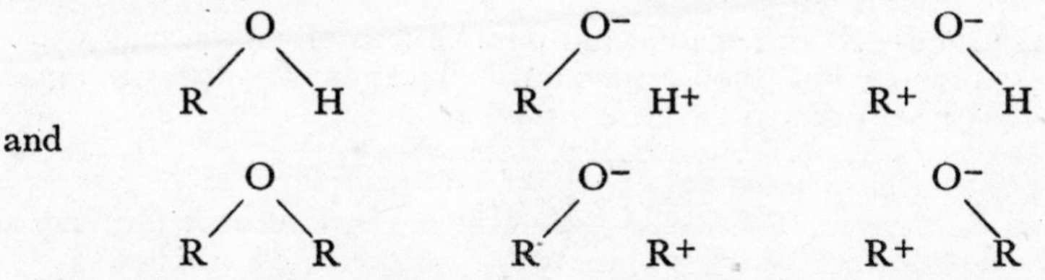

Trivalent positive oxygen is present in oxonium compounds ; water, for example, possesses an affinity for a proton amounting to 180 kcals and thus the hydrogen ion H_3O^+ has the following structures :

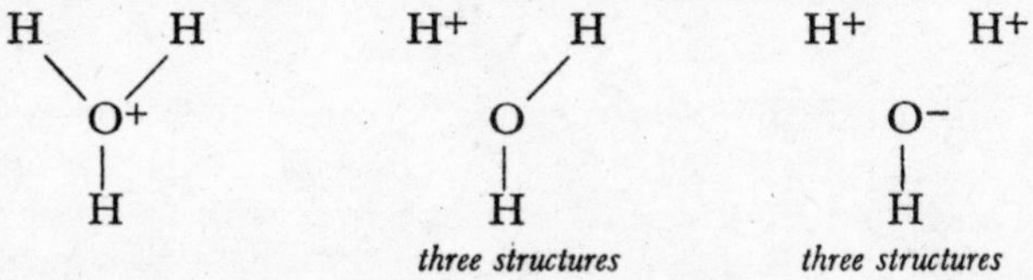

three structures *three structures*

The energy of formation of water from oxygen and hydrogen atoms is 220 kcals. This value will be equivalent to the bond energies of two O—H bonds so that the bond energy of the hydroxyl link is 110 kcals. On the addition of a proton to water there is a further gain of 180 kcals, so that in the ion H_3O^+, 400 kcals is shared between three O—H bonds ; the hydroxyl bond energy in the ion is thus 133 kcals. It is therefore evident that the transition from H_2O to H_3O^+ has caused a strengthening of each bond and this fact is one of the causes of complex formation, hydration and the dissociation of such acids as hydrogen chloride in water.

It was suggested by FRIEDEL and by COLLIE and TICKLE that the compound formed by the addition of hydrogen chloride to an ether has the structure :

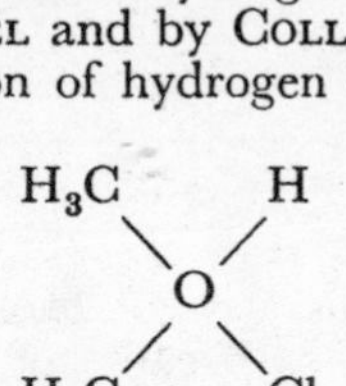

H_3C H
O
H_3C Cl

However, oxygen can be electrically neutral and tetravalent only in the case when one 2*p* electron is excited to the 3*s* state :

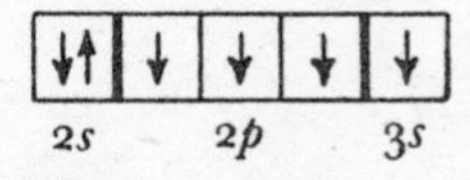

The energy required for this excitation is 273 kcals and is sufficiently large to make the resulting atomic state improbable. Spectroscopic investigation[5] of $(CH_3)_2$ OHCl has confirmed that tetravalent oxygen does not take part in the structure. For a similar reason the tetravalent doubly charged positive ion,

O^{2+} [↓ | ↓ ↓ ↓]
2s 2p

is unlikely to contribute to the structure of molecules containing oxygen, as the energy required to remove one *s* and one *p* electron from the ground state is greater than 1,300 kcals.

Carbon $1s^2 2s^2 2p^2$— Both negative and positive ions of carbon may play a part in the structures of carbon compounds. The gain of an electron gives the singly charged negative trivalent ion,

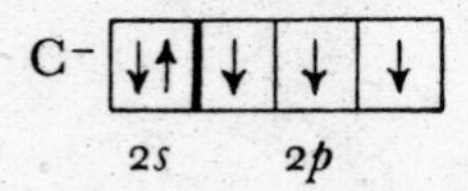

whereas the loss of an electron leads to a singly charged positive trivalent ion:

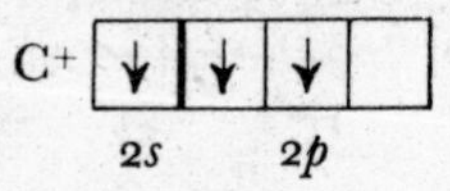

The latter ion occurs in the structures of compounds of the type, CCl_4, $CHCl_3$:

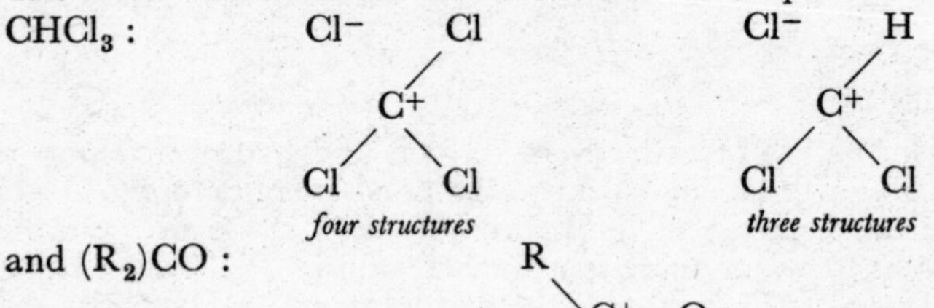

four structures *three structures*

and $(R_2)CO$:

R₂ >C+ O−

and these ionic structures resonate with the corresponding covalent forms. The former negative ion occurs in compounds such as CH_3Li and C_2H_5Na:

H_3C^- Li^+ H₃C—CH₂⁻ Na⁺

Multiply charged carbon ions are not likely to be of significance in the structure of carbon compounds because of the high value of the second ionization potential.

In addition to the states described above, an electrically-neutral divalent state and a singly charged positive monovalent ion can occur:

which exist with other forms in the structures of carbon monoxide,

C=O (*a*) C+—O− (*b*) C−≡O+ (*c*)

The triple bond in the third structure *c* is formed by the transfer of one *p* electron from the oxygen atom, in which it is paired, to the vacant *p* orbital in carbon, thus producing two ions with identical electronic

structure capable of forming the three covalent bonds. Thus the transfer of an electron from one atom to the other has produced, in addition to the Coulombic attraction between the ions, an additional covalent bond. Such bonds have from time to time been given special names, *e.g.* semi-polar, dative or coordinate, and have been represented in structure formulae by an arrow, *viz* $C^- \overset{\leftarrow}{\equiv} O^+$ showing the direction of electron transfer. In view of the fact that such bonds utilize no new binding force, such names now appear unnecessary.

The bond energy of the carbon monoxide molecule, 210 kcals, is the greatest for any diatomic molecule; the bond energy of the nitrogen molecule N_2, in which the two nitrogen atoms are joined by three covalent bonds, is only 170 kcals. This high bond energy is due to the considerable resonance between the three structures *a*, *b* and *c*. The dipole moment of carbon monoxide is very small, which indicates that the contribution of the two ionic forms *b* and *c* will be almost equal. This fact brings out the essential difference between resonance and tautomerism, both the structures *b* and *c* may be used to describe the molecule and contribute to the resultant structure of the molecule, but if carbon monoxide were a tautomeric mixture rather than a resonance hybrid of the structures *a*, *b* and *c* then the experimental dipole moment would be high (about 5×10^{-18} e.s.u) since the two tautomeric forms *b* and *c* would be capable of orienting independently in the applied field.

Similar structures to those given for carbon monoxide are proposed for diethoxymethylene, which is formed by the dissociation of tetraethoxy-ethylene. The molecule is stabilized by resonance between a structure containing divalent carbon *I* and one containing a singly charged, negative, trivalent carbon atom and a singly charged, positive trivalent oxygen atom *II*

C_2H_5O \\ C / C_2H_5O	$C_2H_5O^+$ \\\\ C^- / C_2H_5O
I	*II*
	two structures

In carbon dioxide there exist in addition to the homopolar structure:

$$O{=}C{=}O$$

four ionic structures:

$$O{=}C^+{-}O^- \qquad O^-{-}C^+{=}O$$

$$O^+{\equiv}C{-}O^- \qquad O^-{-}C{\equiv}O^+$$

The last two structures play a significant part, causing the raising of the bond energy and a reduction of the interatomic distances. In a similar way, in carbon suboxide C_3O_2, resonance occurs between the following five structures :

$$O{=}C{=}C{=}C{=}O$$

$$O{=}C{=}C{=}C^{+}{-}O^{-} \qquad O^{-}{-}C^{+}{=}C{=}C{=}O$$

$$O^{-}{-}C{\equiv}C{-}C{\equiv}O^{+} \qquad O^{+}{\equiv}C{-}C{\equiv}C{-}O^{-}$$

Nitrogen $1s^2 2s^2 2p^3$—In addition to the electrically neutral trivalent structure *I*, a singly charged, negative divalent ion *II* and a singly charged, positive, tetravalent ion *III* are important in the valence bond structures of nitrogen compounds.

	2s	2p		
I N	↓↑	↓	↓	↓
II N^-	↓↑	↓↑	↓	↓
III N^+	↓	↓	↓	↓

The doubly and triply charged negative ions *IV* and *V* which are mono- and zerovalent respectively are much less probable structures.

	2s	2p		
IV N^{2-}	↓↑	↓↑	↓↑	↓
V N^{3-}	↓↑	↓↑	↓↑	↓↑

The tetravalent, positive ion *III* has been recognized for some time as it occurs in the ammonium ion $^{+}NH_4$ and in the tetraalkyl ammonium salts *e.g.* $(C_2H_5)_4N^{+}I^{-}$. The other forms are now known to make a contribution to the structures of many nitrogen containing compounds. Thus the following may be considered to be the structures of ammonia,

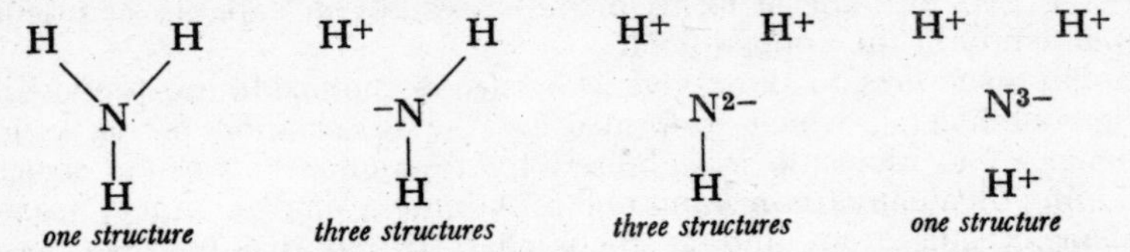

although the first two occur with the greatest weights. Similar ionic structures occur in the amines :

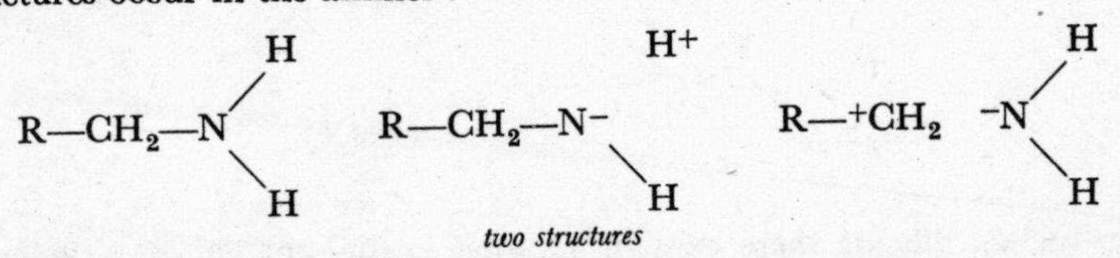

Compounds of the type NH_4-halogen are very stable because in the process of conversion of nitrogen to the tetravalent state, an additional covalent bond is formed and the energy of the molecule is increased by the difference between the electron affinity of the halogen together with the Coulombic energy of the ionic bond between $^{+}NH_4$ and the halogen ion and the ionization potential of ammonia. It is noteworthy in this respect that nitrogen, like boron, tends to assume a tetravalency of the carbon type. This occurs in nitrogen by the loss of an electron to form a positive ion and in boron by the gain of an electron to form a negative ion, *e.g.* BH_4^-. Furthermore as in the case of tetravalent carbon, the four bonds in $>N^+<$ are sp^3 hybrid bonds of equal energy and directed tetrahedrally. That the four N—H bonds in $^+NH_4$ are each stronger than the N—H bond in NH_3 may be shown in the following way. We have the following reactions :

$$N = \tfrac{1}{2}N_2 \qquad \Delta H = -\ 85 \text{ kcals}$$
$$3H = \tfrac{3}{2}H_2 \qquad \Delta H = -\ 154{\cdot}5 \text{ kcals}$$
$$\tfrac{1}{2}N_2 + \tfrac{3}{2}H_2 = NH_3 \qquad \Delta H = -\ 11 \text{ kcals}$$

and hence on summation,

$$N + 3H = NH_3 \qquad \Delta H = -\ 250{\cdot}5 \text{ kcals}$$

and hence the bond energy of an N—H bond in ammonia is 83·5 kcals. For the formation of the ammonium ion from ammonia we have

$$NH_3 + {}^+H = {}^+NH_4 \qquad \Delta H = -\ 206 \text{ kcals}$$

and consequently the heat of formation of the ion $^+NH_4$ from N, 3H and H^+ is 456·5 kcals. The energy of each N—H bond is thus 152 kcals, very much greater than the N—H bond in ammonia.

In order to form pentavalent nitrogen it would be necessary to raise the 2*s* electron to the 3*s* state, a process requiring considerable excitation energy. It is not therefore surprising that in all molecules where five homopolar valencies are ascribed to nitrogen, a large dipole moment is observed. Thus, for example, the nitro group has a dipole moment of $3{\cdot}54 \times 10^{-18}$ e.s.u and in the amine oxides the moment is approximately 5×10^{-18} e.s.u. This fact would agree with the theory that the nitrogen is in the singly charged, positive, tetravalent form in this compound :

```
      O-                 R1
     /                     \
R—N+                   R2—N+—O-
     \\                    /
      O                  R3
```

two structures

This view is substantiated by the work of MEISENHEIMER who showed that in the amino-oxyhydrates :

```
[ R1                ]
[    \              ]
[ R2—N+—OH          ]      OH-
[    /              ]
[ R3                ]
```

the two hydroxyl groups have different properties, one being ionic whereas the other is covalently linked to nitrogen. Additional evidence arises from the reaction between the sodium salt of diphenylamine and tetramethylammonium iodide ; the product, diphenylaminotetramethylammonium, has the properties of a salt and therefore has the structure :

$$[\, N^+(CH_3)_4 \,][\, N^-(C_6H_5)_2 \,]$$

in which there is a singly charged, positive, tetravalent nitrogen and a singly charged, negative, nitrogen instead of one pentavalent and one trivalent nitrogen atom joined by a covalent bond.

When positive, tetravalent nitrogen is bonded to three atoms, a double bond is formed with one of these atoms. In this case, as with carbon, the σ bonds lie in one plane with an angle of 120° between them (sp^2 hybridization) and the π bond is perpendicular to this plane. Thus, for example, the nitrate ion has the structure :

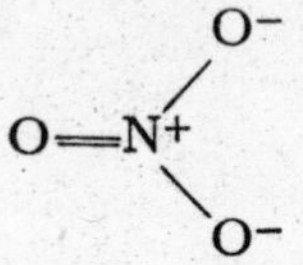

O⁻
/
O═N⁺
\
O⁻

three structures

and the nitro group the structure :

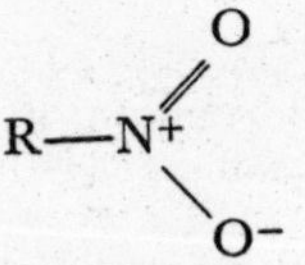

O
//
R—N⁺
\
O⁻

two structures

as suggested above. Experimental data confirm this configuration, the value for the N(O)(O) angle in the nitrate ion being 120°, and in the nitro group 127°. The larger value in the latter case is evidently caused by the repulsion of the two negatively charged oxygen atoms.

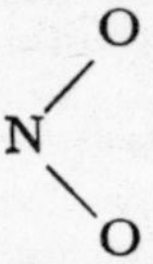

Hydrazoic acid HN_3 is stabilized by resonance between the structures :

$$H—N=N^+=N^-$$
$$H—N^-—N^+\equiv N$$
$$H^+\ \ N^-=N^+=N^-$$

in which the three atoms of nitrogen are linear (sp hybridization, as in acetylene and allene). The third structure, containing a positively charged hydrogen possesses considerable stability owing to the Coulombic attraction between the alternating charges. The large contribution of this structure to the molecule explains the acidic properties of HN_3.

For the free radical, diphenyl nitric oxide, the presence of a neutral tetravalent nitrogen has been suggested (*I*). It will be clear

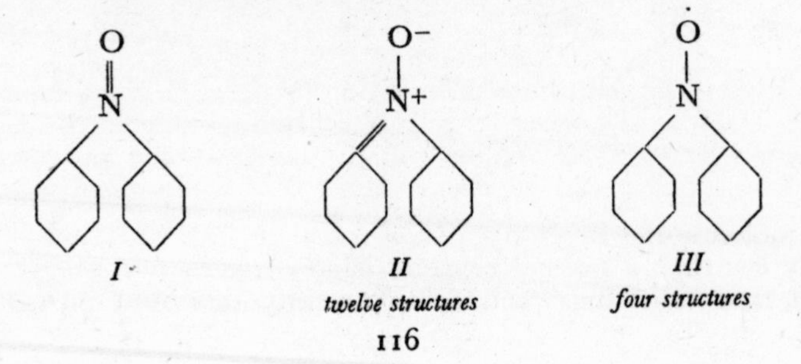

twelve structures *four structures*

from a consideration of the electron configuration of singly charged, positive, tetravalent nitrogen :

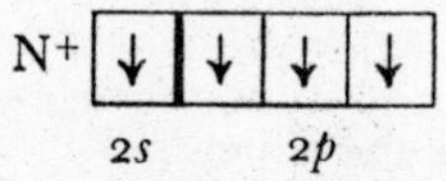

N^+ | ↓ | ↓ | ↓ | ↓ |
2*s* 2*p*

that nitrogen in the tetravalent state cannot be electrically neutral. The structure of the radical will therefore be a resonance hybrid of structures *II* and *III* in which the nitrogen is tetravalent, positive and trivalent, neutral, respectively.

The possibility of boron and nitrogen existing in similar valency states leads to the formation of a series of compounds, one of which, $B_3N_3H_6$, has a hexagonal type of structure. For this compound, in addition to the structure in which both boron and nitrogen are trivalent :

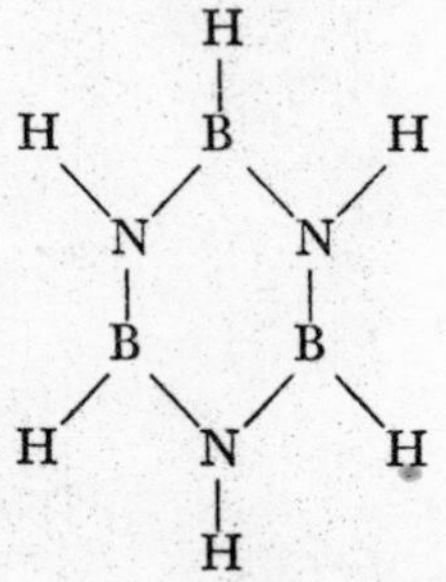

two ionic forms are possible in which the nitrogen is positively charged and tetravalent and the boron negatively charged and tetravalent. The two forms are analogous to the Kekulé structures of benzene :

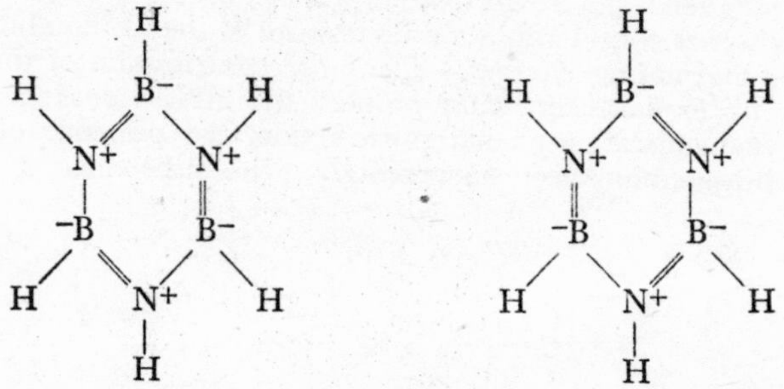

In this molecule the B—N distance is found to be 1·44 Å, which is considerably less than a normal covalent bond between nitrogen and boron (1·58 Å), thus indicating a considerable contribution from the two Kekulé structures. The molecule $B_3O_3(CH_3)_3$ has a rather different structure[6],

CH_3 — B — O — O — B — B — H_3C — O — CH_3

since although the ring is planar, the B—O—B angle is 110° and the O—B—O angle 130°. In this molecule also, structures analogous to the Kekulé structures are possible, but probably contribute less to the final state of the molecule than in the corresponding nitrogen compound. The reason for the apparently anomalous values for the valency angle

CH_3 B− +O O+ −B B− H_3C O+ CH_3 CH_3 B− +O O+ −B B− H_3C O+ CH_3

is that with oxygen in the normal divalent state and in the positively charged trivalent state, the bonding electrons are *p* electrons, which tend to make bonds at an angle of 90° to each other and not at 120°.

Fluorine $1s^22s^22p^5$—Fluorine may be used to illustrate the main valence states of the halogens. The halogens may exist in three different valence states of which the monovalent, neutral atom *I*, the singly charged, negative, zerovalent ion *II* are well known ; in addition, however, there is a third possibility a singly charged, positive, divalent ion *III*.

Hal ↓↑ | ↓↑ ↓↑ ↓ — 2s 2p — *I*

Hal − ↓↑ | ↓↑ ↓↑ ↓↑ — 2s 2p — *II*

Hal+ ↓↑ | ↓↑ ↓ ↓ — 2s 2p — *III*

The first two valence states are present in all X—halogen bonds, *e.g.* H—Cl and $H^+ Cl^-$. The third form occurs where a double or triple bond occurs adjacent to a X—halogen bond. For the molecule

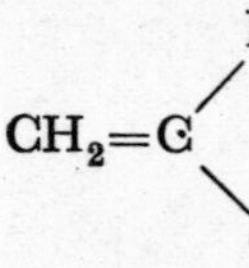

$CH_2{=}C(H)Cl$ for example, there exist the following possible structures :

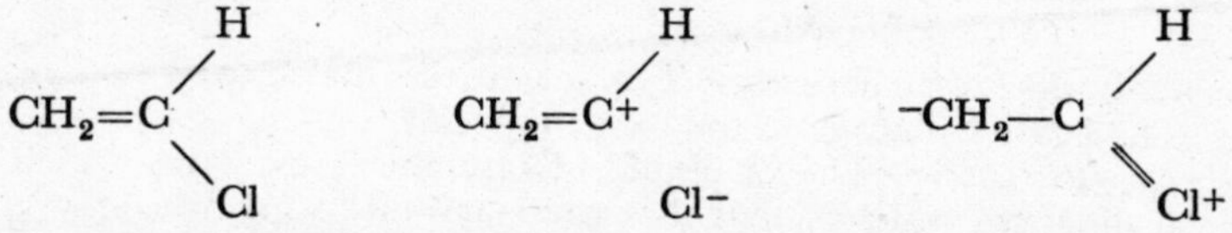

$CH_2{=}C(H)-Cl$ $\quad$ $CH_2{=}C^+(H)\ \ Cl^-$ $\quad$ ${}^-CH_2-C(H){=}Cl^+$

The contribution from the last form, however, will be small. A similar series of structures occurs in chlorobenzene although in this case additional structures are possible in view of the resonance of the benzene ring.

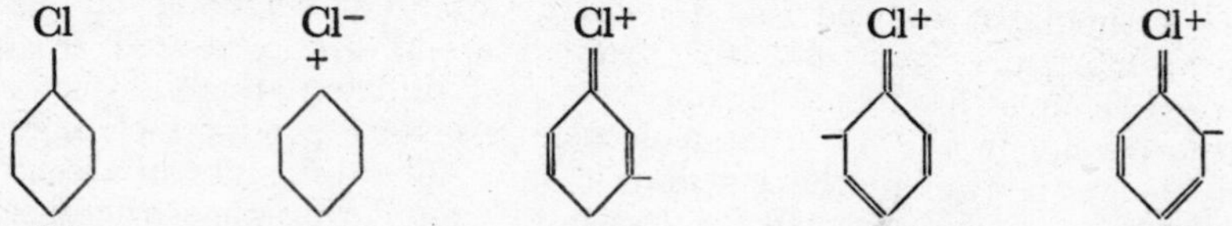

Cl / Cl⁻ + / Cl⁺ / Cl⁺ / Cl⁺

IV $\quad$ *V* $\quad$ *VI* $\quad$ *VII* $\quad$ *VIII*

Of these structures, *IV* and *V* have the greatest weight, the contribution of *VI, VII* and *VIII* being small. The contribution of such states having a positive halogen atom will, however, increase in the series F, Cl, Br, I. It must be emphasized that when it is stated that structures *VI, VII* and *VIII* contribute to the state of the molecule, it does not infer that there exists a positively charged atom of chlorine in the molecule ; the effect of the contribution of such structures will be to reduce the negative character of the chlorine atom. This also occurs in the case of oxygen containing compounds, *e.g.* furan, in which together with the covalent structure *IX*,

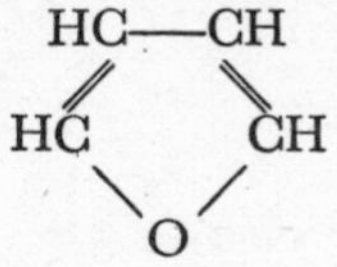

HC—CH
HC CH
O

IX

there will be a contribution from the ionic states with a negative charge on the oxygen atom :

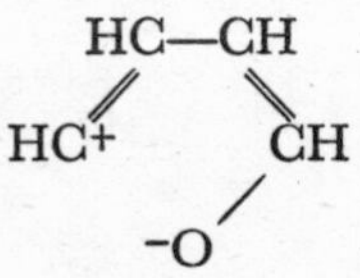

HC—CH $\quad$ HC—CH
HC^+ CH $\quad$ HC ^+CH
^-O $\quad$ O^-

X 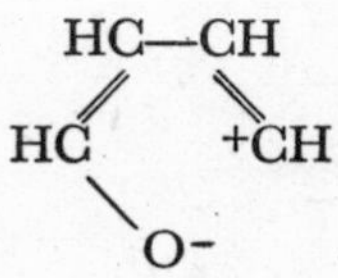 $\quad$ *XI*

and from structures containing the singly charged, positive, trivalent oxygen ion, which are possible owing to the presence of the conjugated system of double bonds.

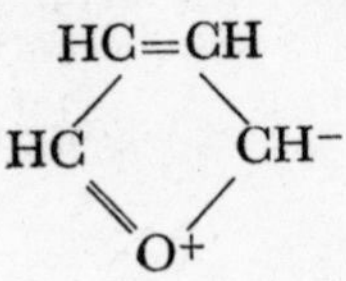

HC=CH HC CH⁻ O+	HC=CH HC⁻ CH O+	HC—C̄H HC CH O+	HC̄—CH HC CH O+
XII	*XIII*	*XIV*	*XV*

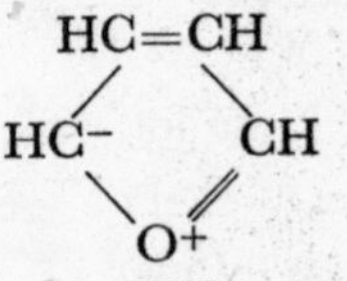

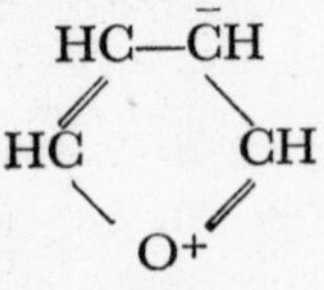

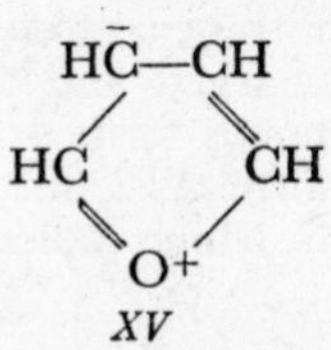

The contribution of structures *XII* to *XV* to the molecular resonance will reduce the negative charge on the oxygen atom.

Molecular Resonance— The examples of resonance structures which have just been discussed indicate that it is necessary to distinguish between two types of resonance involving ionic states : molecular and bond resonance. In the case of bond resonance, valence bond structures exist which possess covalent and ionic forms of one single bond between two atoms *e.g.* resonance between O—H and O^- H^+ H_2C=O and H_2C^+—O^-, H—F and H^+ F^-. Here it should be noticed that the charges occur on neighbouring atoms, but in molecular resonance the charged atoms are separated by one or more neutral atoms. The importance of differentiating between the two forms lies in the fact that molecular resonance produces changes in the valency states of the intermediate atoms. The difference between the two types of resonance may be shown by considering the structures of urea, where in addition to the bond resonance forms *XVI* to *XIX* :

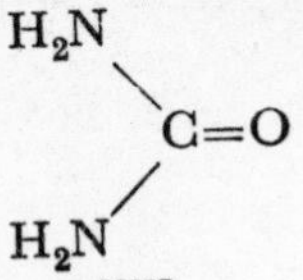

H_2N
C=O
H_2N
XVI

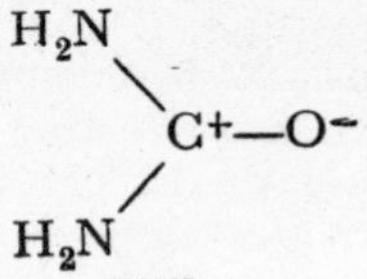

H_2N
C^+—O^-
H_2N
XVII

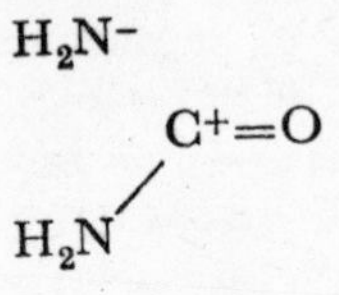

H_2N^-
C^+=O
H_2N

XVIII
two structures

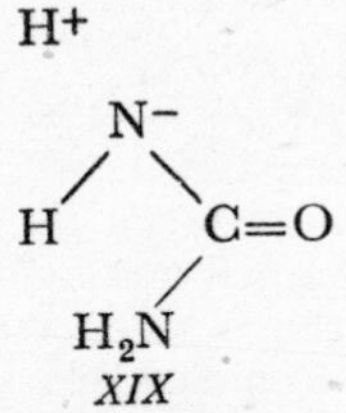

H^+
N^-
H C=O
H_2N
XIX
four structures

there exist also the molecular resonance forms *XX* and *XXI* :

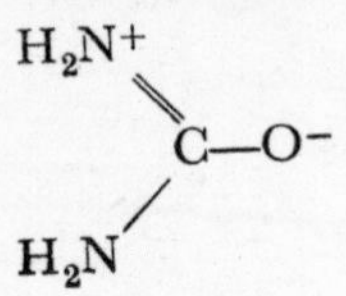

H_2N^+
C—O^-
H_2N

XX
two structures

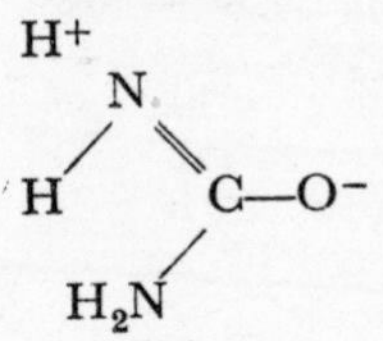

H^+
N
H C—O^-
H_2N
XXI
four structures

In the bond resonance structure *XVII* the oxygen becomes negatively charged and monovalent because the carbon atom to which it is bonded becomes positively charged and trivalent, whereas in the case of molecular resonance *XX*, the oxygen atom is also negatively charged, because the nitrogen atom with which it is not directly bonded, becomes positively charged and tetravalent ; in this valence-bond structure, the number of bonds formed by the carbon atom do not differ from that in the covalent form *XVI* but are only located differently. Other examples of molecules in which molecular resonance occurs are phenol :

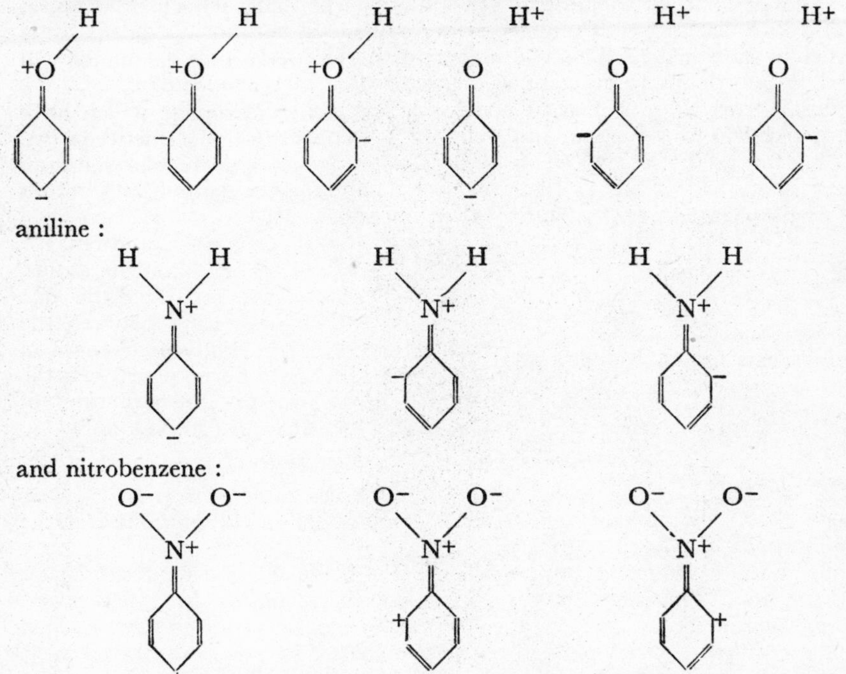

aniline :

and nitrobenzene :

Molecular resonance involving the atom of carbon plays an important part in organic compounds as the carbon atom may be either positively or negatively charged and trivalent.

The most frequently encountered valence states of the elements of the second period are summarized in the accompanying diagram, in which the charges and the number of homopolar valencies are indicated. On the loss of one electron the valencies of Li, Be, B and C are lowered by unity, whilst those of N, O and F are raised by unity. The addition of an electron raises the valency of B by unity and lowers that of C, N, O and F. Carbon occupies a central

Valence States of Second Period Elements

Li	Be	B	C		N	O	F
		4−	4		4+		
		3	3+	3−	3	3+	
	2	2+	2		2−	2	2+
1	1+		1−	1+		1−	1
0+							0−

position in the table, possessing a maximum valency of four and in that valence state is electrically neutral. In carbon the ratio of the valency electrons to the total number of electrons in the atom is 4/6, which is greater than in any other element, excluding hydrogen which has only one electron. The presence of the three valency states of the neutral atom, σ^4, $\sigma^3\pi$ and $\sigma^2\pi^2$, together with the ionic states, account for the great diversity of carbon compounds.

The elements of subsequent periods of the periodic classification reveal certain similarities with the second period, but in addition further possible valency states exist. This is due first to the fact that with the increase of the principal quantum number the excitation energies decrease, thus the transfer from a $3p$ to a $4s$ state requires less energy than the excitation of a $2p$ electron to a $3s$ state, and secondly to the presence of the d orbitals.

Sulphur $1s^22s^22p^63s^23p^4$— Sulphur, like oxygen, is divalent in the ground state since two of the $3p$ electrons are unpaired. On gaining an electron a singly charged negative, monovalent ion is produced :

S^- | ↓↑ | ↓↑ | ↓↑ | ↓ |

$3s$ $3p$

which exists in the valence bond structures of the thioethers,

C_2H_5—S—C_2H_5 $\qquad$ $CH_3\overset{+}{\cdot}CH_2$ $\qquad$ S^-—C_2H_5

and hydrogen sulphide,

H—S—H $\qquad$ H^+ S^-—H

The doubly charged, zerovalent ion is much less important and the structure $H^+ S^{2-} H^+$ makes a very small contribution to the structure of the molecule.

In many compounds, sulphur is shown as being tetravalent, but in order to produce tetravalent sulphur, it is necessary to unpair two $3p$ electrons and transfer one to the $4s$ or a $3d$ orbital, which according to spectroscopic data requires excitation energies of 160 kcals and 200 kcals respectively. The electronic configuration of the sulphur atom would be :

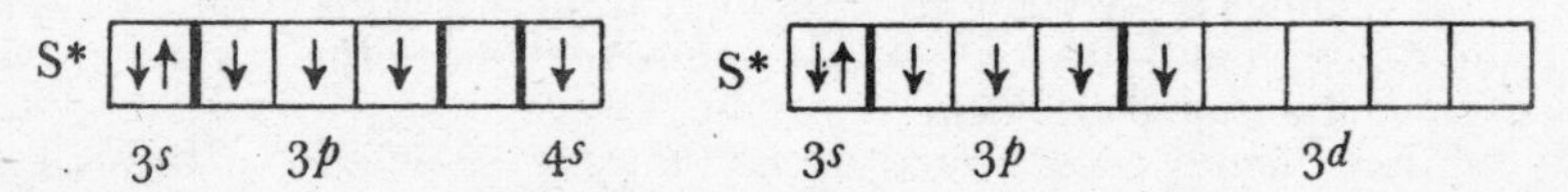

It is not likely, therefore, that such valency states will make a large contribution to the valency state of sulphur, unless the molecule is stabilized in some other way.

The loss of one electron produces a positively charged trivalent ion :

S^+ | ↓↑ | ↓ | ↓ | ↓ |

$3s$ $3p$

which occurs in the structures of SO_2 and $SO_3{}^{2-}$ in addition to the tetravalent form :

O=S=O $\qquad$ O^- \ S^+ // O $\qquad$ O \\ S^+ / O^-

The fact that sulphur dioxide possesses a dipole moment and is triangular in shape lends support to the view that the contribution of the tetravalent structure is very small. A direct indication of the existence of the positively charged trivalent state lies in the existence of the sulphonium compounds $(R_3S)^+ \ Cl^-$ which are formed readily from thioethers and alkyl halides and behave in solution as strong electrolytes containing the $(R_3S)^+$ ion.

If sulphur were to readily form compounds in which the contribution of the tetravalent valence bond structure was considerable, it might be expected that such molecules as SH_4 and SR_4 would be formed by analogy with CH_4 and SiH_4. The fact that such compounds do not exist infers that in compounds frequently shown as containing tetravalent sulphur, structures with trivalent singly charged positive sulphur make a large contribution to the resonance of the molecule. Thus the sulphite ion is best represented by the structure :

O⁻ O⁻
\ /
S⁺
|
O⁻

in which three *p* electrons give a pyramid structure similar to that formed by the *p* orbitals of nitrogen in ammonia. This structure has been confirmed by x-ray data. Similarly in the $SOCl_2$ molecule the main valence bond structures will be :

$O^-{-}S^+(Cl)(Cl)$	$O{=}S^+(Cl)\ \ Cl^-$	$Cl^-\ \ O{=}S^+(Cl)$

In order that sulphur may be hexavalent, it is necessary to unpair two pairs of electrons, one *s* and one *p* and excite one to a 3*d* orbital and the other to the 4*s* orbital, or alternatively both to the 3*d* state, a process

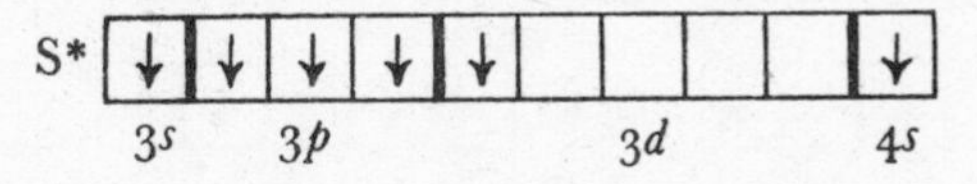

which requires considerable excitation energy. Sulphur may, however, be doubly charged positive and tetravalent :

S^{2+} | ↓ | ↓ | ↓ | ↓ |
3*s* 3*p*

and it is evident that in the sulphur trioxide molecule, in addition to the usual representation of the molecule involving hexacovalent sulphur :

$O{=}S({=}O){=}O$

there are also three further structures of the type :

```
       O⁻
      /
O=S²⁺
      \
       O⁻
```

Since the electronic state of the molecule in this case is similar to carbon, (sp^2), the SO_3 molecule will contain three σ and one π bonds, and the molecule will be planar, the angle between the σ bonds being 120°. The same electronic structure of sulphur will occur in the sulphate ion in which the main structure will be

```
O⁻    O⁻
  \  /
  S²⁺
  /  \
O⁻    O⁻
```

in which the configuration will be tetrahedral since the bonds will be sp^3 hybrid bonds. In SO_2Cl_2, in addition to the less probable hexavalent state of sulphur, the doubly charged positive, tetravalent state makes an important contribution :

```
O     Cl      O     Cl      O⁻    Cl      O     Cl⁻
 \\  /         \\  /          \  /          \\
   S            S²⁺           S²⁺            S²⁺
 //  \         /              /  \          //
O     Cl      O⁻    Cl⁻     O⁻    Cl      O     Cl⁻
```

four structures

In sulphur hexafluoride in which the fluorine atoms are arranged octahedrally about a central sulphur atom it must be assumed that the main valence bond structure is,

```
     F⁻
F         F
  \     /
    S²⁺
  /     \
F         F
     F⁻
```

The charges are not localized on any particular pair of fluorine atoms and there are fifteen different valence bond structures, each bond thus being two thirds covalent and one third ionic.

Phosphorus $1s^2 2s^2 2p^6 3s^2 3p^2$—The electronic structures of phosphorus reveal many similarities with those of nitrogen. The loss of an *s* electron leads to positively charged tetravalent phosphorus which occurs in the acids of phosphorus and in the phosphate ion. All these structures involve

```
      OH               OH              OH               O⁻
      |                |               |                |
⁻O—⁺P—OH        ⁻O—⁺P—OH        ⁻O—⁺P—H         ⁻O—⁺P—O⁻
      |                |               |                |
      OH               H               H                O⁻
```

sp^3 hybrid bonds and are therefore tetrahedral. The formation of pentavalent phosphorus by the excitation of a $3s$ electron to a $4s$ state requires less energy than the corresponding transition in the case of nitrogen ($2s$ to $3s$ state) and therefore compounds such as the phosphorus pentahalides exist which have no nitrogen analogue. The structure of this molecule is a trigonal bipyramid. The pentavalent form of phosphorus may also occur in the valence-bond structures of the acids *e.g.*

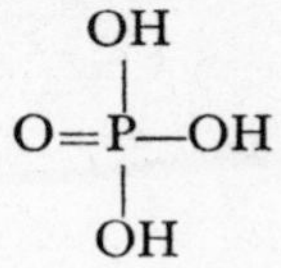

```
      OH
      |
    O=P—OH
      |
      OH
```

Trialkyl phosphines may be oxidized to the corresponding oxycompounds, which will evidently have the following structures :

```
    R                R
    |                |
  R—P=O            R—P+—O−
    |                |
    R                R
```

The decrease of the excitation energy required to form the pentavalent state of phosphorus as compared with nitrogen and its greater electro-positive character, explains the readiness with which the tertiary phosphines undergo addition reactions with chlorine and sulphur.

Chlorine $1s^2 2s^2 2p^6 3s^2 3p^5$— In contrast to fluorine, chlorine forms a series of oxides and oxyacids and exhibits a variable valency. The ion ClO_2^- has been shown to have a triangular structure which would suggest that the chlorine was in the singly charged positive, divalent state :

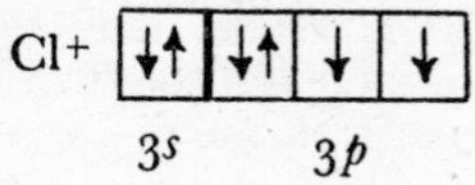

Cl^+	↓↑	↓↑	↓	↓
	$3s$	$3p$		

Two p electrons thus participate in the two bonds which are therefore mutually directed at 90° :

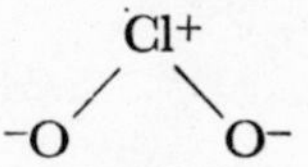

```
     Cl+
    /   \
 −O      O−
```

The ClO_3^- ion is in the form of a pyramid with the chlorine atom at the top :

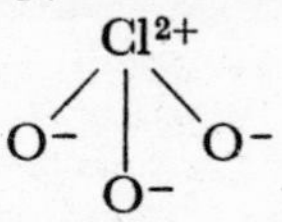

```
     Cl2+
    / | \
  O−  |  O−
      O−
```

which suggests that the chlorine atom is in a doubly charged positive, trivalent state,

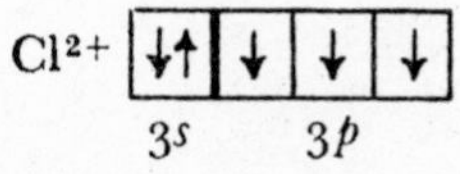

Cl^{2+}	↓↑	↓	↓	↓
	$3s$	$3p$		

and three p electrons participate in the bonds. The ClO_4^- ion is tetra-hedral which would indicate that the four bonding electrons are in the hybrid sp^3 state, with the chlorine in a triply charged positive, tetravalent state :

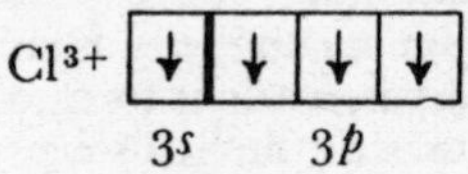

$$Cl^{3+}\ \boxed{\downarrow}\boxed{\downarrow\ \downarrow\ \downarrow}$$
$$3s \quad 3p$$

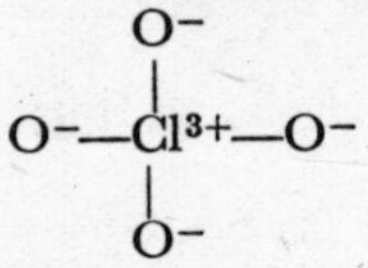

$$\begin{array}{ccc} & O^- & \\ & | & \\ O^-- & Cl^{3+} & --O^- \\ & | & \\ & O^- & \end{array}$$

In addition to the structures given here, it is highly probable that other valence bond structures, involving higher valency states of chlorine, contribute to the resonance of the molecule.

ALTERNATING POLARITY OF ATOMS IN VALENCE BOND STRUCTURES

The bond energy of ionic states of individual bonds is strengthened if alternate positive and negative charges arise on adjacent atoms. As an example, we shall consider first, sulphamide $SO_2(NH_2)_2$, for which the valence bond structure

$$\begin{array}{ccc} O^- & & NH_2 \\ & \diagdown\ \diagup & \\ & S^{2+} & \\ & \diagup\ \diagdown & \\ O^- & & NH_2 \end{array}$$

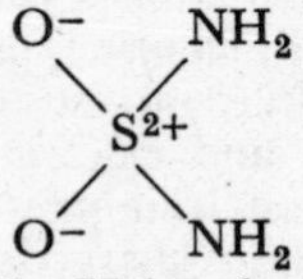

may be written. In each >N—H bond, there is resonance between the covalent and the ionic $>N^-\ H^+$ states, and the formation of a negative charge on the nitrogen atom increases the stability of the molecule in view of the gain of electrostatic energy in the S—N bond. Thus the contribution of the structure :

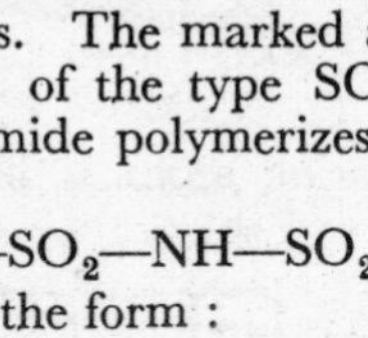

$$\begin{array}{cccc} & & H^+ & \\ O^- & & N^- & \\ & \diagdown\ \diagup & & \diagdown \\ & S^{2+} & & H \\ & \diagup\ \diagdown & & \\ O^- & & NH_2 & \end{array}$$

four structures

will be large in view of the increased stability produced by the alternate positive and negative charges. The marked acid properties of sulphamide and its ability to form salts of the type $SO_2(NHAg)_2$ are in agreement with this structure. Sulphamide polymerizes with the formation of molecules of the type :

$$NH_2—SO_2—NH—SO_2—NH—SO_2—NH—SO_2—NH_2$$

in which the contribution of the form :

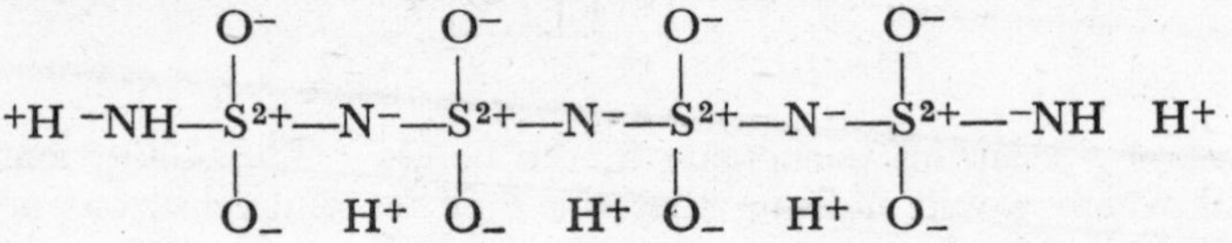

$$\begin{array}{ccccccccc} & O^- & & O^- & & O^- & & O^- & \\ & | & & | & & | & & | & \\ {}^+H\ {}^-NH— & S^{2+} & —N^-— & S^{2+} & —N^-— & S^{2+} & —N^-— & S^{2+} & —{}^-NH\ \ H^+ \\ & | & & | & & | & & | & \\ & O_- & H^+ & O_- & H^+ & O_- & H^+ & O_- & \end{array}$$

will be considerable. Such structures in which there are alternate positive and negative charges on the atoms forming a ring or chain, play an important part in the resonance of certain organic molecules and results in a mutual stabilization of the ionic states in neighbouring bonds[7].

In the case of benzene, resonance is generally considered as occurring between the two Kekulé and the three Dewar structures, but other structures involving a separation of charge can be conceived *e.g.*

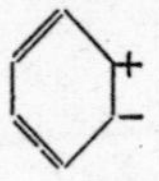

I 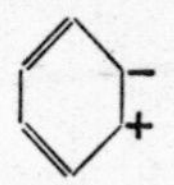 *II*

Such structures do not produce any resultant polarity of the molecule since for each bond the two forms $C^+ \ C^-$ and $C^- \ C^+$ contribute equally to the final state of the molecule. In the case of benzene these structures may in general be ignored in view of the much greater stability of the Kekulé forms. In substituted benzene derivatives, however, this is not always the case, in view of the possibility of the substituent groups being charged. Thus in view of the positively charged nitrogen atom in the trimethyl phenyl ammonium ion :

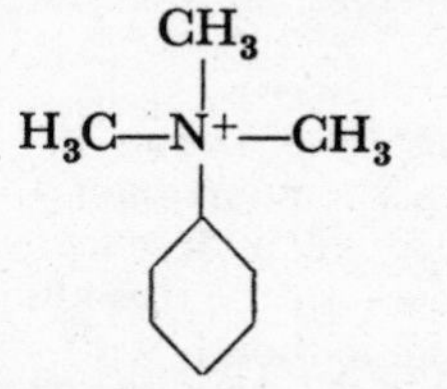

CH_3

$H_3C—N^+—CH_3$

the structures *III* and *IV* are much more probable than in benzene owing to

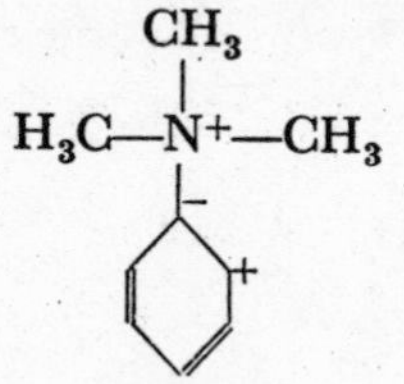

CH_3 CH_3

$H_3C—N^+—CH_3$ $H_3C—N^+—CH_3$

III 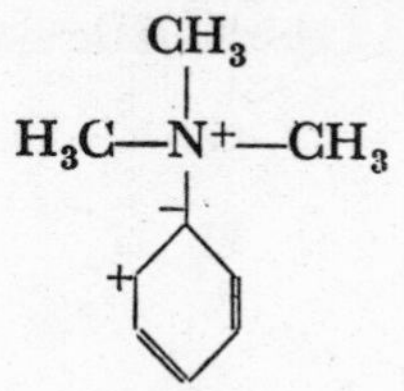 *IV*

the increase of the energy of the molecule in view of the electrostatic energy between the alternate charges, + − +. On the other hand structures of the type *V* are most improbable in view of the repulsion between the adjacent positive charges, + + −

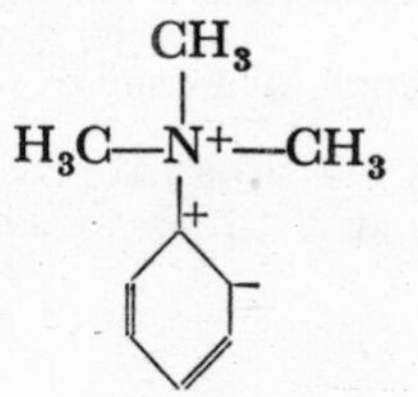

CH_3

$H_3C—N^+—CH_3$

V

Other examples of stabilization in this way are given by benzene-sulphonic acid and nitrobenzene :

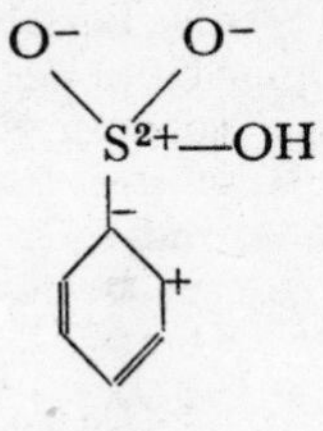

O^- O^- S^{2+}—OH +

VI
two structures

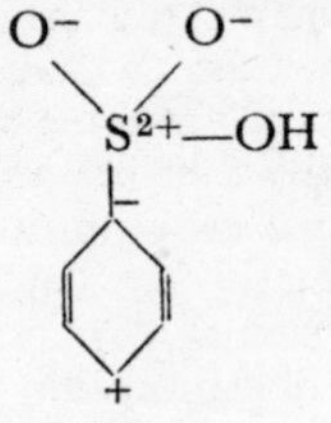

O^- O^- S^{2+}—OH +

VII

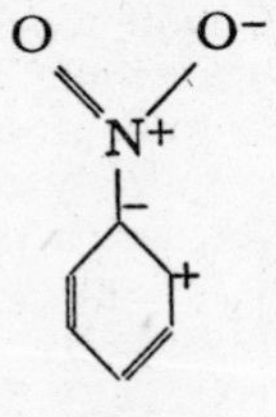

O O^- N^+ +

VIII
four structures

O O^- N^+ +

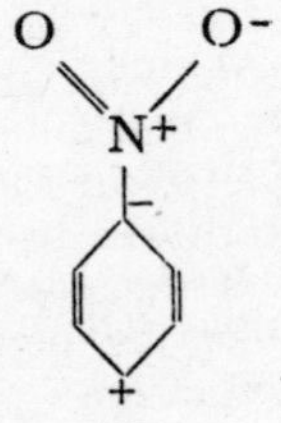

IX
two structures

Alternating polarity may also occur in aliphatic molecules, but is generally present to a lesser extent than in the aromatic series. The resonance in the non-substituted hydrocarbons between the forms C^+ C^- and C^- C^+ will be negligible ; on the introduction of an atom *e.g.* chlorine, which forms a partially ionic bond with carbon, however, alternating polarity can be induced and resonance between the forms *X* and *XI* will occur.

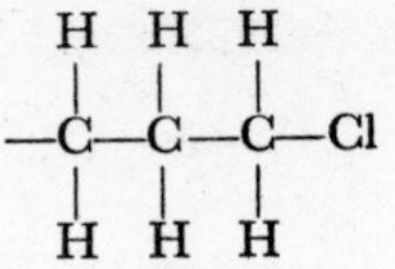

H H H
—C—C—C—Cl
H H H
X

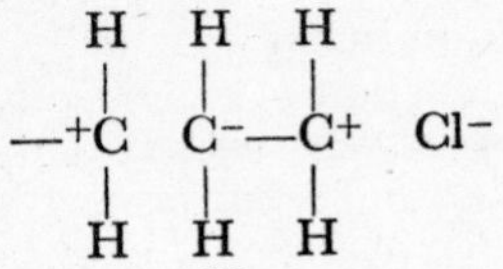

H H H
—$^+$C C^-—C^+ Cl^-
H H H
XI

REFERENCES

[1] PAULING, L. C. *J. Amer. chem. Soc.* 54 (1932) 988
[2] DEBYE, P. *Polar Molecules* New York, 1929
[3] KIRKWOOD, J. G. *Phys. Z.* 33 (1932) 259
GOMBAS, P. and NEUGEBAUER, T. *Z. Phys.* 92 (1934) 375
PSHEZHETSKY, S. Y. *J. phys. Chem. Moscow* 12 (1938) 793
[4] PAULING, L. C. *J. Amer. chem. Soc.* 54 (1932) 3570
[5] GANTMACHER, A. R., WOLKESTEIN, M. V. and SYRKIN, J. K. *J. phys. Chem. Moscow* 14 (1940) 1569
[6] BAUER, S. H. and BEACH, J. Y. *J. Amer. chem. Soc.* 63 (1941) 1394
[7] SYRKIN, J. K. and DYATKINA, M. E. *J. phys. Chem. Moscow* 14 (1940) 1594

7

METHOD OF MOLECULAR ORBITALS

MOLECULAR ORBITALS OF DIATOMIC MOLECULES

THE problem of the nature of the chemical bond may be approached by two different methods. The first treatment, developed mainly by HEITLER, LONDON, SLATER and PAULING, has been discussed in the preceding chapters; the fundamental assumption of this method is that the atoms in the molecule are considered as preserving to a considerable extent their individuality. Thus the electrons in a diatomic molecule are described by functions derived from the atomic wave functions of the constituent atoms, an approximation which is justified only when the interatomic distance is large, since the interaction of the two atoms at distances of the order of 10^{-8} cm is sufficiently great to cause distortion of the atomic orbitals. The second method is that of molecular orbitals[1] which has been developed mainly by HUND, MULLIKAN, HERZBERG and LENNARD-JONES[2]. In this treatment the same principles which have been used for describing the electron states in a single atom (Chapters 1 and 2) are applied to the molecule, with certain modifications which are necessary in view of the fact that the electrons move in the field not of one, but of two nuclei. For our treatment of the electron states of atoms, the simplest atom, hydrogen, was taken as representative and the results obtained applied to the polyelectron atom. In the same way we may consider the simplest diatomic molecule, the hydrogen molecule ion, as a representative molecule and having determined the permissible electron states for the single electron, construct polyelectron molecules, either diatomic or polyatomic, by distributing the electrons in these states. This distribution will be controlled by Pauli's exclusion principle as in the case of atoms.

Each electron in the molecule is described by a wave function ψ, which is the wave function of a molecular orbital. The value of ψ^2 at any point in space may be regarded as representing either the probability of finding the electron at that point or the density of the electron cloud at that point. The calculation of ψ should be made by solving the appropriate Schrödinger equation. This is a mathematical operation of too great a complexity except in the simplest cases and the approximation is made that, when the electron is in the neighbourhood of any one nucleus, the forces acting on it are due mainly to that nucleus and other electrons on that nucleus. The appropriate wave equation and its solution will therefore closely resemble the equation and solution for an isolated atom, and the molecular orbital is assumed to consist of a series of superposed atomic orbitals. This idea which forms the basis of the molecular orbital treatment was first introduced by Lennard-Jones[2] and has been termed by Mullikan[3] the linear combination of atomic orbitals. It must be appreciated clearly that this is an approximation, since the distortion of the atomic orbitals by the adjacent atoms has been ignored in order to simplify the treatment. A detailed study of the hydrogen atom[4] shows that here the assumption is justified.

It has been shown by COULSON[5] that the bonding energy between two atoms is a maximum if the component atomic orbitals of the molecular orbital have the same energy. When these energies are not of comparable magnitude no bonding can be attributed to these particular atomic orbitals.

Thus in the hydrogen chloride molecule, the binding energy of the $1s$ electron of the hydrogen atom to the hydrogen nucleus is much less than that of the electrons of either the K or L electron shells of the chlorine atom to the chlorine nucleus, but is similar to the energy of the $3p_x$ $3p_y$ and $3p_z$ electrons of chlorine. The molecular orbital can thus be formed only by the combination of the H $1s$ atomic orbital and the Cl $3p_x$, $3p_y$, $3p_z$, atomic orbitals, the principle of maximum overlap determining which of the chlorine orbitals are involved. This argument will apply also to homonuclear molecules, *e.g.* Cl_2, when the inner shells of electrons of both atoms have identical energies, since the extent of the overlap of the inner orbitals will be very small and their contribution to the bonding energy negligible. We may therefore conclude that only the electrons of the outer shell, *i.e.* the valency electrons, combine to give molecular orbitals and all other electrons possess non-bonding atomic character.

Turning now to the problem of the hydrogen molecule ion and applying the principles outlined above, we may consider the formation of the molecular orbital in the following manner. When the distance between the nuclei is great, the electron will be represented by the atomic orbital ψ_a; as the nuclei approach the electron may be found at either of the nuclei, a or b. This process of exchange must be regarded as the first step in the formation of the molecular orbital. Neglecting the deformation of the atomic orbitals, we may combine the wave functions to give the molecular orbital,

$$\Psi = \psi_{(a:1s)} + c\psi_{(b:1s)} \qquad \ldots.(7.1)$$

where c is a constant. Such a wave function is interpreted on the basis of quantum theory by regarding the relative probabilities of $\psi_{(a:1s)}$ and $\psi_{(b:1s)}$ as being in the ratio $1^2 : c^2$. Since we are dealing with a homonuclear atom the electron must be equally divided between the nuclei a and b, so that $c^2 = 1$, and there are two possible linear combinations of the atomic orbitals[6] to be considered *viz*,

$$\Psi_g = \psi_{(a:1s)} + \psi_{(b:1s)} \qquad \ldots.(7.2)$$

$$\Psi_u = \psi_{(a:1s)} - \psi_{(b:1s)} \qquad \ldots.(7.3)$$

The subscripts of g and u refer to *gerade* (even) and *ungerade* (odd). When the two nuclei are different as in hydrogen chloride, symmetry no longer exists and separation into g and u orbitals is not possible.

The densities of the electron clouds may be obtained from equations 7.2 and 7.3 and are:

$$\Psi_g^2 = \psi^2_{(a:1s)} + \psi^2_{(b:1s)} + 2\psi_{(a:1s)}\,\psi_{(b:1s)} \qquad \ldots.(7.4)$$

$$\Psi_u^2 = \psi^2_{(a:1s)} + \psi^2_{(b:1s)} - 2\psi_{(a:1s)}\,\psi_{(b:1s)} \qquad \ldots.(7.5)$$

In the first case, to the electron cloud densities of the two atoms is added the cloud density, $2\psi_{(a:1s)}\,\psi_{(b:1s)}$, of the transition structure corresponding to the electron being in the field of both nuclei. As a consequence of this the density of the electron cloud between the nuclei is increased, the nuclei are drawn together and there is an increase of energy. Such an orbital Ψ_g is therefore a bonding orbital. In the second case (equation 7.5) the density of the transition structure is deducted, and the electron is drawn away from the region between the nuclei and, as a result, bonding does not occur. The orbital Ψ_u, is therefore an antibonding orbital.

The transfer of an electron from the atomic orbital to an antibonding orbital involves the loss of energy and therefore the electron will occupy such an orbital only when the bonding orbital is already filled by the two electrons permitted by the Pauli principle. When, however, an electron does exist in an antibonding orbital, it will always tend to return to an atomic orbital and will therefore lower the stability of the molecule. Thus there are two types of molecular orbital, the bonding orbital, in which the electron is located at a lower energy level than in the atom, and the antibonding, in which the electron is in a higher energy state. Each combination of two atomic orbitals will produce two such molecular orbitals. This conception of bonding and antibonding orbitals is fundamental in the molecular orbital treatment as will be seen in the next section where it is applied to simple diatomic molecules. Although the orbitals Ψ_g and Ψ_u have been obtained by the combination of uncorrected atomic orbitals, the division of the molecular orbitals into bonding and antibonding orbitals would still be retained even if it were possible to allow for the distortion of the atomic orbitals which must occur.

The formation of a molecular orbital may be pictured as occurring in another way, in which the nuclei are brought together and imagined to coalesce into a single nucleus. This important idea[7], known as the 'united atom viewpoint', permits a characterization of the molecular orbitals to be made in terms of quantum numbers by analogy to atomic orbitals. An electron moving in a field of central symmetry is described by four quantum numbers n, l, m and s, three of which, *viz*, n, l and m are orbital quantum numbers. In the case of the united atom there will be no difference between the significance of the principal quantum number n, and of the azimuthal quantum number l, compared with a normal atom. If the united atom now divides into the constituent atoms in such a way that the internuclear distance is still very small, the quantum numbers n and l will still be defined as before, but there is a change in the significance of m. In a free atom, m determines the component of the orbital angular momentum of the electron on an arbitrary axis, such as the direction of an applied magnetic field, which has the value $m(h/2\pi)$. In a diatomic molecule, the axis is no longer arbitrary but is the line joining the two nuclei and in this case it is customary to replace m by a new symbol, λ. Thus $\lambda(h/2\pi)$ represents the component of the orbital angular momentum of the electron about the internuclear axis.

The possible values of n are 1, 2, 3, . . . and l may have any value from 0 to $n - 1$. The values of λ, as for m, are $-l, -l+1, \ldots 0, \ldots +l-1, +l$. Only the absolute value of λ is usually of importance since the state with $\lambda = +1$, for example, is of the same energy as that for which $\lambda = -1$; thus the $\lambda = 1$ state is doubly degenerate. If the molecule rotates about an axis perpendicular to the line of centres, the difference between the states described by positive and negative values of λ becomes manifest. This is of importance in the interpretation of the spectra of diatomic molecules, but not in the present discussion. Molecular orbitals with $\lambda = 0$ are termed σ orbitals; with $\lambda = \pm 1$, π orbitals and with $\lambda = \pm 2$, δ orbitals, *etc*. For each value of λ there will be, as we have shown, a bonding and an antibonding orbital and it is customary to represent these as σ and σ^*; π and π^*, *etc* orbitals respectively.

The number of electrons which may exist in each orbital is restricted by Pauli's principle. Thus in each of the σ and σ^* states there may be two electrons; in each of the π and π^* states there may be four electrons, two in the orbital for which $\lambda = +1$ and two for the case when $\lambda = -1$. Similarly, the remaining states: δ and δ^* with $\lambda = \pm 2$, φ and φ^* with $\lambda = \pm 3$, *etc*, there will be four electrons in each state, whether bonding or antibonding.

The molecular orbitals are formed by the combination of atomic orbitals and the electronic states in the constituent atoms will determine the resultant electronic state, *i.e.* the value of λ, in the molecule. Thus in the case of the hydrogen molecule ion the electron is in the 1*s* state in the atom and the molecular orbital that is formed is denoted by $\sigma 1s$ for the bonding orbital and $\sigma^* 1s$ for the antibonding orbital. These orbitals may be represented schematically[1] and are shown in *Figure 25* where the increase and decrease

Figure 25. Schematic Representation of the Formation of Bonding and Antibonding Molecular Orbitals: σ and σ^* and π and π^*

Atomic orbitals / *Molecular orbitals*	*Wave function*	*Symbol*
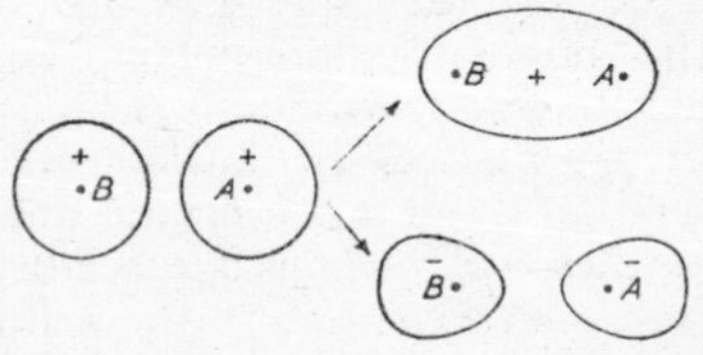	$\Psi_g = \psi_{(a:1s)} + \psi_{(b:1s)}$	$\sigma 1s$
	$\Psi_u = \psi_{(a:1s)} - \psi_{(b:1s)}$	$\sigma^* 1s$
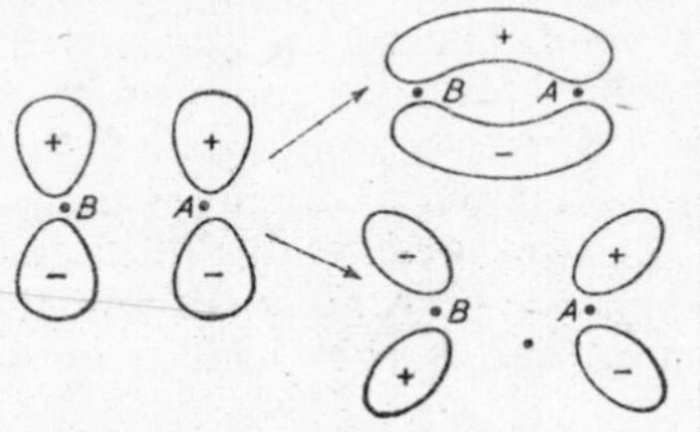	$\Psi_u = \psi_{(a:2p_z)} + \psi_{(b:2p_z)}$	$\pi_z 2p$
	$\Psi_g = \psi_{(a:2p_z)} - \psi_{(b:2p_z)}$	$\pi_z^* 2p$

of the electron density between the nuclei in bonding and anti-bonding orbitals are clearly shown. In the ground state, the hydrogen molecule will have two electrons in this orbital and will therefore be denoted by $(\sigma 1s)^2$. For the combination of p orbitals ($l = 1$) two different types of molecular orbitals will be formed corresponding to the two possible values of λ (0 and ± 1). When $\lambda = 0$ (for example, produced by the combination of two p_x atomic orbitals) we shall have a σ orbital which will be denoted by σp and $\sigma^* p$, which will be similar to the σs and $\sigma^* s$ orbitals respectively. When $\lambda = \pm 1$, however, a new type of molecular orbital, produced by the combination of two p_y or two p_z atomic orbitals, is produced. The general shape of the p_y and p_z atomic orbitals is a figure eight, which, in the constituent atoms, will be at right angles to the line of centres and it will be readily seen that the combination of two such orbitals will produce a new type of orbital (see *Figure 25*) in which there is no symmetry around the line of centres.

The molecular orbital consists of two parts in which Ψ has different signs. For the bonding molecular orbital it is denoted as πp and for the antibonding molecular orbital as $\pi^* p$. Examples of the notation of molecular orbitals formed from different pairs of atomic orbitals are given in *Table XXVII* in which an abbreviated notation due to MULLIAN[8] is also given. The advantages of this notation are that it may be applied to heteronuclear molecules where a molecular orbital may be formed by the combination of atomic orbitals of different atomic shells, *e.g.* H(1*s*) and Cl($3p_x$) in HCl, and it reduces the emphasis laid on the assumption that, for example, the $\sigma 2s$ molecular orbital is entirely composed of atomic 2*s* orbitals. The main disadvantage, apart from the confusion which may arise from the use of the symbols $x, y, z, \ldots$ which have no relation whatever with the Cartesian coordinates, lies in the fact that Mullikan's notation disguises the pictorial relationship between the atomic orbitals of the constituent atoms and the molecular orbital.

Table XXVII. Molecular Orbitals of Homonuclear Molecules

Atomic orbitals	Molecular orbitals		Number of electrons in molecular orbitals
	Full notation	Abbreviated notation	
1*s*, 1*s*	$(\sigma 1s)^2$ $(\sigma^* 1s)^2$	— —	4
2*s*, 2*s*	$(\sigma 2s)^2$ $(\sigma^* 2s)^2$	$z\sigma$ $y\sigma$	4
$2p_x, 2p_x$	$(\sigma 2p)^2$ $(\sigma^* 2p)^2$	$x\sigma$ $u\sigma$	12
$2p_y, 2p_y$ or $2p_z, 2p_z$	$(\pi y 2p)^2 = (\pi z 2p)^2$ $(\pi y^* 2p)^2 = (\pi z^* 2p)^2$	$w\pi$ $v\pi$	

The electronic states of homonuclear diatomic molecules may now be built up by feeding the electrons into the various orbitals, provided that the relative order of molecular orbital energies is known. This has been determined by MULLIKAN[8] from molecular spectra data and is generally found to be :

Full notation:

$$\sigma 1s < \sigma^* 1s < \sigma 2s < \sigma^* 2s < \sigma 2p < \pi_y 2p = \pi_z 2p < \pi_y^* 2p = \pi_z^* 2p < \sigma^* 2p$$

Mullikan's notation :

$$z\sigma < y\sigma < x\sigma < \quad w\pi \quad < \quad v\pi \quad < u\sigma$$

DISTRIBUTION OF ELECTRONS IN HOMONUCLEAR DIATOMIC MOLECULES

H_2^+— When the hydrogen molecule ion is formed from a normal hydrogen atom and a proton, the 1*s* electron is transferred to the lowest bonding σ orbital denoted by the function, $\Psi_g = \psi_{(a:1s)} + \psi_{(b:1s)}$. This may be represented by the equation

$$H(1s) + H^+ = H_2^+(\sigma 1s)$$

H_2— Each atom of hydrogen in the ground state has a single 1*s* electron. If the spins of two atoms are antiparallel they may both occupy the same molecular orbital :

$$H(1s)\downarrow + H(1s)\uparrow = H_2(\sigma 1s)^2$$

If the spins of the electrons of the two atoms are parallel, then only one electron, according to the Pauli principle, may exist in the lowest bonding orbital, the second electron being transferred to the higher energy antibonding σ^*1s orbital denoted by the function $\Psi_u = \psi_{(a:1s)} - \psi_{(b:1s)}$. The reason why the atom is transferred to an antibonding orbital when there exist other bonding orbitals lies in the fact that the latter do not correspond to the ground state of the H_2 molecule but to excited states. Thus we may write

$$H(1s)\uparrow + H(1s)\uparrow = H_2(\sigma 1s)(\sigma^* 1s)$$

The antibonding power of the $\sigma^* 1s$ orbital cancels the bonding power of the $\sigma 1s$ orbital, with the result that no bonding occurs. An attempt to substantiate this argument theoretically has been made by PENIN using the Heitler-London method. The normalized wave functions of the bonding and antibonding orbitals are, according to equations 3.47 and 3.48 :

$$\Psi_g = (\psi_a + \psi_b)/(2 + 2S)^{\frac{1}{2}} ; \; \Psi_u = (\psi_a - \psi_b)/(2 - 2S)^{\frac{1}{2}}$$

and the density of the resultant electron cloud will be given by,

$$\Psi^2 = \Psi_g^2 + \Psi_u^2 = (\psi_a^2 + \psi_b^2 - 2\psi_a\psi_b S)/(1 - S^2)$$

Since the transitional structure term, $2\psi_a\psi_b S$, has a negative sign, the electrons will be drawn away from the region between the atoms and repulsion occurs.

He_2^+—This molecule may be formed by the combination of an helium atom, possessing two electrons in the $1s$ orbital, with an He^+ ion, having one electron in the $1s$ orbital. In the molecule, two of these electrons with opposite spins will occupy the lowest bonding orbital, $\sigma 1s$, whilst the third electron will occupy the antibonding orbital $\sigma^* 1s$, which is the orbital next in the energy sequence. Thus we may write

$$He\,(1s^2) + He^+(1s) = He_2^+(\sigma 1s)^2(\sigma^* 1s)$$

The presence of the electron in the antibonding orbital lowers the stability of the molecule, the occurrence of which may only be detected by spectroscopic means.

He_2—The formation of this molecule may be represented in a similar manner to that used for the He_2^+ ion,

$$2He\,(1s^2) = He_2\,(\sigma 1s)^2(\sigma^* 1s)^2$$

In this case the antibonding power of the $(\sigma^* 1s)^2$ orbital cancels the bonding power of the $(\sigma 1s)^2$ orbital with the well known result that the molecule is not formed.

Li_2—Each atom of lithium has three electrons, two $1s$ and one $2s$. However, we have shown above that the inner orbitals do not take part in bond formation and retain their atomic character in the molecule and only the electrons in the outermost shell need be considered in the formation of the molecular orbital. The two valence electrons in Li_2 will occupy the $\sigma 2s$ or in the abbreviated terminology, the $z\sigma$ molecular orbital.

$$2Li\,(1s^2 2s) = Li_2\,[KK(\sigma 2s)^2]$$

The notation *KK* infers that the two *K* shells of the atoms are filled by non-valence electrons.

N_2—The electron configuration of the nitrogen atom is $1s^2 2s^2 2p^3$; of these the $1s^2$, *i.e.* the *K* shell, will not take part in the formation of a molecular orbital. The remaining electrons, *viz*, $2s^2$ and $2p^3$ will all exist in molecular orbitals and hence contribute to the bonding of the atoms in the molecule. In this fact lies one of the main differences between the molecular orbital treatment and the method of localized pairs, *i.e.* the Heitler, London, Slater and Pauling method, which only regards the three $2p$ electrons as bonding electrons. The result, however, is the same for both

methods as may be shown as follows. The formation of the nitrogen molecule from two nitrogen atoms may be represented by :

$$2N\ (1s^2 2s^2 2p^3) = N_2\ [KK(z\sigma)^2(y\sigma)^2(x\sigma)^2(w\pi)^4]$$

The bonding power of the $(x\sigma)^2$ orbital may be regarded as being cancelled by the antibonding power of the $(y\sigma)^2$ orbital with the result that the bonding is in effect due to the $(x\sigma)^2$ and $(w\pi)^4$ orbitals. This will correspond to a σ bond and two π bonds at right angles to each other, and as six electrons are involved in the bonding, we may term this a triple bond. The conclusion as to the number and types of bonds involved is thus the same as in the electron pair method.

O_2—The atom of oxygen contains one more electron than the nitrogen atom, its configuration being $1s^2 2s^2 2p^4$. On the basis of the electron pair theory it would be expected that the bond between two oxygen atoms would be formed by the two unpaired p electrons which would therefore give rise to a σ and a π bond. Spectroscopic data, however, show that the oxygen molecule has two unpaired electrons and is therefore strongly paramagnetic. These facts cannot be explained by the theory of electron pairs. Application of the molecular orbital treatment leads to the following electron configuration

$$2O\ (1s^2 2s^2 2p^4) = O_2\ [KK(z\sigma)^2(y\sigma)^2(x\sigma)^2(w\pi)^4(v\pi)^2]$$

The bonding $(z\sigma)^2$ is cancelled by the antibonding $(y\sigma)^2$ orbital and the antibonding $(v\pi)^2$ cancels one of the bonding $(w\pi^4)$ orbitals, which is a degenerate state owing to the equivalence of the $\pi_y 2p$ and $\pi_z 2p$ orbitals. The atoms are therefore bonded by a σ and a π bond involving four electrons which may be termed a double bond. The important point about the molecule as represented by the above electron configuration is that two electrons occur in the $v\pi$ or $\pi^* 2p$ molecular orbital. On account of the degeneracy between the π_y and π_z states, this orbital will accommodate four electrons and may be regarded as made up of two orbitals, the $\pi_y^* 2p$ and the $\pi_z^* 2p$ which may each accommodate two electrons. Since only two electrons occur in this state in the oxygen molecule, according to Hund's law (page 24), one will go into each of the $\pi_y^* 2p$ and $\pi_z^* 2p$ orbitals and will have parallel spins. The observed facts regarding the oxygen molecule are thus completely explained.

F_2—In the fluorine molecule there are, in comparison with O_2, two additional electrons, which will fill the $v\pi$ orbital. All electron spins are thus paired and the molecule is not paramagnetic.

$$2F\ (1s^2 2s^2 2p^5) = F_2\ [KK(z\sigma)^2(y\sigma)^2(x\sigma)^2(w\pi)^4(v\pi)^4]$$

The $(z\sigma)^2$ and $(y\sigma)^2$ orbitals practically cancel as do the $(w\pi)^4$ and $(v\pi)^4$ since they are bonding and antibonding respectively. Thus the bond is effectively due to the $(x\sigma)^2$ orbital and as only two electrons take part, it is a single bond.

Ne_2—The electron configuration of the neon atom is $(1s^2 2s^2 2p^6)$, the L shell thus being completely filled. The configuration of the molecule would therefore be :

$$2Ne\ (1s^2 2s^2 2p^6) = Ne_2\ [KK(z\sigma)^2(y\sigma)^2(x\sigma)^2(w\pi)^4(v\pi)^4(u\sigma)^2]$$

Here in addition to the cancellation of the bonding $(z\sigma)^2$ and $(w\pi)^4$ orbitals by the antibonding $(y\sigma)^2$ and $(v\pi)^4$ orbitals as in F_2, the $(x\sigma)^2$ is cancelled by the $(u\sigma)^2$ orbital and molecule formation does not occur.

A similar representation may be made for the homonuclear diatomic molecules occurring amongst elements of the third period, *e.g.* Na_2.

DISTRIBUTION OF ELECTRONS IN HETERONUCLEAR DIATOMIC MOLECULES

When a heteronuclear diatomic molecule is formed, the same principles as those discussed in the previous section may be applied. The criterion that the atomic orbitals, which combine to give a molecular orbital, must have nearly equal energies[5], implies that only the outermost shell of electrons of each atom is involved (see page 129) and these for two different atoms will not generally be in the same electronic state. The two atomic orbitals, however, must have the same component of angular momentum, *i.e.* value of the quantum number m, in the direction of the bond axis. In the following discussion we shall denote by p_x a p orbital having the value $m = 0$, the p_y and p_z orbitals will have the values $m = \pm 1$. The x axis will thus be considered as lying along the line of centres of the nuclei. Thus for the bonding electrons of hydrogen chloride, which will be compounded from $\psi_{(H:1s)}$ and $\psi_{(Cl:3p_x)}$, the molecular orbital, by analogy with equation 7.1 is,

$$\Psi = \psi_{(H:1s)} + c\psi_{(Cl:3p_x)} \quad \ldots.(7.6)$$

The constant c no longer satisfies the relationship $c^2 = 1^2$, since the atoms are not identical, and has to be calculated. However, there will still be two values of c, as in equations 7.2 and 7.3, corresponding to a bonding and an antibonding orbital. These orbitals may be termed the $\sigma 3p$ and $\sigma^* 3p$ respectively. The shape of the resulting molecular orbital will depend on the value of c; if $c > 1$, then there is a greater contribution from the chlorine atomic orbital than from the hydrogen atomic orbital. This is what happens in the case of hydrogen chloride as is well known, since the electronegative character of chlorine, compared with hydrogen, attracts the valency electrons towards the chlorine atom.

The electronic configuration of the hydrogen chloride molecule may be represented as,

$$H\ (1s) + Cl\ (1s^2 2s^2 2p^6 3s^2 3p^5) = HCl\ [KL(3s)^2(\sigma 3p)^2(3p_y)^2(3p_z)^2]$$

It will be clear that only the $\sigma 3p$ orbital is molecular in character, the $3s$, $3p_y$ and $3p_z$ being mainly atomic. The K and L represent the K and L shells of chlorine which remain entirely atomic.

In many cases the molecular orbitals for a heteronuclear diatomic molecule may be worked out in a straightforward manner as for hydrogen chloride. In others, however, certain difficulties arise and we shall take as an example the case of carbon monoxide, the structure of which has been the subject of much controversy. In carbon monoxide, as in the nitrogen molecule, there are fourteen valency electrons and Mullikan[9] has formulated the structure of both molecules as

$$N_2, CO: [KK(z\sigma)^2(y\sigma)^2(x\sigma)^2(w\pi)^4]$$

in which there are four bonding orbitals: $z\sigma$, $x\sigma$, and $w\pi$ which is doubly degenerate, and one antibonding orbital $y\sigma$. The resultant structure is therefore approximately a triple bond. In order to substantiate this similarity of electronic configuration in molecules possessing the same number of electrons (isoelectronic molecules), attention has frequently been directed towards the similarity that exists between certain physical properties, notably the boiling point, critical constants, interatomic distance, solubility *etc* of these molecules, *Table XXVIII.* LONG and WALSH[10] consider,

Table XXVIII. Physical Properties of Isoelectronic Molecules

Electronic configuration	$(z\sigma)^2(y\sigma)^2(x\sigma)^2(w\pi)^4$		$(z\sigma)^2(y\sigma)^2(x\sigma)(w\pi)^4$			$(z\sigma)^2(y\sigma)^2(w\pi)^4(v\pi)$	
Molecules	N_2	CO	CN	$(CO)^+$	N_2^+	NO	O_2^+
Ionization potential (kcals)	359	324	322	—	—	219	—
Excitation potential (kcals)	140*	138*	—	—	—	—	—
Polarizability (Å³) ..	1·76	1·96	—	—	—	—	—
Internuclear distance (Å) ..	1·09	1·13	1·17	1·11	1·12	1·15	1·12
Frequency of vibration (cm^{-1})	2,360	2,168	2,069	2,211	2,207	2,211	1,876
Dissociation energy (kcals) ..	225·1	256·1	175	189	201·3	150	149
Melting point (°K) ..	63	66	—	—	—	—	—
Boiling point (°K)	78	83	—	—	—	—	—
Critical temperature (°K) ..	127	133	—	—	—	—	—
Critical pressure (atm.) ..	33	35	—	—	—	—	—
Density in liquid state ..	0·796	0·793	—	—	—	—	—

* As these values correspond to the transfer of N_2 and CO from the ground state to different excited states: $(z\sigma)^2(y\sigma)^2(x\sigma)^2(w\pi)^3(v\pi)$ for N_2 and $(z\sigma)^2(y\sigma)^2(x\sigma)(w\pi)^4(v\pi)$ for CO, no great significance can be given to their similarity

however, that this argument is not logical, since many of the properties cited infer similar molecular volumes and similar external fields of force rather than similar electronic arrangements. Furthermore, these authors point to the fact that the molecules of nitrogen and carbon monoxide differ in a very significant way. When the nitrogen molecule ionizes to give N_2^+, the bond is weakened, as shown by the increase in the interatomic distance and the decrease of the vibrational frequency, *Table XXVIII.* On the other hand, when the carbon monoxide molecule ionizes to give $(CO)^+$, the interatomic distance decreases and the frequency of vibration increases, thus showing an increase in the strength of the bond. These data are only understandable if, unlike the nitrogen molecule, carbon monoxide contains a double bond and forms on ionization, a third bond. On ionization the nitrogen molecule reverts from a triple to a double bonded structure. Long and Walsh derive a molecular orbital description of carbon monoxide which approximates to a double rather than a triple bond in the following way. It is imagined that the two atoms are brought together without interaction and the molecular orbital is then gradually formed. Thus we start with

$$\mathrm{C}: 1s^2 2s^2 2p_x 2p_y$$
$$\mathrm{O}: 1s^2 2s^2 2p_x 2p_y 2p_z^2$$

where the carbon atom is in the state in which it occurs on the dissociation of carbon monoxide, and we proceed to form the molecular orbitals, the x axis being in the direction of the line of centres. The $1s$ orbital (K shell) will remain unaffected whereas the $2s$ electrons will fill the $z\sigma$ and $y\sigma$ orbitals, which will largely cancel each other. The $2p_x$ electron of carbon interacts with the $2p_x$ electron of oxygen to form a $x\sigma$ orbital and the $2p_y$ electrons of carbon and oxygen may now interact to form a $w\pi$ orbital. The two p_z electrons of oxygen remain and will show a small drift towards the $2p_z$ atomic orbital of carbon by occupying a molecular orbital of the form $c\psi_{(\mathrm{C}:2p_z)} + \psi_{(\mathrm{O}:2p_z)}$. The semipolar or coordinate bond denoted by the arrow in the formula $\mathrm{C} \overset{\leftarrow}{=} \mathrm{O}$, which is sometimes employed to describe carbon monoxide, implies that $c = 1$. There is nothing in the molecular orbital treatment to indicate that this is so and spectroscopic data[10] suggests that the factor c is very small.

The case of nitric oxide is more straightforward and the formation of the molecular orbital may be represented as,

$$\mathrm{N}\ (1s^2 2s^2 2p^3) + \mathrm{O}\ (1s^2 2s^2 2p^4) = \mathrm{NO}\ [KK(z\sigma)^2(y\sigma)^2(x\sigma)^2(w\pi)^4(v\pi)]$$

The $(z\sigma)^2$, $(x\sigma)^2$ and the doubly degenerate $(w\pi)^4$ orbitals are bonding, whereas the $(y\sigma)^2$ and $(v\pi)$ are antibonding. There is thus a predominance of bonding over antibonding orbitals and a stable molecule is formed. The single electron in the antibonding $v\pi$ orbital is responsible for the reactivity and paramagnetism of this molecule.

THE THREE ELECTRON BOND

The introduction of the idea of a three electron bond was an attempt to explain the existence of molecules with unpaired electrons within the framework of the Heitler-London treatment. According to Pauling[11] the bond in He_2^+ occurs by the superposition of the two forms :

$$\underset{a}{\mathrm{He}:} \quad \underset{b}{\cdot\,\mathrm{He}^+}$$

$$\underset{a}{\mathrm{He}\,\cdot^+} \quad \underset{b}{:\mathrm{He}}$$

where the dots represent electrons. Calculation has shown that such resonance leads to a value for the bond energy which is in satisfactory agreement with experiment. In the helium atom both electrons are paired and the atom is chemically inert, but the approach of a helium ion makes possible a gain in energy due to the resonance between the two structures. This method has been extended to other molecules containing unpaired electrons (NO, O_2, ClO, ClO_2 *etc*) and the bond in oxygen, for example, is represented as a resonance between the forms :

$$:\underset{\cdot}{\ddot{\mathrm{O}}} - \underset{\cdot\cdot}{\dot{\mathrm{O}}}: \qquad :\underset{\cdot\cdot}{\dot{\mathrm{O}}} - \underset{\cdot}{\ddot{\mathrm{O}}}:$$

i.e. by one normal covalent bond and two three electron bonds. This is more usually represented by

$$:\mathrm{O}\overset{\cdots}{\underset{\cdots}{-}}\mathrm{O}:$$

In a similar manner the nitric oxide molecule may be represented by resonance between the two forms :

$$:\dot{\mathrm{N}} = \ddot{\mathrm{O}}: \qquad :\ddot{\mathrm{N}} = \dot{\mathrm{O}}:$$

or by the more usual formula

$$:\mathrm{N}\overset{\cdots}{=}\mathrm{O}:$$

I

A comparison of this structure with the electronic configuration according to the molecular orbital treatment brings out an important similarity. The molecular orbitals of nitric oxide are

$$\mathrm{NO}\ [KK(z\sigma)^2(y\sigma)^2(x\sigma)^2(w\pi)^4(v\pi)]$$

Since the $(z\sigma)^2$ and $(y\sigma)^2$ orbitals cancel, these four electrons take no part in the bond and will be represented by the two electrons shown to the left of the nitrogen and two to the right of the oxygen in structure *I*. Of the remaining three orbitals, the $(x\sigma)^2$ and $(w\pi)^4$ (doubly degenerate) are bonding and completely filled, and the $v\pi$ orbital is antibonding and contains only a single electron. The number of bonds will thus be approximately two and a half, in agreement with the calculations of Pauling[11] which show that the three electron bond has half the strength of an ordinary single bond. We thus see that the same conclusion is reached by the two methods, which are simply alternative ways of describing the same idea.

MOLECULAR ORBITALS OF SIMPLE POLYATOMIC MOLECULES

The application of the molecular orbital theory to polyatomic molecules meets certain difficulties which may be overcome only by assuming the existence of localized molecular orbitals. This may best be shown by considering an example. If we apply the principles developed at the beginning of this chapter to the case of the molecule of methane, we conclude that, of the ten electrons of methane, two occupy the *K* shell of carbon and the remaining eight occupy molecular orbitals embracing all five nuclei. Such a treatment does not explain why the characteristic properties of the C—H bond should remain effectively the same in a variety of different molecules, although it does predict a tetrahedral structure for the methane molecule[12]. This difficulty has been overcome (see for example Coulson[1]) by employing localized molecular orbitals, in which it is supposed that each single bond is due to two electrons of opposite spins in a molecular orbital almost completely localized between the two nuclei. Such a modification of the molecular orbital theory produces a similarity with the localized electron pair theory of Heitler, London, Pauling and Slater, but with the important difference that the molecular orbital treatment does not lead to the idea of a resonance between different valence bond structures.

The idea of a localized molecular orbital may be illustrated by the water molecule. The atomic orbitals available for the formation of molecular orbitals are the $2p_x$ and $2p_y$ of oxygen and the two $1s$ of the two hydrogen atoms, which we shall call H_a and H_b. The angle between the $2p_x$ and $2p_y$ orbitals of oxygen is 90° and the maximum overlap between these orbitals and those of the hydrogen atoms will occur in the directions of the $2p_x$ and $2p_y$ orbitals of oxygen. The two molecular orbitals produced will have the form: $\Psi_1 = \psi_{(H_a)} + c\psi_{(O:2p_x)}$ and $\Psi_2 = \psi_{(H_b)} + c\psi_{(O:2p_y)}$ and are quite independent of each other. The replacement of the atom H_b by some other group will change Ψ_2 but have little effect on Ψ_1, thus we see that this treatment leads to the conclusion that the electrons in a particular bond have characteristic wave functions. As pointed out earlier the coefficient c determines the polarity of the orbit and it is therefore unnecessary to consider the bond as a superposition of the pure covalent wave function $\Psi_{(O-H)}$ and the pure ionic wave function $\Psi_{(O^-H^+)}$ which is necessary in the resonance treatment.

The theory of localized molecular orbitals, although most successful when applied to the ground states of molecules containing not more than one double bond, ceases to be correct for excited states and for systems containing conjugated double bonds. The first of these cases may be illustrated by considering methane. If one of the electrons be excited, it is impossible to predict in which localized molecular orbital it will occur and it is necessary to allow for the possibility of the excited electron being at any of the five nuclei and this can only be done in terms of non-localized molecular orbitals.

The second situation referred to above, *viz* systems containing conjugated double bonds, is perhaps more important to the present discussion. The classical example of such a system is benzene. The molecular orbital treatment regards the six C—C bonds and the six C—H bonds as completely localized molecular orbitals compounded out of carbon sp^2 hybrid atomic orbitals and the hydrogen s orbital. So far the treatment is identical with the electron pair theory, discussed in Chapter 4. The C—C bonds will be σ bonds formed by the overlap of two sp^2 hybrid atomic orbitals, one from each carbon atom and the C—H bonds will also be σ bonds formed by the overlap of one sp^2 hybrid atomic orbital of carbon with the s atomic orbital of hydrogen. The six carbon $2p_z$ atomic orbitals that remain will form completely non-localized molecular orbitals. Thus each $2p_z$ electron will be regarded as existing in the field of six nuclei and will possess a wave function of the form :

$$\Psi = c_1\psi_1 + c_2\psi_2 + c_3\psi_3 + c_4\psi_4 + c_5\psi_5 + c_6\psi_6 \qquad \ldots.(7.7)$$

where ψ_1 is the atomic orbital at nucleus 1, ψ_2 that at nucleus 2, *etc* and the coefficients c_1, c_2, *etc* are related to the probabilities of the electron being at any particular nucleus. As there are six $2p_z$ electrons, there will be six distinct molecular orbitals of the form of equation 7.7. Of these, HÜCKEL[13] and COULSON[14] have shown that three are bonding and three antibonding orbitals and in the normal state of benzene the six electrons will be distributed amongst the three bonding orbitals. The most stable of these is the orbital

$$\Psi = \psi_1 + \psi_2 + \psi_3 + \psi_4 + \psi_5 + \psi_6 \qquad \ldots.(7.8)$$

in which the two electrons may be imagined as 'swarming' round all the nuclei, thus bonding them together. There is a distinct similarity between the delocalized electrons of such a molecule as benzene and the conduction electrons of a metal, and any electrical influence in one part of the system is easily propagated to any other part, thus forming the basis for a theory of directional substitution in conjugated compounds.

From the foregoing discussion we may conclude that the main difference between the π bonds of benzene, or any other conjugated system, and a lone π bond, is that the two electrons forming the localized π bond is situated in the field of two nuclei, whereas in benzene each of the six electrons exist in the field of six nuclei. The fact that the electrons in benzene have a greater space in which to move will result in a lower total energy, *i.e.* a greater binding energy, than when paired in localized bonds. This energy which could be termed the 'delocalization energy' (Coulson[1]), is identical with the resonance energy of the valence-bond treatment.

In the molecule of butadiene four non-localized electrons exist in the field of four nuclei and HÜCKEL[13] has shown that of the four possible molecular orbitals, two are bonding and two antibonding. Of the two bonding orbitals the first, *i.e.* the more stable, draws all four nuclei together whereas the second bonds together nuclei 1 and 2, and 3 and 4, more strongly than the two nuclei 2 and 3. Thus calculations[15] predict correctly, that the links in butadiene alternate in length, the two outermost links being the shorter.

COMPARISON OF THE ELECTRON PAIR AND MOLECULAR ORBITAL TREATMENTS

The essential feature of the molecular orbital method is the complete freedom of movement of the electrons in the molecular orbitals. This means that one electron has no influence on the location of another electron and hence the probability of finding simultaneously one electron at a point x_1, y_1, z_1 and another at the point x_2, y_2, z_2 will be the product of the independent probabilities. For two electrons this will be :

$$\psi^2(x_1y_1z_1, x_2y_2z_2) = \psi^2(x_1y_1z_1)\psi^2(x_2y_2z_2) \qquad \ldots.(7.9)$$

Therefore the wave function describing the state of a molecule will be the product of the functions of the separate atoms. If we now apply this conclusion to the atom of hydrogen in which two electrons are located in the molecular orbital $\psi_a + \psi_b$ (see equation 7.2 ; we must of course consider the bonding orbital). The state of the molecule will therefore be described by the function,

$$\psi = [\psi_a(1) + \psi_b(1)][\psi_a(2) + \psi_b(2)] \qquad \ldots.(7.10)$$

which implies that both electrons are quite independent and may both be at nucleus *a* or nucleus *b*. Expanding equation 7.10 we obtain :

$$\psi = \psi_a(1)\psi_b(2) + \psi_b(1)\psi_a(2) + \psi_a(1)\psi_a(2) + \psi_b(1)\psi_b(2) \qquad \ldots.(7.11)$$

The first two terms represent the two electrons as being one at nucleus *a* and the other at nucleus *b* ; the third term describes the ionic state where both electrons are at nucleus *a*, *viz* $H_a^- H_b^+$ and the fourth term represents the alternative and equally probable ionic state where both electrons are at nucleus *b*, *viz* $H_a^+ H_b^-$. Let us compare this expression, with that obtained for H_2 by the Heitler-London method. This is

$$\psi = \psi_a(1)\psi_b(2) + \psi_b(1)\psi_a(2) \qquad \ldots.(6.19)$$

and is identical with the first two terms of the molecular orbital expression. In the application of the Heitler-London method it was found that corrections were necessary to account for the contribution of the ionic terms which are not represented in equation 6.19. On the other hand, the molecular orbital treatment leads to the other extreme and over emphasizes the ionic terms which are given the same weight as the homopolar terms. This is due to the fact that the mutual repulsion of the electrons has been ignored in obtaining equation 7.9 and this repulsion will considerably decrease the probability of finding both electrons on the same nucleus.

For heteronuclear molecules a similar result is obtained employing the expression

$$\Psi = \psi_a + c\psi_b \qquad \ldots.(7.6)$$

in place of equation 7.2. The wave function for the molecule then becomes,

$$\begin{aligned}\psi &= [\psi_a(1) + c\psi_b(1)][\psi_a(2) + c\psi_b(2)] \\ &= c[\psi_a(1)\psi_b(2) + \psi_b(1)\psi_a(2)] + \psi_a(1)\psi_a(2) + c^2\psi_b(1)\psi_b(2)\end{aligned} \qquad \ldots.(7.12)$$

The ratio of the contributions of the homopolar and two ionic forms being in the ratio $c : 1 : c^2$.

A more satisfactory equation than 7.12 would be

$$\psi = c_1[\psi_a(1)\psi_b(2) + \psi_b(1)\psi_a(2)] + c_2\psi_a(1)\psi_a(2) + c_3\psi_b(1)\psi_b(2) \qquad \ldots.(7.13)$$

We may thus conclude that the two methods are both approximate, being based on different limiting conditions. However, both treatments lead to a qualitative picture of the formation of a chemical bond and to the stabilization of the molecule by resonance energy. The quantitative aspect of both approaches is less satisfactory and calculations of bond energy and interatomic distance in satisfactory agreement with experiment have only been made possible by the rejection of simplifying assumptions. Neither method gives a satisfactory description of the polarity of molecules since the Heitler-London theory neglects the contribution of the ionic forms whereas these are over emphasized in the molecular orbital treatment.

The description of such molecules as He_2^+, O_2 and NO is more satisfactory by the molecular orbital method than by the Heitler-London since in the latter an additional concept, that of the three electron bond, must be introduced in order to explain the molecule and its properties. The conception of directional valency is perhaps more easily conceived by the method of localized pairs, but as already pointed out, the molecular orbital treatment of delocalized electrons also leads to the tetrahedral model of methane.

REFERENCES

[1] Van Vleck, J. H. and Sherman, A. *Rev. mod. Phys.* 7 (1935) 167
Coulson, C. A. *Quart. Rev.* 1 (1947) 144
[2] Hund, F. *Z. Phys.* 51 (1928) 759
Mullikan, R. S. *Phys. Rev.* 32 (1928) 186, 761
Herzberg, G. *Z. Phys.* 57 (1929) 601
Lennard-Jones, J. E. *Trans. Faraday Soc.* 25 (1929) 668
[3] Mullikan, R. S. *J. chem. Phys.* 3 (1935) 375
[4] Coulson, C. A. *Trans. Faraday Soc.* 33 (1937) 1479
— *Proc. Camb. phil. Soc.* 34 (1938) 204
[5] — *ibid* 33 (1937) 111
[6] Pauling, L. C. *Chem. Rev.* 5 (1928) 173
Lennard-Jones, J. E. *Trans. Faraday Soc.* 25 (1929) 668
[7] Mullikan, R. S. *Phys. Rev.* 41 (1932) 49
[8] — *Rev. mod. Phys.* 4 (1932) 40
[9] — *ibid* 4 (1932) 1
[10] Long, L. H. and Walsh, A. D. *Trans. Faraday Soc.* 43 (1947) 342
[11] Pauling, L. C. *The Nature of the Chemical Bond* Cornell, 1940
[12] Van Vleck, J. H. *J. Chem. Phys.* 1 (1933) 177, 219
[13] Hückel, E. *Z. Phys.* 70 (1931) 240
— *Z. Elektrochem* 43 (1937) 752, 827
[14] Coulson, C. A. *Proc. roy. Soc. Edinb.* 61A (1941) 115
[15] Lennard-Jones, J. E. and Coulson, C. A. *Trans. Faraday Soc.* 35 (1939) 811

8

SPECTRA OF DIATOMIC MOLECULES

GENERAL CHARACTERISTICS OF MOLECULAR SPECTRA

IN THE preceding chapters we have discussed the quantum mechanical theory of the chemical bond at the present stage of its development. Although the conclusions which have been reached are of fundamental importance, they must not be permitted to overshadow the fact that at the present time the experimental physical methods of studying molecular properties give more precise data concerning the structure of molecules. Thus spectroscopic, x-ray and electron diffraction methods and the determination of electric and magnetic moments have been developed to a stage where accurate determinations of characteristic constants of molecules, such as interatomic distance, valency angle, energies of dissociation and excitation, electric and magnetic polarization and vibrational frequencies, may be made. A description of these physical methods lies outside the scope of this work, and we shall be concerned primarily with the application of the results of such methods to chemical problems.

The interpretation of the spectra of molecules has only become possible through the application of quantum theory; previously, such relationships as were obtained, were entirely empirical and were without theoretical significance. As we have seen, atoms and molecules may exist only in certain permitted energy levels and the transition from one energy level to another is accompanied by the absorption or emission of energy, frequently in the form of light radiation. The absorption spectrum of a molecule is obtained when light possessing a continuous spectrum, *e.g.* white light, is passed through the substance, generally in the gaseous state. The frequency of the absorbed radiation ν, corresponds to a quantum of energy $h\nu$, which has been absorbed by one molecule and which has produced a transition from an energy level E_1, to an excited level E_2, so that

$$h\nu = E_2 - E_1 \qquad \ldots.(8.1)$$

If the molecule is excited, not by the absorption of radiation, but by an electric discharge or some other method, the excitation energy is emitted in the form of radiation of characteristic frequencies, as an emission spectrum.

In atoms, the energy levels correspond to different energy states of the electrons and in just the same way, the electrons in a molecule have a series of possible energy levels. Transitions between these energy levels produce the electronic molecular spectrum. The electronic states of a molecule were discussed in Chapter 7 where it was assumed that the positions of the nuclei were fixed; this, however, is not correct. In the molecule, the nuclei and the completed electronic shells round each of the nuclei, repel each other. This repulsive force, which operates at short distances, is balanced by the bonding forces due to the valency electrons. As a result of these two opposing forces the nuclei vibrate about an equilibrium position at which the repulsive force is just counterbalanced by the binding forces. In addition to this vibration of the molecule, it may also rotate about its centre of gravity.

The electrical forces acting on the nuclei and on the electrons are of the same order of magnitude, but the mass of the electrons is very much smaller than that of the nuclei and it is therefore possible when considering only electronic transitions, to regard the nuclei as fixed. This enables the electronic states of the molecule to be discussed independently of the rotational and vibrational states[1]. The vibration and rotation of a molecule take place simultaneously and interaction between these two modes of oscillation occurs, but to a first approximation it is permissible to regard both as occurring separately and thus to discuss the vibrational and rotational levels independently.

If the vibration of the two nuclei in a diatomic molecule is assumed to be harmonic, then it can be shown (see Chapter 18) that the vibrational energy is given by

$$E_n = (n + \tfrac{1}{2})h\nu \qquad \ldots.(8.2)$$

where ν is the frequency of vibration and n is an integer, termed the vibrational quantum number. The various vibrational energy levels will thus be: $E_0 = h\nu/2$, $E_1 = 3h\nu/2$, $E_2 = 5h\nu/2$, *etc.* It will be noticed that the lowest level has the value $h\nu/2$ and not zero. This energy, termed the zero-point energy, is possessed by all vibrating systems even at the absolute zero of temperature.

The rotational energy is given by,

$$E_J = J(J+1)h^2/8\pi^2 \qquad \ldots.(8.3)$$

where J is the rotational quantum number and I the moment of inertia of the molecule. For diatomic molecules with nuclear masses m_1 and m_2 and internuclear distance r,

$$I = \frac{m_1 m_2}{m_1 + m_2} r^2 \qquad \ldots.(8.4)$$

Since atomic masses are of the order of 10^{-22} to 10^{-24} gm and r^2 will be approximately 10^{-16} sq cm, the values of I will lie between 10^{-38} and 10^{-40} gm sq cm.

The energy levels of diatomic molecules are thus seen to be characterized by three quantum numbers which determine the electronic, vibrational and rotational states of the molecule. We shall now compare the relative magnitudes of the changes in energy accompanying transitions between different electronic, vibrational and rotational levels of the molecule. The relationship between the change in energy and the frequency of the emitted or absorbed radiation is given by equation 8.1 and it is general to give the frequency in terms of wave numbers rather than frequencies. The relationship between the wave number ω and the frequency ν is $\nu = c\omega$, where c is the velocity of light; ω therefore is equal to $1/\lambda$ and has the units cm^{-1}. A wave number of 1 cm^{-1} thus corresponds to a frequency of 3×10^{10} sec^{-1}, and one of 10^3 cm^{-1} to a frequency of 3×10^{13} sec^{-1}. The corresponding energy in the latter case will be $h\nu = 6{\cdot}6 \times 10^{-27} \times 3 \times 10^{13} = 19{\cdot}18 \times 10^{-14}$ ergs per molecule or calculating on the basis of a gram molecule this must be multiplied by the Avogadro number, *i.e.* $19{\cdot}18 \times 10^{-14} \times 6{\cdot}03 \times 10^{23} = 12{\cdot}3 \times 10^{10}$ ergs $= \dfrac{12{\cdot}3 \times 10^{10}}{4{\cdot}18 \times 10^{10}} = 2{\cdot}84$ kcals/gm mol or $0{\cdot}123$ ev/gm mol.

The magnitude of the electronic excitation energy in a molecule is close to that in an atom and corresponds to a frequency of the order of 10^4 cm^{-1} (visible and ultraviolet regions of the spectrum). Vibrational transitions correspond to spectral lines with frequencies of the order of 10^3 cm^{-1} (the near infra-red region) and rotational transitions to frequencies of 10 to 10^2 cm^{-1} (the far infra-red region). It thus transpires that the values of the quanta of rotational energy are much less than those of vibrational energy and during the period of a single rotation the molecule will complete many vibrations.

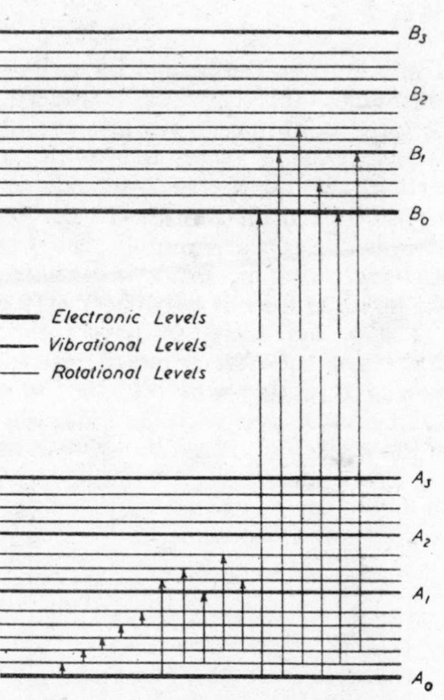

Figure 26. Energy levels of a diatomic molecule. The short arrows denote rotational changes, the medium length arrows vibrational–rotational changes, and the long arrows electronic, vibrational and rotational changes.

The bonding energy of a molecule is dependent on the electronic state of the molecule and therefore a particular equilibrium internuclear distance and a series of vibrational energy levels will exist for each electronic state. Every vibrational level is in turn accompanied by a series of rotational levels and in *Figure 26* there is shown a schematic representation of the energy levels of a diatomic molecule. Molecular spectra may thus be divided into three sections: rotational spectra, vibrational-rotational spectra, and the complete molecular spectrum produced by rotational, vibrational and electronic transitions. The first type occurs through changes in the rotational quantum number and is found to consist of a series of lines. The second type is caused by changes in the vibrational energy. Each vibrational change is accompanied by a number of rotational energy transitions which are represented in the spectrum by a number of lines situated close together, constituting a band. The vibrational-rotational spectrum of a diatomic molecule thus consists of a series of bands, corresponding to the vibrational transitions, each having rotational fine structure. Finally the electronic spectrum consists of many series of bands, each series of bands corresponding to an electronic transition.

This interpretation of the molecular spectra has been confirmed by a large amount of experimental data. Thus, for example, equation 8.3 predicts that for transitions in rotational energy in which $\Delta J = \pm 1$, the lines in the spectrum will have a constant separation equivalent to $h^2/4\pi^2 I$. For hydrogen chloride the separation of lines in the far infra-red is 20·68 cm^{-1}, which gives $I = 2{\cdot}71 \times 10^{-40}$ gm cm^2; substitution in equation 8.4, putting $m_1 m_2/(m_1 + m_2) = 1{\cdot}63 \times 10^{-24}$ gm gives the internuclear distance r, as $1{\cdot}29 \times 10^{-8}$ cm in agreement with values obtained by other methods. As will be described in the following sections of this chapter the data obtained from vibrational-rotational spectra may be used to calculate the dissociation energy of molecules and the values obtained in this way are in excellent agreement with those obtained from thermochemical data.

POTENTIAL ENERGY CURVES

The vibrations performed by a diatomic molecule may not be regarded as harmonic. This is readily understandable since a system of two nuclei performing harmonic vibration would never dissociate into the constituent atoms, since in accordance with the law $F = - Kx$ (*cf* equation 1.12) the farther the internuclear separation, the greater would be the attracting force between the nuclei. In the case of an actual molecule, the restoring force is due to the bonding energy of the electrons which decreases rapidly with increasing internuclear distance and at a separation of 6 to 7×10^{-8} cm the bonding force is effectively zero and the molecule dissociates into atoms.

For a harmonic oscillator, the vibrational quanta, *i.e.* the energy difference between adjacent vibrational levels, all have identical values. This may be shown by reference to equation 8.2 which relates the energy of a vibrational level with the quantum number and the vibrational frequency of the molecule. If the molecule is initially in the state characterized by the

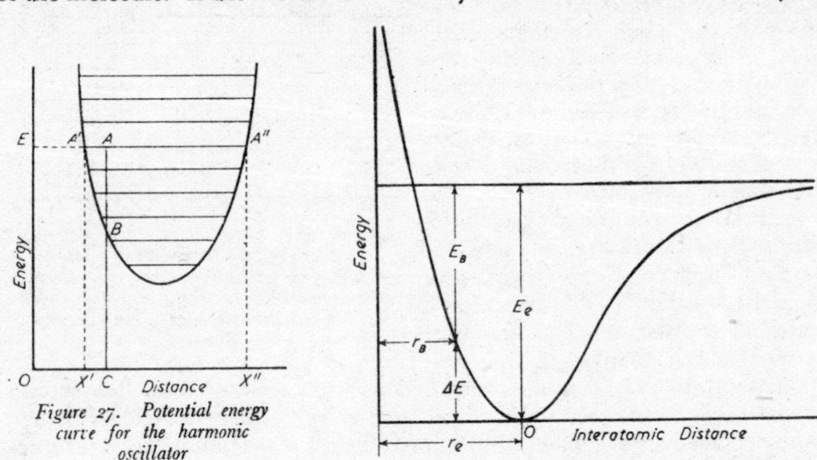

Figure 27. *Potential energy curve for the harmonic oscillator*

Figure 28. *Potential energy curve for a diatomic molecule*

quantum number n, the energy will be : $E_1 = (n + \frac{1}{2})h\nu$; on absorption of one quantum of energy the molecule is transferred to the vibrational level having a quantum number $n + 1$ which will have an energy given by $E_2 = (n + 3/2)h\nu$. The difference in energies will thus always be given by $E_2 - E_1 = h\nu$, irrespective of the value of n, and the energy levels will be situated at regular intervals, the energy difference between adjacent vibrational levels being a constant. *Figure 27* shows the variation of the potential energy with internuclear separation for an harmonic oscillator generally termed a potential energy curve ; the horizontal lines represent the permitted energy levels. The meaning of this curve may best be illustrated by considering an example. If the oscillator has an energy value represented by E, the changes in potential energy during oscillation are represented by the curve $A'A''$ and the nuclear separation varies between OX' and OX''. At a particular point B on the curve, representing some intermediate condition of the system between its extremes of oscillation, the internuclear distance is OC and the total energy AC is made up of kinetic energy AB and potential energy BC. At the extremes of vibration *i.e.* at A' and A'' the kinetic energy is zero.

The potential energy curve of a diatomic molecule is represented diagrammatically in *Figure 28* and possesses a minimum at the equilibrium internuclear distance. At all other values of the internuclear distance the potential energy is greater, since work has to be done either against the molecular bonding energy or against the repulsion energy of the nuclei and their completed electronic shells. The molecule, however, is never found in the non-vibrating state represented by the point O, since the molecule, even in its lowest quantum state, possesses vibrational energy, the zero-point energy. From a comparison of *Figures 27* and *28*, it is seen that the potential energy curve of a diatomic molecule only approximates to the parabola of an harmonic oscillator at low energy levels. A transition between a hypothetical state of the molecule with an internuclear distance equal to r_e (*Figure 28*) to one with an internuclear distance equal to r_B, involves the loss of energy since work has to be done against the forces of repulsion. This amount of energy, $\Delta E = E_e - E_B$ has been converted from potential into kinetic energy of vibration. The curve approaches asymptotically the horizontal line which represents the energy of the free atoms formed by the dissociation of the molecule.

From the potential energy curve the relationship between the force of interaction f and the internuclear distance r, may be obtained since $f = \frac{dV}{dr}$, where V is the potential energy. This variation is represented in *Figure 29*. The value of r equal to r_e represents the minimum in the potential energy curve and hence $\frac{dV}{dr} = 0$; this fixes the zero on the ordinate and positive values of f will represent the force of repulsion and negative values, the force of attraction. The force of repulsion increases rapidly with decrease in r and may be represented either by an expression of the type C/r^n where n has a value close to 10 or by an exponential expression. The force of attraction increases, *i.e.* becomes more negative, as r increases, passes through a maximum, and then decreases approaching zero asymptotically. Only in a small region close to the equilibrium position does this curve approximate to a straight line and therefore it is only in this region, as we have already noticed, that the vibration can be assumed to be harmonic. The deviation of this complex curve (*Figure 29*) from a straight line, emphasizes the very marked deviation from harmonic vibration that occurs and clearly indicates that equation 8.2 :

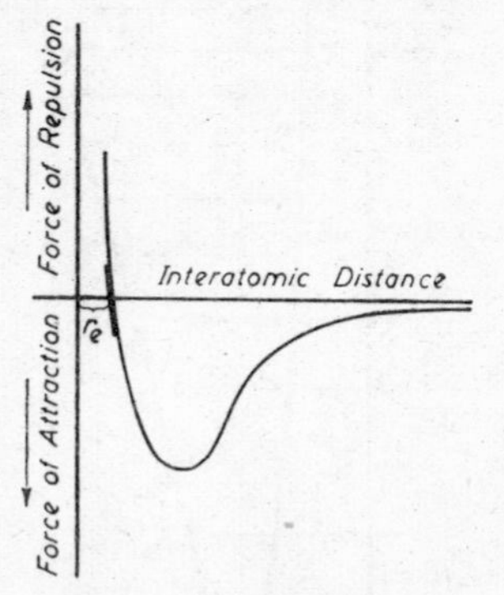

Figure 29. Variation of forces of attraction and repulsion with interatomic distance for a diatomic molecule

$$E = (n + \tfrac{1}{2})\, h\nu \qquad \ldots .(8.2)$$

must be modified before applied to actual molecules. Equation 8.2 has therefore been replaced by,

$$E = (n + \tfrac{1}{2})h\nu - (n + \tfrac{1}{2})^2 a h\nu \qquad \ldots .(8.5)$$

in which the second term may be regarded as a correction term and a is known as the anharmonicity constant. With this equation the difference in energies of the two energy states characterized by the quantum numbers $n + 1$ and n becomes,

$$E_2 - E_1 = [(n+1+\tfrac{1}{2})h\nu - (n+1+\tfrac{1}{2})^2 ah\nu] - [(n+\tfrac{1}{2})h\nu - (n+\tfrac{1}{2})^2 ah\nu]$$
$$= h\nu - 2nah\nu - 2ah\nu \quad \ldots (8.6)$$

and hence the vibrational quanta decrease in value as the quantum number n increases.

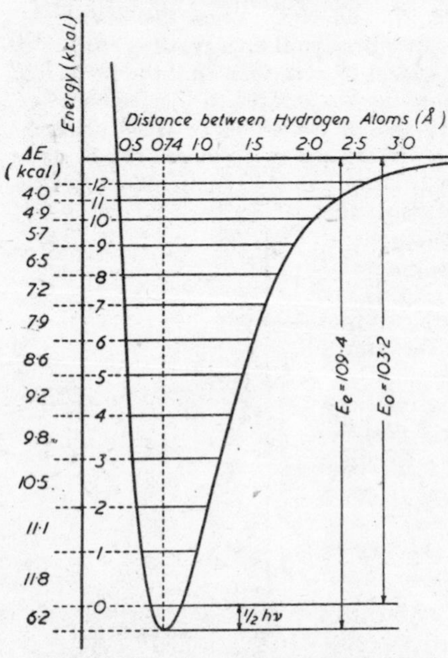

Figure 30. Potential energy curve and vibrational energy levels for the hydrogen molecule. The vertical scale gives the differences in energy between adjacent vibrational levels

The potential energy curve and vibrational energy levels of the hydrogen molecule are shown in *Figure 30*. The minimum of the curve corresponds to a value of 109·4 kcals, but in the ground state the hydrogen molecule has a slightly higher energy value owing to the zero point energy $\frac{1}{2}h\nu$, which is equal to 6·2 kcals. Thus the dissociation energy of the hydrogen molecule is 103·2 kcals/gm molecule. The difference between the values of adjacent energy levels is seen to decrease as the quantum number increases, in the manner indicated by equation 8.5.

From a study of the vibration-rotation spectrum of a molecule, the frequency of vibration, the values of the energy levels, the anharmonicity constant and the dissociation energy may be determined. From the rotation spectrum or from the rotational fine structure of the vibration-rotation spectrum the value of I and hence of the interatomic distance may be determined by using equations 8.3 and 8.4.

The above elementary treatment of molecular spectra is sufficient for our present purpose and for a more extended discussion of the coupling of the vibrational and rotational modes of oscillation, the polarization and intensity of spectral lines, permitted and forbidden transitions, the Frank-Condon principle and the application to thermodynamics, the reader is referred to the many monographs which have been published[2].

The potential energy curve shown in *Figure 30*, for the hydrogen molecule has been obtained experimentally; it is, however, desirable that such curves be represented by a mathematical equation. We have already seen that the parabolic curve only approximates to the potential energy curve at low values of the quantum number and the expression for the variation of energy with internuclear distance obtained by Heitler and London is also a poor approximation, and moreover, has only been derived for the case of the hydrogen molecule. Recourse has therefore to be made to the derivation of empirical equations. The attraction energy may be represented by an expression of the type—A/r^m, and the repulsion energy by $+ B/r^n$. Since the repulsion energy increases very rapidly at small values of r, it is apparent that n must be very much greater than m. The expression for the potential energy V may then be written

$$V = -\frac{A}{r^m} + \frac{B}{r^n} \qquad \ldots (8.7)$$

This expression unfortunately has not been found to be of general application and a more useful approximation has been introduced by MORSE[3] :

$$V_{(r)} = D_e{}^{-2a(r-r_0)} - 2D_e{}^{-a(r-r_0)} \qquad \ldots (8.8)$$

where r is the distance between the nuclei, r_o is the equilibrium internuclear separation and D_e is the dissociation energy together with the zero-point energy. The factor a is related to the anharmonicity constant by the expression

$$a = \left(\frac{8\pi^2 \nu a}{h} \frac{m_1 m_2}{m_1 + m_2}\right)^{\frac{1}{2}} \qquad \ldots (8.9)$$

The importance of equation 8.8 lies in the fact that if it is substituted for the potential energy term in the Schrödinger equation, the latter may be solved for the vibrational energy and yields equation 8.5.

The Morse equation describes the potential energy curve very satisfactorily. Its main disadvantage lies in the fact that when $r = 0$, a finite, although large, value of the potential energy is obtained instead of an infinite value. Various modifications to this formula have been proposed by ROSEN and MORSE and by PÖSCHL and TELLER[4].

RESULTS OF SPECTROGRAPHIC MEASUREMENTS

The most detailed spectroscopic investigations have been carried out with diatomic molecules and at the present time the characteristic constants, obtained from vibrational-rotational spectra are known for more than 250 diatomic molecules. Several of these compounds are not sufficiently stable to exist in the pure state and have only been observed and studied by spectroscopic methods. Such compounds as CH, NH *etc* are of great interest as they undoubtedly occur as intermediate products in many chemical reactions.

The experimental data, which have been taken mainly from the monographs of HERZBERG[2] and GAYDON[5], are grouped into different sections according to the nature of the molecule. Homonuclear molecules are given in *Table XXX*, hydrides in *Table XXXI* and oxides in *Table XXXII*. In order to simplify the discussion, the tables have been compiled according to the position of the element in the periodic table. Three constants (where known) are given for each molecule. Reading downwards these are : the energy of dissociation D in kcals ; the equilibrium interatomic distance r_o in Å ; and the frequency of vibration ν in cm^{-1}. The energy of dissociation represents the difference between the limiting value of the potential energy at infinite separation of the nuclei and the lowest vibrational level, which is $\frac{1}{2}h\nu$ above the minimum value.

It should be pointed out, that in spite of the very great importance of spectroscopic methods, the interpretation of the data is not always unambiguous. For example, the dissociation energy of nitrogen has at various times been given as 268, 220, 206, 180 and 169·7 kcals. The latter figure, accepted by Herzberg[2] has recently been questioned by GAYDON and PENNEY[6] who, by a reinterpretation of the same experimental data, arrive at the value 225·1 kcals. Thus of the values of the dissociation energies of diatomic molecules which have been determined by spectroscopic methods, only about 60 out of the 250 are sufficiently accurate and unambiguous to be regarded as correct. It is unfortunate that carbon monoxide does not fall within this category since if the dissociation energy and hence the heat of formation of carbon monoxide were known exactly, it would be possible by means of the following thermochemical equations to determine accurately the heat of atomization of carbon which is of great importance in the calculation and interpretation of the bond energies of carbon compounds :

$$C_{gas} = C \qquad \Delta H_1$$
$$O = \tfrac{1}{2}O_2 \qquad \tfrac{1}{2}\Delta H_2$$
$$C_{solid} + \tfrac{1}{2}O_2 = CO_{gas} \qquad \Delta H_3$$
$$C + O = CO_{gas} \qquad \Delta H_4$$

Since ΔH_2 and ΔH_3 are known, an accurate knowledge of the value of ΔH_4 would lead to a value of ΔH_1.

The agreement between the data obtained by spectrospcoic methods and by other physical methods is found to be excellent. For example, in *Table XXIX*, the values of the interatomic distances in the molecules Cl_2, Br_2 and I_2 obtained by spectroscopic and electron diffraction methods are compared and the agreement is found to be within the order of accuracy of electron diffraction measurements, ± 0·03Å. Also the heat of formation of NaCl from thermochemical measurements is 96 kcals, close to the value obtained from spectroscopic data of 98 kcals.

Table XXIX. Internuclear Distances for Halogen Molecules

Molecule	Internuclear distance Å	
	Spectroscopy	*Electron diffraction*
Cl_2	1·99	2·01
Br_2	2·28	2·28
I_2	2·67	2·65

Some relationship must exist between the energy of dissociation, the equilibrium internuclear distance and the frequency of vibration, since the greater the value of the dissociation energy, the greater will be the frequency of vibration and the smaller the internuclear distance. Attempts to relate these quantities by an empirical or semi-empirical formula, however, have so far failed.

Homonuclear diatomic molecules—The experimental data for homonuclear diatomic molecules are summarized in *Table XXX* and *Figure 31*, where it is seen that amongst elements of the second period there is a progressive change in the values of the dissociation energy, *i.e.* the bond energy, and the

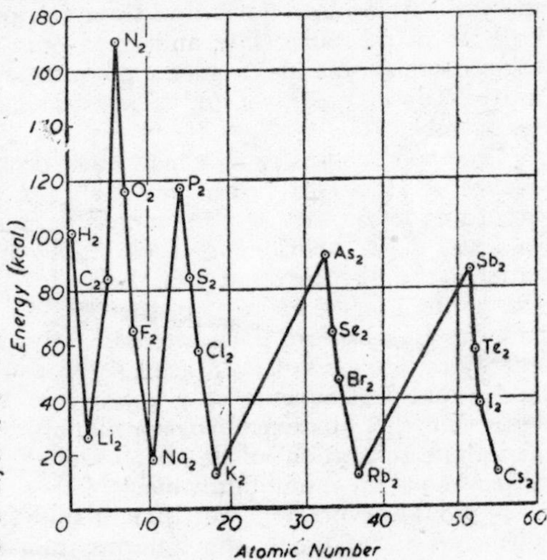

Figure 31. Dissociation energies of diatomic homonuclear molecules

frequency of vibration. The values increase from Li_2 to C_2 and reach maximum values with N_2 and then fall again with O_2 and F_2. These changes are paralleled by the variation of the internuclear distance which is shortest in N_2, greater in O_2 and C_2 and greater still in the cases of F_2 and Li_2. Such behaviour may easily be interpreted on the basis of the molecular orbital treatment. The orbitals concerned in this group of molecules are the $z\sigma$, $y\sigma$, $x\sigma$, $w\pi$ and $v\pi$ of which the $z\sigma$, $x\sigma$, $w\pi$ orbitals are bonding and the $y\sigma$ and $v\pi$ orbitals antibonding. The configurations of the molecules formed by the second group elements is as follows :

$$\begin{array}{ll} Li_2 & [KK(z\sigma)^2] \\ B_2 & [KK(z\sigma)^2(y\sigma)^2(x\sigma)^2] \\ C_2 & [KK(z\sigma)^2(y\sigma)^2(x\sigma)^2(w\pi)^2] \\ N_2 & [KK(z\sigma)^2(y\sigma)^2(x\sigma)^2(w\pi)^4] \\ O_2 & [KK(z\sigma)^2(y\sigma)^2(x\sigma)^2(w\pi)^4(v\pi)^2] \\ F_2 & [KK(z\sigma)^2(y\sigma)^2(x\sigma)^2(w\pi)^4(v\pi)^4] \end{array}$$

If we now assume that the $y\sigma$ and $v\pi$ antibonding orbitals cancel the bonding of the $z\sigma$ and $w\pi$ orbitals (see Chapter 7), we see that the effective number of bonding orbitals in these molecules, remembering that the $w\pi$ and $v\pi$ states are doubly degenerate, is : Li_2, 1 ; B_2, 1 ; C_2, 2 ; N_2, 3 ; O_2, 2 and F_2, 1. Thus the bond energy should increase from Li_2 to N_2 and then decrease to F_2, which is in agreement with the spectroscopic data given below.

Table XXX. Dissociation Energies, Internuclear Distances and Vibration Frequencies of Homonuclear Diatomic Molecules

H_2: 103·2 0·74 4,405							
Li_2: 26 2·67 351	—		B_2: 69 — —	C_2: 83 1·31 1,641	N_2: 225·1 1·09 2,360	O_2: 117·1 1·21 1,580	F_2: 72 1·45*e* —
Na_2: 17·8 3·08 159	—		—	—	P_2: 116 1·89 780	S_2: ≤83 1·89 726	Cl_2: 57·1 1·99 565
K_2: 11·8 3·92 93	—		—	—	As_2: 90·8 — 429	Se_2: 65 2·16 392	Br_2: 45·4 2·28 323
Rb_2: 11·1 — 57	—	Cd_2: 2·1 — —	—	—	Sb_2: 69 — 270	Te_2: 53 2·59*e* 251	I_2: 35·6 2·67 214
Cs_2: 10·4 — 42	—	Hg_2: 1·4 3·3 36	—	Pb_2: (14) — —	Bi_2: 39·6 — 174	—	—

The figures, reading from top to bottom, are the dissociation energy in kcals, internuclear distance in Å and vibration frequency in cm^{-1} ; *e* signifies that the internuclear distance has been measured by electron diffraction

It is particularly interesting in this connection to notice that the dissociation energies of F_2, O_2 and N_2 are very nearly in the ratio 1 : 2 : 3. If we compare the properties of Li_2 and F_2 each of which have a single effective bond we should perhaps expect that owing to the increased electronic repulsion in F_2, the dissociation energy of Li_2 might be greater than that of F_2; actually this is not found to be the case, the bond in Li_2 being weaker: $D = 26$ kcals; $r_e = 2{\cdot}67$ Å, than that in F_2: $D = 64$ kcals; $r_e = 1{\cdot}45$Å. The reason for this behaviour must lie in the difference of the two bonding orbitals, that in Li_2 being a $z\sigma$ orbital (*i.e* $\sigma\ 2s$), whereas in F_2 the effective bonding orbital is the $x\sigma$ (*i.e.* $\sigma 2p_x$). The much greater overlap possible with p orbitals compared with an s orbital causes the difference in bond strength[7]. In this connection it is interesting to note the marked similarity in the values of the dissociation energies of F_2 and B_2, since in both molecules the effective bonding orbital is the $x\sigma$. A similar gradation of properties occurs amongst the elements of the succeeding periods of the periodic table. In every case the maximum values of the dissociation energy and of the vibration frequency, and the minimum values of the internuclear distances are observed with the elements of the fifth group, where the number of effective bonding orbitals has a maximum value and the molecules may be regarded as containing a triple bond. The shortest single bond is that occurring in H_2: $D = 103{\cdot}2$ kcals, $r_e = 0{\cdot}74$ Å, $\nu = 4{,}405\ cm^{-1}$, in which there are only two electrons, both existing in a bonding orbital.

The absence of diatomic homonuclear molecules of the second group (Be_2, Mg_2, Ca_2, Gr_2, and Ba_2) is understandable in view of the fact that in the single atoms there are no unpaired electrons. The electronic configuration of Be_2, for example, would be: $[KK(z\sigma)^2(y\sigma)^2]$ in which the bonding effect of the $z\sigma$ orbital is cancelled by the antibonding effect of the $y\sigma$ orbital and no molecule is formed. In order for a molecule to be formed an atomic s electron would have to be excited to a p state so that the molecule formed would have the configuration Be_2 $[KK(z\sigma)^2(x\sigma)^2]$ in which both the $z\sigma$ and $x\sigma$ are bonding orbitals. The excitation energy involved, however, is too great to be compensated by the bond energy and such molecules are not therefore formed.

Hydrides— The experimental data for the diatomic hydrides are summarized in *Table XXXI*. In LiH, the internuclear distance is much less than in Li_2 which may be attributed to the fact that there is only one inner complete shell, that of lithium. In addition to the homopolar valence bond structure Li—H, the ionic form $Li^+ H^-$ makes an important contribution to the resulting state of the molecule and will thus increase its stability. The reason for the existence of a negative charge on the hydrogen, which is unusual, is that the ionization potential of hydrogen, 312 kcals, is much greater that that of lithium, 123 kcals, and that hydrogen possesses a small, but significant electron affinity of 16·4 kcals compared with the zero electron affinity of lithium. These data all tend to show that the ionic form $Li^+ H^-$ is more probable than the alternative structure $Li^- H^+$. The energy of dissociation is found to decrease progressively in the alkali metal hydrides from LiH to CsH, but the decrease is only from 58 kcals, in the case of LiH to 41 kcals for CsH, compared with the corresponding decrease from 26 kcals to 10·4 kcals in the homonuclear diatomic molecules (see *Table XXX*). The smaller proportional decrease in the hydrides may be attributed to the decrease in the ionization potential from lithium, 123·5 kcals, to caesium, 89·2 kcals, with the corresponding increase in the contribution of the ionic form $Cs^+ H^-$ to the state of the molecule.

The hydrides of the second group of elements can only be formed by the initial excitation of an s electron to a p state. It will be noticed that the

Table XXXI. Dissociation Energies, Internuclear Distances and Vibration Frequencies of Diatomic Hydride Molecules

LiH 58 1·60 1,406	BeH 53 1·34 2,058						BH 58 1·23 2,366	CH 80 1·12 2,821	NH (97)(78) 1·04 3,300	OH 101 0·97 3,728	HF 104 0·92 4,141
NaH 47 1·89 1,171	MgH 46 1·73 1,495						AlH 67 1·65 1,680	SiH — 1·52 (2,080)	PH — 1·43 2,380	—	HCl 102·1 1·27 2,989
KH 42·9 2·24 983	CaH 39·2 2·00 1,299	FeH — (1·48) —	CoH — 1·54 1,890	NiH 60 1·47 1927	CuH 62 1·46 1940	ZnH 19·5 1·59 1,608	—	—	—	—	HBr 83·0 1·41 2,650
RbH 39 — 934	SrH 38 2·15 1,206				AgH 53 1·62 1,760	CdH 15·6 1·76 1,431	InH 58 1·85 —	SnH <74 — —	—	—	HI 63·4 1·60 2,309
CsH 41 2·49 891	BaH 41 2·23 1,172				AuH 69 1·52 2,306	HgH 8·57 1·74 1,387	TlH 46 1·87 1,391	PbH 41 1·84 1,565	BiH 58 1·81 1,699	—	—

The figures reading from top to bottom are the dissociation energy in kcals, internuclear distance in Å and vibration frequency in cm^{-1}

Table XXXII. Dissociation Energies, Internuclear Distances and Vibration Frequencies of Diatomic Oxide Molecules

BeO 101 1·33 1,487						BO 161 1·20 1,885	CO 256·1 1·13 2,168	NO 150 1·15 1,906	O_2 117·2 1·21 1,580
MgO (71) — 666						AlO 87 1·62 977	SiO 184 1·51 1,242	PO 143 1·49 1,231	SO 119·5 1·49 1,124
CaO 136 1·75 843	ScO 138 — 971	TiO 127 1·62 1,008	VO 127 1·89 1,013	CrO 74 — 899	CuO 104 — (620)	GaO 58 — 768	GeO 127 — 986	AsO (113) — 967	SeO 81 — 909
SrO 104 (1·83) (633)	YO 161 — 855	ZrO 150 1·42 937			AgO 32 — 493	InO 25 — 703	SnO 74 1·84 822	SbO 74 — 824	TeO 62·8 — 796
BaO 108 1·80 671	LaO 161 — 812						PbO (76) 1·92 722	BiO 92 — 493	

The figures reading from top to bottom are the dissociation energy in kcals, internuclear distance in Å and vibration frequency in cm^{-1}

vibrational frequencies are noticeably greater and the internuclear distances less than in the corresponding hydrides of the alkali metals, a fact which may be attributed to the stronger bonding of a *p* compared with an *s* electron. But it is important to note that even so, the dissociation energies of corresponding elements of the two groups of compounds are very similar. This is due to the fact that energy is required to produce the initial excitation of the atoms from the s^2 to the *sp* state and the observed value of the dissociation energy represents the difference between the true dissociation energy and that required for the excitation of the atom.

In boron hydride there is a noticeable strengthening of the bond compared with lithium and beryllium hydrides and the dissociation energy continues to increase in the series BH, CH, NH, OH, and HF. For boron and carbon hydrides, this increase of bond energy compared with the corresponding hydrides of the first and second groups will be due to the fact that the bond is formed by an unpaired *p* electron with a greater overlap with an *s* orbital compared with the extent of overlap of two *s* orbitals. The continued increase of the strength of the bond in the nitrogen, oxygen and fluorine compounds will be due to an increasing contribution of the ionic state to the resonance of the molecule.

In the halogen group, the dissociation energy decreases from 104 kcals in HF to 63·4 kcals in HI. This is a much greater relative decrease than in the corresponding alkali metals where the decrease is from 58 kcals in LiH to 41 kcals in CsH. This is due to the fact that whereas the contribution of the ionic form M^+H^- to the molecular state increases from lithium to calcium hydride, owing to the increasing electro positive character of the metal, the contribution of the ionic state H^+ Hal^- to the halogen hydrides decreases from F to I, owing to the decreasing electronegativity of the halogen.

Oxides and Nitrides— It is unfortunate that most of the dissociation energies of the oxides are not known with sufficient exactitude to permit any systematic study. However, on the basis of the data given in *Table XXXII*, it is possible to make a few tentative conclusions. The dissociation energies of the oxides are noticeably greater than those of the hydrides as is to be expected from the fact that the bond will largely possess double bond character and that there will be a considerable contribution to the state of the molecule from ionic forms. The shortest internuclear distances occur with the oxides of the fourth group elements of the periodic table : CO, SiO, *etc*, a fact which may be explained in the same way as the similar property of the homonuclear molecules of the fifth group N_2, P_2, *etc*, with which they are isoelectronic. Thus, employing the molecular orbital treatment, the maximum number of six bonding electrons in three molecular orbitals is characteristic of both groups of molecules, or in terms of the localized electron pair theory, resonance between three valence bond structures occurs :

$$A{=}O \qquad A^+ - O^- \qquad A^- \equiv O^+$$

Since the ionic structures will make a greater contribution in the oxides than in the homonuclear atoms, the fact that the oxides of the group four elements have greater dissociation energies than the corresponding homonuclear molecules of the group five elements *i.e.* $D_{CO} > D_{N_2}$, $D_{SiO} > D_{P_2}$ *etc*, is explained.

The ionization potentials of the elements of group four decrease from carbon to lead and it would be anticipated that the contribution of the form $A^{-}{\equiv}O^{+}$ decreases in the same order. Thus in PbO the main contribution to the molecule will come from the structures Pb=O and Pb^{+}—O^{-}.

Very little data have so far been obtained for the nitrides and the known values are given in *Table XXXIII.* An interesting comparison may be made between the three compounds CN, N_2 and NO which contain 13, 14 and 15 electrons respectively. The electron configurations of these molecules is as follows :

Table XXXIII. Dissociation Energies, Internuclear Distances and Vibration Frequencies of Diatomic Nitrides

Molecule	Dissociation energy	Internuclear distance	Vibration frequency
BN	92	—	—
CN	(175)	1·17	2,069
SiN	104	1·57	1·152
N_2	225·1	1·09	2,360
PN	138	1·49	1,337
AsN	115	—	—
SbN	71	—	—
NO	150	1·15	1,906
SN	115	—	1,220
BrN	58	—	—

The figures reading from top to bottom are the dissociation energy in kcals, internuclear distance in Å and vibration frequency in cm^{-1}

$$\text{CN}\quad [KK(z\sigma)^2(y\sigma)^2(x\sigma)^2(w\pi)^3]$$
$$N_2\quad [KK(z\sigma)^2(y\sigma)^2(x\sigma)^2(w\pi)^4]$$
$$\text{NO}\quad [KK(z\sigma)^2(y\sigma)^2(x\sigma)^2(w\pi)^4(v\pi)]$$

The maximum number of bonding orbitals is present in N_2 (six electrons in three bonding orbitals) and in this molecule the dissociation energy and the vibration frequency are greater and the internuclear distance smaller, than in the other two atoms. The existence of an additional electron in the antibonding orbital $v\pi$ in NO decreases the dissociation energy by 75·1 kcals whereas the absence of an electron in the bonding orbital $w\pi$ only decreases the energy by 49·9 kcals. Unfortunately similar behaviour is not observed in the case of SiN, PN and NS, if the most recent data is considered, and it may be suggested only tentatively that the presence of an electron in an antibonding orbital has a greater relative effect than an electron in a bonding orbital.

Molecular ions—The data for some diatomic molecules and the corresponding molecular ions, given in *Table XXXIV*, show that in certain cases the strength of the bond in the ion is stronger and in others weaker than in the corresponding molecule. This

Table XXXIV. Dissociation Energies, Internuclear Distances and Vibration Frequencies for Some Diatomic Molecules and the Corresponding Molecular Ions

Molecule	Values	Ion	Values	Molecule	Values	Ion	Values
H_2	103·2 / 0·74 / 4,405	H_2^+	61·07 / 1·06 / 2,297	CO	256·1 / 1·13 / 2,168	$(CO)^+$	189 / 1·11 / 2,211
N_2	225·1 / 1·09 / 2,360	N_2^+	201·3 / 1·12 / 2,207	NO	(150) / 1·11 / 2,211	$(NO)^+$	— / (1·07) / —
O_2	117·2 / 1·21 / 1,580	O_2^+	149 / 1·12 / 1,876	HCl	102·1 / 1·27 / 2,989	$(HCl)^+$	104 / — / —
As_2	90·8 / — / 429	As_2^+	46 / — / 314	CH	80 / 1·12 / 284	$(CH)^+$	83 / — / —
Cl_2	57·08 / 1·99 / 565	Cl_2^+	97 / 1·89 / 645	BeH	53 / 1·34 / 2,058	$(BeH)^+$	74 / — / —

The figures reading from top to bottom are the dissociation energy in kcals, internuclear distance in Å and vibration frequency in cm^{-1}

apparently anomalous behaviour, however, may be explained by the sequence of molecular orbitals. The bond in H_2^+ is much weaker than in H_2, since in the ion there is only one bonding electron, whereas in the molecule there are two. Similarly there are six bonding electrons in N_2, as shown by its electronic configuration

$$N_2 \quad [KK(z\sigma)^2(y\sigma)^2(x\sigma)^2(w\pi)^4]$$

$$N_2^+ \quad [KK(z\sigma)^2(y\sigma)^2(x\sigma)^2(w\pi)^3]$$

but only five in the ion N_2^+, thus explaining the weaker bond in the latter. A similar argument will apply to As_2 and As_2^+. The case of CO and CO^+ has already been discussed in Chapter 7, but it should be pointed out that although the internuclear distance decreases and the vibration frequency increases on formation of the ion, indicating a strengthening of the bond, the dissociation energy has decreased considerably.

With O_2 and Cl_2 the position is reversed and the bond in the ion is markedly stronger than in the neutral molecule as indicated by the increase in dissociation energy, decrease of internuclear distance and increase of vibrational frequency. The electronic configuration of these molecules and the corresponding ions is :

$$O_2 \quad [KK(z\sigma)^2(y\sigma)^2(x\sigma)^2(w\pi)^4(v\pi)^2]$$

$$O_2^+ \quad [KK(z\sigma)^2(y\sigma)^2(x\sigma)^2(w\pi)^4(v\pi)]$$

$$Cl_2 \quad [KKLL(z\sigma)^2(y\sigma)^2(x\sigma)^2(w\pi)^4(v\pi)^4]$$

$$Cl_2^+ \quad [KKLL(z\sigma)^2(y\sigma)^2(x\sigma)^2(w\pi)^4(v\pi)^3]$$

It is seen that, in both cases, on ionization an electron in the antibonding $v\pi$ orbital is lost, and the bond strength is increased as shown by the experimental data. According to this argument the addition of an electron to O_2 to give the ion O_2^-, will bring about a weakening of the bond, since the additional electron must enter an antibonding orbital. The energy of the reaction $O_2 = O + O^-$ may be calculated from the dissociation energy of O_2, 117·2 kcals, the electron affinity of the oxygen atom, 71 kcals, and the electron affinity of O_2. The value for the latter has been given as 62 kcals by WEISS[8] and as 18 kcals by KAZARNOVSKY[9]. The latter figure is probably the more accurate since it has been obtained from the lattice energy of crystalline KO_2 which consists of K^+ and O_2^- ions, whereas the calculation of Weiss involves certain assumptions concerning the value of the heats of hydration of ions. Using these values, the dissociation energy of O_2^- is 64 kcals. Thus it is seen again (compare with NO) that the addition of an electron in an antibonding orbital weakens the bond more than the loss of an electron formerly in an antibonding orbital.

For NO^+ only the internuclear distance is at present known. The value is less than for the neutral molecule, thus suggesting a stronger bond in NO^+ than in NO, in agreement with the molecular orbital formula

$$NO \quad [KK(z\sigma)^2(y\sigma)^2(x\sigma)^2(w\pi)^4(v\pi)]$$

$$NO^+ \quad [KK(z\sigma)^2(y\sigma)^2(x\sigma)^2(w\pi)^4]$$

which indicates the absence in the ion, of an electron in the $v\pi$ antibonding orbital.

The experimental data for the hydride ions is as yet insufficient for discussion and furthermore, the electronic arrangement in the molecular orbitals is still somewhat in doubt.

Isotopic molecules— The determination, by spectroscopic methods, of the molecular constants of molecules and their analogues containing an isotope, gives interesting information concerning the dependence of these constants on atomic mass. The greatest amount of data has been accumulated using one of the isotopes of hydrogen, deuterium of atomic weight 2, and these data are summarized in *Table XXXV*. It is clear that those properties which depend only on the electronic configuration and nuclear charge and are independent of mass, remain almost unaltered when deuterium is

Table XXXV. Molecular Constants of Some Hydrides and Deuterides

Molecule	*Reduced mass (atomic units)*	*Dissociation energy kcals*	*Zero-point energy* kcals*	*Inter-nuclear distance* Å	*Moment of inertia gmcm²* × 10^{40}	*Force constant dynes cm⁻¹* × 10^{-5}	*Vibrational frequency cm⁻¹*
H_2	0·5	103·22	6·18	0·74	—	5·71	4,405
HD	0·67	104·02	5·36	0·74	—	5·75	3,817
D_2	1·0	105·02	4·39	0·74	—	5·73	3,119
LiH	0·88	(58)	1·99	1·60	3·68	1·02	1,405
LiD	1·51	(58)	1·51	1·60	6·53	1·03	1,065
NaH	0·96	47	1·66	1·89	5·65	0·77	1,170
NaD	1·84	(51)	1·17	1·89	10·81	0·74	825
CH	0·92	80	4·01	1·12	1·91	4·33	2,824
CD	1·72	81	2·96	1·12	—	4·33	2,073
OH	0·94	101	5·29	0·97	1·45	7·70	3,728
OD	1·77	103·0	—	0·97	—	—	—
HCl	0·99	102·1	4·21	1·27	2·61	5·11	2,989
DCl	1·99	103·4	3·03	1·27	5·08	—	(2,091)
HI	1·0	63·4	3·24	1·61	4·31	3·11	2,309
DI	2·0	6·45	2·31	—	—	—	—

* Certain values of the zero-point energy have been calculated with allowance for the anharmonicity, by the formula $E_0 = h\nu_0 (\frac{1}{2} - \frac{1}{4}a)$

substituted for hydrogen. Properties dependent on mass, such as internuclear distance and force constant, however, change considerably on such substitution. The moment of inertia I is related to the reduced mass m by:

$$I = mr^2 = \frac{m_1 m_2}{m_1 + m_2} r^2 \qquad \ldots.(8.4)$$

and values for the deuterides are almost double those for the corresponding hydrides. The frequency of vibration will be expressed by $\nu = (k/m)^{\frac{1}{2}}/2\pi$ where k is the force constant. This expression is obtained by combining equation 1.27 with 1.12 and 1.13, the displacement in this case referring to that of an harmonic oscillator and the mass m to the reduced mass.

For H_2, $m = \frac{1 \times 1}{1 + 1} = \frac{1}{2}$, in atomic units, and for D_2, $m = \frac{2 \times 2}{2 + 2} = 1$.

Thus the vibrational frequency in H_2 will be $\sqrt{2}$ times greater than in D_2 in agreement with the experimental data. This difference in the value of the vibrational frequency also effects the zero-point energy, with the result that D_2, which has the lower frequency of vibration, has a ground energy state which is 1·79 kcals below that of H_2. The difference in the dissociation energies is therefore due to the difference in the zero point energies, the addition of these two quantities giving the values 109·40 kcals in the case of H_2 and 109·41 kcals for D_2. For a similar reason the energy of activation in chemical reactions involving deuterium is greater than that of the corresponding reactions involving hydrogen. In addition to the influence of the lower ground energy level of deuterium, however, the velocity of the reaction will also be reduced by the smaller velocity of the heavier deuterium molecules.

The differences in molecular properties for the isotopes of other elements is less marked than in the case of H_2 and D_2 where the ratio of the isotopic weights, with the exception of the case of hydrogen and tritium, is a maximum.

ORTHO AND PARA HYDROGEN

In 1927 HEISENBERG[10] and HUND[11] deduced, by the methods of wave mechanics, that pure hydrogen is a mixture of two different types of molecules. This apparently surprising result is due to the fact that spin is not only a property of electrons, but of protons and neutrons also. In the molecule of hydrogen, therefore, two orientations of nuclear spin are possible, the antiparallel ↓↑ and the parallel ↓↓. Corresponding to these two orientations, there are two distinct forms of molecular hydrogen; that with antiparallel spins is called parahydrogen and that with parallel spins, orthohydrogen. By means of this theory it was possible to explain the alternating intensity of the rotational fine structure in the spectrum of H_2 observed by MECKE[12] in 1924 and also the temperature variation of the heat capacity of hydrogen[13]. It was a triumph for the quantum theory when in 1929, BONHOEFFER and HARTECK[14], and EUCKEN and HILLER[15] were able to produce direct experimental evidence for the existence of these two forms. A detailed description of this work is given in the monograph of FARKAS[16].

The complete wave function of the hydrogen molecule must describe the electronic orbital motion, the electronic spin orientation, the vibration of the nuclei, the rotation of the nuclei and the nuclear spin orientation. As a first approximation the various forms of motion must be considered as being independent of each other and the complete wave function may thus be represented as the product of five separate functions:

$$\phi = \overset{1}{\begin{pmatrix}\text{electronic}\\ \text{orbital motion}\end{pmatrix}} \overset{2}{\begin{pmatrix}\text{electronic spin}\\ \text{orientation}\end{pmatrix}} \overset{3}{\begin{pmatrix}\text{nuclear}\\ \text{vibration}\end{pmatrix}} \overset{4}{\begin{pmatrix}\text{nuclear}\\ \text{rotation}\end{pmatrix}} \overset{5}{\begin{pmatrix}\text{nuclear spin}\\ \text{orientation}\end{pmatrix}}$$

For the normal electronic state of the molecule, since Pauli's principle must be obeyed, the entire function must be antisymmetric in the two electrons, *i.e.* when the electrons are transposed, the sign of the wave function must change. Let us consider the symmetry of each of the above five wave functions with reference to the two electrons. The electron orbital motion function is (see Chapter 3),

$$\psi_1 = \psi_a(1)\psi_b(2) + \psi_b(1)\psi_a(2) \qquad \ldots.(8.10)$$

which on transposition of the electrons gives

$$\psi_1' = \psi_a(2)\psi_b(1) + \psi_b(2)\psi_a(1) \qquad \ldots.(8.11)$$

and hence

$$\psi = \psi_1' \qquad \ldots.(8.12)$$

and the function is symmetric. The electronic spin function is antisymmetric and the nuclear vibration function, the nuclear rotation function and the nuclear spin orientation are independent of the electrons and hence symmetric. The signs of the various functions after transposition of the electrons will therefore be :

$$\begin{matrix} 1 & 2 & 3 & 4 & 5 & \\ (+) & (-) & (+) & (+) & (+) & = (-) \end{matrix}$$

The complete wave function, ϕ, of the molecule is thus antisymmetric as required by Pauli's principle.

The Pauli principle must also apply to the nuclei so that the transposition of the nuclei must lead to an antisymmetric function. Let us now consider the symmetry character of these functions with respect to the nuclei. Transposition of the nuclei in equation 8.10 gives :

$$\psi_1'' = \psi_b(1)\psi_a(2) + \psi_a(1)\psi_b(2) \qquad \ldots.(8.13)$$

(note that the subscripts *a* and *b* have been transposed and not the numerals as in expression 8.11). Again $\psi_1 = \psi_1''$ and the electron orbital motion function is symmetric with reference to the nuclei. The electron spin function is independent of the nuclei and consequently symmetric. The nuclear vibration function will be symmetric for all vibrational states, inasmuch as the variable r, the internuclear distance, is unchanged on transposing the nuclei. The nuclear rotation and nuclear spin functions may be either symmetric or antisymmetric with reference to the nuclei. If one is symmetric then the other must be antisymmetric in order to produce a complete wave function that is antisymmetric. The theory of spin functions has already been discussed in connection with the spin of electrons and the same argument may be applied to protons (see Chapter 3). If the spins are oriented in an antiparallel manner as in parahydrogen then we have an antisymmetric function,

$$\alpha(1)\beta(2) - \beta(1)\alpha(2) \qquad \ldots.(8.14)$$

where the symbol $\alpha(1)\beta(2)$ indicates that proton (1) has a spin of $+\frac{1}{2}$ and the proton (2) has a spin of $-\frac{1}{2}$. The nuclear rotation function must in this case, be symmetric and on interchange of the nuclei we have the following distribution of the signs of the functions :

$$\begin{matrix} 1 & 2 & 3 & 4 & 5 & \\ (+) & (+) & (+) & (+) & (-) & = (-) \end{matrix}$$

the full wave function ϕ thus being antisymmetric. When there is a parallel orientation of the spins of the protons (orthohydrogen) there are three symmetrical spin functions (see Chapter 3) *viz*

$$\left.\begin{matrix} \alpha(1)\alpha(2) \\ \beta(1)\beta(2) \\ \alpha(1)\beta(2) + \beta(1)\alpha(2) \end{matrix}\right\} \qquad \ldots.(8.15)$$

The nuclear rotation function must now be antisymmetric and hence transposition of the nuclei must give rise to the following arrangement of the signs of the functions :

$$\begin{matrix} 1 & 2 & 3 & 4 & 5 & \\ (+) & (+) & (+) & (-) & (+) & = (-) \end{matrix}$$

The solution of the Schrödinger equation for a rotating diatomic molecule shows that interchange of the two nuclei causes a change of sign if the rotational quantum number J, is odd and leaves the function unchanged if J is even. Thus the rotational wave function is symmetric when $J = 0, 2, 4, 6$, *etc* and antisymmetric when $J = 1, 3, 5, 7$, *etc*. The energy of rotation is given by

$$E_J = J(J+1)h^2/8\pi^2 I \qquad \ldots (8.3)$$

which may be conveniently written for the present purpose as :

$$E_J = J(J+1)B \qquad \ldots (8.16)$$

where

$$B = h^2/8\pi^2 I$$

Thus molecules of parahydrogen have values of the rotational energy equivalent to :

J	0	2	4	6	8	.....
E_J	0	$6B$	$20B$	$42B$	$72B$	.....

and orthohydrogen may have the energy values :

J	1	3	5	7	9	.....
E_J	$2B$	$12B$	$30B$	$56B$	$90B$	.....

The ortho and para forms of hydrogen thus possess different amounts of rotational energy (*Table XXXVII*, columns 2 and 3) and consequently different heat capacities since $C = \frac{dE}{dT}$. Therefore properties depending on the specific heat, such as thermal conductivity, will not be identical in the two forms and the method of their identification depends on this fact.

At each temperature there will be a thermodynamic equilibrium between the two forms. At the absolute zero, the molecules must be located at the lowest energy level, *i.e.* $J = 0$, so that only the para modification is stable. At higher temperatures molecules may exist in both odd and even energy levels and in consequence both forms exist. The thermodynamic equilibrium between the two forms is governed by the Boltzmann distribution law. According to this law, the fraction of molecules N_J of the total number N_0 in the rotational state J is given by :

$$N_J = N_0 p_J \exp(-E_J/kT) \qquad \ldots (8.17)$$

where p_J is the statistical weight *i.e.* degeneracy and E_J the energy of the rotational state J. In determining the statistical weight of each state it is necessary to consider separate degeneracies. Thus

$$p_J = g_{J\,rot} \times g_{spin} \qquad \ldots (8.18)$$

Each rotational state will have $2J + 1$ orientations of the angular momentum in an applied field *viz* : $+J, +J-1, \cdots\cdots 0, \cdots\cdots, -J+1, -J$, *i.e.*

$$g_{J\,rot} = 2J + 1 \qquad \ldots (8.19)$$

For the spin degeneracy we have seen that for the antiparallel form (parahydrogen) there is only one spin function (8.14) which corresponds to a value $\Sigma s = 0$ (equation 3.113). For the parallel form (orthohydrogen) there are three spin functions (8.15) corresponding to the values of Σs of $+1$, -1, and 0 (equations 3.114, 3.115, 3.116 *et seq*). Thus the statistical weight of states corresponding to even values of J is :

$$p_{J\,even} = 2J + 1 \qquad \ldots (8.20)$$

and to odd values of J

$$p_{J_{odd}} = 3(2J+1) \qquad \ldots.(8.21)$$

The ratio of the number of molecules of parahydrogen to the number of molecules of orthohydrogen thus may be written:

$$\beta = \frac{[pH_2]}{[oH_2]} = \frac{\sum_{J=0,2,4,6..} p_J \exp\left(-E_J/kT\right)}{\sum_{J=1,3,5,7...} p_J \exp\left(-E_J/kT\right)} = \frac{\sum_{J=0,2,4,6...} (2J+1)\exp\left(-J(J+1)B/kT\right)}{\sum_{J=1,3,5,7...} 3(2J+1)\exp\left(-J(J+1)B/kT\right)} \qquad \ldots.(8.22)$$

For the lowest level, $J=0$ and $(2J+1)\exp\left(-J(J+1)B/kT\right)$ becomes 1;

for $J=1$, $3(2J+1)\exp\left(-J(J+1)B/kT\right)$ becomes $9\exp\left(-2B/kT\right)$ *etc*

and hence

$$\beta = \frac{1+5\exp\left(-6B/kT\right)+9\exp\left(-20B/kT\right)+13\exp\left(-42B/kT\right)+\cdots}{3\left\{3\exp\left(-2B/kT\right)+7\exp\left(-12B/kT\right)+11\exp\left(-30B/kT\right)+\cdots\right\}} \qquad \ldots.(8.23)$$

At high temperatures B is very small compared with kT and $\beta = 1/3$. Thus the ratio is determined only by the statistical weights due to nuclear spin. The value of B may be obtained from spectroscopic data and is $1{\cdot}19 \times 10^{-14}$ gm cm^2 sec^{-2}. The values of β calculated according to equation 8.23 at various temperatures together with the percentage of parahydrogen are given in *Table XXXVI.*

At room temperature ordinary hydrogen is an equilibrium mixture, containing 25 per cent of para and 75 per cent of orthohydrogen molecules. The transfer of one modification to the other does not generally take place spontaneously, but is a very slow process. This is explained by the fact that the transfer from an even to an odd rotational level is accompanied by a change in the spin orientation, and according to WIGNER[17] the probability of the transference occurring by the absorption of light radiation is insignificantly small. Thus when normal hydrogen is cooled, the original ratio of the ortho to the para form is maintained although the proportion of parahydrogen must increase slowly as the system is not in thermodynamic equilibrium. It was this constant ratio of the two forms that permitted DENNISON[13] to explain the temperature change of the heat

Table XXXVI. Percentage of Parahydrogen at Various Temperatures

$T°K$	β	*Parahydrogen per cent*	$T°K$	β	*Parahydrogen per cent*
0	—	100	100	0·6262	38·51
20	554·8	99·82	150	0·3994	28·54
30	32·1	96·98	210	0·3463	25·72
40	7·78	88·61	273	0·3357	25·13
50	3·327	79·89	∞	0·3333	25·00
75	1·077	51·86			

Table XXXVII. Rotational Energy of Hydrogen

$T°K$	*Pure parahydrogen kcals*	*Pure orthohydrogen kcals*	*Equilibrium mixture kcals*	*Normal hydrogen kcals*
0	0·00	337·17	0·00	252·88
20	0·00	337·17	0·63	252·88
50	0·20	337·18	78·38	252·94
100	30·56	338·59	219·78	262·17
200	290·22	393·59	366·76	367·75
273·1	473·34	502·16	494·84	494·91
298·1	529·12	546·92	542·46	542·47

capacity of hydrogen. In *Table XXXVII* are given the energy of rotation of the ortho and para forms together with that of the equilibrium mixture and of normal hydrogen. Even at the absolute zero of temperature, therefore, both modifications exist although thermodynamically orthohydrogen should have all passed into the para form. Each modification will be in the lowest possible energy state, *i.e.* $J = 1$ for orthohydrogen and $J = 0$ for parahydrogen. The presence of the orthohydrogen at the absolute zero produces a residual entropy of 4·39 kcals/degree/gm mol.

The rate of conversion of orthohydrogen into parahydrogen may be accelerated by a catalyst such as active carbon, or paramagnetic ions and molecules. In the last case the transformation is presumably produced by the change of the spin orientation under the influence of the very strong heterogeneous magnetic field operating in the vicinity of the ion or molecule. This fact has been used to determine the paramagnetic susceptibility and to detect free radicals.

Ortho and para forms are known for the molecules D_2, N_2, Cl_2^{35} and Br_2^{79} in addition to H_2.

REFERENCES

[1] BORN, M. and OPPENHEIMER, R. *Ann. Phys.* 84 (1927) 457

[2] KRONIG, R. DE L. *The Optical Basis of the Theory of Valency* Cambridge, 1935
TERENIN. *Introduction to Spectroscopy* Leningrad, 1933
HERZBERG, G. *Molecular Spectra and Molecular Structure* New York, 1939
BOWEN, E. J. *The Chemical Aspects of Light* Oxford, 1946

[3] MORSE, P. M. *Phys. Rev.* 34 (1929) 57

[4] ROSEN, N. and MORSE, P. M. *ibid* 42 (1932) 143
PÖSCHL, G. and TELLER, E. *Z. Phys.* 83 (1933) 143

[5] GAYDON, A. G. *Dissociation Energies and Spectra of Diatomic Molecules* London, 1947

[6] GAYDON, A. G. and PENNEY, W. G. *Proc. roy. Soc.* *A* 183 (1945) 374

[7] PAULING, L. C. and SHERMAN, J. *J. Amer. chem. Soc.* 59 (1937) 1450

[8] WEISS, J. *Trans. Faraday Soc.* 31 (1935) 966

[9] KAZARNOVSKY, Y. S. *J. phys. Chem. Moscow* 14 (1940) 320

[10] HEISENBERG, W. *Z. Phys.* 41 (1927) 93

[11] HUND, F. *ibid* 42 (1927) 93

[12] MECKE, R. *ibid* 28 (1924) 261
— — 31 (1925) 709

[13] DENNISON, D. M. *Proc. roy. Soc.* *A* 115 (1927) 483

[14] BONHOEFFER, K. F. and HARTECK, P. *Z. phys. Chem.* *B* 4 (1929) 113

[15] EUCKEN, A. and HILLER, K. Z. *ibid* 4 (1929) 142

[16] FARKAS, A. *Orthohydrogen, Parahydrogen and Heavy Hydrogen* Cambridge, 1935

[17] WIGNER, E. *Z. phys. Chem.* *B* 23 (1933) 28

9

VIBRATIONAL FREQUENCIES AND INTER-ATOMIC DISTANCES IN POLYATOMIC MOLECULES

RAMAN, MANDELSTAM AND LANDSBERG EFFECTS

THE ANALYSIS of the spectrum of a polyatomic molecule presents many difficulties since the motion of the nuclei in such a molecule is invariably complex. If the molecule consists of n atoms, each atom has three degrees of freedom and hence the total number of degrees of freedom of motion in space will be $3n$. Of these, three will represent the translational motion of the molecule in space and another three will describe the rotation of the molecule about three mutually perpendicular axes. The remaining $3n-6$ degrees of freedom will be associated with the motions of the atoms relative to each other, which involve neither a translation nor a rotation of the molecule. There are therefore $3n-6$ vibrational degrees of freedom, which will correspond to $3n-6$ fundamental modes of vibration of the system. In the particular case of the linear molecule, *e.g.* diatomic molecules and such polyatomic molecules as CO_2 and C_2H_2, there are only two degrees of rotational freedom, that about the axis joining the nuclei and that about an axis perpendicular to the line of centres ; the number of vibrational degrees of freedom will therefore be $3n-5$. The energy levels of the molecule will be obtained by adding the energies of the $3n-6$, or $3n-5$ if the molecule is linear, independent oscillating systems.

For the majority of simple molecules the normal modes of vibration may be obtained by a straightforward, if tedious, procedure and the motion of the atoms relative to each other obtained. In certain cases several normal modes possess the same frequency and the system is degenerate ; this point will be discussed later when we consider specific molecules.

The oscillations of a polyatomic molecule may be divided into two types. First, the valency oscillation in which the atoms move in the direction of the line joining the two nuclei and in which only the internuclear distance changes during the course of the vibration. Secondly, the deformation oscillation in which the valency angle changes. Clearly diatomic molecules can only show vibrations of the valency type.

The multiplicity of the modes of vibration and rotation considerably complicates the interpretation of experimental data, and little progress has so far been made with the analysis of the electronic spectra of polyatomic molecules. The study of vibrational-rotational (infra-red) spectra is less difficult and has led to the determination of interatomic distances, valency angles and vibrational frequencies of some of the simpler polyatomic molecules.

The application and scope of infra-red spectra was considerably extended by the discovery by RAMAN and KRISHNAN and independently of them by LANDSBERG and MANDELSTAM, of what is now known as the Raman effect. When a beam of light passes through a gas, liquid or transparent solid, part of the light is scattered in all directions and if the incident light has a line spectrum, it is found that the scattered light contains exactly the same frequencies as the incident beam. This scattering is termed Rayleigh scattering. However, on closer examination, by taking a spectrogram in which the lines due to Rayleigh scattering are strongly over exposed, some weak additional lines are found which do not appear in the line spectrum of the incident light. An examination of the frequency of the additional lines shows that each one of the original lines is accompanied by one or more lines of weak intensity and furthermore that the difference, $\Delta\nu$, between the original frequency ν_0 and the frequency of the additional Raman line, ν, is independent of ν_0 and dependent only on the nature of the scattering substance.

If E_0 be the energy of the molecule before illumination by the incident radiation, then absorption of a light quantum $h\nu_0$ produces a change in the molecule to an excited state with energy E_2:

$$E_2 = E_0 + h\nu_0 \qquad \ldots .(9.1)$$

The molecule may now either return to the original level by emitting a quantum $h\nu_0$, or return to another level with energy E_1 by the emission of a quantum $h\nu_1$. Thus:

$$E_0 + h\nu_0 = E_1 + h\nu_1 \qquad \ldots .(9.2)$$

or

$$E_1 - E_0 = h\nu_0 - h\nu_1 = h\Delta\nu \qquad \ldots .(9.3)$$

The resultant effect of the series of changes represented by equations 9.1 and 9.2 is the same as if the molecule, in the original state with energy E_0, had absorbed a quantum $h\Delta\nu$ and had thereby been transferred from the E_0 to the E_1 energy level (see *Figure 32*). Raman spectra may be divided into two classes, large Raman displacements in which it is found that the value of $\Delta\nu$ corresponds exactly with the frequencies of band heads in the vibration-rotation spectrum, and small Raman displacements in which the value of $\Delta\nu$ agrees exactly with the frequencies of the lines in the far infra-red, rotational spectrum. Thus both vibrational and rotational transitions may be studied by means of the Raman spectrum and since $\Delta\nu$ is independent of the frequency of the incident radiation, the measurements may be made in the visible part of the spectrum. The infra-red and Raman spectra are not, however, identical since the transitions which occur and which are responsible for the two different types of spectra are governed by different selection rules in the two cases.

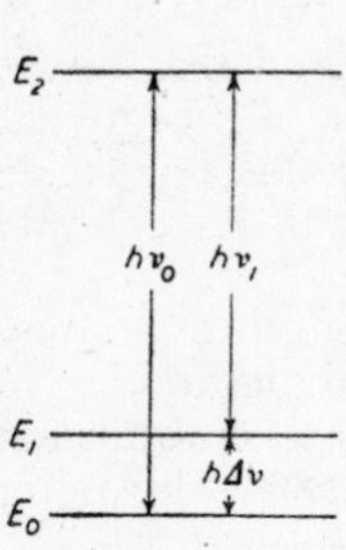

Figure 32. Illustration of the Raman effect

In addition to the frequency ν_1 of the Raman line, which is smaller than that of the incident radiation ν_0, there is also a frequency ν_2 which is greater than ν_0 such that

$$\nu_2 - \nu_0 = \nu_0 - \nu_1 \qquad \ldots .(9.4)$$

This means that a quantum of light $h\nu_2$, greater than the absorbed quantum $h\nu_0$, has been emitted. The explanation of this process is that the molecule was originally in an excited state and returned to a lower energy level after the absorption of light. The lines of smaller frequency than the incident radiation, which will be on the red side of the original line, are termed Stoke's lines, whereas the lines of higher frequency, which will be displaced in the direction of the violet part of the spectrum are termed anti-Stoke's lines. The intensity of the anti-Stoke's lines is much less than that of the corresponding Stoke's lines, since it is less probable that the molecule will be initially in an excited state than in the ground state. The number of molecules in the ground state, with energy E_0 and in an excited state with energy E_1 is governed by Boltzmann's law and the intensities of the Stoke's and anti-Stoke's lines is given by the approximate relation,

$$I_{anti\text{-}Stoke's}/I_{Stoke's} = N_{E_1}/N_{E_0} = \exp\left[-(E_1 - E_0)/kT\right] = \exp(-h\Delta\nu/kT) \quad \ldots.(9{\cdot}5)$$

Certain aspects of infra-red and Raman spectra may be explained on the basis of the classical theory of light absorption and scattering. In order to interact with a stream of electromagnetic waves, a molecule must produce an oscillating electric field. Such homopolar molecules as H_2 and O_2 have no permanent dipole moment and hence during rotation and vibration no fluctuating field is produced. Thus homopolar molecules do not yield a rotation or a vibration-rotation spectrum. Molecules possessing a permanent dipole moment, however, will form a fluctuating electric field during vibration and rotation and therefore give infra-red spectra. It is possible that a molecule in its equilibrium position may have no permanent dipole moment but that on vibration a dipole is produced. This type of behaviour occurs in carbon dioxide. This molecule is linear and although each individual carbon-oxygen bond is polar, *i.e.* there is an equal negative charge on both oxygen atoms, the centres of gravity of the positive and negative charges are at the same point and the molecule as a whole is non-polar.

Let us now consider in detail the possible modes of vibration of the carbon dioxide molecule. In the deformation vibration, the carbon atom is displaced away from the axis of the molecule in one direction and the oxygen atoms are displaced in the opposite direction (see *Figure 33*).

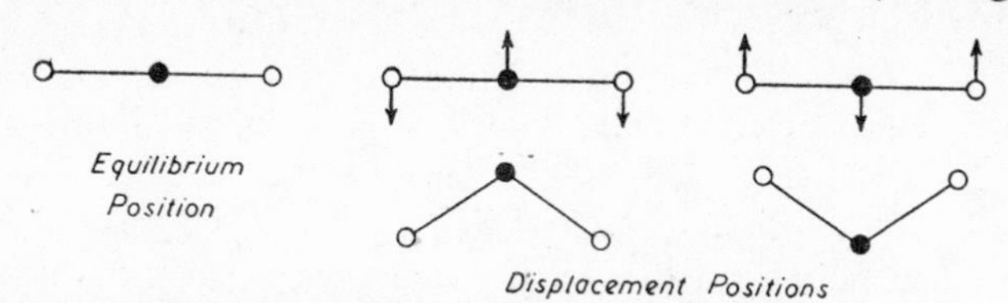

Figure 33. Deformation vibration of carbon dioxide

The previously linear molecule is now bent and the O—C—O angle is no longer 180°. After attaining maximum displacement, the carbon and oxygen atoms return to the axis and are displaced in the opposite directions to those of the initial displacements. During the course of this vibration the centres of gravity of the positive and negative charges separate and a periodically changing dipole moment is produced. Light radiation of corresponding frequency may therefore be absorbed or emitted and this particular mode of vibration of the carbon dioxide molecule produces an infra-red spectrum. In the other two possible modes of vibration of the carbon dioxide molecule the molecule remains linear. In the first case (see *Figure 34*) both oxygen atoms move away from the central carbon atom along the molecular axis and then, after reaching maximum displacement, move back towards the carbon molecule. During the course of this symmetrical vibration no change of dipole moment is produced, the molecule remaining linear and symmetrical. This mode of vibration therefore does not produce an infra-red spectrum. The third possible mode

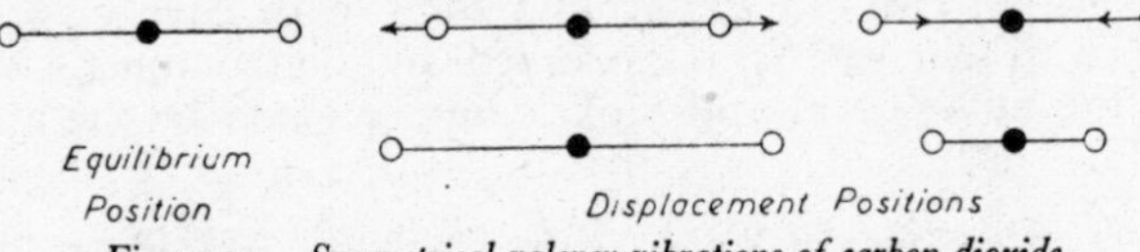

Figure 34. Symmetrical valency vibrations of carbon dioxide

of vibration in the carbon dioxide molecule is shown in *Figure 35*, in which the molecule remains linear, but the vibration is not symmetrical, the carbon atom approaching one oxygen atom whilst receding from the other. This non-symmetrical vibration will give rise to a varying dipole moment and hence give an infra-red spectrum.

Whether or not a particular vibration gives a Raman spectrum depends on a different basis. Under the influence of the incident radiation the molecule is polarized and executes forced vibrations. If a molecule is

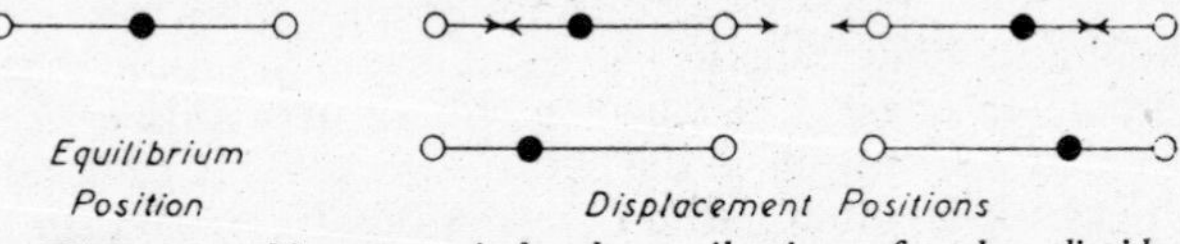

Figure 35. Non-symmetrical valency vibrations of carbon dioxide

introduced into an electric field F, an electric dipole is induced into the system. The resulting dipole moment m is proportional to the strength of the field F and hence we may write,

$$m = \alpha F \qquad \ldots .(9.6)$$

where α is termed the polarizability. The varying electric field due to a light wave of frequency ν_0 is given by

$$F = F_0 \cos 2\pi \nu_0 t \qquad \ldots .(9.7)$$

where t is the time. From equations 9.6 and 9.7 it follows that,

$$m = \alpha F_0 \cos 2\pi \nu_0 t \qquad \ldots .(9.8)$$

During the course of the vibration, the internuclear distance, and consequently the forces acting on the electrons, change. There is therefore no reason why we should assume that α remains constant during the vibration and to a first approximation for small displacements, we may write

$$\alpha = \alpha_0 + \alpha_1 x \qquad \ldots .(9.9)$$

where α_0 is the polarizability in the equilibrium position and $\alpha_1 x$ represents the change in polarizability during the course of the vibration where x is the displacement. For small displacements the molecule may be assumed to execute harmonic vibrations and consequently

$$x = x_0 \cos 2\pi \nu_1 t \qquad \ldots .(9.10)$$

where ν_1 is the vibrational frequency of the molecule. From equations 9.8, 9.9 and 9.10 we obtain

$$\begin{aligned} m &= [\alpha_0 + \alpha_1 x_0 \cos 2\pi \nu_1 t] F_0 \cos 2\pi \nu_0 t \\ &= \alpha_0 F_0 \cos 2\pi \nu_0 t + \alpha_1 F_0 x_0 \cos 2\pi \nu_1 t . \cos 2\pi \nu_0 t \qquad \ldots .(9.11) \end{aligned}$$

and employing the well known trigonometrical expression

$$\cos \alpha \cos \beta = \tfrac{1}{2} \cos (\alpha + \beta) + \tfrac{1}{2} \cos (\alpha - \beta) \qquad \ldots .(9.12)$$

we obtain

$$m = a_0 F_0 \cos 2\pi \nu_0 t + \tfrac{1}{2} a_1 F_0 x_0 \cos 2\pi(\nu_0 + \nu_1)t + \tfrac{1}{2} a_1 F_0 x_0 \cos 2\pi(\nu_0 - \nu_1)t \quad \ldots.(9.13)$$

Thus it is seen that m varies not only with ν_0, the frequency of the incident light, but also with the frequencies $\nu_0 + \nu_1$ and $\nu_0 - \nu_1$. The molecule will therefore emit radiation, not only with the frequency equivalent to the frequency of the absorbed radiation, but also with frequencies $\nu_0 + \nu_1$ and $\nu_0 - \nu_1$. This elementary treatment of the Raman effect shows that the appearance of Raman lines is to be associated with a change of polarizability during oscillation. A more detailed treatment of the Raman effect involves the use of a more complex expression than 9.9 for the variation of α.

If we now return to a further consideration of the symmetrical vibration of the carbon dioxide molecule (see *Figure 34*), it is seen that during the course of the vibration the carbon-oxygen distance changes and consequently the polarizability changes. Thus this mode of vibration which does not give rise to an infra-red spectrum, does produce a Raman spectrum. During the course of the deformation vibration (*Figure 33*), however, the polarizability does not change since the carbon-oxygen distance remains unaltered and hence this particular mode of vibration, although giving an infra-red spectrum, does not produce Raman lines.

In the above discussion we have considered all the possible modes of vibration of carbon dioxide; according to the formula $3n-5$, these should be $(3 \times 3) - 5 = 4$ in number. The four oscillations will be the symmetrical, the non-symmetrical and two deformation vibrations. The deformation oscillation may occur in any plane passing through the axis of the molecule, but all such vibrations may be described by the projections on to two mutually perpendicular planes passing through the molecular axis.

CHARACTERISTIC FREQUENCIES

An extension of the methods described in the preceding section to complicated molecules presents many difficulties, and attempts to analyse the spectra and so determine the molecular constants has been found possible only for relatively simple molecules. For complex organic compounds in particular the complete analysis of the spectra has been found impossible, but information of considerable value may be obtained by following the change in the infra-red spectrum as certain groups are introduced into a particular molecule. This procedure makes possible the formulation of certain empirical rules and leads to the assignment to certain molecular groupings of characteristic frequencies which are generally independent of the structure of the remainder of the molecule. Thus, for example, in the spectra of all saturated mercaptans a line of frequency 2,570 to 2,575 cm^{-1} is found to occur which is absent in the spectrum of the corresponding hydrocarbons. Furthermore, in the spectrum of the hydrogen sulphide molecule, there exists a line of frequency 2,578 cm^{-1} and hence it is concluded that the frequency 2,573 ± 3 cm^{-1} is characteristic of the S—H link. In exactly the same way characteristic frequencies are found for the C≡N and $C{-}NH_2$ groups (see *Table XXXVIII*). The very small variation in the values of the frequencies justifies the conclusion that the corre-

Table XXXVIII.
Characteristic Frequencies [cm^{-1}]

R	*Mercaptans* RSH	*Nitriles* RCN	*Amines* RNH_2
CH_3	2,572	2,249	3,372
C_2H_5	2,570	2,243	3,369
C_3H_7	2,575	2,244	3,377
C_4H_9	2,575	2,240	3,371
C_5H_{11}	2,573	2,242	—
Average value	2,573	2,244	3,372

sponding molecular vibrations are characteristic of a particular bond or group and do not depend on the remaining part of the molecule. Such frequencies as those given in *Table XXXVIII* are termed the characteristic frequencies of a particular bond or group. A knowledge of these characteristic frequencies will clearly be most useful in the analysis of complex spectra, and the assignment of particular lines to certain groups.

However, the use of characteristic frequencies must be carried out with care since variations of the characteristic frequencies from the normal value do occur in certain instances. Such variations are generally due either to the resonance of the molecule between valence bond structures or to the existence of relatively heavy atoms near to the bond concerned. For this reason it is preferable to refer to the characteristic frequency range of a particular bond. Many such frequency ranges are now known and are based on a considerable amount of experimental data. Thus, for example, frequencies greater than 2,500 cm^{-1} are characteristic of bonds involving the lighter elements ; the valency vibrations of the C—H bond lies in the range 2,800 to 3,300 cm^{-1}, the N—H bond at 3,300 cm^{-1}, the O—H bond between 3,350 and 3,450 cm^{-1} and the S—H bond at 2,570 cm^{-1}. The valency vibrations of bonds involving the heavier atoms have lower frequency values, and the deformation vibrations still lower values. Thus the vibrations in $-CH_3$ and $>CH_2$, in which the H—C—H bond angle is deformed, have values between 1,300 and 1,400 cm^{-1}, deformation vibrations involving the first carbon atom of the hydrocarbon chain, *i.e.* the C—C—H bond angle, lie in the range 800 to 1,200 cm^{-1} and the deformation vibrations of the carbon chain, *i.e.* the C—C—C bond angle, fall in the range 300 to 400 cm^{-1}.

In diatomic molecules it was observed that the vibration frequency increased with the multiplicity of the bond and similar behaviour occurs in polyatomic molecules. The frequency of the C—C bond lies in the range 800 to 1,200 cm^{-1} and increases to 1,600 cm^{-1} for the C=C bond and to 2,100 cm^{-1} for C≡C. Similar behaviour is observed in bonds between other atoms and the data are summarized

Table XXXIX. Vibrational Frequencies of Multiple Bonds

Molecule	*Bond*	*Frequency* cm^{-1}
	Triple bonds (*6 bonding electrons*)	
HCCH	C≡C	1,960
CO	C≡O	2,150
RCN	C≡N	2,250
	Nitric oxide (*5 bonding electrons*)	
NO	N⋯O	2,211
	Double bonds (*4 bonding electrons*)	
H_2CCH_2	C=C	1,620
R_2CO	C=O	1,720
CH_3CHNOH	C=N	1,650
CH_3ONO	N=O	1,640
	Single bonds (*2 bonding electrons*)	
H_3CCH_3	C—C	990
CH_3OH	C—O	1,030
CH_3NH_2	C—N	1,030
NH_2OH	N—O	1,000

in *Table XXXIX*. On comparing the frequencies associated with different types of bonds between various atoms it is apparent that the vibrational frequencies of bonds of different multiplicity lie in certain frequency ranges. Thus the frequencies of single, double and triple bonds lie in the region of 1,000 cm^{-1}, 1,600 cm^{-1} and 2,100 cm^{-1} respectively. Some of the bonds whose frequencies are quoted in *Table XXXIX* are not pure covalent bonds but contain a certain proportion of ionic character. The variable amounts of ionic character in different bonds will slightly alter the frequencies but, nevertheless, it is seen that the frequencies remain within the same region and the assignment of particular values or ranges of values to a particular type of bond is not invalidated.

We shall now discuss various types of bonds and consider how the vibrational frequency changes with changes in the rest of the molecule.

The carbonyl group—Compounds containing the carbonyl group have been the subject of many investigations and a considerable amount of experimental data has accumulated concerning the vibrational frequencies of the C=O bond. In a series of saturated ketones the value for the frequency of 1,710 cm^{-1} remains constant irrespective of the chain length; similar behaviour has been observed in the saturated aldehydes where the frequency is slightly different, being 1,720 cm^{-1}. Similar constancy of the vibrational frequency is observed in many other compounds, *e.g.* carboxylic acids, esters and acid chlorides (see *Table XL*). Let us compare the values for the ketones, the carboxylic acids and the acid chlorides. In the carboxylic acids the frequency is noticeably lowered in comparison to the

Table XL. Vibrational Frequency of the C=O *bond* (cm^{-1})

R	$RCOCH_3$	RCHO	RCOOH	$RCOOCH_3$	$RCOOC_2H_5$	RCOCl
CH_3	1,706	1,715	1,663	1,736	1,736	1,798
C_2H_5	1,711	1,722	1,651	1,735	1,731	1,786
n-C_3H_7	1,710	1,718	1,654	1,734	1,731	1,791
iso-C_3H_7	1,709	1,721	1,649	1,733	1,729	—
n-C_4H_9	1,709	1,717	1,652	1,732	1,731	1,792
iso-C_4H_9	1,709	1,717	1,652	1,732	1,734	—
sec-C_4H_9	1,708	1,718	1,646	1,732	1,728	—
tert-C_4H_9	1,702	1,721	1,645	1,729	1,728	—
n-C_4H_{11}	1,709	1,720	1,653	1,738	1,734	—
iso-C_5H_{11}	1,709	1,720	1,653	1,738	1,734	1,794
sec-C_5H_{11}	1,701	1,725	1,643	1,728	1,721	—
n-C_6H_{13}	1,710	1,721	1,654	1,737	1,732	—
n-C_7H_{15}	—	1,723	1,652	1,734	1,737	—
n-C_8H_{17}	—	1,721	1,654	1,736	—	—
n-C_9H_{19}	1,710	1,722	1,649	1,737	—	—

ketones: 1,650 cm^{-1} instead of 1,710 cm^{-1}; in the acid chlorides it is raised to 1,790 cm^{-1}. In the ketones there is a bond resonance in the carbonyl group between the valence bond structures $>C{=}O$ and $>C^{+}{-}O^{-}$, molecular resonance involving the structure

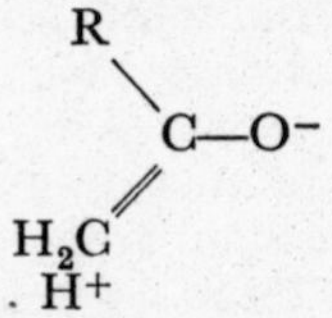

```
       R
        \
         C—O⁻
        //
    H₂C
     . H⁺
```

making a smaller contribution. In the acid chlorides, the strongly electronegative chlorine atom may be regarded as competing with the oxygen atom for the negative charge and new valence bond structures occur which contribute to the final state of the molecule. Apart from the resonance in the CO and CCl bonds we shall have the following structures :

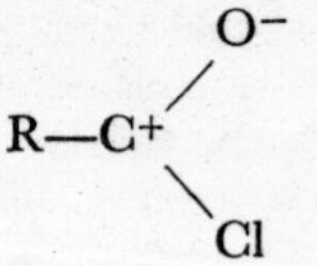

```
          O⁻                        O
         /                         //
   R—C⁺                      R—C⁺
         \
          Cl                        Cl⁻
       I                         II
```

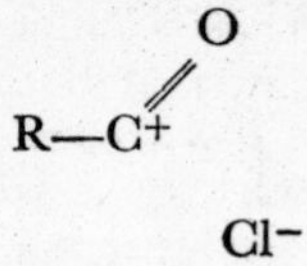

and also a new type of structure in which the chlorine is negative, not with reference to the carbon as in *II*, but with the oxygen,

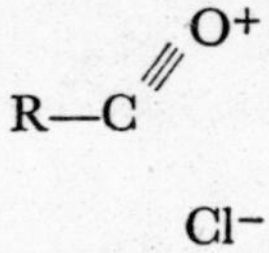

```
          O⁺
         ///
   R—C

          Cl⁻
        III
```

Thus the CO bond becomes partially a triple bond and experimental data (*Table XXXIX*) show that as the multiplicity of a bond increases, so also does the vibrational frequency of the bond, in agreement with the results in *Table XL.* In addition to the above three valence bond structures, there will also be a contribution from structure *IV*,

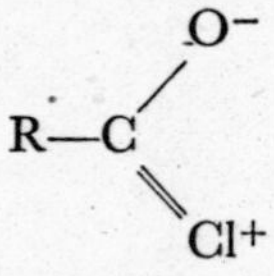

```
          O⁻
         /
   R—C
         \\
          Cl⁺
        IV
```

but in view of the greater electronegativity of chlorine compared with oxygen this structure is less probable than the structures *I*, *II*, and *III*.

In the carboxylic acids an additional valence bond structure occurs. Because of the contribution of the structure *VI*,

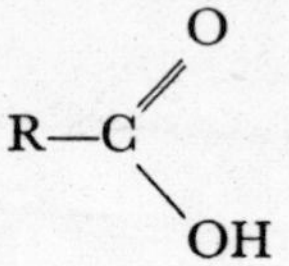

```
          O                         O⁻
         //                        /
   R—C                       R—C
         \                         \\
          OH                        O⁺—H
       V                         VI
```

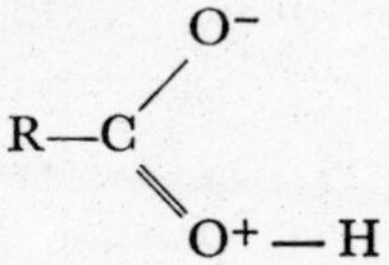

the single bond character of the carbonyl group is increased, with the result that the vibrational frequency is decreased.

Table XLI. Vibrational Frequencies in Carboxylic Acids and Corresponding Anions

Molecule	*Frequency* cm^{-1}		
HCOOH	1,400	—	1,657
$HCOO^-$	1,351	—	—
CH_3COOH	1,370	1,436	1,666
CH_3COO^-	1,347	1,413	—

In the anions of the carboxylic acids the characteristic carbonyl frequency is absent although a characteristic frequency of 1,350 to 1,400 cm^{-1}, present in the acids is retained (see *Table XLI*). This is evidently due to the fact that in the anions, both oxygens are equally charged and the two carbon-oxygen bonds are identical and equivalent to 1·5 bonds. The two structures *VII* and *VIII* will thus contribute equally to the structure of the molecule :

$$R{-}C({=}O){-}O^- \qquad\qquad R{-}C(O^-){=}O$$

VII *VIII*

In gaseous formaldehyde and also in strong solutions of the sodium salts of carboxylic acids, frequencies of 1,768 cm^{-1} have been observed. HIBBEN[1] and KRISCHNAMURTI[2] noticed that in dilute solutions this frequency decreased and there was a certain similarity of the spectrum to that of glycol. These authors have proposed that during the dilution process the formation of $CH_2(OH)_2$ occurs.

In *Table XLII* the values of the vibrational frequency of the carbonyl group in molecules of the type

$$\begin{matrix} R_1 \\ & \diagdown \\ & & C{=}O \\ & \diagup \\ R_2 \end{matrix}$$

are given, and the observed frequencies are in agreement with the resonance structures of the corresponding compounds.

Table XLII. Vibrational Frequencies of Carbonyl Group in Molecules of type $R_1CO\,R_2$ *(*cm^{-1}*)*

R_1	R_2				
	NH_2	C_6H_5	H	OC_2H_5	Cl
NH_2	1,655	1,652	1,671	1,692	1,731
C_6H_5	—	1,653	1,696	1,715	1,768
H	—	—	—	1,715	—
OC_2H_5	—	—	—	1,743	1,772
Cl	—	—	—	—	1,810

In urea, $(NH_2)_2CO$, a considerable lowering of the frequency is observed on account of the contribution of the structure *IX* to the resonance of the molecule.

$$\begin{matrix} {}^+NH_2 \\ & \diagdown\!\!\diagdown \\ & & C{-}O^- \\ & \diagup \\ NH_2 \end{matrix}$$

IX

This view is supported by dipole moment measurements and by other properties. The highest frequency of the carbonyl group exists in phosgene,

$COCl_2$, in which structures *X* and *XI* containing a triple carbon-oxygen bond contribute to the molecule.

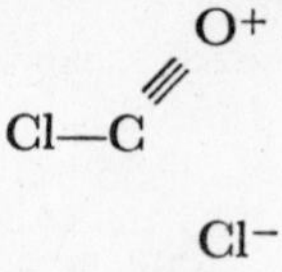

O^+ ≡ C—Cl, Cl^- ^-Cl C ≡ O^+, Cl

X 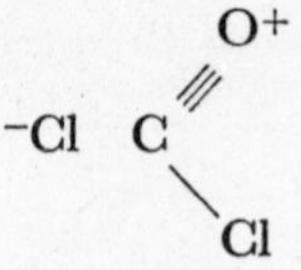   *XI*

The groups OH, NH_2 and C_6H_5 increase the contribution of structures containing a single carbon-oxygen bond, C—O^-, thereby lowering the frequency. On the other hand, the presence of chlorine, as in phosgene increases the contribution of the triple bond structure, C≡O^+, and the frequency is thereby increased. It is interesting to note that in the molecule NH_2COCl, the negative charge is shared between the —NH_2 group and the chlorine atom, with the result that the vibrational frequency of the carbonyl group is raised to a less extent than in the other cases discussed above.

In acetophenone $C_6H_5COCH_3$, the frequency of the carbonyl group has the value 1,684 cm^{-1} which is lower than in the case of acetone 1,706 cm^{-1}. This will be due to the contribution of the structure *XII*, thus increasing the single character of the bond.

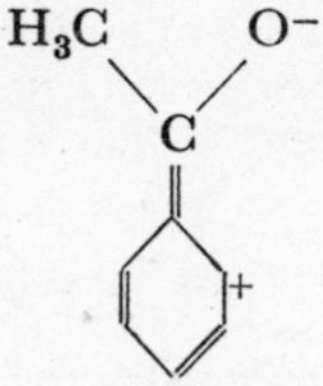

H_3C O^- C   +

XII

In acetyldurene *XIII* and acetylmesitylene *XIV*:

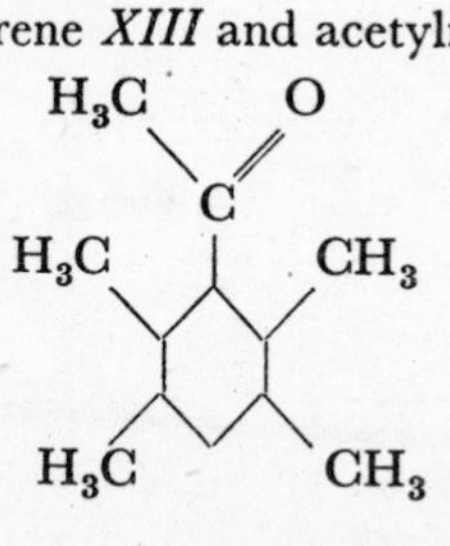

H_3C O   C H_3C CH_3 H_3C CH_3 H_3C O   C H_3C CH_3 CH_3

XIII 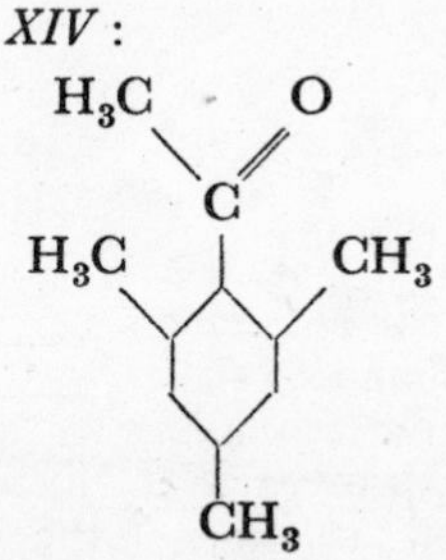   *XIV*

the frequency (1,699 cm^{-1}) is not decreased to any significant extent[3], although it would appear that similar resonance structures involving the ring system would contribute to the structure of the molecule. However, conditions for resonance incorporating structures of the type *XII* are most favourable when the carbonyl group is in the plane of the ring. Only under these conditions is the transfer of the π electrons at a maximum. In acetyldurene and acetylmesitylene, the methyl groups in the *ortho* position prevent the acetyl group from lying in the plane of the ring, the orbitals of the π electrons are thus not parallel and the electron transfer is made more difficult. Thus structures of the type *XII* make a much smaller contribution to the structure of the molecule in the case of acetyldurene and acetylmesitylene and the frequency of the carbonyl group is therefore greater than in acetophenone. In mesitylaldehyde,

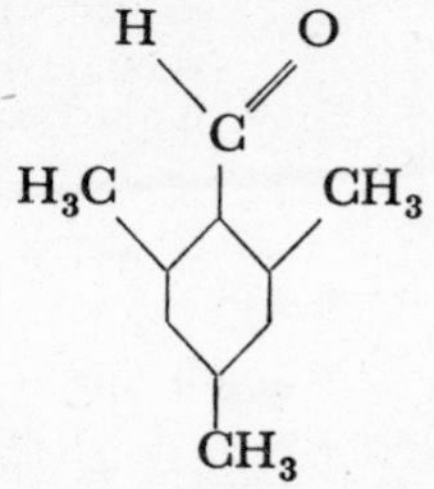

H O

C

H_3C CH_3

CH_3

XV

the aldehyde group has been shown to be in the plane of the benzene ring[4], resonance structures involving the ring will thus be possible in agreement with the low value for the frequency of the carbon-oxygen bond *viz* 1,687 cm^{-1}.

The structural formula of betaine is often given as

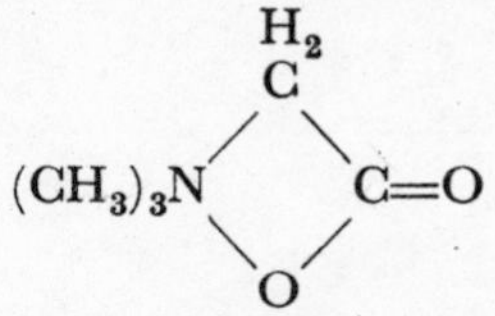

H_2

C

$(CH_3)_3N$ C=O

O

XVI

involving a four membered heterocyclic ring and a pentavalent nitrogen atom. However, a dipolar ionic zwitterionic structure *XVII* is more in accordance with modern views and furthermore is in agreement with

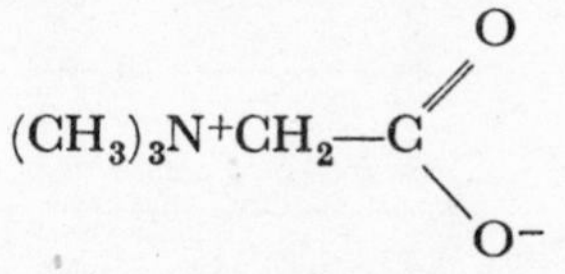

O

$(CH_3)_3N^+CH_2—C$

O^-

XVII

the insolubility of betaine in aprotic organic solvents and its marked solubility in water. If the cyclic structure *XVI* were correct, the spectrum should contain the characteristic frequency for the carbonyl group. In the case of the dipolar ion structure *XVII*, the carbon-oxygen bond would be equivalent to 1·5 bonds and the characteristic frequency of the carbonyl group should be absent. Experiment has shown[5] that in the spectrum of betaine there is no line with a frequency of 1,700 cm^{-1}, although lines are found with frequencies of 1,336, 1,394 and 1,416 cm^{-1}. Evidently the dipolar ionic form represents the correct structure. In the same manner, amino acids exist in the zwitterionic form $^+NH_3RCOO^-$ and give spectral lines at 1,330 to 1,360 and 1,410 to 1,420 cm^{-1}. On conversion to the corresponding hydrochloride, the intensity of the first group weakens

Table XLIII. Vibrational Frequencies in Amino Acids and Derivatives

Molecule	Frequency cm^{-1}	
$^{+}NH_3CH_2COO^{-}$	1,331	1,412
$ClNH_3CH_2COOH$	1,315	—
$^{+}NH_3CH(CH_3)COO^{-}$	1,358	1,416
$ClNH_3CH(CH_3)COOH$	1,356	—
$^{+}NH_3CH(C_2H_5)COO^{-}$	1,358	1,413
$ClNH_3CH(C_2H_5)COOH$	1,363	—

and the second group disappears (see *Table XLIII*)[6].

The spectrum of betaine thus reveals a marked similarity to that of the carboxylate anions and differs considerably from the spectra of compounds containing a carbonyl group. This example illustrates the use of Raman spectra in the solution of structure problems.

The double bond, C=C —The double bond in ethylene and in substitution products of ethylene gives a Raman spectrum in the region 1,600 to 1,680 cm^{-1}. In ethylene the value is 1,620 cm^{-1}, and on the introduction of methyl groups into the molecule the frequency increases, as shown in *Table XLIV*. In the di-substituted compounds the values for the *cis* and *trans* forms are different from each other and different from that in which both methyl groups are attached to the same carbon atom. This distinction may be used as a method of distinguishing between isomers.

Table XLIV. Frequencies of Some Ethylenic Hydrocarbons

Molecule	Frequency cm^{-1}	Molecule	Frequency cm^{-1}
$CH_3CH{=}CH_2$	1,647	$(CH_3)_2C{=}CHCH_3$	1,679
$CH_3CH{=}CH\,CH_3$ *cis*	1,669	$(CH_3)_2C{=}C(CH_3)_2$	1,674
$CH_3CH{=}CH\,CH_3$ *trans*	1,681		
$(CH_3)_2C{=}CH_2$	1,654		

In the monosubstituted ethylenes (*Table XLV*), there is very little change in the frequency as the size of the substituent group is increased and it would appear that with propylene the maximum shift of the frequency had been attained. However, there are a number of substituent groups which lower the value of the frequency by an appreciable amount (*Table XLVI*) and it would appear from the nature of such substituents that this change is associated with the contribution of valence bond structures to the resonance of the molecule in which the ethylenic bond has single bond, rather than double bond character. In the lowering of the frequency, the mass of the substituent

Table XLV. Frequencies of Some Monosubstituted Ethylenes

Molecule	Frequency cm^{-1}	Molecule	Frequency cm^{-1}
$C_2H_5CH{=}CH_2$	1,642	$C_7H_{15}CH{=}CH_2$	1,642
$C_3H_7CH{=}CH_2$	1,642	$C_5H_9CH_2CH{=}CH_2$	1,642
$C_4H_9CH{=}CH_2$	1,642	$CH_2OHCH{=}CH_2$	1,649
$C_5H_{11}CH{=}CH_2$	1,642	$CH_3CH\,OH\,CH{=}CH_2$	1,646
$C_6H_{13}CH{=}CH_2$	1,642		

group may play an important part and a semiquantitative treatment for the halogen vinyl compounds[7] has shown that approximately one third of the frequency shift can be attributed to the influence of mass and the remaining two thirds to the resonance effect. Resonance in vinyl compounds between, for example, the valence bond structures :

Table XLVI. Raman Frequencies in $RCH{=}CH_2$ *Compounds*

R	*Alternative structure*	*Frequency* cm^{-1}	*Frequency lowering compared to* $CH_3CH_2{=}CH_2$
C_6H_5	$^+CH_2{-}CH{=}C_6H_5^-$ (quinonoid ring)	1,631	− 16
$C{\equiv}N$	$^+CH_2{-}CH{=}C{=}N^-$	1,608	− 39
Cl	$^-CH_2{-}CH{=}Cl^+$	1,608	− 39
Br	$^-CH_2{-}CH{=}Br^+$	1,598	− 49
$C{\equiv}CH$	$^+CH_2{-}CH{=}C{=}C^-{-}H$	1,595	− 52
I	$^-CH_2{-}CH{=}I^+$	1,581	− 66
OC_2H_5	$^-CH_2{-}CH{=}O^+{-}C_2H_5$	1,635	− 12

$$CH_2{=}CH{-}Cl \quad \text{and} \quad {}^-CH_2{-}CH{=}Cl^+$$

is supported by the observed increase of the carbon-carbon distance, the decrease of the dipole moment in comparison with the saturated compounds and by the change of chemical behaviour. Where the resonating groups are separated by a group which cannot partake in the molecular resonance the characteristic frequency of the ethylenic group is retained (*Table XLVII*).

Table XLVII. Ethylenic Bond Frequency where Resonance Cannot Occur

Molecule	*Frequency* cm^{-1}	*Molecule*	*Frequency* cm^{-1}
$CH_2{=}CHCH_2OCOCH_3$	1,649	$CH_2{=}CHCH_2Cl$	1,640
$CH_2{=}CHCHOHC{\equiv}CH$	1,646	$CH_2{=}CHCH_2Br$	1,635
$CH_2{=}CHCHOHCH{=}CH_2$	1,646	$CH_2{=}CHCHBrCH_3$	1,638
$CH_2{=}CHCH_2C{\equiv}CC_6H_5$	1,642	$CH_2{=}CHCH_2C_6H_5$	1,642
$CH_2{=}CHCHClCH_3$	1,640		

Molecules containing both ethylenic and carbonyl groups and in which resonance may occur, show a change in the multiplicity of both the CC and the CO bonds. Both give reduced Raman frequencies (*Table XLVIII*), indicating an increase in single bond character. Organic radicals are found to have the following sequence in their effect on the frequency of the ethylenic double bond :

$$COOH < COOC_2H_5 < OC_2H_5 < C_6H_5 < CHO <$$
$$< Cl < COCl < CN < Br < C{\equiv}CH < I$$

Similar general behaviour is observed with the poly-substituted derivatives of ethylene ; if only one of the substituent groups is effective in changing the resonance of the molecule, the change of frequency of the double bond is analogous to that observed with the corresponding monosubstituted derivative. If several of the substituent groups or molecules participate in the resonance of the molecule, however, the problem is more complex and empirical relationships can no longer be formulated.

Table XLVIII. Frequency of C=C *and* C=O *Bonds in Molecules of the type* $CH_2{=}CHR$

R	*Alternative structure*	$\nu_{C=C}$	$\Delta\nu_{C=C}$	$\nu_{C=O}$	$\Delta\nu_{C=O}$
COOH	$^{+}CH_2{-}CH{=}C(OH)(O^{-})$	1,637	−10	1,657	0
COOR	$^{+}CH_2{-}CH{=}C(OR)(O^{-})$	1,635	−12	1,720	−15
CHO	$^{+}CH_2{-}CH{=}C(H)(O^{-})$	1,618	−29	1,692	−30
COCl	$^{+}CH_2{-}CH{=}C(O^{-})(Cl)$; $^{+}CH_2{-}CH{=}C({=}O)\ Cl^{-}$	1,609	−38	1,752	−34

Allene, $CH_2{=}C{=}CH_2$, and its derivatives are an exception among compounds containing a carbon-carbon double bond, in that there is no Raman frequency in the range 1,600 to 1,680 cm^{-1}, although characteristic frequencies occur in the region 1,080 to 1,130 cm^{-1}. This may be explained by the fact that the vibration of two carbon atoms, as in the double

Table XLIX. Raman Frequencies of Triple Bond, C≡C

Molecule	*Frequency* cm^{-1}	*Molecule*	*Frequency* cm^{-1}
$CH_3C{\equiv}CH$	2,123	$CH_3C{\equiv}CCH_3$	2,234
$C_4H_9C{\equiv}CH$	2,121	$C_2H_5C{\equiv}CCH_3$	2,238
$(CH_3)_2CHCH_2C{\equiv}CH$	2,118	$C_3H_7C{\equiv}CCH_3$	2,238
$C_5H_{11}C{\equiv}CH$	2,118	$C_4H_9C{\equiv}CCH_3$	2,235
$C_6H_{13}C{\equiv}CH$	2,119	$C_5H_{11}C{\equiv}CCH_3$	2,233
$CH{\equiv}C(CH_2)_5C{\equiv}CH$	2,119	$C_5H_{11}C{\equiv}CCH_2OH$	2,226
$C_6H_5CH_2C{\equiv}CH$	2,120	$C_5H_{11}C{\equiv}CCH(CH_3)(OCH_3)$	2,240
$CH_3OCH_2C{\equiv}CH$	2,118		
$CH_2OHC{\equiv}CH$	2,118	$(C_5H_{11}C{\equiv}C)_2CHOH$	2,250
$(CH_3)_2(OH)CC{\equiv}CH$	2,120	$(C_5H_{11}C{\equiv}C)_3COH$	2,236

bond C=C, cannot occur in this molecule and will be replaced by the valency vibration of all three carbon atoms.

The triple bond, C≡C — The Raman frequency of the triple bond in acetylene is 1,960 cm^{-1}, on monosubstitution this value is increased to about 2,120 cm^{-1} and with the di-substituted derivatives is raised to approximately 2,235 cm^{-1} (see *Table XLIX*).

Bonds involving Nitrogen — The C≡N bond has a Raman frequency of approximately 2,250 cm^{-1} in saturated aliphatic nitriles. In C_6H_5CN, however, owing to the contribution of the valence bond structure with a double bond between the carbon and nitrogen :

N^-
C
+

the frequency is lowered to the value 2,227 cm^{-1}. In the molecule $C_6H_5CH_2CN$, where molecular resonance involving the benzene ring can no longer take place, the frequency has the value of 2,252 cm^{-1}. A comparison of the nitriles and the isonitriles shows that different valence bond structures in which the charge on the nitrogen molecule is different contribute to the resonance of the molecules. The frequency of the CN bond in CH_3NC is less than in CH_3CN by over 100 cm^{-1} (CH_3CN, 2,261 cm^{-1}; CH_3NC, 2,146 cm^{-1}) which can only signify that the contribution of the structure containing a double bond, *viz* R—N=C, is greater in the isonitrile than in the nitrile, where a separation of charge occurs *viz* R—C^+=N^-.

In the aliphatic nitro derivatives, Raman frequencies characteristic for the nitro group occur at 1,383 cm^{-1} and 1,555 cm^{-1}. These values are between those observed in compounds containing a single N—O bond (approximately 1,000 cm^{-1}) and those containing a double N=O bond (approximately 1,640 cm^{-1}). In nitrobenzene these characteristic frequencies are lower, being 1,345 cm^{-1} and 1,523 cm^{-1} respectively, which is most probably due to molecular resonance with the benzene ring and the contribution of the structure :

O^- O^-
N^+
+

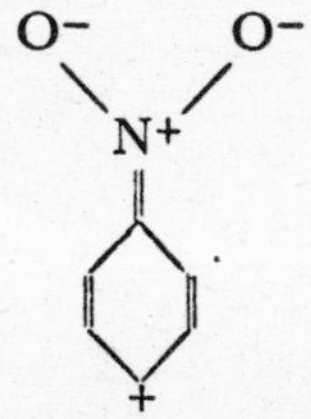

in which the nitrogen-oxygen bond is single. In nitromesitylene the corresponding frequencies are 1,363 cm^{-1} and 1,523 cm^{-1}. The slight shift in the direction of the frequencies of aliphatic nitro compounds has been interpreted[3] as indicating that the methyl groups in nitromesitylene prevent the nitro group from lying in the plane of the ring, thereby reducing the molecular resonance. This view is supported by the dipole moment data (see Chapter 10).

In dimethyl nitrosamine the molecule may be represented as a resonance hybrid of the two structures :

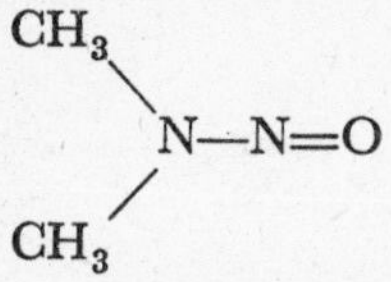

$$(CH_3)_2N{-}N{=}O \quad \text{and} \quad (CH_3)_2N^+{=}N{-}O^-$$

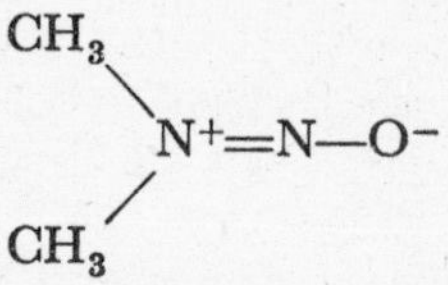

and hence both the NN and the NO bonds will possess double bond character. This view is in agreement with the existence[8] of a Raman frequency of 1,399 cm^{-1} which lies between the single and double bond frequencies of the NO bond (see above).

Applications of the Raman effect— In the above discussion we have seen that the so-called characteristic frequencies may vary, being dependent on the nature of the bond and on the adjacent atoms or groups. Nevertheless, the spectra of homologous substances have many similarities and this fact may be used for analytical purposes. Thus impurities in, for example, pure hydrocarbons can be readily detected by Raman spectra.

The differences in the Raman spectra of *cis* and *trans* isomers may be used to identify these forms. As a result of the greater symmetry of the *trans* isomer, the number of degenerate vibrations is greater and hence there are fewer spectral lines than in the case of the *cis* isomer.

Table L. Raman Frequencies in Acetoacetic Acids

Molecule	*Frequency cm^{-1}*		
$CH_3COC(CH_3)_2COOCH_3$	—	—	1,710
$CH_3COCH(CH_3)COOCH_3$	1,595	—	1,718
$CH_3COCH_2COOCH_3$	1,595	1,655	1,723
$CH_3COCH_2COOCH_3$ *in hexane solution*	1,602	1,641	—

One of the earliest applications of the Raman effect was to *keto-enol* tautomerism. Thus in the case of acetoacetic ester, a characteristic frequency corresponding to that of the C=C bond is observed. In the *keto* form, $CH_3COCH_2COOC_2H_5$, such a bond does not occur, nor does such a bond exist in the hydrolysis products (acetone, CH_3COCH_3 and ethyl acetate, $CH_3COOC_2H_5$). The presence of this frequency shows that in acetoacetic ester the *enol* form, $CH_3C(OH){=}CHCOOC_2H_5$, must exist in equilibrium with the *keto* form. In dimethylated acetoacetic ester, enolization cannot occur and the only observed frequency is that characteristic of the carbonyl group (see *Table L*). The monomethylated derivative shows a weak Raman line at 1,595 cm^{-1}, which is a frequency corresponding to the double bond C=C, together with the frequency for the carbonyl group. The solution of acetoacetic ester in hexane gives a Raman spectrum in which there is no line corresponding to the carbonyl frequency and it must therefore be concluded that this solution consists mainly of the enolic form.

Raman spectroscopy has also been used to identify the intermediate products of exchange reactions. Thus, for example, in the mixed crystal of $SnCl_4$ and $SnBr_4$ new lines occur, which have been interpreted as indicating the existence of $SnBr_3Cl$, $SnBr_2Cl_2$ and $SnBrCl_3$.

INTERATOMIC DISTANCES

For a number of comparatively simple polyatomic molecules the moments of inertia and hence the internuclear distances may be calculated from the rotational fine structure. In addition to the spectroscopic method, interatomic distances and valency angles may also be determined by x-ray and electron diffraction. Thus an exact quantitative picture of the molecule may be made whenever it has been possible to make the necessary calculations. In those cases where the same quantity, *e.g.* the interatomic distance, has been determined by more than one method the agreement between the two values is generally found to be good.

The CC *bond*— The considerable amount of data that has accumulated for various interatomic distances, show that it is almost a constant quantity, almost independent of the nature of the adjacent atoms or groups but dependent on the multiplicity of the bond. This conclusion is illustrated in *Table LI* for the single bond, C—C, which for a wide variety of substances is found to have an interatomic distance of 1·54 Å. In the double bond, C=C, the four bonding electrons hold the atoms together more strongly and the interatomic distance is reduced to 1·34 Å. (Values for : ethylene, 1·34 Å ; stilbene, 1·33 Å ; benzophenone, 1·32 Å ; ketene, 1·35 Å ; allene, 1·34 Å). In acetylene, with six bonding electrons, the internuclear distance is 1·20 Å (values : for diacetylene, 1·20 Å ; dibromacetylene, C_2Br_2, 1·20 Å ; di-iodoacetylene, C_2I_2, 1·18 Å ; and in monohalogen derivatives, HC≡CHal, 1·20 Å).

Table LI. Single Bond Carbon—Carbon Distances

Molecule	*Interatomic distance Å*	*Molecule*	*Interatomic distance Å*
Diamond	1·54	*Butylbromide*	1·55
Ethane	1·55	*Nonacosane*	1·54
Propane	1·54	*Paraldehyde*	1·54
Isobutane	1·54	*Metaldehyde*	1·54
n–Pentane	1·54	*trans–2, 3–Ethoxybutane*	1·54
Cyclopropane	1·53	*cis–2, 3–Ethoxybutane*	1·54
Cyclopentane	1·52	*Tetrahydrofuran*	1·54
Cyclohexane	1·53		

As has been shown previously some links cannot be regarded simply as pure single or pure double bonds, but are of an intermediate type. In benzene for example, the bonds have 50 per cent double bond character and the value for the interatomic distance is 1·40 Å, which is between the values for a single and a double bond. In cyclic molecules similar to benzene, *e.g.* pyridine, pyrazine, pyrrole, thiophene, dibenzyl, tetramethylbenzene, naphthalene, anthracene, chrysene, hexachlorbenzene, *etc*, the value for the interatomic distance of the cyclic carbon atoms varies only between 1·39 and 1·41 Å. In quinone,

where the double and single bonds are fixed, x-ray data show that the double bond distance is 1·32 Å and the single bond distance 1·50 Å.

There exist a number of compounds in which the distance between two adjacent carbon atoms is less than 1·54 Å, although in the structural formula the links are represented as single bonds (*Table LII*). This alteration of the bond length is due to the fact that alternative valence bond structures contribute to the state of the molecule. In these alternative valence bond structures, bonds normally represented as single bonds appear as double bonds and thus in every case, owing to the partial double bond character of these links, the interatomic distance is less than the accepted value for the single bond, C—C (1·54 Å).

Table LII. Carbon-Carbon Distances in Resonating Molecules

Molecule	*Bond*	*Interatomic distance Å*	*Example of alternative valence bond structure*
$CH_2{=}CH{-}CH{=}CH_2$	HC—CH	1·46	$CH_2{-}CH{=}CH{-}CH_2$ (ends joined by dotted line)
(ring, atoms 1, 2, 3, 4, 5)	2—3	1·46	(ring structure)
$CH{\equiv}C{-}C{\equiv}CH$	C—C	1·36	$CH{=}CH{=}CH{=}CH$ (ends joined by dotted line)
$N{\equiv}C{-}C{\equiv}N$	C—C	1·36	$N{=}C{=}C{=}N$ (ends joined by dotted line)
$C_6H_5CH{=}CHC_6H_5$	$C_{al}{-}C_{ar}$	1·44	=CH—CH—
$C_6H_5C{\equiv}CC_6H_5$	$C_{al}{-}C_{ar}$	1·40	=C=C—
$CH_3C{\equiv}CH$	$C{-}CH_3$	1·46	$^{+}H\ CH_2{=}C{=}^{-}CH$
$CH_3C{\equiv}C{-}C{\equiv}CCH_3$	{ $C{-}CH_3$ { C—C	1·46 1·38	$^{+}H\ CH_2{=}C{=}C{=}^{-}CCH_3$
$HC{\equiv}C{-}CH_2Hal$	C—C	1·47	$^{+}CH{=}C{=}CH_2Hal$
(ring, atoms 1, 2, 3, 4, O)	2—3	1·46	− (ring) O+
(ring, atoms 1, 2, 3, 4, N—H) (ring, atoms 1, 2, 3, 4, S)	2—3	1·44	− (ring) +N—H − (ring) S+
(fused rings, atoms 1, 2)	1—2	1·46	(fused ring structure)
$H_3C{-}C{\equiv}C{-}CH{=}GH_2$	{ $H_3C{-}C$ { ≡C—CH=	1·47 1·42	$^{+}H\ CH_2{=}C{=}C^{-}{-}CH{=}CH_2$ $CH_3{-}C{=}C{=}CH{-}CH_2$ (ends joined by dotted line)

Although most of the data given in *Table LII* has been confirmed, there is still some doubt about the value for the $C_{aliphatic}—C_{aromatic}$ bond in methylbenzenes and stilbene. The older data show small values for $C_{aliphatic}—C_{aromatic}$ bonds in polyphenyls and in durene, but more recent measurements on hexamethylbenzene[9] show that the length of this bond is 1·53 Å. Furthermore, there is some doubt as to whether the distance between the benzene rings in diphenyl is less than the bond length of a single C—C bond[10].

The dependence of bond length on the bond multiplicity, however, is not quite so simple as might be imagined from the data given above. This complexity may be illustrated by a more detailed examination of diacetylene, $\underset{1}{HC}\equiv\underset{2}{C}—\underset{3}{C}\equiv\underset{4}{CH}$. The bond length in the 'single' 2–3 bond is less than a normal single bond having a value of 1·36 Å, *i.e.* it has been lowered almost to the value for a double bond. We may consider that this has taken place by a considerable contribution to the resonance of the molecule of the structure HC=C=C=CH (the two terminal carbons joined by a dotted line), but if this is so, it is reasonable to assume that the bond distances in the acetylenic bonds, 1–2 and 3–4 must be correspondingly increased. This is not supported by the experimental data and these acetylenic bond distances have the value 1·20 Å as in acetylene. Other instances are known where the contribution of valence bond structures, involving an alteration of the bond multiplicity, has been shown by independent methods, which is not in agreement with the measured bond length. Thus the dipole moment of isobutylene, 0·49 D, suggests that structures of the type :

$$\begin{array}{l} H^{+}H_2C \\ \quad\quad \diagdown \\ \quad\quad\quad C—C^{-}H_2 \\ \quad\quad \diagup \\ H_2C \end{array}$$

contribute to the resonance of the molecule. Nevertheless, the experimental data give a value of 1·54 Å for the $C—CH_3$ bond distance, thus indicating the absence of double bond character. Anomalies of a similar type occur with such molecules as tetramethylethylene, mesitylene, hexamethylbenzene and 2-butene. It would appear that a re-examination of the molecular constants of molecules showing these anomalous properties is desirable.

The CH *bond*—In methane the C—H bond distance is 1·09 Å and in acetylene 1·06 Å. The greatest bond distance, 1·12 Å is observed in the molecule CH. It is probable that the decrease of the bond distance from this value is related to the nature of the bonding orbitals of the carbon atom. In CH, the bond is formed by a p electron of the carbon atom and an s electron of the hydrogen and in CH_4, C_2H_4 and C_2H_2 the carbon bonding orbital is sp^3, sp^2 and sp respectively. Before any satisfactory theory can be made, however, more exact values for the bond distance must be obtained. Indirect evidence in favour of this sequence is given by the Raman frequencies which are : in CH 2,824 cm^{-1}; in CH_4 2,870 cm^{-1}; in C_2H_4 3,000 to 3,100 cm^{-1} and in C_2H_2 3,320 cm^{-1}, and by the calculated exchange energies of the CH bond which are 50, 91, 96 and 97 kcals for the bond involving a p, sp^3, sp^2 and sp electron of carbon respectively.

Table LIII. Interatomic Distances of Single Bond, C—O

Molecule	*Interatomic distance Å*	*Molecule*	*Interatomic distance Å*
Dimethylether	1·44	*cis*-2, 3–*Ethoxybutane*	1·43
Dioxan ..	1·46	*trans*-2, 3–*Ethyoxybutane*	1·43
Paraldehyde	1·43	*Tetrahydrofuran* ..	1·43
Metaldehyde	1·43	α–*Methylhydroxylamine*	1·44

Table LIV. Interatomic Distance in Multiple Bonds between Carbon and Oxygen

Molecule	*Interatomic distance Å*	*Molecule*	*Interatomic distance Å*
HCHO	1·21	$(HCOOH)_2$	1·25; 1·36
CH_3CHO	1·20	HCOONa	1·27
CO	1·13	COOH | COOH $2H_2O$	1·24–1·30
CO_2	1·15		
COS	1·16	$Be_4O(CH_3COO)_6$	1·29
$CH_2{=}C{=}O$	1·17	$CaCO_3$	1·31
C_3O_2	1·20	BH_3CO	1·13
$CO(NH_2)_2$	1·25		
NH_2CH_2COOH	1·25–1·27	$Ni(CO)_4$	1·15

The CO *bond*—For the single C—O bond a constant characteristic value of the interatomic distance is obtained for a number of molecules (*Table LIII*). The case of the double bond C=O is rather different from that of the ethylenic bond C=C, since the C=O bond is not homopolar and contributions from other valence bond structures, with a separation of charge and a different multiplicity of the bond, always occur. In aldehydes and ketones, for example, the structure $>C^+{-}O^-$ contributes to the resonance of the molecule and in carbon dioxide the structure $O^-{-}C{\equiv}O^+$ occurs. In *Table LIV*, the internuclear distances of this bond in various molecules is given. In aldehydes the CO bond distance is 1·20 Å and very probably the same distance occurs in ketones. In urea, because of the contribution of the structure

$$\begin{matrix} {}^+NH_2 & & \\ & \diagdown & \\ & & C{-}O^- \\ & \diagup & \\ NH_2 & & \end{matrix}$$

in which the carbonyl group has single bond character, the bond distance is lengthened in comparison with the aldehydes. In the carboxylate ion, both CO groups are identical and equivalent to 1·5 bonds, the internuclear distance being 1·27 to 1·29 Å. The data at present available suggest that the carbon-oxygen bond distances are different in the acids, but more exact measurements are required. In the carbonate ion CO_3^{2-}, each bond possesses 0·33 double bond character owing to the resonance that exists between the three structures;

$$\begin{matrix} & O^- \\ O{=}C & \\ & O^- \end{matrix} \qquad \begin{matrix} & O \\ O^-{-}C & \\ & O^- \end{matrix} \qquad \begin{matrix} & O^- \\ O^-{-}C & \\ & O \end{matrix}$$

and the distance is 1·31Å. A contribution from a triple bonded structure will cause a marked decrease in the interatomic distance as in BH_3CO, in which resonance occurs between $H_3B^-—C^+=O$ and $H_3B^+—C\equiv O^-$, and probably also in the acid chlorides where the possible valence bond structures are

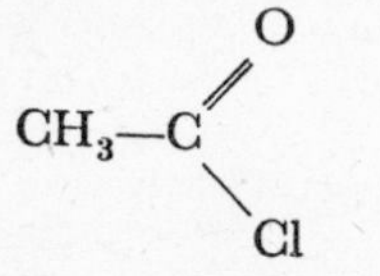

$$CH_3—C(=O)—Cl \quad \text{and} \quad CH_3—C(\equiv O^+)\ Cl^-$$

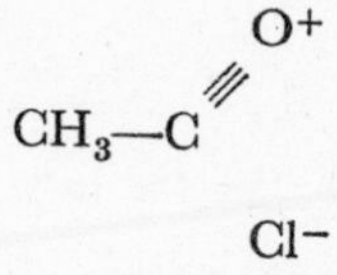

The CS *bond*— The CS bond is very similar in its properties to the carbonyl group. The single bond distance is 1·82 Å in $(CH_3)_2S$. In thiophene it is decreased to 1·74 Å and in thiourea, where similar valence bond structures to those in urea are also possible, the bond distance, according to x-ray data, is 1·64 Å.

The CN *bond*— Values for the internuclear distance in the CN bond are given in *Table LV*. The single C—N bond has a length of 1·47 Å in $N(CH_3)_3$. In pyrrole, pyridine, pyrazine, urea and thiourea it is decreased, a fact evidently connected to the possible contribution of structures containing multiple bonds :

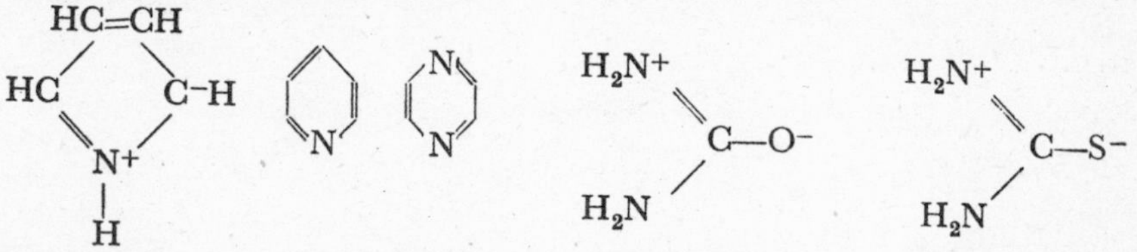

HC=CH, HC, C–H, N+, H (pyrrole); pyridine (N); pyrazine (N, N); H_2N^+=C—O^- with H_2N; H_2N^+=C—S^- with H_2N

According to the experimental data of Boersch[11], the C—N—N atoms of diazomethane are arranged linearly and it therefore follows that the structures :

$$H_2C=N^+=N^- \qquad H_2C^-—N^+\equiv N$$

will make a considerable contribution to the resonance of the molecule. In agreement with this, the C—N distance is lower, having the value 1·34 Å. In dicyanogen, methyl cyanide and methyl *iso*cyanide the CN bond is partly a double and partly a triple bond,

$$N\equiv C—C\equiv N \qquad N=C=C=N \qquad N^-=C^+—C\equiv N$$

$$CH_3—C\equiv N \qquad CH_3—C^+=N^-$$

$$CH_3—N=C \qquad CH_3—N^+\equiv C^-$$

and the bond distance is found to lie between 1·15 and 1·18 Å.

The valency angles, in addition to the bond distances, may be determined from electron diffraction studies and the magnitude of the bond angle may be regarded as an indication of the extent of the contribution of various valence bond structures in which the angle is different. For example, methyl *iso*cyanide is generally considered as being a linear mole-

Table LV. Interatomic Distances in CN *Bond*

Molecule	*Interatomic distance* Å	*Molecule*	*Interatomic distance* Å
$N(CH_3)_3$	1·47	C_4H_5N (*pyrrole*)	1·42
CH_3NO_2	1·46	C_5H_5N (*pyridine*)	1·36
$CH_3{-}N{=}N{-}CH_3$	1·47	$C_4H_4N_2$ (*pyrazine*)	1·36
CH_3N_3	1·47	$CO(NH_2)_2$	1·37
$\overset{1}{CH_3}{-}\overset{2}{N}{=}\overset{3}{C}$	1·44 (1–2) 1·18 (2–3)	$CS(NH_2)_2$	1·35
		CH_2N_2	1·34
$C_6H_{12}N_4$ (*Hexamethylenetetramine*)	1·42	CH_3CN	1·15
		$(CN)_2$	1·16

cule in which a considerable contribution is made by the structure $CH_3{-}N^+{\equiv}C^-$ in which the nitrogen forms two σ bonds at 180° to each other. However, the structure $CH_3{-}N{=}C$, in which the bond angle is 90°, must also make a contribution to the structure of the molecule. Attempts[12] to measure the bond angle in methyl *iso*cyanate show that the angle cannot be measured with the desired accuracy and the conclusion was made that the angle is between 160° and 180°. In certain cases it is impossible to decide the multiplicity of a particular bond. In dicyandiamide the arrangement of the atoms in space according to x-ray data is :

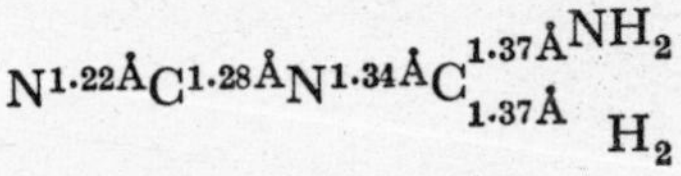

$$N^{1.22\text{Å}}C^{1.28\text{Å}}N^{1.34\text{Å}}C\begin{matrix}^{1.37\text{Å}}NH_2\\ _{1.37\text{Å}}\;H_2\end{matrix}$$

This molecule is generally represented as having the formula

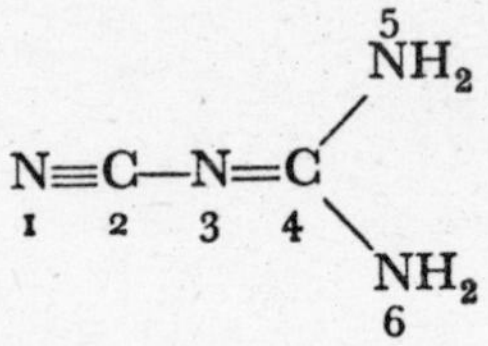

$$\underset{1}{N}{\equiv}\underset{2}{C}{-}\underset{3}{N}{=}\underset{4}{C}\begin{matrix}\diagup \overset{5}{NH_2}\\ \diagdown \underset{6}{NH_2}\end{matrix}$$

I

which is clearly not in agreement with the observed bond distances. Thus the C—NH_2 bond distance (1·37 Å) is only very slightly longer than the C=N (3–4) distance (1·34 Å) and there is no justification for regarding the 3–4 bond as double and the 4–5 and 4–6 as single bonds. Furthermore, the 2–3 distance, represented in formula *I* as a single bond, has a value of 1·28 Å, less than the 3–4 distance, 1·34 Å, which is represented as a double bond. Thus we may conclude that the contribution of the structure *I* is not great and that resonance between formulae *II*, *III* and *IV* involving a separation of charge, gives a more accurate description of the molecule.

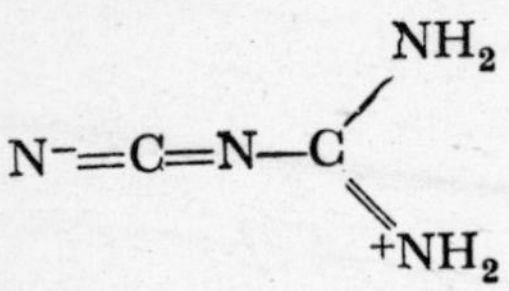

$$N^-{=}C{=}N{-}C\begin{matrix}\diagup NH_2\\ \diagdown\!\!\diagdown {}^+NH_2\end{matrix} \qquad N^-{=}C{=}N{-}C\begin{matrix}/\!/ {}^+NH_2\\ \diagdown NH_2\end{matrix} \qquad N^-{=}C{=}N^+{=}C\begin{matrix}\diagup NH_2\\ \diagdown NH_2\end{matrix}$$

II 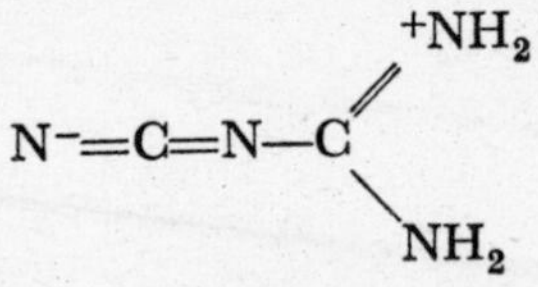 *III* 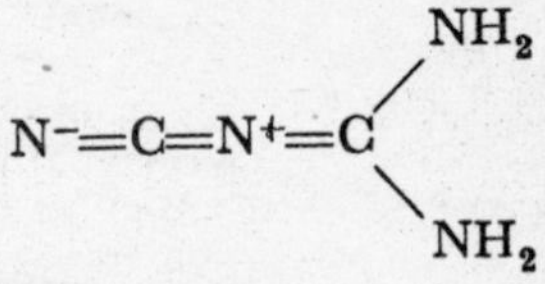 *IV*

Phthalocyanine is generally represented by the structure *V*

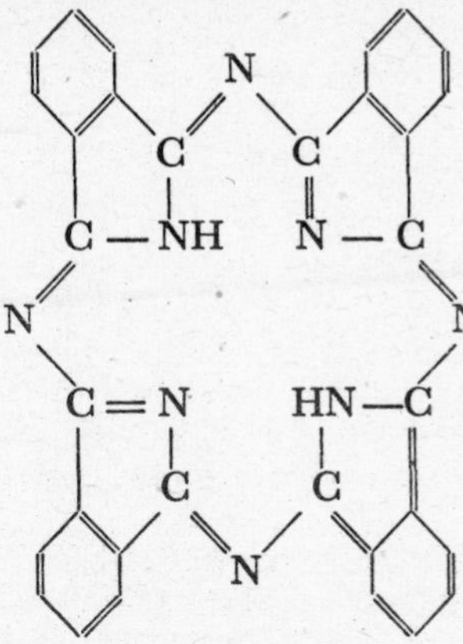

V

and x-ray data [13] have shown that the molecule is flat and that the bond distances and angles are as given in *VI*. The inner system of sixteen alternating nitrogen and carbon atoms is particularly interesting since this system occurs in a number of naturally occurring substances. All the C—N bond distances are found to be equal and have the value 1·34 Å. This fact clearly indicates that any localization of the double bonds as in formula *V* is incorrect and all the bonds have an equal multiplicity.

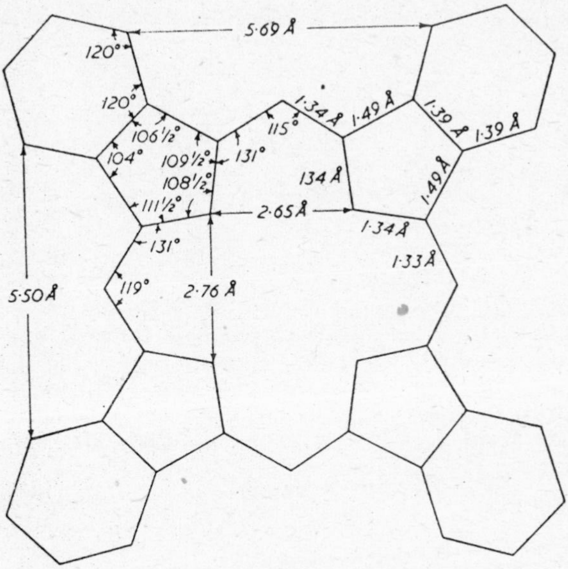

VI

The distance between adjacent carbon atoms in the benzene rings is 1·39 Å and that in the five-membered heterocyclic rings is 1·49 Å, being a little less than the normal value for a single C—C bond, 1·54 Å, owing to the contribution of structure of the type :

The exact position of the two central hydrogen atoms cannot be established by x-ray methods, but since the distances between the central nitrogen atoms are 2·65 Å and 2·76 Å it would appear that the two hydrogen atoms form a hydrogen bridge between those two nitrogen atoms that show the shorter interatomic distance, 2·65 Å. On replacement of the hydrogen by a metal atom, the distance between the nitrogen atoms is somewhat distorted[14].

Interesting information concerning the CN bond is forthcoming from the x-ray data of ROBERTSON[15] and of HAMPSON and ROBERTSON[16] on the *cis* and *trans* isomers of azobenzene. The *trans* form *VII* is flat and

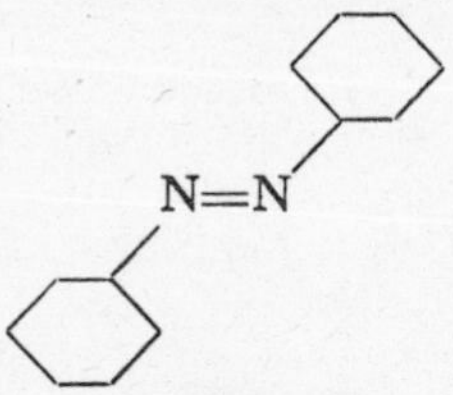

N=N

VII

the C—N distance has the value 1·41 Å, in agreement with the suggestion that the bond will have some double bond character owing to the contribution of the valence bond structure *VIII*,

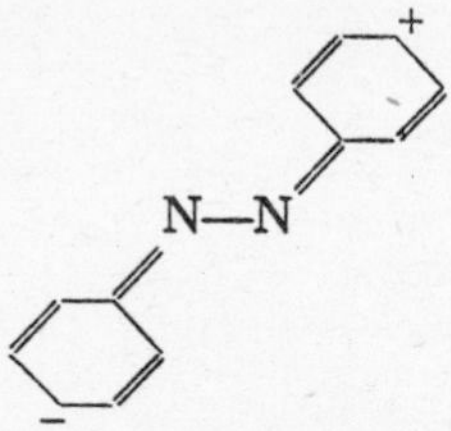

+

N—N

−

VIII

In *cis* azobenzene, steric factors prevent the molecule being flat owing to the interference of the two hydrogen atoms in the *ortho* position, and the C—N—N system (the C being in a benzene ring) is not linear, with the result that a valence bond structure of the type *VIII* cannot contribute to the molecular resonance. The CN bond distance is found to be 1·46 Å as in the single bond and the molecule is represented correctly by the formula *IX*.

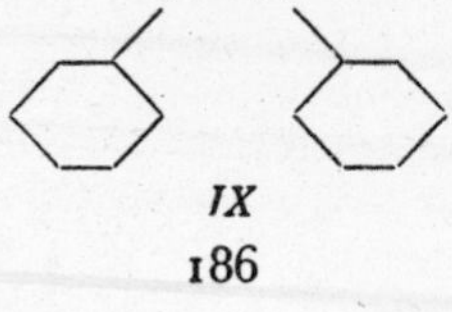

N=N

IX

The Carbon-Halogen bond—In saturated compounds containing halogen, the CCl bond has the value of 1·71 Å (see *Table LVI*). In chlorine substituted vinyl and benzene molecules the distance is decreased (*Table LVII*), which will be due to the contribution of structures of the type :

$$H_2C^-{-}C(=Cl^+){-}H \qquad\qquad C_6H_5^-{=}Cl^+$$

in which the bond between the carbon and chlorine atoms is double. We have already seen that in vinyl chloride the C—C bond is increased to 1·38 Å, in accordance with this structure. These structures are also in agreement with the dipole moment data. In propargyl chloride, H—C≡C—CH_2Cl, the CCl bond distances possess the very high value[17] of 1·82 Å, owing to the contribution of the structure : H—C$^+$=C=CH_2 Cl^- in which the chlorine is in the fully ionic state. In phosgene the distance between the carbon and chlorine atoms is 1·68 Å and in thiophosgene 1·70 Å.

Table LVI. Interatomic Distances in CCl *Bond*

Molecule	*Interatomic distance Å*	*Molecule*	*Interatomic distance Å*
CH_3Cl	1·77	$CHFCl_2$	1·73
CH_2Cl_2	1·77	$CFCl_3$	1·76
$CHCl_3$	1·77	CF_2Cl_2	1·74
CCl_4	1·755	CCl_3CHO	1·76
CH_2FCl	1·76		

Table LVII. Interatomic Distance of CCl *Bond in Unsaturated Molecules*

Molecule	*Interatomic distance Å*	*Molecule*	*Interatomic distance Å*
$CH_2{=}CHCl$	1·69	*p*–$C_6H_4Cl_2$	1·69
$CH_2{=}CCl_2$	1·69	*m*–$C_6H_4Cl_2$	1·69
$CHCl{=}CHCl$ (*cis*)	1·67	*o*–$C_6H_4Cl_2$	1·71
$CHCl{=}CHCl$ (*trans*)	1·69	1, 3, 5—$C_6H_3Cl_3$	1·69
$CHCl{=}CCl_2$	1·71	1, 2, 4, 5—$C_6H_2Cl_4$	1·72
C_2Cl_4	1·73	C_6Cl_6	1·70
C_6H_5Cl	1·69		

In the fluorine derivatives of methane and chloromethanes the variation of the CF bond is somewhat complex. As is seen in *Table LVIII*, the bond length varies from 1·42 Å to 1·35 Å. Pauling considers this to be due to the contribution of structures of the type

Table LVIII. Interatomic Distances of CF *Bond*

Molecule	*Interatomic distance Å*	*Molecule*	*Interatomic distance Å*
CH_3F	1·42	$CHFCl_2$	1·41
CH_2F_2	1·36	$CFCl_3$	1·40
CF_4	1·36	CHF_2Cl	1·36
CH_2FCl	1·40	CF_2Cl_2	1·35

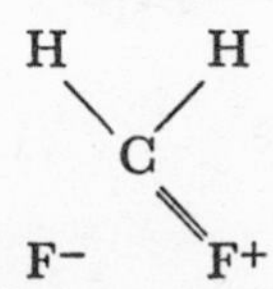

to the resonance of the molecule. This explanation, however, is not in agreement with the dipole moment data for these compounds[18].

The data for the bromine and iodine compounds are as yet insufficient for discussion. The most reliable values of the bond length in CBr and CI bonds are 1·91 Å and 2·12 Å respectively.

The NN, NO *and* OO *bonds*— The interatomic distance between two nitrogen atoms forming a single bond is known from hydrazine in which alternative valence bond structures are not possible, and according to the results of GIGUÈRE and SCHOMAKER[19], the value is 1·48 Å. The double bond distance N=N in azomethane, $CH_3—N=N—CH_3$, is 1·24 Å, whereas in diazomethane the bond distance is 1·13 Å.

The single bond O—O distance is obtained from hydrogen peroxide and is found to be 1·48 Å. SHAND and SPURR[20] established the following configuration for ozone,

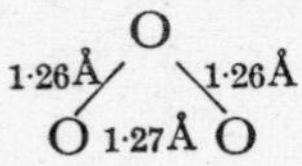

O
1·26Å / \ 1·26Å
O 1·27Å O

which is in agreement with the dipole moment data of PHILLIPS, HUNTER and SUTTON[21], who consider that ozone is best described as a resonance hybrid of the structures

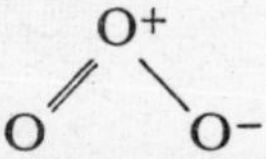

O^+ (=O, —O^-) *two structures* — O (=O, O) *two structures*

The single bond N—O distance in NH_2OCH_3 is 1·37 Å. In the nitro group, where the bonds are equivalent to 1·5 bonds, owing to the resonance of the type

$CH_3—N^+(=O)(—O^-)$ — $CH_3—N^+(—O^-)(=O)$

both bonds have a length of 1·21 Å.

The structure of anhydrous nitric acid is interesting since the three NO bonds are not identical and the experimental evidence[22] suggests that the molecule consists of an hydroxyl group and a nitro group. There are two NO bond lengths of 1·21 Å, and one of 1·4 Å, thus corresponding to the formula

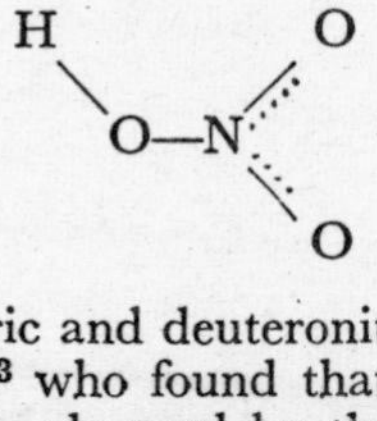

H—O—N(⋯O)(⋯O)

The Raman spectra of nitric and deuteronitric acids have been examined by REDLICH and NIELSEN[23] who found that the characteristic frequencies of the hydroxyl group were changed by the substitution of deuterium for hydrogen. Solution in water brings about the formation of the nitrate ion in which all the oxygen atoms are identical and the O—N—O bond angle is in each case equal to 120° (sp^2 hybridization). The structure of th nitrate ion will therefore be a resonance hybrid of the three forms

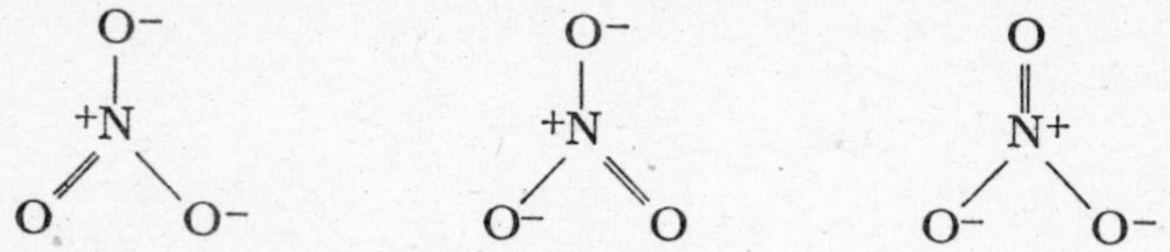

```
     O⁻                    O⁻                   O
     |                     |                    ‖
    +N                    +N                    N+
   //  \                 /  \\                 /  \
  O     O⁻             O⁻     O              O⁻    O⁻
```

in which the bond lengths are all 1·21 Å.

In the oxide of trimethylamine, $(CH_3)_3NO$, the electron diffraction data of LISTER and SUTTON[24] show that the NO bond distance is 1·36 Å which is approximately the value for a single bond. If the nitrogen were pentavalent, the bond would be double and the distance less and evidently, in the amine oxides, structures of the type $(CH_3)_3N—O$, make a large contribution. In nitrosyl chloride and nitrosyl bromide the NO bond length is decreased, from 1·11 to 1·14 Å, which suggests that the bond is a hybrid of the structures

```
    N=O                 N≡O⁺
   /
  X                     X⁻
```

and the multiplicity of the bond is between two and three.

COVALENT RADII

During recent years the application of the methods of x-ray and electron diffraction to the determination of the structure of molecules has permitted interatomic distances of a large number of bonds to be obtained and attempts have been made to find simple additive laws which will describe the observed data. In the case of ionic crystals the suggestion was made that each ion could be regarded as a small sphere, which just touch each other in the crystal. To each ion, therefore, there may be ascribed an ionic radius which is maintained by the ion in all crystals of a particular type, for example, in which the coordination number of the ion remains the same. For different coordination numbers of a particular ion, it is necessary to give different ionic radii.

Although the idea of ions being likened to rigid spheres which are in contact in the crystal state is clearly incorrect when we consider the wave mechanical conception of a molecule or an ion, it has proved of considerable use in studies of the solid state. In the same way also, radii may be ascribed to atoms taking part in a covalent bond, such that the addition of the radii gives the interatomic distance. In this case, different values of the radius will have to be taken, depending on whether a given atom is taking part in a single, double or triple bond. For the construction of a table of covalent radii, half the measured bond lengths in homonuclear molecules are taken. By this means the radii of the atoms in Cl_2, Br_2, Na_2 *etc* may be obtained. The covalent radius of nitrogen is taken as half the N—N single bond distance in hydrazine, and the double bond distance is similarly obtained from azomethane.

The conception of a covalent radius may be tested by considering the hydrides. The covalent radius of the hydrogen atom as measured from molecular hydrogen will be half the bond length, *viz* 0·37 Å. In *Table LIX*,

Table LIX. Covalent Radius of Hydrogen determined from Hydrides

Bond H—X	*Molecule*	*Interatomic distance* H—X *Å*	*Half of interatomic distance* X—X *Å*	*Covalent radius of hydrogen Å*
H—H	H_2	0·74	0·37	0·37
C—H	CH	1·12	0·77	0·35
C—H	CH_4	1·09	0·77	0·32
C—H	C_2H_2, HCN	1·06	0·77	0·29
N—H	NH	1·04	0·74	0·30
N—H	NH_3	1·01	0·74	0·27
O—H	OH	0·97	0·74	0·23
O—H	H_2O	0·97	0·74	0·23
S—H	H_2S	1·35	1·05	0·30
F—H	HF	0·92	0·72	0·20
Cl—H	HCl	1·27	0·99	0·28
Br—H	HBr	1·42	1·14	0·28
I—H	HI	1·60	1·33	0·27
Li—H	LiH	1·60	1·33	0·27
Na—H	NaH	1·89	1·54	0·35
K—H	KH	2·24	1·96	0·28

the value of the covalent radius of the hydrogen atom has been determined from the data for the hydrides, and it is seen that the radius varies from 0·37 to 0·20 Å. This variation might possibly be attributed to the variation of the ionic character of the bond; that this is not so, is shown by the fact that for the case of the most homopolar bonds *e.g.* H—H, H—I, H—C, the variation is still large, being from 0·27 to 0·37 Å, whereas in the series H—Cl, H—Br and H—I, where there is a marked change in the ionic character of the bond, the value of the radius is almost constant (0·27–0·28 Å).

The experimental value of the internuclear distance in gaseous sodium chloride is 2·51 Å; the sum of the covalent radii is 2·53 Å whereas the sum of the ionic radii is 2·48 Å. In obtaining this figure, allowance has been made for the decrease, by about 11 per cent, of the ionic radii in the gaseous molecule compared with that in the ionic lattice. A similar result is obtained in the case of sodium bromide and iodide. Since the radius of the positive ion is less, and that of the negative ion is greater, than the corresponding covalent radii, it would appear that differences have been compensated.

In order to improve the agreement between the calculated and experimental values, Pauling[25] has taken average values. Thus, for fluorine the radius is taken as 0·64 Å rather than 0·72 Å, for hydrogen 0·30 Å instead of 0·37 Å. In *Table LX*, these values of the covalent radii for several elements are given, as corrected by Shomaker and Stevenson[26].

Table LX. Covalent Radii (Å)

H 0·30–0·37	C 0·77	N 0·74	O 0·74	F 0·72
Li 1·34	Si 1·17	P 1·10	S 1·04	Cl 0·99
Na 1·54	Ge 1·22	As 1·21	Se 1·17	Br 1·14
K 1·96	Sn 1·40	Sb 1·41	Te 1·37	I 1·33

In *Tables LXI* and *LXII*, experimental values of bond lengths are compared with the sums of the covalent radii and it will be seen that the agreement is not good. Nevertheless, the idea of covalent radii is often useful in spite of the lack of a theoretical basis, since they permit an approximate evaluation of

Table LXI. Comparison of Experimental Values of Interatomic Distances and Sums of Covalent Radii for Halogen Compounds (Å)

Element	*Compound*	F		Cl		Br		I	
		expt.	*calc.*	*expt.*	*calc.*	*expt.*	*calc.*	*expt.*	*calc.*
B	BX_3	1·30	1·62	1·74	1·89	1·87	2·04	—	—
C	CX_4	1·36	1·49	1·76	1·76	1·94	1·96	2·15	2·10
N	NOX†	—	—	1·98	1·73	2·14	1·88	—	—
O	OX_2	1·41	1·46	1·68	1·73	—	—	—	—
Si	$SiCl_4$	1·54	1·89	2·00	2·16	2·14	2·31	2·43	2·50
P	PX_3	1·52	1·82	2·00	2·09	2·23	2·24	2·52	2·43
S	SX_2	1·57*	1·76	2·00	2·03	—	—	—	—
As	AsX_3	1·72	1·93	2·16	2·20	2·36	2·35	2·58	2·54
Sb	SbX_3	—	—	2·37	2·40	2·52	2·55	2·75	2·74
Pb	PbX_2	—	—	2·46	2·43	—	—	—	—
Cd	CdX_2	—	—	2·23	2·44	2·39	2·59	2·56	2·78

* Obtained from data for SF_6

† The large increase of the NX bond length in NOX is evidently due to the contribution from the structure $^{-}XN{\equiv}O^{+}$

Table LXII. Comparison of Experimental Values of Interatomic Distances with the Sum of Covalent Radii for Bonds involving Carbon (Å)

Bond	*Experimental value, from* X—$(CH_3)_n$	*Sum of radii*	*Bond*	*Experimental value, from* X—$(CH_3)_n$	*Sum of radii*
B—C	1·57	1·67	P—C	1·87	1·87
Al—C	2·05	2·11	As—C	1·98	1·98
Si—C	1·93	1·94	O—C	1·42	1·51
Pb—C	2·25	2·21	S—C	1·82	1·81
N—C	1·47	1·51			

Table LXIII. Interatomic Distances in Gaseous Alkali Halides (Å)

	Cs	*Difference* (CsX—RbX)	Rb	*Difference* (RbX—KX)	K	*Difference* (KX—NaX)	Na
I	3·41	0·15	3·26	0·03	3·23	0·33	2·90
Difference (MI—MBr)	0·27		0·20		0·29		0·26
Br	3·14	0·08	3·06	0·12	2·94	0·30	2·64
Difference (MBr—MCl)	0·08		0·17		0·15		0·13
Cl	3·06	0·17	2·89	0·10	2·79	0·28	2·51

Note—In the vertical column are arranged the differences between the radii of the cations, and in the horizontal columns the differences in the radii of the anions.

the bond lengths in molecules where direct measurement has not been made. The deviation from the correct value is generally not greater than 0·2 Å.

The additivity of the ionic radii of the alkali metals[27] and of the halogen anions is shown in *Table LXIII*, where it is seen that the divergence is of the order of 0·1 Å. The closer agreement is not surprising as the ionic radii of the halogens and the alkali metals are originally obtained from the measurements of the interionic distances in sodium chloride, potassium chloride *etc.*

REFERENCES

[1] HIBBEN, J. H. *J. Amer. chem. Soc.* 53 (1931) 2418
[2] KRISHNAMURTI, P. *Indian J. Phys.* 6 (1931) 7
[3] MURRAY, M. J., CLEVELAND, F. F. and SAUNDERS, R. H. *J. Amer. chem. Soc.* 64 (1942) 1181
[4] KADESCH, R. G. and WELLER, S. W. *ibid* 63 (1941) 1310
[5] SLOVOKHOTOVA, N. A., SYRKIN, J. K. and WOLKENSTEIN, M. V. *Compt. rend. Acad. Sci. U.R.S.S.* 35 (1942) 161
[6] EDSALL, J. T. *J. chem. Phys.* 4 (1936) 1
— *ibid* 5 (1937) 508
[7] PRILEZHAEVA, N. A., SYRKIN, J. K. and WOLKENSTEIN, M. V. *J. phys. Chem. Moscow* 14 (1940) 396
[8] GOUBEAU, J. *Z. Electrochem.* 49 (1943) 438
[9] BROCKWAY, L. O. and ROBERTSON, J. M. *J. chem. Soc.* (1939) 1324
[10] KARLE, I. L. and BROCKWAY, L. O. *J. Amer. chem. Soc.* 66 (1944) 1974
[11] BOERSCH, H. *Sitzungsber. Akad. Wiss. Wien* 144 (1935) 1
[12] GORDY, W. and PAULING, L. C. *J. Amer. chem. Soc.* 64 (1943) 2942
[13] ROBERTSON, J. M. *J. chem. Soc.* (1936) 1195
[14] ROBERTSON, J. M. and WOODWARD, I. *ibid* (1937) 219
[15] ROBERTSON, J. M. *Proc. roy. Soc. A* 171 (1939) 398
[16] HAMPSON, G. C. and ROBERTSON, J. M. *J. chem. Soc.* (1941) 409
[17] PAULING, L. C., GORDY, W. and SAYLOR, J. H. *J. Amer. chem. Soc.* 64 (1942) 1753
[18] SKINNER, H. A. and SUTTON, L. E. *Trans. Faraday Soc.* 40 (1944) 164
[19] GIGUÈRE, P. A. and SCHOMAKER, V. *ibid* 65 (1943) 2025
[20] SHAND, W. and SPURR, R. A. *J. Amer. chem. Soc.* 65 (1943) 179
[21] PHILLIPS, G. M., HUNTER, J. S. and SUTTON, L. E. *J. chem. Soc.* (1945) 146
[22] MAXWELL, L. R. and MOSELEY, V. M. *ibid* 8 (1940) 738
[23] REDLICH, O. and NIELSEN, L. E. *J. Amer. chem. Soc.* 65 (1943) 654
[24] LISTER, M. W. and SUTTON, L. E. *Trans. Faraday Soc.* 35 (1939) 495
[25] PAULING, L. C. *The Nature of the Chemical Bond* Cornell, 1940
[26] SCHOMAKER, V. and STEVENSON, D. P. *J. Amer. chem. Soc.* 63 (1941) 37
[27] MAXWELL, L. R., HENDRICKS, S. B. and MOSELEY, V. M. *Phys. Rev.* 52 (1937) 968

10

DIPOLE MOMENTS

DIELECTRIC POLARIZATION

THE STUDY of the behaviour of molecules in an electric field has shown that the polarizability and the dipole moment of a molecule are important structural characteristics. The fundamental quantity, which is dependent on both the polarizability and the dipole moment of the molecule, is the dielectric constant. Two charges $+e$ and $-e$, separated by a distance r, are attracted to each other according to Coulomb's law. If a vacuum exists between the two charges, then the force of attraction will be e^2/r^2. If, however, there is some medium between the charges, the attractive force is decreased and is given by $e^2/\epsilon r^2$, where ϵ is the dielectric constant which is always greater than unity. The relationship between the dielectric constant and the polarizability is given by the Clausius-Mosotti equation (see Chapter 18) :

$$\frac{\epsilon - 1}{\epsilon + 2} \cdot \frac{M}{d} = \frac{4}{3}\pi N a \qquad \ldots.(10.1)$$

where M is the molecular weight, d the density, N the Avagadro number and a the polarizability. The polarization of a molecule is due to three different, but simultaneous deformations. First, under the action of the applied field, the electrons will be displaced from their mean positions and the polarization produced is termed the electron polarization. The more closely the electrons are bound to the nuclei, the less will be the deformation and hence the smaller the induced moment given by

$$m_{ind} = a_E F$$

Conversely, if the electron polarizability a_E is great, then the electrons will be loosely bound. To a first approximation the electron polarization is independent of temperature. This is due to the fact that the energy difference between the ground and excited electronic states is relatively great and the probability of the electron being in an excited state at normal temperatures is very small. Secondly, the nuclei will be displaced from their mean positions by the action of the applied field and the polarization produced is termed the atom polarization a_A. Finally, if the centres of gravity of the positive and negative charges in the molecule are located at different points, the molecule will have a permanent dipole moment μ and under the action of the field the molecule will tend to become oriented in the position of minimum potential energy. This orientation will be hindered by the thermal agitation of the molecules and in consequence a statistical equilibrium, which will be dependent on the temperature, is set up, in which a slight excess of molecules have their permanent dipoles oriented antiparallel to the direction of the field. The polarization so produced is termed the orientation polarization a_o.

Thus we have

$$a = a_E + a_A + a_o \qquad \ldots.(10.2)$$

and

$$\frac{\epsilon - 1}{\epsilon + 2} \cdot \frac{M}{d} = \frac{4}{3}\pi N(a_E + a_A + a_o) = P \qquad \ldots.(10.3)$$

We shall now introduce the terms :

$$P_E = \frac{4}{3}\pi N a_E \qquad \ldots.(10.4)$$

$$P_A = \frac{4}{3}\pi N a_A \qquad \ldots.(10.5)$$

$$P_O = \frac{4}{3}\pi N a_O \qquad \ldots.(10.6)$$

where P is the total molecular polarization and P_E, P_A and P_O are respectively the electronic, atomic and orientation polarizations.

The nature of the polarization produced in a molecule is dependent on the frequency of the field employed. At relatively low frequencies (10^5) the polarization produced is equal to that obtained by a steady, *i.e.* non-alternating, field and is due to electronic, atomic and orientation polarization. In the alternating field the molecular dipoles must reorient themselves at each reversal of the field and as the frequency is increased a point is reached where the molecules, owing to their inertia, are no longer able to follow the reversals. At high frequencies, therefore, orientation polarization due to permanent dipoles does not occur. At still higher frequencies the nuclei cease to follow the oscillations of the field and the polarization is due entirely to the displacement of the electrons.

The frequency at which the dipoles cease to orient themselves in the alternating field may be obtained by calculating the relaxation time of the molecule, as was first done by Debye. The relaxation time is the period taken by the oriented molecule to return to 1/exp of the original deflection, when the field is removed. According to Debye, the time of relaxation τ is given by :

$$\tau = 4\pi\eta a^3/kT \qquad \ldots.(10.7)$$

where η is the viscosity of the medium, k is the Boltzmann constant, T the absolute temperature and a the radius of the molecule. For the water molecule, $a = 2 \times 10^{-8}$ cm and hence $\tau = 0{\cdot}25 \times 10^{-10}$ sec. Thus at frequencies greater than this value the water molecule will not be able to follow the reversals of the field and the total polarization will be due only to the atomic and electronic polarizations. Knowledge of the polarization at such high frequencies may be obtained by employing a relation, derived by Maxwell, that for measurements carried out at the same frequency, $\epsilon = n^2$, where n is the refractive index of the substance. Substituting this expression in equation 10.1 we obtain

$$\frac{n^2 - 1}{n^2 + 2}\cdot\frac{M}{d} = P \qquad \ldots.(10.8)$$

where P will be equal to either the sum of the atomic and electronic polarizations or to only the electronic polarization, depending on the method of measurement of the refractive index. Since the experimental procedure for determining the refractive index using infra-red light is extremely difficult, it is usual for the majority of substances, which absorb light in the ultra violet region of the spectrum, to measure the molecular refraction using the Na_D line and assume that this gives the sum of the electron and atom polarizations. Alternatively the refractive index is obtained for several wavelengths in the visible region of the spectrum and the refractive index calculated for light of infinite wavelength by the use of an extrapolation formula. The polarization then obtained is regarded as being due only to the distortion of the electrons. These methods, although approximate, are often satisfactory since the atomic polarization is generally small, as will be seen below.

The electronic polarization produced in a molecule is not the same in all directions and the quantity α_E represents an average polarization equal to $(\alpha_1 + \alpha_2 + \alpha_3)/3$, where α_1, α_2 and α_3 represent the electronic polarization in the direction of three mutually perpendicular coordinates. Certain methods of measurement of the polarization (Kerr effect) permit the separation of α into the different components and the determination, for example, of the polarizability in the direction of valency bonds and in the direction perpendicular to the bond. From the data so far obtained, however, no significant conclusions relating to molecular structure have been made.

The polarizability has the dimensions of a volume ; thus we have

$$m = \text{charge} \times \text{length} = \alpha \times \text{pressure} = \alpha \times \frac{\text{charge}}{\text{length}^2} \quad \ldots.(10.9)$$

or

$$\alpha = (\text{length})^3 \quad \ldots.(10.10)$$

Furthermore, we may show that the value of α has the same order of magnitude as that of the third power of the radius of an atom *i.e.* $(10^{-8})^3$ cm. In order to do this we use Bohr's picture of the hydrogen atom. The electron moves in an orbit round the nucleus fixed at the point O (*Figure 36*). Under the influence of the applied field, F, the plane of the orbit is displaced through the distance OA, equal to s. The force acting on the electron is eF, and owing to the displacement of the electronic orbit, there is an induced moment m given by,

$$m = es = \alpha F \quad \ldots.(10.11)$$

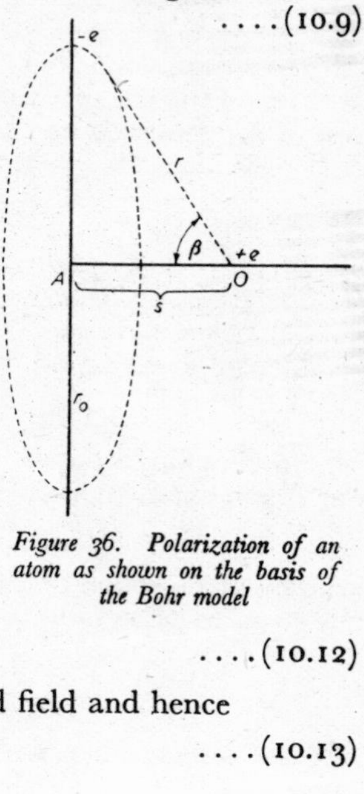

Figure 36. Polarization of an atom as shown on the basis of the Bohr model

The attractive force between the electron and the nucleus is e^2/r^2, which will have a component in the direction OA equal to

$$e^2 \cos\beta/r2 = e^2 s/r^3 \quad \ldots.(10.12)$$

This force neutralizes the influence of the applied field and hence

$$eF = e^2 s/r^3 \quad \ldots.(10.13)$$

or

$$es = Fr^3 \quad \ldots.(10.14)$$

and combining equations 10.11 and 10.14 we have,

$$\alpha = r^3 \quad \ldots.(10.15)$$

Since the distortion is not great, r^3 is very nearly equal to a^3 (a = the Bohr radius) ; exact calculation by the methods of wave mechanics gives $\alpha = 9a^3/2$. This expression may be used to determine the magnitude of the electronic distortion and from the polarizability of helium it may be shown that in a field of 300 volt/cm, the distortion is 2×10^{-16} cm.

Determination of the atomic polarization presents many difficulties. The frequencies corresponding to the vibration of the nuclei lie in the infra-red region of the spectrum and the method generally employed is the determination of the refractive index using infra-red radiation. Generally the atomic polarization is not large as is shown by the data of CARTWRIGHT and ERRERA[1] given in *Table LXIV*. In certain cases, however, the atomic polarization is found to be much larger, thus, for example [2, 3], in 1,3,5-trinitrobenzene, $P_A = 12$ cc, in *p*-benzoquinone, $P_A = 8$ cc and in tetrachloro-*p*-quinone, $P_A = 15$ cc. COOP and SUTTON[3] consider that in these molecules the high atom polarizations are due to the bending of the molecule by the applied field ; thus in the case of *p*-benzoquinone and its derivatives the atom polarization would be largely due to the bending of the highly polar C=O bond relative to the rest of the molecule and perpendicular to the plane of the ring.

Table LXIV. Atom Polarizations

Molecule	*Atomic polarization cc*	*Molecule*	*Atomic polarization cc*
Water	3·2	*Nitrobenzene*	3·8
Acetone	0·9	*Toluene*	0·9
Pyridine	1·5	*Diethyl ether*	3·2
α-Picoline	1·7	*Dioxan*	2·6
β-Picoline	1·0	*Benzene*	0·55
Methyl alcohol	1·9	*Hexane*	0·26
Ethyl alcohol	3·8	*Carbon disulphide*	2·3

For all molecules possessing a permanent dipole moment

$$\frac{\epsilon - 1}{\epsilon + 2} \cdot \frac{M}{d} \gg \frac{n^2 - 1}{n^2 + 2} \cdot \frac{M}{d} \qquad \ldots(10.16)$$

The relationship between the dipole moment and the orientation polarization has been developed by Debye by applying Langevin's theory of paramagnetism to electric dipoles (see Chapter 18). The desired equation is

$$a_0 = \mu^2/3kT \qquad \ldots(10.17)$$

where T is the absolute temperature, k the Boltzmann constant and μ is the dipole moment defined by

$$\mu = ed$$

where e is the value of the charge and d the distance between the charges. Substitution of equation 10.17 into 10.3 gives :

$$\frac{\epsilon - 1}{\epsilon + 2} \cdot \frac{M}{d} = \frac{4}{3}\pi N\left(a_E + a_A + \frac{\mu^2}{3kT}\right) \qquad \ldots(10.18)$$

and the orientation polarization will be given by

$$P_o = \frac{4}{3}\pi N a_o = \frac{4\pi N\mu^2}{9kT} \qquad \ldots(10.19)$$

The Clausius-Mosotti-Debye equation, 10.18, permits the permanent dipole moment of a molecule to be determined from dielectric constant measurements. This may be carried out by either of two general methods : by measuring the dielectric constant at different temperatures it is possible to eliminate a_E and a_A from equation 10.18 and thus calculate μ, or a_E may be obtained by refractive index measurements in the visible region of the spectrum and it is usual either to neglect a_A or to assume that it is equal to a small fraction (*e.g.* 5 per cent) of a_E. Substitution of values of the constants into equation 10.18 gives at 25°C

$$\mu = 0\cdot22\sqrt{P_O} = 0\cdot22\sqrt{P - P_E - P_A} \quad \ldots.(10.20)$$

For molecules possessing a large dipole moment, the orientation polarization is large and any error in the values of P_A or P_E does not significantly affect the values of P_O. For small moments, however, of the order 0·2D (1 Debye = 1D = 10^{-18} e.s.u), P_O is of the order of 1 cc and appreciable errors in the value of the dipole moment may occur.

According to the assumptions made in the derivation of equation 10.19 it is strictly valid only for the case of gases, where there is no molecular interaction and the molecules are oriented independently of one another in the external applied field. However, Debye suggested that measurements in dilute solution of non polar solvents, *e.g.* benzene, hexane, carbon tetrachloride, would be permissible and the validity of this method has been confirmed by the fact that for a number of molecules, the difference between the value of the dipole moment determined in the gas phase and in solution is not greater than 0·2 D. The measurement of dipole moments in solution permits the examination of the polar characteristics of a number of substances which do not lend themselves easily to measurement in the gas phase.

The dipole moment of a molecule may also be directly measured by the molecular beam method in which the beam of molecules is passed through a non-uniform electric field. If only induced polarization exists in the molecule, the molecular beam is deflected in the direction of the stronger electric field, but if the molecules have a permanent polarization, there is a broadening of the beam, the extent of which is dependent on the dipole moment. Exact determinations by this method have not yet been possible, but the method has been of use in determining the dipole moment of ion pairs (molecules) of NaCl, which cannot be measured in any other way.

REFRACTION

Inorganic compounds—Very little data exist on the polarizability of atoms. Values are known for the inert gases, some of the elements of the first group and for iodine. These data are given in *Table LXV* together with a value for the polarizability of the hydrogen atom calculated by quantum mechanical methods. On transfer from hydrogen 1*s* to helium 1*s*² in which the K electronic shell is filled, the polarization increases and the introduction of an *s* electron in the 2*s* orbit, as in lithium, produces a marked increase in the polarizability. This behaviour is repeated with argon and potassium and with xenon and caesium, but the proportionate increase in polarizability decreases as the total number of electrons increases. Thus the ratio of the polarizabilities of the first group elements and the corresponding inert gas decreases from 60 with lithium and helium, to 20·5 with potassium and argon and to 10·1 for caesium and xenon.

Table LXV. Polarizability of Atoms (*cc* × 10^{24})

		H 0·67
	He 0·20	Li 12
	Ne 0·40	
	Ar 1·66	K 34
	Kr 2·54	
I 4·96	Xe 4·15	Cs 42

The polarizabilities of the inert gases neon, argon,

krypton and xenon are in the approximate ratio 1 : 4 : 6 : 10 and it is interesting to note that a similar sequence occurs in the polarizability of the molecules of the halogens, the ratio for fluorine, chlorine, bromine and iodine being 2·91 : 11·67 : 17·43 : 31·97 (in units of 10^{-24} cc which will be used throughout this text). The polarizability of the hydrogen molecule is 0·81, a value which is considerably less than the sum of the polarizabilities of two atoms of hydrogen ; it is thus evident that the two electrons forming the bond, *i.e.* moving in the field of two nuclei, are more closely bound to the nuclei than in the free atoms. In the iodine molecule, on the other hand, the polarizability in the gaseous state is 12·7 and in benzene solution 16·3, values which are more than double the polarizability of the iodine atoms. The increased looseness of the electron cloud in the molecule compared with the atom is probably related to the fact that iodine shows some metallic characteristics.

The polarizabilities of ions have been determined by FAJANS and JOOS from measurements of the refractive indices of salts and have been calculated theoretically by BORN and HEISENBERG, PAULING and others[4]. The polarizabilities of singly and doubly charged ions are given in *Table LXVI*, the values for Li^+ and Be^{2+} have been taken from the data of Pauling and the remainder of the values are those of Fajans. The data show that the polarizability is much greater with anions than with cations ; with cations, the positive charge will tend to counteract the displacement of the electrons by the applied field, but in anions the greater the number of additional electrons there are present, the less strongly is the electron cloud bound to the nuclei and the greater its deformation by the field. Comparison of the values in *Tables LXV* and *LXVI* shows that the polarizabilities of the inert gases fall between the values for the corresponding isoelectronic ions *e.g.* H^-(10·18), He(0·20), Li^+(0·03).

Table LXVI. Polarizability of Ions
(cc × 10^{24})

	H^- 10·18	Li^+ 0·03	Be^{2+} 0·008
O^{2-} 2·74	F^- 0·96	Na^+ 0·19	Mg^{2+} 0·10
S^{2-} 8·94	Cl^- 3·60	K^+ 0·89	Ca^{2+} 0·55
Se^{2-} 11·4	Br^- 5·0	Rb^+ 1·50	Sr^{2+} 1·02
Te^{2-} 16·1	I^- 7·60	Cs^+ 2·60	Ba^{2+} 1·86

In a number of cases it is impossible to relate the refractivity of a molecule to the refractivities of the corresponding ions. For example, the value of the molecular refraction for $SnCl_4$ cannot be regarded as the sum of the refractivities of the ions Sn^{4+} and Cl^-, as the existence of such ions in the molecule is improbable. The field due to the Sn^{4+} ion, with four positive charges, will be so great that the chlorine ion will not preserve its individuality, and the deformation of the electronic cloud of the chlorine ion whilst in the field due to the Sn^{4+} ion cannot be regarded as related to the deformation of the electron cloud of a free chlorine ion. The stannic chloride molecule must be regarded as a resonance hybrid of the covalent and various ionic states in which the charge on the tin ion is relatively small and the contribution of the form containing Sn^{4+} is insignificant.

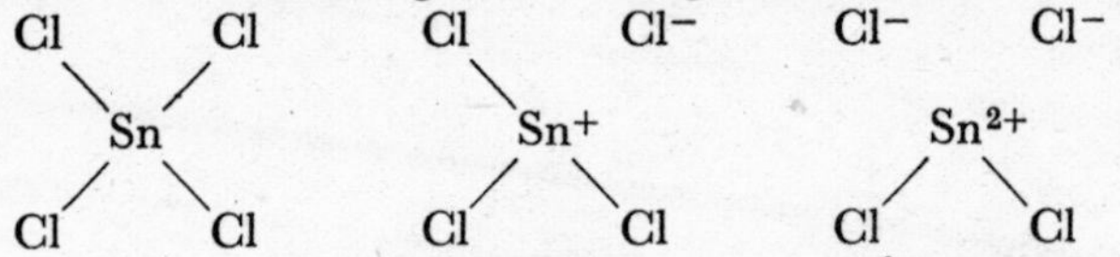

```
Cl      Cl        Cl      Cl⁻        Cl⁻     Cl⁻
  \    /            \
   Sn                Sn⁺                 Sn²⁺
  /    \            /   \               /   \
Cl      Cl        Cl     Cl           Cl     Cl
```

four structures (second form); *five structures* (third form)

In *Table LXVII* the refractions of atoms of the inert gases and of several molecules isoelectronic with the inert gases are given. The refraction has a minimum value for each period at the inert gas, in which the electrons are located in the field of one nucleus. As the number of atoms in the molecules is increased, the electron cloud becomes more and more decentralized and polarization increases. Similar behaviour is noticed with the isoelectronic ions with one negative charge, *e.g.* F^-(2·42) and OH^-(5·10); Cl^-(9·0) and SH^-(13·2). It is interesting to observe from *Tables LXVI* and *LXVII* that the refractions of the hydrogen halides are approximately three quarters of the values for the corresponding negative halogen ions. This may be related to the fact that in the ions F^-, Cl^-, Br^- and I^- there are eight outer electrons whereas in the corresponding isoelectronic molecule, two of the eight outer electrons are bonding electrons, leaving six, *i.e.* three quarters of the total, capable of being polarized

Table LXVII. Refraction of Isoelectronic Atoms and Molecules (cc)

Ne 1·0	HF (1·9)	H_2O 3·75	NH_3 5·67	CH_4 6·58
Ar 4·2	HCl 6·7	H_2S 9·57	PH_3 11·7	SiH_4 11·34
Kr 6·37	HBr 9·16	H_2Se 12·02		
Xe 10·4	HI 13·7			

In order to convert values of the polarization, or molecular or atomic refraction into polarizability it is necessary to divide by $\frac{4}{3}\pi N = 2{\cdot}52 \times 10^{-24}$.

Let us now consider the effect of the variation of charge on the refraction of isoelectronic molecules. As is shown in *Table LXVIII* the refraction falls with a decrease in the negative charge and falls still farther with the formation of a positive charge. But the decrease in negative charge and the increase of positive charge is also accompanied by an increase in the number of nuclei between which the electrons are distributed. This will in itself bring about a decrease in the refraction and therefore the change of refraction with charge is not so great as is indicated by the data in *Table LXVIII*. Nevertheless, it is interesting to note that the refractions of O^{2-}, OH^- and H_2O are approximately in the same ratio as that of the outermost electrons not participating in the formation of bonds, *i.e.* 8 : 6 : 4.

Table LXVIII. Refraction of Isoelectronic Ions and Molecules (cc)

O^{2-}	6·9		
OH^-	5·1		
H_2O	3·75	NH_3	5·67
H_3O^+	3·04	NH_4^+	4·1

The refractions of bonds containing hydrogen are given in *Table LXIX*. These values have been obtained from the refractions of the corresponding molecules by dividing by the number of bonds. The refraction of the bonds of elements of the second period with hydrogen, are very similar, whereas those with elements of the third period increase considerably. The refractions of the bond, O^+—H in H_3O^+ (*Table LXVIII*) is 1·01 cc whilst that of N^+—H in $^+NH_4$ (*Table LXVIII*) is 1·02 cc. Both these values are considerably less than the corresponding values for O—H and N—H (*Table LXIX*). As expected, the refractions of bonds in anions are greater than in the corresponding neutral molecules. Thus in

Table LXIX. Refraction of Bonds Containing Hydrogen

Bond	*Refraction cc*	*Bond*	*Refraction cc*
C—H (CH_4)	1·69	Si—H (SiH_4)	3·0
N—H (NH_3)	1·83	P—H (PH_3)	3·9
O—H (H_2O)	1·88	S—H (H_2S)	4·65
F—H (HF)	(1·9)	Cl—H (HCl)	6·7

$(CN)_2$ the CN bond has a refraction of 5·3 cc whereas in CN^- it has the value 8·3 cc. The latter value is also greater than the values for CO and N_2 (4·4 cc), which are isoelectronic with CN^-.

A comparison of the refractions of different types of bonds between oxygen and carbon, silicon and sulphur (*Table LXX*) shows that two factors may bring about an increase in the value of the molecular refraction, an increase in the multiplicity of the bond and the appearance of a negative charge. The first effect is shown by a comparison of the values for the carbon oxygen bonds occurring in esters, CO_2 and CO. In CO_3^{2-}, each bond possesses only one third double bond character, but owing to the two negative charges, the refraction of the bond is greater than in CO_2. Similar behaviour occurs with SiO_2 and SiO_3^{2-} and with SO_3, in which each bond possesses one third double bond character owing to the resonance between three structures of the type

Table LXX. Refraction of Bonds ContainingOxygen

Molecule	*Refraction in CO bond cc*	*Molecule*	*Refraction in SiO bond cc*	*Molecule*	*Refraction in SO bond cc*
Simple esters	1·51				
CO_2	3·3	$SiO^{2}{}_{2}$–	3·61	SO_3	3·7
CO_3^{-}	4·1	SiO_3	4·46	SO_2	4·9
CO	4·4				

$$O = S^{2+}\!\begin{array}{l} \diagup O^- \\ \diagdown O^- \end{array}$$

and SO_2, in which the bonds possess one half double bond character owing to the resonance between two structures of the form

$$\begin{array}{c} S^+ \\ \diagup\!\!\diagup \quad \diagdown \\ O \qquad O^- \end{array}$$

Organic compounds— For a large number of organic compounds it is found that the bond refraction is an additive quantity. As an example of this relationship between the number and type of bonds and the molecular refraction, *Table LXXI* gives the differences in the values of the molecular refraction of neighbouring members of a homologous series ; these are found to be almost constant. Furthermore, the refractions of isomers are found to be the same, *e.g.* *o*–xylol, 35·75 ; *m*–xylol, 35·9, and *p*–xylol, 35·69. From the molecular refractions the bond refractions may be obtained and the values for some typical bonds are given in *Table LXXII.* The bond refraction increases with the multiplicity as is shown by the data for the CC bond :

Table LXXI. Additivity of Refractions in a Homologous Series

Molecule	*Refraction cc*	*Difference as compared with previous member*	*Molecule*	*Refraction cc*	*Difference as compared with previous member*
n–Pentane	25·28		*n–Nonane*	43·78	4·65
n–Hexane	29·86	4·58	*n–Decane*	48·41	4·63
n–Heptane	34·51	4·68	*n–Undecane*	53·06	4·65
n–Octane	39·13	4·62	*n–Dodecane*	57·67	4·61

C—C, 1·25; C=C, 4·16; C≡C, 6·4. The transfer from a single to a double bond increases the refraction by 2·91 cc and the transfer from a double to a triple bond increases the refraction by the smaller value of 2·24 cc. Thus it appears that for carbon, the σ electrons are polarized less than the π electrons. This is not so, however, with the O—O and N—N

Table LXXII. Bond Refractions

Bond	*Refraction* cc	*Bond*	*Refraction* cc	*Bond*	*Refraction* cc
C—H	1·69	C—Br	9·37	C≡C	6·4
C—N	1·54	C—I	14·55	C—O	1·51
C—F	1·72	C—C	1·25	C=O	3·38
C—Cl	6·53	C=C	4·16		

bonds. The refraction for the single O—O bond may be obtained from the data for hydrogen peroxide and from organic peroxides and peracids and the values obtained are given in *Table LXIII*, from which the mean value for the O—O bond is taken as 2·25 cc. The refraction of the normal oxygen molecule is 4·09 cc and the second pair of bonding electrons produce a

Table LXXIII. Refractions of Peroxides

Molecule	*Molecular refraction* cc	*Bond refraction* cc	*Molecule*	*Molecular refraction* cc	*Bond refraction* cc
H—O—O—H	5·81	2·21	CH_3OOCH_3	15·40	2·15
CH_3OOH	10·74	2·31	$CH_3OOC_2H_5$	20·09	2·22
C_2H_5OOH	15·18	2·17	$C_2H_5OOC_2H_5$	24·72	2·23
$(CH_3)_2CHOOH$	20·01	2·33			

refraction of only 1·84 cc *i.e.* less than that produced by the first pair. Similar behaviour is noticed with nitrogen. The refraction of the single N—N bond, may be obtained from the molecular refractions of hydrazine and the value obtained is 1·72 cc. In molecular nitrogen, where the atoms are bound by a triple bond the molecular refraction is 4·4 cc. Thus the contribution from the four π electrons is 2·68 cc, *i.e.* 1·34 cc for each pair of π electrons, which is a smaller value than that obtained for the σ bond. This difference between the behaviour of carbon and of oxygen and nitrogen, will be discussed again in the next chapter from the point of view of the bond energies.

The refraction of molecules may be calculated by the addition of the appropriate atomic refractions. It is necessary to add to the sum so obtained additional quantities corresponding to the multiplicity of the bonds involved. For a large number of molecules, the calculated and measured values of the molecular refraction agree, within the limits of experimental error. In molecules containing a conjugated system of double bonds, however, deviations from the additivity rule occur, the experimental value always being greater than the calculated. The difference, $R_{exp} - R_{calc}$, may be termed the refraction exaltation and values are given for a variety of

Table LXXIV. Exaltation of Molecular Refraction for Molecules with Conjugated Double Bonds

Molecule	*Exaltation cc*	*Molecule*	*Exaltation cc*
$CH_2=CH-CH=CH_2$	1·42	$C_6H_5-CH=CH-CH=CH_2$	4·74
$CH_2=C(CH_3)-CH=CH_2$	0·88	$C_6H_5-CH=CH-CH=CHCH_3$	4·71
$CH_3CH=CH-CH=CHCH_3$	1·76	$C_6H_5-CH=CH-CH=CHCH_2CH_3$	5·40
$CH_2=CH-CH=C(CH_3)_2$	1·73	$(C_6H_5)CH=CH-CH=CHCH(CH_3)_2$	4·68
$CH_2=C(CH_3)-C(CH_3)=CH_2$	0·75	$(C_6H_5)CH=CH-CH=CHCH_2CH(CH_3)_2$	4·14
$CH_3CH=CH-CH=CHCH_2CH_3$	1·96	$C_6H_5-CH=CH-C_6H_5$	6·20
$CH_2=C(CH_3)-CH=C(CH_3)_2$	0·86	$C_6H_5-CH=C(CH_3)-C_6H_5$	3·98
$CH_3CH=C(CH_3)-CH=CHCH_3$	1·00	$C_6H_5-CH=CH-C_6H_4-CH_3$	6·35
$C_6H_5-CH=CH_2$	1·16	$CH_2=CHC\equiv CCH=CH_2$	2·07
$C_6H_5-CH=CHCH_3$	1·31	$C_6H_5-CH=CH-CH=CH-C_6H_5$ (*cis-trans*)	(3·5)
$C_6H_5-C(CH_3)=CH_2$	0·77	$C_6H_5-CH=CH-CH=CH-C_6H_5$ (*cis-cis*)	7·89
$C_6H_5-C(CH_3)=CHCH_3$	0·82	$CH_2=CHCHO$	0·62
		$CH_3CH=CHCHO$	1·36
$C_6H_5-C(CH_3)=C(CH_3)_2$	0·57	$CH_2=CHCN$	0·31
		$CH_3CH=CHCN$	0·82

molecules containing a conjugated system in *Table LXXIV*. In all such compounds, owing to the contribution of the structure $\underset{\vdots}{CH_2}-CH=CH-\underset{\vdots}{CH_2}$ to the resonance of the molecule, carbon atoms 1 and 4 have partly the character of free radicals and very probably the exaltation is caused by this property, since the number of electrons used in bond formation by the terminal carbon atoms has been reduced. The replacement of a hydrogen

Table LXXV. Exaltation of Molecular Refraction for Cyclic Compounds

Molecule	*Exaltation* cc	*Molecule*	*Exaltation* cc
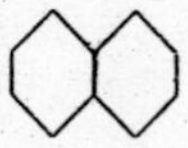	2·55	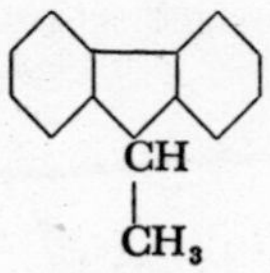 CH CH_3	3·11
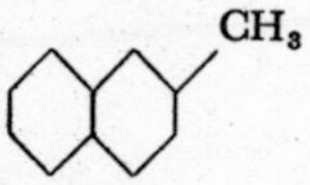 CH_3	2·45	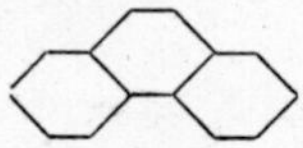	5·53
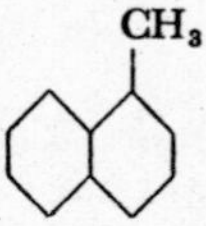 CH_3	2·80	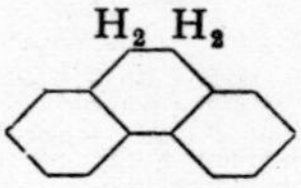 H_2 H_2	3·76
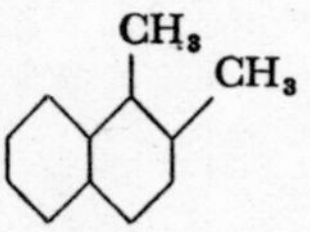 CH_3 CH_3	2·44	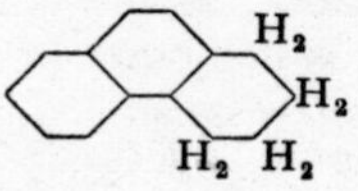 H_2 H_2 H_2 H_2	2·04
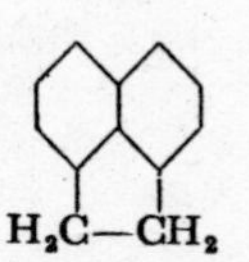 $H_2C—CH_2$	2·97		8·17
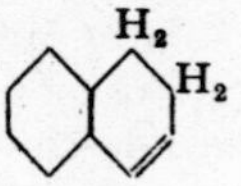 H_2 H_2	1·30	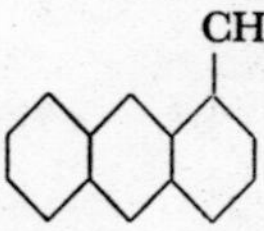 CH_3	3·95
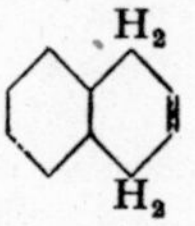 H_2 H_2	0·27	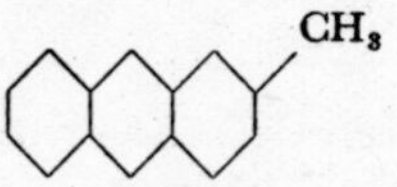 CH_3	4·73
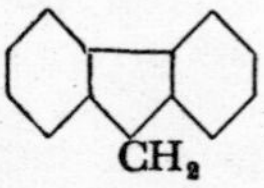 CH_2	2·56	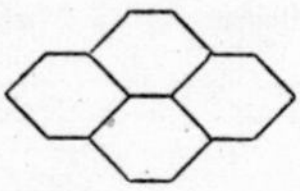	8·03
		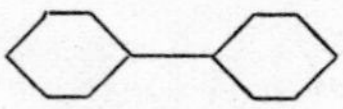	1.80

atom by a methyl group on a carbon atom forming part of the conjugated system, *i.e.* not a terminal carbon atom, as in 1–methylbutadiene (isoprene), 2,3–dimethylbutadiene and *a*–methylstilbene, considerably lowers the exaltation. Molecules containing double bonds which do not form part of a conjugated system, *e.g.* $CH_2{=}CHCH_2CH_2CH{=}CH_2$ (diallyl) or $C_6H_5CH_2CH{=}CHCH_2CH_2CH_3$ do not show exaltation of the molecular refraction.

The absence of exaltation in a number of conjugated ring systems such as benzene, dihydrobenzene, hydrindene, tetralin, cyclopentadiene, cycloheptadiene, cyclo-octadiene is not clearly understood. In polycylic systems, exaltation does appear (*Table LXXV*) and increases with the increase in the number of rings. For α–methyl derivatives of naphthalene and anthracene, the exaltation is somewhat less than for the β–derivatives. Comparison of the 1, 2– and 1, 4–dihydronaphthalenes shows that in the former compound there is a small exaltation (1·30 cc), probably due to the contribution of the structure

H_2

H_2

to the resonance of the molecule. With the latter compound however the double bond is isolated in the 2, 3–position and the exaltation is considerably reduced (0·27 cc).

One of the main difficulties in the interpretation of refraction data, is that reliable measurements, such as those given by EGLOFF[5], are not always available and many of the values recorded must be regarded with suspicion. Furthermore, in the majority of cases, extrapolation to infinitely long wavelengths is not possible owing to the lack of data. It is true that if the substance absorbs in the far ultraviolet the difference between R_D and R_∞ will be small, *e.g.* for benzene $R_D = 26{\cdot}19$ cc and $R_\infty = 25{\cdot}12$ cc, and comparisons of the values for different substances is permissible, but for molecules which absorb in the longer wavelength regions the exaltation may depend considerably on the wavelength at which the refractive index was measured. As an example of this behaviour, the data[6] for *p*–nitraniline are given in *Table LXXVI*, and it is seen that the variation of exaltation with wavelength is very large.

Table LXXVI. Variation of Exaltation of Molecular Refraction of p-Nitraniline with Wavelength

Wavelength Å	4,358	5,460	5,790	6,707	∞ (*extrapolation*)
Exaltation cc	14·85	7·01	6·40	5·23	2·7

The exaltations of molecular refraction for a number of strongly polar substances are given in *Table LXXVII* and it would be of considerable interest to determine the influence of the resonance of the molecule on the exaltation. In certain cases the exaltation is very low, a fact which may be related to a small contribution from the ionic form. In general, however, the existing data is insufficient for any general discussion.

Table LXXVII. Exaltation of Molecular Refractions of Polar Molecules*

Molecule	*Exaltation cc*	*Molecule*	*Exaltation cc*
2,3–*Dinitraniline*	0·9	*o–Nitrophenol*	2·86
2,4–*Dinitraniline*	2·1	*m–Nitrophenol*	−1·06
2,6–*Dinitraniline*	−0·9	*p–Nitrophenol*	−4·90
3,5–*Dinitraniline*	0·2	2,4–*Dinitrophenol*	2·1
2,4,6–*Trinitraniline*	1·7	2,3–*Dinitrophenol*	1·9
Nitrophenylendiamine	4·0	2,6–*Dinitrophenol*	2·4
3–*Nitro–α–naphthylamine*	−0·9	3,4–*Dinitrophenol*	1·7
4–*Nitro–α–naphthylamine*	−1·64	3,6–*Dinitrophenol*	2·0
2,6–*Dimethyl–γ–pyrone*	1·09	*Michler's Ketone*	9·1

* All data given in this table have been obtained from refractions extrapolated to ∞. The data used for the calculated values were obtained from benzene and the monosubstitution products of benzene.

DIPOLE MOMENTS AND THE IONIC CHARACTER OF BONDS

In the diatomic molecule, which must form the basis for a discussion of the experimental data on dipole moments, the relative contributions of the covalent and ionic forms determine the magnitude and direction of the dipole moment. Molecules containing a purely homopolar bond do not possess a permanent dipole moment as is shown by the data for diatomic molecules consisting of identical atoms. However, in Chapter 3, it was found necessary in order to improve the calculations of the bond energy and interatomic distance of the hydrogen molecule, to consider in addition to the homopolar form, H—H, the ionic states H^-H^+ and H^+H^-. Nevertheless, it would be incorrect to ascribe any polarity to the hydrogen molecule as the contribution of the two ionic forms is exactly equal and the electron cloud due to the two electrons forming the bond is symmetrical. The absence of a permanent dipole moment has been proved for all homonuclear diatomic molecules, *e.g.* H_2, N_2, O_2, Cl_2, Br_2, I_2, *etc.*

It is possible to show that for covalent bonds between different atoms, the dipole moment does not exceed 0·1 D. For a purely ionic bond the dipole moment μ must be equal to

$$\mu = ed$$

where e is the charge and d the distance between the centres of the ions. Intermediate values of the dipole moment show that the bond is neither entirely covalent nor purely ionic, but is formed by a superposition of the covalent and ionic forms; a comparison of values of dipole moments of different bonds permits a quantitative assessment of the contributions of the covalent and ionic forms in a bond to be made. It is necessary to appreciate, however, that the magnitude of the dipole moment is dependent on two factors, the charge and the internuclear distance. Thus for a comparatively small effective charge, the dipole moment may be significant if the bond length is considerable. A more significant characteristic of polarity than the dipole moment would perhaps therefore be the ratio between the observed dipole moment and the interatomic distance.

From the experimental values of dipole moments it is possible, in a number of cases, to make a semi-quantitative evaluation of the weights of the various valence bond structures contributing to a bond (see Chapter 18). These calculations must be regarded as only approximate since the bond is described in terms of the Heitler-London theory with the superposition of ionic states. The results cannot, therefore, be more precise than is permitted by the Heitler-London approximation. Nevertheless, the calculations are of significance since they permit an assessment to be made of the more important structures contributing to the bond and thus assist in predicting and explaining the reactivity of bonds.

According to Pauling, a bond in a diatomic molecule may be regarded as a resonance hybrid of only two structures, the ionic and the covalent; the contribution of the transitional structure is thus assigned partly to the ionic and partly to the homopolar states (in Chapter 3, and in particular in Chapter 7, it was shown that the wave function for a bond may be represented by a combination of the following functions: $\psi_a(1)\psi_b(2) + \psi_a(2)\psi_b(1)$, representing the homopolar molecule; $\psi_a(1)\psi_b(2)\psi_b(1)\psi_a(2)$, representing the transitional structure and $\psi_a(1)\psi_a(2) + \psi_b(1)\psi_b(2)$ representing the ionic structure). This treatment causes, in general, an overestimate of the contribution of the ionic structures, as for instance the O—H bond in H_2O, which Pauling does not consider to be correct (see DYATKINA[7]). The calculation of the contribution of the transition structure and its separation from the other two structures is most important since it is in the transitional structure that the quantum mechanical concept of exchange occurs and as we have seen, it is the exchange energy which is largely responsible for the stability of the molecule.

During the following discussion we shall employ wherever possible dipole moment data obtained from measurements on gases, since these values are the most accurate. When such data are not available the values are taken from measurements on dilute solutions in non-polar solvents. Such values are denoted by the subscript *s*.

Table LXXVIII. Dipole Moments and Weights of Structures in Hydrogen Halides

Bond	Dipole moment D	Internuclear distance Å	Weights of bond structures per cent		
			Homopolar	Ionic	Transitional
H—F	2·00	0·92	32	33	35
H—Cl	1·03	1·27	71	6	23
H—Br	0·79	1·41	79	3	18
H—I	0·38	1·61	91	1	8

Table LXXVIII gives the dipole moments and the calculated weights of structures for the hydrogen halides. The data show, in agreement with the chemical behaviour, the increasing homopolar nature of the bond in the series, HF, HCl, HBr, HI, the transitional structure in each step making a greater contribution than the ionic structure.

The resultant dipole moment of a polyatomic molecule is conditioned by the presence of polar groups and bonds, each of which may be regarded as having its own dipole moment; the total dipole moment of the molecule is obtained by adding vectorially the moments of all the bonds. This procedure is supported by the data of EUCKEN and MEYER[8] and may be illustrated by considering the water molecule. The water molecule is triangular in shape, with the H—O—H bond angle having the value 105°. The resultant moment of the molecule will therefore be the vector sum of the moments of two O—H bonds. From the experimental value for the water molecule of $\mu = 1{\cdot}84$ D and the formula that

$$2\mu_{OH}\cos 52° = 1{\cdot}84$$

we obtain

$$\mu_{OH} = 1{\cdot}51\,\mathrm{D}$$

Making a similar calculation for dimethyl ether we obtain $\mu_{CH_3-O} = 1{\cdot}12$ D. Applying these values to methyl alcohol which contains one CH_3—O and one O—H bond,

```
      O
     / \
  H3C   H
```

we find that the calculated value, 1·71 D is very close to the experimental value 1·69 D.

Table LXXIX. Relative Weights of Valence Structures

Molecule	Dipole moment of molecule D	Valency angle	Bond	Dipole moment of bond D	Bond length Å	Weight of structures per cent		
						Homopolar	Ionic	Transitional
H_2O	1·84	105°	O—H	1·51	0·95	53	18	29
$(CH_3)_2O$	1·29	110°	O—CH_3	1·12	1·42	75	7	18
NH_3	1·46	109°	N—H	1·42	1·01	55	15	30
$N(CH_3)_3$	0·65	110°	N—CH_3	0·61	1·47	85	5	10
H_2S	0·93	92°	S—H	0·67	1·35	82	3	15

The vector addition of dipole moments is only permissible if the weights of the ionic states in the various bonds does not alter significantly in the various compounds, such as would be produced if molecular resonance occurred; in these cases only is it possible to assign definite values for the contributions of the various valence bond structures. The data for the bonds OH, OR, NH, NR and SH are given in *Table LXXIX* and the weights of the various structures contributing to the bonds have been calculated and are given in *Tables LXXX* to *LXXXVII*.

Table LXXX.
Relative Weights of Valence Structures in H_2O

Structure		*Weight of structure per cent*
Homopolar		
H—O—H	*I*	27
Single ionic form		
H^+ O^-—H	*II*	$2 \times 9{\cdot}5 = 19$
Double ionic form		
H^+ O^{2-} H^+	*III*	4
Transitional	*I–II*	31
Transitional	*I–III*	8
Transitional	*II–III*	11

It is possible to make certain general deductions from *Tables LXXX* to *LXXXVII*. The contribution of the entirely ionic structures of the type suggested by Kossel, in which the electronic structure of the ions resembles that of an inert gas, is found to be insignificant. Thus in water the contribution of the structure $H^+O^{2-}H^+$ is 4 per cent whereas in dimethyl ether the corresponding structure $^+CH_3$ O^{2-} $^+CH_3$ contributes only 1 per cent. This observation must be connected with the small affinity of oxygen for two electrons, *i.e.* although the electron affinity of O is considerable, that of O^- is negative. The single ionic structures are, however, significant, the contribution of the forms H^+ O^-—H and H—O^- H^+ being 19 per cent.

Table LXXXI. Relative Weights of Valence Structures in CH_3OCH_3

Structure		*Weight of structure per cent*
Homopolar		
CH_3—O—CH_3	*I*	57
Single ionic form		
$^+CH_3$ O^-—CH_3	*II*	$2 \times 5 = 10$
Double ionic form		
$^+CH_3$ O^{2-} $^+CH_3$	*III*	1
Transitional	*I–II*	27
Transitional	*I–III*	3
Transitional	*II–III*	2

In ammonia there is no evidence for the existence of the triply ionic form (*Table LXXXIII*) a fact which is explained by the exceptional endothermic nature of the reaction $N \rightarrow N^{3-}$. Of the possible ionic structures of ammonia, only H_2 N^- H^+ (13·5 per cent) appears to be of significance. The ammonia molecule is a trigonal pyramid with the nitrogen atom at the apex and the three hydrogen atoms in the plane of the base. The NH bond length is 1·01 Å and the distance from the apex of the pyramid to the centre of the base is 0·3 Å. If we assume that there is one negative charge at the apex of

Table LXXXII.
Relative Weights of Valence Structures in CH_3OH

Structure		*Weight of structure per cent*
Homopolar		
CH_3—O—H	*I*	36
Single ionic form		
CH_3—O^- H^+	*II*	16
Single ionic form		
$^+CH_3$ O^-—H	*III*	3
Double ionic form		
$^+CH_3$ O^{2-} H^+	*IV*	2
Transitional	*I–II*	23
Transitional	*I–III*	13
Remaining transitional		7

Table LXXXIII.
Relative Weights of Valence Structures in NH_3

Structure		Weight of structure per cent
Homopolar H—N(H)(H)	*I*	16
Single ionic form H^+N^-(H)(H)	*II*	3 × 4·5 = 13·5
Double ionic form H—N^{2-} (H^+)(H^+)	*III*	3 × 1·3 = 3·9
Triple ionic form H^+ N^{3-} (H^-)(H^-)	*IV*	0·3
Transitional	*I–II*	27·3
Transitional	*I–III*	15
Transitional	*I–IV*	3
Transitional	*II–III*	15
Transitional	*II–IV*	4
Transitional	*III–IV*	2

the pyramid, *i.e.* on the nitrogen atom, and one positive charge in the centre of the base, *i.e.* shared equally amongst the hydrogen atoms, then the dipole moment will be, $\mu = 4{\cdot}8 \times 10^{-10} \times 0{\cdot}3 \times 10^{-8} = 1{\cdot}44 \times 10^{-18}$ e.s.u, which is close to the experimental value of $1{\cdot}46 \times 10^{-18}$ e.s.u. We may thus obtain an approximate picture of the nitrogen molecule as having a single negative charge on the nitrogen atom and one third of a positive charge on each of the hydrogen atoms. From this argument it follows that the nitrogen must be essentially divalent.

Homopolar structures make a sigficant contribution in all the molecules observed and their weight increases in the series water, alcohol, ether (27, 36 and 57 per cent respectively). In hydrogen sulphide the contribution is much greater than in water (67 compared with 27 per cent). Replacement of hydrogen by a methyl group causes a gradual increase in the contribution of the homopolar structure in amines, the values for ammonia, primary, secondary and tertiary amines being 16, 24, 38 and 61 per cent respectively. In methylamine, the structure with a positive charge on one hydrogen atom *i.e.* $CH_3{-}NH\ H^+$ makes a contribution of 6·8 per cent whereas the analogous structure with a positive charge on the carbon, $^+CH_3{-}NH_2$, makes an insignificant contribution. This observation is in conformity with the

Table LXXXIV.
Relative Weights of Valence Structures in CH_3NH_2

Structure		Weight of structure per cent
Homopolar CH_3—N(H)(H)	*I*	24
Single ionic form (two) CH_3—N^- (H^+)(H)	*II*	2 × 6.8 = 13·6
Single ionic form $^+CH_3$ N^-(H)(H)		1
Double ionic form CH_3—N^{2-} (H^+)(H^+)		2
Double ionic form (two) $^+CH_3$ N^{2-} (H^+)(H)		2 × 1 = 2
Triple ionic form $^+CH_3$ N^{3-} (H^+)(H^+)		0·1
Transitional	*I–II*	42
Remaining transitional		15

fact that the single bond C—N is more homopolar than the NH bond.

The data show that the transitional structures make important contributions to the structure of the molecules and may not be ignored. In this respect our data differs from that of Pauling who did not consider the transitional structures separately.

Comparison of the dipole moments for NH_3, PH_3 (0·55 D) and AsH_3 (0·16 D) show that the PH bond is less ionic than the NH bond, whereas the AsH bond is almost entirely homopolar. From the dipole moments of the halides of phosphorus, arsenic and antimony it is possible to calculate the contributions of the ionic states in these molecules. The polarity of the bonds decreases in the series fluorine, chlorine, bromine and iodine: AsF_3 $\mu_s = 2{\cdot}65$ D; $AsCl_3$ $\mu_s = 2{\cdot}15$ D; $AsBr_3$, $\mu_s = 1{\cdot}6$ D; AsI_3, $\mu_s = 1{\cdot}0$ D. The values of the dipole moments of phosphorous halides are less than those of the corresponding halides of arsenic, whereas the values for antimony are greater. Thus, for example, the dipole moments of the bromides are: PBr_3, $\mu_s = 0{\cdot}6$ D; $AsBr_3$, $\mu_s = 1{\cdot}6$ D; $SbBr_3$, $\mu_s = 2{\cdot}5$ D. This change indicates the increase in the ionic character of the bonds and is in agreement with the general conception of the electropositive character of these elements.

Table LXXXV. Relative Weights of Valence Structures in $(CH_3)_2NH$

Structure	*Weight of structure per cent*
$(CH_3)_2N-H$ — *Homopolar* I	38
$(CH_3)_2N^-$ H^+ — *Single ionic form* II	11
$^+CH_3$, CH_3, $N^- - H$ — *Single ionic form (two)* III	2 × 2 = 4
CH_3, $^+CH_3$, N^{2-} H^+ — *double ionic form (two)* IV	2 × 0·7 = 1·4
$^+CH_3$, $^+CH_3$, $N^{2-} - H$ — *double ionic form* V	0·1
$^+CH_3$, $^+CH_3$, N^{3-} H^+ — *triple ionic form* VI	0
Transitional I–II	21
Transitional II–III	10
Remaining transitional	14·5

Table LXXXVI. Relative Weights of Valence Structures in $N(CH_3)_3$

Structure	*Weight of structure per cent*
$(CH_3)_2N-CH_3$ — *Homopolar* I	61
$(CH_3)_2N^-$ $^+CH_3$ — *Single ionic form (three)* II	3 × 3·3 = 9·9
$^+CH_3$, $^+CH_3$, $N^{2-}-CH_3$ — *Double ionic form (three)* III	3 × 0·16 = 0·5
$^+CH_3$, $^+CH_3$, N^{3-} $^+CH_3$ — *Triple ionic form* IV	0
Transitional I–II	23
Remaining transitional	5·6

Table LXXXVII
Relative Weights of Valence Structures in H_2S

Structure		Weight of structure per cent
Homopolar		
H — S — H	*I*	61
Single ionic form (two)		
H^+ S^-—H	*II*	2 × 2·5 = 5
Double ionic form		
H^+ S^{2-} H^+	*III*	0·1
Transitional	*I–II*	24
Remaining transitional		9·9

The dipole moment of nitrogen trifluoride NF_3 is almost zero, which indicates, since the shape of the molecule will be a trigonal pyramid as in NH_3, that the N—F bond is homopolar, notwithstanding the high electronegativity of fluorine. This may be explained by the fact that the positively charged, divalent state of nitrogen, as distinct from the negatively charged, divalent state, is improbable. In oxygen compounds the contribution of the positively charged trivalent state —O^+ (with two further bonds) is not great, the contribution of the corresponding state is, however, greater in sulphur and greater still in selenium. In the case of S_2Cl_2, $\mu_s = 1{\cdot}6$ D and for Se_2Cl_2, $\mu_s = 2{\cdot}6$ D and most probably the structures

Cl—Se^+=Se Cl^- and Cl^- Se=Se^+—Cl

are present to a greater extent than in the corresponding sulphur compound. $TeCl_4$ has the large moment of 2·54 D which is explained by the irregular tetrahedral arrangement of the bonds as shown by electron and x-ray diffraction measurements[9].

If ozone, O_3, were represented as a resonance hybrid of the two ionic structures

O=O^+—O^- and O^-—O^+=O

the dipole moment would be of the order of 1·6 D. The experimental value, $\mu_s = 0{\cdot}49$ D, has been interpreted by PHILLIPS, HUNTER and SUTTON[10] as indicating a considerable contribution from the forms

O=O O and O O=O

In SO_2, however, the experimental value of the dipole moment is 1·60 D in agreement with that calculated from the structures

O=S^+—O^- and O^-—S^+=O

In SO_3 the moment is zero in agreement with a symmetrical, planar configuration. The marked polarity of N_2O_5, $\mu_s = 1{\cdot}39$ D, is most probably explained by the nitrogen being in the positive, tetravalent state and with two negative charges shared by the oxygen atoms. The molecule may thus be represented as a resonance hybrid of the structures

```
O⁻      O      O⁻      O       O       O
  \    / \    /          \\   / \    //
   N+     N+              N+     N+
   ||     ||              |      |
   O      O               O⁻     O⁻
```

The repulsion of the two positively charged nitrogen atoms will tend to increase the N—O—N angle and thus to decrease the dipole moment.

The experimental value for the dipole moment of hydrogen peroxide is $\mu_s = 2{\cdot}13$ D, which is in agreement with the formula proposed by ROBERTSON[11] in which the two O—H bonds are at an angle of 106°, as shown in *Figure 37*.

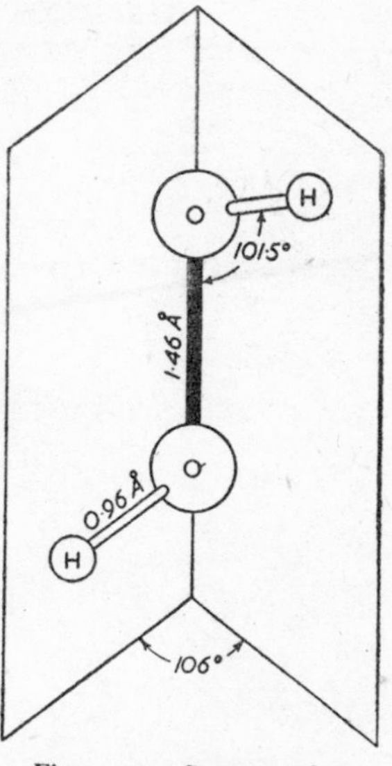

Figure 37. Structure of the hydrogen peroxide molecule

The absence of a dipole moment in molecules such as $HgHal_2$ and $BeHal_2$ is in agreement with the proposed linear configuration of these molecules. The two equal moments of the bonds are directed in mutually opposite directions, with the result that the molecule has a zero moment. A similar compensation of bond moments is responsible for the zero moment of $BHal_3$ molecules, which has a symmetrical planar configuration.

DIPOLE MOMENTS OF HYDROCARBON MOLECULES

Symmetrical tetrahedral molecules such as CH_4, CCl_4, SiH_4, $SiCl_4$ *etc* have a zero dipole moment. Let us consider methane, CH_4, in some detail. We shall let the moment of each CH bond be μ_{CH} and calculate the resultant dipole moment of the $-CH_3$ group in the CH_4 molecule. The configuration of this group will be a regular trigonal pyramid with the carbon atom at the apex and the three hydrogen atoms at the base. The resultant moment due to the three CH bonds will be directed along a line joining the apex to the centre point of the base. This line lies in the direction of the extrapolation of the fourth CH bond in CH_4. The resulting moment of the $-CH_3$ group will thus be equal to the sum of the projection of the three CH bond moments on this line *viz*

$$\mu_{CH_3} = 3\mu_{CH}\cos(180° - 109°28') = \mu_{CH}$$

Thus we see that in molecules such as CH_4, having a symmetrical tetrahedral structure, the resultant moment of the $-CH_3$ group is always exactly equal and opposite to the moment of the CH bond. Thus the moment of CH_4 is zero and furthermore, since $\mu_{CH_3} = \mu_{CH}$, the replacement of a hydrogen atom by a methyl group will not cause an alteration of the moment.

The evaluation of the moment of the CH bond from experimental data has so far proved impossible, although some authors have suggested a value of approximately 0·4 D. It would be best, however, for the present to regard the moment as very small and assume that the bond is almost entirely homopolar. This conclusion is in agreement with the bond energy data.

The symmetrical arrangement of the CH bonds in ethylene, acetylene

Table LXXXVIII. Dipole Moments of Unsaturated Hydrocarbons

Molecule	*Dipole moment* *D*	*Molecule*	*Dipole moment* *D*
$CH_3CH{=}CH_2$	0·35	$C_6H_5C{\equiv}CH$	0·80*s*
$CH_3CH_2CH{=}CH_2$	0·30	$CH_3C_6H_4C{\equiv}CH$	1·01*s*
$(CH_3)_2C{=}CH_2$	0·49	$C_2H_5C_6H_4C{\equiv}CH$	1·05*s*
$CH_3CH{=}CH{-}CH{=}CH_2$	0·68	$(CH_3)_2CHC_6H_4C{\equiv}CH$	1·12*s*
$CH_2{=}C(CH_3){-}CH{=}CH_2$	0·38	CH_2	0·65*s*
$CH_2{=}C(CH_3){-}C(CH_3){=}CH_2$	0·52		
$C_6H_5CH_3$	0·4		
$C_6H_5C_2H_5$	0·6		
$C_6H_5C(CH_3)_3$	0·7		
$C_6H_5CH{=}CH$	0·37*s*	CH_2	0·45*s*
$CH_3C_6H_4CH{=}CH_2$	0·6*s*		
$C_2H_5C_6H_4CH{=}CH_2$	0·6*s*		
$(C_6H_5)_2C{=}CH_2$	0·5*s*		
$CH_3C{\equiv}CH$	0·77*s*	CH_2	0·69*s*
$C_2H_5C{\equiv}CH$	0·80		
$C_3H_7C{\equiv}CH$	0·85		
$C_4H_9C{\equiv}CH$	0·87		
$C_5H_{11}C{\equiv}CH$	0·86	$(C_6H_5)_3CH$	0·21*s*

and benzene results in zero moments for these molecules and it might be expected that their homologues, *e.g.* propylene, methylacetylene and toluene should also have no dipole moment. The experimental data, however, show that many unsaturated hydrocarbons possess a small dipole moment (*Table LXXXVIII*). The carbon atom, as we have seen, may exist in either the positively charged trivalent state, or the negatively charged trivalent state. In saturated hydrocarbons these forms appear only in the bond resonance involving the ionic state, *e.g.* C^-H^+, in the CH bond; in unsaturated hydrocarbons on the other hand, owing to the presence of π bonds, other valence bond structures are possible and contribute to the resonance of the molecule. Thus in propylene, together with the homopolar structure

$$\underset{1}{CH_3}{-}\underset{2}{CH}{=}\underset{3}{CH_2}$$

there are possible three ionic structures, due to the three H atoms in the CH_3 group

$$^+H\ CH_2{=}CH{-}{}^-CH_2$$

in which the localized π bond occurs between the 1–2 carbon atoms in place of the 2–3. Because of the contribution of this structure, the molecule has a permanent dipole moment. The carbon atom in the 3 position thus possesses a negative charge and in the reaction of propylene with hydrogen chloride it would be expected on the basis of the above evidence that the hydrogen atom would bond to carbon atom 3 and the chlorine atom to carbon atom 2. This prediction is in agreement with the empirical rule of MARKOVNIKOV, which states that in the addition of HCl to a double bond the hydrogen atom becomes attached to the carbon atom bonded to the greater number of hydrogen atoms. The product of the reaction is thus $CH_3CHHalCH_3$. The reason why the reaction gives this product, even though the contribution of the ionic structure may be very small, is due to the fact that the problem is largely one of the kinetics of two or more alternative reactions. If the energy of activation is reduced slightly through the contribution of the ionic structure, the rate of reaction will be increased considerably owing to the exponential function in the rate equation. From the dipole moment of propylene, the relative contributions of the different structures may be calculated approximately[12]; these are found to be: homopolar, 94 per cent; ionic, 3 per cent; transitional, 3 per cent. It is evident that the molecule is essentially homopolar, the contributions of the ionic and transitional structures being very small. In isobutylene, $(CH_3)_2C = CH_2$, the dipole moment is appreciable, having the value 0·49 D, which may be attributed to the fact that the number of structures of the type

$$\begin{array}{l} {}^{+}H\ CH_2 \\ \qquad\quad \diagdown \\ \qquad\qquad C{-}{}^{-}CH_2 \\ \qquad\quad \diagup \\ \quad\ \ CH_3 \end{array}$$

is equal to six and the contribution of these forms will therefore be fairly large. In butylene $CH_2{=}CHCH_2CH_3$, the number of analogous structures *viz* $\underset{\qquad\qquad\quad H^{+}}{{}^{-}CH_2{-}CH{=}CH{-}CH_3}$ is only two and the dipole moment is less, being 0·3 D. In acetylene and acetylenic compounds the electron affinity of the carbon atoms taking part in the acetylenic bond is greater than in the case of the ethylenic bond. This is manifested in the acid character of acetylene as in the formation of acetylides, and in the dipole moments of acetylene derivatives which, as is shown in *Table LXXXVIII*, have a moment about 0·4 D greater than in the case of the corresponding ethylene derivative. The contribution of the ionic structures

$$^{+}H\ \ CH_2{=}C{=}^{-}CH$$

in methylacetylene is estimated at 7 per cent, of the transitional structure 6 per cent, and of the homopolar 87 per cent. If the molecule contains both a double and triple bond as in vinylacetylene, $CH_2{=}CH{-}C{\equiv}CH$, then owing to the greater electron affinity of the acetylenic compared with the ethylenic carbon atoms, the contribution of the structure

$$^{+}CH_2{-}CH{=}C{=}^{+}CH$$

is greater than that with the charges reversed. For this reason this compound, on reaction with hydrogen chloride, yields

$$CH_2Cl{-}CH{=}C{=}CH_2$$

Similar behaviour is observed with divinylacetylene,

$$CH_2{=}CH{-}C{\equiv}C{-}CH{=}CH_2$$

in which the two forms:

$$^{+}CH_2{-}CH{=}C{=}C^{-}{-}CH{=}CH_2$$
$$CH_2{=}CH{-}C^{-}{=}C{=}CH{-}^{+}CH_2$$

are the main ionic valence bond structures. On reaction with hydrogen chloride, the molecule

$$CH_2Cl{-}CH{=}C{=}CH{-}CH{=}CH_2$$

is obtained[13]. The polarity of 2–methylbutadiene is accounted for by the contribution of similar structures to those in propylene

$$^{-}CH_2—\underset{\underset{+H\ CH_2}{\|}}{C}—CH=CH_2$$

In 1–methylbutadiene, in addition to the structures :

$$CH_3—CH=CH—CH=CH_2$$
$$^{+}H\ CH_2=CH—^{-}CH—CH=CH_2$$

there is an additional possible structure,

$$^{+}H\ CH_2=CH—CH=CH—^{-}CH_2$$

which will cause an increase in the moment[14].

The polarity of the homologues of benzene is caused by resonance of the benzene ring:

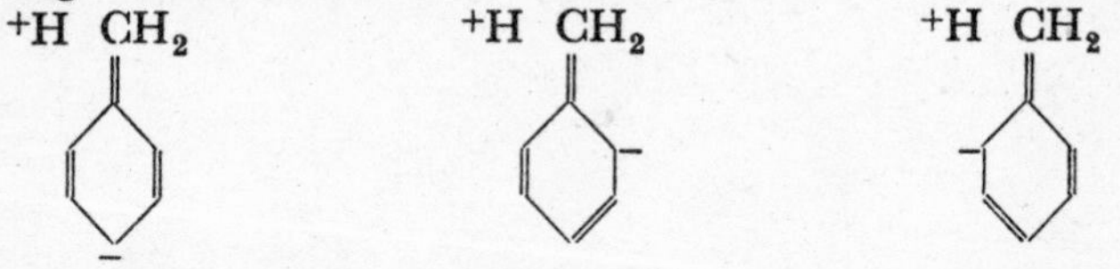

+H CH₂   +H CH₂   +H CH₂

and toluene has a moment of 0·4 D. In fluorene, in addition to four homopolar structures, thirty six ionic structures are possible and are responsible for the existence of a dipole moment,

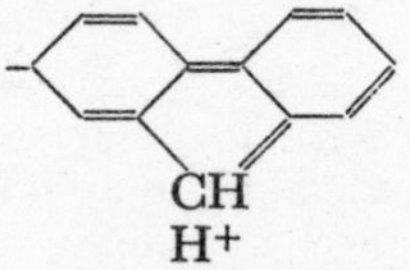

CH
H+

and will be responsible for the acid properties of the hydrogen atom in the 9 position ; indene also has an appreciable moment for the same reason. *Cyclo*pentadiene is polar owing to the resonance of the structures

CH_2 +HCH   +HCH

In symmetrical unsaturated hydrocarbons, *e.g.* $CH_3CH=CHCH_3$, it is necessary to consider the structures

$$^{+}H\ CH_2=CH—^{-}CH—CH_3 \quad \text{and} \quad CH_3—^{-}CH—CH=CH_2H^{+}$$

when discussing the reactivity of the molecule but owing to the symmetry of the molecule, the moments are mutually compensated and the molecule has zero dipole moment.

DIPOLE MOMENTS OF ALIPHATIC COMPOUNDS

The dipole moments of derivatives of the saturated hydrocarbons are generally found to be almost independent of the chain length and of the branching of the chain as shown by the data for the alcohols and for the chloro- and nitro-paraffins (*Table LXXXIX*). The dipole moment is therefore due almost entirely to the polarity of the bond ; thus in alcohols the dipole moment is due to the COH group, in nitro-compounds to the CNO_2 group and in chloro-compounds to the CCl bond.

Table LXXXIX. Dipole Moments of Derivatives of Aliphatic Hydrocarbons

Molecule	*Dipole moment D*	*Molecule*	*Dipole moment D*	*Molecule*	*Dipole moment D*
CH_3Cl	1·92	CH_3OH	1·69	CH_3NO_2	3·54
C_2H_5Cl	2·05	C_2H_5OH	1·70	$C_2H_5NO_2$	3·58
n-C_3H_7Cl	2·10	*n*-C_3H_7OH	1·64	*n*-$C_3H_7NO_2$	3·57; 3·67
n-C_4H_9Cl	2·12	*n*-C_4H_9OH	1·66	*n*-$C_4H_9NO_2$	3·55
$(CH_3)_2CHCl$	2·15	*n*-$C_5H_{11}OH$	1·65	$(CH_3)_2CHNO_2$	3·67
$(CH_3)_2CHCH_2Cl$	2·04	*n*-$C_6H_{13}OH$	1·64	$(CH_3)_3CNO_2$	3·66
$CH_3CH_2 \backslash CHCl / CH_3$	2·12	$(CH_3)_2CHOH$	1·58		
		$(CH_3)_3COH$	1.65		
		$(CH_3)_2CHCH_2OH$	1·63		
$(CH_3)_3CCl$	2·13	$CH_2{=}CHCH_2OH$	1·63		
$CH_2{=}CHCH_2Cl$	1·95				
$CH_2 < (CH_2—CH_2)(CH_2—CH_2) > CHCl$	2·07				

Halogen derivatives— If we assume that the dipole moment of the CH_3 group, and hence of the CH bond, is zero, then it is possible to assign the whole of the moment of the alkyl halide molecules to the CHal bond. The polarity of this bond is caused by the superposition of the two states $\geqslant$ C–Hal and $\geqslant {}^{+}C^{-}$Hal, and the values of the contribution of these structures to the bond are given in *Table XC.* The data shown serve to illustrate the fact that the dipole moment does not indicate, by itself, the ionic character of a bond. Thus the moments of the CF and CI bonds are very close, but the contribution of the ionic form in CF is much greater than in CI, as the interatomic distance is much less.

Table XC. Relative Contributions of Valence Structures in CHal bond

Bond	*Dipole moment D*	*Internuclear distance A*	*Weight of structure per cent*		
			Homopolar	*Ionic*	*Transitional*
C—F	1·83	1·41	58	25	17
C—Cl	2·05	1·76	61	20	19
C—Br	2·04	1·91	71	13	16
C—I	1·80	2·10	77	9	14

If one carbon atom is attached to more than one halogen atom, it is found that the moment of the resulting molecule differs from the vector sum of the constituent bond moments. This behaviour occurs, for example, in

Table XCI. Dipole Moments of Halogen Derivatives of Methane (D)

X / *Molecule*	F	Cl	Br	I
CH_3X	1·83	1·92	1·80	1·63
CH_2X_2	—	1·55	1·43	1·08
CHX_3	1·59	1·02	0·99	0·80

the polyhalogen derivatives of methane, as shown in *Table XCI*. The vector sum of the bond moments in the group $-CX_3$ should be equal to the bond moment of CX, but as is shown in *Table XCI*, this is not the case, and the moments of all the CHX_3 molecules are less than those of the corresponding CH_3X molecules. Similar behaviour occurs in the CH_2X_2 molecules and is also observed in the chloro derivatives of silane (SiH_3Cl, $\mu = 1{\cdot}28$ D ; SiH_2Cl_2, $\mu = 1{\cdot}17$ D ; $SiHCl_3$, $\mu = 0{\cdot}85$ D). This behaviour cannot be attributed to a change in the bond angles, which in every case are close to the tetrahedral angle, nor to molecular resonance, but indicates that in a particular group the ionic states of the various bonds are not independent of each other. In CH_3Cl, the carbon atom possesses a positive charge on account of the presence of one chlorine atom, and on substitution of a second chlorine atom to form CH_2Cl_2 the existing positive charge on the carbon will decrease the ionic character of the second CCl bond. Thus the contribution of the structure

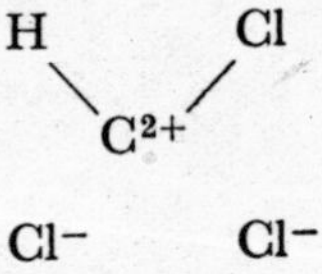

```
H       Cl
 \     /
  C2+

Cl-     Cl-
```

to the resonance of the molecule is less than that of the structure

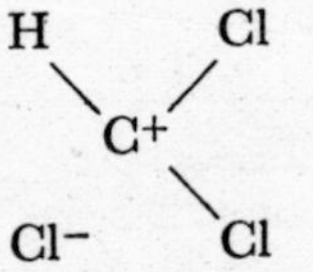

```
H       Cl
 \     /
  C+
     \
Cl-   Cl
```

as is to be expected. The rather higher values of the dipole moment, compared with those given in *Table XCI*, observed for the molecules, CH_3CHCl_2, $\mu=2{\cdot}07$ D ; $CH_3CCl_2CH_3$, $\mu=2{\cdot}25$ D ; CH_3CCl_3, $\mu=1{\cdot}78$ D ; CH_3CF_3, $\mu=2{\cdot}27$ D, might appear to contradict the theory of the mutual suppression of ionic structures developed above ; however in these compounds resonance can occur, since valence bond structures of the type

$$\begin{matrix} CH_2{=}CCl_2 \\ H^+ \quad Cl^- \end{matrix}$$

are possible. In the example given, the number of such structures is nine, more than in CH_3CH_2Cl which is found to have a lower moment. For a similar reason, the moment of $CH_3CCl_2CH_3$ is larger than that of CH_3CHCl_2. In the polyhalogen derivatives of methane, similar structures are only possible if the carbon is assumed to be in the divalent state, $^+H\ CCl_2Cl^-$, which is not very probable.

If the halogen atom is linked to a carbon atom taking part in a double or triple bond the moment is somewhat lower than if the bond is single (*Table XCII*). This fact indicates that in the vinyl halogen derivatives, in addition to the structures

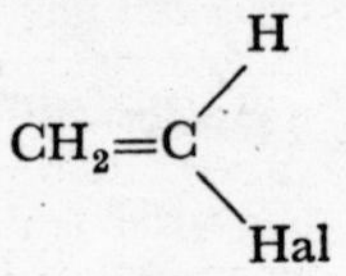

```
          H                       H
         /                       /
CH2=C          and     CH2=C+
         \
          Hal                  -Hal
     I                      II
```

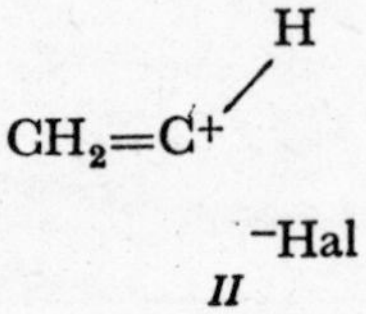

there will be an appreciable contribution from the valence bond structure containing a divalent, positively charged halogen, *viz*

$$^{-}CH_2—CH={}^{+}Hal$$
III

In the halogen derivatives of the acetylenes, the corresponding structure makes an even greater contribution and the values of the dipole moments are less than in the case of the corresponding vinyl derivatives :

$$HC≡CHal \qquad HC≡{}^{+}C^{-}Hal \qquad H—C^{-}=C={}^{+}Hal$$
I   *II*   *III*

Calculation of the relative weights of the structures of the halogen derivatives of the acetylenes shows that the contribution of the valence bond structure *III* is not very great (*Table XCIII*), nevertheless, this small contribution is sufficient to affect the resultant dipole moment as the structures are strongly polar (the distance between the charges in $H—C^{-}=C={}^{+}Cl$, is 2·89 Å and in $H—C^{-}=C={}^{+}Br$, 3·01 Å).

Table XCII. Dipole Moments of Halogen Derivatives of Unsaturated Hydrocarbons (D)

Molecule \ X	Cl	Br	I
$CH_2=CHX$	1·44	1·41	1·26
$CH_2=CXCH=CH_2$	1·42	—	—
$CH≡CX$	0·44	0	—
$C_4H_9C≡CX$	1·23*s*	1·06*s*	0·75*s*
$C_5H_{11}C≡CX$	1·27*s*	1·05*s*	0·80
$C_6H_5CH=CHX$	1·40*s*	1·51*s*	—
$C_6H_5C≡CX$	1·10*s*	0·85*s*	0·55*s*

In the phenyl vinyl halogen derivatives, structures containing a positively charged halogen atom and a negative charge, either in the side chain or in the benzene ring are possible, *e.g.*

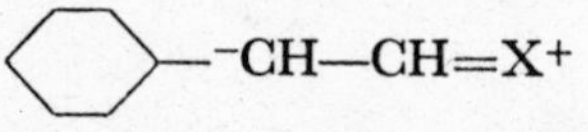

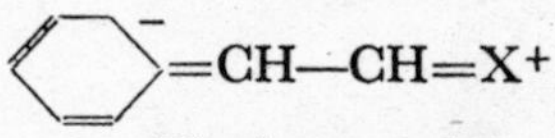

$$C_6H_5{}^{-}CH—CH=X^{+} \qquad {}^{-}C_6H_5=CH—CH=X^{+}$$

The increased resonance due to the benzene ring produces a decrease in the dipole moment.

Table XCIII. Relative Weights of Valence Bond Structures in Halogen Derivatives of Acetylene

Molecule	Dipole[15] moment D	Weight of structure per cent *I*	*II*	*III*	*I–II*	*I–III*	*II–III*
HC≡C—Cl	0·44	49	16	1	20	11	3
H—C≡C—Br	0	57	7	0·5	19·5	13	3

The di-substituted halogen derivatives of ethylene, in which the halogen atoms are located on different carbon atoms form *cis*- and *trans*-isomers. In *trans*-dichlorethylene owing to the mutual compensation of the moments due to the two C–Cl bonds, which are directed in opposite directions in space, the dipole moment is zero. With the *cis* compounds, on the other hand, larger moments are obtained (*cis*- CHCl=CHCl, $\mu = 1·89$ D; *cis*-CHBr=CHBr, $\mu = 1·35$ D;

Table XCIV. Dipole Moments of Aliphatic Aldehydes

Molecule	Dipole moment D	Molecule	Dipole moment D
HCHO	2·27	$CH_3CH_2CH_2CHO$	2·72
CH_3CHO	2·72	$CH_3CH=CHCHO$	3·67
CH_3CH_2CHO	2·73		

cis- CHI=CHI, $\mu = 0{\cdot}75$ D). This difference in the dipole moments of *cis*- and *trans*-isomers may be used as a method of identification and for the analysis of mixture of the two isomers.

Aldehydes— The dipole moments of various aldehydes are given in *Table XCIV*. In formaldehyde resonance can occur only in the carbonyl bond, structures *I* and *II*, since the structure *III*, with a positive charge in one of the hydrogen atoms, involves a divalent carbon atom.

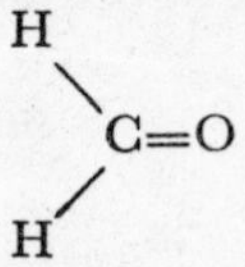

$$\begin{array}{l} H \\ \quad\diagdown \\ \quad\;\; C{=}O \\ \quad\diagup \\ H \end{array} \qquad\qquad \begin{array}{l} H \\ \quad\diagdown \\ \quad\;\; C^{+}{-}O^{-} \\ \quad\diagup \\ H \end{array}$$

I 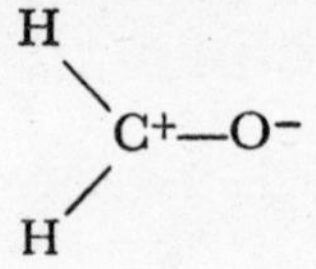 *II*

$$\begin{array}{l} H^{+} \\ \\ \quad\;\; C{-}O^{-} \\ \quad\diagup \\ H \end{array}$$

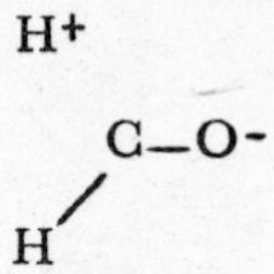

III

If one of the hydrogen atoms is replaced by a CH_3 group, the structures *I* and *II* still contribute to the resonance of the molecule, but in addition the structure *IV* is now possible

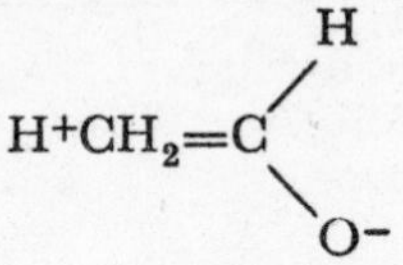

$$\begin{array}{l} \qquad\qquad\quad H \\ \qquad\qquad\;\diagup \\ H^{+}CH_2{=}C \\ \qquad\qquad\;\diagdown \\ \qquad\qquad\quad O^{-} \end{array}$$

IV

three structures

and in agreement with this we see in *Table XCIV* that the dipole moment of acetaldehyde is 2·72 D which is greater than that of formaldehyde, 2·27 D. Furthermore, replacement of the second hydrogen by a methyl group, to give acetone, produces a further increase of the moment to 2·95 D owing to the greater number of structures of type *IV* which are possible.

If the molecule contains an ethylenic group C=C in addition to the carbonyl group, the molecular resonance is increased and the dipole moment raised. Thus in acrolein, $CH_2{=}CHCHO$, the dipole moment measured in solution is 2·88 D, a value greater by 0·39 D than the dipole moment of acetaldehyde also measured in solution, 2·49 D. This is due to the contribution of the structure

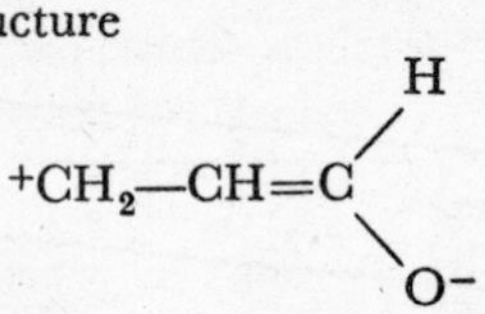

$$\begin{array}{l} \qquad\qquad\qquad\quad H \\ \qquad\qquad\qquad\;\diagup \\ {}^{+}CH_2{-}CH{=}C \\ \qquad\qquad\qquad\;\diagdown \\ \qquad\qquad\qquad\quad O^{-} \end{array}$$

to the resonance of the molecule. In agreement with this picture of the acrolein molecule, the addition of hydrogen bromide to acrolein gives CH_2BrCH_2CHO, the negative bromine atom uniting with the most positive atom and the positive hydrogen atom with the most negative. A still greater increase in dipole moment is observed with crotonaldehyde which will be due to the contribution of the structures

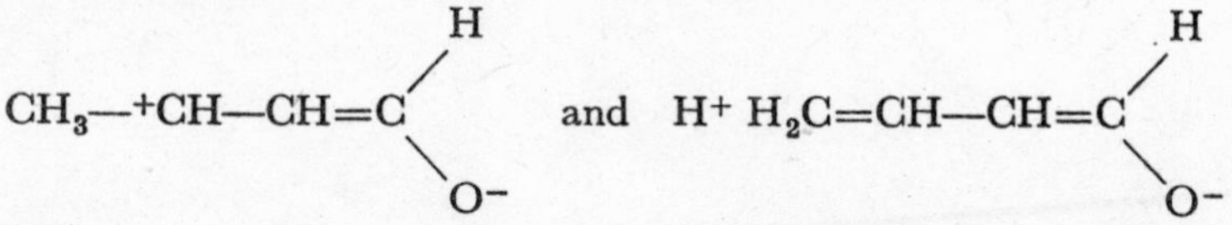

$$CH_3—{}^+CH—CH{=}C\begin{matrix}H\\ \diagup \\ \\ \diagdown \\ O^-\end{matrix} \quad \text{and} \quad H^+\ H_2C{=}CH—CH{=}C\begin{matrix}H\\ \diagup \\ \\ \diagdown \\ O^-\end{matrix}$$

Nitriles— In nitriles, structures of the type $CH_3—C^+{=}N^-$ will be responsible for the dipole moment of the molecule. If the moments of hydrogen cyanide and of methyl cyanide are compared (*Table XCV*) a similar behaviour to that described for the aldehydes is observed. The corresponding valence bond structures are :

I	*II*	*III*
$H—C{\equiv}N$	$H—C^+{=}N^-$	$H^+C{=}N^-$
$CH_3—C{\equiv}N$	$CH_3—C^+{=}N^-$	$H^+CH_2{=}C{=}N^-$

The CC distance in methyl cyanide is 1·49 Å compared with the single bond value of 1·54 Å, indicating an appreciable contribution from the structure *III*. The low moment observed in the case of acrylonitrile is not fully understood, but the high moment for crotononitrile is in agreement with the expected contribution from the structures

$$CH_3—{}^+CH—CH{=}C{=}N^-$$

and

$$H^+CH_2{=}CH—CH{=}C{=}N^-$$

Table XCV. Dipole Moments of Aliphatic Nitriles

Molecule	*Dipole moment D*	*Molecule*	*Dipole moment D*
HCN	2·93	C_4H_9CN	4·09
CH_3CN	3·94	$CH_2{=}CHCN$	3·88
C_2H_5CN	4·02	$CH_3CH{=}CHCN$	4·50
C_3H_7CN	4·05		

DIPOLE MOMENTS OF AROMATIC COMPOUNDS

The difference between the chemical behaviour of the substitution products of benzene and the corresponding aliphatic derivatives are well known and are reflected in the values of their dipole moments (*Table XCVI*). In chlorobenzene, in addition to the bond resonance structures, *I* and *II*, there are three additional structures *III*, *IV* and *V* contributing to the molecular resonance and the dipole moment is lowered in comparison with the alkyl halides.

Table XCVI. Dipole Moments of Aliphatic and Aromatic Compounds

Molecule	*Dipole moment D*	*Molecule*	*Dipole moment D*
CH_3CH_3	0	$C_6H_5CH_3$	0·4
CH_3Cl	1·92	C_6H_5Cl	1·70
CH_3NO_2	3·54	$C_6H_5NO_2$	4·22
CH_3CN	3·94	C_6H_5CN	4·39
CH_3CHO	2·72	C_6H_5CHO	3·16
CH_3NH_2	1·32	$C_6H_5NH_2$	1·48
CH_3OH	1·69	C_6H_5OH	1·40
C_2H_5SH	1·56	C_6H_5SH	1·33
CH_3OCH_3	1·29	$C_6H_5OCH_3$	1·35
		$C_6H_5OC_6H_5$	1·35
CH_3SCH_3	1·40*s*	$C_6H_5SC_6H_5$	1·50*s*

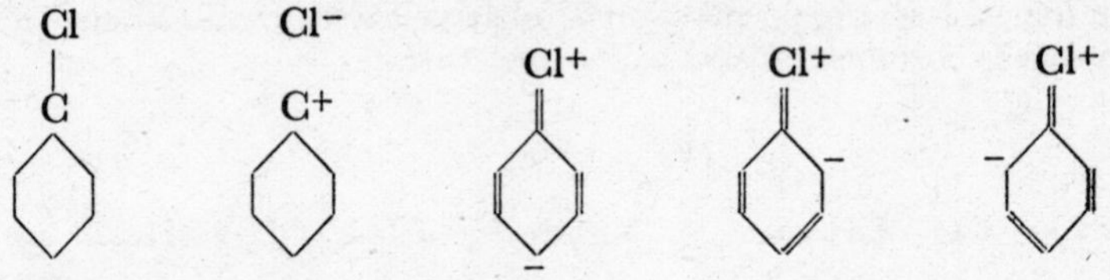

Cl Cl⁻ Cl+ Cl+ Cl+
C C+

I II III IV V

The polar character of nitromethane is due to the formation of a positive charge on the nitrogen and the sharing of the corresponding negative charge between the two oxygen atoms

CH_3—N+ (O, O−) CH_3—N+ (O−, O)

In addition to these structures there will be a contribution from the CN bond in which the carbon atom is negatively charged and the nitrogen positively charged. In nitrobenzene additional structures are possible in which both of the oxygen atoms are negative and the corresponding positive charges occur at the nitrogen atom and at either the *ortho* or the *para* carbon atoms in the benzene ring :

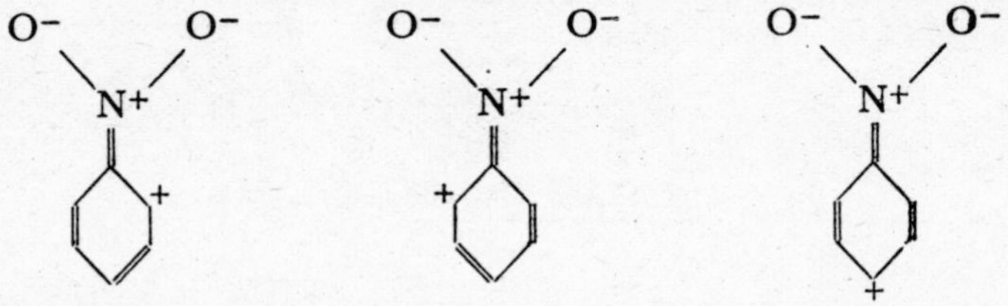

O− O− O− O− O− O−
N+ N+ N+
+ + +

In benzonitrile, C_6H_5CN, the dipole moment is also noticeably greater than in methylcyanide, CH_3CN, since the nitrogen atom may be negative not only with respect to the adjacent carbon atom, but also to the *ortho* and *para* carbon atoms in the ring :

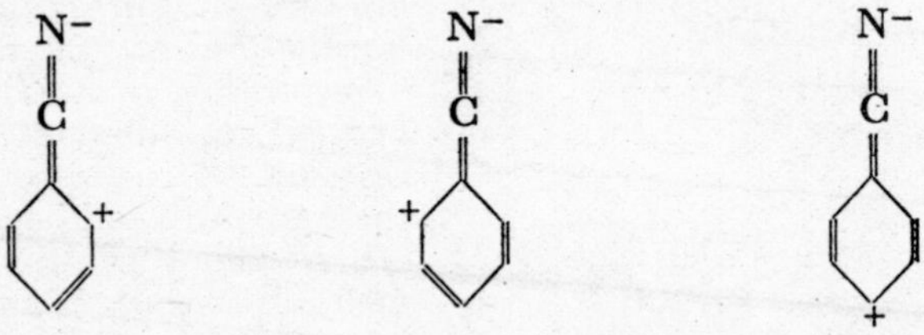

N− N− N−
C C C
+ + +

Similarly, in the case of benzaldehyde, in addition to the bond resonance in the carbonyl bond, >C=O ; $>C^{+}—O^{-}$, there are also the additional structures

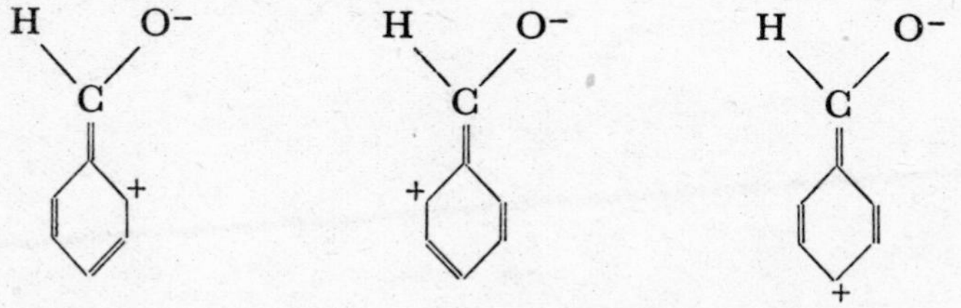

which contribute to the resonance of the molecule and bring about an increase in the dipole moment.

In aniline there are three additional structures containing a tetravalent, positively charged nitrogen atom :

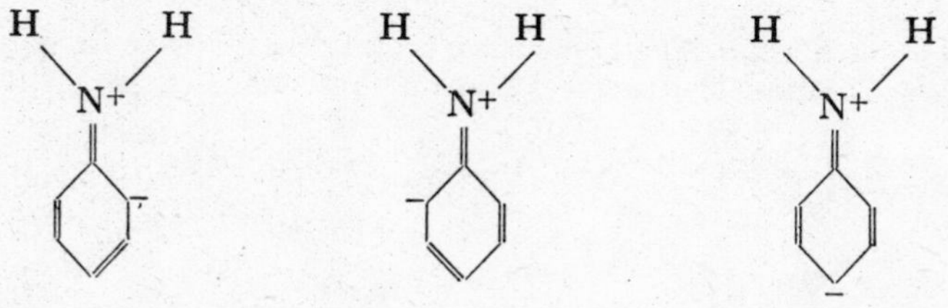

compared with the aliphatic amines. The basic properties of the aromatic amines are thus reduced in comparison with the aliphatic amines since the nitrogen atom is already partially tetravalent, and thus partially neutralized on account of the resonance with the benzene ring.

In the phenols, the structures *I* to *III*, which cannot occur in the alcohols, as well as the structures *IV* to *VI*, tend to reduce the dipole moment. The acid properties of the phenols compared with the alcohols are due to the contribution of the forms *IV* to *VI*.

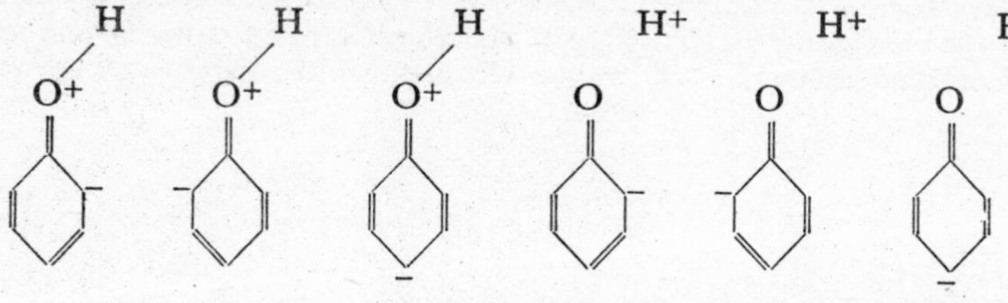

Iodobenzene reacts with chlorine to form phenyliodochloride $C_6H_5ICl_2$, which is considerably more stable than the aliphatic iodochlorides. In phenyliodochloride, the following structures are possible, and the stability of the molecule will be due to the resonance energy of the molecule. In solution the dipole moment is 2·61 D[16], *i.e.* 1·3 D greater than iodobenzene.

Such an increase could not be due to a polar bond between the iodine and chlorine atoms and resonance, involving the benzene ring must occur :

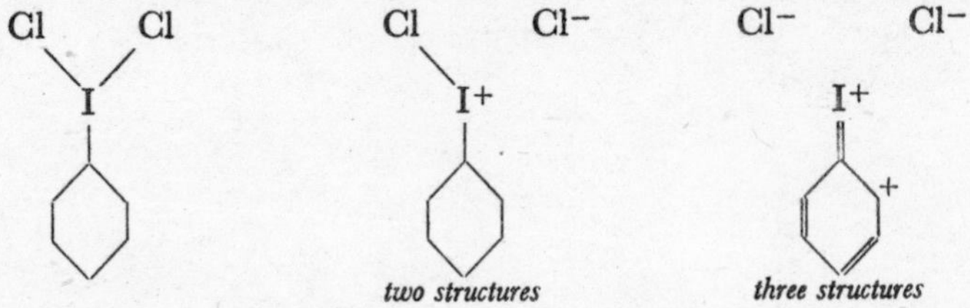

two structures *three structures*

In derivatives of diphenyl, owing to the presence of two benzene rings, the number of possible resonance structures is greater than in the case of the corresponding benzene derivatives and the dipole moment is increased. Thus with *p*-aminodiphenyl :

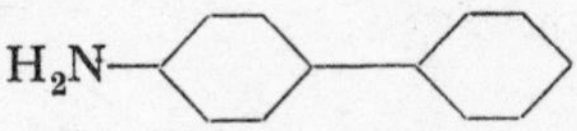

H_2N—

the dipole moment, is 1·76$_s$ D, which is 0·23 D greater than in aniline owing to the contribution of structures showing resonance in both the benzene rings :

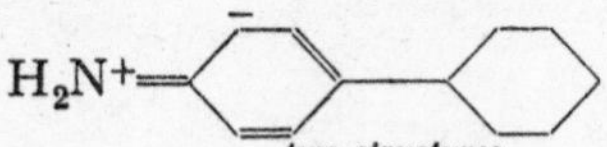

two structures

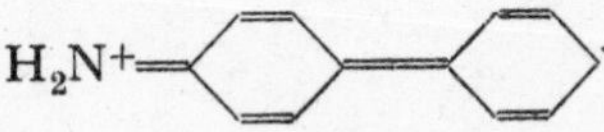

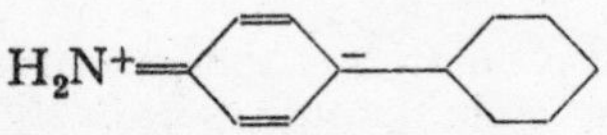

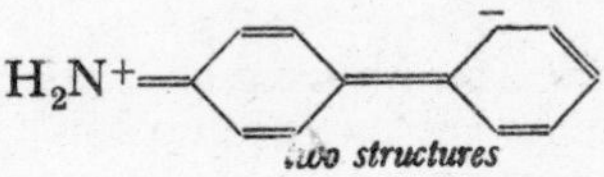

two structures

In *p*-aminoazobenzene, $\mu_s = 2{\cdot}71$ D ; one of the nitrogen atoms in the azo group may be negatively charged.

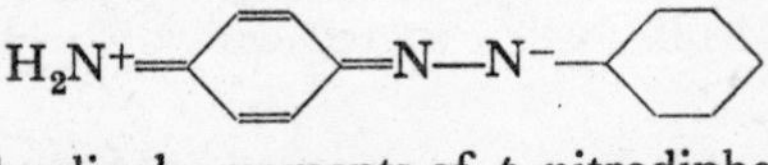

H_2N^+=⟨ ⟩=N—N^-—⟨ ⟩

The difference in the dipole moments of *p*-nitrodiphenyl, *I*, $\mu_s = 4{\cdot}17$ D, and of the *meta* isomer, *II*, $\mu_s = 3{\cdot}40$ D, is due to the exclusion of the second ring from the molecular resonance when the nitro group is in the *meta* position.

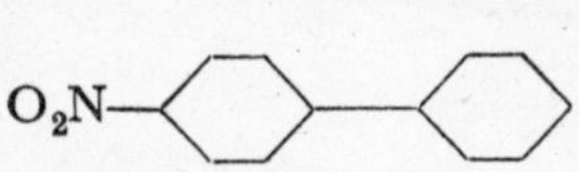

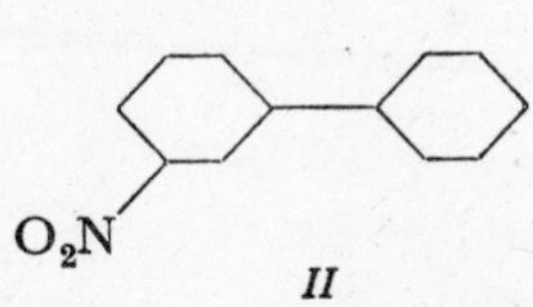

II

The experimental data on the dipole moments of aliphatic and aromatic compounds clearly indicate the existence of molecular resonance in the latter. The resonance, which produces either positive or negative charges on the carbon atoms in the *ortho* and *para* positions, determines the specificity, which has been observed in the substitution of the benzene nucleus. The substituent groups may be divided into two classes depending upon whether their presence gives rise to negative or positive charges on the carbon atoms in the *ortho* and *para* positions. The most important of the groups giving rise to negative charges are: CH_3, Hal, OH, NH_2, OCH_3, $N(CH_3)_2$, and of those giving rise to positive charges: NO_2, CN, CHO, SO_3H, and COOH; the first class lead to substitution predominantly in *ortho* and *para* position and the second class to substitution in the *meta* position. This selective substitution is not only dependent on the nature of the charges in the carbon atoms of the benzene ring and the substituting group, but also on the different energies of activation of reactions involving carbon atoms with different electron densities[17]. The quantitative treatment of the direction of substitution in the benzene ring presents many difficulties, since the difference between the effects producing the different types of substitution is not large. This may best be brought out by considering an example. Let us suppose that the substitution in the *ortho* position proceeds ten times faster than the corresponding reaction in the *meta* position. Since the rate of reaction is proportional to $\exp(-E/RT)$, where E is the energy of activation, it follows that the energy of activation for the *ortho* substitution reaction is only 1·4 kcals less than that for the *meta* substitution reaction. Thus although there is a very noticeable and significant difference in the nature of the reaction product, it has been produced by only a small difference in the properties of the *ortho* and *meta* carbon atoms. In this connection it should be emphasized that the contribution of the valence bond structures showing molecular resonance is not great and the bond is very largely homopolar. Nevertheless, because of their large dipole moment, the small contribution of the polar structures is generally of great significance in determining the properties of the resultant molecule.

Sign and direction of the dipole moment— For the determination of the distribution of positive and negative charges in various structures we have been guided by data on the possible valency states of atoms. The direction of the resulting dipole moment, however, is not always clear. For example, it is necessary to have experimental data in order to determine whether, in toluene, the methyl group carries a positive charge and the benzene ring a negative charge or *vice versa*. For this purpose it is necessary to have a second substituent group in the benzene ring with which there is no doubt as to the directional nature of its dipole moment. Thus, for example, in the halogen derivatives of benzene, there is no doubt that the chlorine atom forms the negative end of the dipole. The effect of structures of the type

$^{-}C_6H_4{=}Cl^{+}$ reduces the dipole moment, but does not cause a change of direction. Returning to the problem of toluene, we find that the dipole moment of *p*-chlorotoluene, $\mu_s = 1{\cdot}90$ D is greater than that of chlorobenzene, $\mu_s = 1{\cdot}55$ D. This result is only possible if the moments act in the same direction *I*. Consequently it is concluded that the methyl group forms the positive end of the dipole.

CH_3—C_6H_4—Cl O_2N—C_6H_4—Cl

$+ \rightarrow -$ $+ \rightarrow -$ $- \leftarrow +$ $+ \rightarrow -$

II

The dipole moment of *p*-nitrochlorobenzene, $\mu_s = 2{\cdot}78$ D, is less than the dipole moment of nitrobenzene, $\mu_s = 4{\cdot}01$ D, which indicates that the moments are directed in different directions, *II*. Consequently in nitrobenzene the moment is directed from the positive ring to the negative oxygen atoms. The lower value of the dipole moment of *p*–chlorobenzonitrile, *p*–ClC_6H_4CN, $\mu_s = 2{\cdot}08$ D, compared with that of benzonitrile, 4·39 D, indicates that the moment is directed from the ring to the nitrogen, in accordance with the resonance structures given above.

The dipole moments of the isonitriles, RNC, are related to the contribution of the structures R—$N^+{\equiv}C^-$ and R—N=C to the resonance of the molecule, and comparison of the moments of C_6H_5NC, $\mu_s = 3{\cdot}49$ D, and *p*–ClC_6H_4NC, $\mu_s = 2{\cdot}07$ D, supports the following charge distribution

Cl—⬡—N=C

− ← + + → −

Owing to the planar configuration of the benzene ring, it will be clear that in $C_6H_5CH_3$, C_6H_5Hal, $C_6H_5NO_2$, C_6H_5NC and $C_6H_5C{\equiv}CH$, the axis of the dipole moment corresponds to a line in the plane of the ring passing through the benzene carbon atom and the substituent atom or group linked to it ; such groups or atoms may be described as being regular. In other cases this is not so. Thus in phenol for example, the moment is not directed along the CO bond since there are two polar bonds, CO and OH, which are at an angle to each other and consequently the resultant moment forms an angle with the axis of the CO bond. The valence bond structures *I* to *III* (see page 221) decrease the moment of the CO bond, whereas structures with positive charge on the hydrogen atom, *IV* to *VI*, influence the direction of the resulting dipole moment of the molecule. Similar irregular structures occur with substituent groups such as NH_2, OH, OCH_3 $N(CH_3)_2$, SH, SCH_3, COOR, CHO. FUCHS and WOLF[18] have calculated from the dipole moment data the values of the valency angles (*Table XCVII*).

Table XCVII. Valency Angles from Dipole Moment Data

Group	*Angle*	*Group*	*Angle*
NO	20°	OCH_3	75°
NH_2	40°	CHO	37°
$N(CH_3)_2$	34°	$COCH_3$	50°
OH	38°		

Di-substituted derivatives of benzene— The comparison of the experimental values of the dipole moment of di-substituted derivatives of benzene with the vector sums of the individual bond or group moments leads to some important results. If in the benzene ring there are two regular groups then the axes of the moments μ_1 and μ_2 in the *ortho* position will form an angle of 60°, in the *meta* position an angle of 120°, and in the *para* position an angle of 180°. The vectorial sum of the moments will be given by :

$$\textit{ortho} \quad \mu = (\mu_1^2 + \mu_2^2 \pm \mu_1\mu_2)^{\frac{1}{2}} \qquad \ldots.(10.21)$$

$$\textit{meta} \quad \mu = (\mu_1^2 + \mu_2^2 \mp \mu_1\mu_2)^{\frac{1}{2}} \qquad \ldots.(10.22)$$

$$\textit{para} \quad \mu = \mu_1 \mp \mu_2 \qquad \ldots.(10.23)$$

The upper signs in formulae 10.21 to 10.23 correspond to the case where the directions of the moments of the substituent groups, relative to the ring, are the same and the lower signs refer to the case when they are opposite.

In the particular case when the substituent groups are identical, as in the dichlorobenzenes, $\mu_1 = \mu_2$ and we have :

$$\text{ortho} \quad \mu = (3\mu_1^2)^{\frac{1}{2}} \qquad \ldots .(10.24)$$

$$\text{meta} \quad \mu = \mu_1 \qquad \ldots .(10.25)$$

$$\text{para} \quad \mu = 0 \qquad \ldots .(10.26)$$

If in an irregular group the angle between the direction of the moment and the axis of the molecule is known, the vector sums of irregular groups may be measured[19]. The dipole moment measurements on di-substituted benzene derivatives have generally been obtained by measurements in dilute solution. Therefore, for calculating the vector sum it is necessary to take data for the monosubstituted derivatives which have been determined in solution. These values differ slightly from the gas phase measurements recorded in *Table XCVI.* The values are : C_6H_5Cl, 1·55 D ; C_6H_5Br, 1·52 D ; $C_6H_5NO_2$, 3·96 D ; C_6H_5CN, 3·92 D ; $C_6H_5NH_2$, 1·53 D ; C_6H_5OH, 1·56 D.

In all the derivatives of toluene it is found that the calculated values almost correspond with the experimental values, *Table XCVIII*, which shows that the two substituent groups have little effect on each other. Most probably this will be due to the small polarity of the methyl group. When the substituent groups are strongly polar, as in the halogen derivatives of nitrobenzene or in the nitroanilines, although good agreement is observed in the case of the *meta* derivatives, considerable deviations occur in certain cases with the *para* and *ortho* derivatives (*Table XCIX*). Thus in *p*-nitraniline the experimental value is greater than the calculated value, owing to the contribution to the molecular resonance of the structure *I*.

Table XCVIII. Dipole Moments of Molecules of the Type $CH_3C_6H_4X$

X	*ortho*		*meta*		*para*	
	μ_{exp}	μ_{calc}	μ_{exp}	μ_{calc}	μ_{exp}	μ_{calc}
Cl	1·35	1·39	1·78	1·79	1·90	1·95
Br	1·44	1·37	1·75	1·76	1·94	1·92
I	1·21	1·15	1·57	1·54	1·71	1·70
NO_2	3·66	3·76	4·17	4·16	4·44	4·35
CN	3·77	3·74	4·18	4·15	4·37	4·30
NH_2	1·58	1·74	1·43	1·46	1·27	1·25
OH	1·41	1·61	1·54	1·60	1·57	1·60

Table XCIX. Dipole Moments of Di-substituted Benzene Derivatives

X	Y	*ortho*		*meta*		*para*	
		μ_{exp}	μ_{calc}	μ_{exp}	μ_{calc}	μ_{exp}	μ_{calc}
NH_2	NO_2	4·26	3·64	4·85	4·74	6·17	5·21
Cl	NO_2	4·59*	5·26*	3·69*	3·68*	2·78*	2·52*
Br	NO_2	4·20	4·88	3·41	3·45	2·60	2·43
I	NO_2	3·92	4·72	3·43	3·48	3·04	2·65
Cl	CN	4·75	4·88	3·38	3·40	2·53	2·35
Cl	ICl_2	2·95	3·6	2·11	2·27	1·30	1·06
Cl	C≡CH	1·69	2·13	1·38	1·36	0·96	0·68

* These values were obtained from measurements in the gas phase ; all other measurements were made in solution.

$$\mathrm{H_2N^+{=}C_6H_4{=}N^+(O^-)_2}$$

I

In a similar way, the contribution of structure *II* in *p*–chloronitrobenzene and of structure *III* in $ClC_6H_4C{\equiv}CH$, decrease the moment of the CCl bond so that the resultant moment of the molecule is increased.

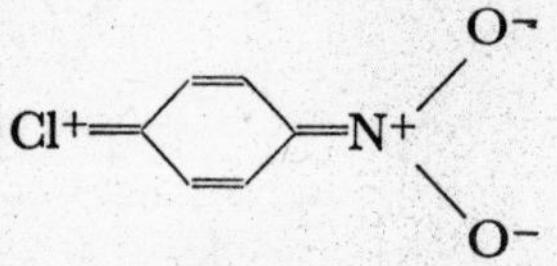

II 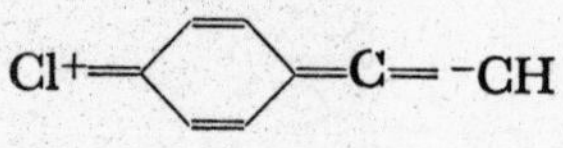   *III*

The difference between the calculated and experimental values in *ortho* derivatives is also due in part to the additional structures *IV* and *V* which are possible in the di-substituted derivatives :

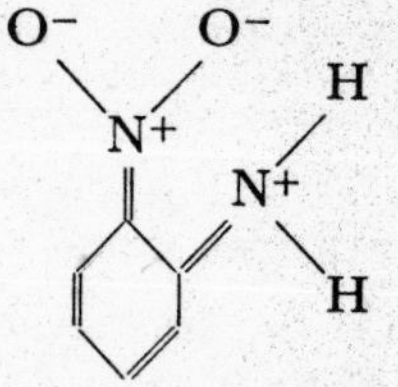

IV 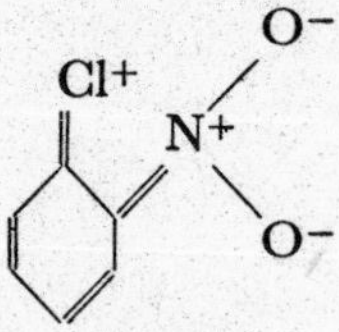   *V*

In addition, however, steric effects may influence the structure of the molecule, especially if the groups are large when, because of their close proximity, they may cause mutually induced moments. These various factors are difficult to separate and the anomalies observed are generally referred to as the *ortho* effect.

The nitro group and the nitrile group give rise to structures in which the *ortho* or *para* carbon atom is positively charged :

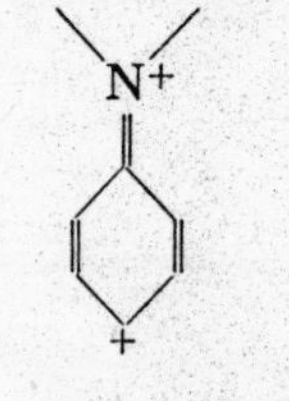

In the nitrobenzonitriles, such resonant structures will be mutually suppressed and consequently no large deviations from the additivity rule occur, such as exist when the two groups are of opposite charge so that the resonance is augmented by additional valence bond structures. The dipole moment of *p*–nitrobenzonitrile is zero, of *o*–nitrobenzonitrile, $6{\cdot}19_5$ D and *m*–nitrobenzonitrile, $3{\cdot}78_5$ D. Similar behaviour is observed with the di-substituted halogen derivatives of benzene and with the phenylenediamines.

In the polysubstituted derivatives the importance of additional valence bond structures is even greater in determining the resultant dipole moment. For example, in picramide, it might be imagined that the moments of the nitro group in the 2, 4 and 6 positions would cancel and the moment be

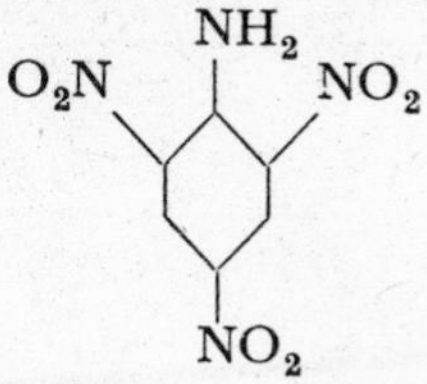

NH_2, O_2N, NO_2, NO_2

equal to that of aniline, $\mu_s = 1{\cdot}53$ D. This is not the case, however, since the nitro groups are distributed in the *ortho* and *para* positions with respect to the amino group, with the result that additional valence bond structures are possible which contribute to the resonance of the molecule. These structures are :

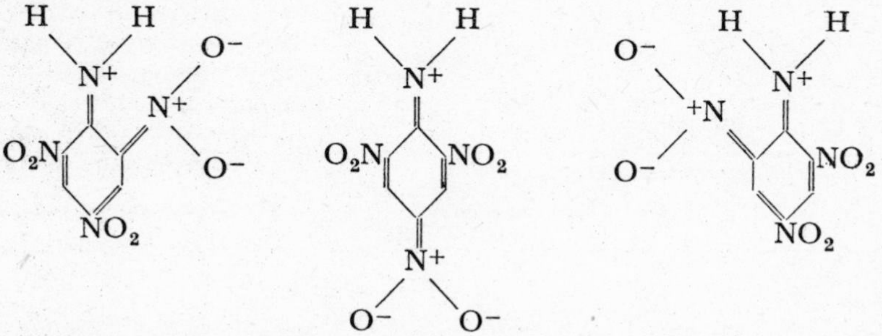

The dipole moment is therefore much greater than that of aniline, being $3{\cdot}25_s$ D, measured in dioxane solution.

Resonance of the type existing in *p*–nitraniline, is also present where several benzene rings are linked together, so long as the resonance of the ring systems is not blocked by a saturated carbon atom as in the diphenyl methane. Thus in 4–nitro–4′–aminodiphenyl (*I*) together with

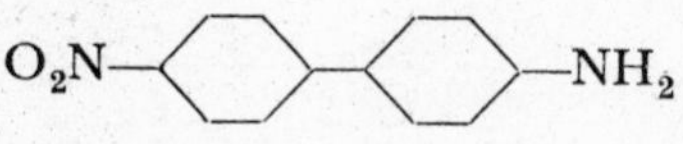

I 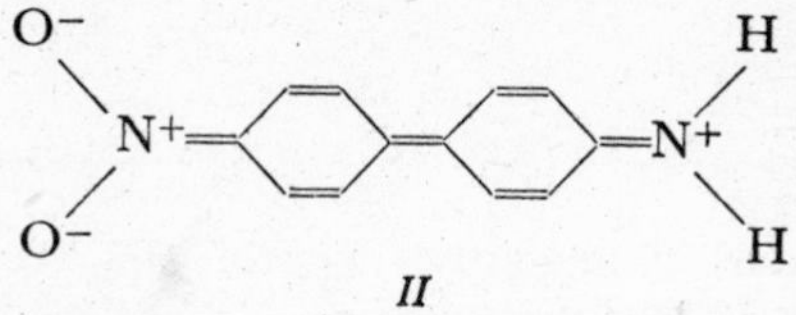   *II*

the resonance structures occurring in nitrobenzene and aniline, structures in which resonance occurs in both rings (*II*) are possible. The contribution of such structures noticeably raises the dipole moment (see *Table C*).

Derivatives of durene and mesitylene— In Chapter 9 it was pointed out that in derivatives of durene and mesitylene steric factors due to the methyl groups may hinder the resonance of the substituent group with the ring system. In *Tables CI* and *CII* the dipole moments of these compounds are compared with the corresponding aromatic and aliphatic derivatives. The dipole moments of the acetyl derivatives of durene and mesitylene are very similar to the value for acetone but lower than that for acetophenone, where resonance with the ring occurs. In aldehydes, on the other hand, where apparently there is no steric hindrance, the moment is almost identical with that of benzaldehyde.

Table C. Dipole Moments of Molecules containing Many Resonating Systems *

Molecule	Dipole moment D
$O_2N—C_6H_4—C_6H_4—NH_2$	6·46
$O_2N—C_6H_4—CH{=}CH—C_6H_4—N(CH_3)_2$	8·3
$O_2N—C_6H_4—N{=}N—C_6H_4—N(CH_3)_2$	8·1
$(CH_3)_2N—C_6H_4—CHO$	4·29
$(CH_3)_2N—C_6H_4—CH{=}CHCHO$	5·4
$(CH_3)_2N—C_6H_4—CH{=}CHCOCH_3$	5·3
$(CH_3)_2N—C_6H_4—CH{=}CHCH{=}CHCOCH_3$	6·7
$(CH_3)_2N—C_6H_4—C({=}O)—C_6H_4—N(CH_3)_2$	5·18
$O_2N—C_6H_4—OCH_3$	4·74
$O_2N—C_6H_4—CH{=}CH—C_6H_4—OCH_3$	7·8
$O_2N—C_6H_4—N{=}N—C_6H_4—OCH_3$	6·5

* All measurements made in solution

The lower values of the dipole moments of, for example, nitrodurene and nitromesitylene in comparison with that of nitrobenzene is regarded as being due to steric hindrance and this view is corroborated by Raman spectra data. It is considered that the methyl groups in the *ortho* positions cause the nitro group to leave the level of the benzene ring. This has the result that the resonance with the ring and with other groups in the *para* position is less probable. A similar argument may be applied to other derivatives. This explanation of the dipole moment data has yet to be substantiated by x-ray diffraction measurements.

Table CI. Dipole Moments of Durene and Mesitylene Compounds with Corresponding Aliphatic and Aromatic Derivatives

X	CH_3X	C_6H_5X	(ring with H_3C, CH_3, H_3C, CH_3)—X	H_3C—(ring with CH_3, CH_3)—X
Br	1·45	1·52	1·55	1·52
$COCH_3$	2·72	2·88	2·68	2·71
CHO	2·49	2·95	2·96	—
COCl	2·40	3·32	—	2·95
NO_2	3·17	3·96	3·39	3·65
NH_2	1·32*	1·53	1·39	1·40

* Measured in the gas phase, all other measurements made in solution

Derivatives of naphthalene and other polycyclic molecules— The dipole moment of the monosubstituted derivatives of naphthalene and tetralin are given in *Table CIII*, and it is observed that there is an appreciable difference in the values of the moments of

Table CII. Dipole Moments of Di-substituted Durene Compounds and Corresponding Aromatic Derivatives

X	Y	X—(ring)—Y	X—(ring with H_3C, CH_3, H_3C, CH_3)—Y
NO_2	NH_2	6·17	4·98
NO_2	OC_2H_5	4·74	3·69
NO_2	$N(CH_3)_2$	6·16	5·11
Br	NH_2	2·99	2·75
Br	NO_2	2·60	2·36
OH	NO_2	5·04	4·08

the α and β derivatives. The values for the α derivatives are close to those of the corresponding monosubstituted benzene compounds but the values of the β derivatives are always greater. This behaviour is also observed in other similar compounds.

*Table CIII. Dipole Moments of α and β Monosubstituted Derivatives of Naphthalene and Tetralin **

Molecule	*Dipole moment D*		*Molecule*	*Dipole moment D*	
	α	β		α	β
Nitronaphthalene	3·98	4·36	*Iodonaphthalene*	1·43	1·56
Naphthylamine	1·49	1·77	*Naphthol*	1·43	1·53
Fluoronaphthalene	1·42	1·52	*Naphthalene sulphonamide*	5·14	5·36
Chloronaphthalene	1·51	1·65	*Nitrotetralin*	3·98	4·81
Bromonaphthalene	1·52	1·70			

* All measurements made in solution

Thus the dipole moment of quinoline, *I*, is $2{\cdot}19_5$ D, a value which is close to that of pyridine, $2{\cdot}25_5$ D, whereas the

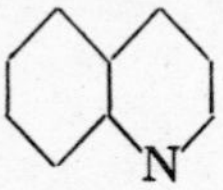

N

I

N

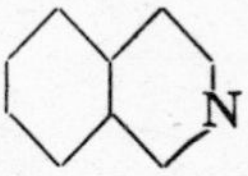

II

moment of isoquinoline, *II*, is $2{\cdot}55_5$ D. Also the moment of 1–nitro–2–naphthylamine[20], *III* is $4{\cdot}47_5$ D and that of 2–nitro–1–naphthylamine, *IV*, is $4{\cdot}89_5$ D

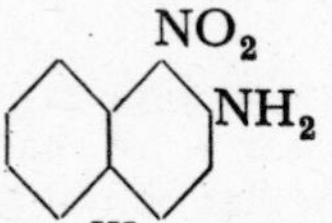

NO_2 NH_2

III

NH_2 NO_2

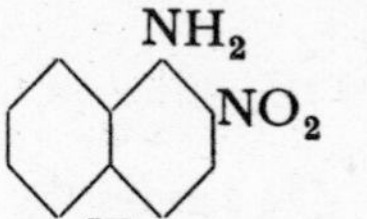

IV

the moment of 4–nitro–2–naphthylamine, *V*, is $4{\cdot}62_5$ D and that of 3–nitro–1–naphthylamine, *VI*, is $5{\cdot}14_5$ D.

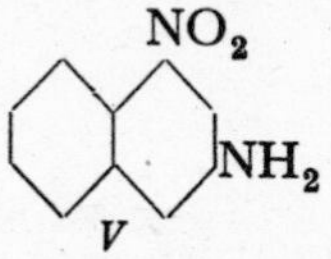

NO_2 NH_2

V

NH_2 NO_2

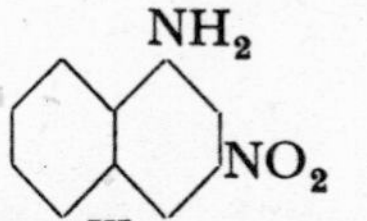

VI

It might be considered that the moments of 4–nitro–1–naphthylamine, *VII*, and of 5–nitro–1–naphthylamine, *VIII*, would be equal.

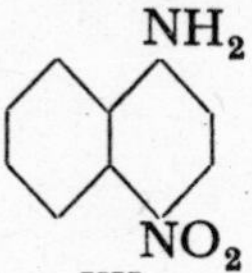

NH_2 NO_2

VII

NH_2 NO_2

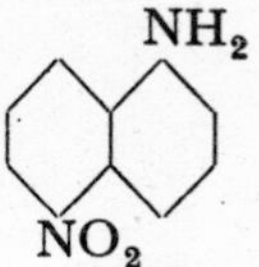

VIII

This, however, is not the case, as the former has a moment of $6{\cdot}67_5$ D and the latter one of 5.22_5 D, which is close to the vectorial sum of the moments in *m*–nitraniline. It will be evident from the above examples, that the conditions of resonance in the various positions of the rings are not the same. In monosubstituted naphthalenes there are seven possible valence bond structures with a separation of charge in the case of the α derivatives and only six for the β derivatives, *viz*

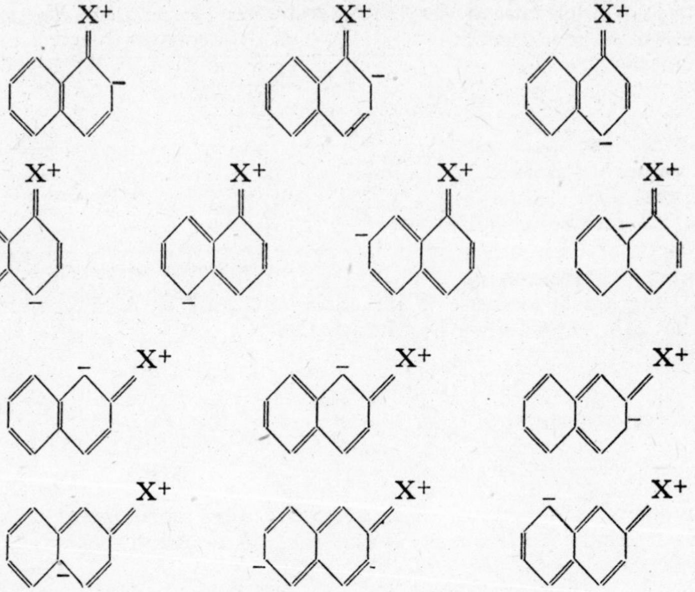

This explains the difference between the α and β derivatives.

In benzene derivatives, the centre of gravity of all charges on the carbon atoms of the ring lies on the extension of the line through C—X.

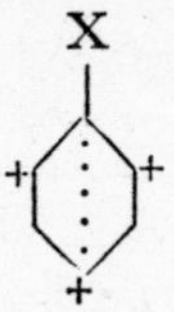

In naphthalene, however, this is not so and irregularities in the values of the dipole moment must therefore occur[21].

In the molecule of phenanthraquinone :

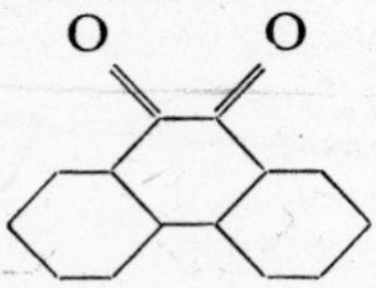

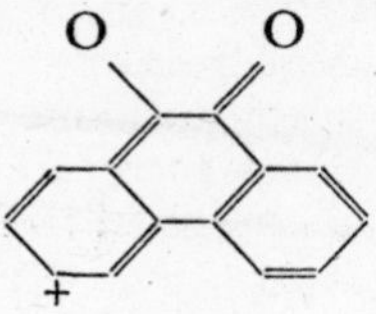

all the rings contribute to the resonance of the molecule, there being several structures of the type

and $\mu_s = 5{\cdot}6$ D. The moment of each CO group in this case is $3{\cdot}23_s$ D, a value which becomes still greater, $3{\cdot}49_s$, in benzanthrone[22] :

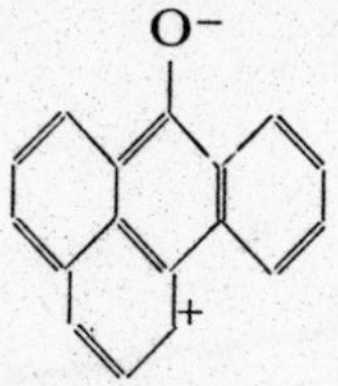

O−

+

where forty two valence bond structures contribute to the resonance of the molecule.

Heterocyclic compounds— The polarity of heterocyclic compounds is due to the formation of ionic valence bond structures. Thus in furan, *I*, structures, similar to those in esters occur, *II*, as well as a structure with a trivalent, positive oxygen atom, *III*, and the moment is $0{\cdot}71_s$ D.

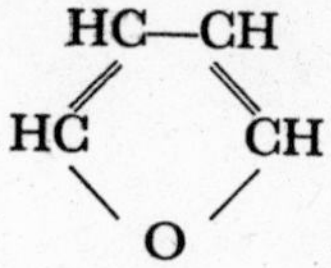

HC—CH HC CH O	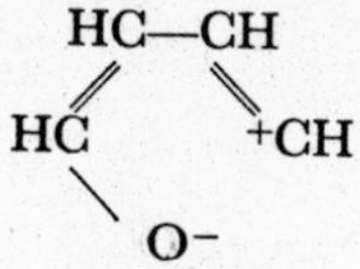 HC—CH HC +CH O−	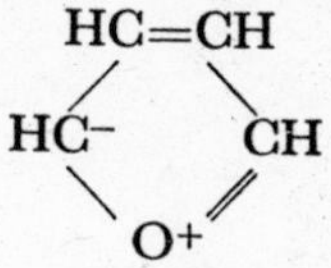 HC=CH HC− CH O+
I	*II* *two structures*	*III* *four structures*

The dipole moment of coumarone,

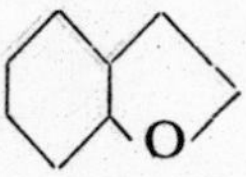

O

is $0{\cdot}79_s$ D and of diphenyleneoxide,

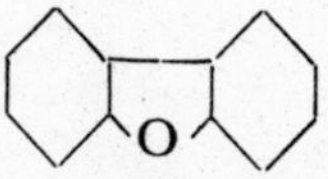

O

$0{\cdot}88_s$ D which is less than the values for simple ethers. If the oxygen atom can be positively charged not only with reference to a carbon atom but also with respect to some more electronegative substituent group, then additional valence bond structures occur. In the first column of *Table CIV* the values of the dipole moment of several such molecules are given. In the case of γ dimethylpyrone[23] the value is $4{\cdot}62_s$ D, whereas the vector sum of the moments due to the carbonyl group and of oxygen in the ring is only $2{\cdot}18_s$ D. This considerable increase must be due to the contribution of the structure :

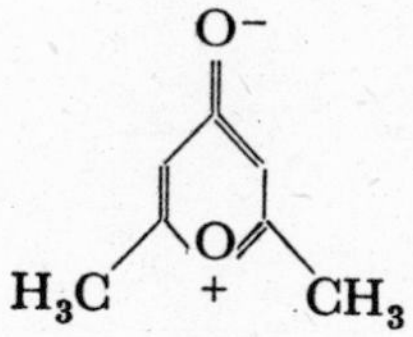

O−

O

H_3C + CH_3

In xanthone and coumarin the analogous structures :

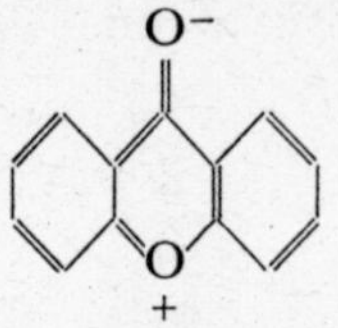

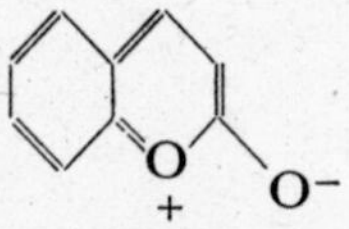

O^- O +   O + O^-

contribute to the molecular resonance. Similar behaviour is noticed with

Table CIV. Dipole Moments of Heterocyclic Compounds

Molecule	*Dipole moment D*	*Molecule*	*Dipole moment D*
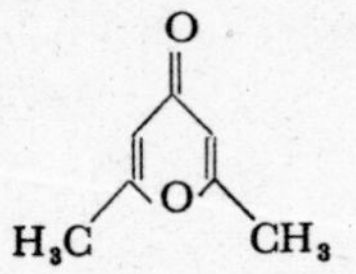 O, O, H_3C, CH_3	4·62	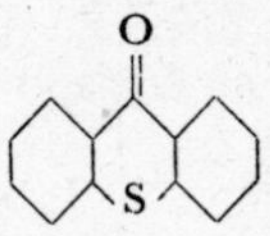 O, S	5·4
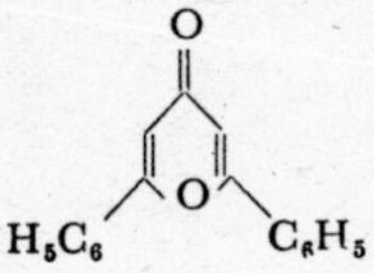 O, O, H_5C_6, C_6H_5	3·82	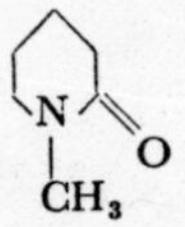 N, O, CH_3	4·01
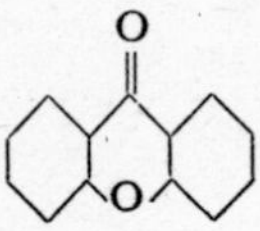 O, O	2·94	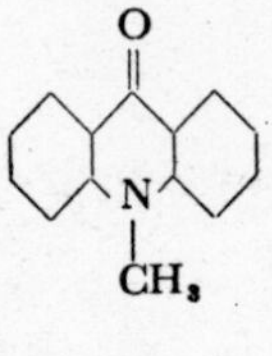 O, N, CH_3	3·5
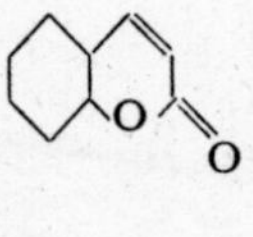 O, O	4·54	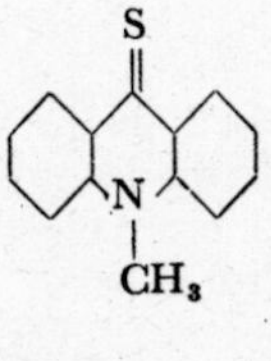 S, N, CH_3	5·2
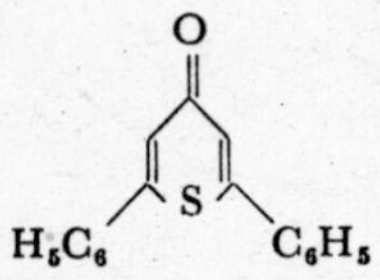 O, S, H_5C_6, C_6H_5	4·39	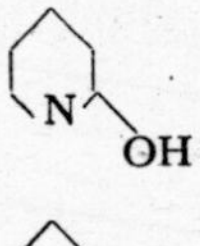 N, OH	1·46
		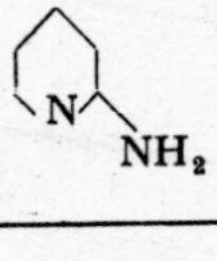 N, NH_2	2·06

heterocyclic compounds containing sulphur and nitrogen (see *Table CIV*) and the contribution of structures containing trivalent, positively charged sulphur is found to be greater than in the case of the corresponding oxygen compounds. In N–methylketopiperidine and in N–methylacridone, the dipole moment differs from the vectorial sum of the group moments owing to the contribution of the structures :

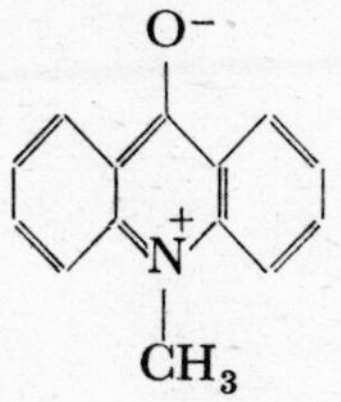

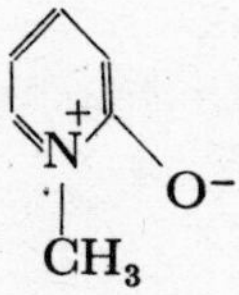

respectively to the final state of the molecules. In α-oxypyridine, the nitrogen can be divalent and negatively charged and the oxygen trivalent and positively charged

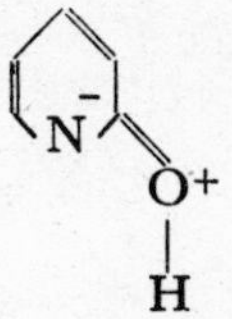

and in α-aminopyridine the structure

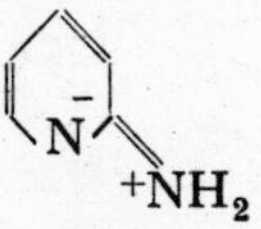

contributes to the resonance of the molecule.

Dipole moment of free radicals— It has already been pointed out in Chapter 5 that in the stabilization of free radicals containing oxygen and nitrogen atoms, the superposition of ionic states plays a significant part. This view is supported by the values of the dipole moments of α,α'–diphenyl–β–picrylhydrazine, *I*, $\mu_s = 4{\cdot}92$ D

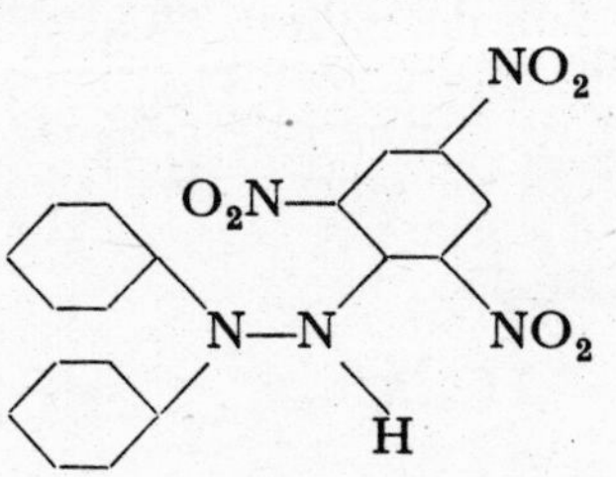

I

and of α,α'–diphenyl–β–picrylhydrazyl[24], *II*, $\mu_s = 3{\cdot}59$ D.

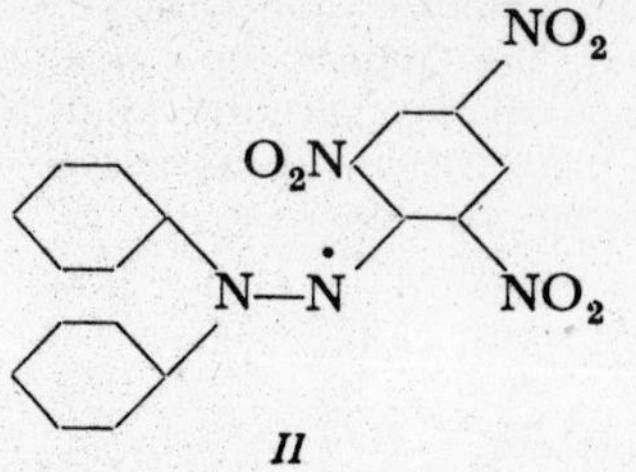

II

The large moment of the molecule *I* is due to the contribution of structures of the type *III*:

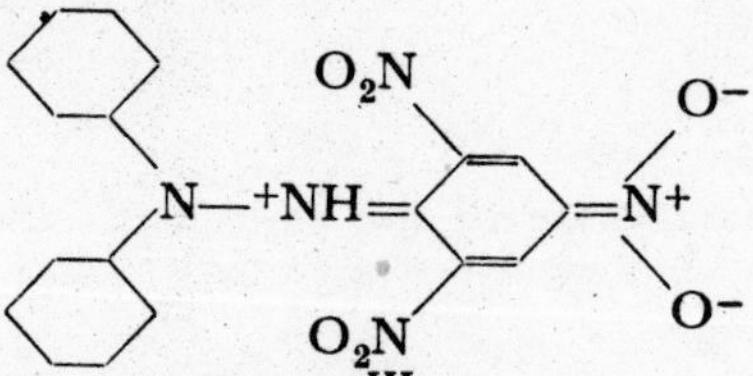

III

The moment of the free radical *II* will also be raised significantly by the contribution of the structures *IV* and *V*:

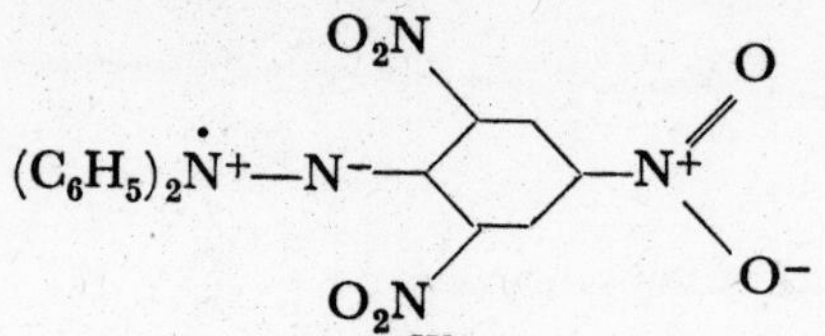

IV

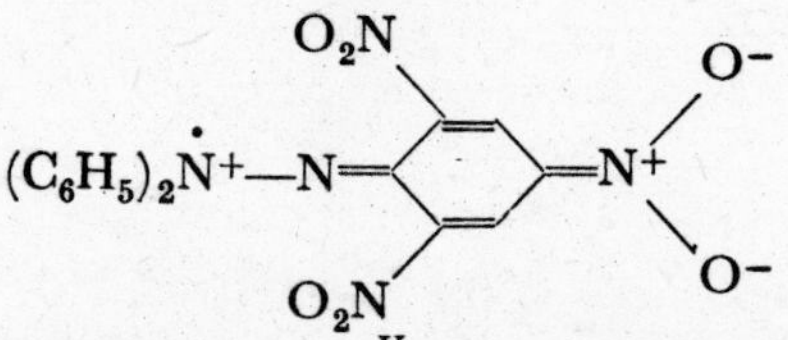

V

In certain cases, the number of carbon atoms which may contain the unpaired electron may, through the resonance with ionic structures, be increased. If this is so the free radical will be stabilized and its formation facilitated. Thus hexa–*p*–nitrophenylethane, $(NO_2C_6H_4)_3C{-}C(C_6H_4NO_2)_3$ dissociates completely into the radical $(NO_2C_6H_4)_3C\cdot$ under conditions in which hexaphenylethane only partially dissociates. In the first case the odd electron is not only shared between the *ortho* and *para* carbon atoms of the ring systems but also with the other carbon atoms, as for example, in the structure

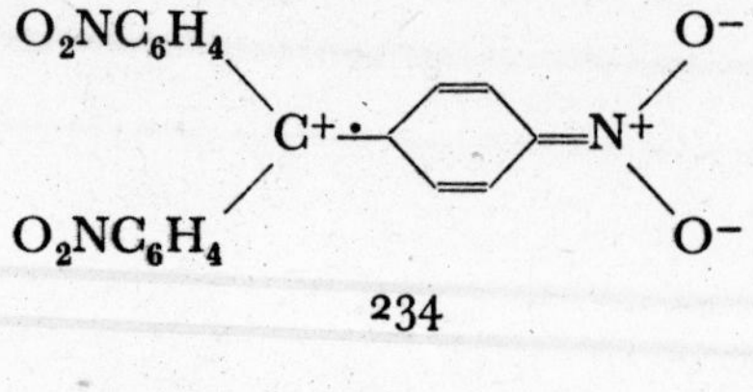

Therefore the free electron is delocalized to a greater extent than in triphenylmethyl, and the radical is more stable.

DIPOLE MOMENTS AND MOLECULAR STRUCTURE

In a number of cases the magnitude of the dipole moment may be used to determine the geometrical configuration of the atoms in a molecule. Thus the first proof of the triangular structure of water arose from dipole moment measurements. Calculation may also be made of the valency angles from dipole moment data, but the values obtained are not as accurate as the more direct methods employing spectra, x-ray and electron diffraction measurements. However, for complex molecules when the application of more exact methods is not possible, the analysis of the dipole moment data may give valuable information. Thus the moment of thianthrene is $1{\cdot}57_5$ D,

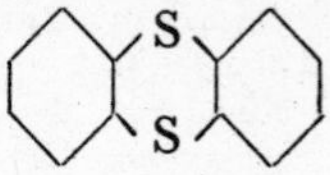

of selanthrene, $1{\cdot}41_5$ D,

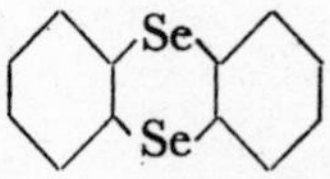

If these molecules were flat they would have a zero dipole moment as is the case with oxanthrene,

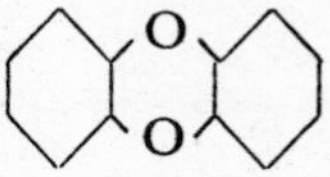

The existence of a permanent dipole moment shows that the sulphur and selenium bonds do not lie in the same plane and the molecules have a bent structure.

Dipolar structure of amino acids—The dipole moment data support the dipolar, zwitterionic, structure of the amino acids, *viz* $N^+H_3RCHCOO^-$. If the molecule at its iso-electric point possesses this structure, it will have a very large dipole moment of the order of 13·9 D since the distance between the charges is approximately 2·9 Å. Unfortunately such compounds are only soluble in polar solvents and it is therefore impossible to measure the dipole moments directly. The dielectric constant of aqueous solutions of amino acids is, however, greater than that of water and furthermore increases in direct proportion to the concentration. The value of $\Delta\epsilon/\Delta c$ *i.e.* the change of the dielectric constant as the concentration is increased by 1 gm mol/l is found to have an approximately constant value for each amino acid. With an increase of the number of carbon atoms between the polar

Table CV. Dielectric Properties of Amino Acids

Amino acid		$-\Delta\epsilon/\Delta c$
$RCH(NH_2)COOH$	(α)	22–26
$RCH(NH_2)CH_2COOH$	(β)	32–36
$RCH(NH_2)(CH_2)_2COOH$	(γ)	51–55
$RCH(NH_2)(CH_2)_3COOH$	(δ)	63
$RCH(NH_2)(CH_2)_4COOH$	(ϵ)	73–77
$RCH(NH_2)(CH_2)_5COOH$	(ς)	87

groups $\Delta\epsilon/\Delta c$ increases almost linearly. These data (*Table CV*) are indirect corroboration of the large dipole moment of the amino acids.

The dipole moments of the esters of amino acids measured in non-polar solutions are generally of the order of 2·1 D, evidently amino acids in the non-zwitterionic form, RNH_2CH_2COOH will also have a small moment.

REFERENCES

[1] CARTWRIGHT, C. H. and ERRERA, J. *Acta Physicochim. U.R.S.S.* 3 (1935) 649
— — *Proc. roy. Soc. A* 154 (1936) 138
[2] PARTO, A. *Z. phys. chem. B* 4 (1929) 227
SHOTT-LVOVA, E. A. and SYRKIN, J. K. *Acta Physicochim. U.R.S.S.* 11 (1939) 659
[3] COOP, I. E. and SUTTON, L. E. *J. chem. Soc.* (1938) 1269
[4] FAJANS, K. and JOOS, G. *Z. Phys.* 23 (1924) 1
FAJANS, K. *Z. phys. Chem. B* 24 (1934) 103
BORN, M. and HEISENBERG, W. *Z. Phys.* 23 (1924) 388
PAULING, L. C. *Proc. roy. Soc.* 114 (1927) 191
MAYER, J. E. and MAYER, M. G. *Phys. Rev.* 43 (1933) 605
[5] EGLOFF, G. *Physical Constants of Hydrocarbons* New York, 1939
[6] VASILIEV, W. G. *Dissertation* Moscow, 1943
[7] DYATKINA, M. E. *J. phys. Chem. Moscow* 15 (1941) 597
[8] EUCKEN, A. and MEYER, L. *Phys. Z.* 30 (1929) 397
[9] DYATKINA, M. E. *Acta Physicochim. U.R.S.S.* 20 (1945) 407
[10] PHILLIPS, G. M., HUNTER, J. S. and SUTTON, L. E. *J. chem. Soc.* (1945) 146
[11] ROBERTSON, J. M. *Annual Rep. Progr. Chem.* 39 (1942) 95
PENNEY, W. G. and SUTHERLAND, G. B. B. M. *Trans. Faraday Soc.* 30 (1934) 898
— *J. chem. Physics* 2 (1934) 492
LU, C. S., HUGHES, E. W. and GIGUERE, P. A. *J. Amer. chem. Soc.* 61 (1939) 1252
[12] DYATKINA, M. E. *J. phys. Chem. Moscow* 15 (1941) 597
[13] COFFMAN, D. D. and CAROTHERS, W. H. *J. Amer. chem. Soc.* 55 (1933) 2040
COFFMAN, D. D., NIEUWLAND, J. A. and CAROTHERS, W. H. *ibid* 55 (1933) 2048
[14] HANNAY, N. B. and SMYTH, C. P. *J. Amer. chem. Soc.* 65 (1943) 1931
[15] BROCKWAY, L. O. and COOP, I. E. *Trans. Faraday Soc.* 34 (1939) 1429
PFLAUM, D. I. and WENZKE, H. H. *J. Amer. chem. Soc.* 56 (1934) 1156
[16] GURGANOWA, E. N. and SYRKIN, J. K. *Acta Physicochim. U.R.S.S.* 11 (1939) 657
[17] WHELAND, G. W. *J. Amer. chem. Soc.* 64 (1942) 900
[18] FUCHS, O. and WOLF, K. L. *Dielektrische polarisation, Hand- und Jahr-buch der chemischer Physik* Leipzig, 1935 *p* 239
[19] ZAHN, E. T. *Phys. Z.* 33 (1932) 400
[20] VASILIEV, W. G. and SYRKIN, J. K. *J. phys. Chem. Moscow* 15 (1941) 254
[21] SYRKIN, J. K. and DYATKINA, M. E. *J. gen. Chem. Russ.* 11 (1941) 626
[22] SHOTT-LVOVA, E. A. and SYRKIN, J. K. *J. phys. Chem. Moscow* 12 (1938) 479
[23] VASILIEV, W. G. and SYRKIN, J. K. *Acta Physicochim. U.R.S.S.* 6 (1937) 639
[24] TURKEVICH, J., OESPER, P. F. and SMYTH, C. P. *J. Amer. chem. Soc.* 64 (1942) 1179

11

BOND ENERGIES

ADDITIVITY OF BOND ENERGIES IN ORGANIC COMPOUNDS

THE BOND ENERGY of a diatomic molecule is equivalent to the energy of dissociation of the molecule, which, as we have seen in Chapter 8, may be obtained in many cases from spectroscopic data. For polyatomic molecules, the bond energies cannot be obtained from spectroscopic measurements and therefore must be calculated from thermochemical data. Thermochemical measurements are somewhat less accurate than spectroscopic measurements, but improvements in experimental technique develcped over several years, particularly by ROSSINI and KISTIAKOWSKI, have reduced the error to the order of 1 in 5,000 kcals. This degree of accuracy has permitted the investigation of the energy changes accompanying several important reactions where small differences in energy are important, such as the heats of formation of isomers.

As is well known, the heat of formation of an organic compound is equal to the sum of the heats of formation of the products of combustion, generally CO_2 and H_2O, from which is subtracted the heat of combustion of the particular substance. Such heats of formation, however, are generally given in terms of a standard reference state of the participating substances which is generally taken as the physical state of the compounds at normal temperatures and pressures, *e.g.* gaseous carbon dioxide, liquid water, solid carbon, gaseous hydrogen, H_2, and gaseous oxygen, O_2. In the evaluation of bond energies, however, we shall be concerned with the heat of formation of the compound in the gaseous state from the constituent atoms, for example, from atomic carbon C, atomic hydrogen H and atomic oxygen O. In order to obtain this value of the heat of formation, it is necessary to add to the heat of formation from the standard states, the necessary latent heats of sublimation and evaporation, and the heats of formation of H_2, O_2 and solid carbon, C_n, from the respective atoms. The heat of evaporation is known for a number of organic liquids ; when it is not known, however, Trouton's rule may be used without very great error. Thus for the hydrocarbon C_nH_{2n+2}, the energy of formation E from gaseous atoms will be

$$E = nQ_{CO_2} + (n+1)Q_{H_2O} - Q + nS + (n+1)Q_{H_2} \quad \ldots\ldots(11.1)$$

where Q_{CO_2} and Q_{H_2O} are the heats of combustion of carbon and hydrogen in the standard state, Q is the heat of combustion of the hydrocarbon in the gaseous state, S is the heat of sublimation of diamond, and Q_{H_2} the dissociation energy of H_2. All these quantities are accurately known from either spectroscopic or thermal measurements except the heat of sublimation of solid carbon (diamond) to gaseous carbon atoms. The latter quantity may be determined either directly, or from the dissociation energy of CO determined spectroscopically. The values recorded in the literature vary from 170 to 80 kcals/gm mol, but the older values are clearly incorrect and on the basis of a critical survey of the data HERZBERG[1] gives the value as 124·1 ± 0·5 kcals. This value has been employed in the following discussion, although GAYDON and PENNEY have suggested a different value[2].

A very large number of organic compounds contain relatively few different types of bonds, *e.g.* C—H, C—C, C=C, C—Cl, and it has been suggested that each bond possesses an energy which is independent of the other bonds in the molecule and that the heat of formation of the gaseous molecule will be equal to the sum of the energies of the various bonds occurring in the molecule. Thus the energy of formation of methane is equal to the energy of four C—H bonds ; of ethane to the sum of the bond energies of one C—C bond and six C—H bonds. In general, for the molecule C_nH_{2n+2} we may write

$$E = (n - 1)E_{C-C} + (2n + 2)E_{C-H} \qquad \ldots .(11.2)$$

where E_{C-C} and E_{C-H} represent respectively the bond energies of the C—C and C—H bonds. The bond energy is often dependent on the actual reaction occurring and in particular on the nature of the molecular fragments formed. For example the average energy of the C—H bond in methane is one quarter of the energy of formation of methane and equals 348·6/4 = 87·15 kcals, whereas the reaction $CH_4 = CH_3 + H$ requires 102 ± 1 kcals and the reaction $C_2H_6 = C_2H_5 + H$ requires 98 ± 2 kcals. In a similar manner the energy required to dissociate C_2H_6 into two CH_3 radicals is 82·6 kcals and for the dissociation of C_4H_{10} into two C_2H_5 radicals, 77·6 kcals, neither energy value being the same as the average energy of the C—C bond. Nevertheless, when additivity is confirmed by experiment, it is frequently possible to speak of the energies of separate bonds.

If the concept of the additivity of bond energies be assumed, the difference in the heats of formation of two adjacent members of a homologous series must be constant. From equations 11.1 and 11.2 it follows that

$$(n-1)E_{C-C} + (2n+2)E_{C-H} = nQ_{CO_2} + (n+1)Q_{H_2O} - Q + nS + (n+1)Q_{H_2} \qquad \ldots .(11.3)$$

Thus in one gram atom of diamond, there are $2N$ carbon to carbon bonds so that the heat of sublimation is twice the bond energy per gm mol, *i.e.* $S = 2E_{C-C}$. In diamond each carbon atom is bonded covalently to four other carbon atoms arranged tetrahedrally and since each bond is common to two carbon atoms, there are twice as many bonds as atoms. Substituting this value for S in equation 11.3 and rearranging, we obtain

$$\frac{Q + Q_{CO_2}}{n + 1} = Q_{CO_2} + Q_{H_2O} + E_{C-C} + Q_{H_2} - 2E_{C-H} \qquad \ldots .(11.4)$$

Thus for a series of saturated hydrocarbons the quantity $(Q + Q_{CO_2})/(n + 1)$ should have a constant value, irrespective of the value of n. The experimental data, however, given in *Table CVI* show that for the *n*-saturated hydrocarbons, the additivity of bond energies is not fulfilled for the first four members of the series but is applicable to all higher members. We may therefore use the data for the molecules from C_5H_{12} to $C_{12}H_{26}$ for the calculation of the energies of the C—C and C—H bonds and we obtain, using the method of least squares

$$E_{C-C} = 62{\cdot}77 \text{ kcals}$$

$$E_{C-H} = 85{\cdot}56 \text{ kcals}$$

These values have been used for calculating the heats of formation of hydrocarbons in *Table CVI* (column 5).

Table CVI. Heats of Formation of n-Saturated Hydrocarbons

Hydrocarbon	Q kcals	Q_f* kcals	E kcals	Heat of formation calc. from bond energies kcals	$\frac{Q + Q_{CO_2}}{n+1}$
CH_4	212·8	18·4	348·6	342·3	153·6
C_2H_6	372·8	21·2	579	576·1	155·8
C_3H_8	530·6	26·2	811·6	810·0	156·3
C_4H_{10}	687·9	31·8	1,044·8	1,043·2	156·5
C_5H_{12}	845·3	37·2	1,277·8	1,277·8	156·6
C_6H_{14}	1,001·6	43·7	1,511·9	1,511·7	156·6
C_7H_{16}	1,158·2	50·0	1,745·8	1,745·6	156·6
C_8H_{18}	1,314·6	56·4	1,979·5	1,979·5	156·6
C_9H_{20}	1,471·3	62·5	2,213·5	2,213·4	156·6
$C_{10}H_{22}$	1,628·2	68·5	2,447·1	2,447·2	156·6
$C_{11}H_{24}$	1,784·4	75·1	2,681·3	2,681·1	156·6
$C_{12}H_{26}$	1,941·9	80·4	2,914·2	2,915·0	156·6

* Q_f is the heat of formation of the substance from the elements in their standard states

In order to calculate by a similar method the energy of the C=C bond we may use either the data of Rossini on the heats of combustion of the hydrocarbons or the values of the heats of hydrogenation obtained by Kistiakowski. The data show, as in the saturated hydrocarbons, that for the straight chain ethylenic hydrocarbons with the double bond in the 1–2 position the additivity concept is not fulfilled in the first three members of the series, but is first observed in 1-pentene. The energy of the C=C bond is found to be 101·16 kcals. Similar calculations for the *n*-alcohols (*Table CVII*) give the sum of the bond energies in the group C—O—H as 185 kcals. The heat of formation of H_2O is 220 kcals, which gives the bond energy of O—H as 110 kcals. Combination of these data gives the energy value of 75 kcals for the single bond between carbon and oxygen (C—O).

These examples show that in a number of cases the bond energy is found to be an additive quantity, but the extension of these calculations to other series of molecules is unfortunately not possible owing to the lack of accurate data. Bond energies of other groups must therefore be obtained by employing approximate data and the values may have to undergo alteration as more accurate data become available. The values calculated from the available data are given in *Table CVIII*, the energy of the bond C≡C is obtained from the heat of formation of acetylene, with the assumption that $E_{C-H} = 85{\cdot}56$ kcals. The homologues of acetylene show a higher value for the energy of the triple bond, and this will be discussed later. In allene, where there is a conjugated series of double bonds, the energy of the C=C bond is low. The value of the bond energy of the carbonyl group in aldehydes has been obtained from heat of hydrogenation of acetaldehyde, 554·4 kcals. In the carboxyl group, owing to the molecular

Table CVII. Heats of Formation of the n-Alcohols

Alcohol	Q kcals	Q_f kcals	E kcals	Difference between adjacent members of series
CH_3OH	182·58	48·60	437·50	
C_2H_5OH	336·78	57·23	673·75	236·25
C_3H_7OH	493·2	63·64	910·74	236·99
C_4H_9OH	649·9	69·77	1,141·47	230·73
$C_5H_{11}OH$	806·75	75·75	1,374·95	233·48
$C_6H_{13}OH$	963·6	81·73	1,608·63	233·68
$C_7H_{15}OH$	1,120·6	87·56	1,842·05	233·42
$C_8H_{17}OH$	1,277·6	93·39	2,075·49	233·44
$C_9H_{19}OH$	1,434·6	99·22	2,308·92	233·43
$C_{10}H_{21}OH$	1,591·6	105·05	2,542·35	233·43

Table CVIII. Bond Energies in Organic Molecules

Bond	*Energy kcals*	*Bond*	*Energy kcals*
C—H	85·56	C—F	104*
C—C	62·77	C—Cl	69
C=C	101·16	C—Br	57
C≡C (*acetylene*)	128·15	C—I	43
O—H	110	N—H (NH_3)	83
C—O (*alcohols*)	75	N—C	53·5
C—O (*ethers*)	75	C≡N (HCN)	146
C=O (*ketones*)	155–157	C≡N (*nitriles*)	149
C=O (CH_2O)	144	N≡C (*isonitriles*)	139
C=O (*aldehydes*)	149·5	C=N	84*
O=C—OH (HCOOH)	348	N=N	80*
		N—N	27 ± 3
O=C—OH (*acids*)	360*	N—O	61*
		N=O	108*
O=C—OC (*formates*)	313	N^{+}(=O)—O^{-}	169 < E < 186
		C=S (CS_2)	107·5
O=C—OC (*esters*)	327	C—S	54
		S—H	82

* approximate values

resonance, it is not possible to assign separate energy values to the C=O, C—O and O—H bonds and in *Table CVIII* the heats of formation of the groups

O=C—O—H in acids, and O=C—O—C

in esters are given. It will be noticed that for formic acid and the esters of formic acid, lower values of the energy are obtained compared with the higher homologues; this is most probably due to the fact that resonance with a structure having a positively charged hydrogen atom, *viz*

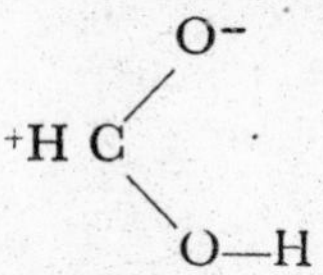

$$^{+}\text{H}\ \text{C}\begin{matrix}\diagup \text{O}^{-} \\ \diagdown \text{O—H}\end{matrix}$$

is improbable since it involves a divalent carbon atom. In the higher members, the corresponding structure

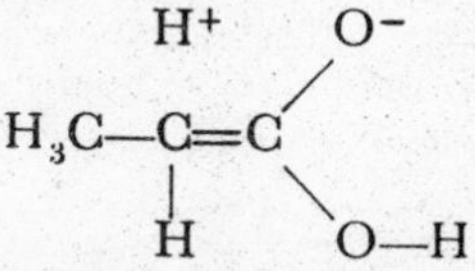

$$\begin{matrix} & \text{H}^{+} & \text{O}^{-} \\ & & \diagup \\ \text{H}_3\text{C—} & \text{C}{=}\text{C} & \\ & | \quad \diagdown & \\ & \text{H} \quad & \text{O—H}\end{matrix}$$

may partake in the resonance of the molecule.

The energy of the C—Cl bond has been obtained from the heat of chlorination of ethylene, 43·65 kcals ; the heats of bromination of several ethylenic hydrocarbons have been determined, which permits the evaluation of a more accurate value for E_{C-Br} than for E_{C-Cl}. The value obtained is 57 kcals which is slightly greater than that obtained from the values of the heat of bromination of methane and ethane, 53 kcals. The C—I bond energy has been obtained from the heats of combustion of alkyl iodides and it is very probable that the value obtained is somewhat low. The energy of the single bond between two nitrogen atoms, E_{N-N}, has been obtained from the heat of dissociation of hydrazine and will be discussed later. The energy of the N—O and N=O bond may not be obtained so directly, but may be calculated from a knowledge of the energies of the following groups : C—O—NO_2 (312 kcals), C—O—N=O (244 kcals), C—NO_2 (240 kcals), N—NO_2 (231 kcals), C—N=O (162 kcals), N—N=O (148 kcals) and C=N—OH (255 kcals).

An examination of the values of the energies of different bonds shows that the bond energy is increased if the bond possesses some ionic character. Homopolar double bonds, in general, have a value of the order of 100 kcals : C=C, 101·16 kcals ; N=N, 80 kcals ; C=N, 84 kcals ; but in the strongly polar carbonyl group the value of the bond energy is much higher, being of the order of 150 kcals. This increase in strength with increase in ionic character is reflected in the internuclear distance which is, for C=C, 1·34 Å and for C=O, 1·20 Å. This behaviour is also shown by the corresponding single bonds, E_{C-C} being 62·77 kcals and E_{C-O} 75 kcals and the bond lengths respectively 1·54 Å and 1·47 Å.

According to the Heitler-London theory of valency, the energy of a molecule consists of the exchange energy A and the Coulomb energy C (see Chapter 3). The exchange energy of a localized bond will include both the attraction and the repulsion energies, and the Coulomb energy will represent the energy of interaction of all the charges in the molecule. In addition, it is necessary to take into account the energy of excitation V required to transfer a carbon atom in its ground state, $1s^2 2s^2 2p^2$, to the excited state, $1s^2 2s 2p^3$, where it may form four identical sp^3 hybrid bonds. The total energy of formation of a bond will thus be

$$E = -V + \Sigma C + \Sigma A - \tfrac{1}{2}\Sigma A' \qquad \ldots. (115)$$

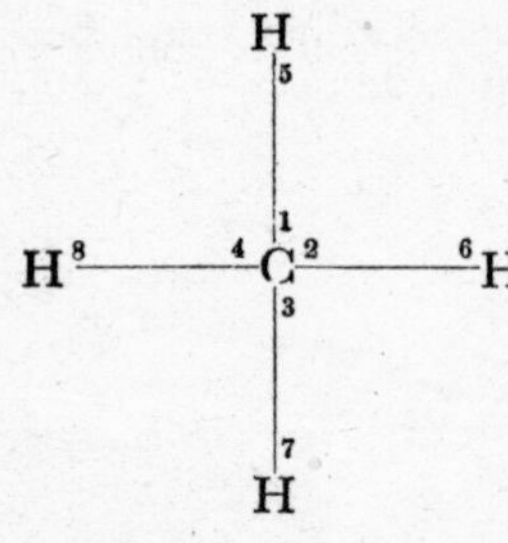

Figure 38. Methane electron pairs

where ΣA represents the exchange energy of all electron pairs forming bonds, and $\Sigma A'$ represents the exchange energy for all other pairs of non-localized electrons.

In methane there are eight valency electrons, four from carbon (*Figure 38*; 1, 2, 3 and 4) and one from each hydrogen atom (5, 6, 7 and 8). The exchange of electrons 1–5, 2–6, 3–7 and 4–8 gives rise to the four C—H bonds with a total exchange energy of $4A_{CH}$. In addition to the above exchange process, each electron of the carbon atom may be exchanged with one of the other hydrogen electrons and there are twelve such interchanges:

1–6, 1–7, 1–8
2–5, 2–7, 2–8
3–5, 3–6, 3–8
4–5, 4–6, 4–7

with a total exchange energy of $-\frac{12}{2}A'_{CH}$. Finally there will be the interaction energies of the four electrons of the hydrogen atoms:

5–6, 5–7, 5–8
6–7, 6–8, 7–8

and we will designate the energy of each such interaction by R. Thus for the energy of formation of methane we have

$$E_{CH_4} = -V + \Sigma C + 4A_{CH} - 6A'_{CH} - 6R \qquad \ldots(11.6)$$

Similarly we may write

$$E_{C_2H_6} = -2V + \Sigma C + 6A_{CH} + A_{CC} - 9A'_{CH} - 7\tfrac{1}{2}A'_{CC} - 6R \qquad \ldots(11.7)$$

$$E_{C_3H_8} = -3V + \Sigma C + 8A_{CH} + 2A_{CC} - 12A'_{CH} - 15A'_{CC} - 7R \qquad \ldots(11.8)$$

where A_{CC} is the exchange energy of electrons forming the C—C bond and A'_{CC} is the exchange energy of the non-localized electrons of the different carbon atoms.

In general we may write

$$E_{C_nH_{2n+2}} = -nV + \Sigma C + (2n+2)A_{CH} + (n-1)A_{CC} - (3n+3)A'_{CH} - 7\tfrac{1}{2}(n-1)A'_{CC} - (n+4)R \qquad \ldots(11.9)$$

As will be evident from equation 11.9 the quantum mechanical treatment has led to the appearance of a number of additional terms in the expression for the energy of formation compared with the simple additive treatment (equation 11.2). The bond energy terms, *e.g.* E_{C-C}, E_{C-H}, are in fact complex functions, including in addition to the exchange and Coulomb energies of a bond, the excitation energy of the valency state of carbon and the repulsion energy of the non-bonding electrons.

The quantum mechanical treatment gives a constant value for the difference in energy of two adjacent hydrocarbons commencing with ethane, *viz*

$$E_{C_nH_{2n+2}} - E_{C_{n-1}H_{2n}} = -V + 2A_{CH} + A_{CC} - 3A'_{CH} - 7\tfrac{1}{2}A'_{CC} - R + \Delta\Sigma C \qquad \ldots(11.10)$$

Thus the quantum mechanical treatment is not in agreement with the experimental values.

DEVIATIONS FROM THE ADDITIVITY RULE

Isomeric effect— The additivity rule for bond energies applies only to compounds in a homologous series and small changes in structure cause deviations in the heats of formation. If the additivity rule were correct, saturated hydrocarbons possessing the same number of carbon and hydrogen atoms would have identical heats of formation. This, however, is not correct as is shown in *Table CIX*, where the experimental data indicate that the heat of formation of a branched chain hydrocarbon is always greater than that of the normal hydrocarbon. This effect is not only shown by the hydrocarbons, but also by other classes of compounds: alcohols, esters, ketones, *etc*.

Table CIX. Heat of Formation of Isomeric Hydrocarbons

Hydrocarbons with branched chain	*Heat of formation of isomeric hydrocarbon kcals*	*Corresponding normal hydrocarbon*	*Heat of formation of normal hydrocarbon kcals*	*Difference kcals*
Isobutane	1,046·4	*Butane*	1,044·8	1·6
Isopentane	1,279·74	*Pentane*	1,277·8	1·94
Tetramethylmethane	1,282·7			4·9
Methylhexane (2– and 3–)	1,747·4	*Heptane*	1,745·8	1·6
3–Ethylpentane	1,746·3			0·5
2, 2–Dimethylpentane	1,746·6			1·8
2, 3–Dimethylpentane	1,747·4			1·6
3, 3–Dimethylpentane	1,748·2			2·4
2, 4–Dimethylpentane	1,747·6			1·8
2, 2, 4–Trimethylpentane	1,982·6	*Octane*	1,979·5	3·1
Hexamethylethane	1,984·6			5·1
2–Methylnonane	2,448·65	*Decane*	2,247·2	1·45
5–Methylnonane	2,448·25			1·05

The difference in the heat of formation of two isomers is relatively small (about 1 to 5 kcals, see *Table CIX*) and since the heats of formation are generally determined at 298° K, the question arises as to whether the difference is due to some contribution to the heat of formation, dependent on the symmetry of the molecule and on the nature of the vibrations. PITSER[3], however, has shown that the transfer from the normal to the branched chain hydrocarbon at 0° K does incur the absorption of energy (*Table CX*).

Table CX. Change of Heat Content on Isomeric Transformation

Reaction	*ΔH at 0° K kcals*	*ΔH at 298° K kcals*
n–Butane → Isobutane	− 1·27 ± 0·21	− 1·6 ± 0·20
n–pentane → Isopentane	− 1·42 ± 0·27	− 1·9 ± 0·27
n–pentane → Tetramethylmethane	− 4·02 ± 0·32	− 4·9 ± 0·3

If we consider this problem from the point of view of the repulsions existing between neighbouring hydrogen atoms, we find that for each CH_3 group there are three such repulsions, but for a CH_2 group only one. Thus in the quantum mechanical equation for the heat of formation of butane, there will be eight repulsion terms and for isobutane, nine such terms. This treatment, therefore, leads to the prediction that the heat of formation of the branched chain hydrocarbons is less than that of the normal hydrocarbons, a conclusion which is the reverse of that obtained from the experimental data. Furthermore, the heat of formation of the molecule is greater, the greater the number of interactions between hydrogen atoms, H . . . . . H. Thus in pentane there are nine, in isopentane ten, and in tetramethylmethane, twelve such interactions ; whereas the heat of formation of isopentane is greater than that of pentane by 1·9 kcals and that of tetramethylmethane by 4·9 kcals. Similarly, in *n*–octane there are twelve H . . . . . H interactions and in hexamethylethane there are eighteen and the heat of formation is increased by 5·1 kcals.

It may be that it is necessary in compounds containing tetravalent carbon atoms, to take into account the resonance with valence bond structures in which carbon is in the divalent, *i.e.* s^2p^2 state. If this be so, then for methane it is necessary to consider the resonance between the orms :

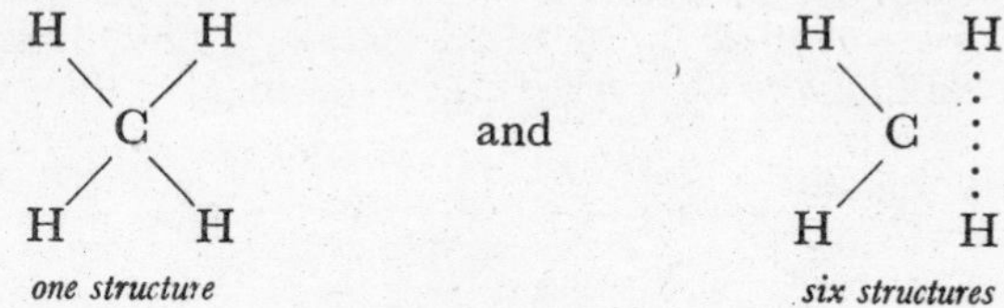

one structure *six structures*

Such resonance will bring about a gain of energy, and the greater the branching, the greater is the number of such structures.

The heat of formation of the ethylenic hydrocarbons is dependent upon both the position of the double bond and the degree of branching. A comparison of the data for butylene and isobutylene shows that the latter compound has a heat of formation greater by 3·5 kcals than that of the former (*Table CXI*). This difference is possibly in part due to the isomeric effect, but there will also be a greater resonance energy owing to the contribution of ionic structures which is suggested by the dipole moment data. In isobutylene ($\mu = 0{\cdot}49$ D) there are six structures of the type,

Table CXI. Heats of Formation of Ethylenic Hydrocarbons

Molecule	*Heat of formation kcals*	*Number of H···· H interactions*	*Number of ionic structures*
$CH_2{=}CHCH_2CH_3$	911·9	5	2
$CH_2{=}C(CH_3)_2$	915·4	7	6
$CH_3CH{=}CHCH_3$ *cis*	913·6	6	6
$CH_3CH{=}CHCH_3$ *trans*	914·6		
$CH_2{=}CHCH_2CH_2CH_3$	1,145·1	6	2
$CH_2{=}CHCH(CH_3)_2$	1,147·0	7	1
$CH_3CH{=}CHCH_2CH_3$	1,147·2	7	5
$CH_3CH{=}C(CH_3)_2$	1,150·4	9	9

$$\begin{array}{l} {}^{+}H\ CH_2 \\ \quad \diagdown\!\!\diagdown \\ \qquad C{-}{}^{-}CH_2 \\ \quad \diagup \\ H_3C \end{array}$$

whereas in butylene ($\mu = 0{\cdot}30$ D) there are only two analogous structures, *viz*

$$\overset{H^+}{CH_3{-}CH{=}CH{-}{}^{-}CH_2}$$

The data for other ethylenic hydrocarbons is given in *Table CXI.*

The energy of the acetylenic bond, C≡C, in acetylene is 128·6 kcals; in methylacetylene the value is 132·2 kcals and in dimethylacetylene, 135·5 kcals. Thus the energy of the C≡C bond is found to increase as the homologous series is ascended, although it is possible that, as in other cases, the value may become constant after the fourth or fifth member ; the necessary experimental data, however, is not available. The increase of the bond energy is most probably associated with the increased contribution of ionic structures to the resonance of the molecule. Thus in methylacetylene there are three structures of the type

$$^{+}HCH_2{=}C{=}^{-}CH$$

and in dimethylacetylene six similar valence bond structures. It should, however, again be emphasized that in calculating the energy of the C≡C bond, the energy of the C—H bond has been assumed to be that in methane, an assumption which is not necessarily valid.

Resonance energy— Where the deviations from the additivity rule are such that the actual energy of formation is greater than the calculated value, it is found possible to describe the molecule by more than one valence bond structure. Thus it is found that every resonating molecule is more stable than it would be if it had the valence bond structure assumed for it in calculating the bond energy. The difference between the calculated and observed values has been termed the resonance energy by PAULING[4]. This quantity we shall denote by the symbol E_R.

In butadiene resonance occurs between the ordinary structure $CH_2{=}CH{-}CH{=}CH_2$ and other structures involving only one double bond, *viz*—$CH_2{-}CH{=}CH{-}CH_2{-}$ and also, but to a lesser extent, $^{+}CH_2{-}CH{=}CH{-}{}^{-}CH_2$. The sum of the energies of the bonds in the ordinary structure is 778·4 kcals and the experimental heat of formation is 782·3 kcals ; the difference, which is the resonance energy E_R, is 4·1 kcals. For 1-methylbutadiene $CH_2{=}CH{-}CH{=}CHCH_3$, $E_R = 6{\cdot}16$ kcals, for 2, 3-dimethylbutadiene $CH_2{=}\underset{CH_3}{\underset{|}{C}}{-}\underset{CH_3}{\underset{|}{C}}{=}CH_2$, $E_R = 4{\cdot}0$ kcals and for isoprene

$CH_3{-}\overset{CH_2}{\overset{\|}{C}}{-}CH{=}CH_2$, $E_R = 8{\cdot}3$ kcals. If the resonance of the molecule is prevented, the additivity rule is found to apply, as in

$$CH_2{=}CH{-}CH_2{-}CH{=}CH_2$$

or in

$$CH_2{=}CH{-}CH_2{-}CH_2{-}CH{=}CH_2$$

A comparison of the resonance energies of structures involving triple and double bonds may be made by considering diacetylene, vinylacetylene and butadiene. Their resonance structures are as follows :

Table CXII. Energies of Structures having Different Multiple Bonds

Molecule	*Arrangement of bonds in first structure*	*Energy of CC bonds in first structure kcals*	*Arrangement of bonds in second structure*	*Energy of CC bonds in second structure kcals*	*Difference*
Diacetylene	≡ — ≡	319·7	= = =	303·5	16·2
Vinyl acetylene	≡ — =	292	= = —	265	27
Butadiene	= — =	265	— = —	226	39

I	II
$HC{\equiv}C{-}C{\equiv}CH$	$HC{=}C{=}C{=}CH$:.....................:
$HC{\equiv}C{-}CH{=}CH_2$	$HC{=}C{=}CH{-}CH_2$:.....................:
$H_2C{=}CH{-}CH{=}CH_2$	$H_2C{-}CH{=}CH{-}CH_2$:.....................:

In *Table CXII* the differences in energy between the two valence bond structures *I* and *II* for the three compounds are given and it is seen that the energy difference increases in the order diacetylene, vinylacetylene, butadiene, and it is therefore to be expected that the contribution of the second structure *II* will decrease in that order, *i.e.* the contribution of structure *II* to the resonance of acetylene will be greater than in the case of butadiene. That this is so is shown by the values for the polarizability. The ease of polarization of the molecule, as shown in Chapter 10, is dependent on the contribution of the valence bond structures with non-saturated carbon atoms and in the hydrocarbons considered here, the polarization increases in the order butadiene, vinylacetylene, diacetylene.

Table CXIII. Resonance Energies of Aromatic Hydrocarbons

Molecule	*Resonance energy kcals*	*Molecule*	*Resonance energy kcals*
Benzene	34·4	*Diphenyl*	6·8
Naphthalene	63·4	*Triphenylmethane*	9·8
Anthracene	86·22	*Diphenylmethane*	3·9
Phenanthrene	193·02	*Toluene*	3·7
Chrysene 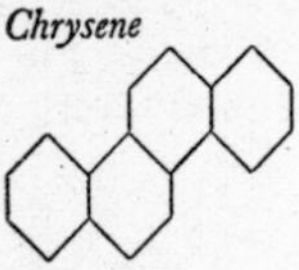	27 ± 7	*o-Xylene*	3·6
		Stilbene	10·2
		Ethylbenzene	4·1
		Styrene	3·8
		Diphenylacetylene	5·7
Perylene 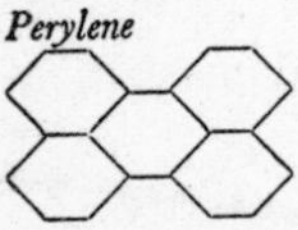	143 ± 7		

The resonance energies of some aromatic hydrocarbons are given in *Table CXIII.* Further insight into the resonance of benzene may be obtained from a study of the three successive stages of the hydrogenation reaction. We have

$$C_6H_6 + H_2 = C_6H_8 \qquad \Delta H = 5{\cdot}57 \text{ kcals}$$
$$C_6H_8 + H_2 = C_6H_{10} \qquad \Delta H = -26{\cdot}78 \text{ kcals}$$
$$C_6H_{10} + H_2 = C_6H_{12} \qquad \Delta H = -28{\cdot}59 \text{ kcals}$$

The first stage is endothermic owing to the high resonance energy of benzene. The value of the heat content for the second stage is less than that of the third, since in 1, 2–dihydrobenzene, resonance with the structure

[structure: cyclohexadiene ring with H_2, H_2]

can occur, and the difference between the heat contents for these two stages will be the resonance energy of 1,2–dihydrobenzene ($E_R = 28{\cdot}59 - 26{\cdot}78 = 1{\cdot}81$ kcals). If E_R is the total resonance energy of benzene, the resonance energy neutralized in the first stage of hydrogenation will be $E_R - 1{\cdot}81$, and if the change of heat content for a normal stage in the hydrogenation is taken as $-28{\cdot}59$ kcals we have that

$$28{\cdot}59 - (E_R - 1{\cdot}81) = -5{\cdot}57 \text{ kcals}$$

and hence $E_R = 35{\cdot}97$ kcals, a value which is in satisfactory agreement with that obtained from the heat of formation of benzene, 34 kcals.

The high resonance energy of benzene frequently determines the course of a reaction, when compared with a similar reaction involving a molecule possessing no resonance energy. For example, cyclohexene may be catalytically transformed to cyclohexane and benzene[5],

$$3C_6H_{10} = C_6H_6 + 2C_6H_{12} \qquad \Delta H = -35{\cdot}97 \text{ kcals}$$

This reaction is thermodynamically favourable since the resonance energy of benzene is gained in the reaction. Similarly, the catalytic dehydrogenation of cyclohexane into benzene at 300° K has been shown by TAYLOR[6] to occur owing to the gain of the resonance energy, whereas the dehydrogenation of cyclopentane and cycloheptane are thermodynamically unfavourable.

Table CXIV. Resonance Energies of Heterocyclic Compounds

Molecule	*Resonance energy kcals*
Pyridine	42·2
Quinoline	67·9
α-Picoline	49·5
β-Picoline	48·2

In pyridine and its analogues, in contrast to benzene, ionic structures of the type

[structure: pyridinium ring with $-N^+$]

contribute to the resonance of the molecule in addition to the Kekulé type structures. This has the effect of increasing the resonance energy of pyridine compared with benzene (see *Table CXIV*).

The resonance of the substituted derivatives of benzene are of particular interest since additional resonance occurs, apart from the resonance of the benzene ring. In *Table CXV* the values of the additional

Table CXV. Additional Resonance Energies of Benzene Derivatives

Molecule	*Resonance energy kcals*	*Molecule*	*Resonance energy kcals*
C_6H_5Cl	2·6	$(C_6H_5)_3N$	5·4
$C_6H_4(OH)(COOH)$ *ortho*	6·9	$C_6H_5NH_2$	6·3
		C_6H_5OH	4·2
		$C_6H_5OC_2H_5$	5·2
$C_6H_4(CO)_2O$	19·5 ± 5	$C_6H_5NO_2$	(2·9)
		$C_6H_5COCH_3$	(−3)
		C_6H_5CHO	1·9
$NH_2C_6H_4C_6H_4NH_2$	12·3	C_6H_5CN	3·9

resonance energy, excluding that of the benzene ring, are given for various benzene derivatives. The presence of two substituent groups, if located in the *ortho* or *para* position will create additional resonance structures. For example, in *p*–nitraniline the following valence bond structure is possible :

$$(H)_2N^+{=}C_6H_4{=}N^+(O^-)_2$$

and its contribution to the molecule resonance has been confirmed by dipole moment measurements. We should, therefore, expect deviations to arise in the values of the bond energies. Unfortunately, however, there have been few thermochemical measurements with compounds of this type and such data as exist are inaccurate. An alternative method based on the heats of neutralization of amines has therefore been employed for the determination of the resonance energies of these compounds. The heats of neutralization of methylamine, ethylamine and ammonia are respectively 13 kcals, 13·2 kcals, and 12·3 kcals, the reaction being

$$RNH_{2\,aq} + H_3O^+{}_{aq} = R^+NH_{3\,aq}$$

In aniline owing to the contribution to the resonance of the molecule of the structure

$$(H)_2N^+{=}C_6H_5^-$$

the nitrogen atom may be regarded as being already partly in the tetravalent state and positively charged, *i.e.* the amino group is already 'partially neutralized'. On neutralization with an acid, therefore, less heat will be given out. Alternatively we may say that a certain amount of energy has been used in overcoming the resonance of the molecule and that therefore the heat of neutralization is $13 - E_R$. This method of calculating E_R is open to criticism as it does not take into account the heats of hydration of the molecules and ions. The heats of neutralization are given in *Table CXVI* and the value obtained by this method for the additional resonance energy of aniline, *viz* $13 - 7{\cdot}4 = 5{\cdot}6$ kcals, is in reasonable agreement with the value calculated from the heat of combustion. The heats of neutralization of *p*–aminoazobenzene and of *o*– and *p*–nitraniline are considerably lower than the normal value owing to the high resonance energy of these molecules. In *p*–aminophenol, which is not a zwitterion, the reverse effect is observed and the heat of neutralization is raised by comparison with aniline. This result is most probably caused by the suppression of the resonance of the amino group with the benzene ring by the presence of the hydroxyl group. The oxygen atom may exist in the positive trivalent state, as in the structure

$$H{-}O^+{=}C_6H_4^{2-}{=}{}^+NH_2$$

and the resonance of the amino group with the benzene ring will thus be lowered and hence the contribution of the $= {}^{+}NH_2$ state to the resonance of the amino group reduced.

Table CXVI. Heats of Neutralization of Aromatic Amines

Molecule	*Heat of neutralization kcals*	*Molecule*	*Heat of neutralization kcals*
Aniline	7·40	*p–Nitraniline*	1·81
α–Naphthylamine	6·44	*o–Nitraniline*	1·81
β–Naphthylamine	5·30	*o–Aminophenol*	8·48
p–Aminoazobenzene	1·77	*p–Toluidine*	7·60

The value of the heat of neutralization of *p*–toluidine, $CH_3C_6H_4NH_2$, is very near that for aniline, being 7·6 kcals; evidently the CH_3 group has a negligible influence on the resonance of the molecule.

The heat of formation of carbon dioxide is 336·9 kcals and since the energy of two C=O bonds is 310 kcals it follows that E_R = 26·9 kcals, the resonance being between the two structures O=C=O and O^-—C≡O^+. By similar calculations using the energies of the C=O, C—O and O—H bonds, we find that for the group COOH, E_R = 20 kcals and for the group COOC, E_R = 22 kcals. A greater deviation from the additivity rule occurs in acetic anhydride

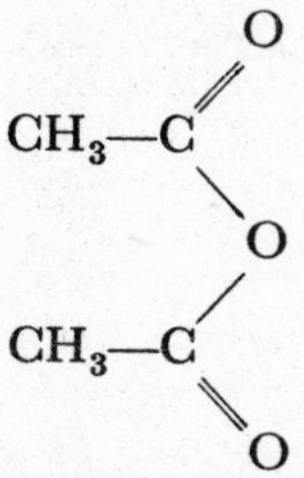

$$\begin{array}{l} CH_3{-}C{=}O \\ \quad\;\; \backslash \\ \qquad O \\ \quad\;\; / \\ CH_3{-}C{=}O \end{array}$$

where, owing to the presence of two C—O bonds, E_R = 28 kcals. In carbonic acid and its derivatives resonance occurs among the three structures:

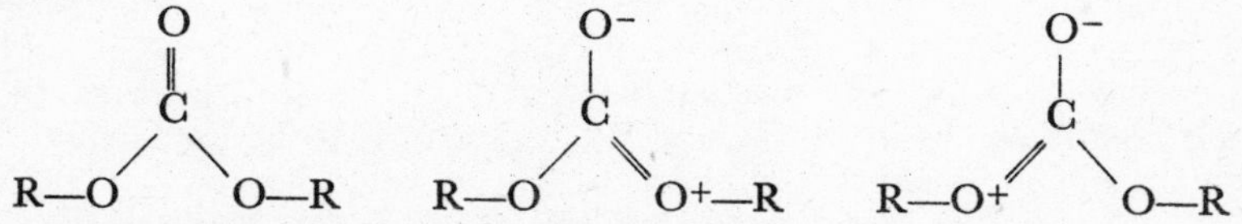

$$R{-}O{-}C({=}O){-}O{-}R \qquad R{-}O{-}C(O^-){=}O^+{-}R \qquad R{-}O^+{=}C(O^-){-}O{-}R$$

the resonance being somewhat inhibited in the esters, but not in the ion. For the esters the resonance energy is 27 kcals.

When the resonance is between purely homopolar valence bond structures, the resonance energy is less than when ionic structures are involved. This general rule may be illustrated by considering the resonance structures of furan and *cyclo*pentadiene. In furan, *I*, the resonance involves

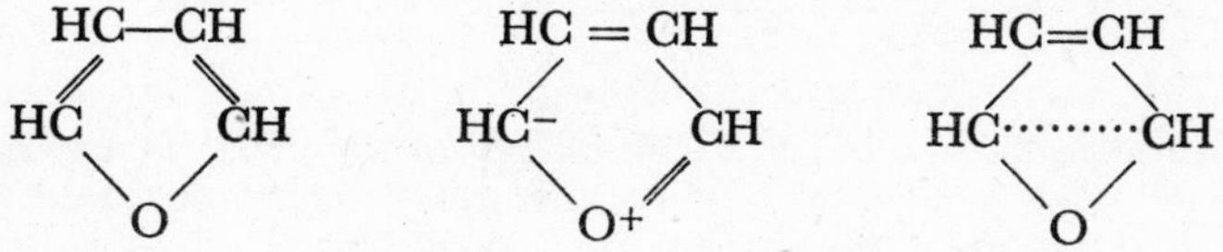

HC—CH HC(=) (=)CH \ O /	HC = CH HC⁻ CH \ O^+ (=)	HC=CH HC·········CH \ O /
I	*II*	*III*

the ionic structure *II*, as well as the cross linked structure *III*. From the heat of formation we find that E_R = 14·4 kcals. It is very probable that this resonance energy is largely due to the resonance between states *I* and *II* since cross linked structures do not generally make large contributions to the resonance of the molecule. This reasoning is substantiated by the fact that the energy of hydrogenation of furan is 36·63 kcals and of *cyclo*-pentadiene 50·56 kcals. Since any resonance that occurs in the *cyclo*-pentadiene molecule can only involve the structures *IV* and *V*, the difference between these values, *viz* 13·93 kcals, represents the resonance energy

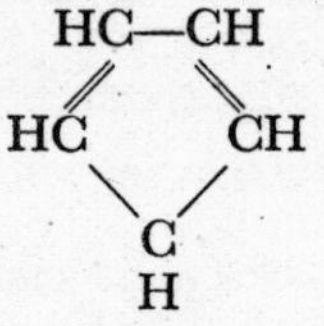

```
   HC—CH              HC=CH
   //   \\            /     \
 HC       CH        HC·········CH
   \     /            \     /
     C                  C
     H                  H
    IV                  V
```

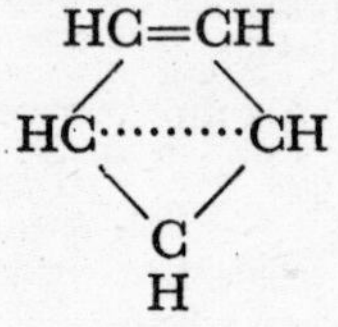

of the normal *I* and ionic *II* states of furan. This behaviour is even more marked in pyrrole, where $E_R = 25$ kcals.

In diacetyl the two neighbouring C=O groups mutually hinder their bond resonance since the ionic structure

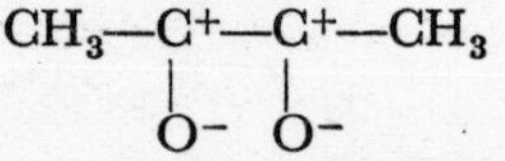

```
CH₃—C⁺—C⁺—CH₃
     |    |
     O⁻   O⁻
```

is improbable owing to the positive charge on each of the adjacent carbon atoms. The bond resonance in both carbonyl groups will thus be reduced and in agreement with this view, the bond energy of the carbonyl groups in diacetyl is found to be 147·30 kcals, a value which is significantly lower than that in normal ketones : 155 to 157 kcals.

In the bond between a carbon and a halogen atom, considerable resonance occurs between the homopolar, C—Hal and ionic, C^+Hal^- states, as indicated by the dipole moment data. This may also be shown by a comparison of the experimental bond energies with the values calculated by a formula suggested by Pauling[4], for the homopolar bond between carbon and halogen. A normal covalent bond AB will be similar in character to the homopolar bonds A—A and B—B, and it is to be anticipated that the energy of the bond AB will lie between the values for the bonds A—A and B—B. Pauling therefore assumes that the energy of a purely covalent bond between the unlike atoms A and B is given by the arithmetic mean of the energies of the bonds A—A and B—B. There is no particular reason why the arithmetic mean has been chosen and in certain cases better results are obtained using the geometric mean. In general, however, the divergence between the values of the two means is small and for convenience the arithmetic mean is generally used (see Chapter 6 for a full account of this method). Thus

$$(E_{A-B})_{\text{covalent}} = \tfrac{1}{2}(E_{A-A} + E_{B-B})$$

Using this formula we find that the energy of the covalent C—F, C—Cl and C—Br bonds are 63, 60, and 54 kcals respectively compared with the experimental values of respectively 104, 70 and 57 kcals. The difference between the experimental and calculated values are : C—F, 41 kcals ; C—Cl, 10 kcals ; C—Br, 3 kcals, an order which is in agreement with the decrease in polarity of the bonds. The experimental value for the energy of the C—I bond is slightly less than the calculated value due, most probably, to experimental error.

In acetyl chloride the energy of the group

$$-\mathrm{C}\begin{matrix}\nearrow\!\!\!\!\!\nearrow \mathrm{O}\\ \searrow \mathrm{Cl}\end{matrix}$$

is lowered by comparison to the sum of the C—O and C—Cl bond energies by 6 to 9 kcals owing to the contribution of the structures

$$\mathrm{CH_3{-}C}\begin{matrix}\nearrow \mathrm{O^-}\\ \searrow\!\!\!\!\!\searrow \mathrm{Cl^+}\end{matrix} \quad \text{and in particular} \quad \mathrm{CH_3{-}C}\begin{matrix}\equiv \mathrm{O^+}\\ \mathrm{Cl^-}\end{matrix}$$

Similarly, deviations from additivity are observed when resonance between C=O and C=C or C≡C groups can occur. Thus the heat of formation of $CH_3CH_2C{\equiv}CCOOC_2H_5$ is 3 kcals greater than that of $CH_3C{\equiv}CCH_2COOC_2H_5$ owing to the contribution of the ionic form

$$\mathrm{CH_3CH_2C^+{=}C{=}\underset{\displaystyle |\atop \mathrm{O^-}}{C}{-}OC_2H_5}$$

which can occur in the former molecule but not in the latter.

Table CXVII gives the resonance energy of several compounds containing the $CONH_2$ group in which resonance with the structure

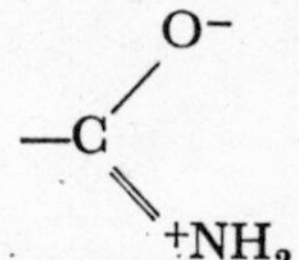

is possible.

The data given in *Table CVIII* show a difference in the energies of the C≡N bond in HCN, nitriles and isonitriles. In the nitrile group, bond resonance occurs between the homopolar structures —C≡N and the ionic form $-C^+{=}N^-$, the contribution of the latter structure being largely responsible for the high dipole moment of the nitriles. The difference between the energy values of the C≡N bond in HCN and RCN lies in the fact that there are fewer ionic structures in HCN compared with RCN. For example, in CH_3CN, in addition to the homopolar structure $H_3C{-}C{\equiv}N$ and the bond resonance structures described above, there are three ionic structures of the type $^+HH_2C{=}C{=}N^-$ with which resonance can occur. In hydrogen cyanide there is only one such structure, *viz* $^+HC{=}N^-$, which is less probable than the corresponding structures for methyl cyanide, since it contains a divalent carbon atom. In the isonitriles, bond resonance will occur between the forms R—N=C and $R{-}N^+{\equiv}C^-$ but molecular resonance of the type described in hydrogen cyanide and the nitriles is not possible. Thus the values of the bond energies are expected to increase in the order isonitrile, hydrogen cyanide, nitrile, in accordance with the experimental data. The value of the energy of the C≡N bond obtained

*Table CXVII. Resonance Energies of Nitrogen Compounds**

Molecule	*Resonance energy kcals*	*Molecule*	*Resonance energy kcals*
$RCONH_2$	11·4	NH—CO CH—NH CO—NH CO NH₂ → NH—CO, CH—NH, CO—NH, CO, NH_2 (*Allantoin*)	70·5
$CO(NH_2)_2$	23·0		
$C_6H_5CONH_2$	17·3		
$(C_2H_5CO)_2NH$	21·7		
CH_3CO NH C_2H_5CO	33·8	NH—CO CH C NH CH N—C N (*Hypoxanthine*)	91·6
$(C_6H_5CO)_2NH$	24·5		
$(C_6H_5CO)_3N$	48·2		
CO C_6H_4 NH CO	19·8		
C_6H_5NHCOH	12·5	NH—CO CO C NH CO NH—C NH (*Uric acid*)	83·9
$C_6H_5NHCOC_2H_5$	19·2		
$(C_6H_5NH)_2CO$	32·8		
$C_6H_5CONHC_6H_5$	23·2		
NH—CO CO CO NH—CO (*Alloxan*)	30·2	NH—CO H_2N—C C NH CH N—C N (*Guanine*)	110·9

* The values have a possible error of ± 5 kcals since only approximate values are known for the heats of sublimation.

from the heat of formation of dicyanogen, C_2N_2, is 142 kcals which is 4 kcals less than the value for hydrogen cyanide. This is most probably due to a suppression of the bond resonance, since the structure $N^-{=}C^+{=}C^+{=}N^-$ is energetically unfavourable owing to the positive charges on the adjacent carbon atoms.

The resonance energy of thiourea is 8·9 ± 5 kcals, considerably lower than that of urea. Evidently oxygen participates more readily in the resonance of the molecule and the structure *I* makes a greater contribution to the resonance of urea than structure *II* to the resonance of thiourea.

$$O^{-}—C(=N^{+}H_2)—NH_2 \qquad S^{-}—C(=N^{+}H_2)—NH_2$$

I *II*

In methyl*iso*thiocyanate, CH_3NCS, the resonance energy (15·3 kcals) is produced by the contribution of the ionic structures :

$$CH_3—N^{+}{\equiv}C—S^{-}, \qquad CH_3—N^{-}—C{\equiv}S^{+}$$

to the resonance of the molecule. In methylthiocyanate the only possible ionic structure is

$$CH_3—S^{+}{=}C{=}N^{-}$$

since the structure involving a positively charged nitrogen atom is impossible ; the resonance energy should therefore be lower in comparison to CH_3NCS.

Distortion of rings— In the cyclic hydrocarbons, the heat of formation is lowered considerably in comparison with the calculated value on account of the distortion of the valency angles. The extent of the distortion decreases in the order *cyclo*propane (C—C—C, angle 60°), *cyclo*butane (C—C—C, angle 90°), *cyclo*pentane (C—C—C, angle 108°). In *cyclo*-hexane and cycloheptane the structures are formed without distortion of the tetrahedral angle. The effect of the distortion of the ring on the heat of formation is shown in *Table CXVIII*. The effect makes itself apparent in other physical properties such as molecular spectra and refractivity and also is the cause of the chemical instability. This effect has been frequently referred to as ring strain. This is an unfortunate term as the energy difference is entirely due to the fact that in these structures, the bonding orbitals do not overlap to the maximum extent, except when the line joining the two nuclei forming the bond happens to lie along the axis of both bonding orbitals. In carbon in the sp^3 state the angle between these axes is the tetrahedral angle.

Table CXVIII. Lowering of Heats of Combustion on Distortion of Bond Angles

Molecule	*Decrease in* C—C *bond energy kcals*
Cyclopropane ..	12
Cyclobutane ..	9
Cyclopentane ..	2·9
Cyclohexane ..	1·8
Cycloheptane ..	1
cis-Dekalin ..	0·9
trans-Dekalin ..	0·4

Keto-enol tautomerism— The change from the keto to the enol form of a molecule generally involves the transfer of a proton from a carbon atom to an oxygen or nitrogen atom and the energy changes incurred in such a process may be studied from the point of view of bond energies. In acetone, for example, there exists an equilibrium between the keto form

$$CH_3—\underset{\underset{O}{\|}}{C}—CH_3$$

and the enol form

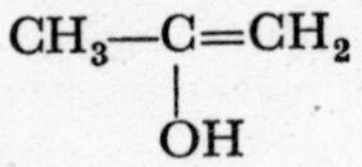

$$CH_3{-}C{=}CH_2$$
$$\quad\;|$$
$$\quad OH$$

In the keto form the bond system

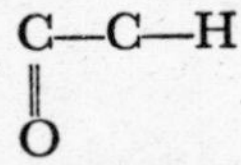

$$C{-}C{-}H$$
$$\|$$
$$O$$

occurs with a total energy of 303·4 kcals whereas in the enol form, the bond system becomes

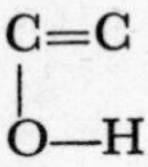

$$C{=}C$$
$$|$$
$$O{-}H$$

which has a total bond energy of 286·2 kcals. Thus the keto form is more stable by 17·2 kcals than the enol form, a value which is sufficiently large to cause the equilibrium mixture to consist almost entirely of the keto form. The equilibrium may favour the enol form if additional factors are present which bring about a gain in energy. Thus phenol is normally regarded as being in the enolic form, but may exist in the keto form :

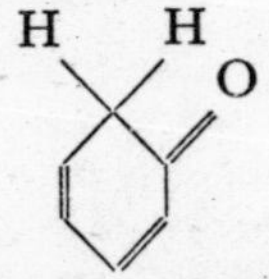

H H O

This structure, however, is much less probable from energy considerations, since although 17·2 kcals have been gained on account of the redistribution of the bonds, this transformation is accompanied by a much greater decrease of the resonance energy of the benzene ring. Thus the keto is much less stable than the enol form and the latter predominates.

Stabilization of another type occurs in the case of acetyl acetone :

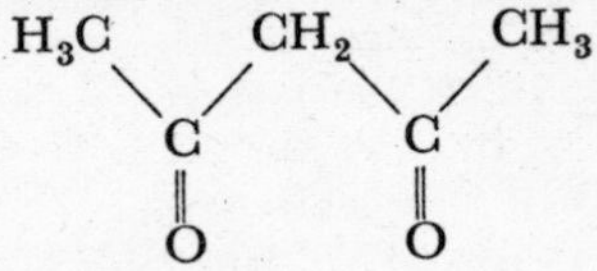

$$H_3C{-}C({=}O){-}CH_2{-}C({=}O){-}CH_3$$

In the enolic form, resonance of the two normal structures *I* and *II* with the ionic structures *III* to *VI* occurs :

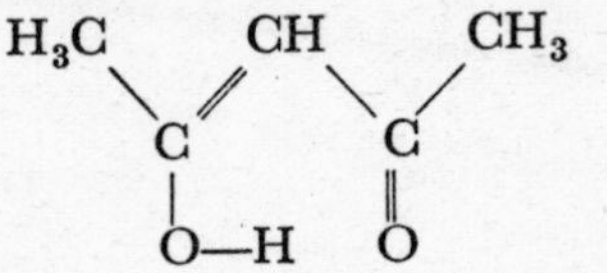

$$H_3C{-}C(OH){=}CH{-}C({=}O){-}CH_3 \qquad (I)$$

$$H_3C{-}C({=}O){-}CH{=}C(OH){-}CH_3 \qquad (II)$$

$$H_3C{-}C(O^-){=}CH{-}C^+(O^-){-}CH_3 \quad H^+ \qquad (III)$$

$$H_3C{-}{}^+C(O^-){-}CH{=}C(O^-){-}CH_3 \quad H^+ \qquad (IV)$$

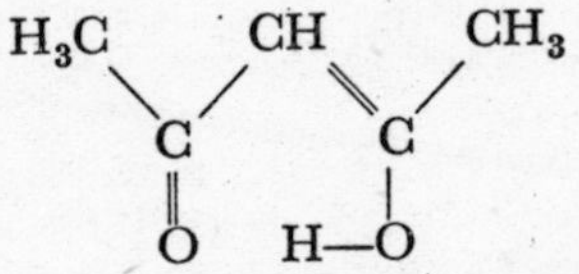

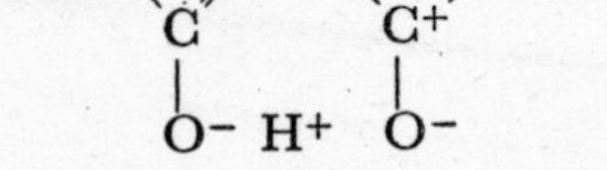

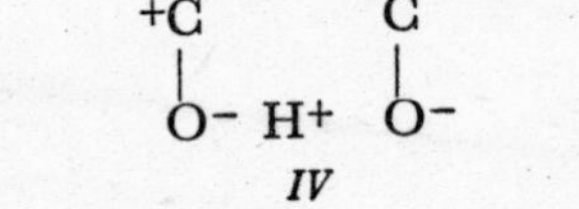

H_3C CH CH_3 — C, C — O^- H—O^+ (V)

H_3C CH CH_3 — C, C — O^+—H O^- (VI)

V *VI*

The result of the contribution of these structures to the molecular resonance will be that the hydrogen is equally bonded to the two oxygen atoms which may thus be regarded as joined by a hydrogen bond (for a discussion of the hydrogen bond, see Chapter 12). The gain in energy owing to the resonance is sufficient to make the enol more stable than the keto form and the equilibrium mixture is found to be 92 per cent enol and 8 per cent keto in the gas phase.

BOND ENERGIES IN INORGANIC COMPOUNDS

In organic chemistry we have a very great variety of molecules which are formed by only a few different types of bonds. It is possible therefore to establish experimentally the constancy of the bond energy of any particular bond. A rather different state of affairs exists in inorganic chemistry where there is both a wide variety of different types of bonds as well as of compounds. We shall consider first the energies of the normal single bond between like atoms. In the case of the elements of the first and seventh groups accurate data are obtained from spectroscopic measurements; this has been discussed in Chapter 8. In P_4 and As_4 the atoms are arranged tetrahedrally and each atom of phosphorus or arsenic therefore forms three single bonds, using the three unpaired *p* electrons. The number of bonds in P_4 and As_4 will be six, corresponding to the number of edges of the tetrahedron, and the energy of one P—P or As—As bond may therefore be taken as equal to one sixth of the heat of formation of the molecule from gaseous atoms. The heat of the reaction $2P_2 = P_4$ may be obtained from vapour pressure measurements and is approximately 30 kcals. Using a spectroscopic value for the dissociation energy of P_2 into atoms (116 kcals) we obtain the value of 262 kcals for the heat of formation of P_4 and hence the energy of the P—P bond is 44 kcals. Similarly we find that the heat of formation of As_4 is 203 kcals, and hence the As—As bond energy is 34 kcals. In addition to the molecules S_2 and Se_2, which are stable only at high temperatures, sulphur and selenium exist in the vapour state as cyclic structures having the formulae S_8, S_6 and Se_8, Se_6. In these structures each atom forms two single bonds, there being eight bonds in S_8 and Se_8 and six in S_6 and Se_6. The bond energies may be calculated from the energies of the reactions $3S_8=4S_6$, $S_6=3S_2$; $S_2=2S$. For the energy of the S—S bond, the value of 52·5 kcals is obtained employing the data for S_8 and 51 kcals using the data for S_6. The corresponding values for the Se—Se bond are 42 kcals and 40 kcals respectively. These values are somewhat different from those given in the literature, since more recent values of the spectroscopic dissociation energies of P_2, As_2, S_2 and Se_2 have been used. The main possibility of error lies in the determination of the heats of formation of the diatomic molecules from the higher polymers.

The energy of the S—S bond may be determined by another method.

If in H_2S_2 the atoms of sulphur form a normal single bond H—S—S—H, then by subtracting from the heat of formation of H_2S_2 twice the energy of the S—H bond, the energy of the S—S bond is obtained. The heat of formation of H_2S_2 is 205 kcals and the energy of the S—H bond is a half of the heat of formation of H_2S (162 kcals) and hence $E_{S-S} = 205 - 162 = 43$ kcals, a value which is somewhat lower than that obtained from the heats of formation of S_8 and S_6. This discrepancy may be due to a difference in the ionic character of the S—H bond in H_2S and H_2S_2.

Table CXIX. Energies of Single and Double Bonds

Atom	*Bond energy in molecule* X_2 *kcals*	*Single bond energy,* X—X *kcals*
P	116	44
As	91	34
S	83	52
Se	62	41

The data obtained may be used to compare the energies of the single and multiple bonds (*Table CXIX*). The single bond energies of phosphorus and arsenic are slightly more than one third of the energy of the triple bond. For sulphur and selenium, the single bond energies are more than half the energy of the double bond. A similar variation of bond energy with multiplicity occurs in carbon: $E_{C-C} = 62$ kcals, $E_{C=C} = 101$ kcals, $E_{C\equiv C} = 128$ kcals. The existence of such molecules as P_4, As_4 and C_n is now understandable since the transfer from multiple to single bonds is accompanied by an increase in the stability of the molecule.

The energy of the single bond between two oxygen atoms may be obtained by a process analogous to that used above for the S—S bond. Hydrogen peroxide has the structure H—O—O—H, thus containing two O—H bonds and one O—O bond. The heat of formation of water is 220 kcals which gives a value of 110 kcals for E_{O-H}. Employing this value and 254·5 kcals as the heat of formation of hydrogen peroxide, we obtain $E_{O-O} = 34{\cdot}5$ kcals. This value must not be regarded as too exact, however, since for the successive dissociation of H_2O we have

$$H_2O = OH + H \qquad \Delta H = 119{\cdot}5 \text{ kcals}$$
$$OH = O + H \qquad \Delta H = 99{\cdot}5 \text{ kcals}$$

Employing the latter value as the energy of the O—H bond we obtain for the dissociation of hydrogen peroxide into two peroxide groups

$$H_2O_2 = 2OH \qquad \Delta H = 55{\cdot}5 \text{ kcals}$$

The energy of the O—Cl bond in Cl_2O is found to be 49 kcals, hence employing Pauling's equation (page 100) we may write,

$$E_{O-Cl} \geqslant \tfrac{1}{2}(E_{O-O} + E_{Cl-Cl})$$

and hence using the value $E_{Cl-Cl} = 57{\cdot}8$ kcals, obtained spectroscopically, we obtain

$$E_{O-O} \leqslant 40{\cdot}2 \text{ kcals}$$

The examination of a considerable amount of data shows that the energy of the O—O bond is to a great extent determined by the nature of the adjacent molecules and we can therefore give only a very approximate value for the bond energy.

The heat of the reaction $2O_2 = O_4$ is practically zero, although the molecule O_4 exists as a separate entity. Pauling rejects the structure

```
O—O
|  |
O—O
```

and the heat of formation of the molecule, 275 kcals, is too great to be accounted for by four single bonds. However, resonance between the homopolar and eight ionic structures of the type

$$\begin{array}{l} {}^{+}O{=}O \\ | \\ O{-}O^{-} \end{array}$$

may occur and thereby increase the heat of formation. The molecule is unstable, however, since the entropy of the O_4 molecule is less than twice the entropy of an O_2 molecule.

The energy of the N—N bond may be obtained from the heat of formation of hydrazine, $H_2N—NH_2$, if the energy of each of the four N—H bonds is assumed to be one third of the heat of formation of ammonia, 249 kcals. The value obtained is 22 ± 2 kcals. This is a particularly low value, especially in view of the fact that the energy of the N_2 molecule is of the order of 170 kcals and hence the energy of the single bond is much less than one third of the energy of the triple bond. There are, however, other data which confirm indirectly the low value of the energy of the N—N bond. First, although the elements phosphorus and arsenic give the stable molecules P_4 and As_4 formed by σ bonds, the corresponding molecule N_4 has never been observed. Evidently in this case, the transfer of π bonds to σ bonds is unfavourable from energy considerations. Secondly, the nitric oxide molecule shows little tendency to dimerise to the molecule N_2O_2. The heat of formation of NO is 122 kcals and if we assume that the energy of the N=O bond is 108 kcals as in organic molecules, it follows that the three electron bond contributes 14 kcals to the energy of the NO molecule. In the formation of the dimer O=N—N=O, the energy of two three electron bonds is lost and that of one N—N bond is gained. Since the heat of this reaction is close to zero it follows that the energy of the N—N bond is of the order of 28 kcals, a value which, although approximate, satisfactorily confirms the previously obtained low value. Finally, the energy of bonds between nitrogen and other atoms is relatively small; thus $E_{N-Cl} = 38$ kcals and E_{C-N}, notwithstanding the resonance with ionic states, is only 53 kcals.

In molecules forming single and multiple bonds, a parallelism is found to exist between the decrease of the internuclear distance and the increase of bond energy on converting a single into a double or triple bond. Thus, where there is a large increase in the bond energy on increasing the multiplicity of the bond, there occurs also a marked decrease of the internuclear distance. The variation of bond distance with bond multiplicity is shown in *Table CXX*.

The heats of formation of the oxides of nitrogen are given in *Table CXXI*. The nitrous oxide molecule is linear, with the oxygen atom at one end of the molecule and is generally represented as a resonance hybrid of the two structures

$$N^{-}{=}N^{+}{=}O \qquad N{\equiv}N^{+}{—}O^{-}$$

The contribution of these forms to the resonance of the molecule must be about equal as nitrous oxide has an almost zero dipole moment, and it is therefore not possible to

Table CXX. Ratio of Internuclear Distances in Single and Multiple Bonds

Bond	r_{double}/r_{single}	Bond	r_{triple}/r_{single}
OO	0·82	NN	0·73
CC	0·86	CN	0·78
SS	0·90	CO	0·79
SeSe	0·93	CC	0·78
		PP	0·85

Table CXXI. Heats of Formation of Nitrogen Oxides

Molecule	Heat of formation kcals	Molecule	Heat of formation kcals
N_2O	208	N_2O_5	462
NO	122	NO_3	(248)
NO_2	194	N_2O_2	(247)
N_2O_3	325	HNO_3	344
N_2O_4	401		

regard either of these formulae as a basis for the computation of bond energies. Pauling[4] has suggested that in nitrogen dioxide resonance occurs between the two structures :

O=N⋯O and O⋯N=O

the dotted line ···· representing a three electron bond. If the bond energies of N—O is taken as 61 kcals, of N=O as 108 kcals and the three electron bond as 14 kcals, we obtain the value 183 kcals for the calculated heat of formation, compared with the observed value of 194 kcals. The difference of 11 kcals represents the resonance energy. Although this resonance stabilizes the molecule, it is insufficient to prevent dimerization to N_2O_4. The structure of this molecule has not been established, but x-ray diffraction measurements suggest that the atoms are arranged in the following manner :

```
O     O
  N  N
O     O
```

For such a configuration it would appear that the arrangement of bonds would be

```
O⁻        O⁻              O       O
  \      /                 \\    //
   N⁺—N⁺         or          N—N
  //     \\                 //   \\
O          O               O       O
      I                        II
```

Structure *I* is unsatisfactory[4], due to the adjacent positive charges, a view which is upheld by an attempt to calculate the heat of formation. The energy of two nitro groups, including resonance energy, lies between 338 and 372 kcals ; therefore since the measured heat of formation is 401 kcals the energy of the bond N⁺—N⁺ cannot be less than 29 kcals, but since the energy of the normal uncharged N—N bond is of this order of magnitude, the bond energy being considered must be less, since there is considerable electrostatic repulsion. Thus a calculation of the bond energy of the structure *I*, with the inclusion of the resonance energy, will fall below the observed value. In structure *II* containing pentavalent nitrogen atoms, the energy of excitation of nitrogen atoms to the pentavalent state ($2s^2 2p^3 \rightarrow 2s2p^3 3s$) is so great that it is most improbable that the molecule would have an energy of 401 kcals. An alternative structure not in agreement with x-ray data would appear to be

```
O⁻        N = O
  \      /
   N⁺—O
  //
O
```

and the calculated value of the heat of formation assuming the molecule to consist of one nitro group, two N—O bonds and one N=O bond, lies between 399 and 416 kcals in agreement with the observed value.

Nitric acid has the structure :

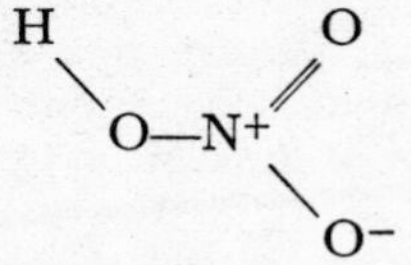

```
H          O
 \        //
  O—N+
      \
       O-
```

and if it be regarded as the combination of a hydroxyl group and a nitro group, we obtain the value 234 kcals as the heat of formation of the nitrate ion. This ion will have the structure :

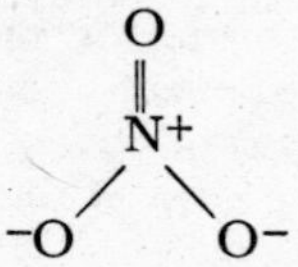

```
     O
     ‖
     N+
    / \
 -O     O-
```

in which, through resonance, all the oxygen atoms are identical. The following structures are possible for N_2O_5

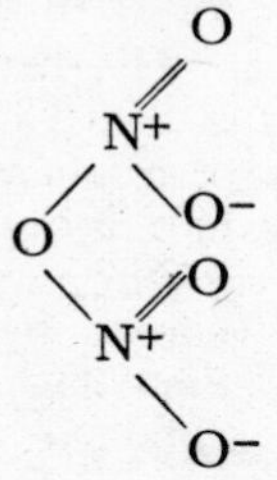

```
      O                 O
     //                //
    N+                N
   /  \              /  \\
  O    O-           O    O
   \  //O            \  //O
    N+                N
     \                 \
      O-                O
      I                 II
```

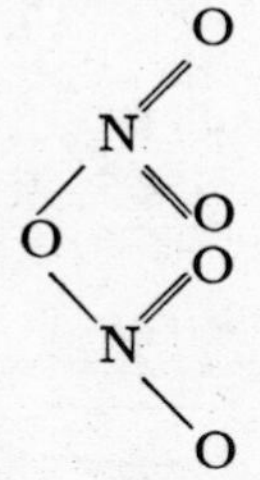

For the purpose of estimating the heat of combustion, structure *I* may be regarded as being composed of two

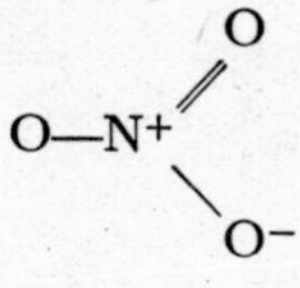

```
        O
       //
  O—N+
      \
       O-
```

groups. This gives a heat formation of the order of 475 kcals in agreement with the observed value. This structure *I* is also supported by the dipole moment data. The formula *II*, involving pentavalent nitrogen, is regarded as improbable owing to the high excitation energy of the valency state. In the decomposition of nitrogen pentoxide, it has been suggested that the molecule NO_3 is formed as an intermediate product. This molecule is a free radical and most probably may be represented by six valence bond structures of the type

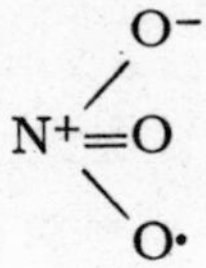

```
     O-
    /
  N+=O
    \
     O·
```

For the dissociation energy of S—O, Herzberg[1] assigns the value 92 kcals; from the heats of formation of SO_2 we find the average value of the SO bond is 122 kcals and from SO_3, 109 kcals. These values are in agreement with the multiplicity of the SO bonds, since in the sulphur dioxide molecule, each bond possesses one half double bond character owing to the resonance between the structures $O{=}S^+{-}O^-$ and $O^-{-}S^+{=}O$ and in sulphur trioxide the bonds possess one third double bond character owing to the resonance between three structures of the type

O
//
O^-—S^{2+}
\
O^-

The electrostatic interaction is greater in SO_3 although the excitation energy of sulphur to the tetravalent, doubly charged, positive state is greater than that to the trivalent, positively charged state.

If in the molecule S_2Cl_2, the energy of the S—S bond is taken as 52 kcals, each S—Cl bond has an energy of 61 kcals. Such an apportionment of the energy of the molecule is only approximate since in addition to the normal homopolar structure Cl—S—S—Cl, the ionic forms:

$^-Cl\ S{=}S^+{-}Cl$ and $Cl{-}S^+{=}S\ Cl^-$

will contribute to the molecular resonance. The heat of formation of $SOCl_2$ is 214 kcals, of SO_2Cl_2, 316 kcals and of $S_2O_5Cl_2$, 615 kcals. With these molecules, owing to the great variety of resonance structures, it is not possible to apportion particular energy values to individual bonds.

The energies of bonds involving hydrogen (MH) and the halogens (MHal) may be obtained by dividing the heats of formation of the molecules MH_x and $MHal_x$ by x. The values obtained are given in *Table CXXII*. The values for the energies of the Si—O and Si=O bonds, which are also given in *Table CXXII* are obtained in the former case from the heat of formation of silica $(SiO_2)_n$, in which each silicon atom is bonded to four oxygen atoms, and in the latter from the heat of formation of gaseous (molecular) SiO_2.

Table CXXII. Bond Energies for Hydrides and Halogen Compounds

Bond	Energy kcals	Bond	Energy kcals	Bond	Energy kcals
SiH	75	BBr	77	PCl	75
NH	83	AlCl	91	PBr	61
PH	75	SiF	143	PI	44
AsH	56	SiCl	85	AsCl	69
OH	110	SiBr	69	AsBr	53
SH	81	SiI	51	AsI	34
SeH	65	GeCl	104	SbCl	73
TeH	51	SnCl	77	OF	59
BeCl	107	PbF	105	OCl	49
BeI	68	TiCl	96	SiC	58
BF	155	NF	69	Si—O	89
BCl	96	NCl	38	Si=O	161

An examination of the data given in *Table CXXII* shows that there is a steady decrease in the energy of the MH bond as a periodic group is descended. This behaviour is probably associated with the repulsion of filled electronic shells and a decrease in the contribution of the ionic state. The bonds of the elements of the sixth group with hydrogen are more stable than those of the fifth group since the ionic structures M^-H^+ will be present in oxygen and its analogues to a greater extent than in nitrogen.

From the values for the bonds involving halogen, no generalization can be made. On descending a periodic group there will occur an increase both of the repulsion due to the electronic shells, and resonance involving the ionic state M^+Cl^-. It would appear that these two opposing factors more or less cancel each other.

The energies of the bonds in polyhalogen compounds $MHal_x$, do not correspond in the majority of cases, with the dissociation of the corresponding sub-halogen, MHal. Unfortunately, the relevant experimental data are neither complete nor accurate and it is hardly possible therefore on the basis of the existing data to make any generalizations. It may be pointed out, however, that in a number of instances the observed data are in agreement with ideas developed in Chapter 2 for the excitation of valency states. For example, with mercury and beryllium, the energy of formation of the molecules MHal is less than that for the second stage of the reaction $MHal + Hal \rightarrow MHal_2$:

Be + Cl = BeCl	$\Delta H = -99$ kcals	BeCl + Cl = $BeCl_2$	$\Delta H = -116$ kcals
Hg + Cl = HgCl	$\Delta H = -27$ kcals	HgCl + Cl = $HgCl_2$	$\Delta H = -52$ kcals
Hg + Br = HgBr	$\Delta H = -25$ kcals	HgBr + Br = $HgBr_2$	$\Delta H = -45$ kcals
Hg + I = HgI	$\Delta H = -11$ kcals	HgI + I = HgI_2	$\Delta H = -35$ kcals
Ca + F = CaF	$\Delta H = -29$ kcals	CaF + F = CaF_2	$\Delta H = (-285$ kcals)

Mercury and beryllium in the ground state have no unpaired electrons and for the formation of a chemical bond it is necessary to unpair the two *s* electrons and excite one to a *p* state. This excitation is necessary before bonding can occur. Thus the energy of the reaction Hg + Cl = HgCl does not indicate the energy of the Hg—Cl bond, but that bond energy reduced by the electronic excitation energy. In the formation of the second bond, the bonding electron is already unpaired and the correct bond energy is liberated as the heat of reaction. In the case of boron and aluminum on the other hand, the energy of the first stage is greater than that of the middle stage in the formation of $BHal_3$ and $AlHal_3$. The energies of the first stage are : AlCl, 110 kcals, BBr, 101 kcals, BCl, 117 kcals and for the middle stage 91 kcals, 77 kcals and 16 kcals respectively. The electronic configuration of these atoms are s^2p and hence the first bond is formed by the unpaired *p* electron whereas, in the second stage an *s* electron has to be excited to the *p* state and the heat of reaction is equal to the bond energy less the excitation energy. Similarly in PCl_3, the energy of each P—Cl bond is 75 kcals, for the reaction $PCl_3 + 2Cl = PCl_5$ the heat of reaction is only 78 kcals, *i.e.* 39 kcals for each bond. In phosphorus the electronic configuration is s^2p^3 so that in the formation of PCl_3 all the unpaired electrons are used and the formation of further bonds will require an additional expenditure of energy to transfer the atoms to the new valency state.

REFERENCES

[1] HERZBERG, G. *Chem. Rev.* 20 (1937) 145
[2] GAYDON, A. G. and PENNEY, W. G. *Proc. roy. Soc. A* 183 (1945) 374
[3] PITSER, K. S. *J. chem. Phys.* 5 (1937) 473
[4] PAULING, L. C. *The Nature of the Chemical Bond* Cornell, 1939
[5] ZELINSKY, N. and PAWLOW, G. *Ber. dtsch. chem. Ges.* 57 (1924) 1066
[6] TAYLOR, H. S. *J. Amer. chem. Soc.* 60 (1938) 627

12

INTERMOLECULAR ATTRACTION

VAN DER WAAL'S FORCES

THE FORCES of attraction between molecules are responsible for the changes in the physical state of substances which occur when the temperature or pressure is changed. Since the molecules do not fall into one another, there must also exist forces of repulsion which will be operative at short intermolecular distances in contrast to the attractive forces which exert their influence over comparatively long distances. In gases the forces of attraction are responsible for the divergence of behaviour from that predicted by the perfect gas equation $PV = RT$. In liquids the forces of attraction play a considerable part in determining the physical behaviour, and the magnitude of these forces may be obtained from the heat of evaporation of liquids. If 1 gm mol of a liquid is evaporated at constant pressure, an amount of work $P(V_{\text{vapour}} - V_{\text{liquid}})$, is obtained. If this quantity is subtracted from the latent heat of evaporation λ, we obtain a value for the energy spent in overcoming the attractive forces between the molecules. A comparison of such values for different substances must be made at corresponding states, and it is general to assume that the boiling point of the liquid fulfils this condition since it is, for many substances, 0·64 of the critical temperature. The term $P(V_{\text{vapour}} - V_{\text{liquid}})$ may then be replaced by RT without great loss of accuracy. Some values of the intermolecular attraction energy for different compounds are shown in *Table CXXIII* and it is seen that the values vary over a wide range, but in every case are very much lower than the energy value normally associated with a chemical bond. In solids, which consist of an ordered array of molecules, the energy of attraction may be obtained from the heat of sublimation in a similar way to that described for liquids.

Table CXXIII. Heats of Evaporation

Substance	*Boiling point* °*K*	$\lambda - RT$ *kcals*	*Substance*	*Boiling point* °*K*	$\lambda - RT$ *kcals*
Helium ..	4·2	0·013	*Ammonia* ..	239·6	4·98
Hydrogen ..	20·4	0·21	*Propionic acid*	327·4	6·26
Nitrogen ..	77	1·21	*Ethyl alcohol*	351·4	8·74
Oxygen ..	90·1	1·46	*Water* ..	373·1	8·90
Krypton ..	119·9	1·92	*Aniline* ..	457	9·59
Xenon ..	165·1	2·69			

Many substances are known to associate in the gaseous or the liquid phase or in solution and in certain cases pairs of molecules or higher associated groups are known to exist. The nature of the forces of attraction which cause this molecular association is electrical in origin, and is due ultimately to the fact that matter is composed of positively charged nuclei and negatively charged electrons. For polar molecules it is necessary to distinguish between two types of electrostatic interaction, dipole–dipole and dipole–induced dipole. When molecules possess a permanent dipole moment, the oppositely charged portions of the molecules are attracted to each other and the portions with like charge repelled. The resulting force between the molecules, whether it be attractive or repellant, depends on the mutual orientation of the molecules and if all configurations were equally probable the repulsion would compensate the attraction and no association would occur. However, the distribution law favours those orientations leading to attraction, since when the positive end of one dipole is attracted towards the negative end of the other, the molecules are drawn together and the energy of attraction increases. On the other hand when the ends of like charge approach, the repulsion increases and the molecules are repelled. Attraction therefore prevails over repulsion.

Molecular association will be opposed by thermal agitation and thus a high degree of association only exists at very low temperatures ; at high temperatures all orientations will tend to become equally probable. This behaviour is analogous to the orientation of a molecular dipole in an external field, since in the present instance we are considering the orientation of a molecule in the field due to the surrounding polar molecules.

The induced dipole interaction is due to the polarization of one molecule by the dipole of a second molecule, or more generally by the field due to the surrounding polar molecules. The induced polarization is superimposed on the dipole–dipole association and since it will have the effect of increasing the dipole moment of the molecule, the attraction energy is increased. This effect is reciprocal, each dipolar molecule polarizing the other.

The average energy of dipole–dipole interaction (see Chapter 18) is given by

$$E_o = -\frac{2}{3}\frac{\mu^4}{r^6 kT} \qquad \ldots.(12.1)$$

where μ is the dipole moment, r the distance between the centres of the dipoles, k Boltzmann's constant and T the absolute temperature. This equation may be applied at fairly high temperatures and only when the distance between the dipoles is considerably greater than the length of the dipole. The energy of attraction due to the induced dipoles is given by

$$E_{ind} = -2\mu^2 a/r^6 \qquad \ldots.(12.2)$$

where a is the polarizability. We thus see that on the basis of classical electrostatics it is possible to develop a theory which will account for the two types of intermolecular interaction of polar molecules.

In order to account for the attraction between non-polar molecules on the basis of the electrostatic theory, it is necessary to regard the molecule as a quadrupole, which may be pictured as a molecule with two identical dipoles directed in opposite directions. The quadrupole may be either linear or rectangular as depicted in *Figure 39*. Such a treatment may be applied not only to molecules such as CO_2, which consist of two identical polar bonds pointing in opposite directions, but also to homopolar molecules such as H_2. It is possible to calculate the field due to the quadrupole and to consider, in a way similar to that described above, two types of interaction, mutual orientation of the quadrupoles and polarization of one molecule in the field of another. The calculation shows that the field due to the quadrupole decreases more rapidly with the distance from the molecule than does the field due to the dipole. The attractive force is thus a short range force which rapidly falls to zero as the distance from the molecule is increased.

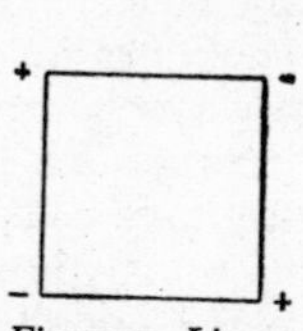

Figure 39. Linear and rectangular quadrupoles

A value for the quadrupole moment of the hydrogen molecule may be obtained by the methods of wave mechanics, but it is found to give too low a value for the van der Waal's energy. Furthermore, the quadrupole treatment would also appear unsatisfactory when applied to the atoms of the inert gases, which have electron clouds possessing spherical symmetry. Nevertheless, the inert gases interact with each other in a similar manner to other substances, as shown by their physical behaviour. Evidently, quadrupole interaction, although occurring in certain cases is not a general phenomenon and may be regarded as being supplementary to the interaction of permanent dipoles. However, experimental data show that even with polar molecules, another attractive force in addition to those produced by the dipoles is operative. This fact is illustrated by the data given in *Table CXXIV*. The heats of sublimation of the hydrogen halides increases in the order HCl, HBr, HI, whereas the dipole moment and therefore the dipole–dipole interaction decreases in the same order. Although the polarizability increases in this order, the induced dipole interaction is proportional to $\mu^2\alpha$, and the square of the dipole moment decreases more rapidly than the polarizability increases. We must therefore conclude that electrostatic theory does not account for a force which causes interaction between all molecules both polar and non-polar.

Table CXXIV. Heats of Sublimation of Hydrogen Halides

Molecule	*Distance between molecules in solid state* Å	*Dipole moment D*	*Polarizability* ($cc \times 10^{24}$)	*Heat sublimation kcals*
HCl	3·89	1·07	2·63	5·05
HBr	4·17	0·78	3·58	5·52
HI	4·50	0·38	5·39	6·21

An alternative and more acceptable theory of intermolecular forces was developed by LONDON by quantum mechanical methods. We shall illustrate the basis of this theory by considering the interaction of two atoms of hydrogen when they are sufficiently far apart so that no electron exchange occurs *i.e.* at a 'van der Waal's distance' of 3 to 4 Å. Each atom possesses no dipole moment, since owing to the spherical symmetry of the electron cloud, it is equally probable for the electron to be found on any side of the nucleus. This, however, only means that the average dipole moment, taken over a period of time, is zero. At any given instant, the nucleus and the electron are located at a certain distance from each other in a particular configuration relative to an arbitrary set of coordinates. Thus each atom always has a momentary dipole moment and such momentary dipoles interact one with another in the same way as permanent dipoles. Although we have considered the particular case of the hydrogen atom, the same ideas may be applied to any atom or molecule.

According to the relative orientation of the momentary dipoles, either attraction, *Figure 40a*, or repulsion, *Figure 40b*, may occur. A gain in energy of the system leading to attraction will occur if the motion of the electrons in adjacent molecules is synchronized, for example, moving from the first to the second position in *Figure 40a* and then back again. The position of the electron in the atom is not fixed even at the absolute zero, and this random movement of the electrons will tend to oppose the effect of synchronization, having the same effect as thermal energy on the orientation of permanent dipoles.

+ − + − I } a
− + − + II

+ − − + I } b
− + + − II

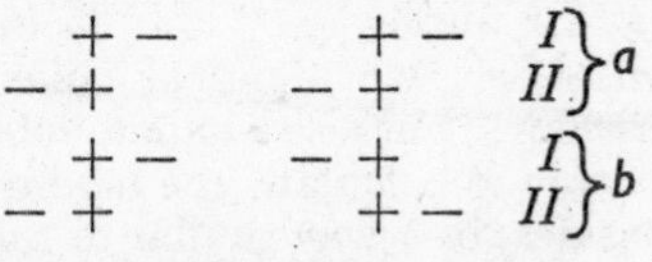

Figure 40. Dipolar interaction, a attraction b repulsion

The momentary dipoles set up a field which polarizes the adjacent molecules or atoms and the induced moments tend to keep in phase with the oscillation of the original dipoles. Calculation for the ideal case of the interaction of two harmonic oscillators leads to the following expression for the energy of interaction (see Chapter 18).

$$E = -\frac{3}{4}\frac{\alpha^2}{r^6}h\nu_0 \qquad \ldots.(12.3)$$

where ν_0 is the frequency and α the polarizability. This equation may be applied to any atom or molecule and we find that the interaction of temporary dipoles always leads to an attraction energy which is independent of the presence of a permanent dipole. The energy, represented in equation 12.3 is generally referred to as the dispersion energy. A more detailed treatment shows that that term $h\nu_0$ in the expression 12.3 may be replaced by the ionization potential without significant error. Ionization potentials are known for a number of molecules and in *Table CXXV* the data of SUGDEN, WALSH and PRICE[1] and of STEVENSON and HIPPLE[2] are summarized. It is seen that the ionization potentials of molecules do not vary over wide limits and for an approximate evaluation of the dispersion energy a value of 230 kcals may be used ; thus the magnitude of the dispersion energy is mainly determined by the polarizability of the different molecules.

Table CXXV. Ionization Potentials of Molecules

Molecule	*Ionization potential kcals*	*Molecule*	*Ionization potential kcals*	*Molecule*	*Ionization potential kcals*
H_2O	289	NH_3	249	$CH{\equiv}C{-}C{\equiv}CH$	247
CH_3OH	249	CH_3NH_3	226	$CH_2{=}CHCl$	229
C_2H_5OH	247	$(CH_3)_2NH$	221	$CHCl{=}CHCl$ *cis*	221
C_3H_7OH	247	$(CH_3)_3N$	217	$CHCl{=}CHCl$ *trans*	228
$(CH_3)_2O$	242	HCHO	250	C_6H_6	212
$(C_2H_5)_2O$	235	CH_3CHO	235	$C_6H_5C_6H_5$	191
H_2S	240	$(CH_3)_2CO$	233	$C_6H_5CH_3$	202
C_2H_5SH	224	$CH_2{=}CHCHO$	232	$C_6H_4(CH_3)_2$	191
$(CH_3)_2S$	217	$CH_3CH{=}CHCHO$	235	$(CH_3)_2C{=}CH_2$	204
$(C_2H_5)_2S$	214	$CH_3CH_2CH_2$	258	$CH_3C{\equiv}CH$	259
$(n\text{-}C_3H_7)S$	212	$CH_3CH{=}CH_2$	225		

An important difference between dispersion forces, on the one hand and dipole and induced dipole forces on the other, lies in their additive properties. Let us consider first induced dipole forces. Let the dipole *AB* (*Figure 41*) polarize the molecule located at *C*. If on the other side of *C* and at an equal distance from *C*, there is located a second dipole *DE* with a moment acting in the opposite direction, it will polarize the molecule *C* to an equal extent, but in the opposite direction to that induced by dipole *AB*, and the molecule *C* will not be polarized. Thus we may conclude generally that the polarization of a molecule due to one dipole may be weakened or neutralized, if the

A B C D E
+ − − +

Figure 41. Cancellation of induced moments

fields due to other dipoles are superimposed on that of the original dipole. The same conclusion applies to dipole-dipole interaction; if two dipoles are so arranged that they are attracted towards a third dipole they will be prevented from occupying positions which are most favourable to their own mutual interaction. Thus, in liquids and solids, as a result of the ordered arrangement of molecules, dipole-dipole and induced dipole forces may be compensated to a considerable extent.

The dispersion forces, however, possess different properties. As LONDON[3] has pointed out, if several molecules interact simultaneously with one another, each molecule will introduce into the other molecules a series of coordinated periodic dipoles, which are in phase with the exciting dipoles. Each molecule thus produces a number of induced periodic dipoles each of which is always oriented so that it is attracted to the corresponding inducing molecule. The resulting simultaneous interaction of several molecules leads to the additive superposition of the forces of attraction of individual pairs of molecules. Thus, for example, if we have three molecules, the dispersion energy will be

$$E = E_{12} + E_{13} + E_{23} \qquad \ldots.(12.4)$$

where E_{12}, E_{13} and E_{23} represent respectively the interaction energies of the pairs of molecules 1 and 2, 1 and 3, and 2 and 3.

The van der Waal's forces are generally considered as the combination of the three individual attractions described above. The average attraction energy between two molecules will therefore be

$$E = -\frac{1}{r^6}\left(\frac{2\mu_1{}^2\mu_2{}^2}{3kT} + \mu_1{}^2\alpha_2 + \mu_2{}^2\alpha_1 + \frac{3}{4}h\alpha_1\alpha_2\frac{\nu_1\nu_2}{\nu_1 + \nu_2}\right) \qquad \ldots.(12.5)$$

where μ_1 is the dipole moment, α_1 the polarizability and ν_1 the frequency of the first molecule and μ_2, α_2 and ν_2 the corresponding quantities for the second molecule. The first term in the bracket represents the dipole-dipole interaction, the second and third terms the induced dipole interaction and the fourth term the dispersion interaction.

In equations 12.1, 12.2, 12.3 and 12.5 the energy of interaction is found to be proportional to $1/r^6$. This arises from the fact that the interaction is between dipoles, either permanent or induced, and the field F due to a dipole is proportional to $1/r^3$. Since the energy of interaction is $\alpha F^2/2$, we see that it will be proportional to $1/r^6$. In order to obtain the force of interaction, the energy must be differentiated with respect to the distance r and hence is proportional to $1/r^7$.

In addition to a dipole, a molecule may possess a constant or periodic quadrupole or moment of higher order. The equation 12.5 obtained above does not include all possible energy terms and is only the first term of an infinite series. For example, the energies of the dipole-quadrupole or quadrupole-quadrupole interactions are proportional respectively to $1/r^8$ and $1/r^{10}$ and

Table CXXVI. Relative Contributions of Dipole, Induced Dipole and Dispersion Effects in van der Waal's Forces

Substance	Dipole association	Induced dipole association	Dispersion	Substance	Dipole association	Induced dipole association	Dispersion
CO	0	0	100	H_2O	77·0	4·0	19·0
HI	0·1	0·4	99·5	CH_3OH	63·4	14·4	22·2
HBr	3·3	2·2	94·5	C_2H_5OH	55·0	12·6	32·4
HCl	14·4	4·2	81·4	C_6H_{14}	0	0	100
NH_3	44·6	5·4	50·0				

hence at large distances make an insignificant contribution to the interaction energy.

The relative contribution of the various interactions in the van der Waal's forces are given for a series of substances in *Table CXXVI.* As pointed out above, the dispersion energy is present in every case and only makes a relatively small contribution in strongly polar molecules in which dipole-dipole association prevails. The variation of the dipole-dipole interaction energy is very great, being zero in non-polar molecules but increasing to 77 per cent for water owing to the fact that it is proportional to μ^4. Although the values of the dipole moments of methyl and ethyl alcohol are almost identical, the polarizability of ethyl alcohol is greater and the dispersion energy is correspondingly increased.

In the van der Waal's equation of state for real gases, the interaction energy of the molecules is represented by the term a. The interaction of the molecules produces the so-called 'inner pressure' given by the term a/V^2. The work done in overcoming this attraction will be

$$\int_V^\infty \frac{a}{V^2} dV = \frac{a}{V} \qquad \ldots.(12.6)$$

and consequently a/V is a measure of the energy required to overcome the forces of intermolecular attraction. The quantity b in the van der Waal's equation is related to the volume of the molecules. The introduction of this quantity, by regarding the molecules as rigid spheres, takes into account the repulsion of the molecules. Measurement of these rigid spheres gives the so-called van der Waal's diameter of the molecule.

The forces of interaction between molecules are fundamental in determining the physical properties of liquids. Although, at the present time, there exists no comprehensive theory of the liquid state it is possible, nevertheless, to observe some quantitative relationships. For example, the boiling point rises as the number of carbon atoms increase in an homologous series. This behaviour will be related to the increase of the polarizability as the molecule increases in size which will cause an increase of the dispersion forces. If we consider molecules of approximately the same polarizability but with different dipole moments, as with the strongly polar RNO_2 and the much less polar esters of nitrous acid RONO, then it is found that the former boil at a much higher temperature (*Table CXXVII*). In the case of the nitriles and isonitriles, the dipole moments are approximately the same and there are correspondingly smaller differences in the boiling points. As the hydrocarbon chain is increased in length, however, the relative contribution of the dispersion forces is increased and the differences in the boiling points of corresponding members of the two series of compounds become less.

Table CXXVII. Influence of Dipole Moment on Boiling Point

Substance	*Dipole moment in solution D*	*Boiling point °C*	*Substance*	*Dipole moment in solution D*	*Boiling point °C*	*Difference in boiling point °C*
CH_3NO_2	3·17	101	CH_3ONO	—	−12	113
$C_2H_5NO_2$	3·19	113	C_2H_5ONO	2·20	17	96
$C_3H_7NO_2$	—	126	C_3H_7ONO	2·28	57	69
CH_3CN	3·51	81·5	CH_3NC	—	60	21·5
C_2H_5CN	3·57	98	C_2H_5NC	3·47	78	20
C_3H_7CN	3·57	116	C_3H_7NC	—	99·5	16·5

In the gaseous phase, polar molecules may be oriented without hindrance by an external field and experiment shows that this is also so in dilute non-polar solutions. In a polar liquid, however, each molecule is closely surrounded by neighbouring dipoles which make rotation impossible in an external field. It is therefore necessary to consider the inner field due to the polar molecules of the liquid; the direction and size of this field will be dependent on the momentary orientation and arrangement of the neighbouring molecules. As a result, the total polarization of the liquid, *i.e.* $(\epsilon - 1)M/(\epsilon + 2)d$, may be less than in the gaseous phase. Thus for example in the case of CH_3I, polarization in the gas phase is 77 cc and in the liquid 42 cc; in CH_3COCH_3 the figures are respectively 176 and 63 cc and in $C_2H_5OCH_3$ 62 and 52 cc. In the gas phase the orientation polarization will be

$$\frac{4}{3}\pi N \frac{\mu^2}{3kT}$$

and in a pure polar liquid the effective orientation polarization will be

$$P_{\text{eff}} = \frac{\epsilon_{\text{liquid}} - 1}{\epsilon_{\text{liquid}} + 2} \cdot \frac{M}{d} - (P_E + P_A) \qquad \ldots.(12.7)$$

where ϵ_{liquid} is the dielectric constant of the pure liquid and P_E and P_A are the electron and atom polarizations. A number of attempts (DEBYE[4], ONSAGER[5], PIEKARA[6] and KIRKWOOD[7]) have been made to obtain a relation between the effective and ideal (*i.e.* gas) orientation polarization and SYRKIN[8] has proposed the following relationship:

$$\frac{4}{3}\pi N \frac{\mu^2}{3kT} = \frac{\dfrac{(\epsilon_{\text{liquid}}-1)}{(\epsilon_{\text{liquid}}+2)} \cdot \dfrac{M}{d} - (P_E + P_A)}{1 - \left(\dfrac{\epsilon_{\text{liquid}}-1}{\epsilon_{\text{liquid}}+2}\right)^2} \qquad \ldots.(12.8)$$

or

$$P_{\text{ideal}} = \frac{P_{\text{eff}}}{1 - \left(\dfrac{\epsilon_{\text{liquid}}-1}{\epsilon_{\text{liquid}}+2}\right)^2} \qquad \ldots.(12.9)$$

Table CXXVIII. Dipole Moments Calculated from Dielectric Constants of Pure Liquids

Molecule	*Density*	*Dielectric constant of liquid D*	*Refractivity cc*	*Dipole moment D*	
				Calculated from equation 12·8	*Measured in non-polar solvent*
CH_3I	2·286	7·1	19·26	1·40	1·37
C_2H_5Br	1·43	9·5	19·11	1·99	2·01
CH_3COCl	1·1051	15·9	16·31	2·59	2·68
$HCOOC_2H_5$	0·92	8·27	17·71	1·94	1·92
CH_3COOCH_3	0·9338	7·03	18·1	1·74	1·78
C_2H_5CN	0·783	27·7	15·88	3·45	3·87
$C_6H_5NO_2$	1·207	34·09	32·72	4·28	3·96
$C_6H_5CH_3$	0·8659	2·39	30·81	0·4	0·4
$C_6H_5OCH_3$	0·994	4·41	33·0	1·29	1·23
C_9H_7N	1·093	9·0	39·5	2·18	2·19
α-$C_{10}H_9Br$	1·4868	5·17	51·32	1·47	1·52

By means of equation 12.8 it is possible to obtain the dipole moment from measurements of the density, refractive index and dielectric constant of the pure liquid. In *Table CXXVIII* the application of this formula is illustrated by comparing the values of dipole moments employing equation 12.8 and the experimental values determined in non-polar solvents. The agreement is good in most cases, but with strongly associated molecules containing intermolecular hydrogen bonds, formula 12.8 is not applicable since it gives values which are too high (*e.g.* 3 D instead of 1·84 D for water).

MOLECULAR COMPOUNDS INVOLVING VAN DER WAAL'S FORCES

The action of van der Waal's forces between molecules brings about the formation of a number of molecular compounds from molecules in saturated valency states. For example, the inert gases form molecular compounds with water (hexahydrates), phenol and cresol[9], the association being due to dipole-induced dipole forces and to dispersion forces. More stable molecular compounds are formed, however, between organic nitro compounds and aromatic hydrocarbons. The nitro group is strongly polar and the double bonds of aromatic hydrocarbons possess a high polarizability. Thus conditions are very favourable for dipole-induced dipole interaction. Dispersion forces will only play a small part as hydrocarbons do not generally form molecular compounds with each other. The structure of the association compound will be such that the nitro group is as close as possible to the polarized double bonds. This will generally result in the two molecules lying side by side and hence the dipole, which is induced into the hydrocarbon, will be in the opposite direction to the original dipole. The resulting moment of the molecular compound is therefore less than that of the original dipolar molecule. This behaviour is illustrated by the fact that the moment of nitrobenzene, 4·22 D, is reduced, when measured in naphthalene solution to 3·73 D and the molecular compound[10] of *m*–dinitrobenzene, $\mu = 3{\cdot}79$ D, with naphthalene, has a dipole moment of 3·43 D, measured in benzene solution.

The heat of formation of molecular compounds of this type depends upon the number and configuration of the nitro groups in the molecule. In the case of the dinitrobenzenes the most stable compounds are formed by the *ortho* derivative and the least stable by the *para* derivative. In order to illustrate the order of magnitude of the heats of formation of molecular compounds, the values for the compounds of trinitrobenzene with a number of unsaturated hydrocarbons are given in *Table CXXIX*. As is to be expected, the heat of formation increases with the polarizability of the hydrocarbon.

Table CXXIX. Heats of Formation of Molecular Compounds between Trinitrobenzene and Hydrocarbons

Hydrocarbon	*Heat of formation kcals*	*Hydrocarbon*	*Heat of formation kcals*
Benzene	0·6	*Phenylbutadiene*	2·1
Naphthalene	3·4	*Diphenylbutadiene*	2·9
Phenanthrene	4·0	*Diphenylhexatriene*	2·4
Anthracene	4·4 ; 3·6	*Phenylacetylene*	0·6
Styrene	1·8	*Diphenylacetylene*	2·07

MOLECULAR COMPOUNDS INVOLVING CHEMICAL BONDS

In addition to the molecular compounds which we have so far discussed and in which the dipole moment of one of the molecules is the primary factor in causing the association, intermolecular compounds exist in which, in addition to the purely physical van der Waal's forces, chemical forces play a part by the formation of additional valency bonds. The inorganic halogen derivatives form two distinct classes of compounds with organic substances depending upon whether they form an ionic or molecular crystal lattice. In the former type, the organic molecules surround the central ion, by which they are polarized, whilst the halogen ions are displaced from their original positions, the interionic distance being increased. This type of compound is similar to those discussed in the previous section, the only difference being that the forces of attraction involved are ion-induced dipole forces in place of dipole-induced dipole forces. With the halogen compounds of boron, aluminium and tin, which form molecular and not ionic crystal lattices, association compounds involving chemical bonds are formed. Several of these compounds have been extensively studied. According to the data of LAUBENGAYER and FINLAY[11] the heat of formation of gaseous $BF_3 \cdot (CH_3)_2O$ from gaseous BF_3 and $(CH_3)_2O$ is 13·9 kcals, and VAN DER MEULEN and HELLER[12] have shown that the heat of formation of $BF_3 \cdot C_5H_5N$ is 51 kcals. Electron diffraction data[13] show that in $BF_3 \cdot (CH_3)_2O$, the B—O distance is 1·52 Å and the configuration of the dimethyl ether molecule remains unchanged. The B—F distance however is increased from 1·30 Å in BF_3 to 1·41 Å. Thus we may conclude that the actual energy of the B—O bond is greater than 13·9 kcals, since the deformation of the molecule and the lengthening of the B—F bond distance will be endothermic processes.

Table CXXX. Dipole Moments of Molecular Compounds and their Organic Components

Molecular Compound	*Dipole Moment D*		*Molecular Compound*	*Dipole Moment D*	
	Molecular Compound	*Organic Molecule*		*Molecular Compound*	*Organic Molecule*
$BeCl_2 \cdot 2(C_2H_5)_2O$	6·84	1·18	$AlCl_3 \cdot p\text{-}ClC_6H_4NO_2$	7·79	2·78
$BeBr_2 \cdot 2(C_2H_5)_2O$	7·57	1·18	$AlCl_3 \cdot o\text{-}NO_2C_6H_4CH_3$	8·92	3·7
			$AlCl_3 \cdot p\text{-}NO_2C_6H_4CH_3$	9·68	4·4
$BF_3 \cdot (CH_3)_2O$	4·35	1·29	$AlBr_3 \cdot (C_2H_5)_2O$	6·43	1·18
$BF_3 \cdot C_2H_5OCH_3$	5·07	—	$AlBr_3 \cdot C_6H_5NO_2$	9·13	4·00
$BF_3 \cdot (C_2H_5)_2O$	4·92	1·18	$AlBr_3 \cdot H_2S$	5·14	0·93
$BCl_3 \cdot (C_2H_5)_2O$	5·98	1·18			
$BCl_3 \cdot CH_3CN$	7·65	3·94	$TiCl_4 \cdot C_2H_5CN$	6·05	4·05
$BCl_3 \cdot C_2H_5CN$	7·75	4·05	$TiCl_4 \cdot C_6H_5CN$	6·16 ; 7·06	4·39
$AlCl_3 \cdot (C_2H_5)_2O$	6·54	1·18			
$AlCl_3 \cdot C_2H_5NH_2$	6·86	1·37	$SnCl_4 \cdot (C_2H_5)_2O$	3·60	1·18
$AlCl_3 \cdot C_6H_5NO_2$	9·05	4·00	$SnCl_4 \cdot 2(CH_3)_2CO$	7·7	2·95
$AlCl_3 \cdot C_6H_5OCH_3$	6·54	1·35	$SnCl_4 \cdot 2C_6H_5COCH_3$	8·7	2·96
$AlCl_3 \cdot (C_6H_5)_2CO$	8·72	3·13	$SnCl_4 \cdot 2C_6H_5CHO$	7·5 ; 8·1	3·00
$AlCl_3 \cdot o\text{-}NO_2C_6H_4Cl$	9·48	4·59	$SnCl_4 \cdot C_6H_5CN$	6·55	4·39

The dipole moments of various non-ionic molecular compounds are given in *Table CXXX* and in each case the moment of the compound is greater than that of the organic molecule from which it is formed. Furthermore, the moment is also greater than that obtained for the inorganic compound when dissolved in an organic solvent: AlI_3 and $AlCl_3$ in benzene have moments of 2·5 D and 5 D respectively[14] and for BCl_3 and $AlCl_3$ in dioxane the values 4·86 D and 2·02 D have been obtained[15]. Although dipole-dipole and dispersion forces will undoubtedly play some part in the formation of such compounds, in view of the magnitude of the bond energies and of the dipole moments they cannot be the only bonding forces and must be regarded as supplementary to the valency forces. The boron atom may acquire an electron and thus become negatively charged and tetravalent, thereby being able to form four homopolar bonds. If in the associating organic molecule there exists an atom such as oxygen or nitrogen, which can increase its valency by the loss of an electron, the formation of a chemical bond is possible. The compound between BF_3 and $(CH_3)_2O$ evidently involves a bond between a tetravalent, positive boron atom and a trivalent, negative oxygen atom and the structure *I* will contribute to the resonance of the molecule.

$$\begin{array}{ccccc} F & & & & CH_3 \\ & \diagdown & & \diagup & \\ F\text{—} & B^- & \text{—} & O^+ & \\ & \diagup & & \diagdown & \\ F & & & & CH_3 \end{array}$$

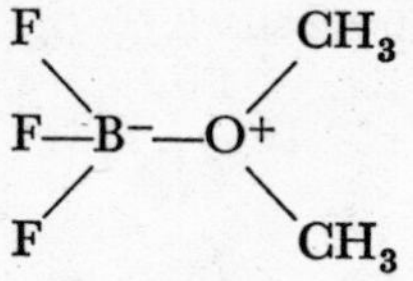

I

This structure is strongly polar and evidently explains the large dipole moment of the compound. It has been suggested that the large dipole moments of this type of compound may be due to the deformation of the BF_3 molecule to a pyramid structure. Although this configuration of the bonds does occur in the B^+ ion in which the four bonds are tetrahedral, the value of the moment could not be due to the BF bond without assuming the completely ionic structure $B^{3+}3F^-$, which is improbable. From the experimental value for the dipole moment of $BF_3 \cdot (CH_3)_2O$, *viz* 4·35 D, it is possible to calculate by vector addition the contribution of the B—O bond to the moment of the molecule. The value obtained is 2·1 D, which is much lower than the calculated value for the moment of a unit positive and a unit negative charge separated by a distance of 1·52 Å, *viz* 7·4 D. There must therefore be a superposition of structure *I* with the van der Waal's structure *II*,

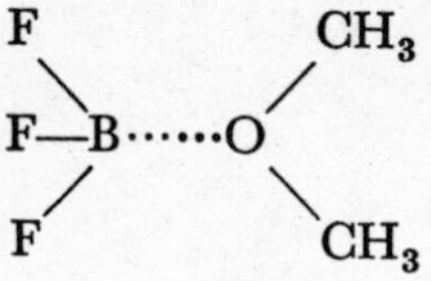

$$\begin{array}{ccccc} F & & & & CH_3 \\ & \diagdown & & \diagup & \\ F\text{—} & B & \cdots\cdots & O & \\ & \diagup & & \diagdown & \\ F & & & & CH_3 \end{array}$$

II

thus giving to the molecule the observed stability and dipole moment. It is very probable that in addition to the structure *I* the ionic structure *III* may contribute to the resonance of the molecule.

$$\begin{array}{ccccc} F^- & & & & CH_3 \\ & & & \diagup & \\ F\text{——} & B & \text{——} & O^+ & \\ & \diagup & & \diagdown & \\ F & & & & CH_3 \end{array}$$

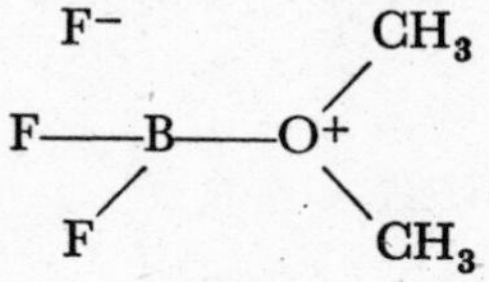

(*three structures*)

III

Such structures will certainly be present in the molecular compounds of titanium and tin *e.g.*

```
Cl⁻       Cl      CH3
           /      /
     Sn———O+                 (four structures)
    /    \      \
  Cl      Cl      CH3
```

and their existence is substantiated by the fact that on substituting a chlorine atom by methyl radical, as in $SnCl_3(CH_3)$ or $B(CH_3)_3$, the tendency to form molecular compounds decreases.

Molecular compounds of BF_3 with $(C_2H_5)_2O$ and (*iso*–$C_3H_7)_2O$ are somewhat less stable than those formed with $(CH_3)_2O$. This has been explained on the basis of steric hindrance caused by the CH_3 groups:[16]

```
                BF3
   H       H    :   H       H
    \     /     :    \     /
      C         O      C
    /   \     /   \  /   \
   H     CH2       CH2     H
```

Tetrahydrofuran, on the other hand, gives a more stable compound :

```
            CH2—CH2
           /      |
F3B······O        |
           \      |
            CH2—CH2
```

The compound between aluminium chloride and ammonia, $AlCl_3 \cdot NH_3$, is remarkably stable and may be distilled without decomposition at 400° C. The energy of the Al—N bond in $AlCl_3 \cdot NH_3$, $AlBr_3 \cdot NH_3$ and $AlI_3 \cdot NH_3$ have been found to be 40, 38 and 30 kcals respectively[17]. Evidently resonance exists between the following valence bond structures

```
Cl              H               Cl              H+
   \           /                   \
Cl—Al+—N⁻—H                     Cl—Al⁻—N—H
   /       \                       /      \
Cl          H                   Cl          H
   one structure                    three structures

Cl⁻         H+                  Cl⁻             H
                                               /
Cl—Al—N—H                       Cl—Al—N+—H
   /     \                         /      \
Cl        H                     Cl          H
   nine structures                  three structures
```

Analogous structures will contribute to the resonance of $AlCl_3 \cdot H_2S$, $PH_3 \cdot CuHal$ and $PH_3 \cdot AlHal_3$. In the complexes formed between aluminium chloride and unsaturated hydrocarbons, valence bond structures are possible in which the aluminium becomes negatively charged with respect to a carbon atom, *i.e.*

```
Cl
   \
Cl—Al⁻—CH2—+CH2
   /
Cl
```

which will resonate with both the alternative ionic structures :

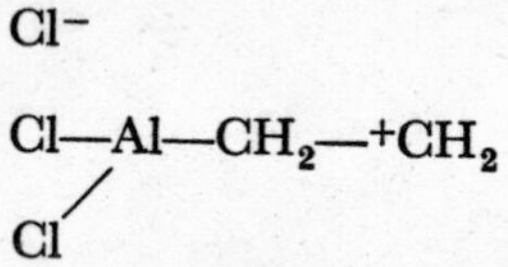

$$\begin{array}{l} Cl^- \\ Cl—Al—CH_2—{}^+CH_2 \\ \quad / \\ Cl \end{array}$$

three structures

and that involving van der Waal's forces :

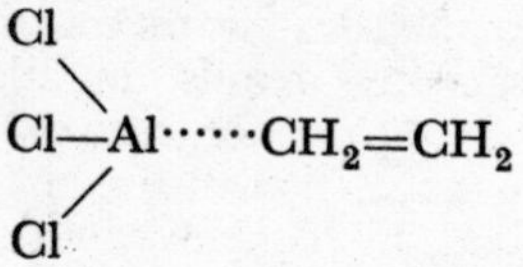

$$\begin{array}{l} Cl \\ \quad \backslash \\ Cl—Al\cdots\cdots CH_2{=}CH_2 \\ \quad / \\ Cl \end{array}$$

THE HYDROGEN BOND

The term hydrogen bond has been introduced to cover a type of molecular interaction of considerable significance, the qualitative effects of which have been extensively observed. The interaction generally occurs between a hydrogen atom, chemically linked to one molecule and an O, S, N, Cl or F atom in a different or in the same molecule. The latter case, where the bonding is intramolecular, will be discussed in the next section and we shall confine ourselves here to intermolecular bonding, which may arise in the solid, liquid or gaseous states to produce molecular association. Some values of the bond distance of hydrogen bonds are given in *Table CXXXI*.

Most of the characteristic properties of the hydrogen bond may be illustrated by a consideration of the dimer of formic acid which has been studied by electron diffraction methods[18]. The dimeric form, which is dissociated only to the extent of 7 per cent in the gaseous phase at 3° C has the following structure

Table CXXXI. Lengths of Some Hydrogen Bonds

Hydrogen Bond	*Bond length Å*	*Substance*
O—H····O	2·76	*Ice*
	2·70	$C(CH_2OH)_4$
	2·70	o–$C_6H_4(OH)_2$
	2·55 ± 0·15	$(COOH)_2$
	2·71 ± 0·15	
	2·76	$(CF_3COOH)_2$
	2·73	$(HCOOH)_2$
	2·76	$(CH_3COOH)_2$
	2·55	$NaHCO_3$
	2·78	HIO_3
	2·63	$CO(NH_2)_2{\cdot}H_2O_2$
F—H····F	2·25 ± 0·2	KHF_2
	2·51 ± 0·2	$NaHF_2$
N—H····N	2·96	NH_4N_3
	2·65	*Phthalocyanine*
N—H····O	2·98 ; 3·03	$CO(NH_2)_2$
	2·76 ; 2·88	NH_2CH_2COOH
	2·85	*Diketopiperazine*
N—H····F	2·63	NH_4F
	2·76	NH_4HF_2
O—D····O	2·76	$CH_3(COOD)_2$

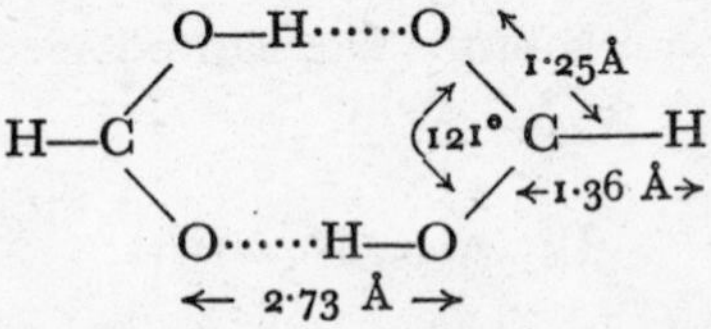

```
        O—H······O  ↖
       /          \   1·25Å
   H—C          (121° C——H
       \          /←1·36 Å→
        O······H—O
      ← 2·73 Å →
```

The hydrogen of the hydroxyl group is located between the oxygen atom to which it was originally joined by a covalent bond, and the carbonyl oxygen of the second molecule. The atom of hydrogen has only one unpaired electron and consequently can participate in only one covalent bond. Therefore we shall have to consider bonding mechanisms other than the homopolar bond to account for the formation of the hydrogen bond.

In the hydroxyl and carbonyl bonds, in addition to the homopolar structures —O—H and > C=O, the ionic states —O⁻H⁺ and > C⁺—O⁻ contribute to the bond resonance. When the bonds are located adjacently, as in the dimer of formic acid, the contributions of the ionic structures will be increased owing to the mutual induction of the two groups. The additional electrostatic attraction energy, between the positively charged hydrogen atom and the negatively charged oxygen atom of the carbonyl group produced thereby, will increase the stability of the molecule. The dimer may therefore be regarded as a resonance hybrid of the structures *I* to *V* of which *I* and *II* are ionic, *III* and *IV* homopolar and *V* a charged homopolar structure :

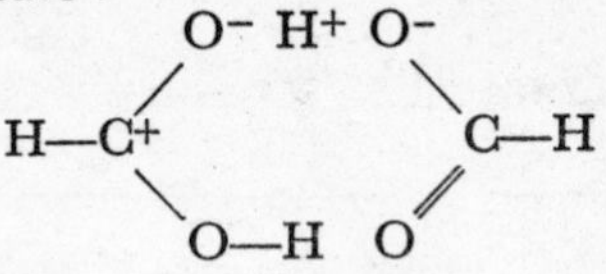

```
       O⁻ H⁺ O⁻                         O  H—O
      /        \                       //      \
  H—C⁺          C—H                H—C          C⁺—H
      \        //                      \       /
       O—H  O                           O⁻ H⁺ O⁻
         I                                 II

       O  H—O                           O—H  O
      //      \                        /      \\
  H—C          C—H                 H—C          C—H
      \       //                       \\      /
       O—H  O                           O  H—O
        III                                IV

                 O⁺—H  O⁻
                //       \
            H—C           C—H
                \        //
                 O⁻  H—O⁺
                     V
```

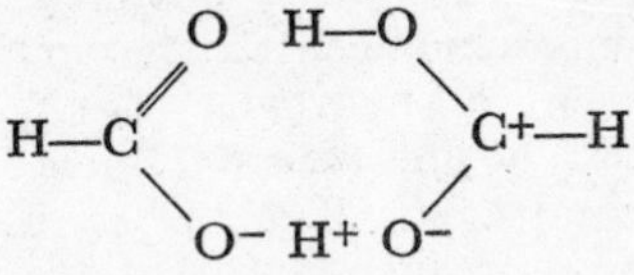

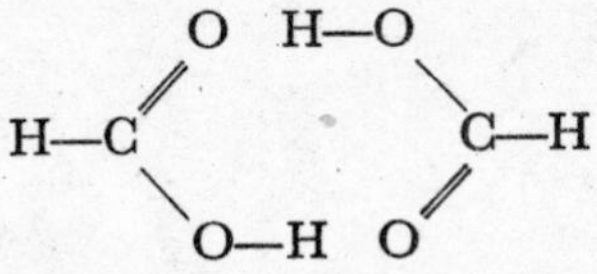

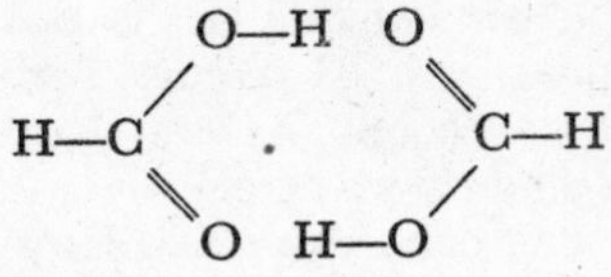

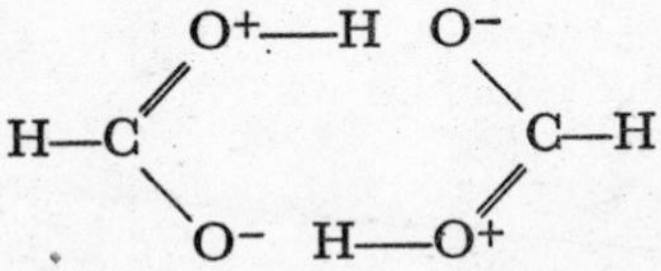

The resonance in the carboxyl group between the homopolar and charged structures *VI* and *VII* will assist in the formation of the hydrogen

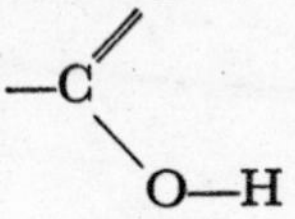

```
        O                          O⁻
       //                         /
     —C                         —C
       \                          \\
        O—H                        O⁺—H
      VI                           VII
```

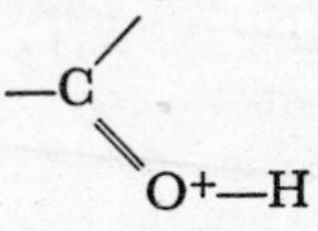

bond, as it increases the negative charge on the carbonyl oxygen atom and also increases the ionic character of the O—H bond since, in structure *VII*, the positive charge on the oxygen atom of the hydroxyl group will, most probably, be transferred to the hydrogen atom.

The nature of the forces responsible for the hydrogen bond are still not completely understood. However, it is now considered[19] that the forces are largely van der Waal's forces on which valency forces are superimposed, thereby strengthening the bond. The main evidence on which this conclusion is based is the fact that the X—H bond distance is not appreciably increased when the hydrogen atom takes part in a hydrogen bond. Thus in the case of the dimer of formic acid, DAVIES and SUTHERLAND[20] have found that the O—H bond distance is 1·04 Å, compared with the value of 0·98 Å in the monomer, and since the O—H……O distance is 2·73 Å it follows that the H……O bond distance is 1·69 Å, which is a much greater value than the covalent bond distance. Thus we see that hydrogen forms an almost normal homopolar bond with one oxygen atom and that the bond to the other oxygen atom is due very largely to van der Waal's forces. The main contributions to the molecular resonance in formic acid will thus be from structures *I*, *II* and *III*.

The suggestion which has sometimes been put forward, that the hydrogen atom is not localized but is spread out in the form of a proton cloud, in a similar manner to the single electron in the hydrogen molecule ion, appears most improbable in view of the much greater mass of the proton and the fact that similar bonds occur in deuterium compounds.

The heats of dimerization of formic, acetic and benzoic acids have been determined and are 14·1, 16·4 and 8·7 kcals respectively. Since in each case two hydrogen bonds are formed, we obtain the values 7·05, 8·2 and 4·35 kcals for the energy of a hydrogen bond. The magnitude of these values is much lower than for a homopolar bond and these figures therefore confirm that the bond is produced largely by forces of the van der Waal's type.

As will be clear from an examination of the structures *I*, *II* and *V* for formic acid on page 274, the dipole moment is reduced considerably on dimer formation, since the moments of the two molecules will compensate each other.

The frequency of the valency vibration of the O—H bond in molecules containing this group, lies in the neighbourhood of 3,500 cm^{-1} and the first overtone at 7,000 cm^{-1}. The N—H bond gives a similar absorption bond at 6,850 cm^{-1}. In compounds, however, where the O—H or the N—H groups are involved in strong hydrogen bond formation it is found that radiation is not absorbed at these characteristic frequencies and instead of a sharp peak, the spectra of these substances show only a broad diffuse band in these regions. This effect has now been observed for so many substances giving hydrogen bonds, that it may be regarded as a criterion of hydrogen bond formation.

In gaseous hydrogen fluoride, long chain or cyclic polymeric molecules, $(HF)_n$ are formed, the energy of the intermolecular bond being between 4 and 7 kcals. The formation of these polymers is due to hydrogen bond formation between fluorine atoms. In molecular hydrogen fluoride, in addition to the homopolar structure H—F there is a considerable contribution of the ionic form H^+F^- and if the two fluorine atoms are located side by side this contribution is increased owing to the mutual induction produced by the configuration $H^+F^-H^+F^-$. Further stability may be given to the structure if a covalent bond occurs between the atoms of hydrogen and fluorine of different molecules. The polymer may thus be represented as a resonance hybrid of the structures

H—F H—F	$H^+F^-H^+F^-$	H F—H F
I	*II*	*III*

The distance between two atoms of fluorine is 2·26 Å and in the isolated hydrogen fluoride molecule the HF bond distance is 0·92 Å, thus making the H ··· F bond approximately 1·34 Å in length. In the hydrogen bond it is characteristic that the hydrogen atom is bound to not more than two atoms, although structures in which the hydrogen is bound to more than two atoms are not theoretically impossible. Pauling considers that this is due mainly to steric effects, so that in hydrogen fluoride, for example, one proton is surrounded by two large negative ions which prevent a third negative ion approaching sufficiently close to produce bonding.

The tendency for atoms to take part in hydrogen bond formation decreases in the order F, O, N, Cl and S. This sequence follows the decrease in electronegativity of the atoms and hence of the ionic character of the X—H bond. There is some indication that bromine and iodine take part in hydrogen bond formation, but as is to be expected these are very weak in character.

In Chapter 6 it was shown that in the compound $(CH_3)_2O \cdot HCl$, the structure

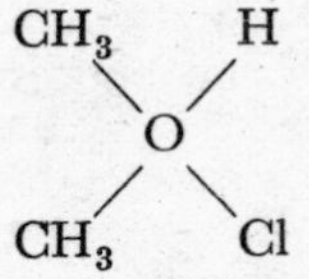

```
CH3     H
   \   /
     O
   /   \
CH3     Cl
```

involving tetravalent oxygen was clearly incorrect. A recent examination[21] of the equilibrium between $(CH_3)_2O$ and HCl between 260° and 303° K shows that the heat of reaction is 6·7 kcals and the energy of activation very small. Evidently this compound is brought about by the formation

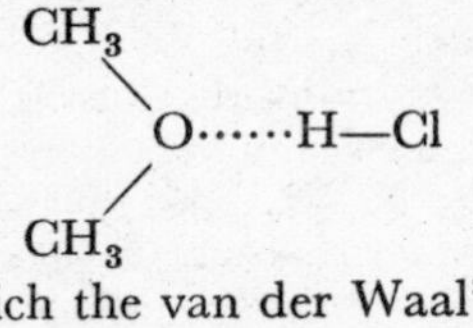

```
CH3
   \
    O······H—Cl
   /
CH3
```

of a hydrogen bond in which the van der Waal's forces are augmented by the superposition of the oxonium structure :

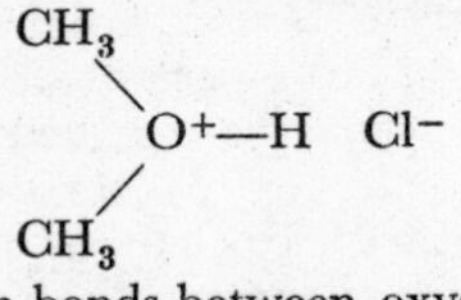

```
CH3
   \
    O+—H  Cl−
   /
CH3
```

The energies of hydrogen bonds between oxygen and nitrogen are given in *Table CXXXII*. There is some evidence for the existence of hydrogen bonds involving the C—H group. Although such bonds will be very weak, they may be responsible for the formation of molecular compounds between chloroform and acetone, $(CH_3)_2CO \cdots HCCl_3$ and ether, $(CH_3)_2O \cdots HCCl_3$.

Association in solution— It has been known for a long time that certain substances in solution associate to form dimers or higher polymers, the first systematic work on this subject being that of BECKMANN and VON AUWERS[22]. More recently a considerable amount of data has been accumulated using the cryoscopic method which has shown that the most important cause of molecular association between organic compounds in solution is intermolecular hydrogen bonding[23]. The important groupings are again found to be those between H and O, N and S. Thus ethyl alcohol is associated in solution, whereas diethyl ether is not.

Table CXXXII. Heats of Formation of Molecular Compounds Containing Hydrogen Bonds

Molecular Compound	*Heat of formation kcals*
Pyridine–o–chlorophenol	6·8
Quinoline–o–chlorophenol	6·8
Toluidine–o–chlorophenol	3·5
Toluidine–p–chlorophenol	4·2

The nature of the solvent determines to a large extent whether a solute is associated in solution or not and this behaviour is closely related to the solubility of the solute. Compounds possessing an intermolecular hydrogen bonded structure will preserve that structure only in aprotic solvents such as benzene and the solubility is generally less than with similar compounds or isomers in which the hydrogen bonded structure is lacking. In polar solvents, which can take part in hydrogen bond formation, however, the intermolecular hydrogen bond may be destroyed in favour of a hydrogen bonded structure between the solute and the solvent, with the result that the solubility is increased. For example, benzoic acid and phenol dissolve in benzene, chloroform, carbon tetrachloride and other aprotic solvents to form an associated complex, whereas in solvents of the type $CH_3C_6H_4X$, the association decreases in the series

$X = CH_3$, Cl, Br, I, NO_2, COOR, CN, CHO, NH_2, COOH, OH

and in acetone, ethyl ether, ethyl alcohol, acetic acid and ethyl acetate solution, no association occurs owing to the preferential formation of hydrogen bonds between solute and solvent molecules, *e.g.*

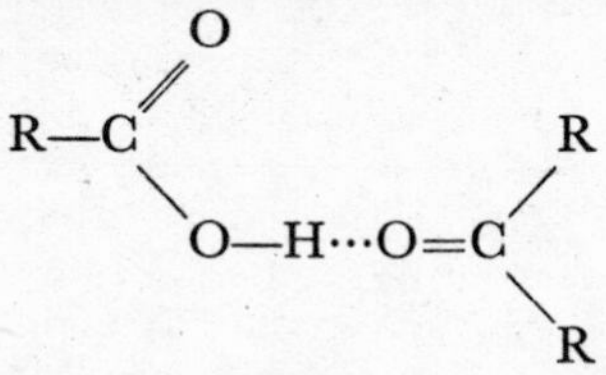

```
        O
       //
  R—C                R
       \            /
        O—H···O=C
                    \
                     R
```

This behaviour may also be illustrated by the case of formanilide, C_6H_5NHCOH, which dissolves in toluene to form polymers produced by intermolecular hydrogen bonding ; the addition of pyridine considerably reduces the degree of polymerization owing to the formation of hydrogen bonds between the formanilide and pyridine :

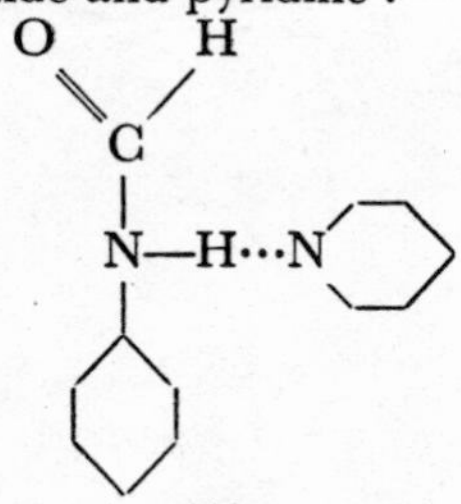

```
  O     H
   \\  /
     C
     |
     N—H···N(pyridine ring)
     |
   (benzene ring)
```

In addition to solubility and cryoscopic studies, the association of solute molecules may be investigated by the variation of the dielectric constant with concentration. If the solution is non-polar, the value of the dipole moment calculated from the value of the dielectric constant at infinite dilution, obtained by extrapolation, may be close to the value obtained in the gaseous phase. If this be so, there are no anomalous solvent effects, but cases exist where this is not so and such behaviour may be explained by two theories. The first assumes that association of solute molecules persists at low concentrations and may be illustrated with reference to the curious variation of polarization of ethyl alcohol in hexane solution. As the concentration is increased, the polarization falls, passes through a minimum, rises to a maximum value and then falls to the value for the polarization of pure ethyl alcohol. In dilute solution the molecules are evidently associated in such a way that the dipole moment is decreased, this may occur through the formation of quadrupoles by means of hydrogen bonds, *viz*

```
R—O····H
  |    |
  H····O—R
```

On increasing the concentration, larger complexes will be formed and this can only occur by the formation of linear polymers of the type :

```
R      R      R
|      |      |
O—H···O—H···O—H
```

in which the O—H bond moment is increased through mutual induction. At high temperatures, the formation of such complexes will be opposed by thermal agitation and the variation of polarization with concentration is very slight.

In the second theory the formation of intermolecular complexes is not assumed and the variation of the dipole moment with concentration is considered to be caused by the limited orientation of the dipole molecules in the external field, due to the field of the surrounding polar molecules.

The dioxan effect — For the measurement of dipole moments in solution it is usual, for reasons which have been discussed above, to use non-polar solvents. However, this is not always practicable since, as we have already pointed out, solubility is to a large extent dependent on solute-solvent interaction and in inert solvents such interaction is considerably reduced and the solubility thereby restricted. For this reason dioxan,

```
   CH2—CH2
  /       \
O           O
  \       /
   CH2—CH2
```

has been used as a solvent for the measurement of dipole moments. The

Table CXXXIII. Dipole Moments of Organic Compounds in Benzene and Dioxan Solution

Molecule	*Dipole Moment D*	
	In benzene	*In dioxan*
Nitrobenzene	4·01	4·03
Trimethylamine oxide	5·04	5·02
Aniline	1·54	1·77
p–Nitraniline	6·17	6·81
β–Naphthylamine	1·77	2·10
Fluorene	0·53	0·65
Triphenylmethane	0·20	0·46
Pyrrole	2·2	3·2
4–Methylglyoxaline	4·8	6·2
Pyrazole	1·7	2·2
α–oxypyridine	1·46	3·1

bond moments of the two ether linkages are largely compensated and it has only a small dipole moment : 0·4 D. It is to be expected that the oxygen atoms will form hydrogen bonds with X—H groups in the solute molecule and this will lead to an increase in the ionic character of the X—H bond and hence to an increase in the dipole moment of the solute molecule. In *Table CXXXIII* the dipole moments measured in benzene and dioxan solution are given for a number of substances. In the case of nitrobenzene and trimethylamine oxide, the moment in the two solvents is practically the same since the only bonds of the X—H type, are the C—H bonds, which are not sufficiently polar to take part in hydrogen bond formation. In the case of aniline, the dipole moment in dioxan solution is greater by 0·23 D than in benzene solution on account of the structures :

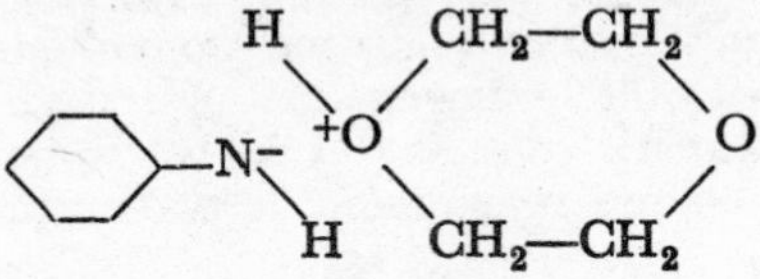

two structures

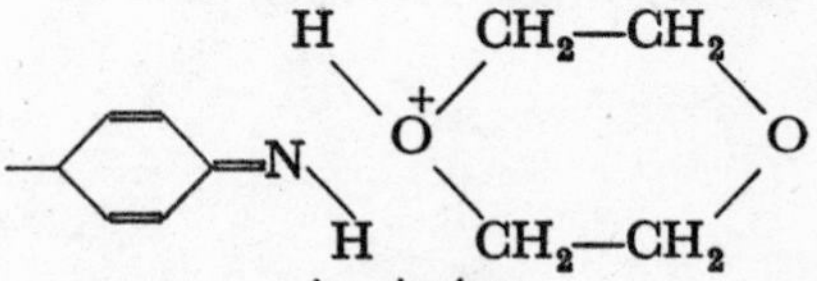

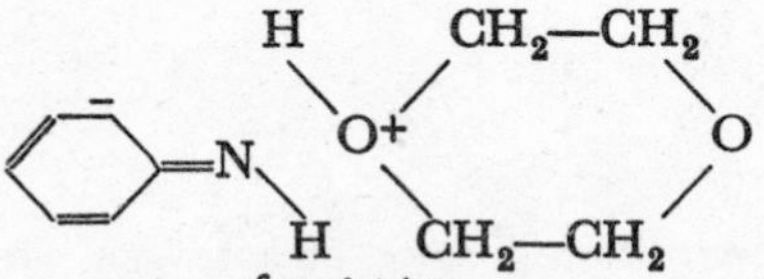

two structures

four structures

In *p*–nitraniline the effect is still greater owing to the additional possible structure :

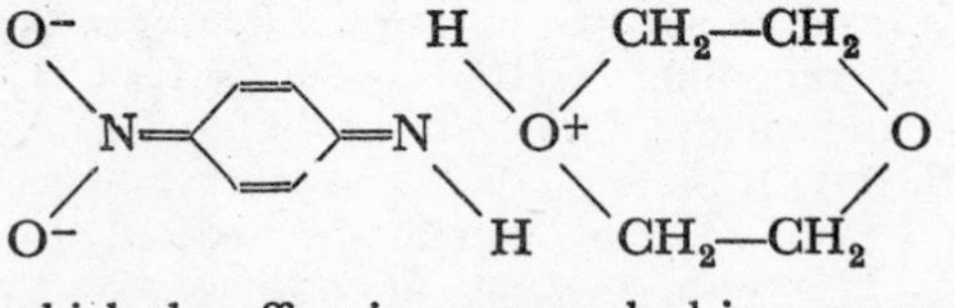

An example in which the effect is most marked is *α*–oxypyridine for which the moment in dioxan is greater than that in benzene by 1·6 D. This will be due to the large contribution to the resonance of the molecule from the structures :

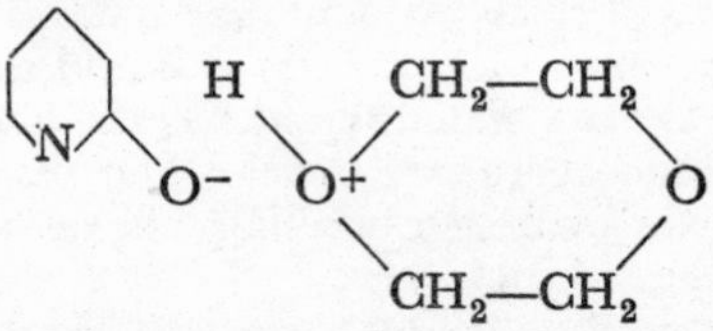

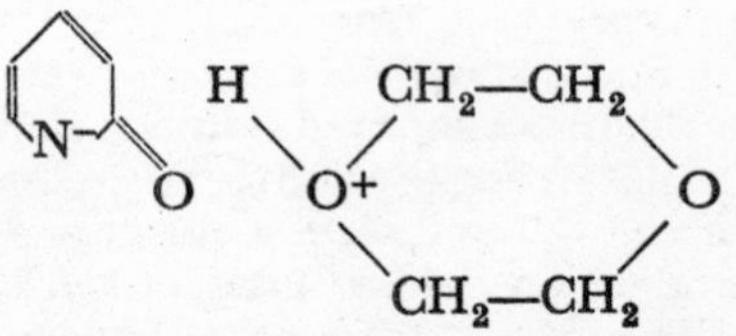

Effect of hydrogen bonds on the properties of liquids— The effect of hydrogen bonded structures is to produce certain anomalies in the physical properties of liquids. Thus, for example, in the series H_2Te, H_2Se, H_2S, the boiling points and the heats of evaporation are lowered and it might therefore be expected that the next member of the series H_2O would boil at a lower temperature than H_2S, whereas in fact it boils at a temperature 160° higher. The same behaviour is noticed in the hydrides of the fifth group elements, where NH_3 boils at a higher temperature than PH_3 and in the seventh group elements where the boiling point of HCl (— 85° C) is only slightly less than that of HBr (— 69° C) and HF boils at 19° C. Normal behaviour is only found to occur in the fourth group where the boiling point increases in the series CH_4, SiH_4, GeH_4. The cause of this behaviour is that the molecules HF, H_2O, NH_3 and HCl form association complexes by means of hydrogen bonds. In the isoelectronic series CH_4, NH_3, H_2O and HF, methane, in which there is no association, has the lowest boiling point (— 112° C); ammonia has a higher boiling point (— 33° C) since a nitrogen atom of one molecule forms a weak hydrogen bond with the hydrogen atom of a neighbouring molecule. The boiling point of water is considerably higher owing to the formation of two hydrogen bonds by one oxygen atom to two neighbouring water molecules, thus:

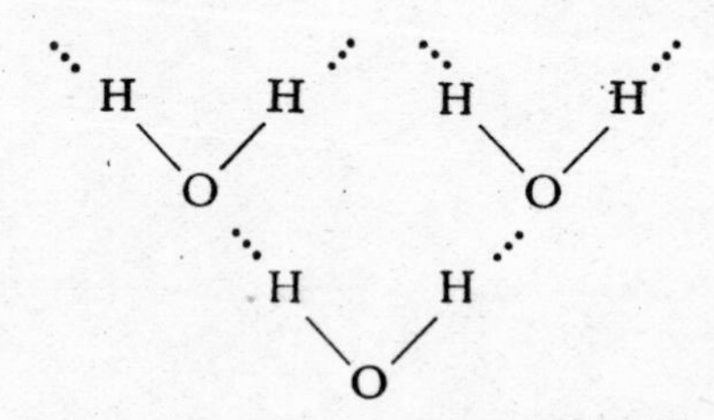

These hydrogen bonds are more stable than those formed by nitrogen. In HF, as we have seen, each atom of fluorine gives only one stable hydrogen bond and as a result the boiling point is lower than that of water. Thus it is essential, when considering the effect of hydrogen bonds, to take into account both the stability and the number of hydrogen bonds formed.

In the series of compounds CH_3CH_3, CH_3NH_2, CH_3OH and CH_3F, ethane (— 88° C) and methyl fluoride (— 78° C), where hydrogen bonding is absent, have the lowest boiling points and methyl alcohol has the highest boiling point (+ 65° C). This behaviour was originally considered in terms of an anomalous Trouton's constant, λ/T, where λ is the latent heat of evaporation per gm mol and T is the boiling point, which in the associated liquids is always greater than the normal value given by Trouton's law: $\lambda/T = 21$ cals/degree/gm mol. This law, stated in another way, indicates that the entropy change on evaporation is a constant. The fact that on transformation from the gaseous state (ideal state, with no association) to the liquid state, the entropy change is greater in the associated liquid than in the non-associated liquid, means that the associated liquid has the lower absolute entropy and is, therefore, the more ordered state. The reason for this ordered state is now apparent since hydrogen bonding will tend to produce an ordered array of hydrogen bonded molecules.

The mutual solubility of liquids is also conditioned by the extent of intermolecular action. Although ideally the mixing of liquids is a natural process accompanied by an increase in entropy, in real systems the heat of mixing may be positive or negative, as it is dependent on three different quantities, the energies of attraction of like molecules in the two original liquids and the energy of attraction of the two unlike molecules in the mixture. The empirical rule that similar substances are mutually soluble is found to hold generally. Thus hydrocarbons dissolve other hydrocarbons. If one liquid is polar and the other is not, mixing will occur only if the polar molecule has a large non-polar section capable of dispersion interaction with the first, *e.g.* nitrobenzene and benzene. If both substances are capable of forming hydrogen bonds, *e.g.* water and the short chain alcohols, solution will occur. If the chain length of the alcohol is increased, the OH groups of the alcohol are screened by the hydrocarbon chain and the extent of hydrogen bond formation with water molecules is correspondingly decreased. In addition, there is little dispersion interaction between the water molecules and the hydrocarbon chain and hence as a result of the combination of all these effects, the solubility of the higher alcohols in water is small. Similar behaviour occurs with the ketones and the ethers. In the latter case the screening of the polar group is particularly effective even in relatively short chain compounds, such as diethyl ether

```
H     H          H     H
 \   /            \   /
   C                C
  / \      O       / \
H     C         C      H
     / \       / \
   H     H   H     H
```

When liquids of similar chemical structure and polarity are mixed, there is generally little change in volume, only small deviations from Raoult's law and very small heats of solution. This behaviour occurs on mixing methyl and ethyl alcohols, methyl and ethyl acetates *etc.* If however, the substances interact strongly, as occurs, for example with acetone and chloroform where hydrogen bonding occurs, there is generally observed a decrease in volume, a lowering of vapour pressure compared with that predicted by Raoult's law and a positive heat of solution. These results will be due to the energy of interaction of the unlike molecules being greater than the sum of the energies of interaction of the like molecules. Sometimes, on mixing a polar and a non-polar liquid the reverse effect is observed and there is an increase in volume, an increase in the vapour pressure compared with that predicted by Raoult's law and a negative heat of solution. Examples of the different kinds of behaviour are given in *Table CXXXIV*.

Table CXXXIV. Deviations from Ideal Behaviour in Liquid Mixtures

Mixture	ΔV *per cent*	Δp *per cent*	ΔH *kcals*
C_6H_6—$(C_2H_5)_2O$	− 0·6	0	0
C_6H_6—CH_2ClCH_2Cl	+ 0·34	0	+ 0·1
CH_3OH—C_2H_5OH	+ 0·05	− 0·8	− 0·09
CH_3COOCH_3—$C_2H_5COOCH_3$	+ 0.08	+ 1	+ 0·21
CS_2—CH_3OH	+ 1·3	+ 22	+ 3·1
C_6H_4—CH_3OH	—	+ 69	+ 2·4
CH_3COCH_3—CS_2	+ 1·4	+ 59	+ 5·0
CH_3COCH_3—$CHCl_3$	− 0·2	− 22	− 5·56

INTRAMOLECULAR HYDROGEN BONDS

The physical properties of a number of *ortho*-di-substituted derivatives of benzene show a marked difference from those of the corresponding *meta*– and *para*– isomers. This effect was first noticed by VON AUWERS and PFIEFFER for the nitrophenols and hydroxybenzaldehydes. *o*–Nitrophenol melts at 45° C which is much lower than the melting point of either *m*–nitrophenol (96° C) or of *p*–nitrophenol (113° C), is less soluble in water than the *m*– and *p*–isomers, does not give addition compounds with triphenyl chloromethane unlike most compounds containing an hydrcxyl group, and in solution it does not associate, in contrast to the *m*– and *p*–isomers. These properties may all be explained if an intramolecular hydrogen bond is considered to exist between one oxygen atom of the nitro group and the oxygen atom of the hydroxyl group, thus,

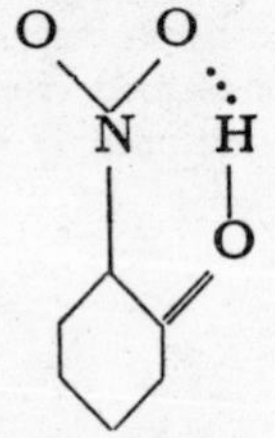

and similarly for *o*–hydroxybenzaldehyde

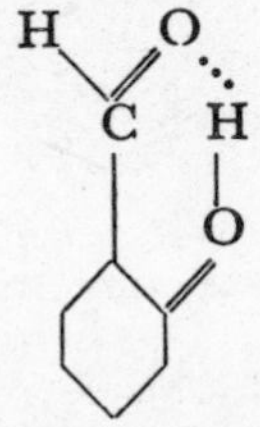

These substances have subsequently been shown not to absorb radiation in the 7,000 cm^{-1} region, which is a characteristic frequency of the valency vibration of the OH bond, thus confirming the hydrogen bonded structure.

The formation of intramolecular hydrogen bonds, sometimes referred to as chelation, occurs in a very large number of organic compounds and only a few of the more important examples may be referred to here[24]. In 2–nitroresorcinol both oxygen atoms of the nitro group take part in hydrogen bond formation with the hydroxyl groups :

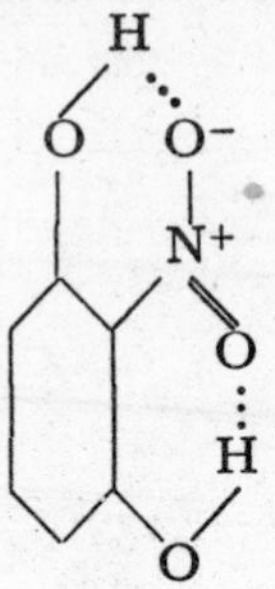

and similar ring formations are possible, whenever groups such as —N=O, —$CONH_2$, —$COCH_3$ are in the *ortho*-position to a hydroxyl group.

Salicylic acid is as strong an acid as *o*–chlorobenzoic acid, in spite of the acid weakening resonance of the hydroxyl group and is much stronger than the *o*– and *p*–isomers[25]. This increase of acid strength is due to the partial neutralization of the carboxylate ion by the proton from the hydroxyl group and the resulting increase in the stability of the ion by the contribution to the molecular resonance of the structure :

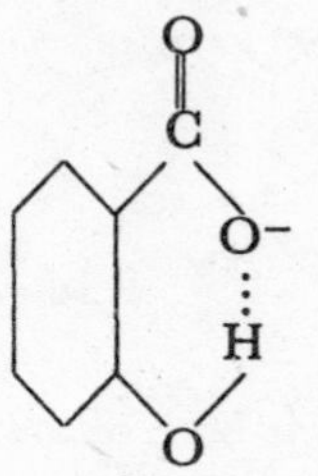

The increase in acid strength due to hydrogen bonding of this type is even more marked in 2, 6–dihydroxybenzoic acid ($K_a = 5 \times 10^{-2}$) in which the stability of the ion is increased by the contribution of the structures :

to the molecular resonance.

It is important to appreciate the difference between the hydrogen bonding occurring in salicyclic acid, which leads to an increase of acid strength and that existing in *o*–nitrophenol which leads to a decrease in the acid strength of the hydroxyl group. In the first case, the proton of the primary acid group (COOH) does not take part in the hydrogen bond and it is the ion that is stabilized, whereas in the second case, the hydrogen atom of the acid group (OH) is involved in the hydrogen bond formation and the acid strength is decreased, because of the increased stability of the acid.

When dissolved in benzene or carbon tetrachloride, salicylic acid forms a dimer and the infra red spectrum shows no absorption at the normal OH frequencies. The structure of the dimer must therefore be in which the hydrogen atoms both of the hydroxyl and the carbonyl groups take part in hydrogen bond formation.

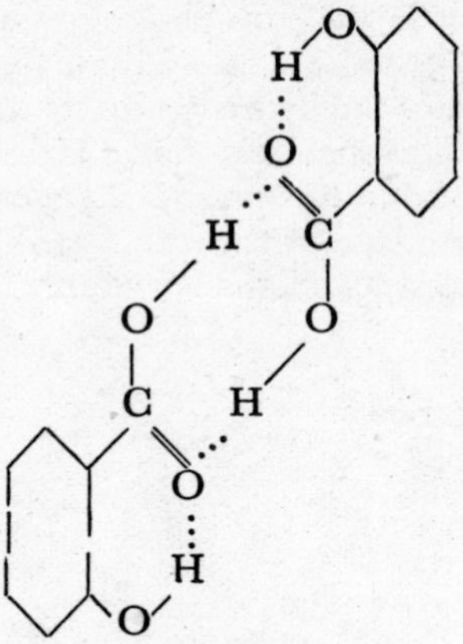

Intramolecular hydrogen bond formation may also occur in a carboxyl group :

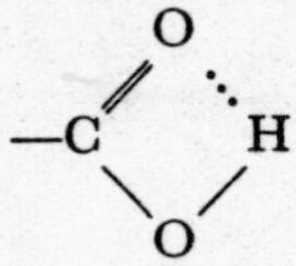

Such bonding, although sufficient to partially inhibit the free rotation of the hydroxyl group, is very weak on account of the long O .... H distance. Therefore wherever possible intermolecular hydrogen bonds are formed where the O···H bond is shorter and the resulting structure more stable.

Acetoacetic ester can exist in both the keto and enol tautomeric forms and it might be expected that the enol form would have a higher boiling point and would dissolve more readily in water, than the keto form. This is not the case, however, and the enol form has the lower boiling point and dissolves in water approximately twenty times less readily than the keto form. This behaviour is explained by the formation of a hydrogen bond in the enol form as in structure *I*,

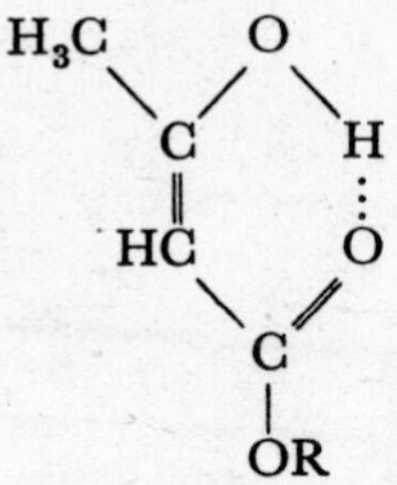

I

which is probably stabilized by resonance with structure *II*,

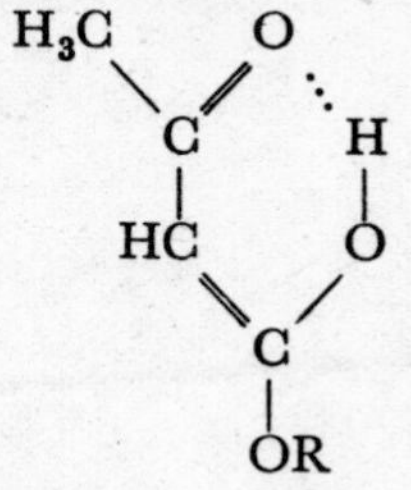

II

Similar structures occur in the case of acetylacetone (*III* and *IV*)

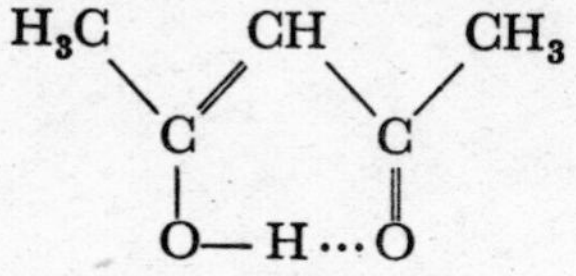

III 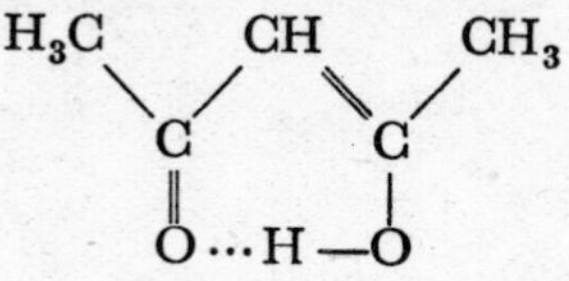 *IV*

which exhibits anomalous behaviour of the same type.

Hydrogen bonds may also occur with nitrogen-containing compounds such as the oxime formed from aniline and salicylaldehyde (*V* and *VI*)

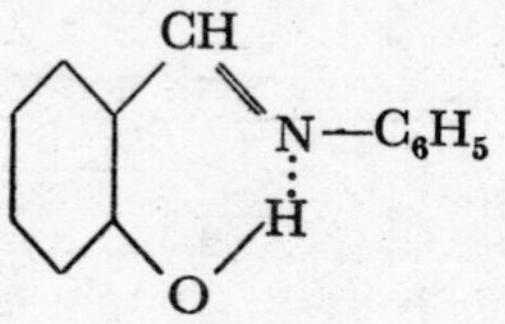

V 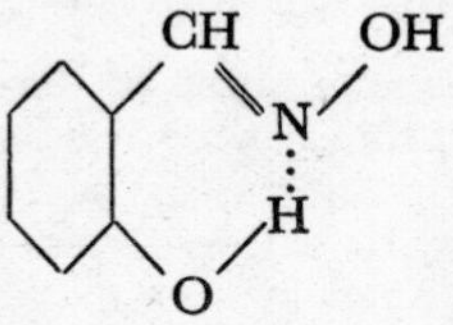 *VI*

The formation of such hydrogen bonds, permits a distinction to be made between the *cis* and *trans* forms of compounds such as *VII*

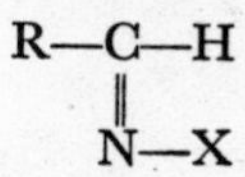

R—C—H
‖
N—X

VII

For example, two oximes of *o*–oxybenzophenol *VIII* are known :

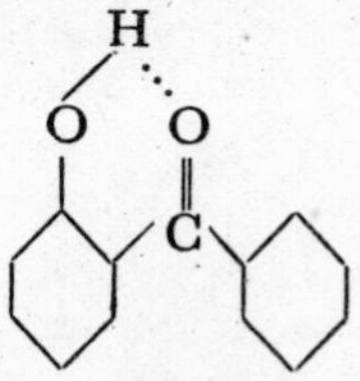

VIII

and the infra-red spectra of the acetyl derivatives shows that the characteristic hydroxyl frequencies are absent for one of the isomers. This must be the *trans* form *IX*, in which the formation of a hydrogen bond is possible

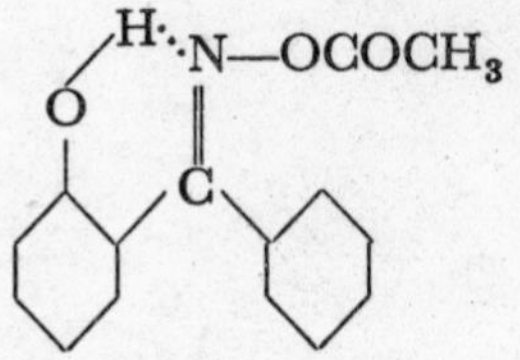

IX

since such bonding is impossible in the *cis* form *X*:

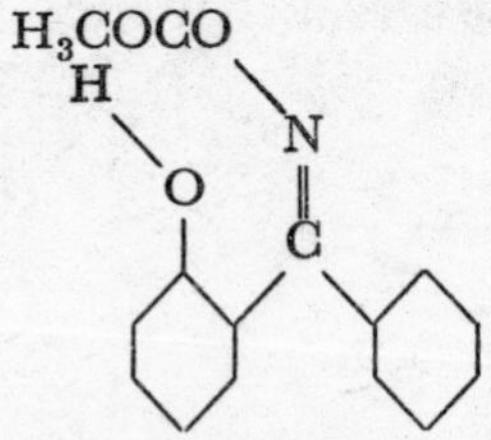

X

From a consideration of the above examples it is possible to define the conditions favouring the formation of an intramolecular hydrogen bond as follows:

1 The configuration of the atoms in the molecule must be such that the hydrogen atom can be situated between two electronegative atoms.

2 The distance of the hydrogen atom from the adjacent electronegative atoms must lie within certain limits. Thus in *o*–oxybenzonitrile, there is no hydrogen bond in spite of the fact that the hydroxyl group is adjacent to the nitrogen atom:

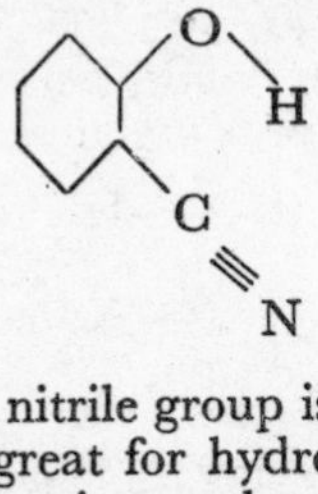

The reason for this is that the nitrile group is linear and the H···N distance is about 3·5 Å, which is too great for hydrogen bond formation.

3 The *o*–positions of a planar six-membered ring are most favourable for hydrogen bond formation and the molecular resonance involving the ring will generally stabilize the hydrogen bond.

INTERNAL ROTATION

The various forces which we have hitherto only regarded as producing interaction between different molecules *viz*, dipole-dipole, dipole-induced dipole and dispersion forces, and the repulsion between non-bonding electrons, may also produce interaction between the non-bonded groups of the same molecule. Such interaction will determine the extent of the freedom of rotation of various groups in the molecule and factors, such as the dipole moment, which are dependent on the average configuration of the molecule, may therefore serve as an indication of this interaction.

VAN'T HOFF postulated free rotation round a single bond in order to explain the lack of *cis* and *trans* isomers in molecules of the type of dichlorethane. In the light of the quantum mechanical theory of the chemical bond, the free rotation is explained by the axial symmetry of the σ bond between the two carbon atoms. Thus the σ bond is not in itself a hindrance to free rotation, but as the rotation occurs the relative configurations of the atoms will be changed, so that the distances between the non-bonded atoms and consequently their energies of interaction will alter.

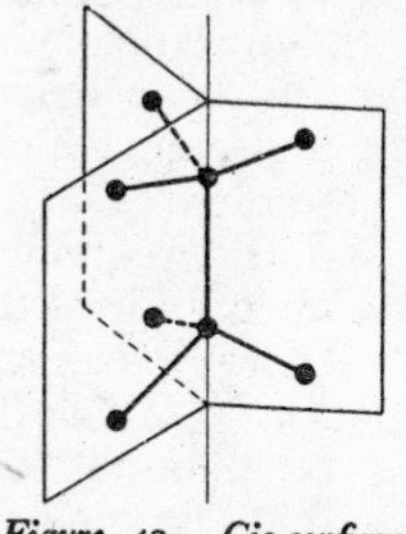

Figure 42. Cis-configuration of ethane

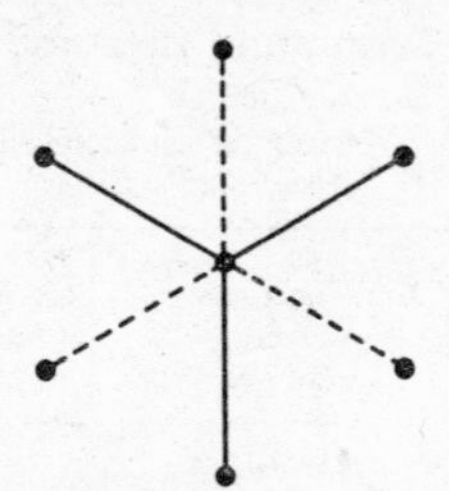

Figure 43. Trans-configuration of ethane

In the ethane molecule, it is possible to conceive various configurations of the two methyl groups with respect to each other. In one limiting configuration (*cis*) the hydrogen atoms of one methyl group are situated directly above the atoms of hydrogen of the other (*Figure 42*). As one of the methyl groups is rotated with respect to the other, the distance between the atoms of hydrogen changes and after rotation through an angle of 60° from the original *cis* configuration, the *trans* configuration is obtained (*Figure 43*). On further rotation, a similar series of configurations are obtained, but in the reverse order until at an angle of 120° to the original structure, the *cis* configuration is again obtained. Different distances between the hydrogen atoms and hence different interaction energies, characterize the different configurations.

Of the infinite number of configurations obtained during the rotation, one will be the most favourable and this particular configuration will be adopted by all the molecules at absolute zero. At higher temperatures, however, the molecule may, by the absorption of energy, exist in configurations other than that corresponding to a minimum potential energy. The probability of the different configurations will be determined by the exponential term of the Maxwell-Boltzmann distribution law, *viz* exp $(-E/kT)$, where E is the energy and T is the absolute temperature. A rotation of 60° will take the molecule from the most probable configuration, with minimum potential energy, to the most improbable configuration with maximum potential energy. The form of the potential energy curve for ethane is given in

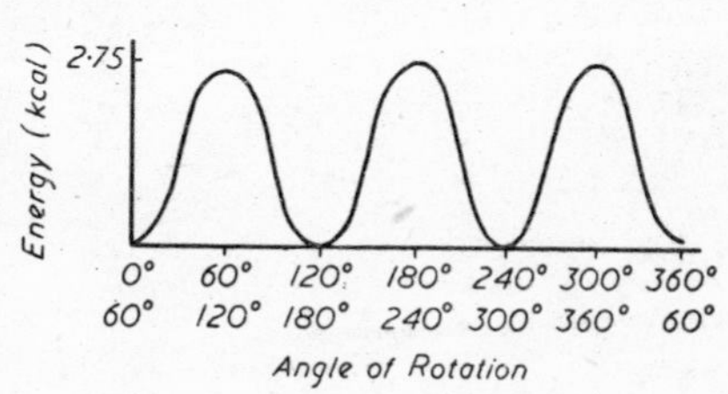

Figure 44. Change of potential energy with internal rotation for ethane

Figure 44, where the most favourable positions are separated from one another by an energy barrier, which must be surmounted if rotation is to occur. If the height of the energy barrier is E, then in accordance with the rate equation in unit time there will be approximately

$$\left(\frac{kT}{h}\exp\left(-E/kT\right)\right)$$

transfers across the barrier. Thus the presence of internal rotation is determined by the height of the potential energy barrier. The experimental data obtained by as many methods as possible (spectroscopic, dipole moment, electron diffraction and thermodynamic) show that internal rotation is very largely restricted in the molecules which have been studied. For a number of different molecules the magnitude of the potential energy barriers is given in *Table CXXXV*. It should be pointed out, however that the majority of these values must be regarded as approximate since accurate determinations are, as yet, not possible. Nevertheless all the values for the energy of rotation of the C—C bond in saturated hydrocarbons are of the order of 3 kcals. In ethane the value is 2·75 kcals and we shall first consider the reason for this rather unexpectedly high value. The obvious explanation of the hindered rotation is the repulsion of the non-bonded electrons of the hydrogen atoms of the two methyl groups. In the *trans* configuration the distance between the hydrogen atoms is at a maximum, there being six H—H distances of 2·47 Å and three of 3·07 Å. If the configuration is, in fact, determined by the repulsion forces between the hydrogen atoms, then this structure, in which this repulsion

Table CXXXV. Energies of Activation of Internal Rotation About Single Bonds

Molecule	Bond about which rotation occurs	Energy of activation kcals	Literature reference
$CH_3\cdot CH_3$	C—C	2·75	26
$CH_3\cdot CH_2\cdot CH_3$	CH_3—CH_2	3·3	27
$CH_3CH_2CH_2CH_3$	CH_3—CH_2	3·4	28
	CH_2—CH_2	3·8	28
$(CH_3)_2CHCH_3$	CH_3—CH	3·8	28
$(CH_3)_4C$	CH_3—C	4·2	28
$CH_3\cdot CCl_3$	C—C	2·7	29
$CH_3\cdot CF_3$	C—C	3·45	30
$CH_3\cdot CH{:}CH_2$	CH—CH	<0·8	27, 31, 32
		2·1	
$CH_3CH_2CH{:}CH_2$	CH_3—CH_2	3·4	28
	CH_2—CH	<0·8	28
$(CH_3)_2C{:}CH_2$	CH_3—C	1·8	28
$CH_3CH{:}CHCH_3$	CH_3—CH	<0·8	28
$CH_3C{:}CCH_3$	CH_3—C	<0·5	33
CH_3OH	CH_3—O	>2·5	34
		1·34	35
		3·4	36
		6·4	37
CH_3CH_2OH	CH_3—CH_2	3·0	38
	CH_2—OH	9·0	38
$(CH_3)_2CHOH$	CH_3—CH	3·4	38
	CH—OH	6·0	38
CH_3COCH_3	CH_3—C	1·25	38
$(CH_3)_2O$	CH_3—O	2·5	39
		3·1	40
$(CH_3)_2S$	CH_3—S	2·0	41
CH_3NH_2	CH_3—N	1·5	42
$(CH_3)_2NH$	CH_3—N	3·5	43
$CH_2Cl\cdot CH_2Cl$	C—C	>5·0	44
$CH_2Br\cdot CH_2Br$	C—C	>5·0	44
$CH_2Cl\cdot CH_2Br$	C—C	>5·0	44
$CH_2CN\cdot CH_2CN$	C—C	1·2	45
Si_2H_6	Si—Si	0	46
B_2H_6	B—B	4·0—6·0	47
$Si(CH_3)_4$	Si—C	1·3	48

will be a minimum, is the most probable. In the *cis* position where there are three H—H distances of 2·27 Å and six of 2·89 Å, the energy of repulsion will be a maximum, and EYRING has shown that on the basis of this theory the magnitude of the energy barrier is only the order of 0·3 kcals. Clearly, therefore, this theory is not able to explain the high value for the height of the energy barrier obtained experimentally and GORIN, WALTER and EYRING[49] have put forward the suggestion that the hindered rotation is due to resonance in the ethane molecule between the structures :

```
H         H           H         H
 \       /             \       /
H—C—C—H       and      H—C=C—H
 /       \
H         H            H.........H
```

In this case the *cis* configuration will be the most probable, since in the *trans* form, the resonance energy will be less.

Certain tentative conclusions may be drawn from the data given in *Table CXXXV*. In unsaturated compounds, the rotation in a single bond adjacent to a double bond is less restricted than in saturated compounds. This behaviour cannot be satisfactorily explained on the basis of the theory of Gorin, Walter and Eyring. PITZER's data suggest that the height of the energy barrier is greatest in the non-linear hydrocarbons, the energy increasing in the order $CH_3CH_2CH_2CH_3$, $(CH_3)_2CHCH_3$, $(CH_3)_4C$. The energy barrier decreases with an increase of distance between the interacting groups, *e.g.* the energy barrier is much lower in $Si(CH_3)_4$ than in $C(CH_3)_4$ and in Si_2H_6 the rotation is almost completely unrestricted.

In dichlorethane, $ClH_2C—CH_2Cl$, various configurations may also exist. In the first limiting case (*cis*), the two chlorine atoms are arranged above each other, with the distance between them at a minimum. On revolution of one $—CH_2Cl$ group through 180°, a second limiting position is obtained (*trans*) in which the distance between the chlorine atoms is a maximum. These two configurations may be represented diagrammatically in the following manner :

I cis *II trans*

In addition to these configurations, two other forms are possible in which the angle of revolution of the $—CH_2Cl$ group from the *cis* configuration is 60° (*III*).

Cl

C

III
two structures

In this molecule the most important factor in determining the repulsion of the non-bonded atoms will be the repulsion of the two negatively charged chlorine atoms. It is therefore to be expected that that position possessing minimum potential energy will be the *trans* configuration and electron diffraction data[50] is in agreement with this conclusion. The variation of the potential energy with rotation shown in *Figure 45*, has been calculated assuming that the *trans* configuration is the most stable and that the probability of deviation from this position is determined by the Maxwell-Boltzmann law. The *cis* configuration, since it possesses maximum potential energy, cannot exist as a stable isomer.

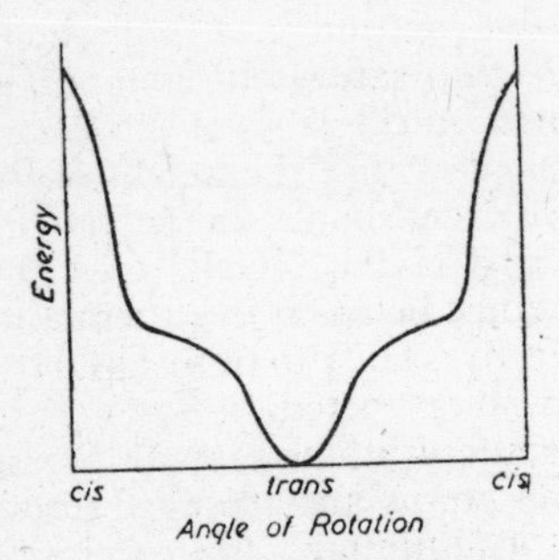

Figure 45. Potential energy curve for internal rotation of dichlorethane

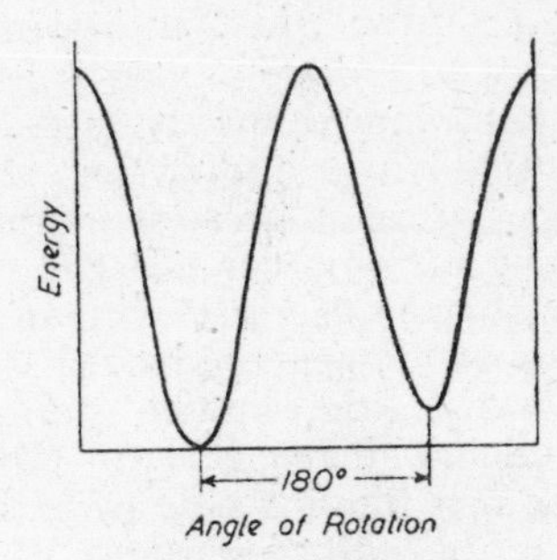

Figure 46. Potential energy curve for internal rotation of ethylene derivatives

The dipole moment of the *trans* form of dichlorethane will be zero, whereas configurations obtained during revolution will have finite moments. Since the probability of configurations other than *trans* will increase with temperature the dipole moment must also increase. This prediction is in agreement with the experimental data as shown in *Table CXXXVI.* The Raman spectrum of dichlorethane contains, in addition to lines which may be ascribed to the *trans* form, additional frequencies, disappearing

Table CXXXVI. Temperature Variation of Dipole Moment of the Di-substituted Derivatives of Ethane

$ClH_2C\cdot CH_2Cl$		$ClH_2C\cdot CH_2Br$		$BrH_2C\cdot CH_2Br$		$NCCH_2\cdot CH_2CN$	
T°C	*Dipole moment D*	*T°C*	*Dipole moment D*	*T°C*	*Dipole moment D*	*T°C*	*Dipole moment D*
32	1·12	66	1·09	66	0·94	−90	2·94
68	1·24	95	1·14	95	0·99	−60	3·16
103	1·32	132	1·20	132	1·03	−30	3·36
146	1·40	163	1·28	163	1·10	0	3·54
184	1·45	—	—	—	—	30	3·68
207	1·48	—	—	—	—	60	3·80
212	1·48	—	—	—	—	90	3·90
271	1·54	—	—	—	—	—	—

at low temperatures, which correspond to a second isomer having the configuration *III*. If these data are correct, the potential energy curve (*Figure 45*) must show shallow minima corresponding to the isomer formed by rotation through 120° from the *trans* configuration.

In certain cases rotation may be inhibited by the formation of a weak hydrogen bond. This is considered to be the case in the carboxyl group for which the dipole moment is close to the value to be expected for the fixed configuration

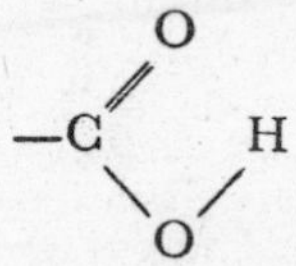

```
       O
      //
   —C      H
      \   /
       O
```

in which the hydrogen atom is situated as close as possible to the oxygen atom of the carboxyl group.

The bond between the two carbon atoms in ethylene consists of a σ and a π bond. The σ bond permits free rotation, but in the π bond two configurations, at 180° to each other, in which overlap of the π orbitals is at a maximum, give minimum potential energy and maximum stability. The variation of the potential energy in such cases is therefore marked by a very high potential energy barrier (*Figure 46*), the height of which corresponds approximately to the energy of a π bond. Thus rotation requires a very high energy of activation and is not possible at ordinary temperatures. In ethylene, the two configurations are indistinguishable but in the di-substituted derivatives one configuration refers to the *cis* and the other to the *trans* form. In these cases the potential energy curve will no longer be symmetrical and the value of the minimum energy will be different in the two cases. Nevertheless, in view of the high energy barrier, the transfer of one form into the other is generally not possible.

The photochemical transformation of maleic and fumaric acids

```
HCCOOH                HCCOOH
  ‖        ⇌            ‖
HCCOOH              HOOCCH
```

occurs on absorption of ultraviolet radiation of wavelength of 2,800 Å. This reaction evidently proceeds as the result of the excitation of one of the π electrons, thus permitting rotation of the C—C bond.

If, owing to resonance, the double bond possesses some single bond character, the height of the energy barrier will be lower than in the case of a pure ethylenic bond. This evidently occurs in the case of *p*-nitro-*p*-aminostilbene[51] :

$$H_2N—C_6H_4—CH{=}CH—C_6H_4—NO_2$$

in which resonance occurs amongst a number of structures containing a single bond between the two central carbon atoms *e.g.*

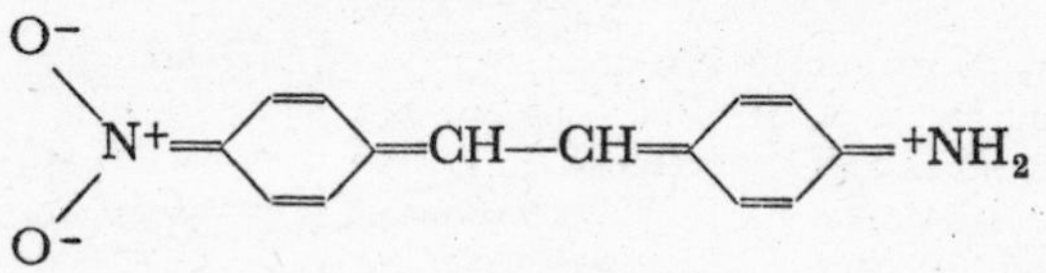

```
O⁻
 \
  N⁺=<ring>=CH—CH=<ring>=⁺NH₂
 /
O⁻
```

REFERENCES

[1] SUGDEN, T. M., WALSH, A. D. and PRICE, W. C. *Nature, Lond.* 148 (1941) 372
[2] STEVENSON, D. P. and HIPPLE, J. A. *J. Amer. chem Soc.* 64 (1942) 2766
[3] LONDON, F. *Trans. Faraday Soc.* 33 (1937) 8
[4] DEBYE, P. *Phys. Z.* 36 (1935) 100
[5] ONSAGER, L. *J. Amer. chem. Soc.* 58 (1936) 1486
[6] PIEKARA, A. *Proc. roy. Soc. A* 172 (1939) 360
[7] KIRKWOOD, J. G. *J. chem. Phys.* 7 (1939) 911 ; 8 (1940) 205
[8] SYRKIN, J. K. *Compt. rend. Acad. Sci. U.R.S.S.* 35 (1942) 45
[9] NIKITIN, B. A. *J. gen. Chem. Moscow* 9 (1929) 1167
— *Compt. rend. Acad. Sci. U.R.S.S.* 24 (1939) 562
[10] SHIALOWSKI, and SYRKIN, J. K. Unpublished data
[11] LAUBENGAYER, A. W. and FINLAY, G. R. *J. Amer. chem. Soc.* 65 (1943) 884
[12] VAN DER MEULEN, D. A. and HELLER, H. A. *ibid* 54 (1932) 4404
[13] BAUER, S. H., FINLAY, G. R. and LAUBENGAYER, A. W. *ibid* 65 (1943) 889
[14] PLOTNIKOV, V. A., SHEKA, I. A. and JANKELIVICH, Z. A. *J. gen. Chem. Moscow* 9 (1939) 868
[15] CURRAN, B. C. *J. Amer. chem. Soc.* 63 (1941) 1470
— *ibid* 64 (1942) 830
MCCUSKER, P. A. and CURRAN, B. C. *ibid* 64 (1942) 614
LANE, T. J., MCCUSKER, P. A. and CURRAN, B. C. *ibid* 64 (1942) 2076
[16] BROWN, H. C. and ADAMS, R. M. *J. Amer. chem. Soc.* 64 (1942) 255
[17] KLEMM, W., CLAUSEN, E. and JACOBI, H. *Z. anorg. Chem.* 200 (1931) 367
[18] KARLE, J. W. and BROCKWAY, L. O. *J. Amer. chem. Soc.* 66 (1944) 574
[19] DAVIES, M. M. *Ann. Rep. chem. Soc.* 43 (1946) 5
[20] — and SUTHERLAND, G. B. B. M. *J. chem. Phys.* 6 (1939) 755
[21] GLADYSHEV, A. I. and SYRKIN, J. K. *Compt. rend. Acad. Sci. U.R.S.S.* 20 (1938) 145
[22] VON AUWERS, K. *Ber.* 70 (1937) 966
[23] HUNTER, L. *Ann. Rep. chem. Soc.* 43 (1946) 141
[24] PAULING, L. C. *The Nature of the Chemical Bond* Cornell, 1939
WHELAND, G. W. *The Theory of Resonance* New York, 1944
[25] BRANCH, G. E. K. and YABROFF, D. L. *J. Amer. chem. Soc.* 56 (1932) 2568
[26] KISTIAKOWSKY, G. B. and NICKLE, A. G. *J. chem. Phys.* 10 (1942) 78, 146
[27] LACHER, J. R. and RANSOM, W. W. *ibid* 8 (1940) 970
[28] PITZER, K. S. *ibid* 5 (1937) 473
[29] RUBIN, T. R., LEVEDAHL, B. H. and YOST, D. M. *ibid* 66 (1944) 16
[30] RUSSELL, H., GOLDING, D. R. V. and YOST, D. M. *ibid* 66 (1944) 16
[31] KISTIAKOWSKY, G. B., LACHER, J. R. and RANSOM, W. W. *ibid* 6 (1938) 900
[32] PITZER, K. S. and GWINN, W. D. *ibid* 9 (1941) 485
[33] OXBORNE, D. W., GARNER, C. S. and YOST, D. M. *ibid* 8 (1940) 131
[34] HALFORD, J. O. and PECHERER, B. *ibid* 6 (1938) 571
[35] KOEHLER, J. S. and DENNISON, D. M. *Phys. Rev.* 57 (1940) 1006
[36] CRAWFORD, B. L. *J. chem. Phys.* 8 (1940) 744
[37] KASSEL, L. S. *ibid* 4 (1936) 276
[38] SCHUMANN, S. C. and ASTON, J. G. *J. Amer. chem. Soc.* 60 (1938) 985
[39] KISTIAKOWSKY, G. B. and RICE, W. W. *J. chem. Phys.* 8 (1940) 618
[40] KENNEDY, R. M., SAGENKAHN, M. and ASTON, J. G. *J. Amer. chem. Soc.* 63 (1941) 2267
[41] OSBORNE, D. W., DOESCHER, R. N. and YOST, D. M. *J. chem. Phys.* 8 (1940) 506
[42] ASTON, J. G. and DOTY, P. M. *ibid* 8 (1940) 743
[43] — EIDINOFF, M. L. and FORSTER, W. S. *J. Amer. chem. Soc.* 61 (1939) 1539
[44] BEACH, J. W. and PALMER, K. J. *J. chem. Phys.* 6 (1938) 639
[45] LEWIS, G. L. and SMYTH, C. P. *ibid* 7 (1939) 1085

[46] STITT, F. and YOST, D. M. *ibid* 5 (1937) 90
[47] — *ibid* 8 (1940) 981
[48] ASTON, J. G. and KENNEDY, R. M. *J. Amer. chem. Soc.* 62 (1940) 2567
[49] GORIN, E., WALTER, J. and EYRING, H. *ibid* 61 (1939) 1876
[50] BEACH, J. Y. and PALMER, K. J. *J. chem. Phys.* 6 (1938) 639
— and TURKEVICH, J. *J. Amer. chem. Soc.* 61 (1939) 303
— and STEVENSON, D. P. *J. chem. Phys.* 6 (1938) 635
[51] CALVIN, M. and BUCKLES, R. E. *J. Amer. chem. Soc.* 62 (1940) 3324

13

THE CHEMICAL BOND IN CRYSTALS

CRYSTAL STRUCTURE OF THE ELEMENTS

A CRYSTAL consists of an ordered three dimensional array of atoms, molecules or ions, which undergo only slight fluctuations from their mean position. The importance of studies of the crystalline state lies in the fact that these investigations lead to information on the spatial arrangement of the elementary particles forming the crystal, the nature of these particles, *i.e.* whether they are atoms, molecules or ions, the type of force or bond existing between the particles and the relationship between the structure of the crystal and its physical and chemical properties. The spatial configuration of the elementary particles forming the crystal may be determined by x-ray analysis. The particles are found to be arranged in simple structural units whose repetition throughout the whole crystal forms the macroscopic solid.

The close packing of equivalent spheres— The atoms of the elements may be regarded as spheres and we should expect that their crystals would be formed by packing the spheres on top of each other in the closest possible way. This is what actually occurs. There are, however, two possible ways of arranging equivalent spheres so that the interstitial space is as small as possible, one with cubic and one with hexagonal symmetry. There is only one way of arranging the spheres as close as possible in a single layer, *i.e.* when each sphere is surrounded by six others (*Figure 47*). In the layer around each sphere are six interstitial spaces or holes formed by three spheres in contact. A second layer may be superimposed on the first layer in only one way, by placing each sphere of the second layer in contact with three spheres of the lower layer. By this means, one half of the holes are covered by spheres of the second layer (*Figure 47*). The third layer can now be added in one of two possible ways, either with spheres directly above those of the first layer, or over the holes of the first layer

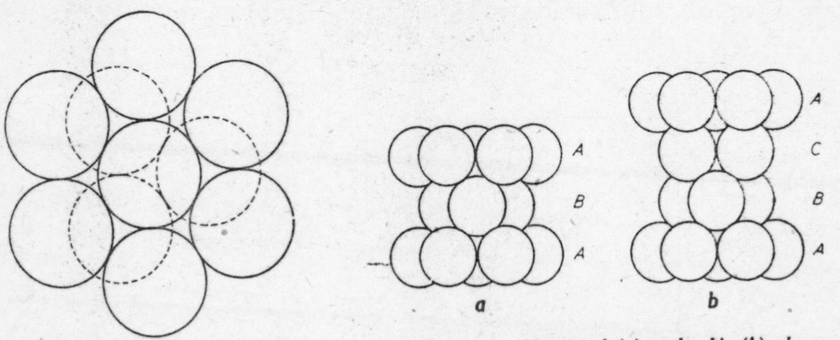

Figure 47. Close packing of spheres

Figure 48. Hexagonal (a) and cubic (b) close packing of spheres

not covered by the second layer. The first structure, which has hexagonal symmetry, is termed hexagonal close packing (*Figure 48a*) and the second structure with cubic symmetry is termed cubic close packing (*Figure 48b*).

A convenient method of describing these structures uses the symbols

A, B and C to represent the three layers of close packed spheres which differ from one another in their relative positions. Thus hexagonal close packing follows the sequence ABABAB...... (or BCBC......, or ACAC......) and the cubic close packing the order ABCABC...... (or CABCAB......, or BCABCA......). In both types of close packed structures, each sphere is in contact with twelve other spheres. This number is generally referred to as the coordination number. Six of these spheres lie in the same layer in the form of a hexagon, and the other six are located three above and three below in the form of two triangles. In hexagonal close packing, the upper triangle has the same configuration as the lower and in cubic close packing it has been rotated through 60°.

The cubic close packed structure may also be represented as a face centred cubic structure in which eight spheres are located at the centres of the faces (*Figure 49*). The relationship between this representation of the cubic close packed structure and that given in *Figure 48b*, is that the plane 111, which cuts the cube in *Figure 49*, represents a layer of spheres in *Figure 48a*.

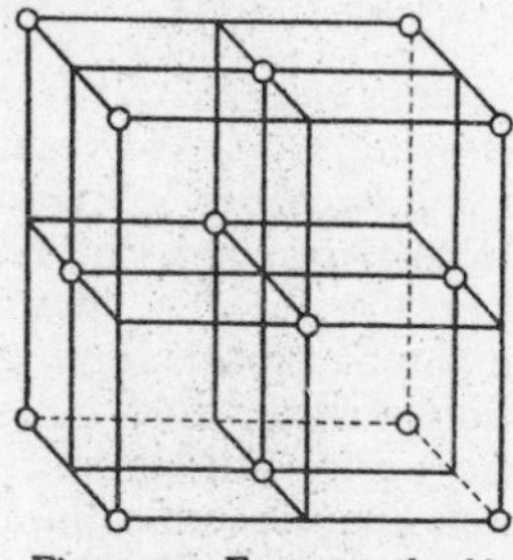

Figure 49. Face-centred cubic lattice

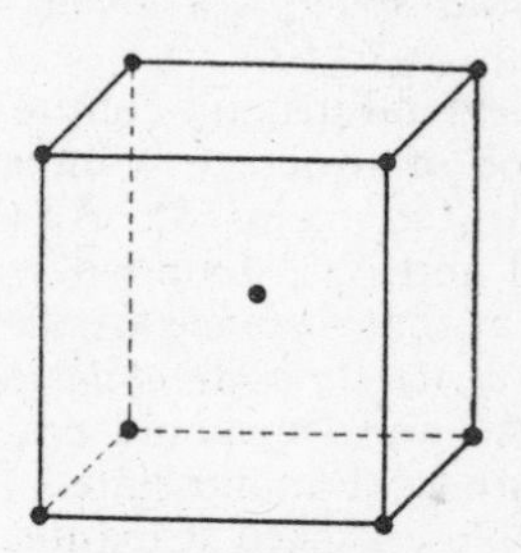

Figure 50. Body-centred cubic lattice

In addition to the close packed structures, other more open structures exist. The most important of these are the body centred cubic and the diamond, or zinc blende, structures. In the former structure, eight spheres are arranged at the corners of a cube and a ninth sphere at the centre of

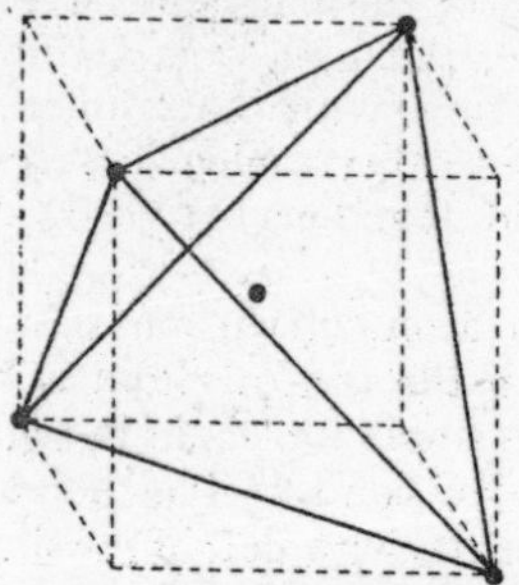

Figure 51. Tetrahedral lattice

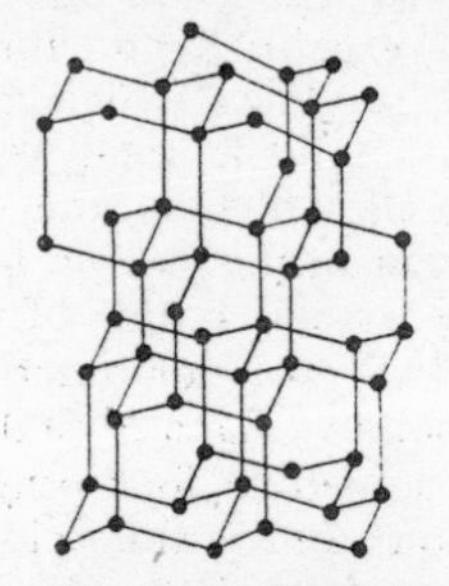

Figure 52. Diamond lattice

the cube (*Figure 50*). The central sphere is thus surrounded by only eight nearest neighbours (coordination number eight) ; in addition to these eight neighbours, six more (at the centres of the six adjacent cubes) are found at a distance only about 15 per cent greater. The effective coordination number is therefore sometimes considered to be fourteen. The diamond (zinc blende) lattice is obtained by removing four of the spheres from alternate corners of the body centred cubic lattice (*Figures 51* and *52*), leaving a central sphere surrounded tetrahedrally by four others. The coordination number is thus four.

Even in the close packed structures, a considerable part of the total volume remains unfilled, since between the spheres there are holes of considerable volume. This volume is greater in the body centred cubic structure and in the diamond lattice. The relative volumes occupied by the spheres and by the interstitial space are given in *Table CXXXVII*.

Table CXXXVII. Relative Volumes occupied by Spheres and Interstitial Holes in different Close Packed Structures

Types of packing	*Coordination number*	*Volume occupied by spheres per cent*	*Volume not occupied by spheres per cent*
Close packed	12	74·05	25·95
Body centred cubic	8	68·02	31·98
Cubic	6	52·36	47·64
Tetrahedral	4	34·0	66·0

The crystal structure of the elements is given in *Table CXXXVIII* in which the type of structure is indicated in the following way: A1 : cubic close packed (face centred), A2 : body centred cubic, A3 : hexagonal close packed and A4 : diamond. The interatomic distances and the number of atoms at that distance are also given.

The crystal structure of the non-metals— The atoms of the inert gases are spherical and we should naturally expect them to exist in a close packed structure in the solid state. This does in fact, occur and of the two alternative close packed structures the inert gases choose the cubic close packed. The only forces which exist between the atoms are van der Waal's forces and in view of the absence of a permanent dipole moment, these will be dispersion forces.

The molecules N_2 and O_2, although far from spherical, crystallize approximately in a close packed form. Each atom has one nearest neighbour to which it is bound covalently and the molecules will be bound together by dispersion forces. The lattices of the halogens have a similar structure except that in the case of iodine, the high polarizability of the molecule produces a high dispersion attraction, with the result that iodine exists as a solid at room temperature when other molecules, *e.g.* Cl_2, F_2, O_2, N_2, *etc* which in the crystal are held together by weak dispersion forces, exist in the gaseous form.

In the crystal lattice of diamond, each atom of carbon is surrounded tetrahedrally by four other atoms to which the central atom is bound by four σ bonds. Each crystal is thus a large single molecule in which every atom is joined to four others by homopolar bonds. The bond between the carbon atoms is almost identical in properties with that of the single C—C bond in hydrocarbons, thus the interatomic distance in diamond is 1·54 Å and the value of the dielectric constant, 5·3, leads to a value for the polarizability of the bond of 1 cc, which is only slightly less than the value for the C—C bond in hydrocarbons.

The x-ray investigation of diamond using the methods of Fourier analysis enables the variation of the electron density in the vicinity of the carbon

Table CXXXVIII. Crystal Structure of the Elements

Li A2 3·04 (8)	Be A3 2·22 (6) 2·27 (6)												C A4 (1·54) 4	N molecular 1·07 (1) 3·44	O molecular		Ne A1 3·20 (12)
Na A2 3·72 (8)	Mg A3 3·19 (6) 3·20 (6)											Al A1 2·86 (12)	Si A4 2·34 (4)	P molecular 2·20 (3) 3·87 (3)	S molecular 2·10 (2) 3·3 (4)	Cl molecular 1·99 (1) 2·79	Ar A1 3·83 (12)
K A2 4·62 (8)	Ca A1 3·93 (12) A3 3·94 (6) 3·96 (6)		Ti A3 2·91 (6) 2·95 (6)	V A2 2·63 (8)	Cr A2 2·49 (8) A3 2·71 (6) 2·72 (6)	Mn various forms	Fe A1 2·52 (12) A2 2·48 (8)	Co A1 2·51 (12) A3 2·50 (6) 2·51 (6)	Ni A1 2·49 (12) A3 2·49 (12)	Cu A1 2·55 (12)	Zn A3 2·66 (6) 2·91 (6)	Ga 2·44 (1) 2·71 (2) 2·74 (2) 2·79 (2)	Ge A4 2·44 (4)	As 2·51 (3) 3·15 (3)	Se 2·32 (2) 3·46 (4)	Br molecular 2·27 (1) 3·30	Kr A1 3·94 (12)
Rb A2 4·87 (8)	Sr A1 4·30 (12)	Y A3 3·60 (6) 3·66 (6)	Zr A2 3·13 (8) A3 3·17 (6) 3·22 (6)	Nb A2 2·85 (8)	Mo A2 2·72 (8)		Ru A3 2·64 (6) 2·70 (6)	Rh A1 2·68 (12)	Pd A1 2·74 (12)	Ag A1 2·88 (12)	Cd A3 2·97 (6) 3·29 (6)	In 3·24 (4) 3·37 (8)	Sn A4 2·80 (4) — 3·02 (4) 3·17 (2)	Sb 2·90 (3) 3·36 (3)	Te 2·86 (2) 3·46 (4)	I molecular 2·70 (1) 3·54 (2)	Xe A1 4·34 (12)
Cs A2 5·24 (8)	Ba A2 4·34 (8)		Hf A3 3·14 (6) 3·20 (6)	Ta A2 2·85 (8)	W A2 2·73 (8) and other forms	Re A3 2·73 (6) 2·76 (6)	Os A3 2·67 (6) 2·73 (6)	Ir A1 2·71 (12)	Pt A1 2·77 (12)	Au A1 2·88 (12)	Hg 3·00 (6) 3·46 (6)	Tl A1 3·42 (12) A3 3·40 (6) 3·45 (6)	Pb A1 3·49 (4)	Bi 3·10 (3) 3·47 (3)			
			Th A1 3·59 (12)		U A2 2·97 (8) and other forms												

A1 = cubic close packed
A2 = body centred cubic
A3 = hexagonal close packed
A4 = diamond
The figures give the interatomic distance in Å, together with the number of atoms at that distance

Figure 53. Variation of electron density in the diamond lattice

atoms to be determined. The electron density diagram is shown in *Figure 53*, in which the contours connect points of equal intensity and the figures refer to the number of electrons per 1 sq Å. Between the atoms, 'electron bridges' exist which show that the electrons are not localized on particular atoms, but are exchanged between them. This electron exchange is a characteristic of the homopolar bond and the fact that the electron bridges are directed along the line joining two atoms is direct corroboration of the localization of electrons in a σ bond.

In the diamond lattice, even when it is assumed that the atoms are in contact, the proportion of the available space occupied by the atoms is only 34 per cent. From this point of view the diamond lattice might appear unstable. It is, however, extremely stable as shown by the physical properties of diamond and this stability is due to the fact that the forces acting between the atoms are homopolar valency forces. Any attempt to increase the coordination number would involve the deformation of valency angles which would be accompanied by a considerable loss of energy. Thus in crystals formed from atoms joined by homopolar bonds, the coordination number is determined by the valency of the atom. Such crystals will therefore be characterized by a small coordination number.

Another form of crystalline carbon, graphite, has a layer lattice (*Figure 54*). Each layer represents a two dimensional crystal formed from condensed benzene rings. Each carbon atom forms three σ bonds, by means of three sp^2 hybrid orbitals, which are in one plane at an angle of 120° to each other. The fourth electron of the carbon atom is located in a p orbital forming a figure of eight perpendicular to the layer. This electron will participate in a π bond with the three adjacent carbon atoms, with the result that each bond possesses one third double bond character in contrast to benzene where the C—C bond possesses one half double bond character. The C—C distance in graphite (1·42 Å) is thus somewhat greater than in benzene. The non-localization of the π electrons, as described by the molecular orbital treatment, explains the high electrical conductivity of graphite. The various layers of graphite are held together by van der Waal's forces, the distance

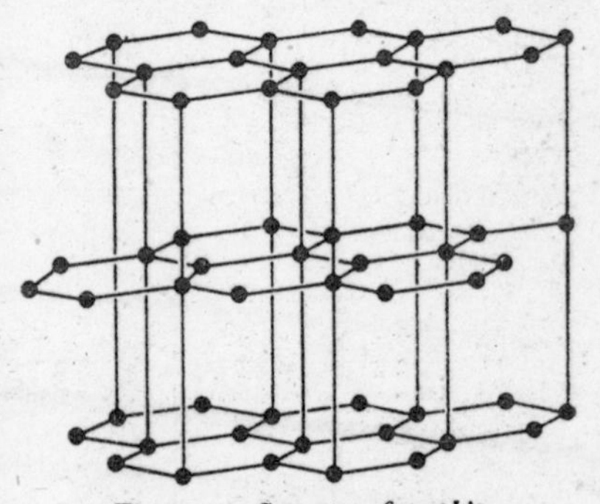

Figure 54. Structure of graphite

between two adjacent layers being 3·45 Å. The relative configuration of adjacent layers is generally considered to be that shown in *Figure 54*, in which the same configuration is repeated every two layers. LIPSON and STOKES[1], however, have suggested on the basis of x-ray measurements that in about 10 per cent of the graphite the configuration is repeated every three layers. Boron nitride has a similar structure to graphite, being composed of six membered rings containing alternate boron and nitrogen atoms. In addition to the homopolar structure *I*, the ionic form *II*, containing tetravalent positively charged nitrogen and delocalized double bonds, will contribute to the resonance of the molecule.

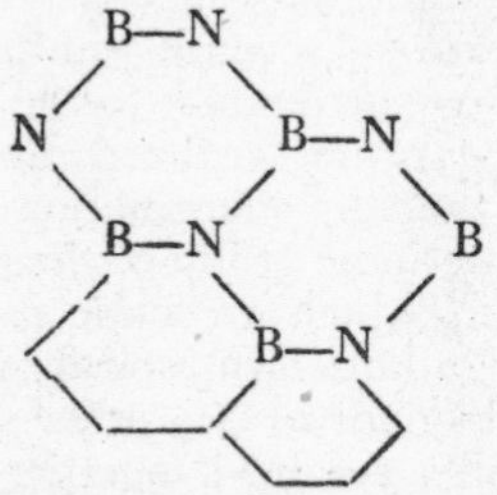

B—N
N B—N
B—N B
B—N

I

B⁻═N⁺
—⁺N B⁻—N⁺
B⁻—⁺N B⁻ —
B⁻═N⁺

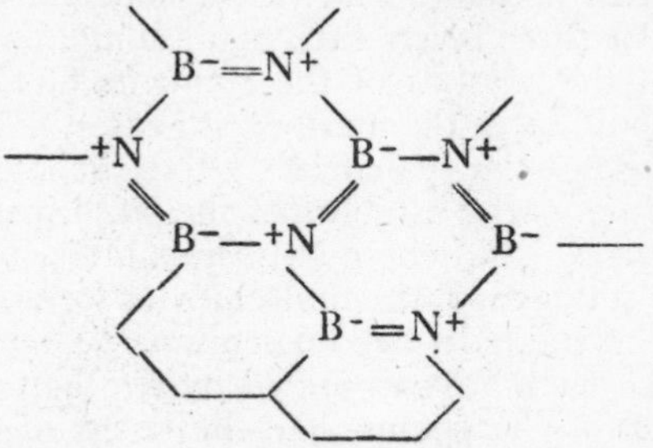

II

The heats of formation of diamond and graphite are very close, since although in diamond each atom has four σ bonds and in graphite each atom forms only three σ bonds and one weaker π bond, in the latter there is an increase of stability owing to resonance of a similar type to that occurring in benzene.

The dispersion energy existing between the graphite layers is not great and calculation by formula 12.3 gives a value of only 1 to 2 kcals. Because of this weak attraction, it is possible for many different atoms or radicals to be taken up between the layers, thereby forming compounds or salts. In this process the graphite crystal retains its original form, except that an expansion occurs in a direction perpendicular to the layers.

The action of strong oxidizing agents, such as nitric acid and potassium chlorate on graphite produce the so called graphitic oxide. During the course of the reaction, the graphite swells in one direction and the colour changes from black to green or brown according to the conditions and the electrical conductivity of graphite is lost. Measurement of the distance between the layers shows that in these compounds it has increased from 3·45 Å to a value between 6 and 11 Å. It is clear that oxygen atoms have penetrated between the layers and formed bonds with the π electrons, the atoms being bonded to both sides of the same layer. The presence of the oxygen atoms renders the graphite hydrophilic and it may readily be dispersed in water to form a colloidal solution. The ratio of the number of carbon and oxygen atoms is not constant but varies between 2·9 and 3·5 to 1.

Graphite also absorbs molten potassium to form two compounds C_8K and $C_{16}K$. The metal may be dissolved out of the graphite by mercury. Also known are the graphite salts formed by suspending graphite in concentrated sulphuric acid to which a small quantity of an oxidizing agent has been added. The graphite develops a blue or purple colour and swells owing to the absorption of HSO_4^- and SO_4^{2-} ions between the layers. Not every layer takes part in the absorption process and various structures in which every second, fourth or sixteenth layer absorbs the ions have been proposed. Graphite also forms a compound with fluorine known as carbon monofluoride, in which the separation between the layers increases to 8·17 Å. The conductivity is decreased to 10^{-5} times that of graphite.

All forms of so-called amorphous carbon are graphitic in character being formed of microcrystals having a graphite structure. The number of regularly arranged laminations and the extent of the layers varies from one form to another. In lamp black, the layers are approximately 40 to 50 Å in diameter and the crystals 10 Å thick. This corresponds to about two or three layers each containing about one hundred rings.

In the crystals of the elements of the fourth to seventh groups of the periodic table the number of nearest neighbours corresponds to the number of homopolar valencies. This behaviour was first realized by HUME-ROTHERY who established the empirical law that the coordination number equals 8 — N, where N is the number of the periodic group of the element. The halogens form molecules of formula Hal_2 which are close packed in the crystal. In solid selenium the selenium atoms form spiral chains in which each atom is joined by two homopolar bonds to two other selenium atoms. The chains, like the layers of graphite, are held together by van der Waal's forces and possibly by weak forces similar to those occurring in metals. Rhombic sulphur consists of cyclic S_8 molecules in which the rings are puckered, each sulphur atom forming two bonds with a bond length of 2·10 Å. The distance between the atoms in the different rings which are held together by van der Waal's forces, is 3·3 Å. At 119° C rhombic sulphur melts to give a transparent liquid which on heating to 200° C changes to a red viscous modification in which it is believed that the S_8 rings have been broken, thus forming S_8 chains. The unstable modification, known as plastic sulphur, also consists of chains of sulphur atoms. For the group VI elements other than oxygen, which is an exception to the 8 — N rule, the ratio of the distance between corresponding atoms of different molecules to the interatomic bond distance is 1·56 for sulphur, 1·48 for selenium and 1·21 for tellurium.

In group V, the 8 — N rule requires an element to have three nearest neighbours. Thus four atoms form a tetrahedral structure, with an atom at each corner and in which the bond angles are not distorted far from the theoretical 90° for the bonds involving *p* electrons. Two types of tetrahedral structure are possible, either an infinite layer in which the atoms lie in two parallel planes so that each forms three pyramidal bonds with its nearest neighbours, or a tetrahedral molecule. Arsenic, antimony and bismuth generally form the layer structure, although the very unstable yellow forms of arsenic and antimony are believed to contain tetrahedral molecules. Phosphorus forms tetrahedral P_4 molecules in the white modification and layer molecules in the black modification. The ratios of the longer interatomic distances between the tetrahedral or layer molecules and the bond distances are : phosphorus, 1·76 ; arsenic, 1·25 ; antimony, 1·17 ; bismuth, 1·12. This sequence is in agreement with the increase of polarity and of metallic character, with increase of atomic number.

In group IV the formation of four tetrahedral bonds results in a three dimensional complex extending throughout the crystal. This occurs in all the elements of this group (carbon, silicon, germanium and tin) with the exception of lead. Carbon and tin form two other modifications, graphite and white tin respectively. We have already considered the structure of graphite; white tin possesses a deformed octahedral structure.

Nitrogen and oxygen do not obey Hume-Rothery's rule, since in both cases there is only one nearest neighbour and not 8 − N. This is evidently due to the fact that the bonds in O_2 and N_2 are more stable than two single O—O bonds and three single N—N bonds respectively.

In the first and second groups of the periodic table the 8 − N rule does not give the number of possible covalent bonds, furthermore the elements of these groups, together with those of the transition groups do not form homopolar or ionic bonds but a metallic bond possessing definite characteristics.

The structure of metallic crystals— Of the characteristic properties of metals which distinguish them from non-metals, the high thermal and electrical conductivities are perhaps the most significant. We shall, however, be concerned here mainly with the problem of the nature of the bond between two atoms in metallic crystals and we must refer those who are

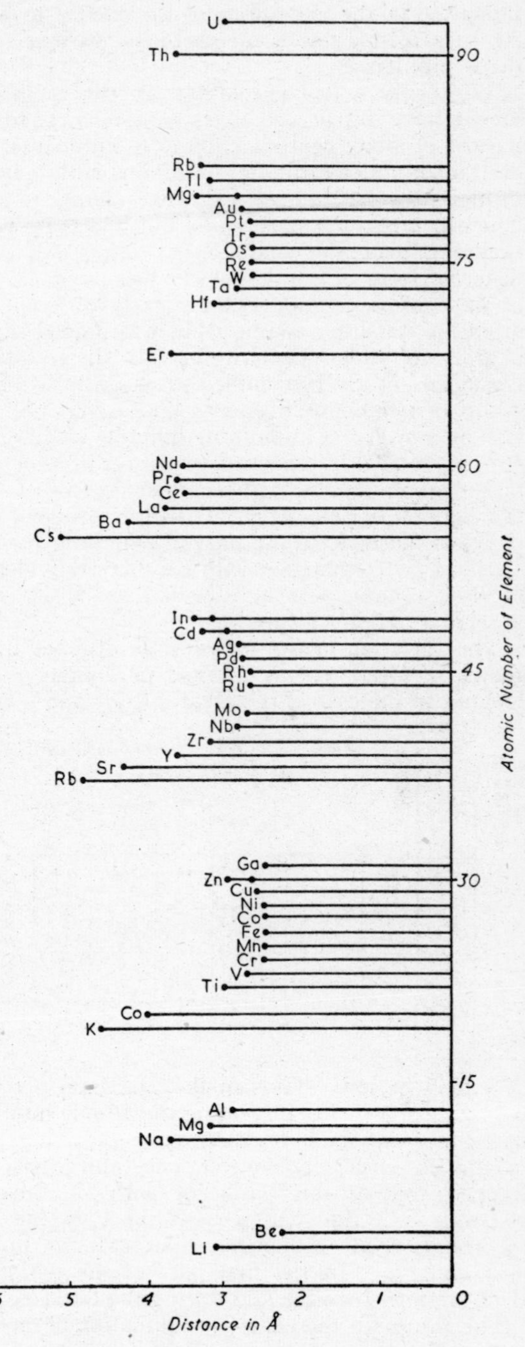

Figure 55. Interatomic distances in metallic crystals

interested in the extensions of the theory to account for the thermal and electrical properties of metals to the various monographs which deal with these problems[2].

With only a few exceptions all the metals whose crystal structure is known have a structure which is either hexagonal close packed, cubic close packed or body centred cubic. A number of metals *e.g.* caesium, which crystallize under ordinary conditions with a body centred cubic structure, at high pressures (22,000 kg/sq cm) change to a close packed modification[3]. The exceptions are zinc, cadmium, mercury, aluminium, gallium, indium, thallium, lead and manganese. Zinc and cadmium crystallize with a distorted form of hexagonal close packing, in which there are two groups of six nearest neighbours at slightly different distances from the central atom. Crystalline mercury has a distorted simple cubic lattice (rhombohedral) in which each atom has six nearest neighbours and gallium crystallizes in a very complex structure in which an atom has the following group of neighbours : one at 2·44 Å, two at 2·70 Å, two at 2·73 Å and two at 2·79 Å. Aluminium, indium, thallium and lead crystallize with approximately close packed structures in which the interatomic distance is rather larger than would be expected from a comparison with the values of neighbouring elements. It is interesting to note that all these elements possessing distorted close packed structures have lower melting points than expected by comparison with neighbouring elements in the periodic classification. Manganese may crystallize in one of three complex structures unrelated to other forms.

The variation of the interatomic distance in crystals of the elements is shown in *Figure 55*. A marked periodicity is observed, the values being greatest in the case of the alkali metals and least with the middle members

Table CXXXIX. Heats of Sublimation of Metals (kcals)

Li 39	Be 75												
Na 26	Mg 36											Al 55	
K 20	Ca 47	Sc 70	Ti 100	V 85	Cr 88	Mn 74	Fe 94	Co 85	Ni 85	Cu 81	Zn 27	Ga 52	Ge 85
Rb 19	Sr 49	Y 90	Zr 110		Mo 160		Ru 120	Rh 115	Pd 110	Ag 68	Cd 27	In 52	Sn 78
Cs 19	Ba (73)	La 90	Hf (> 72)	Ta (> 97)	W 210		Os 125	Ir 120	Pt 127	Au 92	Hg 15	Tl 40	Pb 47
			Th 177										

of a long period. Thus in the first long period the largest value occurs with potassium. On increasing the atomic number the interatomic distance decreases to about the seventh element, manganese, then remains constant to the eleventh element, copper, and then increases up to selenium. PAULING relates this variation with the possible number of unpaired electrons. In the long periods the *s*, *p* and *d* orbitals are being filled (9 orbitals in all) and hence the maximum number of unpaired electrons may equal 9. In the first part of the period the number of unpaired electrons may increase and during the latter part decrease.

The values for the heats of sublimation of metals given in *Table CXXXIX* although only approximate, bring out some important relationships. In the same period, the value of the heat of sublimation increases with increasing number of valency electrons, *e.g.* Na, 25·9 kcals ; Mg, 36·3 kcals ; Al, 55 kcals. The effect of completely filled *d* orbitals on the heat of sublimation is shown by comparing the values for the alkali metals, *viz*, K, 20 kcals ; Rb, 19 kcals and Cs, 19 kcals, with Cu, 81 kcals ; Ag, 68 kcals and Au, 92 kcals respectively. These data confirm the suggestion made above, based on the variation of the atomic distance with atomic number, that the *d* electrons take part in the interatomic bond. The effect of the *d* electrons is also shown by the high values of the heat of sublimation of all the transition elements, the values being particularly high for platinum (127 kcals), molybdenum (160 kcals) and tungsten (210 kcals). The relatively low values for zinc, cadmium and mercury are presumably related to their distorted close packed lattices.

The electrical properties of metals require that a metal should contain free electrons and the spectroscopic properties indicate that the number of free electrons should be comparable with the number of atoms present. The latter requirement is based on the fact that the second ionization potential of an element is generally very much greater than the first, *e.g.* for sodium, the values are 118 and 1,084 kcals respectively. The density of the electron cloud of an isolated atom, as shown in Chapter 1, increases at first with increasing distance from the nucleus, passes through a maximum and then rapidly falls to a low value and approaches zero at infinite distance. In the metallic state, however, the density of the electron cloud does not fall to zero, but falls to a constant value in the space between the ions. This permits the metal to be regarded as a close packed structure of positively charged ions existing in an electron cloud of fluctuating density. Such a general qualitative picture of the structure of a metal is supported by the x-ray data for the variation of the electron density in magnesium. The method of Fourier analysis applied to the x-ray data for magnesium[4] gives the curve shown in *Figure 56* for the variation of the electron density between the magnesium ions.

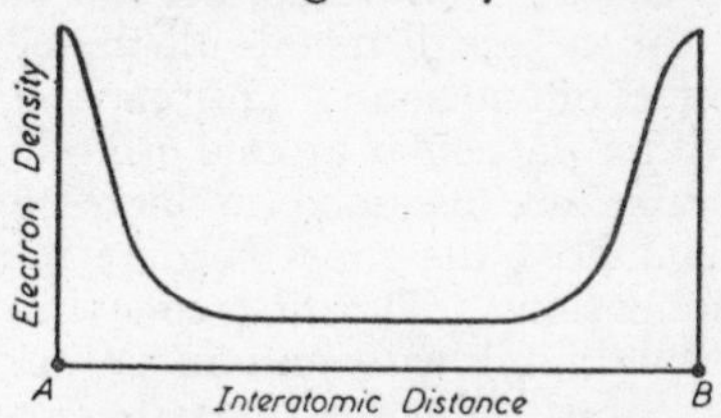

Figure 56. Variation of electron density in metallic magnesium with distance between two neighbouring atoms A and B (by Fourier analysis)

As in a simple molecule, the electronic states in a metallic crystal must be defined by molecular orbitals and not by reference to the quantum levels originally occupied in the uncombined atoms. The single crystal is thus regarded as a very large molecule and the energy of the crystal will consist of the interaction energies of the electrons and nuclei, and of the kinetic energy of the electrons. The latter quantity can be obtained by considering the electrons located in a box of volume V, and assuming that the electrons move in a field of constant potential. We then obtain (see Chapter 18)

$$E = \frac{h^2}{8mV^{2/3}}\left(n_1^2 + n_2^2 + n_3^2\right) \qquad \ldots.(13.1)$$

where h is Planck's constant, m is the mass of the electron and n_1, n_2 and n_3 are three quantum numbers which may have only positive integral values, *i.e.* 1, 2, 3 .... *etc.* The energies of the possible electronic states are thus characterized by the squares of the three positive integers. Each state, according to Pauli's principle, may contain only two electrons, therefore only two electrons occupy the lowest level when $n_1^2 = n_2^2 = n_3^2 = 1$, the next electron pair must occupy the next higher energy level and hence even at the absolute zero of temperature, the electrons will still possess kinetic energy. At the absolute zero the levels will be successively filled by electrons and the total kinetic energy will be a minimum ; if there are N electrons, then $N/2$ states are filled. At higher temperatures, higher energy levels may be occupied by the electrons. The interval between successive energy levels is $h^2/8mV^{2/3}$ and since h is of the order of 10^{-27} erg sec and m is of the order of 10^{-28} gm, the interval between successive levels becomes appreciable only when V is of atomic dimensions. When V is large compared with atomic dimensions and the number of electrons is considerable *e.g.* 10^{22}, the energy levels are so close together that the uncertainty principle prevents us from assigning a particular electron to a particular state and the states may be regarded as forming a continuous series of energy levels, although it must be remembered that the Pauli exclusion principle still holds.

In a real metallic crystal, however, the potential field is not constant but periodic and increases, as we have seen (*Figure 56*), to a maximum at each metal ion and falls to a minimum between the ions. The solution of the appropriate wave equation shows that the electrons cannot assume any value between zero and the maximum energy value, but that there are certain permitted zones of energy values between which there are discontinuities or bands of forbidden energies. Within the limits of any one zone the arrangement of the electronic energy levels does not differ significantly from that of the free electron in a constant potential field.

In the alkali metals all the electrons may be accommodated within the limits of one zone. This may be shown by comparing the zone in a crystal with a particular atomic orbital. If the interatomic distances in the crystal lattice are assumed to increase, but with the retention of the original symmetry, the zones become narrower and are finally reduced to atomic dimensions. The first zone in a crystal of sodium corresponds to the *s* orbital and will contain N energy levels, *i.e.* it can accommodate $2N$ electrons. But for these there are only N electrons for which $N/2$ levels are sufficient for their accommodation. Therefore one half of the levels of the first zone remain unoccupied. The differences in energy between the individual levels of the zone is not great and excitation of the electrons takes place easily ; in this fact lies the explanation of metallic properties.

In other metals the situation may be more complex. Sometimes the first zone may be insufficient to accommodate all the electrons, or overlapping of the zones may take place. In the former situation, the electrons are divided amongst zones separated by forbidden regions, and excitation as in the case of sodium cannot occur. This occurs in diamond where the zones corresponding to the atomic orbitals of carbon are divided and the electrons are concentrated along lines joining neighbouring atoms, thus forming localized, homopolar bonds.

In the analogues of carbon having higher atomic number, the *s* and *p* orbitals are more spread out and in consequence overlapping of zones occurs, causing the appearance of metallic properties. Thus there is a gradual transition of the bond type from the metallic to the homopolar.

For example, in bismuth, the electrons of each atom participating in homopolar bonds with its three nearest neighbours may be partially free and hence responsible for the metallic properties and for the bonds between the layers of covalently bonded atoms.

The structure of alloys— When two or more metals are melted together in suitable proportions a homogeneous solution often results. On cooling, the homogeneous solid is termed a solid solution, since as in a liquid solution, the atoms are distributed in a random fashion. If the structure of the solid solution is identical with that of one of the components (the solvent) the solution is termed a primary or α solid solution. Primary solid solutions are of two types : interstitial solid solutions, in which the atoms of the dissolved substance are situated in the holes between the atoms of the solvent and substitution solid solutions in which the solute atoms have taken the place of solvent atoms in the lattice of the latter.

In a close packed array of atoms, two kinds of holes are formed between the spheres. The first is formed by four spheres in contact and a solute atom placed in such a hole will have four nearest neighbours arranged tetrahedrally around it. Such holes are generally referred to as tetrahedral holes. The second is formed by six spheres in contact, and a solute atom placed at the centre would have six nearest neighbours forming an octahedral group around it, and the holes are therefore referred to as octahedral holes. Clearly there is an upper limit to the size of atoms that can be accommodated in such holes and taking the radius of the close packed atoms as unity, the maximum radii are 0·41 for an atom in a tetrahedral hole and 0·59 in an octahedral hole. Solid solutions in which the maximum radius is exceeded, with resulting deformation of the original lattice, are known, but the divergence from the theoretical radius is generally not very great ; *e.g.* for carbon dissolved in iron the ratio is 0·63.

Interstitial solid solutions are only formed between the non-metals possessing small atoms : hydrogen, boron, carbon and nitrogen, and the metals of the transition group. Other metals of the first and second groups generally tend to form with these non-metals, not interstitial solutions, but ionic lattices, *e.g.* calcium carbide. Since the total proportion of the volume occupied by the atoms, as represented by spheres of two sizes, has increased, the interstitial compounds are much harder and melt at much higher temperatures compared with the original metal.

In a substitution solid solution two possibilities arise : the distribution of the atoms may be entirely random throughout the lattice, or at particular ratios of the constituent atoms an ordered arrangement may exist in the crystal. Such a solid solution is termed a superlattice.

A number of factors determine the formation of solid solutions :

1 The two substances must be chemically similar ; if they differ considerably in electronegativity, the tendency will be for the formation of compounds rather than solid solutions.

2 The relative size of the atoms is important. According to HUME-ROTHERY, MABBOTT and EVANS[5], a continuous series of solid solutions may be formed over the whole range of concentrations if the sizes of the atoms of the two metals do not differ by more than 15 per cent. The limiting value of this ratio is by no means definitely established and depends to some extent on other factors such as the coordination number.

3 The mutual solubilities of metals are not reciprocal. A metal of low valency is more likely to dissolve one of higher valency than *vice versa.* For example, in the solid solutions of copper and silicon, a silicon atom may replace four copper atoms in the copper lattice, but a copper atom, with only a single valency electron, cannot replace a silicon atom which is linked tetrahedrally with four other silicon atoms. Hence the solubility of silicon in copper is 14 per cent but that of copper in silicon only 2 per cent. In a similar way tin dissolves only 1 per cent of silver whereas silver can dissolve up to 12·2 per cent of tin.

When the α phase, *i.e.* the primary solid solution, has only a limited range of stability, other intermediate phases are formed. At particular concentrations of the second component a transformation from one crystal structure to another takes place. In a large number of binary systems, *e.g.* Cu-Au, Cu-Al, Cu-Sn, a transition from the cubic close packed structure of copper to a body centred cubic structure (β phase) occurs at a particular concentration. The β phase is stable over a particular range of concentration and at higher concentrations is generally converted to the γ-phase which has a complex structure, followed by the ϵ and η phases which are hexagonal close packed structures. Each phase has a definite range of stability and Hume-Rothery obtained empirical rules connecting the composition of the phases with the ratio of the number of valency electrons N to the number of atoms N_A. In order to obtain these values it was found necessary to consider that the number of valency electrons of the elements iron, copper, nickel, ruthenium, rhenium, palladium, osmium, iridium and praseodymium was zero. The values of the ratio N/N_A are given in *Table CXL* and it is evident that each particular phase coincides with a particular ratio of the number of valency electrons to atoms, although the phase may be stable over a considerable range of concentration.

An attempt at a theoretical approach to this problem has been made

Table CXL. Ratio of Number of Valency Electrons to Number of Atoms

β Phase	
CuZn, CuBe, AgZn, AgCd, AgMg, AuZn	$\frac{1+2}{2} = \frac{3}{2}$
Ag_3Al, Cu_3Al	$\frac{3+3}{4} = \frac{3}{2}$
Cu_5Sn	$\frac{5+4}{6} = \frac{3}{2}$
γ Phase	
Cu_5Zn_8, Cu_5Cd_8, Ag_5Zn_8, Au_5Zn_8	$\frac{5+16}{13} = \frac{21}{13}$
Cu_9Al_4, Cu_9Ga_4, Ag_9Al_4	$\frac{9+12}{13} = \frac{21}{13}$
$Cu_{31}Sn_8$, $Ag_{31}Sn_8$	$\frac{31+32}{39} = \frac{21}{13}$
Fe_5Zn_{21}, Pt_5Zn_{21}, Ni_5Zn_{21}	$\frac{0+42}{26} = \frac{21}{13}$
ε Phase	
$CuZn_3$, $CuCd_3$, $AgZn_3$, $AgCd_3$, $AuZn_3$, $AuCd_3$, $CuBe_3$, $AuHg_3$	$\frac{1+6}{4} = \frac{7}{4}$
Cu_3Sn, Cu_3Ge	$\frac{3+4}{4} = \frac{7}{4}$
Ag_5Al_3, Au_5Al_3	$\frac{5+9}{8} = \frac{7}{4}$

by MOTT and JONES[6]. It might be expected that the structure of a definite phase would be stable so long as all the electrons can be arranged in the energy levels of a particular zone. When this zone has become fully occupied, the remaining electrons must occupy levels in a higher zone separated from the first by a forbidden region. On the basis of the assumption of a continuous sequence of levels in a field of constant potential, the energy of the highest occupied energy level is given by :

$$E_{max} = \frac{h^2}{8m}\left(\frac{3N}{\pi V}\right)^{2/3} \quad \ldots.(13.2)$$

where N is the number of electrons in volume V (for derivation see Chapter 18). To each electron with a kinetic energy $E = \frac{1}{2} mv^2$, there will correspond a wavelength given by :

$$\lambda = h/mv = h/(2mE)^{1/2} \quad \ldots.(13.3)$$

If the electrons occupy all possible levels up to E_{max}, then the minimum wave length will be :

$$\lambda_{min} = 2(\pi/3)^{1/3}.(V/N)^{1/3} \quad \ldots.(13.4)$$

The greater the number of electrons N, the greater will be the number of energy levels occupied and hence the larger the value of E_{max}. From equation 13.4, however, the greater the value of N, the smaller will be λ_{min} and it may become sufficiently small to satisfy Bragg's law of reflexion,

$$\lambda = 2d \sin \theta \quad \ldots.(13.5)$$

where d represents the distance between the planes of the crystal and θ is the angle or reflexion. It is possible to show that if λ satisfies this equation it corresponds to the upper limit of the filled zone and the electron may no longer enter the crystal, since if it did it would undergo total reflexion. If the energy of the electron were increased, however,

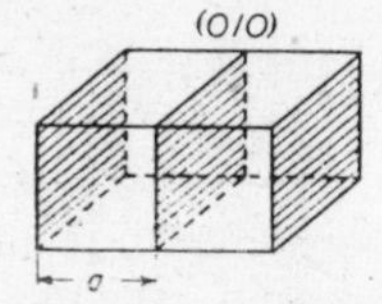

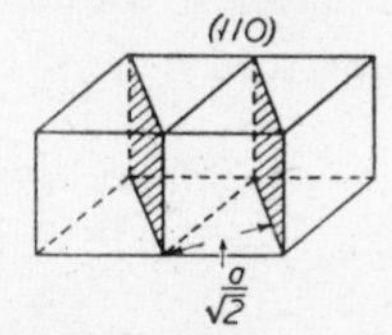

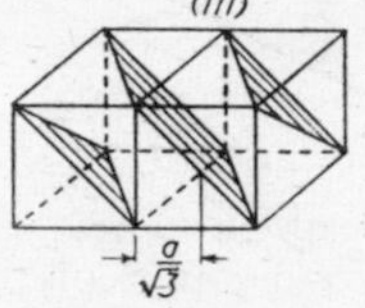

Figure 57. Distances between planes in a cubic crystal

it would occupy a level in a higher zone. A structure in which the number of electrons is less than critical is stable, but the addition of electrons above the critical value produces an unstable condition which is compensated by a rearrangement of the structures with a different sequence of zones and another critical wavelength. The maximum value of the wavelength which will cause reflexion at a given distance between the planes is

$$\lambda_{crit} = 2d \quad \ldots.(13.6)$$

For face centred cubic crystals the lattice planes (010), (110) and (111) are represented in *Figure 57*. The distance between the (111) planes is $a/\sqrt{3}$, where a is the lattice constant given by :

$$d = a/(h^2 + k^2 + l^2)^{1/2}$$

and h, k and l are the indices of the faces. From equation 13.6 the critical wavelength will be given by

$$\lambda_{crit} = 2a/\sqrt{3} \quad \ldots.(13.7)$$

In the unit cell of such a crystal with volume a^3 there are four atoms, so that

$$a^3 = 4V/N_A \quad \ldots.(13.8)$$

where N_A is the number of atoms in the volume V. From equations 13.7 and 13.8 we have

$$\lambda_{crit} = \frac{2}{\sqrt{3}}\left(\frac{4V}{N_A}\right)^{1/3} \quad \ldots.(13.9)$$

The dependence of λ on the number of electrons is given by equation 13.4 and on combining 13.4 with 13.9 we obtain the condition for reflexion of the electrons :

$$2(\pi/3)^{1/3}(V/N)^{1/3} = \frac{2}{\sqrt{3}}\left(\frac{4V}{N_A}\right)^{1/3} \quad \ldots.(13.10)$$

From equation 13.10 it follows that the ratio of the number of electrons to the number of atoms at the critical state is

$$N/N_A = \pi\sqrt{3}/4 = 1{\cdot}362 \quad \ldots.(13.11)$$

Thus the α phase will become unstable when $N/N_A = 1{\cdot}362$ and this electronic concentration limits the region in which the structure of the solid solution can be identical with that of the solvent. The experimental values for N/N_A at the limit of stability of the α phase for several systems is given in *Table CXLI.* For two metals with the same number of valency electrons $N/N_A = 1$ at all concentrations of the components, so that there is no obstruction to the formation of a complete series of solid solutions.

In the β phase, which has a body centred cubic structure, the planes which are the greatest distance apart are the (110) planes. For these

$$\lambda_{crit} = 2a/\sqrt{2} \quad \ldots.(13.12)$$

In a unit cell there are two atoms, and making a similar calculation to that given above we obtain :

$$N/N_A = \pi\sqrt{2}/3 = 1{\cdot}480 \quad \ldots.(13.13)$$

The experimental values of N/N_A for the β phase vary from 1·48 to 1·50 with the exception of the Cu-Al alloy which gives 1·37. An analogous treatment for the γ and ϵ phases may be made, but is more complex. In these cases also the agreement between the theoretical values and the experimental data is good. The electron : atom ratio is not always correct, however, because other factors, such as the dimensions of the atoms and other energy relationships, may introduce complicating factors.

MOLECULAR CRYSTALS

The crystals of such inorganic substances as carbon dioxide and the hydrogen halides and of the majority of organic substances are composed of molecules bound together by van der Waal's forces. If the molecule has a relatively simple structure and only a small polarity, the heat of sublimation is found to be small and for such molecules, LONDON[7] has calculated the heats of sublimation assuming that only dispersion forces are responsible for the intermolecular attraction. The attraction energy is considered to be given by $E = -C/r^6$ where r is the distance between the molecules and $C = \frac{3}{4}\alpha^2 I$ (see equation 12.3). In addition to non-polar or weakly polar molecules, *e.g.* N_2, CO, CH_4, *etc*, London considered also certain dipolar molecules, *e.g.* HCl, HBr, HI, *etc*; disregard of the dipole-dipole forces in these cases was considered justifiable since in the crystals such molecules are in a state of constant rotation so that the effect of the dipole is considerably reduced. The various quantities necessary for such calculations, together with the calculated and experimental values of the heats of sublimation are given in *Table CXLII*. The lack of agreement between the values is not surprising since repulsion, dipole and quadrupole forces were neglected[8]. Nevertheless, it is seen that dispersion forces do give values for the heats of sublimation which are of the right order of magnitude.

Table CXLI. Electron : Atom Ratios for Maximum Solubility in α Phase

α–phase	N/N_A	*α–phase*	N/N_A
Cu–Zn	1·384	Ag–Cd	1·425
Cu–Al	1·408	Ag–Zn	1·378
Cu–Ga	1·406	Ag–Hg	1·35
Cu–Si	1·420	Ag–In	1·40
Cu–Ge	1·360	Ag–Al	1·408
Cu–Sn	1·270	Ag–Ga	1·380
		Ag–Sn	1·366

More complex molecules possess greater polarizabilities and the dispersion forces between the molecules in the crystal are greater. Furthermore, other complicating factors may be introduced, such as the existence of polar groups which will produce strong dipole-dipole or dipole-induced dipole forces, and the distribution of the polar groups throughout the molecule. The latter factor is illustrated by the different heats of sublimation of the isomeric fumaric and maleic acids (*Table CXLIII*). The effect[9] of increasing size and polarity of the molecule on the heat of sublimation is shown in the *Table CXLIII*.

Table CXLII. Heats of Sublimation Calculated from Dispersion Forces between Atoms and Molecules

Substance	*Density gm/cc*	*Ionization Potential kcals*	*Polarizability cc*	*Heat of sublimation kcals*	
				Theoretical	*Experimental value extrapolated to 0°K*
Ne	1·46	494	0·40	0·40	0·59
Ar	1·70	361	1·66	1·80	2·03
Kr	3·2	321	2·54	3·10	2·80
N_2	1·03	391	1·74	1·61	1·86
O_2	1·43	299	1·57	1·48	2·06
CO	1·0	329	1·99	1·86	2·09
CH_4	0·53	334	2·58	2·47	2·70
Cl_2	2·00	419	4·60	7·18	7·43
HCl	1·56	315	2·63	4·04	5·05
HBr	2·73	306	3·58	4·53	5·52
HI	3·58	292	5·4	6·7	6·21
NO	1·58	235	1·76	2·04	4·29

As is to be expected from the difference in the nature of chemical and van der Waal's forces, the distances between atoms in a molecule and between adjacent atoms of different molecules in a crystal, differ considerably. The bond length between two atoms is a fairly constant quantity, differing only slightly from one molecule to another. Intermolecular distances on the other hand, in addition to being much greater

Table CXLIII. Heat of Sublimation of Organic Crystals

Substance	*Heat of sublimation kcals*	*Substance*	*Heat of sublimation kcals*
Benzene ..	9·8	*o–Dinitrobenzene*	20·7
Naphthalene	15·9	*m–Dinitrobenzene*	19·4
Phenanthrene	20·1	*p–Dinitrobenzene*	21·2
Anthracene ..	22·3	*p–Nitraniline*	23·6
Diphenyl ..	16·4	*Fumaric acid*	32·5
Benzoic acid	20·1	*Maleic acid*	26·3

(see *Table CXLIV*), are also more variable. For example, the distance between adjacent carbon atoms in different molecules varies from 3·4 Å to 4·1 Å.

The shape and size of a molecule are the factors which determine the form of the crystal lattice, and BERNAL has distinguished between five main classes of organic molecules : simple molecules, *e.g.* CH_4, $CO(NH_2)_2$; molecules containing a long hydrocarbon chain, *e.g.* the higher paraffins and their derivatives ; molecules composed of planar rings, *e.g.* aromatic compounds ; complex molecules in three dimensions, *e.g.* the terpenes ; high polymeric compounds.

Table CXLIV. Interatomic Distances in One Molecule and Neighbouring Molecules in a Crystal

Substance	*Distance between atoms Å*			
	Within the molecule		*Between atoms in neighbouring molecules*	
Ethane	C—C,	1·54	C...C	3·64
Ethylene	C=C,	1·34	C...C	3·8
Hexamethylbenzene	C_{ar}—C_{ar}	1·42	C_{ar}...C_{ar}	3·69
Hexamethylenetetramine			C...C	3·72
m-Dinitrobenzene			C...C	3·82
Naphthalene	C_{ar}—C_{ar}	1·41	C...C	3·6
Anthracene	C_{ar}—C_{ar}	1·41	CH_3...CH_3	3·7
Durene	C_{ar}—C_{ar}	1·41	CH_3...CH_3	3·9
Dibenzyl	C_{ar}—C_{ar}	1·41	CH_2...CH_2	4·1
	C_{al}—C_{al}	1·58	C_{ar}...C_{ar}	3·7
Chrysine	C_{al}—C_{ar}	1·41	C...C	3·4
Nonacosane	C—C	1·55	CH_2...CH_2	3·6–3·9
Carbon dioxide	C—O	1·07	O...O	3·23 and 3·45

In the methane crystal, the molecules are in constant rotation and therefore possess spherical symmetry. The crystal lattice of methane may therefore be regarded as a close packed structure of spheres with a radius of 2·28 Å. The cubic type of close packed structure is adopted and the distance between atoms of hydrogen of neighbouring molecules is not less than 2·5 Å compared with the interatomic distance in the molecule of 1·78 Å. Carbon tetrabromide and carbon tetraiodide also give a cubic lattice and in the tetradiodides of both carbon and silicon the iodine atoms form an approximately face centred cubic lattice, the distance between the atoms of iodine in different molecules being only slightly greater than the distance in one molecule, the dispersion forces between the readily polarizable iodine atoms being responsible for the compact structure. The crystal of ethane may be regarded as a close packed system of ellipsoids, formed as a result of the rotation of the H_3C—CH_3 molecules.

Molecules containing a long hydrocarbon chain are arranged in the crystal so that the chains are parallel, the chains themselves being close packed ; in such an arrangement the dispersion interaction between the molecules is at a maximum. As the hydrocarbon chain length is increased, the number of bonds per molecule taking part in dispersion interaction with the neighbouring molecules is increased and it is consequently more difficult to separate the molecules. Heats and temperatures of melting and sublimation therefore increase with increasing chain length.

Where one end of the molecule is polar and the other end non-polar, as in the mono-carboxylic acids, it is possible to distinguish between two types of intermolecular bonding, produced either by the interaction of the polar groups, which will be caused by van der Waal's forces of the dipole-dipole type, and in carboxyl and certain other groups by hydrogen bonding, or by dispersion interaction of the non-polar hydrocarbon chains. The structure in the lattice of a carboxylic acid will therefore be :

```
                                          O  H—O
                                         //      \
—CH2—CH3  CH3—CH2 ..... CH2—C              C—CH2..... CH2—CH3  CH3—CH2—
                                          \      //
                                          O—H  O
```

Molecules will always tend to become arranged in that position which permits maximum bonding, whether this be due to dispersion forces, dipole forces or hydrogen bonding. For example, the molecules of urea in the crystal are arranged so that each $-NH_2$ group is surrounded by the atoms of oxygen of the neighbouring molecules. The O ···· H—N distance is between 2·98 and 3·03 Å.

Ice— The formation of hydrogen bonds between the oxygen atoms of the H_2O molecule plays a significant part in the structure of the ice crystal. The molecules are arranged so that the oxygen atom of a given molecule is linked by hydrogen bonds to the oxygen atom of two other molecules, whilst both hydrogen atoms of the given molecule form, in turn, hydrogen bonds with the atom of oxygen of two other neighbouring molecules :

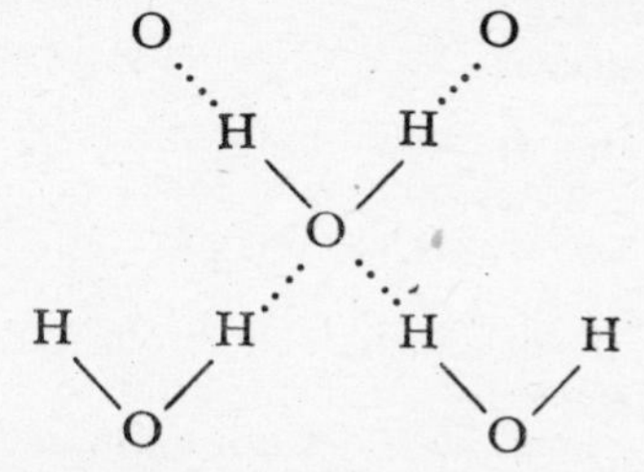

Each oxygen atom is therefore surrounded tetrahedrally by four other oxygen atoms and it takes part in two homopolar and two hydrogen bonds ; the distance between the oxygen atoms is 2·76 Å. The structure is very similar in general configuration to one of the forms of the SiO_2 lattice.

The lattice obtained by arranging the water molecules in this way is an open network with considerable space between the molecules. The crystal could be constructed in a much more compact manner by arranging the separate molecules in one of the close packed structures, thus surrounding each molecule by twelve others. Such a structure, composed of spheres 2·76 Å in diameter, would have a molecular volume of 9 cc, compared with the actual value for ice of 19·6 cc. In the close packed structure, although the dispersion forces between the molecules would be increased, the gain of energy would not offset the loss of energy due to the breaking of the hydrogen bonds since with the close packed structure it is impossible to achieve the most favourable mutual orientation of all the polar OH groups of the molecules.

The x-ray investigation of water shows that the tetrahedral lattice present in ice is preserved to a considerable extent in the liquid state. The intermolecular distances, however, are not constant, indicating that the intermolecular bonds in the liquid state are less strong than in the solid state, thus permitting movement of the molecules, *i.e.* free diffusion, to occur. The molecular volume of liquid water is 18 cc. The decrease of the value compared with that of ice is evidently due to the partial destruction of the open lattice of ice, thereby permitting single molecules to occupy the spaces in the lattice. This tendency to form the close packed structure, however, is not great, as is shown by a comparison of the values for the molecular volume : water, 18 cc ; ice, 19·6 cc ; close packed structure 9 cc. Furthermore, the heat absorbed on melting is only 1·44 kcals/gm mol, whereas that absorbed on sublimation, when all the intermolecular bonds are broken is 12·2 kcals/gm mol.

From the foregoing discussion, it is apparent that water may be regarded as very similar in structure to ice, the crystal lattice being somewhat disrupted. This introduces an important generalization, first suggested by DEBYE, that from the point of view of structure and of properties, liquids are much closer to solids than to gases. On increasing the temperature, thermal motion of the molecules will decrease their orientation and the bond between the molecules is therefore weakened. This will tend to produce an increased molecular volume, but since this process also produces single molecules which may occupy the holes in the lattice and thus decrease the volume, we have two opposing effects. It is these two effects which are responsible for the maximum density of water occurring at 4°C.

COORDINATION LATTICES

The majority of inorganic compounds form a coordination lattice in the crystalline state. In such a lattice each atom or ion is surrounded by a particular number of nearest neighbours, corresponding to its coordination number. The bonding forces between the atoms or ions are covalent and electrostatic respectively and it is an important feature of these compounds that a simple molecule, corresponding to the ratio of the various atoms and ions in the compound does not exist, the whole crystal being a single molecule.

A very large number of inorganic compounds crystallize in a relatively small number of simple lattice forms which we shall now describe briefly.

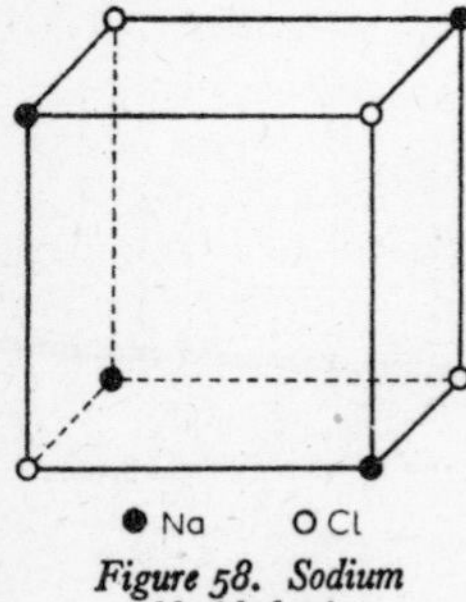

Figure 58. Sodium chloride lattice

The sodium chloride lattice is a simple cubic lattice in which the sodium and chloride ions are located at the alternate corners of a cube (*Figure 58*). Each sodium ion is thus surrounded by six chloride ions and each chloride ion by six sodium ions.

Caesium chloride crystallizes in a body centred cubic lattice, the coordination number of both the caesium and the chloride ions being eight. The caesium chloride lattice may be regarded as two simple cubic systems, one of caesium ions and one of chloride ions, placed so as to interlace with each other.

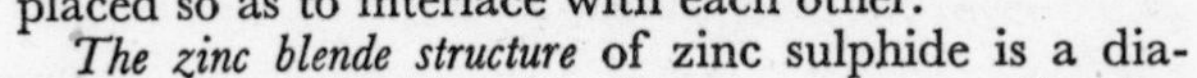

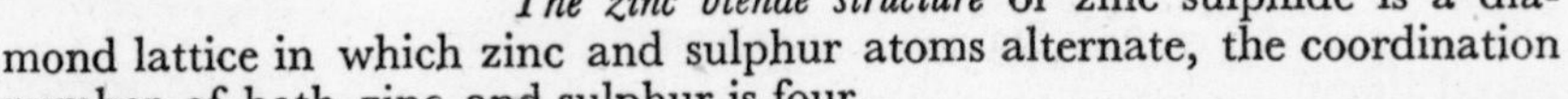

The zinc blende structure of zinc sulphide is a diamond lattice in which zinc and sulphur atoms alternate, the coordination number of both zinc and sulphur is four.

The wurtzite structure of zinc sulphide and of zincite, ZnO, is also a tetrahedral structure (*Figure 59*) and the coordination number of both elements is four ; the difference between the wurtzite and the zinc blende structures is that in the latter the atoms of the various layers are located above each other, whereas in the diamond (zinc blende) structure, the

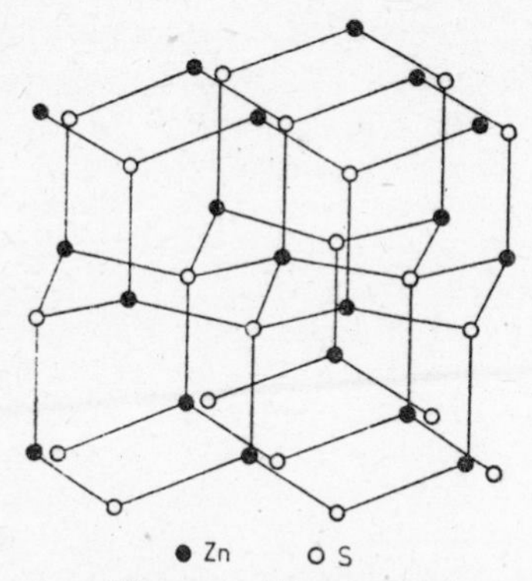

Figure 59. Wurtzite lattice

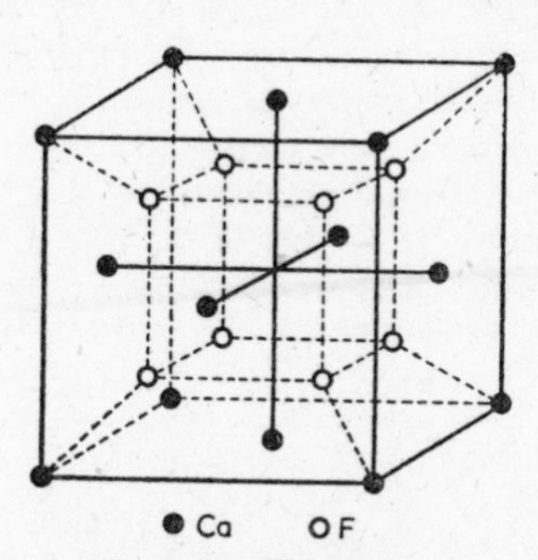

Figure 60. Fluorite lattice

tetrahedra are displaced so that the holes of one layer are occupied by an atom in the adjacent layer.

The fluorite (CaF_2) *lattice* is closely related to the body centred cubic structure of caesium chloride. Since the calcium carries a double positive charge, there are only half the number of calcium ions compared with fluoride ions. If we remove every other ion from the body centred cubic structure we obtain the fluorite lattice (*Figure 60*) in which every Ca^{2+} ion is surrounded by eight F^- ions and every F^- ion surrounded by four Ca^{2+} ions.

The rutile (TiO_2) *lattice* is somewhat more complex. The titanium atoms (black circles in *Figure 61*) are located at the apices and at the centre of a right angled parallelepiped. Two atoms of oxygen (open circles, *Figure 61*) lie along the diagonal of the upper face and two on the diagonal of the lower face. The numbers given refer only to the atoms of oxygen within the unit cell; in *Figure 61* some of the oxygen atoms lying in adjacent crystal

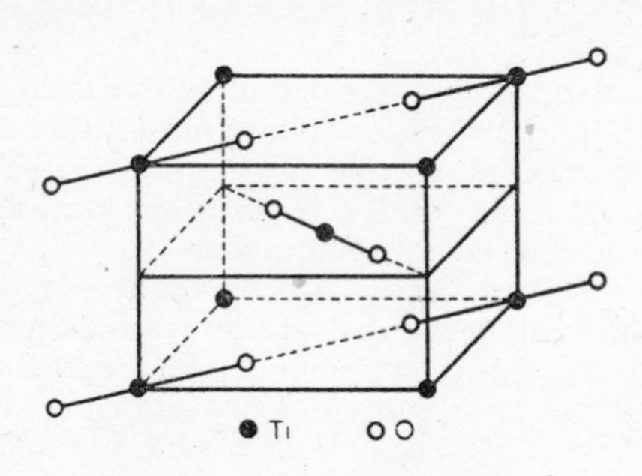

Figure 61. Lattice of Rutile TiO_2

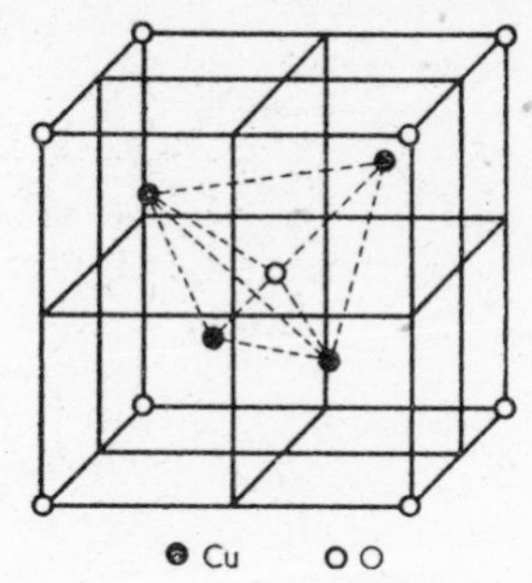

Figure 62. Cuprite lattice

cells are also shown. A further two oxygen atoms lie in the plane of the central titanium atom. Each atom of titanium is thus surrounded by six atoms of oxygen and each oxygen atom by three atoms of titanium. This lattice may be regarded as a transitional type between the ionic and the molecular in that it is possible to distinguish molecules of TiO_2.

The cuprite (Cu_2O) *lattice* is shown in *Figure 62* and consists of a body centred cubic arrangement of oxygen atoms. If this cube is divided into eight smaller cubes and at the centre of each alternate small cube is placed a copper atom, we obtain the cuprite structure. The copper atoms thus form a tetrahedron within the body centred cubic structure of oxygen atoms. Each oxygen atom is thus surrounded tetrahedrally by four copper atoms and each copper atom is located between two oxygen atoms, the three atoms being linear.

Silica (SiO_2) forms six different structures, α and β quartz, α and β tridymite and α and β cristobalite. The tridymite structure is analogous to the zinc blende and cristobalite to the wurtzite structure of zinc sulphide each oxygen atom being located linearly between two atoms of silicon. The exact details of these structures have not, however, been worked out and the nature of the α to β transition is not known. The structure of α and β quartz which is more common than the other two forms is also not known with certainty ; the Si—O—Si angle, however, is not 180°.

The cadmium iodide lattice is shown in *Figure 63* and is an example of a layer lattice. Each plane consists of a cubic close packed structure consisting of three layers only of cadmium and iodine atoms. The cadmium atoms form the central layer and in the unit cell (*Figure 63*) the close packed elementary layer of seven cadmium atoms has two groups of three

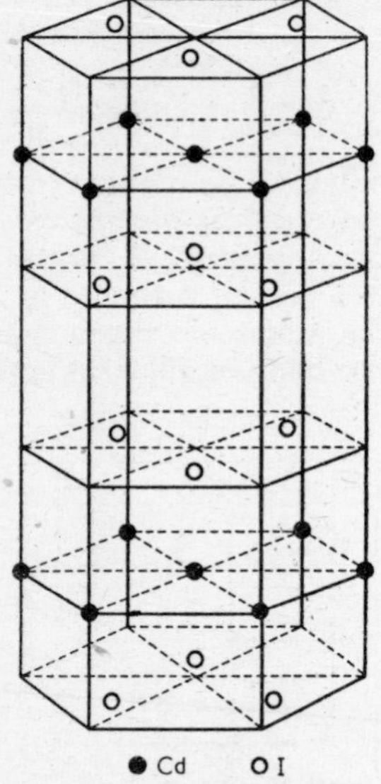

Figure 63. Cadmium iodide lattice

Cl^- Na^+

Figure 64. Sodium chloride ion pair

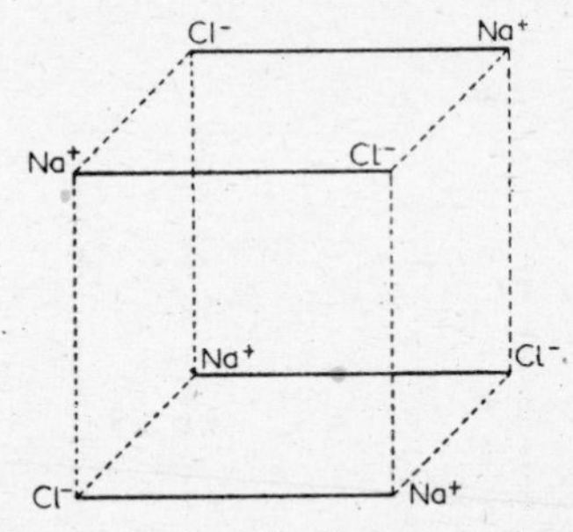

Figure 65. Four sodium chloride ion pairs forming a cube

iodine atoms arranged as a triangle above and below. The mutual orientation of the two triangles is such that the holes not filled by one layer are filled by the other (the configuration, according to *Figure 48*, is CAB). Each cadmium atom is thus surrounded by six iodine atoms, three above and three below, and by six other cadmium atoms. The various planes of cadmium and iodine atoms are placed one on top of the other to form a layer lattice.

Of the various lattices considered above, in those of NaCl, CsCl, CaF_2,

ZnS, SiO_2 and CdI_2 the division of the crystal into single molecules is impossible. Only in TiO_2 is there a suggestion of a molecular unit. Such formulae as NaCl, CsCl *etc* thus represent the ratio of the different species of atoms or ions present in the crystal and not the formula of a single molecule. We must now consider the nature of the forces producing the various crystal structures.

IONIC CRYSTALS

The crystal of sodium chloride consists of an ordered array of Na^+ ions and Cl^- ions which are held in a stable configuration by the Coulomb forces acting between the ions. In the gaseous state, where the NaCl ion-pair (molecule) has a separate existence, the force between the ions is $-e^2/r$. Unlike homopolar forces, electrostatic forces do not show saturation and electrostatic interaction will occur with all the neighbouring ions, so that when two NaCl ion pairs are brought together to form a rectangle, as shown in *Figure 64*, the energy of attraction will be the sum of the various attraction energies between ions of different charge and the repulsion energies of ions of like charge, *i.e.*

$$E = -4e^2/r + 2e^2/r\sqrt{2} = -2{\cdot}57e^2/r = -1{\cdot}285 . 2e^2/r$$

This value is greater than the sum of the energies of the two ion-pairs taken individually, *viz* $-2e^2/r$, and hence the rectangular configuration is the more stable. If four molecules are arranged in the form of a cube (*Figure 65*) the total interaction energy becomes

$$E = -12e^2/r - 4e^2/r\sqrt{3} + 12e^2/r\sqrt{2} = -5{\cdot}8e^2/r = -1{\cdot}45 \times 4e^2/r$$

which is to be compared with the value $-4e^2/r$, the sum of the ionic attraction in four separate ion-pairs. We see, therefore, that the union of ions into large aggregates brings about a gain of energy which is of the same order of magnitude as a single ionic bond. Thus on bringing two ion-pairs together, the increase in energy over $2e^2/r$ is 28 per cent, for four molecules the gain over the value of $4e^2/r$ is 45 per cent, and in the limiting case for an infinite crystal the gain in energy is 75 per cent. These figures are based on the assumption that the interionic distance in the crystal is the same as in the lone ion-pair. This is not so and as will be shown later the equilibrium interionic distance in the crystal is 13 per cent greater than in the gaseous molecule. The gain in energy of the

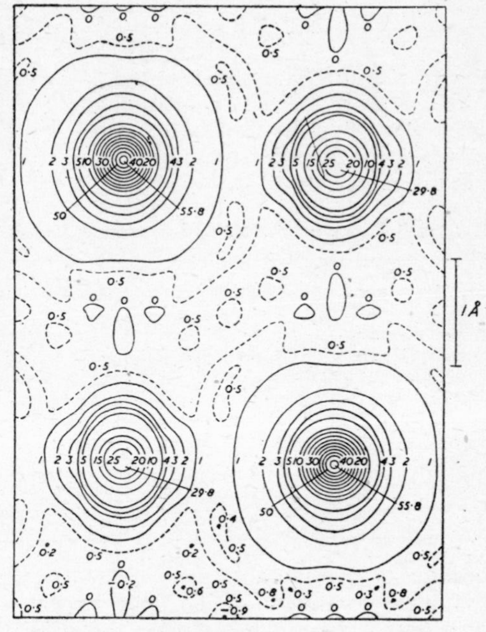

Figure 66. Variation of electron density in sodium chloride lattice

infinite lattice is therefore somewhat less than 75 per cent. This gain in energy is indicated by the stability of ionic lattices and their large heats of sublimation *e.g.* for NaCl, 55 kcals/gm mol.

When two sodium chloride molecules are arranged as shown in *Figure 64*, the weight of the ionic state in each molecule will be increased, since this will cause a further gain of electrostatic energy. The crystals of salts similar to sodium chloride, though not necessarily of the same crystal structure, will thus consist almost entirely of ions. This picture is confirmed by x-ray data, which shows (*Figure 66*) that the electron cloud is concentrated on the ionic centres and rapidly decreases with increase of distance. Between the ions the density falls to zero. From the x-ray data the number of electrons centred on each atom may be obtained and for the NaCl crystal the values are found to be sodium 9·98 and chlorine 17·72, which closely correspond to the theoretical figures of 10 and 18 for Na^+ and Cl^- respectively. In the liquid state and in solution these substances have high conductivity owing to the existence and freedom of motion of the ions.

The electronic energy of the ionic crystal may be obtained from the sum of the energies of all possible pairs of ions of like and unlike charge :

$$E = \Sigma \frac{z_i z_k e^2}{r_{ik}} \qquad \ldots .(13.14)$$

where z_i and z_k represent the charges on two ions i and k, and r_{ik} represents the interionic distances. Each value of r_{ik} may be expressed in terms of r, the shortest distance between two ions of unlike charge in the crystal. We can then write equation 13.14, for 1 gm mol of a crystal, in the form :

$$E = -NAe^2/r \qquad \ldots .(13.15)$$

where N is the Avagadro number and A is Madelung's constant. Different methods exist for the calculation of Madelung's constant and these have been described by SHERMAN[10] and FRENKEL[11]. Values for Madelung's constant for different types of crystal, calculated on the basis of 1 gm mol are given in *Table CXLV*.

Table CXLV. Values of Madelung's Constant for Various Crystals

Crystal structure	*Coordination number*		*Madelung's constant*
Sodium chloride	Na 6	Cl 6	1·74456
Caesium chloride	Cs 8	Cl 8	1·76267
Zincblende ..	Zn 4	S 4	1·63806
Wurtzite ..	Zn 4	S 4	1·641
Fluorite ..	Ca 8	F 4	5.03878
Cuprite ..	Cu 2	O 4	4·11552
Rutile.. ..	Ti 6	O 3	4·816
β-Quartz ..	Si 4	O 2	4·4394

In addition to the attraction and repulsion between the ions as expressed by the function $-Ae^2/r$, repulsion forces also arise between the filled electron shells of the ions. These forces fall off very rapidly with increasing distance from the ion and are sometimes represented by the expression B/r^n, where n is sufficiently large to produce a considerable decrease of the function as r increases. In the simplified treatment of the ionic crystal, it is usual to assume that the repulsion term is the same for the different charged ions, hence in the simple cubic lattice, round each ion there are 6 ions at a distance r, 12 at

$r\sqrt{2}$, 8 at $r\sqrt{3}$ *etc.* The total repulsion energy of this type will therefore be given by :

$$\frac{B}{r^n}\left(6+\frac{12}{(\sqrt{2})^n}+\frac{8}{(\sqrt{3})^n}+\ldots\ldots\right)$$

Generally, within the limits of order of the calculation, it is sufficient to consider only the first term, *i.e.* to consider only the repulsion due to the nearest neighbours. The repulsion energy then becomes BK/r^n, where K is the coordination number of the ion. The total energy of the crystal per gm mol then becomes

$$E = N(-Ae^2/r + BK/r^n) \qquad \ldots.(13.16)$$

At the equilibrium distance when $r = r_o$, the energy will have a minimum value and differentiation of equation 13.16 and equating to zero gives

$$r_o = (nBK/Ae^2)^{1/(n-1)} \qquad \ldots.(13.17)$$

and

$$E_o = -N\frac{Ae^2}{r_o}\left(1-\frac{1}{n}\right) \qquad \ldots.(13.18)$$

The quantity E is termed the lattice energy, and represents the energy required to transfer 1 gm mol of the salt from the crystalline to the gaseous state in which all the ions have a separate existence. The lattice energy is generally taken as the positive quantity $-E$.

In equation 13.18 values of A, e and r_o are known. The value of n is generally obtained from experimental data on the compressibility of the crystal. The compressibility $\varkappa$ is defined as the relative decrease in volume per unit of applied pressure. This may be written as

$$\varkappa = -V^{-1}\frac{dV}{dP} \qquad \ldots.(13.19)$$

where V is the molecular volume and P the applied pressure. If all the energy of the crystal is potential energy, $dE = -PdV$, and hence

$$\frac{dP}{dV} = -\frac{d^2E}{dV^2}$$

and combining with equation 13.19 we have,

$$\frac{d^2E}{dV^2} = -1\Big/\frac{dV}{dP} = 1/\varkappa V \qquad \ldots.(13.20)$$

V is proportional to r^3, provided that the atoms remain in the same relative positions. Let us call the proportionality constant a, which can readily be found from the geometry of the crystal. E is a function of r, as shown in equation 13.16 and hence the terms in equation 13.20 may be evaluated. It is found that

$$-4NAe^2/9a^2r^7 + n(n+3)BK/9a^2r^{n+6} = 1/\varkappa ar^3 \qquad \ldots.(13.21)$$

If $\varkappa$ is measured under conditions in which $r = r_o$, then equations 13.21 and 13.17 both give relationships between n and B and these quantities may therefore be evaluated. The values for n which have generally been used are as follows[12] : for ions with an electron structure of He, 5 ; Ne, 7 ; Ar, 9 ; Kr, 10 ; Xe, 12. Frequently the value $n = 9$ is used since the actual value is not critical.

Table CXLVI. The Contribution of Various Factors to the Lattice Energy as a percentage of the Electrostatic Energy Ae^2/r

Crystal	Repulsion according to the law B/r^n	Repulsion according to the law $\exp(-\alpha r)$	Van der Waal's interaction	Zero-point energy	Difference between E calc. from equation 13.18 and by Born and Mayer
NaCl	12·8	11·5	1·4	0·8	− 3
NaBr	7·8	10·7	1·4	0·7	4
NaI	12·6	9·6	1·8	0·6	− 7
KCl	11·4	11·3	2·1	0·8	− 2
KBr	11·0	10·6	2·0	0·7	− 2
KI	10·8	9·9	2·3	0·6	5
CsI	10·5	10·0	4·5	0·5	− 6

BORN and MAYER[18] have attempted to improve the accuracy of equation 13·18 by making certain corrections. The additional factors considered were the van der Waal's forces between the ions, the zero-point energy, and in place of the function B/r^n they introduced an exponential expression of the form $\exp(-\alpha r)$. These corrections, however, do not appreciably effect the values obtained as shown in *Table CXLVI.*

The second column of *Table CXLVII* gives the lattice energies of various crystals calculated by the method of Born and Mayer. These values must not be regarded as theoretical values, as the repulsion energy has been obtained by an empirical method. Comparison of these values with experimental values for the heat of dissociation of the crystal into gaseous ions is possible only in a few instances owing to lack of experimental data but the agreement obtained is within the limits of experimental error. An alternative method of obtaining experimental values, when the direct thermal data is lacking, is by means of the Born-Haber cycle. From thermochemical data the heats of formation of the solid crystalline salts of the alkali metal halides from the solid alkali metal and gaseous molecular halogen are known, *e.g.* for sodium chloride :

Table CXLVII. Lattice Energies

Crystal	Calculated according to Born and Mayer	Experimental value for heat of dissociation $MX_{solid} = M^+_{gas} + X^-_{gas}$	Experimental value obtained by the Born-Haber cycle
LiF	245		246
NaF	216		217
KF	193		192
RbF	183		185
CsF	176		178
LiCl	200		200
NaCl	184	181[14]	
KCl	168		167
RbCl	163		163
CsCl	156		157
LiBr	190		189
NaBr	176	176[15]	
KBr	162	160[15]	
RbBr	157	151[14]	
CsBr	150		149
LiI	176		177
NaI	166	166[15]	
KI	153	151[15] ; 154[14]	
RbI	148	146[16]	
CsI	143	141[14]	

$$Na_{solid} + \tfrac{1}{2}Cl_{2\,gas} = NaCl_{solid} \qquad \Delta H = -Q \qquad \ldots\ldots(i)$$

We also have the following data :

$$Na_{solid} = Na_{gas} \qquad \Delta H = S$$

$$Na_{gas} = Na^+_{gas} + e \qquad \Delta H = I$$

$$\tfrac{1}{2}Cl_{2\,gas} = Cl_{gas} \qquad \Delta H = \tfrac{1}{2}D$$

$$Cl_{gas} + e = Cl^-_{gas} \qquad \Delta H = -F$$

$$Na^+_{gas} + Cl^-_{gas} = NaCl_{solid} \qquad \Delta H = -E_0$$

Summing we obtain

$$Na_{solid} + \tfrac{1}{2}Cl_{2gas} = NaCl_{solid} \qquad \Delta H = S + I + \tfrac{1}{2}D - F - E_0 \qquad \ldots.(ii)$$

Combination of i and ii gives

$$S + I + \tfrac{1}{2}D - F - E_0 = - Q$$

and hence

$$E_0 = Q - F + S + I + \tfrac{1}{2}D \qquad \ldots.(iii)$$

This equation permits the calculation of the lattice energy if we know F, the electron affinity of the halogen atom, S, the heat of sublimation of the alkali metal, I, the ionization potential of the metal and D, the dissociation energy of the molecular halogen. These quantities are known, but to different orders of accuracy, and furthermore, the values should all refer to the same standard temperature, either absolute zero or room temperature, a condition which is not always fulfilled. However, the agreement between the calculated and observed values is sufficiently good to indicate that the theory developed for the lattice energy on the basis of ionic interaction is basically correct.

The theory of Born and Mayer has been extended by the work of LANDSHOFF[17] using the methods of quantum mechanics. Taking sodium chloride as an example, Landshoff accepts the assumption that the lattice consists of Na^+ and Cl^- ions and calculates the ionic interaction energy on the basis of the Heitler-London theory using the known distributions of electrons in the Na^+ and Cl^- ions. In addition to the correction terms of Born and Mayer, additional interactions related to the superposition of the electron clouds, the attraction between electrons and nuclei and the mutual repulsion of electrons are incorporated. The values obtained by this more exact method, however, differ from the values given in *Table CXLVII* by only a few kcals, the value for sodium chloride being 183 kcals.

INTERIONIC DISTANCES IN CRYSTALS

The distance between the ions in a crystal is determined by the equilibrium between the forces of attraction and repulsion. Values of the interionic distances may be obtained from x-ray data. On the basis of the Born theory of lattice energies we have,

$$r_0 = (nBK/Ae^2)^{1/(n-1)} \qquad \ldots.(13.17)$$

and r_0 is dependent on the nature of the law of repulsion, *i.e.* on n and B, the coordination number K and Madelung's constant A. If the same substance can crystallize in both a NaCl and a CsCl type lattice, then the equilibrium distances between the ions must be related by

$$\frac{r_{CsCl}}{r_{NaCl}} = \left(\frac{K_{CsCl} \cdot A_{NaCl}}{K_{NaCl} \cdot A_{CsCl}}\right)^{\frac{1}{n-1}} = \left(\frac{8}{6} \cdot \frac{1{\cdot}7476}{1{\cdot}7627}\right)^{\frac{1}{n-1}}$$

and when $n = 9$ this ratio becomes 1·036 and when $n = 12$, 1·207.

Ammonium chloride, NH_4Cl, crystallizes in a CsCl lattice up to a temperature of 174·3° C and above that temperature, in the NaCl lattice. Similar behaviour is observed with ammonium bromide (temperature of transformation 137·8° C) and ammonium iodide (temperature of transformation − 17·6° C). The interionic distances in the CsCl lattice are actually found to be approximately 3 per cent greater than in the NaCl lattice. Pauling has given the following ratios of the interionic distances for various lattices assuming $n = 9$:

$$K = 8 \rightarrow K = 6 \qquad \frac{r_{\text{CsCl}}}{r_{\text{NaCl}}} = 1{\cdot}036 \qquad \frac{r_{\text{fluorite}}}{r_{\text{rutile}}} = 1{\cdot}031$$

$$K = 4 \rightarrow K = 6 \qquad \frac{r_{\text{wurtzite or zinc-blende}}}{r_{\text{NaCl}}} = 0{\cdot}957 \qquad \frac{r_{\text{quartz}}}{r_{\text{rutile}}} = 0{\cdot}960$$

The equilibrium interionic distance in the crystal is not the same as that in the gaseous molecule (ion-pair) since in the latter the distance is determined only by the mutual interaction of two ions, whereas in the former case each ion is located in the field of all its nearest neighbours. The equilibrium interionic distance in the molecule (ion-pair) is obtained from equation 6.8 which may be written in the form

$$r_0' = (nB/e^2)^{1/(n-1)} \qquad \ldots.(13.22)$$

From equations 13.17 and 13.19, on combining we have,

$$r_0/r_0' = r_{\text{cryst}}/r_{\text{gas}} = (K/A)^{1/(n-1)} \qquad \ldots.(13.23)$$

If the value of n is taken as 9, then the ratio $r_{\text{cryst}}/r_{\text{gas}}$ becomes 1·18 for the NaCl and 1·21 for the CsCl type lattice. The experimental values obtained are: 1·13 for NaCl, NaBr, NaI, KCl, KBr, KI, RbCl, RbBr and RbI and 1·16 — 1·18 for CsCl, CsBr and CsI.

Ionic radii— The experimental determination of the interionic distance in crystals has led to the suggestion that in many crystals these distances may be correlated by assuming that each ion has a definite and constant radius, such that the sum of the ionic radii of two ions gives the interionic distance in the corresponding crystal. This concept of the additivity of the ionic radius is illustrated by the data given in *Table CXLVIII*, where the interionic distances in the crystals of the halogen compounds of the alkali metals are given. The data for CsCl, CsBr and CsI, which crystallize with a body centred cubic lattice, are shown in parentheses. All other structures are of the simple cubic type. If additivity of ionic radii is achieved, the difference between the interionic distances in such pairs of compounds as KI and KBr, NaI and NaBr, LiI and LiBr should be constant since it equals the difference of the ionic radii of iodine and bromine. These differences are found to be very approximately constant, the deviations being of the order of 0·1 Å. We may conclude therefore that for the halogen compounds of the alkali metals the conception of the ions as spheres in contact with each other is approximately correct.

Table CXLVIII. Verification of the Additivity of Ionic Radii in Ionic Lattices

Cation / Anion	Distance Å								
	Cs	Cs–Rb	Rb	Rb–K	K	K–Na	Na	Na–Li	Li
I	(3·95)	(0·29)	3·66	0·13	3·53	0·30	3·23	0·23	3·00
I–Br	(0·24)		0·23		0·24		0·25		0·25
Br	(3·71)	(0·28)	3·43	0·14	3·29	0·31	2·98	0·23	2·75
Br–Cl	(0·14)		0·16		0·15		0·17		0·18
Cl	(3·57)	(0·30)	3·27	0·13	3·14	0·33	2·81	0·24	2·57
Cl–F	(0·57)		0·45		0·48		0·50		0·56
F	3·00	0·18	2·82	0·16	2·66	0·35	2·31	0·30	2·01

The experimental data, however, give values only of the distance between two ions and therefore in order to obtain values for the individual ionic radii certain assumptions have to be made. Where the anion is large and the cation small, *e.g.* LiI, it may be assumed[18] that in the crystal the anions touch and that the radius of the anion is half the interatomic distance. In other crystals where such an assumption may not be made, other methods have to be employed to determine the ionic radii. WASASTJERNA[19] used a method based on the assumption that the molecular refraction of an ion is proportional to the cube of the radius. These values were used by GOLDSCHMIDT[20] to give a systematic table of ionic radii. The most satisfactory method, however, is that of PAULING[21]. In a crystal such as KCl, the two ions K^+ and Cl^- have the same electronic structure and differ only in the charge on the nucleus. Clearly, the K^+ ion, which has the greater nuclear charge, will draw the electrons closer to the nucleus than the Cl^- ion, so that the radius of the K^+ ion will be smaller than that of the Cl^- ion. The difference in size will depend on the effective charges on the nucleus of the ions and Pauling proposed that for the isoelectronic ions, *e.g.* K^+ and Cl^-, Na^+ and F^-, the radii are inversely proportional to the effective nuclear charges. The effective nuclear charge is equal to the actual nuclear charge, Ze, minus the screening effect, Se, of the other electrons in the ion. Values of the screening constant, S, have been obtained by theoretical calculation and experimentally[21]. The value of S for ions with the neon structure is 4·52 and the effective nuclear charges for Na^+ and F^- are thus $6{\cdot}48e$ and $4{\cdot}48e$ respectively. By dividing the interionic distance in the sodium fluoride crystal, 2·31 Å, in the inverse ratio of these values we obtain the values 0·95 Å for the ionic radius of the Na^+ ion and 1·36 Å for that of F^-. By a similar method the values for K^+, Cl^-; Rb^+, Br^-; Cs^+, I^- ions are obtained. Furthermore, knowing the ionic radius of the K^+ ion and the ratio of the effective nuclear charges of the isoelectronic ions K^+ and Ca^{2+}, the radius for the Ca^{2+} ion may be obtained. However, using the value for the ionic radius of the calcium ion obtained in this way, the calculated interionic distances for the crystals of calcium compounds do not agree with the observed values. This discrepancy was ascribed by Pauling to the doubly charged character of the calcium ion and it can be considered that the value obtained by the method described above represents the radius that the calcium ion would have, if it possessed only a single charge, *i.e.* its energy of interaction with, for example, the Cl^- ion is $-e^2/r$ and not $-2e^2/r$. The dependence of the interatomic distance on the charge on the ion, z, is given by the general form of equation 13.17

$$r_z = (nBK/Az^2e^2)^{1/(n-1)} \qquad \ldots.(13.24)$$

For singly charged ions we have,

$$r_1 = (nBK/Ae^2)^{1/(n-1)} \qquad \ldots.(13.17)$$

and hence the radii of ions with charge z and unit charge are related by

$$r_z/r_1 = z^{2/(n-1)} \qquad \ldots.(13.25)$$

By this means and using the value of n given above, Pauling derived values for the radii of a large number of ions of different charge[22] and the values are given in *Table CXLIX*. In this table we have omitted many of the poly-charged ions, such as Cl^{7+} and N^{5+} which are never encountered. The gradual variations of the radii in members of the same group and of the same period are to be expected. It is interesting to note, however, that the radii of Cu^+, Ag^+ and Au^+, which possess filled *d* orbitals, are less than those of K^+, Rb^+ and Cs^+. Similar behaviour is observed with Zn^{2+}, Cd^{2+}, Hg^{2+} and Ca^{2+}, Sr^{2+}, Ba^{2+}.

Table CXLIX. Ionic Radii (Å) *according to Pauling*

		Li^+ 0·60	Be^{2+} 0·31		
O^{2-} 1·40	F^- 1·36	Na^+ 0·95	Mg^{2+} 0·65		
S^{2-} 1·84	Cl^- 1·81	K^+ 1·33	Ca^{2+} 0·49	Cu^+ 0·96	Zn^{2+} 0·74
Se^{2-} 1·98	Br^- 1·95	Rb^+ 1·48	Sr^{2+} 1·13	Ag^+ 1·26	Cd^{2+} 0·97
Te^{2-} 2·21	I^- 2·16	Cs^+ 1·69	Ba^{2+} 1·35	Au^+ 1·37	Hg^{2+} 1·10

If the ionic radii are used to calculate the interionic distances in crystals of the sodium chloride type, good agreement is obtained with the experimental values for the salts of potassium and rubidium, but it is less satisfactory with the salts of sodium and agreement is poor for lithium. Thus in LiCl, the experimental interionic distance is 2·57 Å whereas the sum of the ionic radii is 2·41 Å, in LiBr the values are respectively 2·75 Å and 2·55 Å and in LiI 3·02 Å and 2·76 Å. In NaI the difference is 3·23 Å and 3·11 Å. On the basis of the concept of ionic radii, these discrepancies are explained by the fact that lithium ions are very small and occupy the hole formed by the packing of the large anions which are considered to be in contact. Thus the anions are not in contact with the cations, which is the basic assumption on which the conception of ionic radii rests. This explanation, however, is not entirely satisfactory since the interionic distance in lithium iodide, for example, is not twice the ionic radius of the I^- ion. In fact the equilibrium distance is established as a result of the balancing of the forces of attraction and repulsion and is not dependent on the dimensions of hypothetical stable spheres with radii equivalent to the ionic radii.

The introduction of the concept of ionic radii must make an implicit assumption concerning the variation of the repulsion energy with the interionic distance. The curve showing variation of the repulsion energy with distance which shows a steep rise as the distance is decreased, is replaced by a vertical straight line parallel to the ordinate and at a distance from it equal to the sum of the radii of the two ions. Thus it is clear that the ionic radii have no real physical meaning. This may be illustrated in another way. In *Figure 67* the variation of the density of the electronic cloud with the distance from the nucleus for the K^+ ion is shown. The vertical line at 1·33 Å corresponds to the ionic radius of K^+ (1·33 Å) and it is clear the electron density at this distance is almost insignificant and the radius does not correspond to any definite limit of the electron cloud. On the basis of *Figure 67* the value of the 'radius' might have been taken equally well at a value greater or less than 1·33 Å.

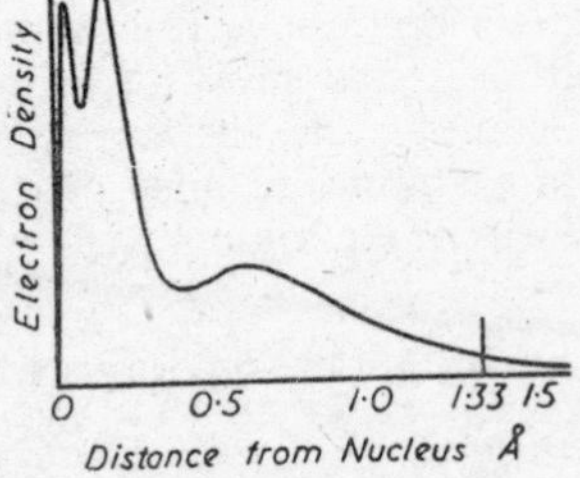

Figure 67. Variation of the electron density with distance from nucleus in potassium (K^+) *ion*

From the above discussion it will be appreciated that the magnitude of the radius assigned to a particular ion will be dependent on the particular lattice structure of the crystal. This fact explains the divergences which have been noticed for CsCl, CsBr and CsI in *Table CXLVIII*. The interionic distances in body centred cubic lattices are approximately 3 per cent greater than the sum of the radii (*Table CL*), due to the calculation of ionic radii being made almost invariably from lattices of the sodium chloride (simple cubic) type.

The wide variation of the radii of different ions has been considered as a possible explanation of the formation of different lattices, possessing different coordination numbers. In the case of the close packing of equivalent spheres it is possible, as we have seen, to pack twelve spheres round a central sphere. If, however, the surrounding ions are larger than the central ion, it is not possible for it to be in contact with more than eight, thus replacing a close packed lattice by a body centred cubic lattice. The coordination number would thus appear to be dependent on the ratio of the ionic radii. This problem may be considered quantitatively. Let us consider the CsCl type lattice and let r_a and r_c be the radii of the anion and cation respectively. The distance between the nuclei when the ions are in contact will be $r_a + r_c$, which is half the length of the diagonal of the cube. If the values for the radii are close, *i.e.* $r_a \sim r_c$, the anions will not touch. On increasing the radii of the anions, there is reached a limit when the anions are in contact. At this limiting condition the length of the edge of the cube is twice the radius of the anion, *i.e.* $2r_a$, and since the ratio of the diagonal of a cube to an edge is $\sqrt{3}/1$ we have for anion contact

Table CL. Experimental Interionic Distances and Sums of Radii in CsCl type Lattices

Salt	Experimental distance Å	Sum of radii Å	Ratio
CsCl	3·56	3·50	1·027
CsBr	3·72	3·64	1·022
CsI	3·96	3·85	(1·029)*
RbI	3·75	3·64	1·030

* Pauling's value of the radius of the Cs^+ ion given in *Table CXLIX* was obtained from the interionic distance in CsI and decreased by 2·7 per cent to conform with an NaCl lattice.

$$(r_a + r_c)/2r_a = \sqrt{3}/2$$

or

$$r_c/r_a = \sqrt{3} - 1 = 0{\cdot}732$$

This relationship establishes the lower limit of the radius ratio for which the CsCl type lattice may occur. The condition of its formation being that

$$r_c/r_a \geqslant 0{\cdot}732$$

If the radii are such that $r_c/r_a < 0{\cdot}732$, the cation cannot be in contact with eight anions, the coordination number falls to six and a lattice of the NaCl type is formed. In this case the distance between the nuclei of the anion and cation, $r_a + r_c$, is equal to the side of the cube, and the distance between the nuclei of two anions is equal to the diagonal of the face of the cube. If all the ions are in contact, we have

$$(r_a + r_c)\sqrt{2} = 2r_a$$

or

$$r_c/r_a = \sqrt{2} - 1 = 0{\cdot}414$$

This ratio gives the lower limit for the formation of the NaCl type lattice and the condition for its formation is therefore,

$$r_c/r_a \geqslant 0{\cdot}414$$

By a similar method, we may obtain the analogous expression for the tetrahedral structure, where the coordination number is four. This is :

$$r_c/r_a \geqslant \sqrt{6} - 1 = 0{\cdot}225$$

If $r_c/r_a < 0{\cdot}225$, the coordination number is reduced to three, and the three ions are arranged round the central ion in a planar configuration. The lower limiting ratio is then :

$$r_c/r_a = 2/\sqrt{3} - 1 = 0{\cdot}155$$

The significance of these critical ratios was first pointed out by MAGNUS[23] for ionic complexes and later applied by GOLDSCHMIDT[20] to crystals. In the case of CsCl, CsBr and CsI, the value of the ratio r_c/r_a is greater than 0·73. It is therefore understandable that these salts form crystals with a coordination number of eight. There are, however, many exceptions to the conditions formulated above. For example, the halides of rubidium, potassium chloride and potassium fluoride, which crystallize with a NaCl lattice, have a value of r_c/r_a greater than 0·732.

Some alkali halides which at normal pressures crystallize with the NaCl lattice are transformed at higher pressures into the more compact CsCl lattice[24]. The choice of the lattice, however, is not determined by the most suitable arrangement of the hypothetical spheres, but by the attainment of minimum free energy. The theoretical prediction of the type of lattice that is formed is made difficult by effects other than the electrostatic interaction, which may be decisive factors. MAYER, and MAYER and LEVY[25] calculated for the salts of silver, thallium and copper the change of energy on the transformation from one type of lattice to another. These authors took into consideration all the terms in the energy expression. Unfortunately the values obtained can only be regarded as approximate and moreover the calculation is only correct for the crystal structure at absolute zero. The calculations show correctly, that for silver fluoride, the NaCl lattice is more stable than the tetrahedral lattice by 8 kcals and more stable than the CsCl lattice by 2·5 kcals. For silver iodide, however, the theoretical predictions are not in agreement with the experimental observations, a result explained by the authors on the grounds that silver iodide cannot be treated on the basis of an elementary ionic model.

The concept of ionic radii is useful as a means of assisting in the determination of structure, but in the opinion of the authors its extension to such structures as that of silica, with the suggestion of the existence of the Si^{4+} and O^{2-} ions, is unwarranted.

HALOGEN COMPOUNDS

The crystals of the halides of copper and silver are rather different in their properties compared with the halides of alkali metals. In *Table CLI* are given the lattice energies calculated by electrostatic theory and by the Born-Haber cycle. The agreement between the values is clearly not as good as that indicated in *Table CXLVII* for the halides of the alkali metals and although the accuracy of the figures is not very great, the divergencies cannot be attributed to experimental error. It would therefore appear that electrostatic theory alone is insufficient to use as a basis for the calculation of these lattice energies. The variation of $(E_{exp} - E')$ which is observed shows that agreement is best in the case of AgF and increases in the order AgCl, AgBr, AgI, *i.e.* in the order of decreasing electronegativity of the halogen. It would therefore appear that the discrepancies are due to the partial covalent character of the bond in these crystals. The copper salts appear to be more covalent than the silver salts, and the covalent character of the bond again increases in the order chlorine, bromine, iodine.

AgF, AgCl and AgBr crystallize with a sodium chloride lattice and CuCl, CuBr, and CuI with the lattice given in *Figure 62* in which copper has a coordination number of four. This difference in crystal structure of the two salts is not determined by the difference in the dimensions of the Ag^+ and Cu^+ ions, since according to Pauling the latter has the value 0·96 Å, which is not outside the limits for a sodium chloride lattice. The decrease of the coordination number from six to four and the formation of a tetrahedral configuration are more probably determined by the covalent character of the bonds between copper and chlorine. However, it is to be emphasized that the bonds are not entirely covalent any more than they are entirely ionic, but are of an intermediate type.

Table CLI. Lattice Energies of Silver and Copper Halides

Salt	*Lattice energy*			
	By electrostatic method E kcals	*By electrostatic method corrected for van der Waal's forces E′ kcals*	*By Born-Haber cycle E_{exp} kcals*	*Difference $E_{exp} - E'$ kcals*
CuCl	201	216	233	17
CuBr	293	208	228	20
CuI	182	199	224	25
AgF	194	219	228	9
AgCl	174	203	213	10
AgBr	170	197	209	12
AgI	159	190	204	14

At low temperatures silver iodide forms a structure in which silver has a coordination number of four. On raising the temperature the lattice is deformed so that three iodine atoms are closer to the silver atom than the fourth. Above 146° C a further transformation occurs to give a structure in which the iodine ions form a body centred cubic lattice and the silver ions move freely in the interstices. Owing to the free mobility of the silver ions, the high temperature form conducts electricity.

The inter-atomic distances in crystals where the bond is known to be of an intermediate type have frequently been compared with the corresponding ionic and covalent radii. There is, however, considerable difficulty in arriving at these two quantities and it is doubtful whether any of the values recorded in the literature can be regarded without suspicion. For example, Goldschmidt obtained the ionic radius of the Ag^+ ion by assuming that the bond in silver fluoride was entirely ionic and subtracted from the Ag—F distance the ionic radius of the F^- ion, thus obtaining the value 1·13 Å, which he considered to be the ionic radius of the Ag^+ ion. The value obtained by Pauling for the ionic radius of Ag^+, 1·26 Å does not agree with Goldschmidt's value, but owing to the assumptions made during the course of the calculation the error may be of the order of 0·15 Å. The covalent radius of silver is obtained on the assumption that the bond in AgI is entirely homopolar and substracting from the bond distance one half of the interatomic distance of I_2. Clearly these calculations are very approximate and it is doubtful whether the values so obtained, not only for Ag^+, but also for copper, platinum, zinc, *etc*, are of great significance.

In the solid state the halides of ammonium consist of NH_4^+ and Hal^- ions arranged in a lattice. From the value for the lattice energy it is possible to obtain the affinity of ammonia for a proton, by considering the following thermochemical processes :

$$NH_3 + H^+ = NH_4^+ \qquad \Delta H = -P$$

The heats of formation of crystalline ammonium salts, NH_4Hal from N_2, H_2 and Hal_2 are known from thermochemical data ; we have

$$\tfrac{1}{2}N_{2_{gas}} + 2H_{2_{gas}} + \tfrac{1}{2}Cl_{2_{gas}} = NH_4Cl_{solid} \quad \Delta H = -Q \qquad \ldots.(i)$$

We can also proceed from the reactants to solid ammonium chloride by a different method :

$$\tfrac{1}{2}N_{2_{gas}} + \tfrac{3}{2}H_{2_{gas}} = NH_3 \qquad \Delta H = -Q_1$$
$$\tfrac{1}{2}H_{2_{gas}} = H \qquad \Delta H = D_1/2$$
$$H = H^+ + e \qquad \Delta H = I$$
$$\tfrac{1}{2}Cl_{2_{gas}} = Cl \qquad \Delta H = D_2/2$$
$$Cl + e = Cl^- \qquad \Delta H = -F$$
$$NH_3 + H^+ = NH_4{}^+{}_{gas} \qquad \Delta H = -P$$
$$NH_4{}^+{}_{gas} + Cl^-{}_{gas} = NH_4Cl_{solid} \qquad \Delta H = -U$$

Summing we obtain,

$$\tfrac{1}{2}N_{2_{gas}} + 2H_{2_{gas}} + \tfrac{1}{2}Cl_{2_{gas}} = NH_4Cl_{solid}$$

and

$$\Delta H = D_1/2 + I + D_2/2 - Q_1 - F - P - U \qquad \ldots(ii)$$

From equations i and ii we obtain

$$P = Q - Q_1 + D_1/2 + I + D_2/2 - F - U \qquad \ldots.(iii)$$

Table CLII gives the values of Q and U for different ammonium salts together with the values of P calculated by means of equation iii. It is interesting to notice that the values increase in the order I, Br, Cl and F, and that the value for the fluoride is significantly greater than the other values. NH_4Cl, NH_4Br, NH_4I crystallize in lattices of the sodium chloride and caesium chloride type. The lattice of NH_4F, however, is of the tetrahedral, wurtzite type. The NH_4^+ ion is tetrahedral and in NH_4F, the fluorine ions are arranged along the continuation of the direction of the N—H bond. The hydrogen bonds N—H···F so formed stabilize the molecule, resulting in a gain in energy which is responsible for the high value of P for NH_4F given in *Table CLII*.

Table CLII. Proton Affinity of Ammonia

Salt	*Q* *kcals*	*U* *kcals*	*P* *kcals*
NH_4F	111·9	177·5	220
NH_4Cl	75·1	153·3	210
NH_4Br	64·0	147·4	206
NH_4I	48·6	143·6	201
		Average	209

The halides of the elements of the second and higher groups of the periodic classification are evidently not ionic compounds in view of the improbability of the formation of poly-charged ions such as

Al^{3+}. We would therefore expect that the bonds in such crystals would possess considerable covalent character. It is not possible to determine the nature of the bond directly from the melting point of the crystals as will be apparent from the following discussion. The melting points of several fluorides are given in *Table CLIII*; the values for LiF, BeF_2, NaF, MgF_2 and AlF_3 are very much higher than those of the remainder of the compounds. Such a sharp change in the melting point as indicated by these data cannot be regarded as evidence as a transfer from one limiting type of bond to the other, since the substances differ from one another in the type of lattice formed. The fluorides of sodium, magnesium and aluminium all crystallize in coordination lattices, the coordination number of fluorine being six in NaF, three in MgF_2 and two in AlF_3. In these crystals, as in all coordination lattices, there cannot be any suggestion of individual molecule formation. In the process of melting, chemical bonds are broken, and the melting point is therefore high. In the case of the fluorides possessing low melting points, molecular lattices are formed in which separate molecules are held together in the crystal lattice by van der Waal's forces. In the process of melting it is these forces which are overcome by the thermal energy of the molecules and the nature of the bond between the element and halogen have little influence on the melting point. The character of the bond in these compounds will vary with the nature of the electropositive element. In LiF, BeF_2, NaF and MgF_2 the bond is essentially ionic. In BF_3 and AlF_3 there will be resonance between the ionic and homopolar states and in CF_4, NF_3, OF_2 and F_2 the contribution of the covalent form increases considerably.

Table CLIII. Melting Points of some Fluorides °C

LiF	BeF_2	BF_3	CF_4	NF_3	OF_2	F_2
842	800	−127	<−15	<−210	<−146	−233
NaF	MgF_2	AlF_3	SiF_4	PF_3		
980	1,400	1,040	−77	−160		

Although it is not possible, therefore, to determine the nature of the bond from the melting point, it is evident that the bond type is important in determining the type of lattice. The greater the ionic character of the bond, the more probable is the formation of a coordination lattice. *Table CLIV* gives the melting points of various chlorides, together with their electrical conductivity, λ, in the fused state. There is an obvious correlation between the two properties; chlorides with high melting points have a high conductivity and those with low melting points, low conductivity. It is, however, important to observe that there is a much greater difference in the conductivities of the

Table CLIV. Melting Points of Chlorides and Electrical Conductivity of the Fused Salts

	HCl	LiCl	NaCl	KCl	RbCl	CsCl
T °C	−114	606	800	768	717	645
λ *ohms*$^{-1}$	10^{-6}	166	134	104	78	67
		$BeCl_2$	$MgCl_2$	$CaCl_2$	$SrCl_2$	$BaCl_2$
T °C		404	718	774	870	960
λ *ohms*$^{-1}$		0·066	29	52	56	65
		BCl_3	$AlCl_3$	$GaCl_3$	$InCl_3$	$TlCl_3$
T °C		−107	<183*	75·5	586	25
λ *ohms*$^{-1}$		0	15×10^{-6}	10^{-7}	14·7	10^{-3}

* boiling point

corresponding elements of the first and second periodic groups than in their melting points. This evidence clearly indicates a type of bond which is less ionic in the second group elements compared with the first. In diamond, the bond between the carbon atoms is homopolar. Nevertheless, since the carbon atoms form an infinite network of carbon atoms arranged tetrahedrally, the melting point is extremely high. Thus we may conclude that the melting point of a crystal is, to a very large extent, a characteristic of the type of lattice formed and not of the nature of the bond between the atoms.

Certain metals, such as thallium, may give rise to two zero valent ions with different charges, *e.g.* Tl^{+} ($5d^{10}$ $6s^{2}$) and Tl^{3+} ($5d^{10}$). In the monohalides of thallium, according to MAYER and LEVY[25], van der Waal's forces contribute a significant amount, approximately 30 kcals, to the lattice energy. When this is taken into consideration, agreement between the calculated and experimental values of the lattice energies is obtained (*Table CLV*). This result would tend to indicate that in these compounds the bond between thallium and halogen is largely ionic. In the trihalogen compounds, however, the experimental evidence tends to show that the bond possesses greater homopolar character, *e.g.* the electrical conductivity data (*Table CLVI*) clearly shows that in the fused state InCl, TlCl, $SnCl_2$ and $PbCl_2$ have a higher ionic character than $InCl_3$, $TlCl_3$, $SnCl_4$ and $PbCl_4$.

Table CLV. Lattice Energies of the Thallium Halides

Salt	*Calculated value by the method of Born and Mayer kcals*	*Calculated by Born's cycle kcals*	*Van der Waal's energy kcals*
TlCl	167	168	28
TlBr	164	169	28
TlI	154	160	30

Table CLVI. Electrical Conductivities of Halides

Salt	*Energy of emission of one electron from metal kcals*	*Boiling point of chlorides °C*	*Electrical conductivity of fused chlorides ohms^{-1}*
InCl	133	—	130
$InCl_3$	403	550	17
TlCl	140	806	46·5
$TlCl_3$	430	100	0
$SnCl_2$	253	605	21.9
$SnCl_4$	529	113	0
$PbCl_2$	257	954	40·7
$PbCl_4$	554	105*	$< 2 \times 10^{-5}$

*decomposes

A study of the subhalides of the alkaline earth metals has been made by GUNTZ and BENOIT[26]. The heats of formation of CaCl, SrCl and BaCl are as follows:

$$Ca + CaCl_2 = 2CaCl \qquad \Delta H = -\ 2{\cdot}7 \text{ kcals}$$
$$Sr + SrCl_2 = 2SrCl \qquad \Delta H = -\ 14{\cdot}6 \text{ kcals}$$
$$Ba + BaCl_2 = 2BaCl \qquad \Delta H = -\ 16{\cdot}5 \text{ kcals}$$

If the subhalides form entirely ionic lattices, then it follows that the lattice energy of SrCl would not be greater than the corresponding value for RbCl. If this were so the reaction $Sr + SrCl_2 = 2SrCl$ would occur with the absorption of 112 kcals whereas it actually occurs with the evolution of 14·6 kcals. Such a large discrepancy cannot be due to experimental error and it can only be concluded that the simple ionic structure does not give rise to the entire lattice energy, it being possible that the unused valency electrons of the Sr^+ ion give rise to a bond of the type occurring in metals. The data on the subhalides are, however, very incomplete.

CdI_2, PbI_2 and $NiCl_2$ crystallize with layer lattices of the CdI_2 type. A layer lattice of a somewhat different type is given by $MgCl_2$, $ZnCl_2$, $CdCl_2$, $MnCl_2$, $FeCl_2$ and $CoCl_2$. The layer lattice must be regarded as a transitional type between the coordination lattice and the molecular lattice. Each infinite layer represents a large coordinate molecule in which the bonds between the atoms will be a resonance hybrid of the covalent and ionic forms. The layers will be bonded by van der Waal's forces. In contrast to the halides discussed here, the fluorides of some elements, where the bond is largely ionic in character, give lattices of the CaF_2 and TiO_2 type.

HYDRIDES, OXIDES, HYDROXIDES AND THE ANIONS OF THE OXYACIDS

The hydrides of the alkali metals in the solid state are salt like compounds, constructed from the ions M^+ and H^- as indicated by the electrical conductivity of the fused compounds in which hydrogen is liberated at the anode. x-ray data show that the crystal lattice is of the sodium chloride type ; the interionic distances are given in *Table CLVII*. The calculation of the lattice energy by equation 13.18 is not possible owing to the absence of data on the compressibility of the hydrides, but the electron affinity of hydrogen (16·4 kcals) has been calculated by the methods of quantum mechanics, and the knowledge of this value permits the calculation of the lattice energy by the Born-Haber cycle (third column of *Table CLVII*). A quantum mechanical calculation of the lattice energy of LiH has been made by HYLLERAAS[27] who obtained the value 219 kcals, in excellent agreement with the value obtained by the Born-Haber cycle, 220 kcals. The value obtained for the interionic distance was 2·20 Å, compared with the observed value of 2·04 Å.

Table CLVII. Lattice Energies of the Hydrides of the Alkali Metals

Hydride	*Interatomic distance Å*	*Lattice energy kcals*
LiH	2·04	220
NaH	2·44	193
KH	2·85	165
RbH	3·02	162
CsH	3·19	156

From the heat of formation of solid LiH,

$$L_{solid} + \tfrac{1}{2}H_{2_{gas}} = LiH_{solid} \qquad \Delta H = -21{\cdot}6 \text{ kcals}$$

and the heat of formation of the gaseous molecule, it is possible to determine the heat of sublimation. The value obtained is 55 kcals, but the value of the dissociation energy of the gaseous molecule is not known accurately, so that this value has no great significance. If, however, it is of the correct order of magnitude, the high value would suggest that LiH forms a coordination lattice.

The oxides of the alkaline earth metals crystallize in a sodium chloride lattice although in SrO and BaO the radius ratio is greater than 0·732. It has been proposed that the crystals are constructed from the ions M^{2+} and O^{2-}; the electron affinity of the oxygen atom calculated on this assumption by the Born-Haber cycle for the different oxides give rather divergent values (*Table CLVIII*, column three), a result which may be interpreted as indicating that the bond is not entirely ionic. A more accurate calculation of this affinity by MAYER and MALTBIE[28], taking into account the van der Waal's forces and the zero-point energy, shows an even greater range of values, from — 190 to — 144 kcals.

If it be assumed that the average of the values given in column three of *Table CLVIII*, *viz* — 166 kcals, is the affinity of the oxygen atom for two electrons, it is possible by means of the Born-Haber cycle to determine the lattice energies of other oxides and to compare them with the values calculated by equation 13.18. The values obtained are given in *Table CLVIII* and although the agreement is good in certain cases, in others there is a wide discrepancy, indicating the inadequacy of the simple ionic theory. The data suggest, however, that the crystals of Li_2O, K_2O and Na_2O are ionic; these oxides crystallize in an anti-fluorite lattice (Li^+ replace F^- ions and O^{2-} replace the Ca^{2+} ions in the fluorite lattice).

Table CLVIII. Lattice Energies of Metallic Oxides in kcals

Oxide	Lattice energy calculated by equation 13.18	Affinity of oxygen atom for two electrons	Oxide	Lattice energy calculated by equation 13.18	Lattice energy calculated by Born-Haber cycle	Oxide	Lattice energy calculated by equation 13.18	Lattice energy calculated by Born-Haber cycle
MgO	940	−175	Li_2O	695	692	Cu_2O	644	788
CaO	842	−171	MnO	912	929	Ag_2O	585	714
SrO	791	−160	FeO	944	937	CdO	867	913
			CoO	950	963			
			NiO	968	965	SnO_2	2,734	2,812
BaO	747	−157	ZnO	977	964	PbO_2	2,620	2,829
						Al_2O_3	3,708	3,613

Table CLIX. Coordination Number of Oxygen in Oxides

Coordination number of oxygen	Compound
8	Li_2O, Na_2O, K_2O
6	CaO, MgO, SiO, BaO, CdO, MnO, FeO, CoO, NiO
4	ZnO, BeO, PbO, SnO, PtO, PdO, Cu_2O, Ag_2O
3	TiO_2, SnO_2, PbO_2, VO_2, NbO_2, TeO_2, MoO_2, WO_2, MnO_2, RuO_2, OsO_2, IrO_2, GeO_2
2	SiO_2, GeO_2

In its compounds, oxygen shows a wide range of coordination numbers (*Table CLIX*). The higher coordination numbers will be determined by the ratio of the radii of the participating ions, but the lower co-ordination numbers will be due to an increased contribution of the covalent structure to the bonds in the crystal.

The x-ray and electron diffraction data reveal that the ZnO crystal is intermediate between the coordination lattice and a molecular lattice. The general structure is tetrahedral, the zinc atom being surrounded tetrahedrally by four oxygen atoms. The structure, however, is not regular, the zinc atom being located not at the centre of the tetrahedron but nearer to one oxygen atom than to the remaining three. Furthermore, the electron density diagram shows that the electrons are not arranged symmetrically around the zinc and oxygen atoms as if all were in the ionic form, but there is an increased density between the zinc atom and the nearest oxygen atom[29]. It would therefore appear that the bond between the zinc atom and this oxygen has considerable covalent properties. In a similar manner in the sesquioxides, Al_2O_3, Fe_2O_3, Cr_2O_3, Ti_2O_3, V_2O_3 and Ga_2O_3, it is possible to distinguish a molecular group *e.g.*

```
      O
    /   \
Al—O—Al
    \   /
      O
```

in the crystal lattice. In these examples the lattice, although primarily ionic, does show a trend towards the formation of molecular groups and the lattices must therefore be regarded as intermediate between the coordination and molecular types.

The oxides of antimony (senarmontite) and arsenic (arsenolite), to which the formulae Sb_2O_3 and As_2O_3 are normally ascribed, give molecular lattices consisting of packed Sb_4O_6 and As_4O_6 molecules. In these molecules, the six oxygen atoms form an octahedron (*Figure 68*), and the atoms of arsenic and antimony are located outside the octahedron on the perpendiculars from the centre of every other face. Thus each atom of arsenic (or antimony) forms a pyramid structure with three oxygen atoms, corresponding to the three *p* electrons of arsenic or antimony. The AsO bond distance in the crystal is 2·01 Å, and the SbO distance 2·22 Å. In the gaseous state, the structure of molecules As_4O_6 and Sb_4O_6 is retained, although the AsO distance is less, being 1·80 Å and the As—O—As angle is 126° compared with a tetrahedral angle in the solid state[30]. In the bonds between arsenic and oxygen, resonance between the homopolar $>$As—O and the ionic $>$$As^+O^-$ structures will occur. The contribution of the ionic form is probably of significance even though the structure is mainly homopolar, since the alternating charges produced throughout the structure will increase the stability. In the crystalline state the contribution of the ionic form will be increased by mutual induction between the molecules, compared with the molecule in the gaseous state. This is the probable cause of the deformation of bond angles and bond distances on crystallization. It is clear from the experimental evidence discussed above, that the poly-charged ionic states of arsenic and oxygen *viz* As^{3+} and O^{2-} make no contribution to the structure of the molecule.

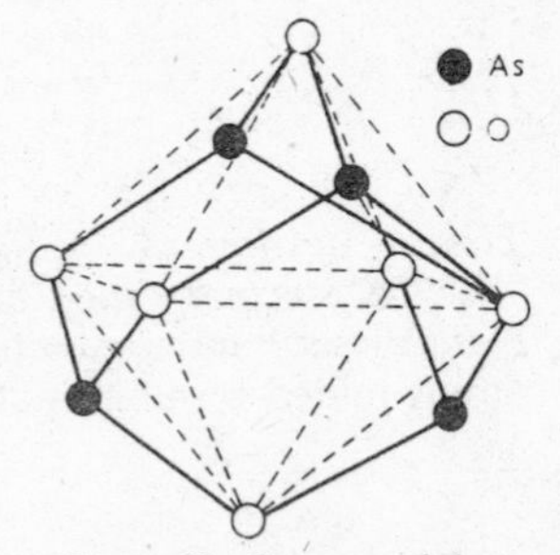

Figure 68. Structure of the As_4O_6 molecule

The separate As_4O_6 and Sb_4O_6 molecules are arranged in the crystal in a diamond structure, the distance between the oxygen atoms of the neighbouring molecules being 2·8 Å. This value is smaller than usual for a molecular crystal and the closeness of the packing is evidently due to strong dispersion forces. In addition there will be some electrostatic interaction of arsenic and oxygen atoms of different molecules. These strong intermolecular forces are responsible for the melting point being unusually high for a molecular lattice (Sb_4O_6, 656° C).

The structure of hexamethylenetetramine, $C_6H_{12}N_4$ is similar to that of As_4O_6 and Sb_4O_6. The nitrogen atoms occupy the corresponding position to that of the arsenic atoms and the CH_2 groups correspond to the oxygen atoms. The structure of P_4O_6 is also similar, and in P_4O_{10} each phosphorus atom is bonded to four oxygen atoms, so that the structure resembles that of P_4O_6 (As_4O_6 type), but with an additional oxygen atom located on the same perpendicular from the octahedral face as the phosphorus atom, but farther away from the centre of the molecule. The fourth PO bond is different (interatomic distance = 1·39 Å) from the other three, resonance occurring between the structures :

```
—O                 —O
   \                  \
—O—P=O             —O—P+ — O−
   /                  /
—O                 —O
```

The structure of $P_4O_6S_4$ is similar, the PS distance being 1·85 Å.

In a second modification of Sb_2O_3 (valentinite), BUERGER and HENDRICKS[31] have concluded that the crystal consists of endless chains of atoms joined by homopolar bonds :

```
   /        \
  O          O
   \        /
    Sb    Sb
   /  \  /  \
  O    O     O
   \        /
    Sb    Sb
   /  \  /  \
  O    O     O
   \        /
```

The SbO distance is 2·00 Å, *i.e.* less than in senarmontite, the Sb—O—Sb angles are 132° and 116° and the O—Sb—O angles are 81°, 93° and 99°.

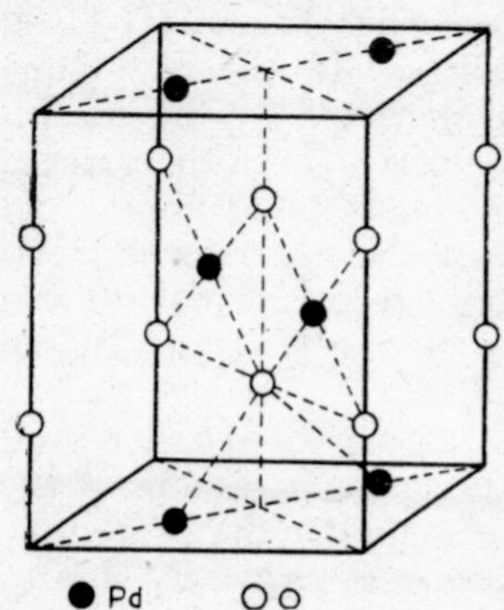

Figure 69. Palladium oxide (PdO) *lattice*

The monoxides of lead and tin, PbO and SnO, form layer lattices[32]. Each oxygen atom is surrounded tetrahedrally by four atoms of the metal. The PbO distance is 2·30 Å and the SnO distance 2·21 Å. For the distance between the metal atoms the following values have been obtained :

Pb—Pb	(in one layer)	3·95 Å
Pb—Pb	(in different layers bonded by van der Waal's forces)	3·82 Å
Pb—Pb	(in the same layer but separated by an oxygen atom)	3·67 Å

In SnO the corresponding values for the Sn—Sn distance are 3·80 Å, 3·70 Å and 3·51 Å respectively.

The structure of the PtO and PdO crystals[32] (*Figure 69*) are of considerable interest. Four oxygen atoms (open circles) are arranged round each platinum or palladium atom (black circles) in a plane, thus forming a rectangle (almost a square). This arrangement of bonds is shown in the following chapter to be characteristic of these metals in this valency state. The oxygen atoms are surrounded by four atoms of the metal which are located at the apices of a rather deformed tetrahedron. The configuration of the atoms is determined by the direction of the covalent bonds of platinum and palladium. The Pt—O distance is 2·02 Å and the Pd—O distance 2·01 Å. It is very probable that CuO has the same configuration.

The hydroxides of the metals give layer lattices. The layers of crystalline LiOH consist of three sheets of Li atoms and OH groups, the Li atoms lying between the two sheets of OH groups and in such a way that each Li atom is surrounded by four OH groups :

x • x • x •

o x o x o x

x • x • x •

o x o x o x

x Li atoms

• OH groups below sheet of Li atoms

o OH groups above sheet of Li atoms

$Mg(OH)_2$, $Mn(OH)_2$, $Ca(OH)_2$, $Ca(OH)_2$, $Co(OH)_2$, $Ni(OH)_2$ and $Fe(OH)_2$ all form lattices of the CdI_2 type in which each layer consists of two parallel sheets of hydroxyl groups, between which is located the layer of metal atoms. The hydroxyl groups of different layers form a close packed layer in which each hydroxyl group from one layer is surrounded by three hydroxyl groups of the other. The structure of $Al(OH)_3$ is similar to that of $Mg(OH)_2$ but two aluminium atoms take the place of three magnesium atoms, which causes a rearrangement of the sheets of atoms in the layers. The mutual arrangement of the layers, however, is quite different, each hydroxyl group of the upper layer being directly above that of the lower layer.

Hydrogen bond formation may play an important part in the stability of the hydroxide lattices. In LiOH the bond between lithium and the hydroxyl group is almost entirely ionic. This will reduce the ionic character of the OH bond since the structures $Li—O^-H^+$ and $Li^+ O^{2-} H^+$ are much less probable than the form $Li^+ O^-—H$. A similar argument will apply to $Mg(OH)_2$, and this effect will tend to reduce the possibility of hydrogen bond formation. In $Al(OH)_3$ the conditions for the formation of hydrogen bonds will be more favourable, and the layers of $B(OH)_3$ molecules in boric acid are strongly linked by hydrogen bonds, since resonance may occur between the forms $B—O^- H^+$, B—O—H and $B^+ O^-—H$. The distances between the hydroxyl groups in the various hydroxides are given in *Table CLX*; these values enable the effect of hydrogen bonding in these structures to be

Table CLX. The O · · · · O Distance in Hydroxides

Hydroxide	*Distance Å*	*Hydroxide*	*Distance Å*
LiOH	3·61	$Fe(OH)_2$	3·06
$Mg(OH)_2$	3·22	$Cd(OH)_2$	2·98
$Ca(OH)_2$	3·22	$Zn(OH)_2$	2·83
$Mn(OH)_2$	3·18	$Al(OH)_3$	2·79
$Co(OH)_2$	3·14	$B(OH)_3$	2·71
$Ni(OH)_2$	3·10		

assessed, since the shorter the distance the greater is the hydrogen bonding.

The salts of the oxyacids contain anions such as SO_4^{2-}, NO_3^-, CO_3^{2-} *etc*, and in the crystal lattices these ions exist as separate structural units. In *Table CLXI* the structure of these ions is given as determined from x-ray analysis. The directional characteristics of the bond in such ions have been discussed in Chapter 4. The structure of the salts of iodic acid, MIO_3, was at one time regarded as consisting of IO_6 and MO_6 octahedra, the bonding in the latter case being entirely ionic. The data of ROGERS and HELMHOLZ[33] for periodic acid, however, has established the fact that in the crystal the IO_3^- ion exists as a unit, the ion having a pyramidal structure, the O—I distance being 1·80 Å and the O—I—O angles having a value between 96° and 101°. At considerably greater distances from the iodine atom there exist three other oxygen atoms (the values being 2·45 Å, 2·70 Å and 2·95 Å). The six atoms of oxygen form a strongly distorted octahedron. The three short I—O bonds are evidently largely covalent and the O—I—O angle is that characteristic for *p* bonds. For this ion the following structure is suggested

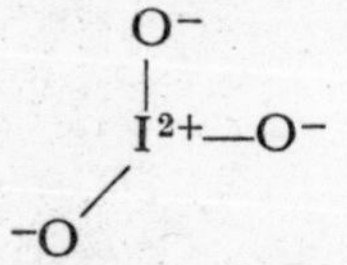

```
        O⁻
        |
        I²⁺—O⁻
       /
   ⁻O
```

Table CLXI. Some Ionic Configurations

Triangular ions (p^2) :					
	NO_2^-	ClO_2^-			
Planar configuration, bond angle 120° (sp^2) :					
	BO_3^{3-}	CO_3^{2-}	NO_3^-		
Pyramidal ions (p^3) :					
	SO_3^{2-}	ClO_3^-	BrO_3^-		
Tetrahedral ions (sp^3) :					
SiO_4^{4-}	CrO_4^{2-}	WO_4^{2-}	MoO_4^{2-}	MnO_4^-	
PO_4^{3-}	SO_4^{2-}	SeO_4^{2-}	ClO_4^-	IO_4^-	
ReO_4^-	VS_4^{3-}	AsS_4^{3-}	SnS_4^{4-}	BeF_4^{2-}	BF_4^-

The bond between iodine and the more distant oxygen atoms is considered to be due to electrostatic attraction, the distances being too great for a covalent bond and too short for van der Waal's forces. This view is confirmed by the I—O—I angle which is much greater (114°—138°) than the normal valency angle of oxygen. The distance between the oxygen atom of one IO_3^- ion and the two oxygen atoms of a neighbouring ion is 2·78 Å and in this triangular zone is located the hydrogen atom which will form two hydrogen bonds with the neighbouring oxygen atoms.

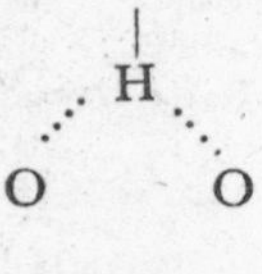

```
      O
      |
      H
    ·   ·
  O       O
```

SILICATES

In silica and the silicates, each atom of silicon is surrounded tetrahedrally by four atoms of oxygen. This structure is in agreement with the tetravalency of silicon and with the directional character of the four sp^3 hybrid bonds. In such an SiO_4 group, only one of the two valencies of oxygen are used, and two possible structures may therefore exist; either the oxygen is present as a monovalent ion —O^-, or forms a second covalent bond with another silicon atom. The various possible combinations of these two forms of oxygen are responsible for the complex structures of the silicates. In silica, the four oxygen atoms of an SiO_4 group are all bonded covalently to four other silicon atoms, each oxygen thereby forming a bridge between two atoms of silicon. An infinite network is thus built up and the different possible ways of grouping the SiO_4 tetrahedra are responsible for the six different crystalline forms of silica mentioned above. Thus in silica the coordination numbers of silica and oxygen, *viz* four and two respectively, are identical with the number of bonds. These bonds, however, being between two unlike atoms, are not homopolar as in diamond, and in addition to the homopolar structure

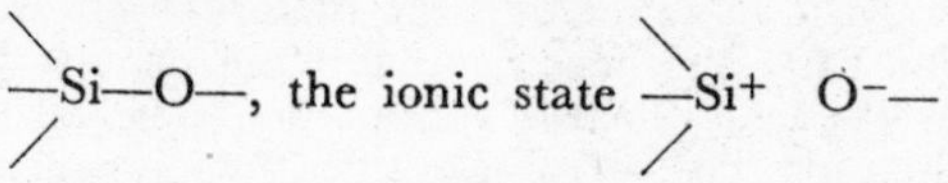

```
\                         \
—Si—O—, the ionic state  —Si+  O-—
/                         /
```

will contribute to the resonance of the molecule. Such a structure as that given below, having alternate positive and negative charges,

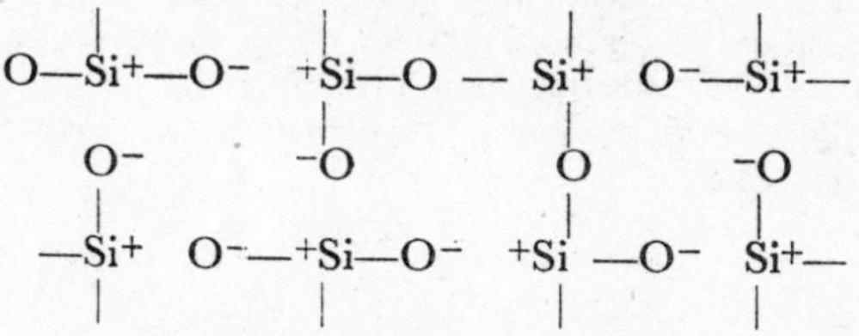

```
     |          |            |       |
O—Si+—O-   +Si—O  —  Si+  O-—Si+—
                |            |
   O-         -O            O       -O
   |                         |        |
 —Si+   O-—+Si—O-    +Si —O-   Si+—
   |           |            |        |
```

would increase considerably the stability of the molecule. An indication that such structures do in fact contribute to the resonance of the molecule is given by the fact that the Si—O—Si angle is very much greater than the normal value for the valency bonds of oxygen (theoretically 90°) and is close to 180°, the value depending on the type of lattice. The coordination numbers of silicon and oxygen, however, are not determined by the close packing of ions but by the valency of the uncharged atoms. If silicon and oxygen existed respectively in the form Si^{4+} and O^{2-}, each ion would possess ten electrons and BRAGG[34] has shown that this does not agree with the x-ray diffraction data. BRAGG and WEST[35] have shown by Fourier analysis that in beryl ($Be_3Al_2Si_6O_{18}$) it is possible to ascribe 12·47 electrons to the silicon atoms and 8·95 electrons to the oxygen atoms. Even though these results are not very accurate owing to experimental difficulties it is clear that the silicon and oxygen atoms are closer to the Si^+ and O^- ionic states than to the Si^{4+} and O^{2-} states. In confirmation of the partial covalent nature of the SiO bond, BRILL, HERMANN and PETERS[36] have shown that in silica the electronic density does not fall to zero between the atoms, as in NaCl, but only to a minimum value of 2·25 electrons per $Å^2$. This value is less than that to be expected if the bond were homopolar and on the basis of the above evidence it is fairly certain that the SiO bond in SiO_2 is intermediate between the homopolar and the ionic.

The very great difference between the crystal structure of SiO_2 and CO_2 is of particular interest. Although carbon and silicon belong to the same group of the periodic table, the crystal lattices are quite different.

The CO_2 lattice is molecular and possesses typical properties of such a lattice, for example, it possesses a low heat of sublimation, as sublimation occurs at $-79°$ C. SiO_2 on the other hand, forms an infinite lattice in which there are no separate SiO_2 molecules and the melting point is 1,625° C. The energy of the single C—O bond is 75 kcals compared with the appreciably higher value for the SiO bond of 89 kcals which is the result of the greater electropositive character of silicon (the ionization potential of silicon is 70 kcals less than that of carbon) which causes an increased contribution from the $Si^+ O^-$ ionic state. The heat of formation of gaseous CO_2 is 336 kcals and of gaseous SiO_2, 322 kcals. The heat of formation of a molecular lattice of SiO_2 molecules would therefore be approximately 330 kcals, the van der Waal's forces being assumed to be 8 kcals, whereas the heat of formation of the coordination lattice is $4 \times 89 = 356$ kcals. The latter form, with the greater heat of formation is thus the stable modification. For CO_2 on the other hand the heat of formation of the molecular lattice, 342 kcals (heat of sublimation is 6 kcals), is greater than that of a coordination lattice of the silica type, which has the value $4 \times 75 = 300$ kcals.

We have already pointed out that the two forms of oxygen in which it is divalent, and monovalent and singly charged, are responsible for the wide number of silicates. The crystal of silica, in which the oxygen atoms are divalent form one extreme structure, and the so called orthosilicates in which the silicon and oxygen atoms form a tetrahedral ion possessing four negative charges :

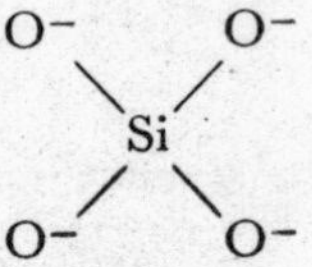

```
O⁻      O⁻
  \    /
    Si
  /    \
O⁻      O⁻
```

forms the other extreme. In this ion the Si—O distance is 1·6 Å and the distance between two atoms of oxygen is 2·6 Å. The ions are held in the lattice by the electrostatic attraction with the cations which exist between the close packed $(SiO_4)^{4-}$ ions and the distance between the oxygen atoms of different tetrahedra varies from 2·8 to 2·9 Å. Typical silicates of this type are Mg_2SiO_4 and Fe_2SiO_4. The oxygen ions are arranged in an approximate hexagonal close packed structure, each silicon atom being surrounded by four oxygen atoms. The ions of magnesium or iron are arranged so that they are surrounded by six oxygen atoms. One might thus describe the structure of these silicates as a hexagonal close packed structure of oxygen ions, in which the tetrahedral holes were filled by silicon atoms and the octahedral holes by magnesium or ferrous ions. In zirconium orthosilicate a different structure arises in which each zirconium ion, Zr^{4+}, is surrounded by eight oxygen atoms, four at a distance of 2·05 Å and four at 2·41 Å.

In the silicates containing hydroxyl groups, the latter are not bound to the silicon atoms. For example, in enclase, $BeAlSiO_4(OH)$, there are independent $(SiO_4)^{4-}$ ions and OH^- ions. Thus each aluminium ion is surrounded by five oxygen atoms and one hydroxyl group and each beryllium ion is located between three oxygen atoms and an hydroxyl group.

In addition to these two limiting cases, intermediate structures occur in which oxygen atoms may be shared between two tetrahedra (*Figure 70*). Thus in the ion $(Si_2O_7)^{6-}$ one oxygen atom is common to two tetrahedra :

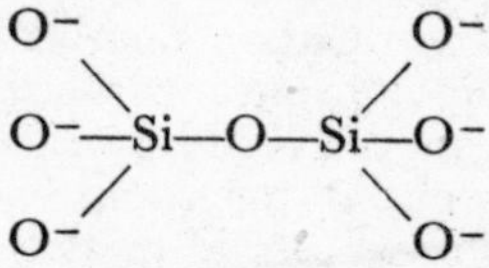

```
O⁻                O⁻
   \            /
O⁻—Si—O—Si—O⁻
   /            \
O⁻                O⁻
```

In this structure the oxygen atoms are not all in identical valency states. The six outer oxygen atoms are singly charged and monovalent, whereas the seventh, central oxygen atom is divalent. Such an atom is sometimes termed inactive and in the lattice the cations are located nearer to the active, *i.e.* negatively charged atoms, than to the inactive. Three, four or six SiO_4 tetrahedra may be united in ring structures to form the ions $(Si_3O_9)^{6-}$ which occurs in benitoite, $BaTiSi_3O_9$, $(Si_4O_{12})^{8-}$ and $(Si_6O_{18})^{12-}$ which occurs in beryl, $Be_3Al_2Si_6O_{18}$. The structures of these ions are shown in *Figure 70*. In addition to the cyclic structures, infinite chains of SiO_4 tetrahedra may be formed (*Figure 71*) such as occur in the pyroxenes, $CaMg(SiO_3)_2$. In such a chain, each tetrahedron has two active and two inactive oxygen atoms and such chains may be represented by the empirical formula $(SiO_3)_n^{2-}$. It is important to realize that there is no separate $(SiO_3)^{2-}$ anion, the position being similar to that of the SiO_4 group in silica. The individual covalently bonded chains will be held together in the lattice by the cations spaced between the chains. In the amphiboles, *e.g.* $(OH)_2Ca_2Mg_5(Si_4O_4)_2$, two pyroxene are joined together with a common oxygen atom (*Figure 72*). In this structure, some of the SiO_4 groups have three inactive oxygen atoms and others only two, the structure may be represented by the empirical formula $(Si_4O_4)_n^{6-}$. Such minerals as the pyroxenes and the amphiboles readily cleave between the chains, a process which does not involve the breaking of any covalent bonds. Further polymerization of the SiO_4 groups produces infinite layers in which in every SiO_4 tetrahedron, three oxygen atoms are inactive and only one active.

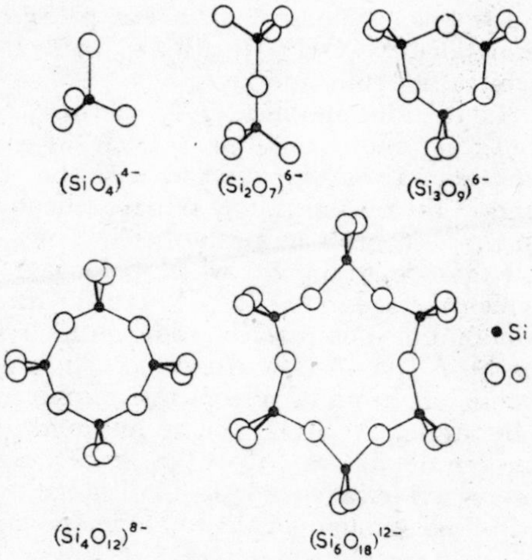

Figure 70. Structure of silicate ions formed from $(SiO_4)^{4-}$ *tetrahedra*

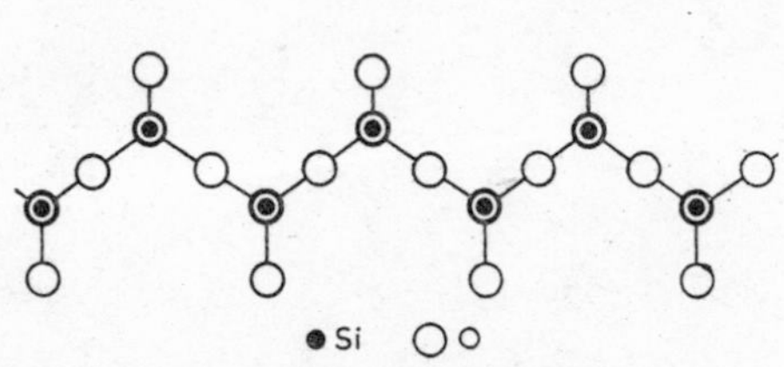

Figure 71. Chains formed from $(SiO_4)^{4-}$ *tetrahedra*

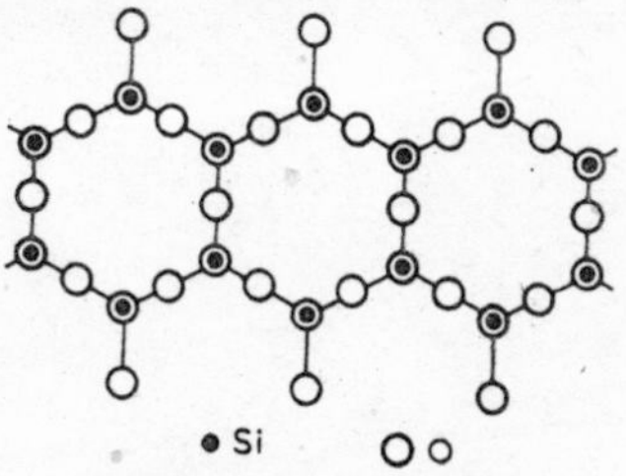

Figure 72. Sheets formed from $(SiO_4)^{4-}$ *tetrahedra*

Such layer type structures are present in mica, $(OH)_2KMg_3(AlSi_3O_{10})$ and talcum, $(OH)_2Mg_3(Si_4O_{10})$ which are characterized by the ease in which they split into layers.

In the aluminosilicates, *e.g.* felspar, $NaAlSi_3O_8$ and zeolite, $NaAlSi_2O_6$, the aluminium may be present in either of two forms. In the first, aluminium may function as a cation, with a coordination number of six and in the second it may replace silicon from the SiO_4 tetrahedron thereby having a coordination number of four. The first type is illustrated by the mineral $Ca_3Al_2Si_3O_{12}$, which belongs to a sub-group of the granites and in which the separate $(SiO_4)^{4-}$ tetrahedra are held together in the lattice by aluminium ions (coordination number 6) and calcium ions (coordination number 8). In this structure each oxygen atom has as its nearest neighbours one atom of silicon, one aluminium ion, and two calcium ions. In sillimanite, Al_2SiO_5, the aluminium occurs in the form of cations in oxygen octahedra (Al—O distance 1·9 Å) and also alternates with silicon in oxygen tetrahedra (Al—O distance 1·7 Å). In the tetrahedra, the bonds will possess more covalent character than in the octahedra.

Germanium oxide, GeO_2 differs from SiO_2 in that in addition to a quartz type structure in which the coordination numbers of germanium and oxygen are respectively 4 and 2, there exists a second modification with a rutile structure (coordination numbers respectively 6 and 3). The reason for the formation of the second structure is not clear, but it may be due to an increased contribution from the ionic form of the GeO bond.

Ions with an infinite chain structure, analogous to that occurring in the silicates, are formed by the borates, *e.g.* CaB_2O_4. Each boron atom is surrounded by three oxygen atoms, all four atoms being in one plane. Two neighbouring boron atoms are joined through a common oxygen atom with the result that an infinite chain, having the empirical formula $(BO_2)_n^-$ is formed *viz*

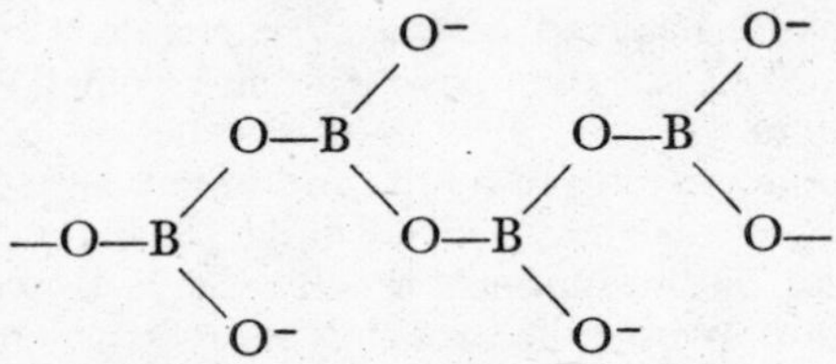

```
                  O⁻              O⁻
                 /               /
             O—B           O—B
            /    \         /    \
     —O—B        O—B          O—
          \          \
           O⁻         O⁻
```

In $K_3B_3O_6$ the BO_3 groups form a ring structure,

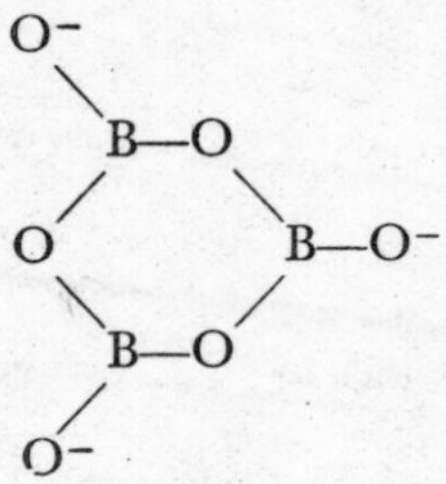

```
      O⁻
        \
         B—O
        /    \
      O       B—O⁻
        \    /
         B—O
        /
      O⁻
```

which is probably stabilized by resonance involving the structure containing tetravalent negatively charged boron :

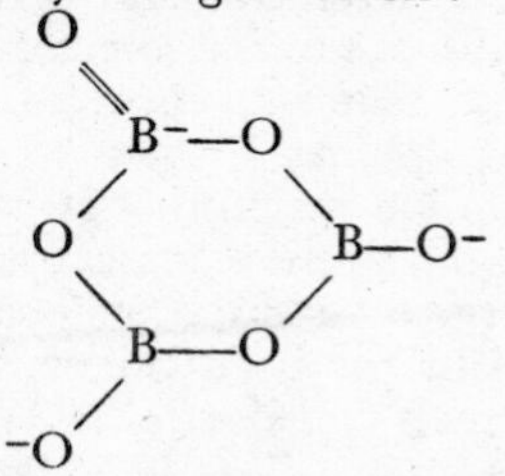

```
         O
          \\
           B⁻—O
          /     \
        O        B—O⁻
          \     /
           B——O
          /
       ⁻O
```

The BO distance in CaB_2O_4 is 1·36 Å ; in $K_3B_3O_6$ the distance between boron and an inactive oxygen atom is 1·38 Å and between boron and an active oxygen 1·33 Å, the smaller value in the latter being due to the partial double bond character of the link.

On cooling fused SiO_2, B_2O_3 or certain silicates, glasses are formed in place of the corresponding crystalline state. Glasses as distinct from crystals, give a diffuse x-ray pattern indicating a lack of an ordered structure. This arises not from a loss of the symmetry of the SiO_4 tetrahedra but from the random manner in which they are joined together. This may be illustrated by reference to the planar BO_3 group. In the crystal the groups are bonded together to form identical repeating units, whereas in the glass there exists a variety of ring structures containing different numbers of BO_3 groups (*Figure 73*), in which the O—B—O angle is preserved but the B—O—B angle may be changed.

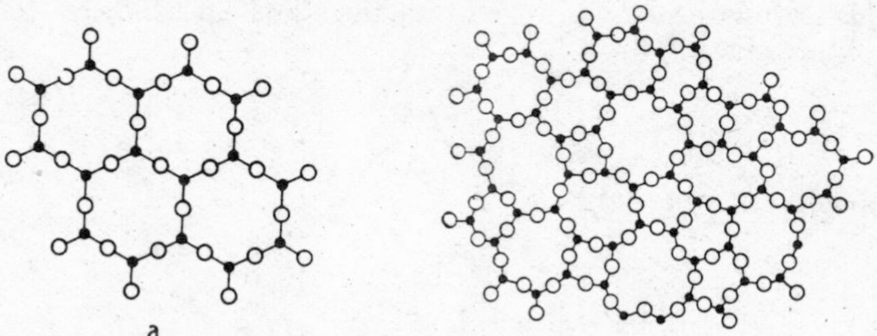

a

b

Figure 73. (a) *Two-dimensional crystal* (b) *Two-dimensional glass*

The difficulty in transforming a glass into a crystal is due to the fundamental characteristics of the Si—O and B—O bonds. These are covalent and therefore directional. A change of a glass-like structure into a crystal would thus involve the breaking of covalent bonds, followed by a molecular rearrangement and the reformation of the bonds. Such a process requires considerable energy of activation and therefore those bonds which already exist in the liquid state are retained on solidifying and in this sense the glass may be regarded as a supercooled liquid. In ionic compounds *e.g.* MgO there also occurs a disordered grouping of the ions in the liquid and in the rapidly cooled solid. But since electrostatic forces are not directional a disorder-order reaction can take place yielding, at equilibrium, an ordered structure. Substances which may give rise to glass formation are those which have a three dimensional infinite lattice structure ; orthosilicates, on the other hand, rarely give glasses[37].

SULPHIDES AND SOME OTHER COMPOUNDS

In the sulphides, selenides, tellurides and arsenides, all types of bond, ionic, covalent and metallic occur. The compounds of the alkali metals with sulphur, selenium and tellurium form an ionic lattice with an anti-fluorite structure and the sulphides of the alkaline earth metals form ionic lattices with a sodium chloride structure. If in MgS, CaS, SrS and BaS, the bond is assumed to be entirely ionic, the lattice energies may be calculated from equation 13.18 and from these values the affinity of sulphur for two electrons obtained by the Born-Haber cycle. The values obtained vary from -71 to -80 kcals and if van der Waal's forces are considered, from -83 to -102 kcals.

The type of lattice formed by a particular compound does not necessarily define the character of the bond. Thus, although PbS, PbSe and PbTe crystallize with a sodium chloride type lattice which is normally associated with a purely electrostatic force between the ions, these compounds possess, in some part, the properties of a metal[38].

Among compounds of this type, zinc blende and wurtzite structures often occur *viz*, (BeS, BeSe, BeTe, ZnS, ZnSe, ZnTe, CdS, CdSe, CdTe, HgS, HgSe, HgTe, MgTe, AlN, AlP, AlAs, AlSb, GaP, GaAs, GaSb). In these structures where the coordination number is 4, the bond is predominantly covalent, as we have seen previously.

The type of lattice is not always determined by the radius ratio. For example, the ratio of the ionic radii in CaS and CdS is identical (0·53) but nevertheless CaS crystallizes in a sodium chloride lattice and CdS in a zinc sulphide type. Similar behaviour is observed with the corresponding tellurides. For sulphur, nitrogen and their analogues where the valency state of nitrogen is sp^3

$$\diagdown\diagup\; N^+ \;\diagup\diagdown$$

and of sulphur either sp^3,

$$\diagdown\diagup\; S^{2+} \;\diagup\diagdown \quad \text{or } p^3d \quad \diagdown\diagup\; S \;\diagup\diagdown$$

the formation of four covalent bonds is characteristic. In sp^3 hybridization four homopolar valencies are directed towards the corners of a tetrahedron, and the tetrahedral configuration is therefore encountered in a large number of nitrogen and sulphur compounds.

The structure of zinc sulphide on the basis of an ionic bond, would consist of Zn^{2+} and S^{2-} ions arranged tetrahedrally. The covalent structure, however, requires the sulphur to be doubly charged, positive and tetravalent and the zinc to be doubly charged negative and tetravalent, both the Zn^{2-} and the S^{2+} thereby being in an sp^3 valency state. The actual molecule will be a superposition of these two extreme states and although the contribution of the covalent form may be small, it does nevertheless determine both the configuration of the atoms and their coordination numbers.

In pyrites, FeS_2, it is possible to distinguish the S_2 group in which the bond distance is 2·10 Å as in the homopolar bond of pure sulphur. The sum of the ionic radii of two S^{2-} ions is 3·5 Å. In the crystal lattice surrounding each atom of iron are six S_2 groups, each of which is in turn surrounded by six atoms of iron. This structure may be pictured in another way. Each atom of sulphur is joined on one side to a second atom of sulphur in the S_2 group by a covalent bond, and on the other side there are located three atoms of iron, the five atoms thus forming a tetrahedral arrangement in which the coordination number of the sulphur is four. The Fe—S distance is 2·26 Å. Similar structures involving diatomic groups of S_2, P_2, As_2, AsS and SbS are observed in marcasite (another modification of FeS_2) and in $FeAs_2$, FeAsS, FeSbS, $PtAs_2$, $PtSb_2$ and PtP_2.

The structure of covelline, CuS, is more complicated than would be anticipated from its simple stoichiometric formula. In this crystal there are two types of sulphur atoms, the S_2 groups located between six copper atoms as in pyrites and, in addition, isolated atoms of sulphur surrounded by five atoms of copper, three in the form of a triangle at a distance of 2·19 Å and two, one above and one below, at a distance of 2·35 Å. The copper atoms are also arranged in different ways, some being located at the centres of tetrahedra and others at the centres of triangles of sulphur atoms. In view of this complex structure the formula Cu_3SS_2 has been suggested. The PtS crystal possesses a similar structure to the PtO crystal.

In SiS_2, each silicon atom is at the centre of a tetrahedron of four atoms of sulphur, and each sulphur atom is joined to two atoms of silicon thus forming an infinite chain in which the bonds are almost entirely covalent.

```
         S       S
 \     /   \   /   \     /
   Si        Si       Si
 /     \   /   \   /     \
         S       S
```

It is possible to distinguish three methods of joining tetrahedral structures, *i.e.* with common points as in SiO_2, with common sides, as in SiS_2, and with common faces as in Al_2O_3. Pauling considers that a transfer from a common point structure to a common side structure is related to an increase in the covalent character of the bonds.

From the data on the structure of crystals discussed in this chapter we may make the same conclusion as that reached for gaseous molecules, namely, that the homopolar and the ionic bond are only limiting cases and that actual bonds, as characterized by the distribution of the electron cloud may be described in terms of the relative contributions of the limiting structures. In the crystalline state diamond and sodium chloride may be taken as characteristic of the limiting structures. A satisfactory theory of crystals, intermediate between these extremes, will only be attained when, by wave mechanical methods, it is found possible to describe the motion of electrons in the periodic field due to the atoms arranged in the crystal.

REFERENCES

[1] LIPSON, H. and STOKES, A. R. *Nature, Lond.* 149 (1942) 328

[2] SOMMERFELD, A. and BETHE, H. *Electronentheorie der Metalle, Handbuck der Physik* Berlin, 1933

MOTT, N. F. and JONES, H. *The Theory and the Properties of Metals and Alloys* Oxford, 1936

SEITZ, F. *The Modern Theory of Solids* New York, 1940
HUME-ROTHERY, W. *The Metallic State* Oxford, 1931
— *Atomic Theory for Students of Metallurgy* London, 1947
WILSON, A. H. *The Theory of Metals* Cambridge, 1936
[3] BRIDGMAN, P. W. *Phys. Rev.* 48 (1935) 893
[4] BRILL, R. and HERMANN, C. *Ann. Phys. Lpz.* 41 (1942) 1937
[5] HUME-ROTHERY, W., MABBOTT, G. W. and EVANS, K. M. C. *Phil. Trans.* *A* 233 (1934) 1
[6] MOTT, N. F. and JONES, H. *The Theory and the Properties of Metals and Alloys* Oxford, 1936
[7] LONDON, F. *Z. phys. Chem* *B* 11 (1930) 222
[8] DEITZ, V. *J. Franklin Inst.* 219 (1935) 459
SPONER, H. and BRUCK-WILLSTÄTTER, M. *J. chem. Phys.* 5 (1937) 745
[9] WOLF, K. L. and WEGHOFER, H. *Z. phys. Chem. B* 39 (1938) 194
[10] SHERMAN, J. *Chem. Rev.* 11 (1932) 93
[11] FRENKEL, J. *Theory of Solids* Leningrad, 1924
[12] PAULING, L. C. *J. Amer. chem. Soc.* 49 (1927) 772
[13] BORN, M. and MAYER, J. E. *Z. Phys.* 75 (1932) 1
[14] MAYER, J. E. *ibid* 61 (1930) 798
— and HELMHOLZ, L. *ibid* 75 (1932) 22
HELMHOLZ, L. and MAYER, J. E. *J. chem. Phys.* 2 (1934) 245
[15] TANDON, A. N. *Proc. Nat. Acad. Sci. Ind.* 7 (1937) 102
— *Ind. J. Physics* 11 (1937) 99
[16] SRIVASTAVA, B. N. *Proc. Nat. Inst. Sci.* 4 (1938) 365
[17] LANDSHOFF, R. *Z. Phys.* 102 (1936) 201
— *Phys. Rev.* 52 (1937) 246
[18] LANDÉ, A. *Z. Phys.* 1 (1920) 191
[19] WASASTJERNA, J. A. *Soc. Sci. Fenn, Comm. Phys. Math* 1 (1923) no. 38
— *Z. phys. Chem.* 101 (1922) 193
[20] GOLDSCHMIDT, V. M. *Geochemische Verteilungsgesetze der Elemente* Oslo, 1923–27
[21] PAULING, L. C. *Proc. roy. Soc.* *A* 114 (1927) 181
— and SHERMAN, J. *Z. Kristallogr.* 81 (1932) 1
[22] — *The Nature of the Chemical Bond* Cornell, 1939 p 346
[23] MAGNUS, A. *Z. anorg. Chem.* 124 (1922) 288
[24] JACOBS, R. B. *Phys. Rev.* 54 (1938) 468
[25] MAYER, J. E. *J. chem. Phys.* 1 (1933) 270, 327
— and LEVY, R. B. *ibid* 1 (1933) 647
MAY, A. *Phys. Rev.* 52 (1937) 339
[26] GUNTZ, A. and BENOIT, F. *Bull. Soc. chim. Fr.* 35 (1924) 709
[27] HYLLERAAS, E. A. *Z. Phys.* 63 (1930) 771
[28] MAYER, J. E. and MALTBIE, M. *ibid* 75 (1932) 748
[29] YEARIAN, H. J. and LARK-HOROWITZ, K. *Phys. Rev.* 42 (1932) 905
LARK-HOROWITZ, K., YEARIAN, H. J. and LOWE, J. *ibid* 47 (1935) 331
YEARIAN, H. J. *ibid* 48 (1936) 631
LARK-HOROWITZ, K. and EHRHARDT, C. H. *ibid* 55 (1939) 605
JAMES, H. M. and JOHNSON, V. A. *ibid* 56 (1939) 119
[30] MAXWELL, L. R., HENDRICKS, S. B. and DEMING, L. S. *J. chem. Phys.* 5 (1937) 626
HAMPSON, G. C. and STOSICK, A. J. *J. Amer. chem. Soc.* 60 (1938) 1814
[31] BUERGER, M. J. and HENDRICKS, S. B. *Z. Kristallogr.* 98 (1937) 1
[32] MOORE, W. J. and PAULING, L. C. *J. Amer. chem. Soc.* 63 (1941) 1392
[33] ROGERS, M. J. and HELMHOLZ, L. *ibid* 63 (1941) 278
[34] BRAGG, W. L. *Trans. Faraday Soc.* 25 (1929) 291
[35] — and WEST, J. *Proc. roy. Soc.* *A* 111 (1926) 691
[36] BRILL, R., HERMANN, C. and PETERS, C. *Ann. Phys. Lpz.* 41 (1942) 233
[37] GASSELL. *Crystal Chemistry* Leningrad, 1938
[38] BRAGG, W. L. *Atomic Structure of Minerals* Cornell, 1937

14

COMPLEX COMPOUNDS

VALENCY STATES OF ATOMS INVOLVING *d* ELECTRONS

THE EXPERIMENTAL evidence shows that a complex compound such as $K_4Fe(CN)_6$ cannot be regarded as a mixed crystal, $4KCN.Fe(CN)_2$, since in solution it may be demonstrated that the ion $Fe(CN)_6^{4-}$ exists as an independent species. In such an ion each CN group will be at an equal distance from the atom of iron and bound to it by an identical type of bond. The existence of such compounds clearly involves a valency greater than the classical di- or trivalency of iron and this was originally accounted for by WERNER by supplementing the classical valency theory by the idea of the coordinate bond. The modern views on the nature of the chemical bond, however, permit a somewhat more rigorous approach to the problem of complex compounds.

A particular atom may exist in one or more valency states and so far we have considered only those cases involving *s* and *p* electrons, but nevertheless we have observed cases where the normal valency of an atom does not correspond to the number of unpaired electrons in the ground state, but to that in some excited electronic state. This occurs in divalent beryllium, trivalent boron and tetravalent carbon (see Chapter 2). The loss or gain of an electron also incurs a change of valency, as shown in the compounds of nitrogen, oxygen, boron and carbon. This production of new valencies by the transformation of the atom to a new valency state forms the basis for the understanding of complex compounds owing to the great number of possible valency states of atoms containing *d* electrons in the penultimate electronic shell. In these atoms the electrons are located in the five *d* orbitals in accordance with Hund's rule, so that the number of unpaired electrons, N, is a maximum. The ground states of some atoms having *d* electrons are given in the following diagram.

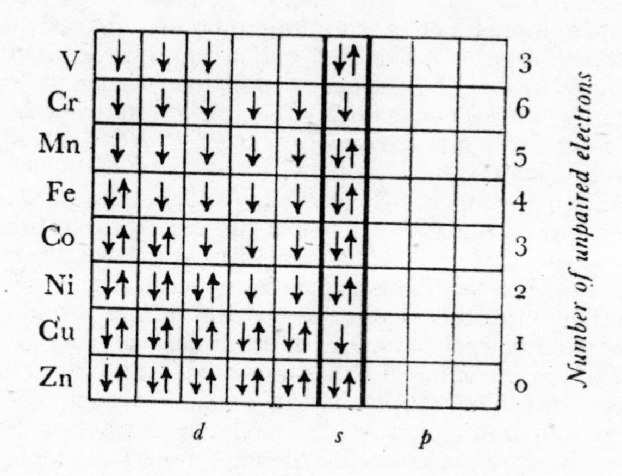

For atoms possessing *d* electrons, the energy of the *d* and *s* states is very close and in *Table CLXII* are given the energy differences for various distributions of electrons in the *d* and *s* orbitals in which the number of unpaired electrons in each state remains constant. In scandium, titanium, vanadium, manganese, iron, cobalt and nickel in the ground state, there are two paired *s* electrons and the transfer of one electron to the *d* shell, thereby pairing with a *d* electron already occupying an orbital, requires in the case of scandium the absorption of 58 kcals. On increasing the number of *d* electrons, however, the excitation energy falls as shown by the values given in the first row of *Table CLXII*, until with nickel the transfer requires the absorption of only 0·6 kcals, a value which is of the same order as RT. The transfer of both the *s* electrons in nickel to the *d* shell ($d^8s^2 \rightarrow d^{10}$) with the pairing of all electrons, requires the absorption of 42 kcals. In platinum the corresponding excitation energy ($d^9s \rightarrow d^{10}$) is 17 kcals and in palladium the d^{10} state is the ground state.

Table CLXII. Difference in the Energies in kcals of d and s States in Different Atoms

Sc $ds^2 \rightarrow d^2s$ 58	Ti $d^2s^2 \rightarrow d^3s$ 43	V $d^3s^2 \rightarrow d^4s$ 42	Mn $d^5s^2 \rightarrow d^6s$ 48	Fe $d^6s^2 \rightarrow d^7s$ 20	Co $d^7s^2 \rightarrow d^8s$ 10	Ni $d^8s^2 \rightarrow d^9s$ 0·6
Y $ds^2 \rightarrow d^2s$ 53	Zr $d^2s^2 \rightarrow d^3s$ 36			Ru $d^7s \rightarrow d^6s^2$ 21	Rh $d^8s \rightarrow d^7s^2$ 36	
						Pt $d^9s \rightarrow d^8s^2$ 2

In addition to the formation of new valency states by transitions between the *s* and *d* states, the *p* orbitals may also be filled, since, for example, the difference in the energy of the 3*d*, 4*s* and 4*p* levels is not great and electronic transitions can readily occur between these levels. Such transitions increase the number of unpaired electrons without involving energy changes of any considerable magnitude. The maximum number of unpaired electrons that is possible is therefore nine : five in *d*, one in *s* and three in *p* orbitals. In addition, the gain or loss of electrons by the atom to give an ion may also cause a change in the valency state. The valency states of various atoms possessing *d* electrons is summarized in *Table CLXIII*, the number of unpaired electrons being given for each.

With vanadium, owing to the existence of unoccupied *d* orbitals, in addition to the ground state d^3s^2 in which the two electrons in the *s* orbital are paired, an excited state in which the electronic configuration is d^4s or d^3sp is possible in which the number of unpaired electrons has been increased from three to five. In other neutral atoms and in ions, in addition to the ground state various excited states exist similar to that described for vanadium in which the value of N has increased. It is interesting to notice that the maximum values of N in the case of vanadium (5), chromium (6), manganese (7), and iron (8) correspond with the number of the group in which these atoms were placed in the Mendeléeff periodic table, but owing to the somewhat artificial nature of this grouping, there is no group into which chromium (9) may be placed. Chromium and molybdenum are the

Table CLXIII. Valency States of Atoms containing d Electrons

Atom	No. of unpaired electrons	Electronic configuration	Atom	No. of unpaired electrons	Electronic configuration	Atom	No. of unpaired electrons	Electronic configuration	Atom	No. of unpaired electrons	Electronic configuration	Atom	No. of unpaired electrons	Electronic configuration	Atom	No. of unpaired electrons	Electronic configuration	Atom	No. of unpaired electrons	Electronic configuration	Atom	No. of unpaired electrons	Electronic configuration
V	3 5 {	d^3s^2 d^4s d^3sp	Cr	6	d^5s	Mn	5 7	d^5s^2 d^5sp	Fe	4 6 8	d^6s^2 d^6sp d^5sp^2	Co	3 5 7 9	d^7s^2 d^7sp d^6sp^2 d^5sp^3	Ni	2 4 6 8	d^8s^2 d^8sp d^7sp^2 d^6sp^3	Cu	1 3 5	$d^{10}s$ d^9sp d^8sp^2	Zn	0 2 4	$d^{10}s^2$ $d^{10}sp$ d^9sp^2
V^+	4 {	d^4 d^3s	Cr^+	5 {	d^5 d^4s	Mn^+	6	d^5s	Fe^+	5 { 7	d^6s d^5s^2 d^5sp	Co^+	4 { 6 8	d^7s d^6s^2 d^6sp d^5sp^2	Ni^+	3 { 5 7 9	d^8s d^7s^2 d^7sp d^6sp^2 d^5sp^3	Cu^+	0 2 4	d^{10} d^9s d^8sp	Zn^+	1 { 3	$d^{0}s$ d^9s^2 d^9sp
V^{2+}	3	d^3	Cr^{2+}	4	d^4	Mn^{2+}	5 {	d^5 d^4s	Fe^{2+}	4 6	d^6 d^5s	Co^{2+}	3 5 7	d^7 d^6s d^5sp	Ni^{2+}	2 4 { 6 8	d^8 d^7s d^6s^2 d^6sp d^5sp^2	Cu^{2+}	1 3 5	d^9 d^8s d^7sp	Zn^{2+}	0 2 4	d^{10} d^9s d^8sp
V^{3+}	2	d^2	Cr^{3+}	3	d^3	Mn^{3+}	4	d^4	Fe^{3+}	5	d^5	Co^{3+}	4 6	d^6 d^5s									
V^-	6	d^5s	Cr^-	7	d^5sp	Mn^-	8	d^5sp^2	Fe^-	9	d^5sp^3	Co^-	8	d^6sp^3	Ni^-	7	d^7sp^3	Cu^-	2 4	$d^{10}sp$ d^9sp^2	Zn^-	3	$d^{10}sp^2$
			Cr^{2-}	8	d^5sp^2	Mn^{2-}	9	d^5sp^3	Fe^{2-}	8	d^6sp^3	Co^{2-}	7	d^7sp^3	Ni^{2-}	6 4	d^8sp^3 d^9sp^2	Cu^{2-}	5	d^9sp^3	Zn^{2-}	4	$d^{10}sp^3$
			Cr^{3-}	9	d^5sp^3				Fe^{3-}	7	d^7sp^3	Co^{3-}	6	d^8sp^3				Cu^{3-}	4	$d^{10}sp^3$			
									Fe^{4-}	6	d^8sp^3												

only elements in which, in the ground state, there are six unpaired electrons. With these atoms, excitation of the *d* or *s* electrons to a *p* orbital does not lead to an increase of *N*. Of the various possible electronic configurations of the negative ions, only those are given in *Table CXLIII* for which *N* has a maximum value. The greatest possible number of unpaired electrons, 9, is achieved in Cr^{3-}, Mn^{2-}, Fe^{-}, Co and Ni^{+}. In these cases the further addition of electrons brings about a decrease of *N*. Similar valency states are possible in the analogous atoms of the fifth and sixth periods.

The spectroscopic data for the energies of excitation of atoms with *d* electrons to states with an increased value of *N* are rather limited; the available values are given in *Table CLXIV*. The energies of excitation of *s* electrons to the *p* state in scandium, titanium, manganese, iron, cobalt, nickel, ytterbium and zirconium are of the same order as in the alkaline earth elements and it is found that the energy of excitation increases considerably with the increase of the number of inner *d* electrons. In order to transform a nickel atom from the ground state to that in which *N* is six or eight, it is necessary to unpair two or three pairs of electrons respectively; in iron, to produce the same values of *N*, it is necessary to unpair only one or two pairs of electrons. Furthermore, the excitation energy in the case of the first electron pair (Fe, $d^6s^2 \rightarrow d^6sp$; Ni, $d^8s^2 \rightarrow d^8sp$) is less for iron (54 kcals) than for nickel (73 kcals). This evidence indicates that the production of atoms with six unpaired electrons requires more energy for nickel than for iron, thus explaining why, with nickel, complexes with a coordination number of four are characteristic whereas with iron the value is six.

Table CLXIV. Excitation Energies of Atoms Containing d Electrons

Atom	Transition	Excitation energy kcals	Atom	Transition	Excitation energy kcals
Sc	$ds^2 \rightarrow dsp$	45	Cu	$d^{10}s \rightarrow d^9sp$	111
Y	$ds^2 \rightarrow dsp$	43	Au	$d^{10}s \rightarrow d^9sp$	129
Ti	$d^2s^2 \rightarrow d^2sp$	45	Sc	$ds^2 \rightarrow d^2s$	33
Zr	$d^2s^2 \rightarrow d^2sp$	42	Y	$ds^2 \rightarrow d^2s$	31
Mn	$d^5s^2 \rightarrow d^5sp$	52	La	$ds^2 \rightarrow d^2s$	8
Fe	$d^6s^2 \rightarrow d^6sp$	54	Ti	$d^2s^2 \rightarrow d^3s$	19
Co	$d^7s^2 \rightarrow d^7sp$	67	Zr	$d^2s^2 \rightarrow d^3s$	14
Ni	$d^8s^2 \rightarrow d^8sp$	73	V	$d^3s^2 \rightarrow d^4s$	6
Zn	$d^{10}s^2 \rightarrow d^{10}sp$	92	W	$d^4s^2 \rightarrow d^5s$	8
Cd	$d^{10}s^2 \rightarrow d^{10}sp$	86	Pd	$d^{10} \rightarrow d^9s$	19
Hg	$d^{10}s^2 \rightarrow d^{10}sp$	108			

The energies of excitation of zinc, cadmium and mercury are greater than those of calcium, strontium and barium, where there are no *d* electrons in the penultimate electronic shell, and also greater than in the case of manganese, iron, cobalt and nickel. The existence of compounds, however, in which zinc, cadmium and mercury form covalent bonds, *e.g.* $Hg(CH_3)_2$ indicates that unpairing of electrons must occur.

Very little data exist on the transfer of *d* electrons to *p* orbitals. For chromium the excitation energy of one *d* electron to a *p* orbital without change of *N*, $d^5s \rightarrow d^4sp$, is 71 kcals. For copper and gold the excitation energies for the transfer $d^{10}s \rightarrow d^9sp$ involving change of *N* from one to three, are respectively 111 kcals and 129 kcals. Although these values are rather large, the existence of compounds involving trivalent gold indicates that the loss of the excitation energy is compensated by the gain of energy due to bond formation.

The low values of the excitation energy for vanadium and tungsten shown in *Table CLXIV* indicates that the excitation of an s electron to a d state requires only a very small absorption of energy.

Directional nature of bonds involving d orbitals— The atoms of the transition elements may take part in both σ and π bonds in the formation of a compound. The number of σ bonds formed by the central atom cannot exceed the number of surrounding atoms or groups since between any pair of atoms, only one σ bond is permissible, but the number of σ bonds may be less than the number of neighbours, since bonds other than the covalent are possible, *e.g.* bonds due to ion-dipole and dispersion forces.

A very large number of complex compounds exist in which the coordination number is either six or four. By the methods of classical stereochemistry it was established that the coordination number of six corresponded to an octahedral configuration of the atoms or groups about the central atom and that when the coordination number is four the configuration was either planar or tetrahedral. More recently these configurations have been confirmed by x-ray analysis.

It has been shown by PAULING[1] that six stable and equivalent σ bonds may be formed if the electrons of the central atom are located in states described by a hybrid function composed of the functions of two d, one s and three p orbitals, generally termed d^2sp^3 hybridization. The six equivalent σ bonds are formed by the overlapping of the d^2sp^3 hybrid orbitals with orbitals of the surrounding atoms, and are directed towards the six corners of a regular octahedron. Each of the d^2sp^3 hybrid orbitals is represented by an electron cloud which is almost entirely concentrated along one axis, thus permitting considerable overlap of the orbitals to occur. In the case of a coordination number of four, similar calculations lead to two possible linear combinations of the atomic orbitals, the first being the four sp^3 hybrid orbitals which are directed towards the four corners of a tetrahedron and which have been discussed in Chapter 4, and a second type of hybridization due to the combination of one d, one s and two p functions leading to the formulation of four dsp^2 hybrid orbitals, which are situated in one plane and are directed towards the four corners of a square.

The most complete discussion of the various possible combinations of atomic orbitals to form hybrid atomic orbitals is that of KIMBALL[2], who considers the problem of directed valence from the point of view of group theory. The various spatial arrangements of the surrounding atoms which are possible are considered in turn and the hybrid atomic orbitals, necessary to form a σ bond between the central atom and each surrounding atom, are derived from the s, p and d atomic orbitals. All coordination numbers from two to eight are considered and the results are given in *Table CLXV*.

Where the coordination number is two, linear and triangular configurations of the three atoms are possible, and Kimball's results show that the former case may result from sp or from dp hybridization and the latter case from p^2, d^2 or ds hybridization. In addition to a σ bond between a pair of atoms there may be two π bonds. The axes of the π bonds are perpendicular to the axis of the σ bond and perpendicular to each other. In the case of the linear configuration, four π bonds may be formed, two by p electrons and two by d electrons. In the angular configuration, however, as Kimball points out, the four π bonds are not equivalent. If the σ bonds are formed by two p electrons (p^2 hybridization), then the π bonds are of two types :

Table CLXV. Spatial Arrangement of Hybrid Bonds and Possibility of Multiple Bond Formation

Coordination number	Configuration of σ bonds	Electrons participating in σ bonds	Electrons participating in π bonds	
			Strong	Weak
2	*Linear*	sp	p^2d^2	—
		dp	p^2d^2	—
	Angular	p^2	dp or d^2	ds or d^2
		ds	dp or d^2	p^2 or dp
		d^2	dp or d^2	sp or p^2 or dp
3	*Trigonal plane*	sp^2	pd^2	d^2
		dp^2	pd^2	d^2
		d^2s	pd^2	p^2
		d^3	pd^2	p^2
	Unsymmetrical plane	dsp	pd^2	pd or d^2
	Trigonal pyramid	p^3	—	d^4s or d^5
		d^2p	—	sp^2d^2 or p^2d
4	*Tetrahedral*	sp^3	d^2	d^3
		d^3s	d^2	p^3
	Irregular tetrahedron	d^2sp	—	d
		dp^3	—	s
		d^3p	—	s
	Tetragonal plane	dsp^2	d^3p	—
		d^2p^2	d^3p	—
	Tetragonal pyramid	d^4	d	sp or p^2
	$TeCl_4$ *configuration (Cl–T–Cl in linear configuration, other two bonds in planes perpendicular to this line)*[3]	p^3d	d	d^3
		d^2sp	d	d^2p^2
		dp^3	d	sd^3
		d^4	d	sp^3
5	*Bipyramid*	dsp^3	d^2	d^2
		d^2sp	d^2	p^2
	Tetragonal bipyramid	d^2sp^2	d	pd^2
		d^4s	d	p^3
		d^2p^3	d	sd^2
		d^4p	d	sp^2
	Pentagonal pyramid	d^5	—	sp^2 or p^3
	Pentagonal plane	d^3p^2		
6	*Octahedron*	d^2sp^3	d^3	—
	Trigonal prism	d^4sp	—	p^2d
		d^5p	—	p^2s
	Trigonal antiprism	d^3p^3	—	sd
7	*Octahedron with one extra atom in centre of face*	d^3sp^3	—	d^2
		d^5sp	—	p^2
	Trigonal prism with one extra atom at centre of one square face	d^4sp^2	—	dp
		d^4p^3	—	ds
		d^5p^2	—	ps
8	*Dodecahedron*	d^4sp^3	d	—
	Antiprism	d^5p^3	—	s
	Face centred prism (only two square faces occupied)	d^5sp^2	p	—

two π bonds are obtained from one d and one p electron, or from two d electrons, whilst the remaining two π bonds, which are weaker, are formed by either one d and one s electron or by two other d electrons.

With a coordination number of four, the tetrahedral configuration arises by the formation of sp^3 or d^3s hybrid orbitals. The remaining electrons form π bonds which may be strong (d^2 hybridization), or weak (d^3 or p^3 hybridization). The planar configuration, due to either dsp^2 or d^2p^2 hybridization may have four stable π bonds between the central atom and the surrounding atoms, depending on the number of available electrons.

MAGNETIC CRITERION OF BOND TYPE

The investigation of the magnetic properties of compounds gives information concerning the valency states of the individual atoms in the compound. Before dealing with the magnetic properties of complex compounds we shall discuss briefly the magnetic properties of simpler compounds[4].

When any substance is placed in a magnetic field a magnetic polarization is produced which may be represented by

$$J = \Sigma M \quad \ldots .(14.1)$$

where J is the magnetic moment per unit volume and M is the magnetic moment of the atoms, molecules or ions forming the compound. For reasons which will be apparent later the polarization may either oppose or augment the applied field, the substance being termed diamagnetic or paramagnetic respectively. In addition to these two main classes, certain substances in which the paramagnetism is very strong are termed ferromagnetic. Ferromagnetism is not a molecular or atomic property but a property of the crystal and will not concern us here. In paramagnetic and diamagnetic substances J is proportional to the strength of the applied field H,

$$J = \chi H \quad \ldots .(14.2)$$

The proportionality coefficient χ is termed the magnetic susceptibility and in paramagnetic substances has a positive value whereas in diamagnetic substances it is negative. In order to indicate the order of magnitude of the magnetic susceptibility in the three types of magnetism, the diamagnetic susceptibility of water per gm is $-0{\cdot}72 \times 10^{-8}$ c.g.s units, for the paramagnetic susceptibility of copper sulphate the value $+6 \times 10^{-6}$ c.g.s units has been obtained, and for ferromagnetic substances the value is of the order of $+40$ c.g.s units.

On the basis of classical theory, the motion of an electron in an orbit around the nucleus will give rise to a magnetic moment and as shown by LANGEVIN, the presence of an external magnetic field will exert an accelerating influence on the electrons and results in the formation of an induced magnetic moment directed against the applied field. A quantum mechanical derivation leads to the same expression for the diamagnetic susceptibility as the classical treatment. It will be evident that diamagnetism will be inherent in all substances irrespective of whether they are also para- or ferromagnetic.

PASCAL[5] has attempted to account for the diamagnetic susceptibility of organic compounds by considering it as an additive quantity in a similar manner to induced electric polarization. The data show that the addition of the same group to different molecules often changes the diamagnetic

Table CLXVI. Additivity of Diamagnetic Susceptibilities

Substance	$-10^6\chi$	*Difference*
Ethyl acetate ..	55·2	17·1
Ethyl chloroacetate	72·3	
Acetone	33·7	17·2
Chloroacetone ..	50·9	
Benzene	55·1	3 × 17·1
Trichlorobenzene ..	106·5	

susceptibility by the same amount (*Table CLXVI*) and Pascal suggested that the diamagnetic susceptibility of a molecule is equal to the sum of the susceptibilities of the individual atoms constituting the molecule. However, in order to produce agreement between the calculated and observed values it was found necessary to introduce additional constants for double and triple bonds and for other structural factors. The relative magnitude of these structural constants compared with the molecular values was much greater than in the analogous case of molecular refractions and furthermore, many more structural factors were found to be necessary. For example, a constant had to be introduced for the group $CH_2{=}CH{-}CH_2$ ($4·5 \times 10^{-6}$ c.g.s units) in *cyclo*hexene and in *cyclo*pentene. Different increments were necessary for halogen atoms in mono-, di- and polyhalogen derivatives since if only one value is assumed for the chlorine atom, the deviation from additivity is found to be : in CH_2Cl_2, 9 per cent ; CH_2Br_2, 10 per cent ; CH_2I_2, 7 per cent ; $CHCl_3$, 19 per cent ; $CHBr_3$, 25 per cent ; C_2Cl_6, 17 per cent ; C_2Br_6, 31 per cent and CBr_4, 32 per cent. These observations tend to show that there is little evidence for considering the diamagnetic susceptibility as an additive quantity in the same sense that additivity occurs in molecular refraction. An alternative system of addition of atomic and group diamagnetic susceptibilities suggested by GRAY and CRUICKSHANK[6] is equally unsatisfactory.

In paramagnetic substances, the atoms or molecules possess a permanent magnetic moment, which are oriented in the external magnetic field. As in the orientation of permanent electric dipoles, the orientation is opposed by the thermal motion of the molecules and atoms. The classical theory of paramagnetism was developed by Langevin and was later applied by Debye to the case of electrical polarization. The application of quantum mechanics to the problem introduced certain modifications to the theory of Langevin, the most important being that only certain limited orientations are permissible. The total susceptibility of a substance is thus composed of the diamagnetic susceptibility χ_a which is a property of all substances, the paramagnetic susceptibility χ_μ which is dependent on the temperature, and an additional paramagnetic susceptibility χ_R independent of temperature and conditioned by electronic excitation. We thus have

$$\chi = \chi_a + \chi_\mu + \chi_R \qquad \ldots.(14·3)$$

The value of the paramagnetic susceptibility in those molecules and atoms possessing a permanent moment is much greater than that of the diamagnetic susceptibility. The diamagnetism, although present, is thus invariably more than compensated by the paramagnetism and all such substances have a resultant paramagnetic susceptibility. Sometimes, however, *e.g.* $KMnO_4$ where $\chi_\mu = 0$, χ_R may be greater than χ_a and the substance possesses a small paramagnetic susceptibility which is independent of temperature.

The paramagnetic susceptibility may be attributed almost entirely to the electrons since the magnetic moments of the nuclei are relatively so small that to a first approximation they may be ignored. The electric moment of the electrons is due in part to the spin magnetic moment and in part to the magnetic moments associated with the motion of the electron relative to the nucleus. Since in Bohr's theory the electrons were represented as moving in definite orbits, the latter quantity is frequently referred to as the orbital magnetic moment.

On the basis of the Bohr theory the orbital magnetic moment may be obtained in the following way. The electron, during rotation about a closed orbit, is equivalent to an electric current, $e\nu$, where ν is the number of rotations of the electron in the orbit per second and e is the electronic charge. For such a system, the magnetic moment will be equal to the product of the area of the orbit, πr^2, and the current flowing, *i.e.*

$$\mu = \pi r^2 e\nu \qquad \ldots.(14.4)$$

We also have the angular momentum p, given by

$$p = mvr \qquad \ldots.(14.5)$$

and also that

$$v = 2\pi\nu r \qquad \ldots.(14.6)$$

From which it follows on combination of equations 14.5 and 14.6 that,

$$p = 2\pi m\nu r^2 \qquad \ldots.(14.7)$$

Then from equations 14.4 and 14.7

$$\mu/p = e/2m \qquad \ldots.(14.8)$$

The angular momentum of the electron may, however, only have the values given by

$$p = \sqrt{l(l+1)}.h/2\pi, \text{ where } l = 0, 1, 2, 3, \ldots. \qquad \ldots.(14.9)$$

Combining equations 14.8 and 14.9 we obtain

$$\mu = \sqrt{l(l+1)}.eh/4\pi m = \sqrt{l(l+1)}.\mu_B \qquad \ldots.(14.10)$$

or on transfer to electromagnetic units,

$$\mu = \sqrt{l(l+1)}.eh/4\pi mc \qquad \ldots.(14.11)$$

The term $eh/4\pi m$, generally denoted by μ_B, is termed the Bohr magneton. The value of μ_B is $0{\cdot}9273 \times 10^{-20}$ ergs/gauss.

The spin angular momentum of the electron is given by

$$p_s = \sqrt{s(s+1)}.h/2\pi = \sqrt{3}.h/4\pi \qquad \ldots.(14.12)$$

The spin magnetic moment of the electron will be,

$$\mu_s = 2\sqrt{s(s+1)}.\mu_B = \sqrt{3}.\mu_B \qquad \ldots.(14.13)$$

thus

$$\mu_s/p_s = e/m \qquad \ldots.(14.14)$$

i.e. twice the value given for the corresponding ratio for the orbital moment in equation 14.8.

In an atom with N electrons there are $2N$ magnetic vectors (N spin vectors and N orbital vectors). The resulting spin magnetic moment will be

$$\mu_s = \sqrt{4S(S+1)}.\mu_B \qquad \ldots.(14.15)$$

where S is the resultant spin quantum number, *i.e.* $S = |\Sigma s|$, 1/2 for one electron, for two electrons with antiparallel spins 0, or with parallel spins 1, for three electrons 1/2 or 3/2, *etc*). The resultant orbital magnetic moment is

$$\mu_L = \sqrt{L(L+1)}.\mu_B \qquad \ldots.(14.16)$$

where L is the resultant orbital quantum number. If, for example, there are two electrons with quantum numbers l_1 and l_2, then L may assume any integral values from $(l_1 + l_2)$ to $(l_1 - l_2)$, and similarly for more than two electrons.

The resultant spin and orbital angular momenta are coupled, employing the method of RUSSEL and SAUNDERS, to give a total angular momentum characterized by the quantum number J which may assume the values :

$$(L+S), (L+S-1), (L+S-2), \cdots\cdots (L-S+2), (L-S+1), (L-S)$$

For example, if $L = 2$ and $S = 3/2$, J may have any of the values $7/2$, $5/2$, $3/2$ and $1/2$.

The resultant magnetic moment of the atom is given by

$$\mu_J = g\sqrt{J(J+1)} \cdot \mu_B \qquad \ldots.(14.17)$$

where g is termed the splitting factor for which Landé deduced the empirical relation :

$$g = 1 + \frac{J(J+1) + S(S+1) - L(L+1)}{2J(J+1)} \qquad \ldots.(14.18)$$

The resultant angular momentum is

$$p_J = \sqrt{J(J+1)} \cdot h/2\pi \qquad \ldots.(14.19)$$

and

$$\mu_J / p_J = ge/2m \qquad \ldots.(14.20)$$

It will be seen from equation 14.18 that when $L = 0$ *i.e.* when the magnetic moment is due only to the electron spin,

$$g = 2 \qquad \ldots.(14.21)$$

and when $S = 0$ and the magnetic moment is due only to the orbital motion of the electron

$$g = 1 \qquad \ldots.(14.22)$$

The ratio of the magnetic and mechanical moments may be determined experimentally by means of the gyromagnetic[7] effect (SUCKSMITH[8], by rotation during magnetization and BARNETT[9], by the converse method, of magnetization by rotation). If for a particular substance this ratio is found to be equal to e/m, the paramagnetism will be due entirely to electron spin ; if the ratio has the value $e/2m$, the paramagnetism will be due to the orbital motion of the electron. Intermediate values will indicate that the magnetization of the substance is determined partly by spin and partly by the orbital motion of the electron. In all atoms with completely filled electronic shells, both S and L will be zero since all the electrons will be paired, hence $J = 0$ and the atom has no permanent magnetic moment.

Atoms and ions with unpaired electrons will possess constant magnetic moments. The paramagnetism is due in every case to the incomplete electronic shell, since the completed inner shells in which all the electrons are paired cannot contribute to the magnetic moment. By means of equation 14.17, using the appropriate values of L, S and J it is possible to calculate the moments of atoms and ions containing unpaired electrons. We are more interested here, however, in the magnetic moments of molecules rather than of atoms and ions ; in a very large number of molecules the resultant magnetic moment is zero owing to the complete pairing of the electrons and the only compounds which we have so far discussed which are paramagnetic are nitric oxide, the free radicals and molecular oxygen (O_2).

Compounds incorporating elements of the transition, lanthanon or actinon groups which contain *d* or *f* electrons, possess permanent magnetic moments. For example ferrous chloride, $FeCl_2$, is paramagnetic. The iron atom in the ground state contains four unpaired electrons ; in different ionic states this may increase, but in $FeCl_2$ there are only two Fe—Cl bonds and on the formation of these bonds, whatever their character (*i.e.* ionic, covalent or intermediate), only two of the four unpaired electrons are used. If the bonds are ionic, two electrons will be transferred from an atom of iron to two chlorine atoms to form two Cl^- ions with a completed electronic shell. If on the other hand the bonds are covalent, two electrons from the atom of iron would form electron pairs with unpaired electrons of the chlorine atoms. Thus, whatever the nature of the bond, two electrons of the atom of iron are excluded from contributing towards the magnetic moment of the atom. Such a state of the iron atom, where two of the electrons are employed in bond formation, we shall designate Fe^{II}. The two remaining unpaired electrons are responsible for the magnetic moment of the molecule.

The magnetic moment of ferrous chloride must be compared with the calculated moment of the atom of iron containing only two unpaired electrons, *i.e.* with the calculated moment of the Fe^{2+} ion. It must be stressed again that the agreement which is obtained does not indicate that the bond in $FeCl_2$ is ionic ; the comparison only permits us to establish the number of unpaired electrons in the molecule. The same is true of zinc chloride, which is diamagnetic. In the covalent structure both the two unpaired *s* and *p* electrons of Zn ($d^{10}sp$) participate in covalent bond formation ; in the ionic structure both ions Zn^{2+} (d^{10}) and Cl^- are diamagnetic. In certain instances the magnetic data does permit a conclusion to be made regarding the nature of the prevailing bonds. For example in the covalent structure of $PtCl_2$, the two unpaired electrons in the ground state of platinum (d^9s) become paired so that the substance would be diamagnetic. In the ionic structure, the ion Pt^{2+} (d^8) is formed, which in its ground state will have two unpaired electrons. The formation of the diamagnetic Pt^{2+} ion in which all the eight *d* electrons are paired, would involve the loss of energy and this state is therefore less probable. The experimental magnetic properties of $PtCl_2$ show that it is diamagnetic and hence the covalent structure represents the actual state of the molecule. Similar examples are observed in the complex compounds to be discussed later in this chapter.

The magnetic moments of the sulphates of the lanthanons have been measured and the experimental values are compared with those calculated by equation 14.17, in *Table CLXVII*.

Table CLXVII. Magnetic Moments of the Sulphates of the Lanthanons, in Bohr magnetons

Atom	Electronic configuration of *f* shell in ion	*S*	*L*	*J*	Calculated magnetic moment $\mu = g\sqrt{J(J+1)}$	Experimental magnetic moment
La^{III}	—	0	0	0	0	*Diamagnetic*
Ce^{III}	f^1	1/2	3	5/2	2·54	2·50
Pr^{III}	f^2	1	5	4	3·58	3·55
Nd^{III}	f^3	3/2	6	9/2	3·62	3·59
Sm^{III}	f^5	5/2	5	5/2	0·84	1·47
Eu^{III}	f^6	3	3	0	0	3·38
Gd^{III}	f^7	7/2	0	7/2	7·94	8·03
Tb^{III}	f^8	3	3	6	9·7	9·3
Dy^{III}	f^9	5/2	5	15/2	10·6	10·55
Ho^{III}	f^{10}	2	6	8	10·6	10·4
Er^{III}	f^{11}	3/2	6	15/2	9·6	9·5
Tm^{III}	f^{12}	1	5	6	7·6	7·35
Yb^{III}	f^{13}	1/2	3	7/2	4·5	4·5
Lu^{III}	f^{14}	0	0	0	0	*Diamagnetic*

The agreement in the majority of instances is very close and it should also be pointed out that the values of the Landé splitting factor, calculated by equation 14.18 and determined experimentally from gyromagnetic measurements are in good agreement (*Table CLXVIII*). For an explanation of the discrepancies occurring between the experimental and calculated values for samarium and europium the appropriate monographs[4] should be consulted.

Table CLXVIII. Landé Splitting Factor from Gyromagnetic Effect

Atom	calc	exp
Nd^{III}	0·73	0·78
Gd^{III}	2·00	2·12
Dy^{III}	1·32	1·36

The position is rather more complicated with the transition elements of the fourth period for which data are given in *Table CLXIX*. The agreement between the experimental values and those calculated by equation 14.17 is not good, but when it is assumed that the magnetic moment is due only to the electron spin and the moments are calculated by equation 14.15, the agreement is more satisfactory. It would thus appear that the magnetic moment of these atoms is due only to the spin magnetic moment and that the contribution from the orbital motion of the electron has been quenched. This is generally attributed to the influence of the fields of the neighbouring molecules, atoms or ions. In the case of the lanthanons, the *f* electrons lie sufficiently deep in the atom to be effectively screened from the influence of the fields of neighbouring ions and the total magnetic moment is given by

Table CLXIX. Magnetic Moments of Salts of Transition Elements, in Bohr Magnetons

Atom	Electronic configuration of unfilled d shell	Number of unpaired electrons	S	L	J	$\mu_J = g\sqrt{J(J+1)}$	$\mu^*_{\text{experimental}}$	$\mu_S = \sqrt{4S(S+1)}$
Mn^{VI}	d^1	1	1/2	2	3/2	1·55	K_2MnO_4, 1·71; $BaMnO_4$, 1·80	1·73
V^{III}	d^2	2	1	3	2	1·63		2·83
Cr^{III}, Mn^{IV}, V^{II}	d^3	3	3/2	3	3	0·78	$CrCl_3$, 3·81; $Cr_2O_3 7H_2O$, 3·85; $2KClMnCl_4$, 3·89	3·88
Mn^{III}	d^4	4	2	2	0	0	$Mn_2(SO_4)_3$, $5{\cdot}19_s$; $MnCl_3$, $5{\cdot}08_s$	4·90
Mn^{II}, Fe^{III}	d^5	5	5/2	0	5/2	5·91	$MnCl_2$, 5·65–5·92; $MnSO_4$, 5·90; $Fe_2(SO_4)_3$, 5·86	5·91
Fe^{II}	d^6	4	2	2	4	6·76	$FeCl_2$, 5·23; $FeSO_4$, 5·26	4·90
Co^{II}	d^7	3	3/2	3	9/2	6·68	$CoCl_2$, 5·04; $CoSO_4$, 5·04–5·25	3·88
Ni^{II}	d^8	2	1	3	4	5·61	$NiCl_2$, 3·24–3·42; $NiSO_4$, 3·42	2·83
Cu^{II}	d^9	1	1/2	2	5/2	3·56	$CuCl_2$, 2·02; $CuSO_4$, 2·01	1·73

* Subscript s indicates that value has been obtained from measurements made in solution

the sum of the orbital and spin moments. With the transition elements the *d* electrons form the outermost shell and interaction with neighbouring ions, leading to the quenching of the orbital moment, is apparently almost complete. The discrepancy between the experimental values and those calculated assuming complete quenching of the orbital moments, is greatest in Co^{II}, Ni^{II} and Cu^{II}. This difference is dependent on several factors such as the nature of the surrounding atoms or groups and, if measured in solution, on the concentration. The magnetic moments of Ni^{II} and Cu^{II} are decreased on complex formation[10], approaching more closely the theoretical values calculated on the basis of complete quenching of the orbital moments (from 3·42 to 3·09μ_B for Ni^{II} and from 2·01 to 1·85μ_B for Cu^{II}).

In the majority of instances, it will be evident that the magnetic data permit the number of unpaired electrons to be determined[11]. The salts of cobalt are an exception since the moment for $CoCl_2$, which must contain a considerable contribution from a moment due to the orbital electronic motion, has a value not only greater than three, but also greater than four unpaired electrons calculated on the basis of spin moments. In the complex compounds of cobalt, where evidently there is the same number of unpaired electrons as in $CoCl_2$, the magnetic moments vary considerably (*e.g.* $Co(N_2H_4)_2(CH_3COO)_2$, 4·56 μ_B; $Co(N_2H_4)_2Cl_2$, 4·93 μ_B; $Co(N_2H_4)_2SO_3H_2O$, 4·31 μ_B; $Co(NH_3)_6Cl_2$, 5·3 μ_B).

The magnetic data indicate the nature of the atomic or ionic valency states in atoms containing a number of unpaired electrons (*Table CLXX*). In compounds of chromium, for example in $CrCl_3$, three electrons are employed in bond formation leaving three which, from the value of the magnetic moment, are unpaired. The original configuration of the atoms with six unpaired electrons is therefore d^5s. In other compounds of chromium, more than three electrons may participate in the bonds, thus the ion CrO_4^{2-} may be represented by the following structures between which resonance occurs:

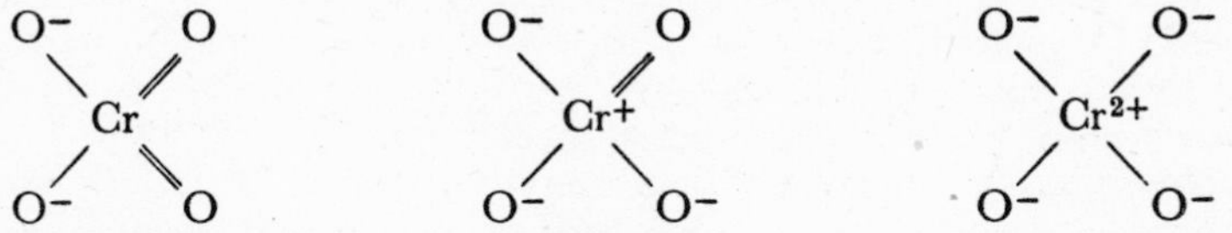

O^- O Cr O^- O	O^- O Cr^+ O^- O^-	O^- O^- Cr^{2+} O^- O^-
six structures *I*	*four structures* *II*	*one structure* *III*

In these structures all the six electrons of chromium are employed in bond formation. In the covalent structure *I*, all the bonds are homopolar, in the other structures electrons have been transferred to the oxygen atoms, pairing with the electrons of the latter. The tetrahedral configuration of this ion indicates that four σ bonds are formed with d^3s hybrid electrons and π bonds are formed with the remaining *d* electrons (*Table CLXV*). The other elements of the same group, *viz*, molybdenum and wolfram, give halides with four, five or six halogen atoms ($MoCl_4$, WI_4, $MoCl_5$, WBr_5, MoF_6, WCl_6).

The manganese atom possesses seven unpaired electrons (d^5sp) which indicates that the atom is in an excited state compared with its normal ground state (d^5s^2). All seven electrons are employed in bond formation in $KMnO_4$, whereas in K_2MnO_4 only six electrons are so used and there remains one

Table CLXX. Electronic States of Atoms in the Original State and in Complex Molecules

Compound		*Number of electrons occupied in bond formation*	*Number of unpaired electrons*	*Number of unpaired electrons in initial state*
Cr, Mo	$CrCl_3$	3	3	6
	K_2CrO_4	6	0	
	MoF_5	5	1	
	MoF_6	6	0	
Mn	$MnCl_2$	2	5	7
	$MnCl_3$	3	4	
	$MnCl_4$	4	3	
	K_2MnO_4	6	1	
	$KMnO_4$	7	0	
Fe, Os	$FeCl_2$	2	4	6
	$FeCl_3$	3	5	8
	OsF_8	8	0	
Co	$CoCl_2$	2	3	5
	$CoCl_3$	3	4 and 6	7 and 9
Ni, Pt	$NiCl_2$	2	2	4
	$PtCl_4$	4	0	
Cu, Au	CuCl	1	0	1
	$CuCl_2$	2	1	3
	$AuCl_4$	3	0	

unpaired electron. In $MnCl_4$ there are four bonds and three unpaired electrons, in $MnCl_3$ three bonds and four unpaired electrons and finally in $MnCl_2$ two electrons participate in bonds and five remain unpaired.

The iron atom has four unpaired electrons in the ground state d^6s^2 and also in $FeCl_2$. This indicates that the valency state of the ion in $FeCl_2$ is d^6sp and of the six unpaired electrons two are employed in bond formation. In $FeCl_3$ in addition to the three electrons used in the formation of bonds, there are five unpaired electrons, showing that the valency state of iron in $FeCl_3$ is d^5sp^2. In osmium, which also has the same valency state as iron in $FeCl_3$, all eight electrons are used in bond formation in OsO_4 and OsF_8.

If we assume that the magnetic moment of $CoCl_2$ corresponds to three unpaired electrons (see above), then cobalt is in the d^7sp state in $CoCl_2$. In Co^{III} compounds, the magnetic moment corresponds to 5 or 7 and the number of unpaired electrons is not certain, being either four or six. The cobalt atom is therefore in either the valency state d^6sp^2 ($N = 7$) or d^5sp^3 ($N = 9$). With nickel and platinum compounds, the valency state in compounds is generally that in which there are four unpaired electrons, d^8sp. In $NiCl_2$, two of these are employed in bond formation and two remain unpaired. In $PtCl_4$ all four unpaired electrons are employed in bond formation.

With copper, two types of compound are characteristic, a diamagnetic form, *e.g.* CuCl and a paramagnetic series $CuCl_2$, $CuSO_4$ *etc.* In the first group only the single unpaired *s* electron of copper ($d^{10}s$) forms a chemical bond. In salts of divalent copper (d^9sp) only two of the three unpaired electrons are used in bond formation, presumably the *s* and *p* electrons, whereas the third *d* electron remains unpaired and is responsible for the paramagnetism of these compounds. These examples show that in many compounds of elements containing *d* electrons, a number of electrons remain unpaired. In atoms containing only *s* and *p* electrons, or a completely filled and screened *d* shell, the unpaired electrons almost invariably bring about bond formation with other atoms, so long as this leads to a considerable gain in stability. Molecules with unpaired electrons are, therefore, only comparatively stable when additional stabilizing factors exist. This occurs, for example, in the organic free radicals of the triphenylmethyl type in which stabilization is caused by delocalization of the unpaired electrons and by the resonance of a great number of structures.

The compounds of the transition elements containing unpaired *d* electrons may be regarded as a particular type of free radical and the question arises as to how these molecules are stabilized. We consider that this behaviour may be explained on the basis of intra-atomic resonance. In the same way that electron transfer may occur between different atoms, so also will there be transfer of the electrons between the different electronic levels of one atom. In the former instance the exchange integrals are negative and the transfer of electrons with antiparallel spins leads to a decrease of the energy of the system and with parallel spins to an increase in energy. Within the atom, however, the exchange integrals are positive and the transfer of electrons with parallel spins gives stability to the atom[12]. On the formation of chemical bonds the nature of the intra-atomic resonance may change. If an unpaired electron of the atom enters into bond formation with another atom, the system gains energy and the conditions for resonance within the atom may be less favourable. The explanation of the preservation of unpaired electrons in simple and complex molecules evidently lies in this concept. The formation of bonds will occur only if the energy gained compensates for the loss of energy of intra-atomic resonance. In compounds containing *d* electrons a number of factors exist which tend to decrease the bond energies. First, the electrons of the surrounding atoms are repelled by the many non-bonding electrons of the central atom (the number of outer electrons not taking part in bond formation in an atom of a transition element is greater than in bonds formed by *s* and *p* electrons). This will result in a lowering of the bond energy. Secondly, there occurs a repulsion between the electrons of the coordinating atoms, which is increased if the interatomic distance between the central atom and a coordinating atom is small and if the latter are themselves large. This second factor is evidently the explanation of why high valencies generally occur with fluorides but not with other halides, and with the atoms of the fifth and sixth periods but not of the fourth, *e.g.* molybdenum and wolfram give MoF_6 and WF_6 and OsF_8 exists, but FeF_8 and $OsCl_8$ do not occur. The formation of multiple bonds decreases the effect of the steric factors. For example, chromium is hexavalent only in CrO_4^{2-}, where it is necessary to arrange only four atoms round the central atom. It should be pointed out, however, that the six electrons of the chromium atom in the d^5s state do not form six equivalent σ bonds, but invariably form multiple bonds, *e.g.* four σ and two π bonds, as in CrO_4^{2-}. Only by this means can the six electrons be employed in bond formation. In this connection the data of BRAUNE and PINNOW[13] are interesting. These show that in WF_6 and MoF_6 the fluorine atoms are not arranged in a perfect octahedron but the arrangement round the central atom is distorted. The fluorine atoms may be separated into three groups arranged at different distances from the central atom. EWENS and LISTER[14], however, have shown that the chlorine atoms in WCl_6 form a regular octahedron and in $MoCl_5$ a regular bipyramid. The problem of the equivalence of the bonds in such molecules still requires further investigation.

METALLIC CARBONYLS

None of the metallic carbonyls are paramagnetic, a fact which indicates that all the unpaired electrons existing in the ground state of the metal are paired in the molecule. The pairing of electrons could come about in two ways, either by the pairing of the electrons in the *d* orbitals of the atom, or by the formation of chemical bonds with the carbon monoxide molecule. However, spectroscopic data show that the pairing of electrons in the atom requires considerable excitation energy, *e.g.* the pairing of two electrons in iron requires 59 kcals, in cobalt 47 kcals, and in nickel 38 kcals. These values are greater than could be compensated for by van der Waal's attraction between the central atom and the surrounding CO groups and since the diamagnetic properties of the carbonyls also confirm that such a method of bonding is not possible, it is therefore concluded that covalent bonds are formed between the metal and the CO groups. Electron diffraction data show that in the metallic carbonyls the carbon and not the oxygen is bonded to the metal atom.

We have already shown that the carbon monoxide molecule may be represented by the following structures among which resonance occurs :

$$C{=}O \qquad C^{-}{\equiv}O^{+} \qquad C^{+}{-}O^{-}$$

and it is to be expected that in the carbonyl, the metal atom will participate in the resonance by virtue of the existence of different valency states. Thus the CO group may form a double bond with the metal atom by the pairing of two electrons of the metal with two electrons of carbon, *I* :

$$M{=}C{=}O$$
I

In addition to this structure, the CO group may donate one electron to the metal thereby permitting the structure to be

$$M^{-}{-}C{\equiv}O^{+} \qquad\qquad M^{-}{-}C^{+}{=}O$$
II *III*

The bond between the metal atom and the carbon atom may be considered as formed by two electrons from the carbon atom, which thus move in the field of two nuclei. The carbon and oxygen atoms may also exist in the singly charged negative trivalent and singly charged negative, monovalent states respectively, thus leading to the structures :

$$M^{+}{-}C^{-}{=}O \qquad\qquad M^{+}{\equiv}C{-}O^{-}$$
IV *V*

and the much less probable structure,

$$M^{+}{-}C{-}O^{-}$$
VI

involving a divalent carbon atom. In these structures the metal atom contributes either one or three electrons to a covalent bond and also donates one electron to the carbon or oxygen atom. In the metallic carbonyls all the above structures *I–VI* contribute to the resonance of the molecule and the numbers of electrons contributed to the bond by the metal may be summarized as follows : zero in structures *II* and *III* where an empty orbital is occupied by electrons from the carbon atom ; 2 instructures *I*, *IV* and *VI*; and 4 in structure *V*.

The formula and bond distances of the metallic carbonyls are given below, the latter being obtained from electron diffraction data. (Compounds of the alkali and alkaline earth metals with formulae of the type $K_6(CO)_6$ have been shown to be phenolates of hexahydroxybenzene.)

Cr	Mn	Fe	Co	Ni
$Cr(CO)_6$ Cr—C 1·92 Å	unknown	$Fe(CO)_5$ Fe—C 1·84 Å $Fe_2(CO)_9$ $Fe_3(CO)_{12}$	$Co_2(CO)_8$ $Co_4(CO)_{12}$	$Ni(CO)_4$ Ni—C 1·82 Å
Mo	**Tc**	**Ru**	**Rh**	
$Mo(CO)_6$ Mo—C 2·08 Å	unknown	$Ru(CO)_5$ $Ru_2(CO)_9$ $[Ru(CO)_4]_n$	$Rh_2(CO)_8$ $[Rh(CO)_3]_n$	
W	**Re**	**Os**		
$W(CO)_6$ W—C 2·06 Å	$Re_2(CO)_{10}$	$Os(CO)_5$ $Os_2(CO)_9$		

Although those metals which contain in the atom an even number of outer *d* and *s* electrons (Cr, 6; Fe, 8; Ni, 10; Mo, 6; Ru, 8; W, 6) give carbonyls, it is interesting to notice that Mn, Tc, Re and Co which contain an odd number of *d* and *s* electrons in the atom do not give carbonyls containing only one metal atom in the molecule.

The MCO group of atoms in the carbonyls is linear, as would be expected from the multiple nature of the bonds shown in structures *I* to *VI*. The CO distance is 1·15 Å compared with 1·13 Å in the carbon monoxide molecule. According to the data of ANDERSON, the Raman spectrum of $Ni(CO)_4$ shows the presence of a frequency at 2,038 cm^{-1} which evidently corresponds to the vibration of the CO group. In carbon monoxide the frequency is 2,158 cm^{-1} and the decrease of the frequency in the carbonyl group is evidently an indication that in the carbonyls, the contribution of the structure with the triple bond is smaller than in the carbon monoxide molecule. This conclusion is in agreement with the slight lengthening of the CO bond as indicated by the data given above.

The values of M—C distances given above are, as pointed out by Pauling, about 0·1 to 0·2 Å less than the sum of the covalent radii for single bonds. From this it is concluded that the M—C bond has some multiple bond character. Although this is evidently correct, the evidence based on the summation of covalent radii must not be regarded as of great significance.

The heat of formation of $Fe(CO)_5$ in the gaseous state from gaseous Fe and 5CO, is 138 kcals and for $Ni(CO)_4$ from Ni and 4CO in the gaseous state is 121 kcals. These data give for the M—CO bond the value of 28 to 30 kcals. The actual bond energy is probably greater, since the energy of the CO bond in the carbonyl group is probably less than that in the free carbon monoxide molecule, *i.e.* the CO group in the molecules $M(CO)_n$ possesses more carbonyl character than in carbon monoxide. In addition, the bond energy as determined from the heat of formation will be low, since in the formation of the carbonyl, the metal atom has been raised from the ground electronic state to its valency state.

The nickel atom possesses ten outer electrons and of these a maximum number of eight may be unpaired. Nickel forms a tetracarbonyl, $Ni(CO)_4$, the four CO groups being arranged tetrahedrally about the central nickel atom ; four σ bonds are therefore formed involving either sp^3 or d^3s hybridization. The structure *VII* is therefore possible in which the nickel atom makes four double bonds with the carbon atoms :

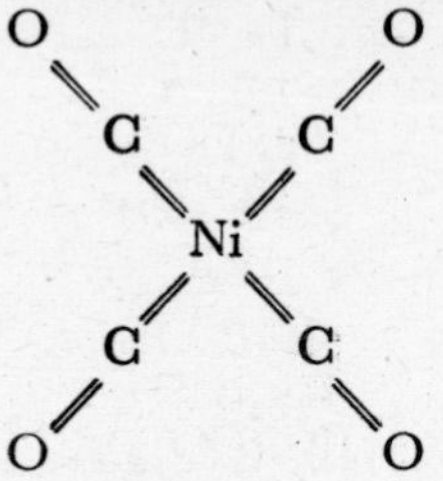

O O
C C
Ni
C C
O O

VII

In addition, the structures *VIII* and *IX*, in which a distribution of charge occurs, must also be considered.

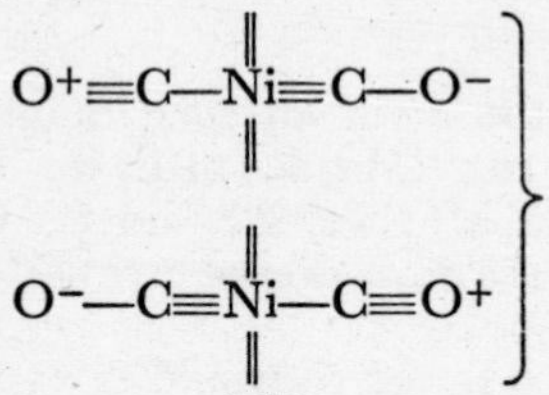

$O^+\equiv C—Ni\equiv C—O^-$ $O=C^+—Ni\equiv C—O^-$

$O^-—C\equiv Ni—C\equiv O^+$ $O^-—C\equiv Ni—C^+=O$

VIII 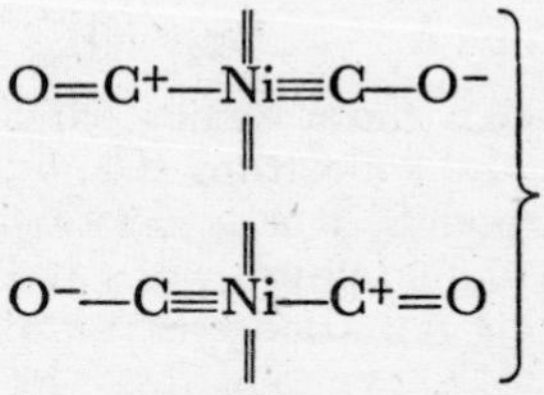 *IX*

Other possible structures for nickel carbonyl are *X*, in which the nickel is positively charged and employs nine unpaired electrons in bond formation :

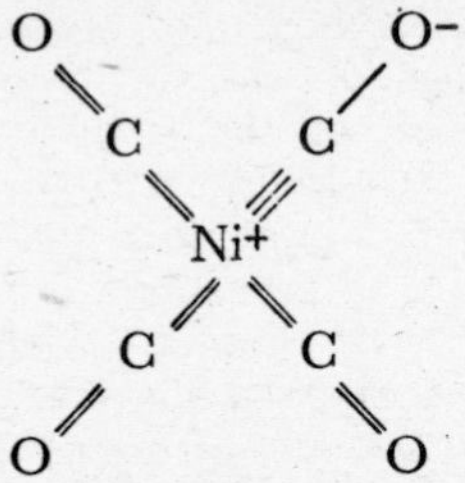

O O⁻
C C
Ni⁺
C C
O O

X

and *XI* and *XII* in which the nickel atom, having accepted one electron from a carbonyl group, possesses seven unpaired electrons :

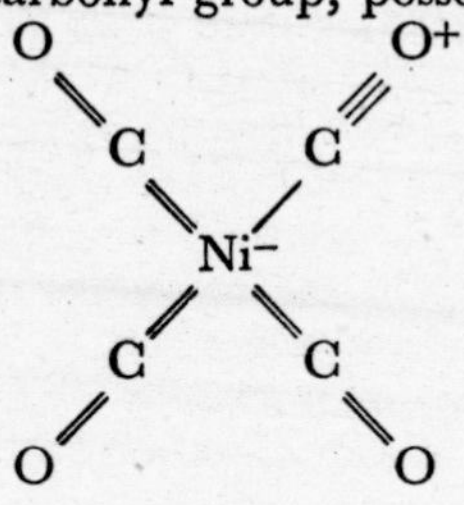

O O⁺ O ·O
C C C C⁺
Ni⁻ Ni⁻
C C C C
O O O O

XI 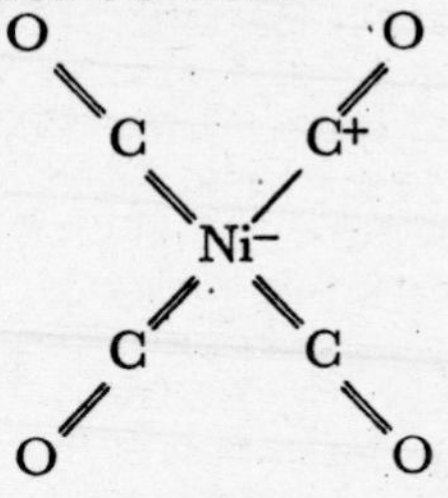 *XII*

KIMBALL[2] has pointed out that with the tetrahedral configuration, only two strong π bonds are formed (*Table CLXV*) and he therefore suggests the structure *XIII* as being perhaps more stable than the other structures which involve three, four and five π bonds

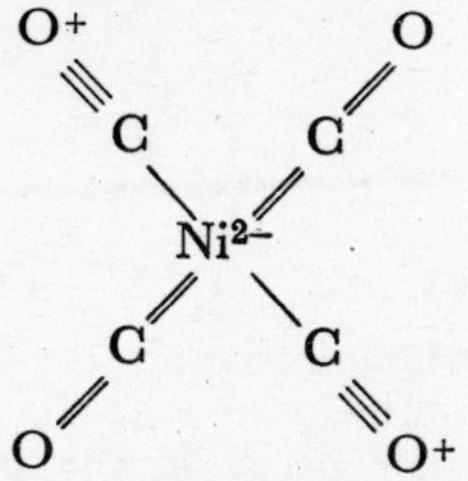

O^+ O
C C
Ni^{2-}
C C
O O^+

XIII

It is clear, however, that the structure of the $Ni(CO)_4$ molecule is a resonance hybrid of several structures in which varied localization of π bonds and of charges occur ; the valency state of nickel varying in the different structures from six to nine.

In compounds of elements involving *d* electrons our understanding of the term valency must be somewhat modified. In simple molecules, involving only *s* and *p* electrons, *e.g.* H_2O and NH_3, it is possible to consider the oxygen as being predominantly divalent and the nitrogen as trivalent, in spite of the fact that resonance occurs with other states in which, for example, the oxygen atom may be negatively charged and monovalent. This is due to the fact that in these compounds the contribution of the other structures, although significant, is relatively small. With the transition elements, however, the position is different. The structures with 9, 8, 7 and 6 valent nickel in $Ni(CO)_4$ evidently vary little in their relative stabilities and it is impossible to assign one dominating structure to the compound. We cannot, therefore, consider a particular valency as being typical for nickel, but must consider a range of valencies.

All eight of the outer electrons of iron and ruthenium may be unpaired (d^5sp^2). This makes it possible for each atom to link with four CO molecules. However, there still remains an empty *p* orbital which permits a fifth CO group to form a bond of the type

$$^{-}Fe{-}C{\equiv}O^{+}$$

on account of the lone pair of electrons in the CO group. Therefore in iron pentacarbonyl, or ruthenium pentacarbonyl, the five structures *XIV* will predominate.

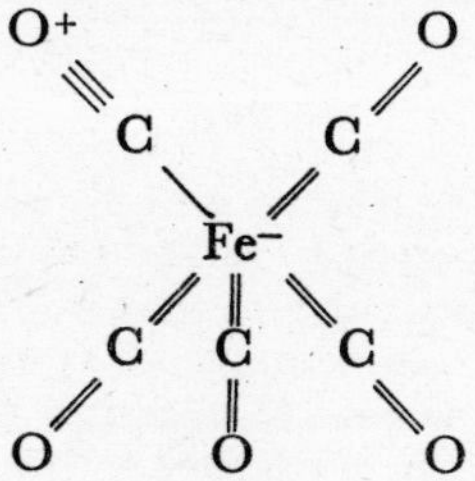

O^+ O
C C
Fe^-
C C C
O O O

Five structures

XIV

Structures with an octavalent neutral iron atom :

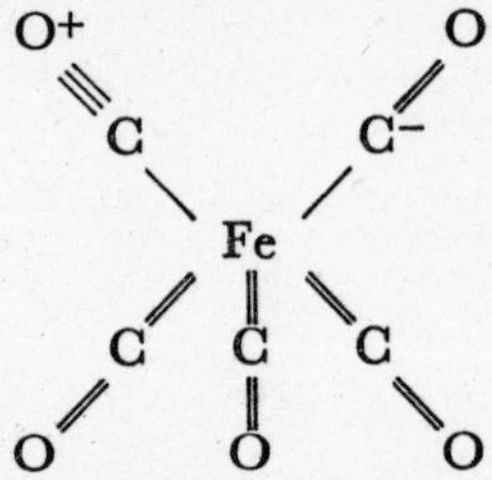

$$\begin{array}{ccccc} O^{+} & & & & O \\ \| \! \backslash & & & & / \\ C & & & & C^{-} \\ & \backslash & & / & \\ & & Fe & & \\ & / & | & \backslash & \\ C & & C & & C \\ / & & \| & & \backslash \\ O & & O & & O \end{array}$$

are less probable in view of the negative charge being located on the carbon atom and not on an oxygen atom.

In addition, resonance can occur in the pairs of double bonds and structures *XV* and *XVI* will contribute to the structure of the molecule.

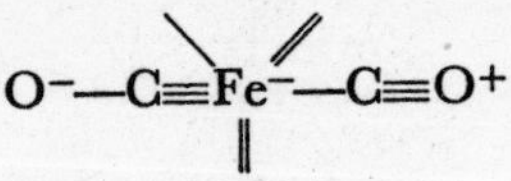

$O^{-}—C{\equiv}Fe^{-}—C{\equiv}O^{+}$

XV

$O^{-}—C{\equiv}Fe^{-}—C^{+}{=}O$

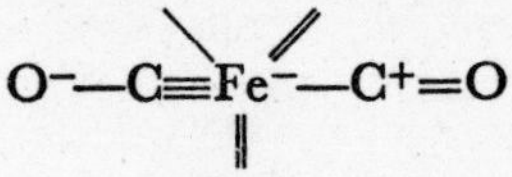

XVI

The five CO groups in iron pentacarbonyl form a bipyramid, three CO groups being arranged around the Fe atom in a plane with one CO group above and another below the plane of the triangle. All five CO groups are equidistant from the central atom, and the dipole moment should be zero. The value of 0·6 to 0·8 D reported by BERGMANN and ENGEL[15] and by GRAFFUNDER and HEYMANN[16], is probably due to atom polarization as in symmetrical trinitrobenzene.

In addition to $Fe(CO)_5$ iron forms a carbonyl with the formula $Fe_2(CO)_9$. The configuration of the molecule has been established by POWELL and EWENS[17] by a detailed x-ray crystallographic study and is shown to possess trigonal symmetry (distribution of charges not shown in *XVII*) :

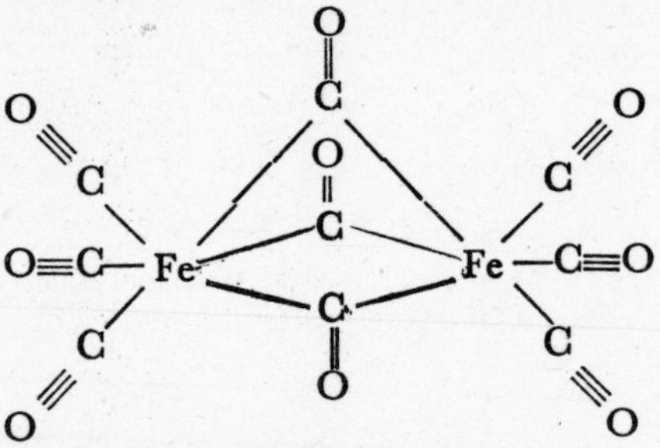

$(OC)_3Fe(\mu\text{-}CO)_3Fe(CO)_3$

XVII

In this molecule three of the carbonyl groups, which are linked to two atoms of iron, possess different properties to the other six. The CO distance in these three groups, 1·3 Å, is similar to that in organic carbonyl groups and is due to the absence of the contribution of structures of the type $—C{\equiv}O^{+}$ to the bond resonance. The Fe—C distances are different also, the value being 1·9 Å for the inner carbon atoms, *i.e.* those linked to two iron atoms, and 1·8 Å for the others. This shorter value indicates that the bond must have a partial double bond character. The distance between the two iron atoms is approximately the same as that in metallic iron, 2·48 to 2·52 Å, so that bonding between the iron atoms is not impossible. Although these data give a precise picture of the positions of the atoms relative to each other in the molecule, the exact nature of the various bonds is somewhat more obscure. The structure *XVII* in which the iron is represented as being hexavalent is not entirely satisfactory since it does not indicate any difference between the Fe—C bonds. The molecule is best represented as a resonance hybrid of the following structures which satisfies the observed diamagnetism of the molecule[18].

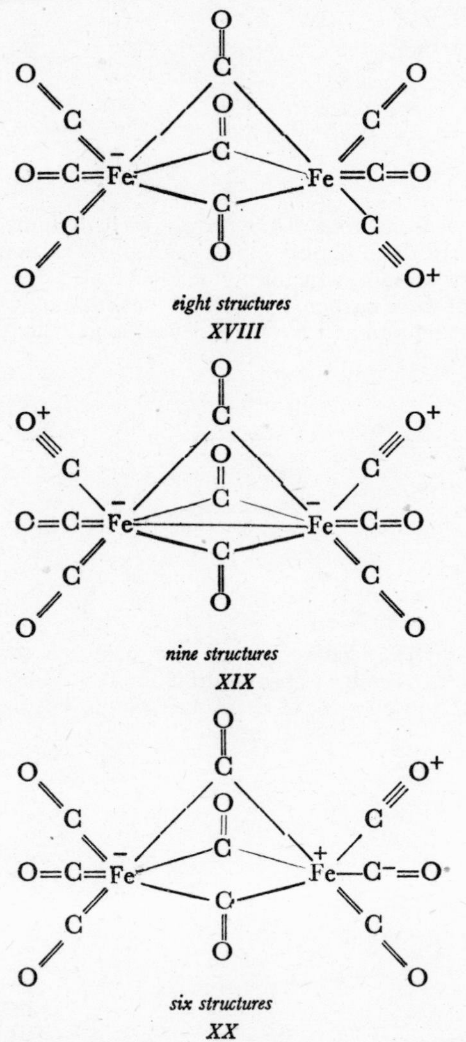

eight structures

XVIII

nine structures

XIX

six structures

XX

The Fe—C—Fe angle is 87°, and has therefore been considerably decreased in comparison with the normal valency angle of carbon with a coordination number of three (120°). This may be due to the strength of the Fe—Fe bond.

For the molecule $Fe_3(CO)_{12}$ an analogous series of valence bond structures may be considered. The geometry of the molecule is represented by the structure *XXI*, which in all probability, represents one of the main resonance forms.

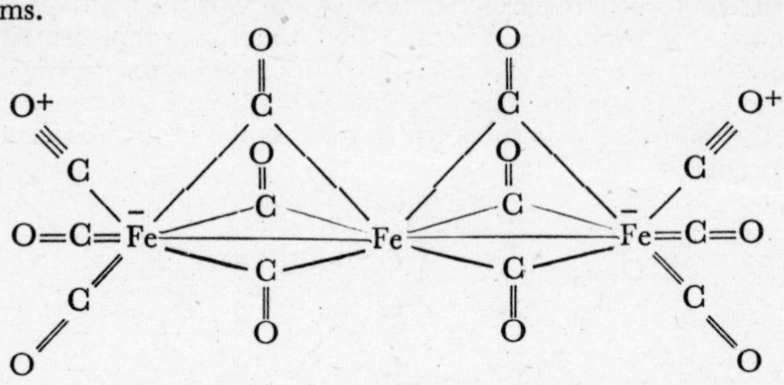

XXI

The six unpaired electrons of the atoms of chromium, molybdenum and tungsten may form three double bonds with three carbonyl groups. Three unfilled *p* orbitals remain, which may be filled by the donation of an electron pair from each of three carbonyl groups. The structure of these compounds will therefore be represented by the valence-bond structure *XXII*:

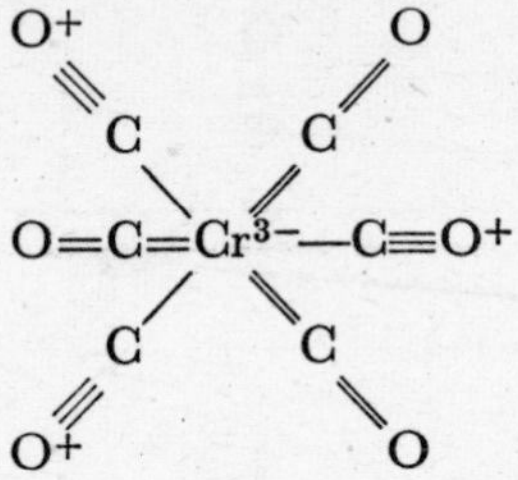

XXII

which is one of several such resonance structures. A distinctive feature of many complex compounds of chromium is the fact, which will be discussed again later, that the chromium is present as the ion Cr^{3-}. The valence bond structures:

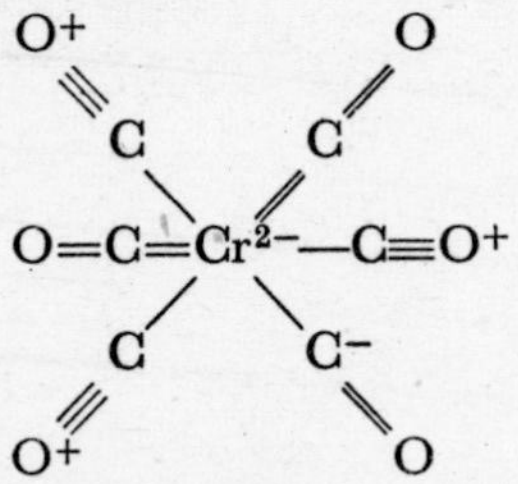

XXIII 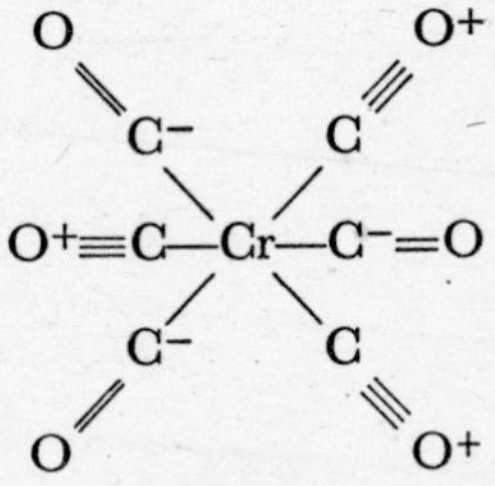 *XXIV*

in which the charges on the chromium atom have been delocalized and shared between the CO groups are less probable than the structure *XXII*, in view of the fact that the CO groups are arranged round the central atom in the form of a regular octahedron which must be due to d^2sp^3 hybridization and the bonds formed by the chromium ion (Cr^{3-}) will be six σ and three π bonds.

If cobalt were to form a tetracarbonyl, one electron in the atom would remain unpaired, and therefore the carbonyl $Co_2(CO)_8$ is formed in which two tetracarbonyls are joined by a Co—Co bond *i.e.*

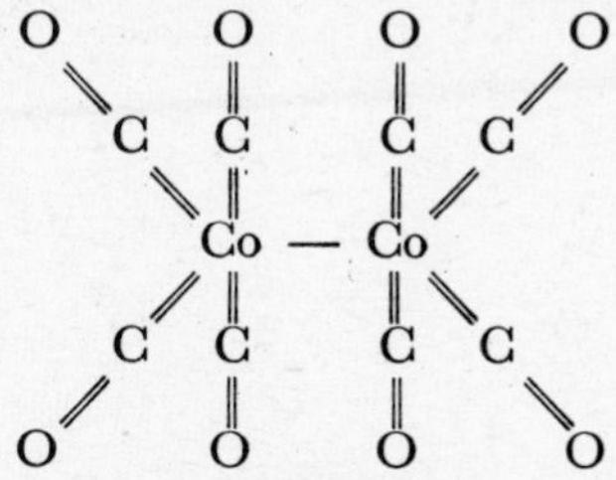

XXV

Many of the metallic carbonyls form hydrides, *e.g.* $Fe(CO)_4H_2$, $Co(CO)_4H$, $Os(CO)_4H_2$, $Ir(CO)_4H$. The structures of the first two compounds have been investigated by EWENS and LISTER[19] by electron diffraction methods. An exact determination of the position of the hydrogen atoms was not possible, owing to the small scattering produced by these atoms. The data, however, show conclusively that the hydrogen atoms are attached to the oxygen atoms of the carbonyl group and not directly to the metal. Both compounds have a tetrahedral configuration as in $Ni(CO)_4$ which is iso-electronic with the ions $Co(CO)_4^-$ and $Fe(CO)_4^{2-}$. The tetrahedra are, however, somewhat distorted, there being two different M—C distances. In $Fe(CO)_4H_2$ these are 1·84 Å, which is considered by Ewens and Lister to be the Fe—CO distance, and 1·89 Å which is the Fe—COH distance. To this hydride it is therefore possible to ascribe the structures :

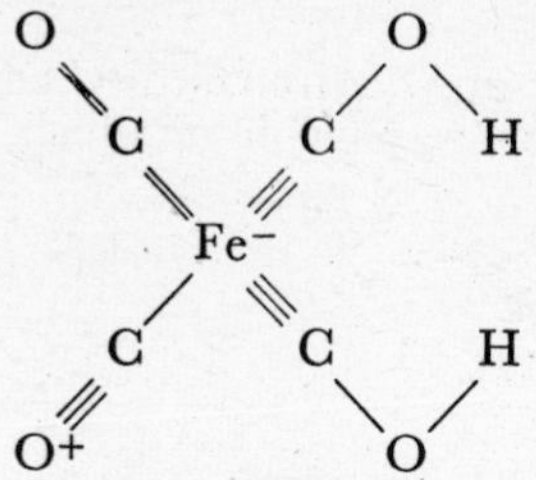

XXVI

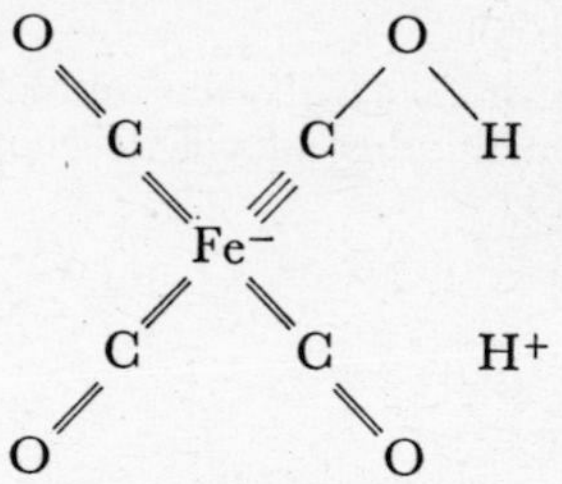

XXVII

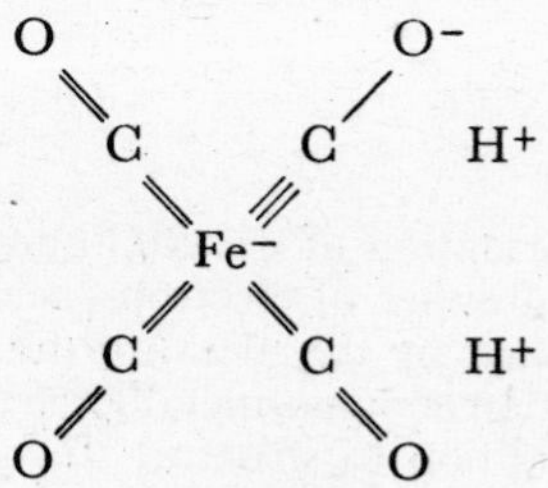

XXVIII

It would, therefore, be more correct to give the formula of this compound as $Fe(CO)_2(COH)_2$. In $Co(CO)_4H$ the CO distance is 1·83 Å and the C—COH distance 1·75 Å and its structure may be represented by

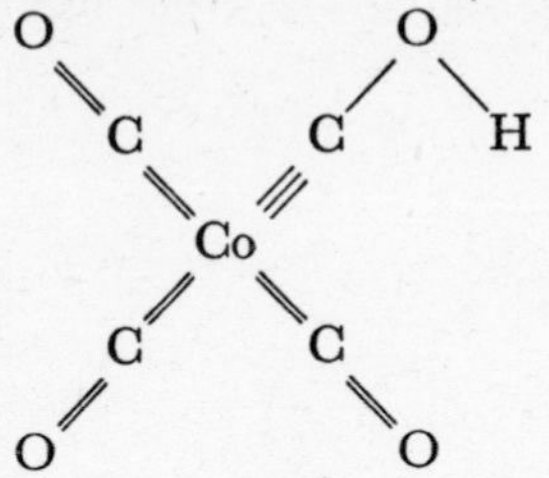

XXIX

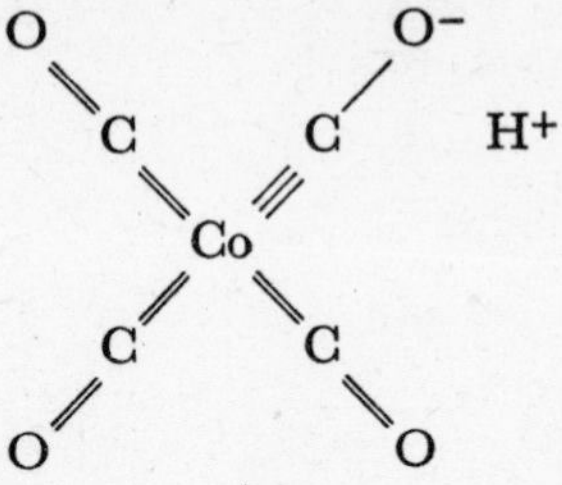

XXX

The shorter M—C distance in the M—COH group compared with M—CO may be regarded as due to a greater contribution from the structures with a triple bond than from those with a double bond for the MC linkage. The hydrogen of the hydrides of the carbonyl may be replaced by metals with the formation of salts such as $KCo(CO)_4$ and $K_2Fe(CO)_4$ *etc.*

NITROSYL AND NITROCOMPOUNDS

The tendency of nitric oxide to form addition compounds is related to the possible formation of different valency states of nitrogen and oxygen and to the presence in NO of an unpaired electron. For the bond of a metal with NO the following structures are possible:

$$M—N=O$$
$$M^-=N^+=O$$
$$M^+=N—O^-$$
$$M \equiv N^+—O^-$$

and resonance will occur amongst these structures. In iron nitrosyl $Fe(NO)_4$, a large number of valence bond structures are possible of which *I* is an example

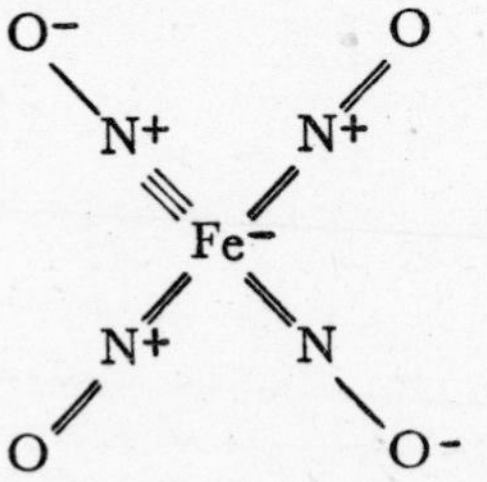

I

The fact that in the formation of the MC bond in carbonyls the metal always donates an even number of electrons, and that in the nitrosyls the number of electrons donated by the metal to the MN bond is always odd, is the reason for the formation of mono-metallic carbonyl-nitrosyl compounds, *e.g.* $Co(CO)_3NO$. In addition to structure *II* for $Co(CO)_3NO$, in which the nine electrons (d^7sp) are employed in the formation of σ and π bonds,

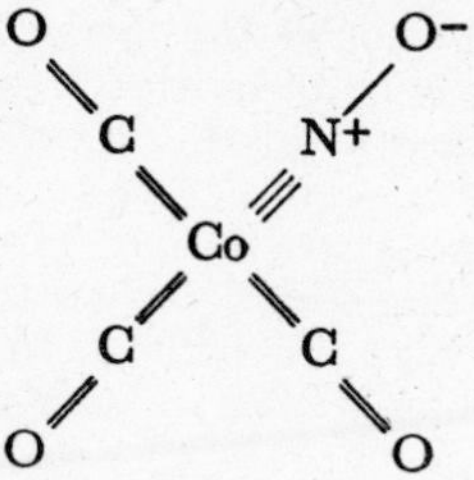

II

there will be additional structures in which the nitrogen becomes positively charged with respect to an oxygen atom of a carbonyl group,

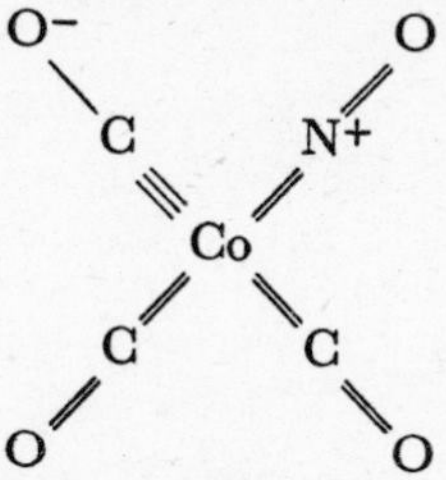

III

In addition to the two valence bond structures *II* and *III*, represented above, other structures may be considered in view of the possibility of cobalt existing in other valency states (*Table CLXX*).

In $Fe(CO)_2(NO)_2$ a large number of possible structures may be considered of which we give only four (*IV–VII*):

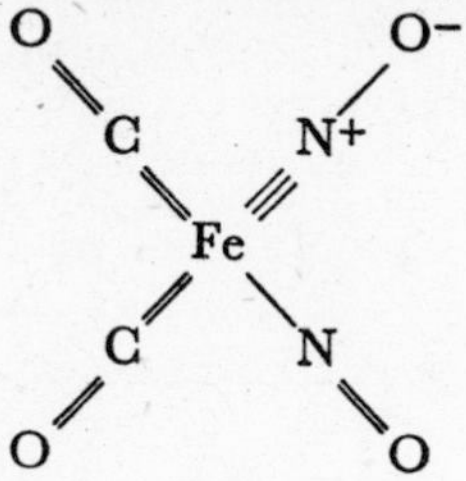

IV

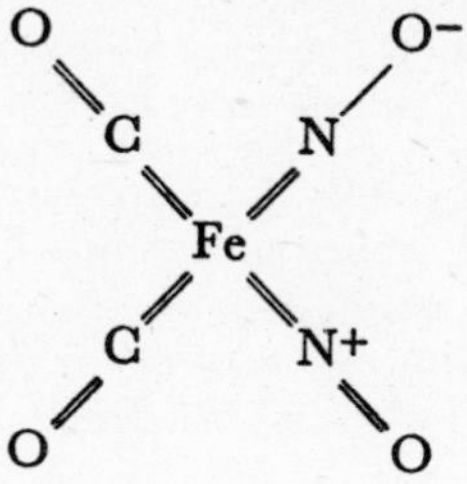

V

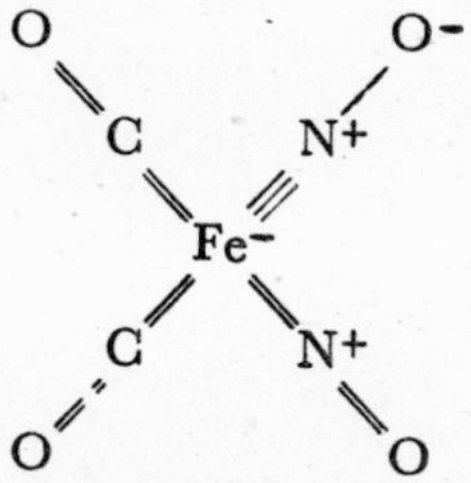

VI

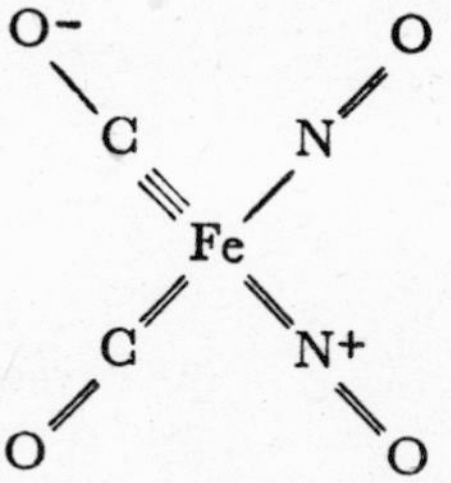

VII

In these compounds the NO distance is 1·11 Å, thus being somewhat shorter than in the molecule of NO (1·14 Å).

The capacity of both carbonyl and nitrosyl groups to assume both a positive and negative charge, as illustrated by the formulae given above, is related to the existence of the nitrosyl and carbonyl compounds as neutral molecules, in contrast to other complex molecules which may exist only as ions whose charge is compensated by ions of opposite sign in the crystal. Such is the case for example in complexes where the central atom is bonded only to nitro groups, as in $K_2NaCo(NO_2)_6$. In the nitro group, in contrast with nitric oxide, the nitrogen atom is already positively charged and tetra-

```
      O
     //
  —N+
     \
      O−
```

valent and in the bond with the metal, resonance of the following valence bond structures are therefore possible :

```
       O                      O−
      //                     /
  M—N+                   M—N+
      \                      \\
       O−                     O

              O−
             /
         M=N+
             \
              O−
```

The formation of the latter structure in which the metal atom is joined to the nitrogen atom by a double bond, would be improbable, if by so doing, a positive charge were formed on the metal atom, since we should then have two adjacent atoms both positively charged. For this reason the complexes formed between metals and nitro groups are all negative ions, the charge being equalized by cations in the crystal. The structure of the $Co(NO_2)_6^{3-}$ ion has been shown by x-ray methods to be octahedral and we may represent the structure as follows, in which the cobalt atom forms six σ and three π bonds (d^2sp^3-hybridization).

```
          O−   O
     O−    \  //      O−
     |      N+       /
     N+     |      N+
    /  \\   |    //  \
  O−     \\ |  //     O−
            Co
  O        / || \      O
   \\     /  ||  \    //
     N+      ||    N+
     |       N+    |
     O−     /  \   O−
          O−    O−
```

VIII

Several structures other than that given above, *VIII*, are possible with a varied localization of the π bonds and distribution of charges on the nitro groups.

CYANIDES

In the bond between a metal atom and the cyanide group, resonance will occur among the following structures :

$$\begin{array}{l} M{-}C{\equiv}N \\ M{=}C{=}N^- \\ M \quad C^-{\equiv}N \\ M \quad C{=}N^- \end{array}$$

The last two structures, which represent an electrostatic bond between the metal atom and the cyanide ion, may be conveniently written as $M(CN)^-$ since the localization of the charge in the (CN) group is unimportant to the present discussion. Theoretically there should also occur a bond of the isocyanide type, in which the metal atom is joined to the nitrogen atom of the (CN) group. The x-ray analysis of these substances cannot, in general, permit the distinction of the carbon and nitrogen atoms because of their similarity, but there is, however, some evidence in the case of $K_4Mo(CN)_8$ that the metal is bound to the carbon and not to the nitrogen atom.

Of the simple cyanides, $Hg(CN)_2$, $Cd(CN)_2$ and $Zn(CN)_2$, it has been established[20] that $Hg(CN)_2$ is linear and it may therefore be represented by the formula

$$\underset{I}{NC{-}Hg{-}CN}$$

in which two σ bonds are formed by the s and p electrons of the mercury atom in the valency state $d^{10}sp$. A significant contribution to the structure of the molecule will also be made by the structure

$$\underset{II}{NC{-}Hg^+ \quad CN^-}$$

in which the mercury is positively charged and monovalent ($d^{10}s$) and by

$$\underset{III}{NC{-}Hg^+{=}C{=}N^-}$$

in which the mercury is positively charged and trivalent (d^9sp). Less significant structures are

$$\underset{IV}{NC^- \quad Hg^{2+} \quad CN^-} \qquad \text{and} \qquad \underset{V}{N^-{=}C{=}Hg^{2+}{=}C{=}N^-}$$

As a result of the contribution of the structures *III* and *V* it is to be expected that the HgC distance will be somewhat less than in a single Hg—C bond as occurs for example in $Hg(CH_3)_2$.

The complex ion $Ag(CN)_2^-$ is analogous to $Hg(CN)_2$ and it may be described in terms of the following structures :

$$N^-{=}C{=}Ag{-}C{\equiv}N$$

in which the silver atom is uncharged and trivalent, forming two σ bonds at an angle of 180°, on account of sp electrons and a π bond formed by the unpaired d electron,

$$N^-{=}C{=}Ag^+ \quad (CN)^-$$

and

$$(CN)^- \quad Ag{-}C{\equiv}N$$

The complex cyanides formed by the transition elements have frequently been discussed in terms of the simple compounds formed by these atoms. Thus, for example, $K_4Fe(CN)_6$ has been referred to as a compound of ferrous iron and $K_2Fe(CN)_6$ as a compound of ferric iron. This procedure, however, is not correct as the valency state of iron in $K_4Fe(CN)_6$ is quite different from that in $Fe(CN)_2$ or $FeCl_2$; thus $FeCl_2$ has a magnetic moment corresponding to four unpaired electrons, whereas $K_4Fe(CN)_6$ is diamagnetic. The suggestion that the diamagnetism of $K_4Fe(CN)_6$ is caused by the pairing of electrons in the Fe^{2+} ion under the influence of the strong electric field due to the $(CN)^-$ ions, appears inadequate since $(NH_4)_3FeF_6$, where the field due to the F^- ions is stronger, is paramagnetic[21]. These facts can only mean that in $FeCl_2$ some of the outer electrons of the iron atom are not used in bond formation and remain unpaired, whereas in $K_4Fe(CN)_6$ all the outer electrons are paired in bonds with the (CN) groups. The suggestion has been made by Pauling that the formation of such covalent complexes occurs as the result of the pairing of all the outer six electrons of the Fe^{2+} ion in three *d* orbitals. The ion will therefore have two *d*, and one *s* and three *p* orbitals empty, *viz*,

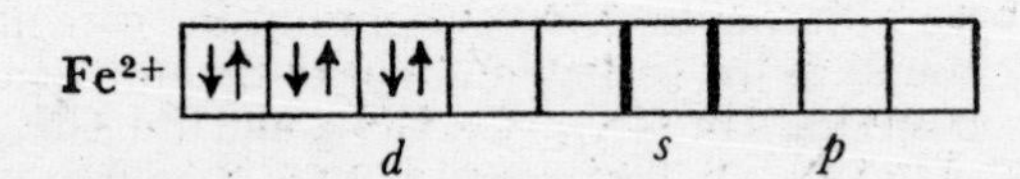

The vacant orbitals are then used in the formation of six coordinate (donor-acceptor) bonds with six $(CN)^-$ ions ; this may be represented as the donation of six electrons (one from each $(CN)^-$ ion) to each of the six orbitals with the formation of an Fe^{4-} ion containing six d^2sp^3 unpaired electrons :

Fe^{4-} | ↓↑ | ↓↑ | ↓↑ | ↓ | ↓ | ↓ | ↓ | ↓ | ↓ |

d *s* *p*

These electrons then take part in six covalent bonds with six unpaired electrons in the CN groups. If this representation of the structure of $K_4Fe(CN)_6$ were correct, it would be represented by the structure *VI*.

$$\left[\begin{array}{ccc} NC & & CN \\ & \diagdown \; \diagup & \\ NC- & Fe^{4-} & -CN \\ & \diagup \; \diagdown & \\ NC & & CN \end{array}\right] 4K^+$$

VI

However, VAN VLECK and SHERMAN[22] and PAULING[21] have shown that such a structure is improbable owing to the high negative charge on the central iron atom, since iron generally tends to assume a positive charge.

We consider that for a description of this and similar complexes there is no need to assume that the outer electrons of the Fe^{2+} ion are paired and that the union of the ion with the $(CN)^-$ ions occurs through coordinate bonds. The structure of these complexes may be understood if the valency states of the metal ion, as described above and in Chapter 2 for simple ions, are considered. The ground state of the iron atom is d^6s^2 in which there are four unpaired *d* electrons, two paired *d* electrons and two paired *s* electrons. Excitation of the paired electrons to the *p* state leads to an atom of iron in the d^5sp^2 state in which there are eight unpaired electrons, which may therefore take part in the formation of eight covalent bonds. If the iron atom accepts an electron into the vacant *p* orbital from a $(CN)^-$ ion, then the Fe^- ion will be formed with the electronic configuration d^5sp^3, which may thus take part in the formation of nine covalent bonds. This therefore leads to the structure *VII* for $K_4Fe(CN)_6$:

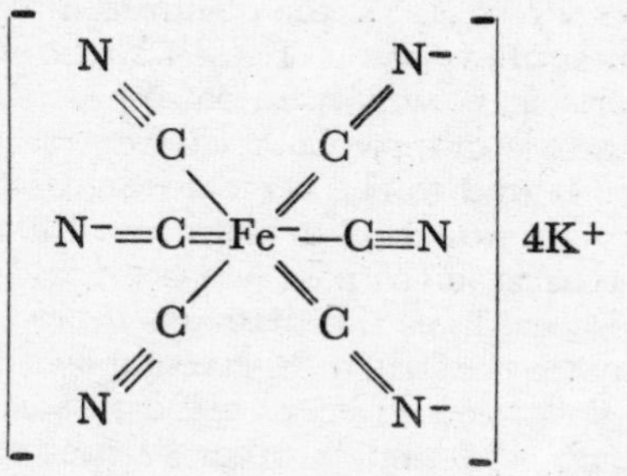

```
 ┌                          ┐
    N           N⁻
     ⫽         /
      C       C
       \     /
 N⁻=C=Fe⁻—C≡N               4K⁺
       /     \
      C       C
     ⫽         \
    N           N⁻
 └                          ┘
```

VII

in which the four negative charges occur, one on the iron atom and three on three nitrogen atoms. This formula has also been proposed by Pauling[21]. The nine covalent bonds between the Fe^- ion and the six (CN) groups will consist of six σ bonds, formed by d^2sp^3 hybrid electrons, arranged octahedrally and three π bonds (formed by three *d* electrons), in accordance with the data of Kimball (*Table CLXV*). The structure *VII* represents only one of many resonance structures with various localizations of the π bonds and of the negative charge on the nitrogen atoms, and the stability of such a complex will compensate for the energy absorbed in the excitation of the iron atom. In addition to structure *VII*, resonance is possible with the form *VIII* in which the iron atom is octavalent:

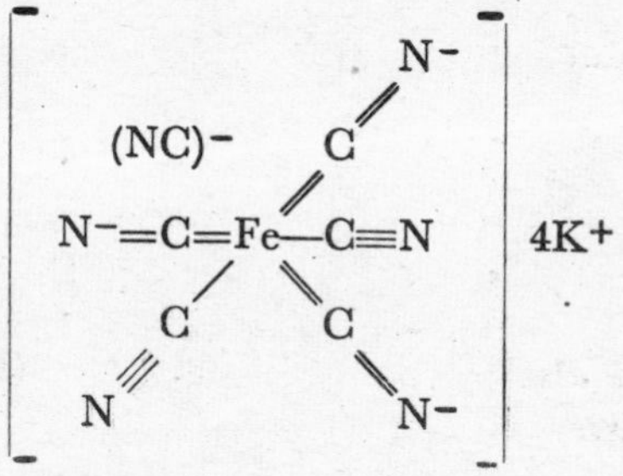

```
 ┌                          ┐
                N⁻
               /
    (NC)⁻     C
             /
 N⁻=C=Fe—C≡N                4K⁺
       /     \
      C       C
     ⫽         \
    N           N⁻
 └                          ┘
```

VIII

and other structures, *VIII* and *IX*, in which the iron is hepta- and hexa-valent :

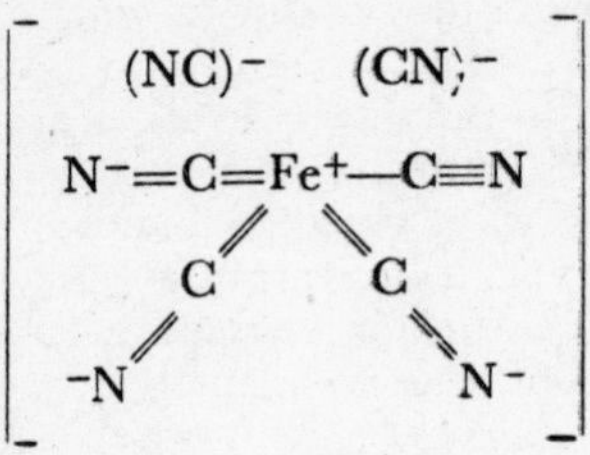

$$\left[\begin{array}{c}(NC)^- \quad (CN)^- \\ N^-{=}C{=}Fe^+{-}C{\equiv}N \\ C \qquad C \\ {}^-N \qquad\quad N^- \end{array}\right] 4K^+ \qquad \left[\begin{array}{c}(NC)^- \quad (CN)^- \\ N^-{=}C{=}Fe^{2+}\ (CN)^- \\ C \qquad C \\ {}^-N \qquad\quad N^- \end{array}\right] 4K^+$$

IX 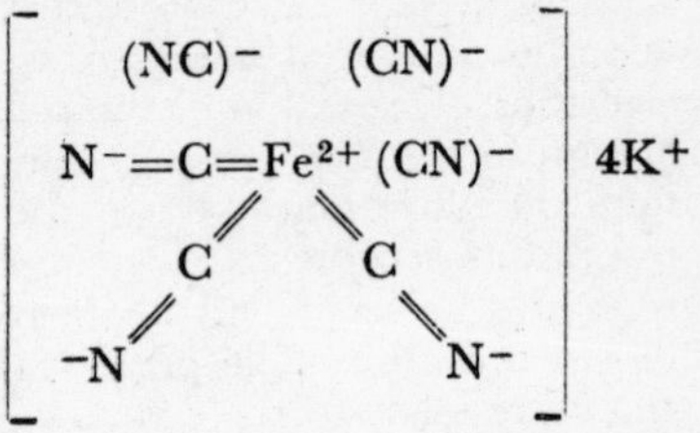 *X*

In the structures *VI* to *X*, all the electrons are paired, so that the total spin angular momentum is zero. These structures may therefore resonate with each other and it is important to appreciate that, although certain CN groups, for example in formula *X*, are represented as being in the ionic state and therefore bound to the central iron atom by electrostatic forces, all the CN groups are attached to the central atom by the same type of bond which is in part ionic, in part a σ bond and in part a π bond. The pairing of spins also explains the diamagnetic character of this substance.

Let us now compare the structures given above, *VII* to *X*, for $K_4Fe(CN)_6$ with hypothetical structures in which the iron atom is in the same valency state as in $FeCl_2$, *viz*, d^6sp and in other valency states in which there are four unpaired *d* electrons. In the following formulae we shall represent the unpaired electrons by dots :

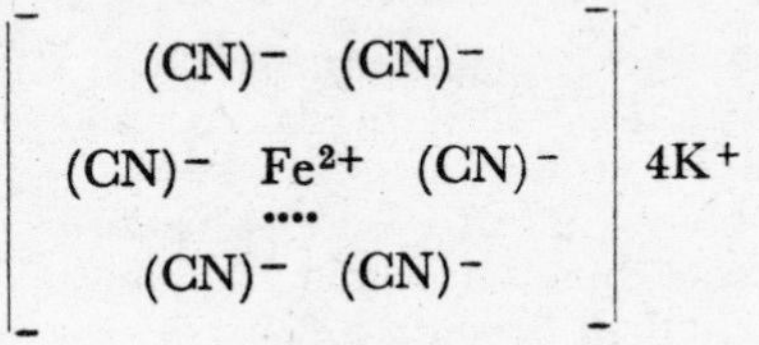

$$\left[\begin{array}{c}(CN)^- \quad (CN)^- \\ (CN)^- \quad \underset{\cdots\cdot}{Fe^{2+}} \quad (CN)^- \\ (CN)^- \quad (CN)^- \end{array}\right] 4K^+$$

$(Fe^{2+} = d^6)$

XI

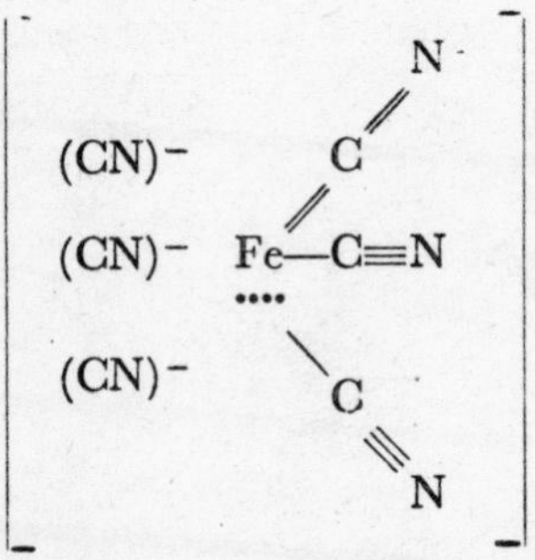

$$\left[\begin{array}{c} N \\ (CN)^- \qquad C \\ (CN)^- \quad \underset{\cdots\cdot}{Fe}{-}C{\equiv}N \\ (CN)^- \qquad C \\ N \end{array}\right] 4K^+ \qquad \left[\begin{array}{c} N \\ (CN)^- \qquad C \\ (CN)^- \quad \underset{\cdots\cdot}{Fe^-}{-}C{\equiv}N \\ C \qquad C \\ N \qquad\quad N \end{array}\right] 4K^+$$

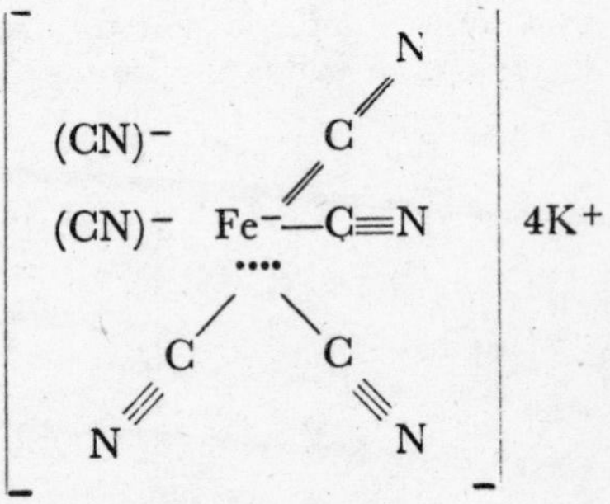

$(Fe = d^5sp^2)$ $(Fe^- = d^5sp^3)$

XII *XIII*

The similarity between structures *X* and *XI*, *VIII* and *XII*, and *VII* and *XIII*, is evident, but in the forms *VII*, *VIII* and *X* there are additional covalent bonds of the type $Fe{=}C{=}N^-$, in which the unpaired electrons are employed in bond formation with a consequent loss of paramagnetism and increase in stability of the complex.

The entirely ionic form of $K_4Fe(CN)_6$:

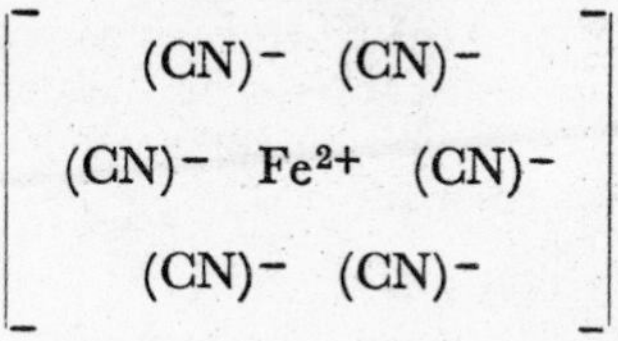

$$\left[\begin{array}{ccc} & (CN)^- \quad (CN)^- & \\ (CN)^- & Fe^{2+} & (CN)^- \\ & (CN)^- \quad (CN)^- & \end{array}\right] 4K^+$$

XIV

can only be compatible with the observed diamagnetism of the compound if the six *d* electrons of the Fe^{2+} ion are all paired. The molecule could then also participate in the resonance between structures *VII* to *X*. The pairing of the electrons to give the configuration,

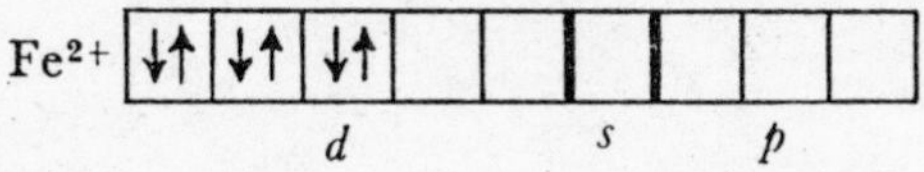

Fe^{2+}	↓↑	↓↑	↓↑						
			d			*s*		*p*	

involves the absorption of energy ; such an electronic state is therefore unfavourable for the stability of the molecule and the corresponding structure *XIV* is hence improbable.

It is not possible to formulate a diamagnetic structure for $K_3Fe(CN)_6$ since the total number of electrons in this molecule is uneven. The experimental data show that the magnetic moment is $2{\cdot}33\mu_B$, thus corresponding approximately to the presence of one unpaired electron. It is therefore clear that here the electronic state of the atom of iron in the complex is essentially different from that in $FeCl_3$ in which the Fe^{3+} iron possesses five unpaired electrons. It is possible to describe the structure of the complex by the following :

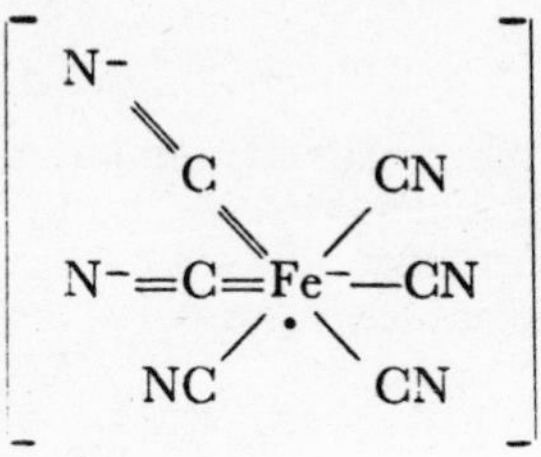

$$\left[\begin{array}{l} N^- \\ \quad \diagdown \\ \quad\ C \qquad\quad CN \\ \qquad \diagdown \quad \diagup \\ N^-{=}C{=}Fe^{-}{-}CN \\ \qquad\ \diagup \cdot \diagdown \\ \quad NC \qquad\ CN \end{array}\right] 3K^+ \qquad \left[\begin{array}{l} N^- \\ \quad \diagdown \\ \quad\ C \qquad\quad CN \\ \qquad \diagdown \quad \diagup \\ N^-{=}C{=}Fe{-}CN \\ \qquad\quad \cdot \diagdown \\ \quad (NC)^- \quad CN \end{array}\right] 3K^+$$

XV 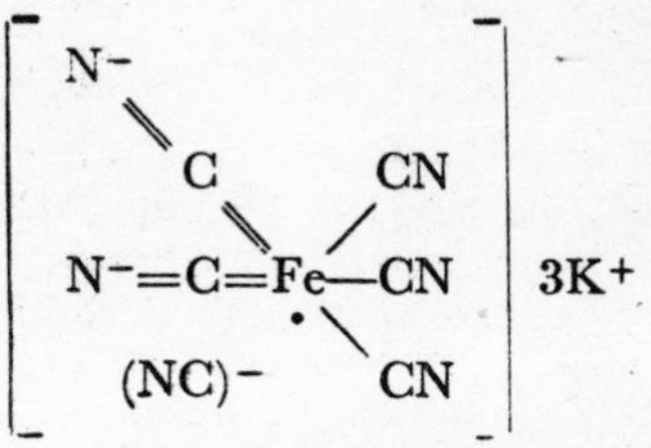 *XVI*

Similarly the magnetic moments of the complex cyanides of manganese, K_3MnCN_6, $3{\cdot}25\ \mu_B$, corresponding to two unpaired electrons, and of $K_4Mn(CN)_6$, $2{\cdot}18\ \mu_B$, corresponding to one unpaired electron, indicate that in these compounds the valency states of the manganese atoms are different from those in $MnCl_2$ ($\mu = 5{\cdot}92\ \mu_B$) and MnCl ($\mu = 5{\cdot}1\ \mu_B$). In $KMn(CN)_3$, $\mu = 4{\cdot}22\ \mu_B$, corresponding to three unpaired electrons, and it is possible that this compound possesses the formula $K_2[Mn(Mn(CN)_6)]$, where the inner manganese atom has one unpaired electron as in $K_4Mn(CN)_6$ and the outer manganese atom, five unpaired electrons[23] as in $MnCl_2$. According to the treatment discussed above the molecule $K_5Mn(CN)_6$ will be represented predominantly by the covalent structure *XVII* in which the manganese atom is monovalent and doubly charged negative, *i.e.* in the electronic state d^5sp^3 corresponding to the ion Mn^{2-}. In such a structure there are no unpaired electrons and the complex should be diamagnetic. In addition to the covalent structure *XVII*, ionic structures, such as *XVIII* and *XIX* will contribute to the molecular resonance.

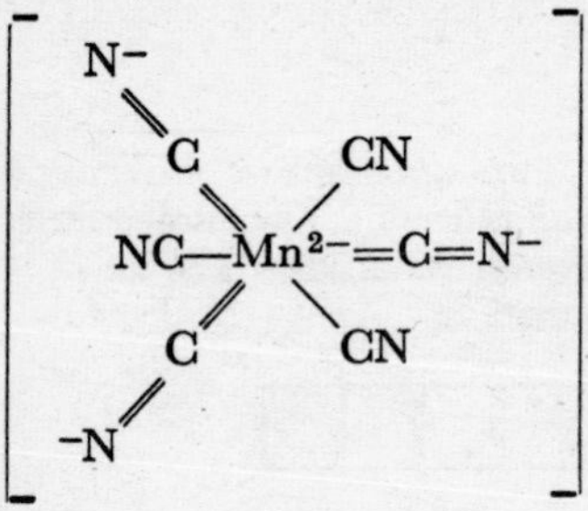

N^- — C; CN
$[NC—Mn^{2-}=C=N^-]$ $5K^+$
C; CN
^-N

XVII

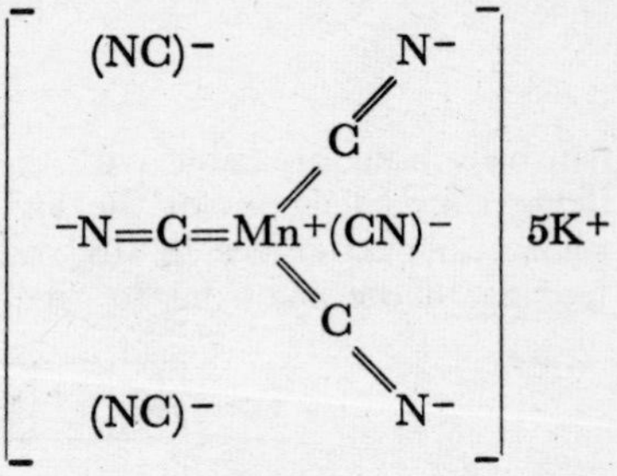

$(NC)^-$ N^- = C
$[^-N=C=Mn^+(CN)^-]$ $5K^+$
C = N^-
$(NC)^-$

XVIII

$(NC)^-$ N^- = C
$[(NC)^-\ Mn=C=N^-]$ $5K^+$
C; CN
^-N

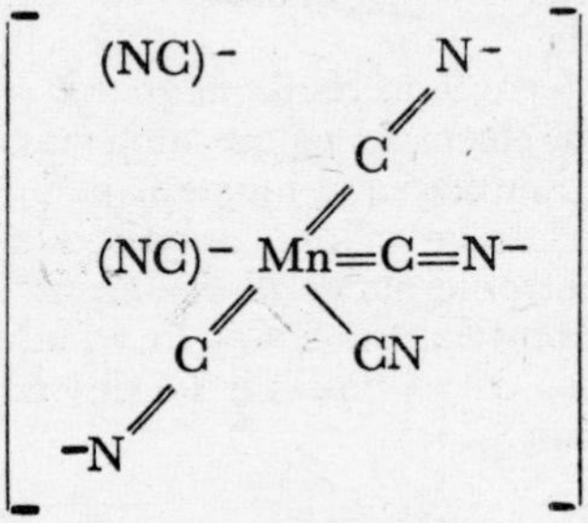

XIX

GOLDENBERG'S[23] measurements show that the magnetic moment of $K_5Mn(CN)_6$ is 1·05 μ_B, which is less than the calculated value for one unpaired electron. From the above possible structure this cannot be due to electron spin, so it is evidently due to incomplete quenching of the orbital moment.

The limiting covalent and ionic structures of $K_4Mn(CN)_6$, in which there is one unpaired electron, are

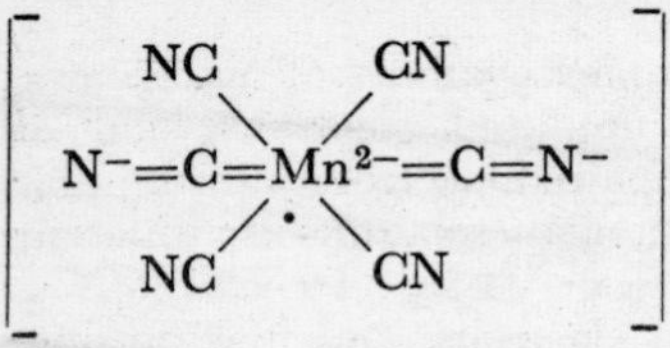

NC CN
$[N^-=C=Mn^{2-}=C=N^-]$ $4K^+$
NC CN

XX

$(NC)^-$ $(CN)^-$
$[N^-=C=Mn^{2+}=C=N^-]$ $4K^+$
$(NC)^-$ $(CN)^-$

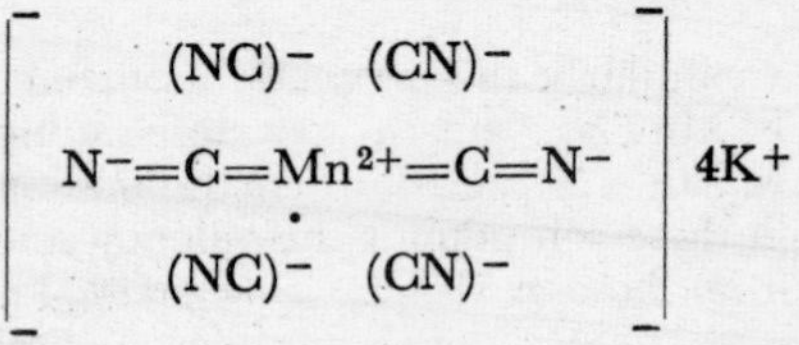

XXI

and similarly for $K_3Mn(CN)_6$ in which there are two unpaired electrons, we have

```
 _                        _            _                                _
|  N-                      |          |  N-                              |
|    \\                    |          |    \\                            |
|      C        CN         |          |      C           (CN)-           |
|       \      /           |          |       \                          |
|  NC—Mn²⁻—CN              |   3K+    |  (NC)-  Mn³⁺   (CN)-             |   3K+
|       / ••  \            |          |          ••                      |
|    NC        CN          |          |  (NC)-         (CN)-             |
 -                        -            -                                -
```

XXII *XXIII*

In $K_3Cr(CN)_6$, the experimental data show that there are three unpaired electrons and, since both the Cr^{3+} ion and $CrCl_3$ also contain three unpaired electrons, the complex is sometimes written in the form *XXIV*:

```
 _                                _           _                        _
|    (CN)-   (CN)-                 |         |  NC          CN          |
|                                  |         |     \      /             |
|  (CN)-   Cr³⁺   (CN)-            |  3K+    |  NC—Cr³⁻—CN              |  3K+
|          •••                     |         |      •••                 |
|                                  |         |     /      \             |
|    (CN)-   (CN)-                 |         |  NC          CN          |
 -                                -           -                        -
```

XXIV *XXV*

However, $K_3Cr(CN)_6$ may be equally well represented by an alternative limiting structure, which also satisfies the observed magnetic moment, represented by *XXV*. In this structure it is assumed that the chromium atom in the $[Cr(CN)_6]^{3-}$ ion is in a d^5sp^3 electronic state and possesses three negative charges. Six of the nine electrons are employed in covalent bond formation (d^2sp^3 hybridization) with the CN groups, and three remain unpaired. We have already postulated that chromium is in this electron state in the carbonyl compounds. Both the structures, *XXIV* and *XXV* may at first sight appear improbable owing to the high charge, either positive or negative, carried by the central atom. However, we consider that the structure of $K_3Cr(CN)_6$ may be represented as a resonance hybrid of the forms *XXIV* and *XXV* and of other structures in which the central atom possesses the same number of unpaired electrons, *e.g.*

```
 _                            _
|     (NC)-     CN             |
|              /               |
|  (NC)-   Cr⁺—CN              |   3K+
|          •••                 |
|     (NC)-    (CN)-           |
 -                            -
```

XXVI

The description of a molecule or complex in terms of resonance among several structures is, as we have emphasized before, only a convenient way of describing the real state of the molecule which is intermediate between these extreme forms. In fact the twelve electrons of the central atom and of the surrounding groups or atoms are located in the field of all the nuclei in molecular orbitals. In $K_4Fe(CN)_6$ all the electrons of the complex ion occupy molecular orbitals in pairs, thereby neutralizing their spins[21]. In $K_3Fe(CN)_6$, one electron in the outermost molecular orbital remains unpaired as in NO and in other instances it is possible that an electronic configuration is more favourable when some electrons occupy molecular orbitals, not in pairs, but singly as in the molecule of oxygen, O_2. This is evidently what occurs in $K_3Cr(CN)_6$ and in other paramagnetic complexes.

Twelve electrons take part in bond formation in $K_3Cr(CN)_6$ and hence all the CrC bonds may be regarded as single, as in the limiting covalent structure *XXV*. In $K_4Cr(CN)_6$, however, the limiting covalent structure, *XXVII*, must include one double bond, since the magnetic moment corresponds to only two unpaired electrons.

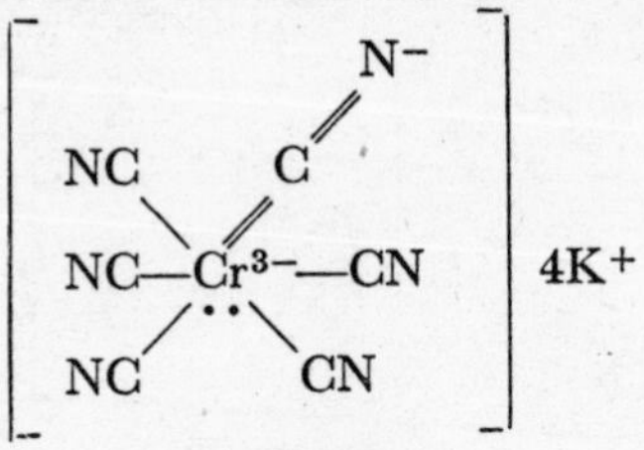

$$\left[\begin{array}{ccc} & & N^- \\ & & /\!\!/ \\ NC & & C \\ & \diagdown \; /\!\!/ & \\ NC— & \underset{\cdot\cdot}{Cr^{3-}} & —CN \\ & / \; \diagdown & \\ NC & & CN \end{array}\right] 4K^+$$

six structures

XXVII

A limiting ionic structure with a doubly charged positive chromium ion and six CN^- ions is not in agreement with the magnetic data, since the Cr^{2+} ion has four unpaired electrons. Furthermore, such a structure cannot resonate with the form *XXVII* since resonance can only occur when the value of the total spin is identical in both forms. The ionic limiting structure must, therefore, be given by *XXVIII*. An example of an intermediate resonance structure is given by *XXIX*.

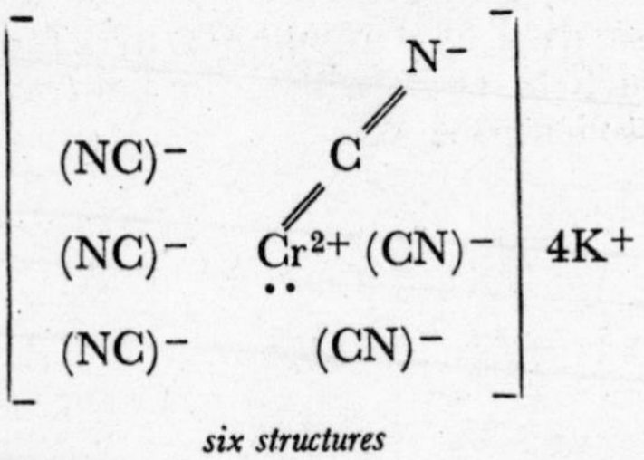

$$\left[\begin{array}{ccc} & & N^- \\ & & /\!\!/ \\ (NC)^- & & C \\ & /\!\!/ & \\ (NC)^- & \underset{\cdot\cdot}{Cr^{2+}} & (CN)^- \\ (NC)^- & (CN)^- & \end{array}\right] 4K^+ \qquad \left[\begin{array}{ccc} & & N^- \\ & & /\!\!/ \\ (CN)^- & & C \\ & /\!\!/ & \\ (CN)^- & \underset{\cdot\cdot}{Cr} & —CN \\ & \diagdown & \\ (CN)^- & CN & \end{array}\right] 4K^+$$

six structures *XXVIII*

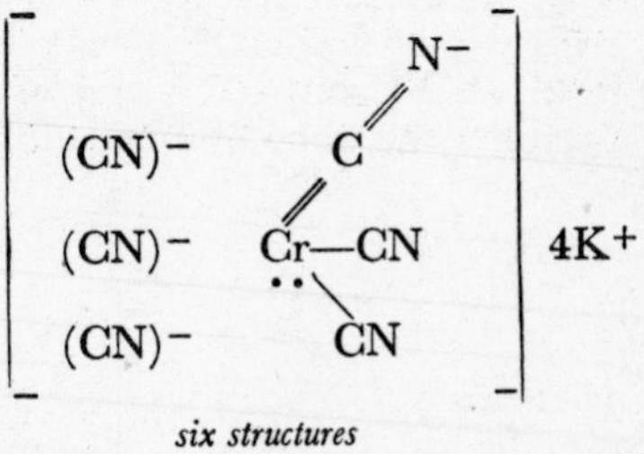

six structures *XXIX*

The diamagnetic octacyanides $K_4Mo(CN)_8$ and $K_4W(CN)_8$ are known in which resonance between all possible structures from the limiting covalent form *XXX* to the limiting ionic form *XXXI* will occur.

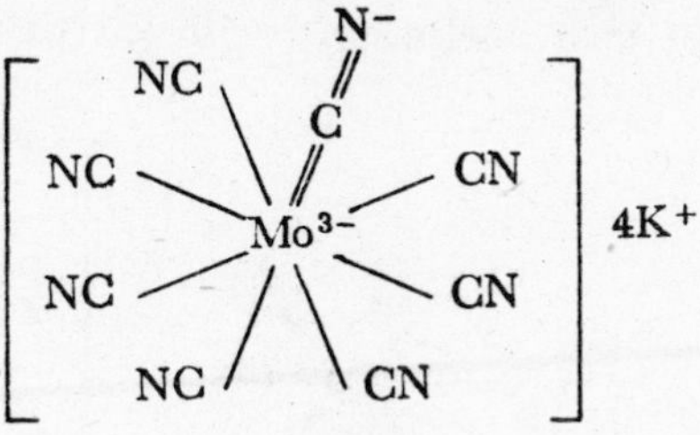

$$\left[Mo^{3-}(CN)_7(C{=}N^-) \right] 4K^+$$

eight structures

XXX

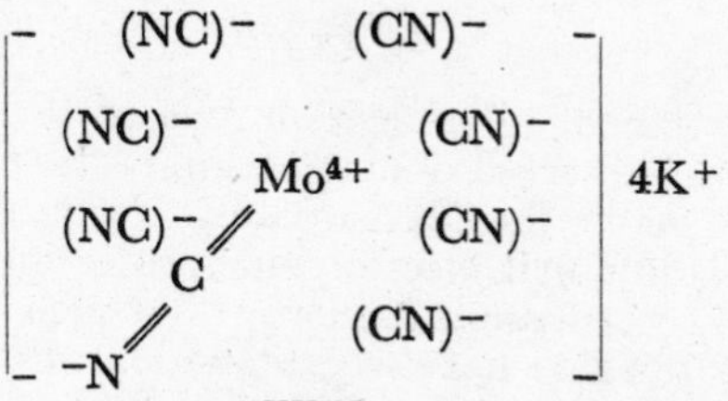

$$\left[(NC)^- (CN)^- (NC)^- (CN)^- \; Mo^{4+} \; (NC)^- {=}C{=}N^- \; (CN)^- (CN)^- \right] 4K^+$$

XXXI

There now arises the problem of why the ion Cr^{3-} uses only six unpaired electrons in the cyanide complex ion and has a coordination number of six, whereas the ion Mo^{3-} may use all nine unpaired electrons to form a complex with a coordination number of eight. There are probably two different reasons. First, the large size of the atom of molybdenum permits the packing of eight atoms or groups round it much more easily than in chromium and secondly, the loss of intra-atomic resonance in molybdenum and tungsten on bond formation is less than in chromium, owing to the greater principal quantum number of the outermost electrons of these elements.

For $K_3Mo(CN)_8$ which must have one unpaired electron, the following limiting structures are possible,

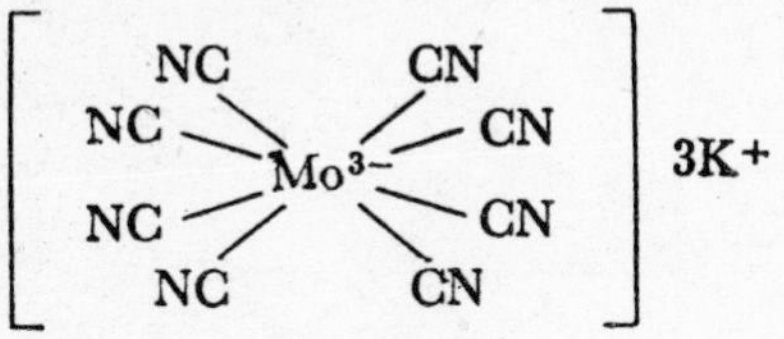

$$\left[Mo^{3-}(NC)_4(CN)_4 \right] 3K^+ \qquad \left[Mo^{5+} \; 4(NC)^- \; 4(CN)^- \right] 3K^+$$

XXXII 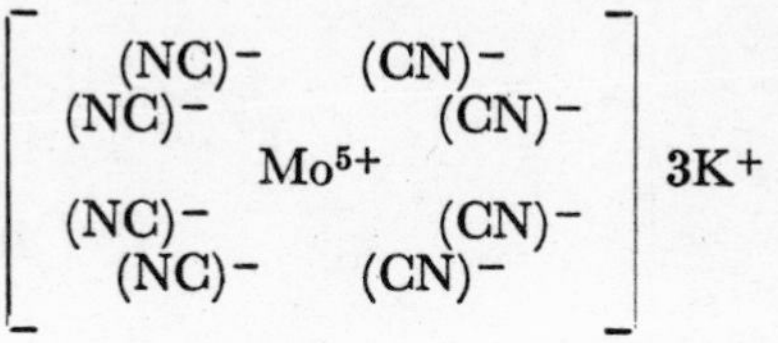 *XXXIII*

The x-ray diffraction data show that the complex $[Mo(CN)_8]^{3-}$ ion has a dodecahedral structure in agreement with the prediction of KIMBALL (*Table CLXV*). A coordination number of eight, involving d, s and p electrons may correspond to a dodecahedron (d^4sp^3) or to a quadratic antiprism (d^5p^3). The alternative geometric arrangement of the groups at the apices of a cube is not permissible since it has been shown to require the participation of f electrons[24].

The ion $[Co(CN)_6]^{3-}$ is isoelectronic with $[Fe(CN)_6]^{4-}$ and the most probable structure will be

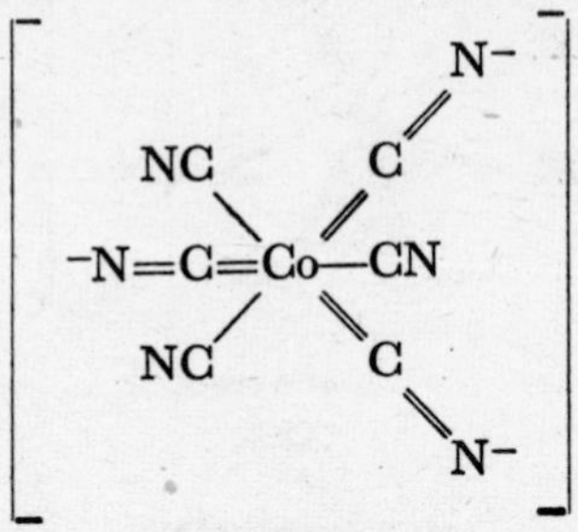

$$\left[\begin{array}{c} \text{structure: Co bonded to NC, NC, CN (single bonds), to } {}^{-}N{=}C{=} \text{ and to two } C{=}N^{-} \text{ groups (double bonds)} \end{array} \right]$$

XXXIV

and the participation of all nine electrons of the cobalt atom in bond formation causes the observed diamagnetism of the molecule. The complex $K_4Co(CN)_6$ is less stable than $K_3Co(CN)_6$. From the structure *XXXIV* it is clear that the additional electron may enter into $[Co(CN)_6]^{3-}$ to form $[Co(CN)_6]^{4-}$, only by utilizing a higher orbital such as the 4 *d* or 5 *s* of the cobalt atom. In this fact lies the explanation of the observed differences in the oxidation-reduction potentials of the complex cyanides of cobalt compared with those of iron :

$$[Fe(CN)_6]^{4-} \rightarrow [Fe(CN)_6]^{3-} \qquad -0{\cdot}36\,v$$
$$[Co(CN)_6]^{4-} \rightarrow [Co(CN)_6]^{3-} \qquad +0{\cdot}83\,v$$

The oxidation of $[Co(CN)_6]^{4-}$ to $[Co(CN)_6]^{3-}$ occurs very readily since it will be accompanied by the liberation of the excitation energy of the additional electron to the orbital of higher energy. The oxidation of $[Fe(CN)_6]^{4-}$ to $[Fe(CN)_6]^{3-}$ does not occur readily, since all the electrons are employed in bond formation and one electron is left upaired in $[Fe(CN)_6]^{3-}$.

In $K_2Ni(CN)_4$ and in the analogous complexes of palladium and platinum, various valence bond structures are possible of which *XXXV* and *XXXVI* are examples and are in agreement with the observed diamagnetism of these substances.

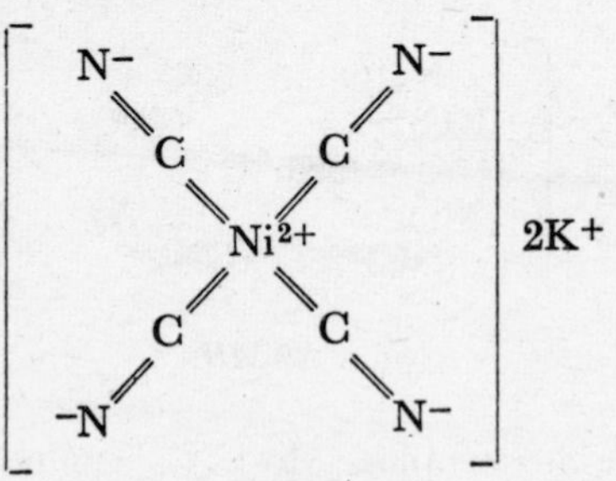

$$\left[\text{Ni}^{2+} \text{ bonded to four } C{=}N^{-} \text{ groups} \right] 2K^{+} \qquad \left[\text{Ni bonded to two } C{\equiv}N \text{ and two } C{=}N^{-} \text{ groups} \right] 2K^{+}$$

XXXV 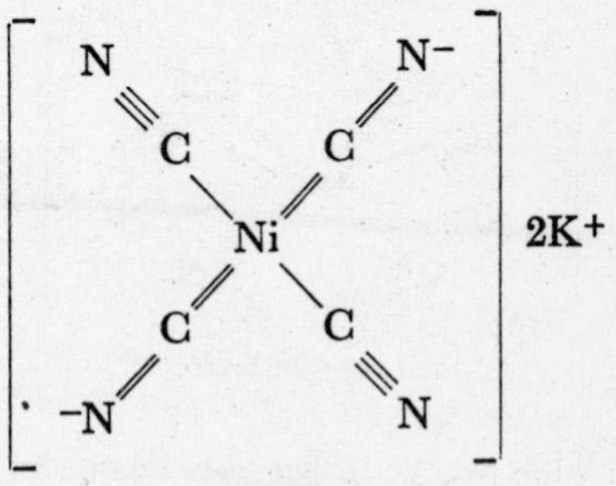 *XXXVI*

The x-ray diffraction data show that the $[Ni(CN)_4]^{2-}$ ion is planar, the four CN groups being arranged symmetrically at the four corners of a square around the central atom. Such a distribution of σ bonds corresponds to dsp^2 or d^2p^2 hybridization and up to four π bonds may be formed by d^3p electrons.

In contrast to the cyanides, other complexes of nickel with a coordination number of four, *e.g.* $[Ni(NH_3)_4]^{2+}SO_4^{2-}$, show paramagnetism corresponding to one or two unpaired electrons, which has been regarded as evidence for a tetrahedral structure of the complex ion. This has not been confirmed experimentally.

$K_4Ni(CN)_4$ may be represented by the structures :

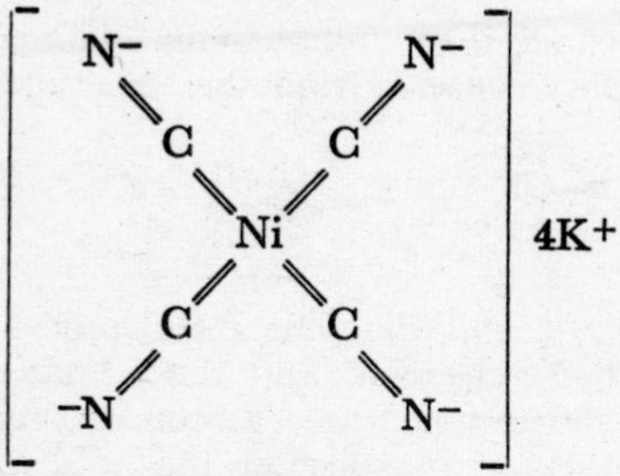

XXXVII 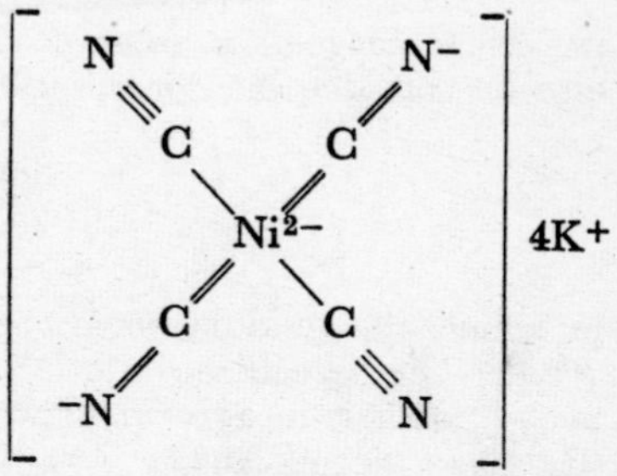 *XXXVIII*

Of the other compounds in which the central atom possesses a high valency, $K(OsO_3N)$ is worthy of mention, in which according to the x-ray evidence, the oxygen and nitrogen atoms are bonded directly to the osmium atom, and we may therefore represent the complex by the structures *XXXIX* to *XLI*.

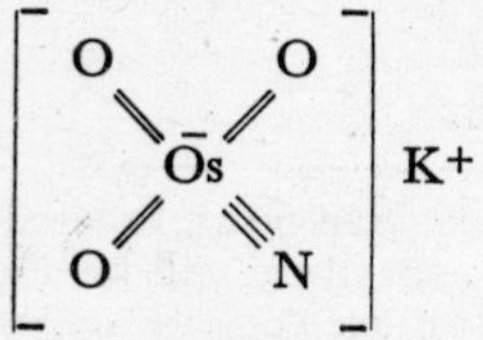

XXXIX 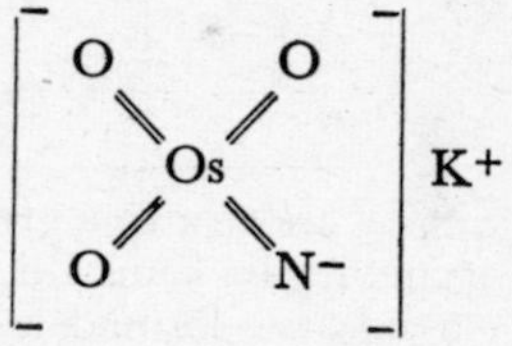 *XL*

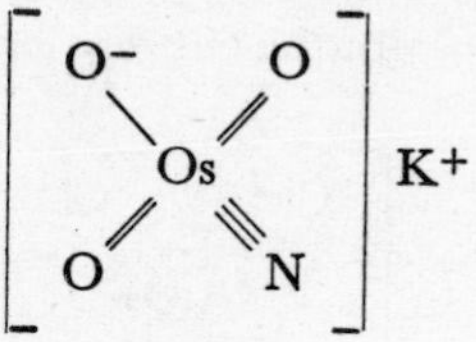

three structures
XLI

HALOGEN COMPOUNDS

In the complex halogen compounds, as in the complexes we have discussed above, the number of halogen atoms bonded to the central atom is greater than the normal valency of the latter. In the case of the complex chloride of gold, $CsAuCl_3$, the crystal structure consists of an aggregation of Cs^+ cations and two different anions, $AuCl_2^-$ which is linear and $AuCl_4^-$

which is planar. In the $AuCl_2^-$ ion, resonance will occur between the forms :

$Cl^- \quad Au^+ \quad Cl^-$ (*I*)

$Cl—Au \quad Cl^-$ (*two structures*, *II*)

in which the gold is either positively charged or monovalent. There will also be considerable contribution to the resonance from the structure

$$Cl—Au^-—Cl$$

III

in which the gold is negatively charged and divalent (electronic state, $d^{10}sp$). The hybridization of all the *s* and *p* electrons and the formation of two σ bonds is in agreement with the linear structure. In considering the structures of the $AuCl_4^-$ ion, it is necessary to consider the gold atoms initially in the excited, trivalent state, d^9sp. This leads to the structure *IV*.

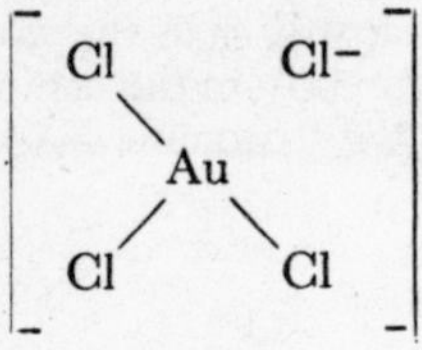

IV: $[Cl(—Au)Cl^-;\ Cl—Au—Cl]^-$ (Au bonded to three Cl, with one Cl^-)

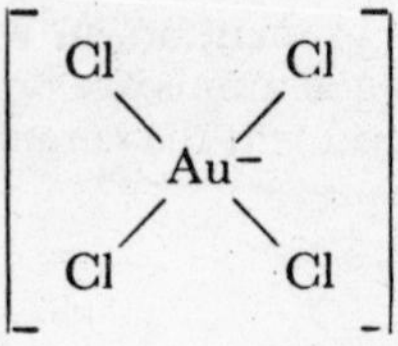

V: $[Au^-$ bonded to four Cl$]^-$

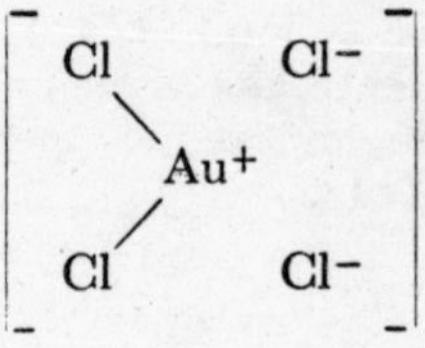

VI: $[Au^+$ bonded to two Cl, with two $Cl^-]^-$

The gain of an electron gives the negatively charged tetravalent state of gold, occurring in *V* in which the electronic structure will be d^9sp^2, so that four σ bonds are formed by four dsp^2 hybrid electrons in agreement with the observed planar configuration. The loss of an electron giving the positively charged divalent ion d^9s leads to the structure *VI*. In the $AuCl_4^-$ ion resonance will occur among all three structures, all of which have a total spin moment of zero. In the entirely ionic structure *VII*,

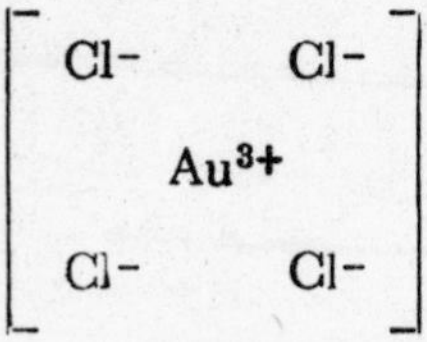

$$\left[\begin{matrix} Cl^- & & Cl^- \\ & Au^{3+} & \\ Cl^- & & Cl^- \end{matrix}\right]$$

VII

the electronic configuration of the gold atom is d^8 and in the ground state, six of the eight electrons would be paired and two unpaired. Since the total spin is not the same as that in the structures *IV* to *VI*, resonance may only occur when the Au^{3+} ion is excited to the state in which all of the eight *d* electrons are paired. Owing to the magnitude of this excitation energy, the form *VII* will not contribute significantly to the resonance of the ion. The position is the same in K_2PtCl_4, which may be described by the two limiting structures :

$$\left[\begin{array}{ccc} Cl & & Cl \\ & Pt^{2-} & \\ Cl & & Cl \end{array}\right] 2K^+ \qquad \left[\begin{array}{ccc} Cl^- & & C^- \\ & Pt^{2+} & \\ Cl^- & & Cl^- \end{array}\right] 2K^+$$

VIII *IX*

together with a number of intermediate structures. As in the case of the $AuCl_4^-$ ion, the completely covalent structure *VIII* has a total electronic spin of zero, whereas in the ionic form *IX* the Pt^{2+} ion will be in the electronic state d^8 and in order to pair all the eight electrons in four *d* orbitals, considerable excitation energy is required and the structure *IX* does not therefore contribute significantly to the structure of the molecule. The planar configuration of the $PtCl_4^{2-}$ ion is evidently caused by the contribution to the molecular resonance of the covalent structure *VIII* in which the tetravalent Pt^{2-} ion forms four dsp^2 hybrid orbitals. In neutral $PtCl_4$, a different configuration is to be expected since non-charged tetravalent platinum has the electronic configuration d^8sp, formed by the excitation of one *d* electron in the ground state, d^9s. Here the bonds will be formed by d^2sp electrons which according to *Table CLXV* will give rise to a non-symmetrical tetrahedral configuration. This is what is found to be the case in $(CH_3)_3PtCl$ in which the bonds are mainly covalent, but in which there is a small contribution from the ionic form $(CH_3)_3Pt^+Cl^-$.

In K_2PtCl_6 there exists resonance between the covalent and ionic structures. The K_2PtCl_6 crystal consists of K^+ ions and octahedral $PtCl_6^{2-}$ ions arranged in a similar manner to the Li^+ and O^{2-} ions in an anti-fluorite lattice. Each potassium ion is surrounded by twelve chlorine atoms and the closeness of the packing will evidently be due to the attraction between the positive potassium ions and the partially negative atoms of chlorine.

On the basis of the above discussion of the complex compounds of gold and platinum an explanation of the formation of the ICl_4^- ion, as in $KICl_4$, is possible. The entirely ionic structure *X* is improbable in view of the magnitude of the charge on the central atom. In the atom of iodine,

$$\left[\begin{array}{ccc} Cl^- & & Cl^- \\ & I^{3+} & \\ Cl^- & & Cl^- \end{array}\right] K^+$$

X

or in the iodide ion, however, the excitation energy of an electron in the $6p$ state to a $6d$ or $7s$ orbital is not great and such a valency state is not without possibility. Such an excitation of two of the $6p$ electrons in the ion I^-, leads to the valency states p^4ds or p^4d^2, both of which give rise to a planar configuration (*Table CLXV*). Thus we have the limiting covalent structure *XI*.

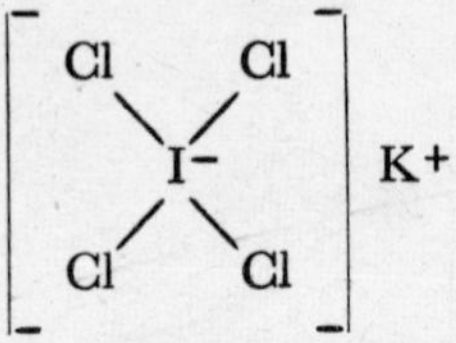

```
┌  Cl     Cl  ┐
     \   /
      I⁻        K⁺
     /   \
   Cl     Cl
└             ┘
```

XI

Resonance can only occur between structures *X* and *XI*, if the I^{3+} ion (s^2p^2) has a zero spin moment. The electronic configuration in which this condition holds is not necessarily the ground state of the ion.

In contrast to $K_3Fe(CN)_6$ the complex molecule $(NH_4)_3FeF_6$ has a magnetic moment of 5·9 μ_B, which corresponds to five unpaired electrons. The central atom of iron in $FeF_6{}^{3-}$ is therefore in the same electronic state as the atom of iron in $FeCl_3$. Only three of the eight available electrons of iron can participate in bond formation and it is therefore generally assumed that this compound is entirely ionic (*XII*).

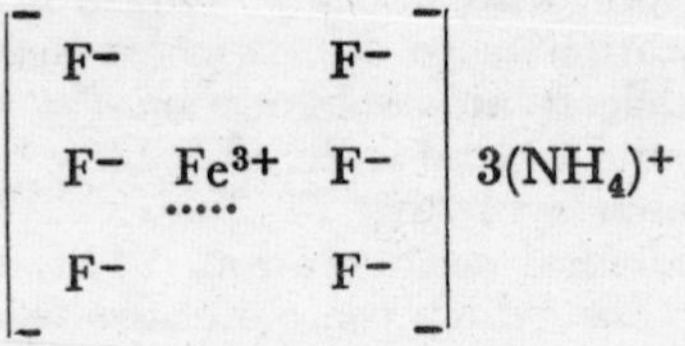

```
┌ F⁻          F⁻ ┐
  F⁻   Fe³⁺   F⁻    3(NH₄)⁺
       •••••
  F⁻          F⁻
└                ┘
```

XII

Structures in which the bonds are partially ionic, however, are possible, *viz*

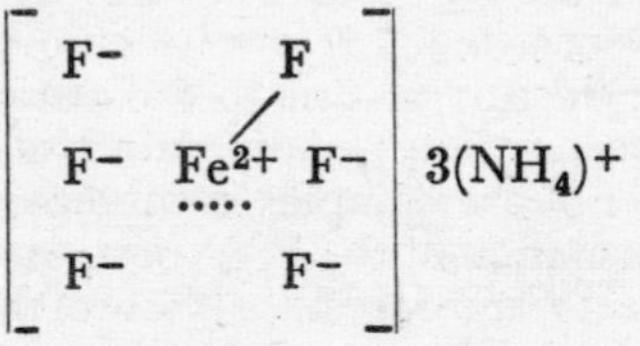

```
┌ F⁻         F ┐                     ┌ F⁻         F ┐
            /                                    /
  F⁻   Fe²⁺  F⁻    3(NH₄)⁺              F⁻  Fe⁺——F      3(NH₄)⁺
       •••••                                •••••
  F⁻         F⁻                          F⁻         F⁻
└              ┘                     └              ┘
```

XIII 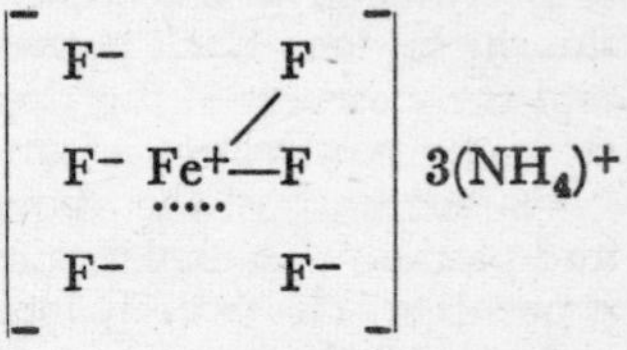 *XIV*

```
┌ F⁻         F ┐
            /
  F⁻   Fe——F      3(NH₄)⁺
       •••••
            \
  F⁻         F
└              ┘
```

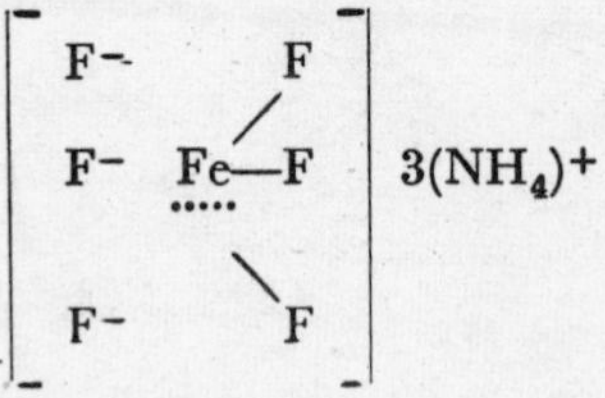

XV

The resonance of these structures will produce an increased stability of the molecule. Thus it is evident that it is not possible to decide the exact nature of the bond in these complexes simply on the basis of magnetic data, except in certain cases (see page 353) and in general it is only possible to determine the valency state of the central atom. The existence of the unpaired electrons in FeF_6^{3-} may be in part due to the fact that in the bond between a halogen atom and a metal atom, only bond resonance between the covalent M—F and ionic M^+F^- forms is possible and in contrast to the CN group a covalent bond between the metal and the F^- ion is not possible.

AMMINO COMPOUNDS AND SALT HYDRATES

A very large number of metals, including the alkali and alkaline earth metals which do not generally form complexes, give ammino derivatives and hydrates. In the complex $NaCl(NH_3)_x$, the bond between the metal ion and the ammonia molecules is due to ion-dipole forces. The

$$M^+ \quad NH_3$$
I

bond is therefore not strong and these substances often possess an appreciable vapour pressure of ammonia. More stable ammino compounds are formed, however, with metals possessing *d* electrons. In such cases the attraction is not only due to ion-dipole forces but, since nitrogen may exist in the positively charged tetravalent state, there is a tendency for electrons to be transferred from the nitrogen to a vacant orbital in the metal atom with the formation of a compound of the type *II*. The possibility of the

$$F_3B^-—^+NH_3$$
II

transfer of electrons from ammonia molecules to a metal atom is determined by the number of available orbitals in the metal and if the metal has a high electron affinity, a donor-acceptor (coordinate) bond between the metal and the ammonia molecule is formed. By this means, bonds of the type :

$$M^-—^+NH_3 \qquad\qquad X^- \quad M—^+NH_3$$
III *IV*

occur. In the $—^+NH_3$ group, the positive charge is not localized on the nitrogen atom, but is shared by the hydrogen atoms. This is shown by the fact that the ammonia molecule, NH_3, forms coordination compounds much more readily than trimethylamine, $N(CH_3)_3$. Pyridine, on the other hand, behaves in this connection as a primary amine owing to the contribution of resonance structures in which the nitrogen atom is negatively charged and divalent. Although ion-dipole forces may play some part in the bond between the metal ion and the ammonia molecule, the bond is predominantly homopolar, since molecules such as CH_3Cl and CH_3NO_2, which have a greater dipole moment than ammonia and which are smaller in molecular size than pyridine, do not form complex compounds since carbon is unable to exert a valency greater than four. If the electrostatic attraction between the ion and the dipoles were of great significance in complex formation, the tendency towards complex formation would be greater, the smaller the radius and the greater the charge of the central ion (the energy of ion-dipole interaction is given by $ze\mu/r^2$ where ze is the charge of the ion, μ the dipole moment, and r the distance between the ion and the dipole). The ions Be^{2+} and Al^{2+} would thus form complexes more readily than iron, platinum, cobalt and nickel, which does not occur.

On the basis of the above discussion, in stable complexes, such as

$Au(NH_3)_4Cl_3$, there will evidently be resonance between a number of different structures, the limiting forms being :

$$\left[\begin{array}{ccc} H_3N & & NH_3 \\ & Au^{3+} & \\ H_3N & & NH_3 \end{array}\right] 3Cl^- \qquad \left[\begin{array}{ccc} H_3N^+ & & {}^+NH_3 \\ & \diagdown \; \diagup & \\ & Au^- & \\ & \diagup \; \diagdown & \\ H_3N^+ & & {}^+NH_3 \end{array}\right] 3Cl^-$$

V   *VI*

In structure *VI*, the gold is in the negatively charged tetravalent state, in which the four bonds are formed by dsp^2 electrons. The planar configuration of the $[Au(NH_3)_4]^{3+}$ complex, as determined by experiment, is in agreement with the prediction that four dsp^2 hybrid bonds are formed.

In $Cd(NH_3)_4Cl_2$ a similar limiting covalent structure occurs, *VII*, but here the four valency electrons of the ion Cd^{2-} are in sp^3 orbitals so that the complex ion has a tetrahedral configuration. The configuration of the ions $[Ag(NH_3)_2]^+$ and $[Cd(NH_3)_2]^{2+}$ has been shown by experiment to be linear, a fact which is in conformity with the sp hybridization of the valency electrons :

$$H_3N^+—Ag^-—{}^+NH_3$$
$$H_3N^+—Cd—{}^+NH_3$$

The limiting covalent structure of the complex $Cu(NH_3)_4Cl$, *VII*, contains copper in the doubly charged negative tetravalent state :

$$\left[\begin{array}{ccc} H_3N^+ & & {}^+NH_3 \\ & \diagdown \; \diagup & \\ & Cu^{2-} & \\ & \diagup \; \cdot \; \diagdown & \\ H_3N^+ & & {}^+NH_3 \end{array}\right] 2Cl^-$$

VII

The electronic structure of the Cu^{2-} ion, however, is d^9sp^3 in which there are five unpaired electrons and therefore one electron must remain unpaired in the tetrammino compound. Two forms of hybridization can occur in the Cu^{2-} ion, either dsp^{2-} or sp^{3-} the former leading to a planar structure and the latter to a tetrahedral configuration.. Experiment shows that the ion is planar, which would indicate that dsp^{2-} hybrid bonds are more stable than sp^3 bonds.

The magnetic moment of $Cr(NH_3)_6Cl_3$ indicates the existence of three unpaired electrons in agreement with the resonance between structures *VIII* and *IX* and other types which are intermediate between the limiting ionic and covalent forms.

$$\left[\begin{array}{ccc} & H_3N \;\; NH_3 & \\ H_3N & \underset{\cdots}{Cr^{3+}} & NH_3 \\ & H_3N \;\; NH_3 & \end{array}\right] 3Cl^- \qquad \left[\begin{array}{ccc} H_3N^+ & & {}^+NH_3 \\ & \diagdown \; \diagup & \\ H_3N^+— & \underset{\cdots}{Cr^{3-}} & —{}^+NH_3 \\ & \diagup \; \diagdown & \\ H_3N^+ & & {}^+NH_3 \end{array}\right] 3Cl^-$$

VIII   *IX*

In all the examples considered above, the total electron spin is the same in both of the limiting structures, *i.e.* that in which the bonding forces are entirely ion-dipole and that in which they are homopolar, resonance between these and possible intermediate structures may therefore occur. The experimentally determined dia- and paramagnetism does not indicate that one or other of the valence bond structures is to be preferred, since in these structures the number of unpaired electrons does not change. Here also, the number of unpaired electrons is the same in the simple salt and in the ammino compound. Thus, for example, $AuCl_3$ and $Au(NH_3)_4Cl_3$ are both diamagnetic, $CuCl_2$ and $Cu(NH_3)_4Cl_2$ both have a single unpaired electron, and $CrCl_3$ and $Cr(NH_3)_6Cl_3$ have three unpaired electrons each. In the ammino compounds of cobalt, however, the position is different, $Co(NH_3)_6Cl_3$ being diamagnetic, whereas $CoCl_3$ is strongly paramagnetic. Pauling considers this fact as evidence for the covalent character of the bonds in $Co(NH_3)_6Cl_3$, which therefore corresponds to the structure *X*,

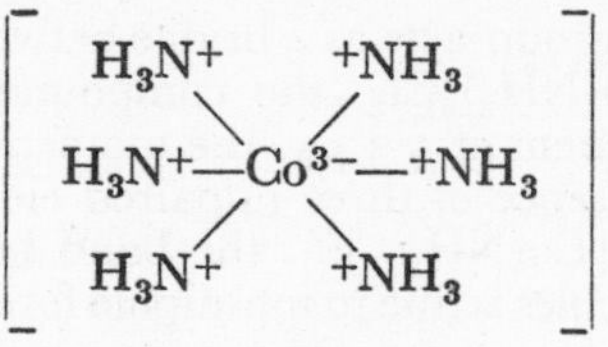

$$\left[\begin{array}{ccc} H_3N^{+} & & {}^{+}NH_3 \\ & \diagdown \quad \diagup & \\ H_3N^{+}\!-\!\!\! & Co^{3-} & \!\!\!-{}^{+}NH_3 \\ & \diagup \quad \diagdown & \\ H_3N^{+} & & {}^{+}NH_3 \end{array}\right] 3Cl^{-}$$

X

An ionic structure in order to be diamagnetic would have to include the unusual triply charged, positive cobalt ion *XI*:

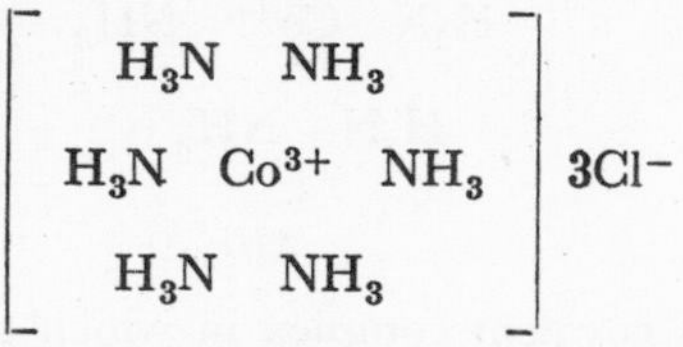

$$\left[\begin{array}{ccc} & H_3N \quad NH_3 & \\ H_3N & Co^{3+} & NH_3 \\ & H_3N \quad NH_3 & \end{array}\right] 3Cl^{-}$$

XI

in which the electronic structure is as follows:

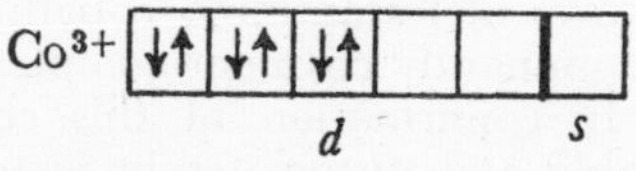

$$Co^{3+}\ \begin{array}{|c|c|c|c|c||c|} \hline \downarrow\uparrow & \downarrow\uparrow & \downarrow\uparrow & \quad & \quad & \quad \\ \hline \end{array}$$

$$\qquad\qquad d \qquad\qquad\qquad s$$

with all six *d* electrons paired in three *d* orbitals. In view of the energy necessary to produce this excited state from the ground state in which there will be four unpaired electrons, a considerable absorption of energy would be involved and it is unlikely that this would be compensated to any great extent by the ion-dipole forces repsonsible for the bonding in structure *XI*. It thus appears that here the magnetic properties do lead to a decision as to the nature of the bonds in the complex, the covalent structure *X* being preferable to the ionic form *XI*. In the ion $[Co(NH_3)_6]^{3+}$ of all the valency electrons (nine in Co and twelve in six NH_3 groups), three are transferred to the chlorine atoms and the remaining eighteen are located in pairs in molecular orbitals in the field of an atom of cobalt and six atoms of nitrogen.

These electrons may be regarded as taking part in six σ bonds between the d^2sp^3 hybrid orbitals of cobalt and the sp^3 orbital of nitrogen ; the remaining six electrons will form three π bonds. The structure of the complex ammine containing two atoms of cobalt,

$$[(NH_3)_5Co—NH_2—Co(NH_3)_5]\ \ X_5$$

will have a similar covalent structure to *X*, *i.e.*

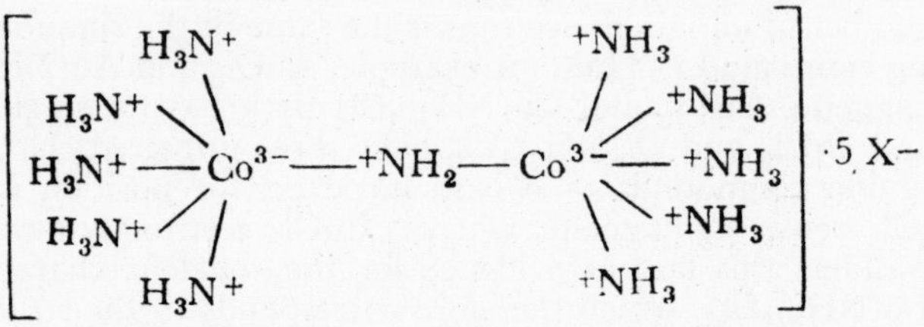

$$\left[\begin{array}{ccccc} & H_3N^+ & & {}^+NH_3 & \\ H_3N^+ & \diagdown\ \backslash & & /\ \diagup & {}^+NH_3 \\ H_3N^+ — & Co^{3-} & —{}^+NH_2— & Co^{3-} & — {}^+NH_3 \\ H_3N^+ & \diagup\ / & & \backslash\ \diagdown & {}^+NH_3 \\ & H_3N^+ & & {}^+NH_3 & \end{array}\right] \cdot 5\,X^-$$

XII

in which the—$^+NH_2$—group acts as a bridge between the two cobalt atoms.

In contrast with $Co(NH_3)_6Cl_3$, the compound $Co(NH_3)_6Cl_2$ is paramagnetic and has a moment of 5·3 μ_B, the moment of $CoCl_2$ being 5·04 μ_B, which indicates the presence of three unpaired electrons. Hence it is concluded that in the ion $[Co(NH_3)_6]^{2+}$, the bond between the central atom and the ammonia molecules is due to ion-dipole forces. The structure of the complex is therefore

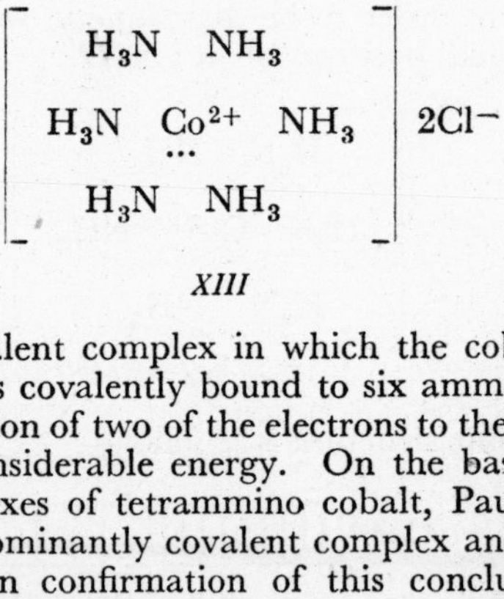

$$\left[\begin{array}{ccc} & H_3N\ \ NH_3 & \\ H_3N & \underset{\cdots}{Co^{2+}} & NH_3 \\ & H_3N\ \ NH_3 & \end{array}\right]\ 2Cl^-$$

XIII

The formation of a covalent complex in which the cobalt possesses three unpaired electrons and is covalently bound to six ammonia molecules can only occur by the excitation of two of the electrons to the 5*s* and 5*p* orbitals, which would require considerable energy. On the basis of the magnetic properties of the complexes of tetrammino cobalt, Pauling has described $[Co(NH_3)_6]^{3+}$ as a predominantly covalent complex and $[Co(NH_3)_6]^{2+}$ as predominantly ionic. In confirmation of this conclusion we find that $Co(NH_3)_6Cl_2$ is not stable and dissociates in water yielding ammonium ions, whereas the $Co(NH_3)_6Cl_3$ complex is quite stable and the ion $[Co(NH_3)_6]^{3+}$ does not decompose in solution. The Co—N distance in $[Co(NH_3)_6]^{3+}$ is 1·9 Å, considerably shorter than that in $[Co(NH_3)_6]^{2+}$ which is 2·5 Å.

The magnetic moments of $Mn(NH_3)_6Br_2$, and $Fe(NH_3)_6Cl_2$ and $Fe(H_2O)_6Cl_2$ correspond to those of $MnSO_4$ and $FeCl_2$ respectively and in these compounds, as in $Co(NH_3)_6Cl_2$, the bond is largely ionic in character.

In $Co(NH_3)_6Cl_3$ the complex ion $[Co(NH_3)_6]^{3+}$ has been formed by the transference of three electrons to the chlorine atoms ; no such process is necessary in the case of $Co(NH_3)_3(NO_2)_3$, since the NO_2 groups possess an odd number of electrons. The structure of this compound will therefore be

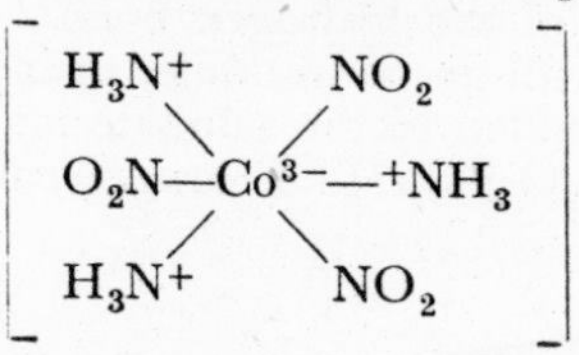

$$\left[\begin{array}{ccc} H_3N^+ & & NO_2 \\ & \diagdown \quad \diagup & \\ O_2N - & Co^{3-} & - {}^+NH_3 \\ & \diagup \quad \diagdown & \\ H_3N^+ & & NO_2 \end{array}\right]$$

XIV

in which all the bonds are covalent. The negative charge will not necessarily be located on the cobalt atom but may be distributed on the oxygen atoms. We thus have an alternative structure, *XV*, in which the cobalt atom is monavalent, with six σ and three π bonds

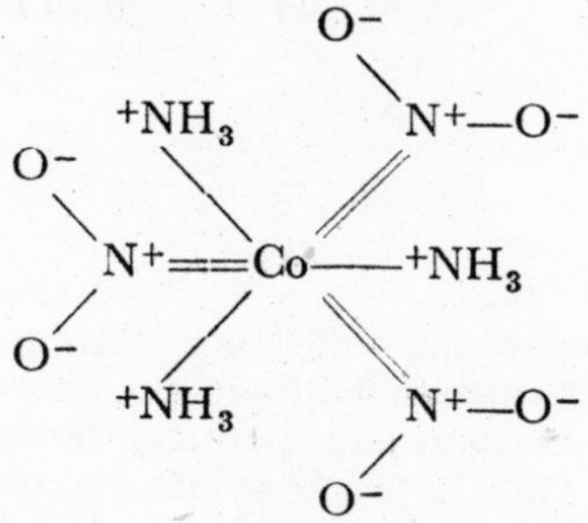

$$\begin{array}{ccccc} & & & O^- & \\ & & & \diagdown & \\ & {}^+NH_3 & & N^+ - O^- & \\ O^- & & \diagdown & /\!/ & \\ \diagdown & & & & \\ & N^+ = & Co & - {}^+NH_3 & \\ \diagup & & & & \\ O^- & & \diagup & \backslash\!\backslash & \\ & {}^+NH_3 & & N^+ - O^- & \\ & & & \diagup & \\ & & & O^- & \end{array}$$

XV

Since in many of the ammino complexes the bond $M-{}^+NH_3$ occurs, in which the nitrogen is tetravalent and positively charged, the basic properties of the nitrogen atom are reduced and its acidic properties correspondingly increased. The loss of a proton is evidently facilitated by increase of the positive charge on the hydrogen atom owing to the resonance between $M-{}^+NH_3$ and $M-NH_2H^+$.

The nature of the bonding forces in ammino compounds which has been discussed above may, in general, be applied to the hydrates. Here the ion-dipole forces occur in addition to the coordinate bond formed by the donation of a pair of electrons by the oxygen atom. We thus obtain structures of the type,

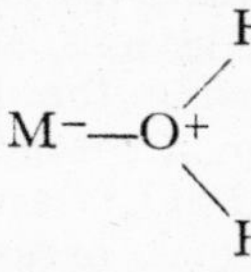

$$\begin{array}{c} \quad\quad H \\ \quad \diagup \\ M^- - O^+ \\ \quad \diagdown \\ \quad\quad H \end{array} \quad \text{and} \quad X^- \begin{array}{c} \quad\quad H \\ \quad \diagup \\ M - O^+ \\ \quad \diagdown \\ \quad\quad H \end{array}$$

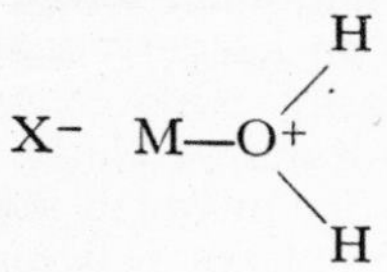

In addition to the formation of hydrated cations, bonding of water molecules to anions may occur by means of hydrogen bonds as in, for example, the sulphate ion *XVI*

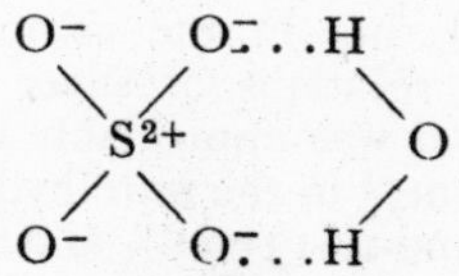

$$\begin{array}{ccccc} O^- & & O^- \cdots H & & \\ & \diagdown \; \diagup & & \diagdown & \\ & S^{2+} & & & O \\ & \diagup \; \diagdown & & \diagup & \\ O^- & & O^- \cdots H & & \end{array}$$

XVI

The negatively charged oxygen atoms of the sulphate ion will appreciably increase the strength of the hydrogen bond. We thus find that several sulphates crystallize with an odd number of molecules of water of crystallization, one being bonded to the sulphate ion and the remainder to the cation, *e.g.* $CuSO_4{\cdot}5H_2O$ (*XVII*). Four molecules of water are arranged in

```
                      H
                      |
                      O
                    /   \
     H2O           /     H        H···O⁻     O⁻
        \         /       ·.     /      \   /
         Cu²⁺                  O          S²⁺
        /    \            .·     \      /   \
     H2O      \          H        H···O⁻     O⁻
                \       /
                  O
                  |
                  H
```

XVII

a plane round each copper ion, while the oxygen atom of the fifth molecule of water is tetrahedrally surrounded by four atoms of oxygen to which it is bound by a system of covalent and hydrogen bonds. The first two stages in the dehydration of $CuSO_4{\cdot}5H_2O$ evidently consist in the removal of the four molecules bound to the copper ion, the fifth molecule is bound more firmly, and the structure of $CuSO_4{\cdot}H_2O$ is evidently that shown by *XVIII*

```
               H···O⁻     O⁻
              /      \   /
     Cu²⁺—O            S²⁺
              \      /   \
               H···O⁻     O⁻
```

XVIII

With the hydrates of various salts, it is possible to trace a gradation of the stability of the bond. This is greatest when it is caused by the superposition of covalent and ion-dipole forces and weakest where the molecules of water are adsorbed in an irregular manner between the ions, as in NaCl, when the water is easily removed without destroying the lattice structure. Such crystal hydrates as $Na_2SO_4{\cdot}10H_2O$ form a special class which are best regarded as ice in which the ions Na^+ and SO_4^{2-} are dissolved. The formation of complexes between water and such organic molecules as ethylene, butadiene and other unsaturated organic compounds is due to the possibility of the carbon existing in other valency states. This view is borne out by the Raman spectroscopic data of TAUFEN, MURRAY and CLEVELAND[25] who showed that in the complexes formed between the olefines and concentrated solutions of silver nitrate, the characteristic frequency of the C=C bond was appreciably lowered (1,584 cm^{-1} in the complex in place of 1,653 cm^{-1} in the pure hydrocarbon ; for *cyclo*hexene the values are 1,539 cm^{-1} and 1,613 cm^{-1}, and for *cyclo*pentene, 1,598 cm^{-1} and 1,660 cm^{-1}). This shows that the formation of the complex involves the double bond and the nature of the bonds in the complex may be regarded as due to resonance between the forms :

```
 \      /          \       /          \      /
  C----C+           C+----C            C==C
 /  \    \         /     / \          /      \
     Ag                Ag                 Ag+
```

the last structure being formed by van der Waal's forces. Similar observations have been made for the complex formed between $HgCl_2$ and acetylene by FREIDLINA and NESMEYANOV[26].

INNER COORDINATION COMPOUNDS

A particular type of non-localized bond occurs in the so-called inner co-ordination compounds. This group of compounds may be illustrated by reference to the copper salt of aminoacetic acid (glycine). This compound dissociates only weakly in solution, it possesses a colour similar to the ammino complexes of copper and does not react with ammonia. These properties all tend to show that copper atom has a saturated valency and may be explained by considering the copper as bound to both the hydroxyl and the amino groups. In accordance with our concept of the nature of the bond between a metal and an amino group in such a compound, the structure of the complex will be represented by resonance amongst the forms *I* to *IX* :

```
O=C—O        O—C=O            O=C—O         O—C=O
  |    \    /    |              |    \     /    |
  |     Cu2-     |              |     Cu-       |
  |    /  · \    |              |    /  ·       |
H2C—+NH2   +NH2—CH2           H2C—+NH2     NH2—CH2
         I                               II

              O=C—O-        O—C=O
                |          /    |
                |      Cu-      |
                |    /  ·  \    |
              H2C—+NH2    +NH2—CH2
                       III*

O=C—O        O—C=O            O=C—O-        O-—C=O
  |    \    /    |              |                |
  |     Cu       |              |       Cu       |
  |     ·        |              |     /  · \     |
H2C—NH2      NH2—CH2          H2C—+NH2    +NH2—CH2
         IV                              V*

O=C—O-       O—C=O            O=C—O-        O—C=O
  |         /    |              |          /    |
  |     Cu       |              |      +Cu      |
  |   /  ·       |              |       ·       |
H2C—+NH2     NH2—CH2          H2C—NH2      NH2—CH2
        VI*                             VII*
```

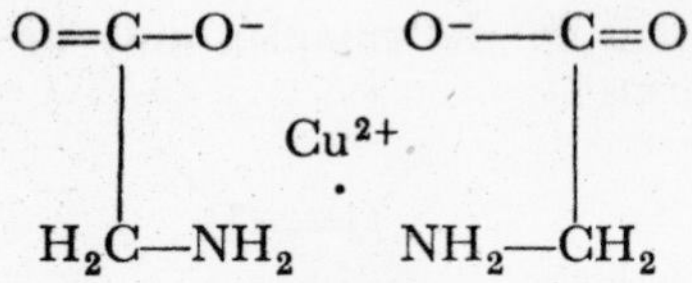

$$\begin{array}{ccc} O{=}C{-}O^- & & O^-{-}C{=}O \\ | & Cu^{2+} & | \\ H_2C{-}NH_2 & \cdot & NH_2{-}CH_2 \end{array}$$

*VIII**

$$\begin{array}{ccc} O{=}C{-}O & & O^-{-}C{=}O \\ | & \diagdown Cu & | \\ H_2C{-}NH_2 & \cdot \diagdown & {}^+NH_2{-}CH_2 \end{array}$$

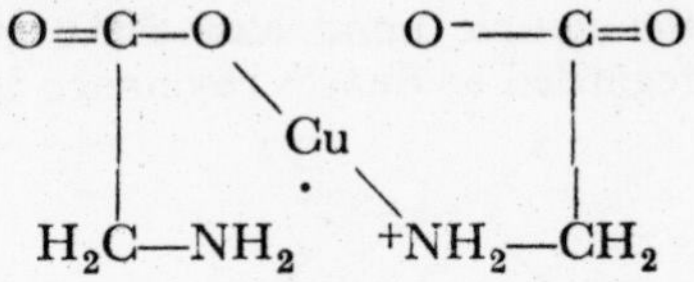

*IX**

Resonance will also occur in the structures marked with an asterisk between the types $O{=}\underset{|}{C}{-}O^-$ and $O^-{-}\underset{|}{C}{=}O$ and both oxygen atoms will have identical charge.

It was thought originally that in these complexes, the main bond was that formed between the copper atom and the carboxylate ion, the bonds existing with the amino group being auxiliary. It is now considered, however, that all the bonds, whether to oxygen or nitrogen atoms, are identical. This is evident since the reaction of the silver salts of the amino acids with alkyl halides results in the formation not only of the ester but also of the N–alkyl compound,

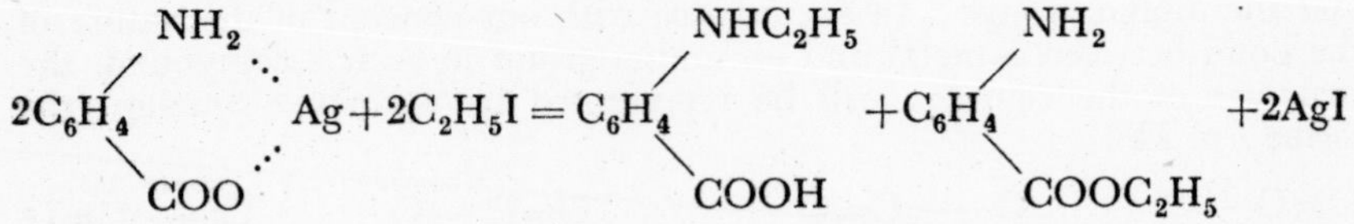

$$2C_6H_4\begin{matrix}\diagup NH_2 \cdots \\ \diagdown COO \cdots\end{matrix}Ag + 2C_2H_5I = C_6H_4\begin{matrix}\diagup NHC_2H_5 \\ \diagdown COOH\end{matrix} + C_6H_4\begin{matrix}\diagup NH_2 \\ \diagdown COOC_2H_5\end{matrix} + 2AgI$$

The formation of inner coordination compounds is connected with the presence in the organic molecule of atoms which may exist in more than one valency state, *e.g.*

$$=O, \quad -O-, \quad -OH, \quad -NH_2, \quad =NH, \quad =NOH, \quad \equiv N, \quad =N-, \quad -SH \quad \textit{etc}$$

The formation of such complexes is conditioned by steric factors; in the α- and β- amino acids, when the ring consists of five or six atoms respectively, a coordination compound is formed, but an increase in the number of atoms separating the amino and carboxylic acid groups (in γ, δ, ϵ, *etc* amino acids) generally inhibits the formation of cyclic inner coordination compounds.

The same principles determine bond formation in the complexes formed by the β-diketones. The ability of diketones to form metallic derivatives is determined by the extent of enolization, *e.g.*

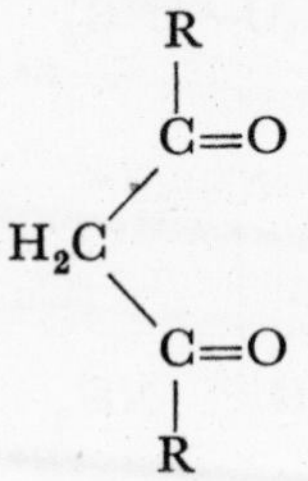

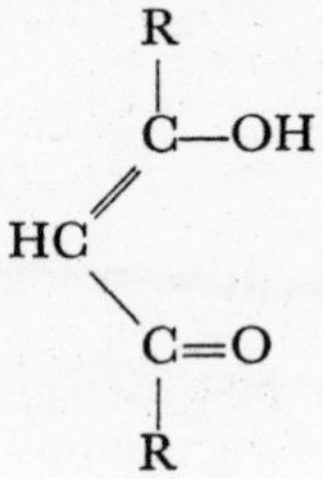

$$H_2C\begin{matrix}\diagup C(R){=}O \\ \diagdown C(R){=}O\end{matrix} \qquad HC\begin{matrix}\diagup\!\!\diagup C(R){-}OH \\ \diagdown C(R){=}O\end{matrix}$$

The metal may replace the hydrogen atom of the enolic form with the formation of a salt having a structure which resonates between *X* and *XI* :

```
       R                         R
       |                         |
       C—O⁻                      C—O
      //                        /    \
   HC          Na⁺           HC       Na
      \                         \
       C=O                       C=O
       |                         |
       R                         R

       X                         XI
```

Owing to the conjugated system of double bonds, the structures *XII* and *XIII* are also possible.

```
       R                         R
       |                         |
       C=O                       C=O
      /                         /
   HC          Na⁺           HC       Na
      \\                        \\    /
       C—O⁻                      C—O
       |                         |
       R                         R

       XII                       XIII
```

Thus owing to the resonance between the four structures *X* to *XIII* the sodium atom has a coordination number of two.

The triacetylacetone derivatives of aluminium, cobalt and iron are very different in their magnetic properties, the first two being diamagnetic and the last paramagnetic, having a moment of $5{\cdot}9\,\mu_B$ corresponding to five unpaired electrons. Hence it has been suggested that the bonds in aluminium and cobalt compounds are covalent whereas those in the iron compound are ionic, but SUGDEN[27] has pointed out that this conclusion is not in accordance with the properties of the iron compound, which is volatile and soluble in non-polar solvents. The formation of donor-acceptor (coordination) bonds, as proposed by Pauling, does not explain the difficulty, but if the formation of ordinary electron pair bonds are assumed the observed behaviour of iron may be satisfactorily explained. Thus the aluminium complex forms the structure *XIV*.

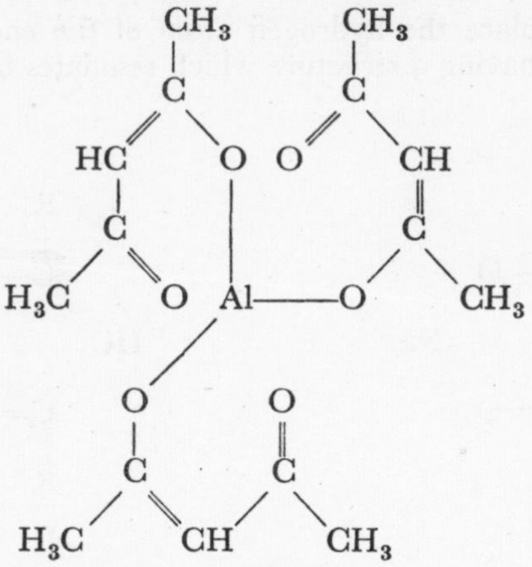

XIV

Since aluminium has the electron configuration s^2p, which becomes sp^2 when trivalent, this compound will be diamagnetic. The analogous structure for iron, d^6s^2, will leave five electrons unpaired in the d orbitals in agreement with the magnetic properties. In cobalt, d^7s^2, it must be assumed that the bonds are formed by pairing of the three unpaired electrons with the formation of a diamagnetic complex.

The experimental data show that the compounds of copper with the β-diketones are planar which indicates dsp^2 or d^2p^2 hybridization. Commencing with the ion Cu^{2+} (d^9), it is impossible to consider the bond as formed by the donation of an electron pair from the oxygen atom, since Cu^{2+} has no vacant d orbital[27]. It is, therefore, clear that the structure is best represented as a resonance hybrid of all possible structures from the completely ionic, *XV* and *XVI*, to the completely covalent, *XVIII*

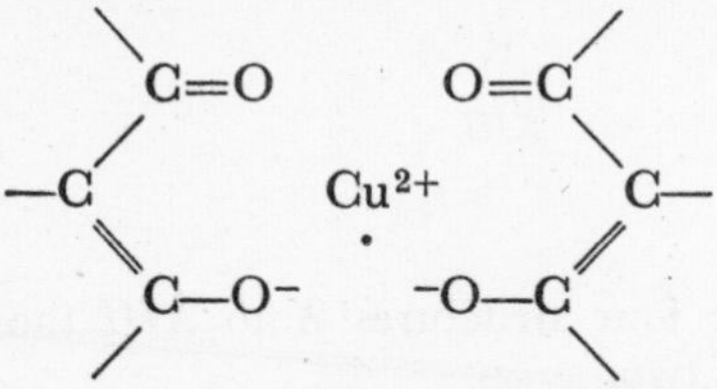

XV

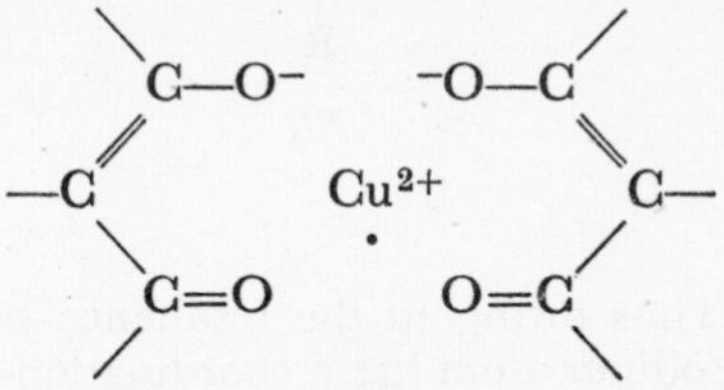

XVI

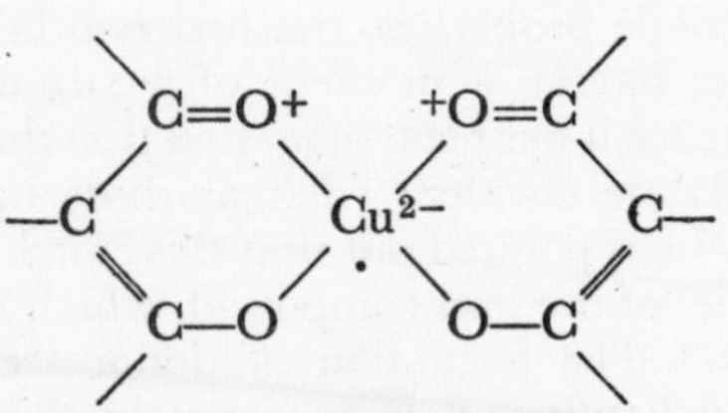

XVII

In the covalent structure *XVII*, copper is in the Cu^{2-} state with five unpaired electrons, four of these take part in the formation of four covalent bonds, dsp^2 hybrid electrons, and the fifth remains unpaired and is responsible for the observed magnetic moment of 1·73 μ_B.

CONCLUSIONS

From the above discussion it is possible to draw certain general conclusions.

Complex formation occurs most extensively with those atoms possessing *d* electrons since, owing to the similar energy values of the *d*, *s* and *p* levels, electronic excitation to form new valency states occurs readily.

In the simple compounds of atoms containing *d* electrons, not all the *d* electrons are, in general, used in bond formation. The preservation of unpaired electrons in the molecule may be related to the intra-atomic electronic resonance.

In the complex compounds, bonds may be formed with all unpaired electrons of the central atom or ion, the maximum number of unpaired electrons able to participate in bond formation being nine.

Such groups as CO, NO, CN, NO_2 *etc*, in which the atoms can assume various valency states, are able to form σ and π bonds with the central atom.

Resonance amongst various valence bond structures occurs with varied localization of the π bonds and different valency states of the central atoms. Thus the valency state of the central atom cannot always be defined and a range of valency exists.

The formation of complexes involving ammonia and water *etc*, cannot be explained solely on the basis of ion-dipole attraction. A significant part is played by the different valency states of nitrogen and oxygen and by the formation of donor-acceptor bonds.

The observed configurations of the atoms are in agreement with the direction of homopolar valencies of the central atom in the limiting covalent structure.

REFERENCES

[1] PAULING, L. C. *J. Amer. chem. Soc.* 53 (1931) 1367 3225
[2] KIMBALL, G. E. *J. chem. Phys.* 8 (1940) 188
[3] DYATKINA, M. E. *Acta physicochim. U.R.S.S.* 20 (1945) 407
[4] VAN VLECK, J. H. *The Theory of Electric and Magnetic Susceptibilities* Oxford, 1932
KLEMM, W. *Magnetochemie* Leipzig, 1936
SELWOOD, P. W. *Magnetochemistry* New York, 1943
[5] PASCAL, P. in GRIGNARD, V. *Traité de chimie organique*, vol. 2 Paris, 1936
[6] GRAY, F. W. and CRUICKSHANK, J. H. *Trans. Faraday Soc.* 31 (1935) 1491
CLOW, A. *ibid* 33 (1937) 381
[7] VAN VLECK, J. H. *ibid*
STONER, E. C. *Magnetism and Atomic Structure* London, 1926
[8] SUCKSMITH, W. *Proc. roy. Soc.* *A* 128 (1930) 276
[9] BARNETT, S. J. see VAN VLECK, J. H. *ibid*
[10] RUSSELL, C. D., COOPER, G. R. and VOSBURGH, W. C. *J. Amer. chem. Soc.* 65 (1943) 1301
[11] SCHUTH, W. and KLEMM, W. *Z. anorg. Chem.* 220 (1934) 193
KLEMM, W. and FRISCHMUTH, G. *ibid* 230 (1937) 220
— and STEINBERG, H. *ibid* 227 (1936) 193
[12] HEISENBERG, W. *Z. Physik* 39 (1926) 499
[13] BRAUNE, H. and PINNOW, R. *Z. phys. Chem.* *B* 35 (1937) 239
[14] EWENS, V. G. and LISTER, M. W. *Trans. Faraday Soc.* 34 (1938) 1358
[15] BERGMANN, E. and ENGEL, L. *Z. phys. Chem.* *B* 13 (1931) 232

[16] GRAFFUNDER, W. and HEYMANN, E. *ibid* 15 (1932) 377
[17] POWELL, H. M. and EWENS, R. V. G. *J. chem. Soc.* (1939) 286
[18] KLEMM, W. JACOBI, H. and TILK, J. *Z. anorg. Chem.* 201 (1931) 1
[19] EWENS, R. V. G. and LISTER, M. W. *Trans. Faraday Soc.* 35 (1939) 681
[20] ZHDANOV, G. S. and SHUGAM, E. A. *J. phys. Chem. U.R.S.S.* 19 (1945) 433
[21] VAN VLECK, J. H. *J. chem. Phys.* 3 (1935) 803
PAULING, L. C. *The Nature of the Chemical Bond* Cornell, 1939
[22] VAN VLECK, J. H. and SHERMAN, A. *Rev. Mod. Phys.* 7 (1935) 167
[23] GOLDENBERG, N. *Trans. Faraday Soc.* 36 (1940) 847.
[24] RACAH, G. *J. chem. Phys.* 11 (1943) 214
MARCHI, L. E., FERNELIUS, W. C. and MCREYNOLDS, J. P. *J. Amer. chem. Soc.* 65 (1943) 329
[25] TAUFEN, H. J., MURRAY, M. J. and CLEVELAND, F. F. *ibid.* 63 (1941) 3500
[26] FREIDLINA, R. K. and NESMEYANOV, A. N. *C. R. Acad. Sci. U.R.S.S.* 26 (1940) 60
[27] SUGDEN, S. *J. chem. Soc.* (1943) 328

15

THE STRUCTURE OF THE BORON HYDRIDES

DIBORANE B_2H_6

THE BORON HYDRIDES[1] occupy a special position among chemical compounds owing to the structural problems that they present. In the case of the simplest boron hydride, diborane B_2H_6, the problem arises from the fact that this molecule contains twelve valency electrons which must take part in the formation of seven bonds, six B—H and one B—B bond. The molecule BH_3, does not exist and is evidently rapidly dimerized on formation to B_2H_6. It will be clear that diborane is deficient in electrons and cannot therefore be represented by a valency structure involving seven electron pair bonds. To overcome this difficulty, SIDGWICK, LEWIS, PAULING and others have suggested that the B—B and four of the B—H bonds are electron pair bonds and that the remaining two bonds between hydrogen and boron are single electron bonds. As evidence for the possible formation of such a bond, attention is generally drawn to its existence in the hydrogen molecule ion, where the bond energy is as high as 61 kcals. However, the single electron bond occurs only in the hydrogen molecule ion and in no other molecule and the suggestion that it occurs in diborane is due largely to the fact that no suitable alternative was considered to exist.

Recently the bridge structure *I*, originally suggested by DILTHEY[2] has been revived by several authors[3–6],

```
H   H   H
 \ / ·. /
  B     B
 / ·. / \
H   H   H
```

I

who have put forward different suggestions concerning the exact nature of the electronic structure. NEKRASSOV[3] considered that the stability of the molecule was due to resonance between the two forms *II* and *III* :

```
H   H   H          H   H   H
 \ /   /            \   \ /
  B   B              B   B
 /   / \            / \   \
H   H   H          H   H   H
    II                 III
```

SYRKIN and DYATKINA[4], however, have shown by a quantum mechanical calculation, that in these entirely covalent structures the resonance energy does not compensate for the repulsion of the electrons not taking part in bond formation and it is therefore suggested that other possible valency states of boron, in addition to the tricovalent form, should be considered. Hence the additional valence bond structures *IV* to *VIII* have been formulated amongst which resonance occurs as well as with the structures *II* and *III*. In the structures *IV* to *VIII* boron, as well as being trivalent, is present in the positively charged divalent and negatively charged tetravalent states. The forms *VI* to *VIII* are much less probable than *IV* and *V*, owing to the very small $B\hat{B}H$ bond angle:

```
H   H     H            H     H   H
 \ /     /              \   / \ /
  B⁻    B+               B+    B⁻
 / \     \              /     / \
H   H     H            H     H   H
     IV                     V

H   H+    H            H+    H   H
 \   \   /                  /   /
  B⁻———B                B———B⁻
 /   \   \             /   /   \
H    H    H            H   H    H
 four structures       four structures
     VI                     VII

      H+    H    H
           /    /
       ⁻B————B
       /   \    \
      H     H    H
    four structures
         VIII
```

Calculation[4] shows that the energy obtained by such resonance is sufficient to stabilize the molecule. This conception of the structure of diborane has been criticized by LONGUET-HIGGINS and BELL[5] and by BELL and EMELEUS[1] who point out that there is some distortion of the valency angles in these structures since BH_3 is planar (sp^2 hybridization), H_2B^+ linear (sp hybridization) and $^-BH_4$ tetrahedral (sp^3 hybridization) and furthermore although there is considerable evidence that molecules with alternate valence bond structures may be stabilized by resonance, it is not generally considered that two parts of a molecule can be held together only by this method of bonding.

An alternative structure has been suggested by PITZER[7] which may be referred to as a protonated double bond and is represented schematically in *IX*:

```
H           H
 \   H+    /
  ⁻B====B⁻
 /   H+    \
H           H
     IX
```

The protons are regarded as being embedded in the π orbital of the double bond. This model accounts for the hindrance of internal rotation which occurs in this molecule (see later), but the B—B distance is greater, and the force constant lower, than is to be anticipated for a double bond, even if allowance is made for some weakening of the bond by the protons. From this formula acidic properties are to be expected, but they are not observed. Another alternative structure, *X*, has been suggested by WALSH[8]

```
H    H    H
 \  /  ↘ /
  B ↖    B
 /    \/  \
H     H    H
      X
```

in which it is assumed that the bonding orbitals in a normal B—H bond may be used to fill the vacant orbitals of the other boron atom. This is in fact only another way of describing the resonance formula *II* and *III*.

The method of molecular orbitals has been applied to the problem of diborane by MULLIKAN[9] who considered both the ethane-like structure and the bridge structure *XI* which is really identical with the protonated double

H H H
B═B
H H H

XI

bond structure *IX* and which resembles ethylene rather than ethane. The latter structure appears most satisfactory and the molecule may be represented by molecular orbitals, identical with those of ethylene, which embrace the two protons in addition to the boron nuclei.

The formation of such molecules as $B(CH_3)_3$ and BF_3 and not the corresponding dimers and the absence of the monomer BH_3, is due to the stabilization by trigonal conjugation, the most important empirical evidence for this being the very short B—X distances. This conjugation results from the interaction of the excess π electrons of the outer atoms with the vacant orbital of the central atom. In BH_3, there are no such excess electrons. The structure of BF_3 may thus be represented as a resonance hybrid of the four structures represented by *XII* and *XIII*.

XII *XIII*

It is thus apparent that a choice between the various theoretical treatments of the structure of diborane cannot yet be made. We shall now consider the experimental evidence for the structure of the molecule which is generally interpreted in terms of either the bridge structure *I*, the ionic structure *IX*, or an ethane type of configuration.

The x-ray investigation[10] of crystalline diborane has permitted the determination of the position of the boron atoms in the crystal lattice, but not of the hydrogen atoms. Consequently these data do not provide evidence for the structure of this molecule.

The diffraction of electrons by gaseous diborane has been studied by BAUER[11], who originally interpreted the data in terms of the ethane model and obtained the following values for the interatomic distances: B—B = 1·86 Å and B—H = 1·27 Å. More recently[12,13], however, it has been shown that the data agree equally well with distribution of atoms in the bridge model, the values for the distances being as follows:

$$B—B = 1{\cdot}80 \pm 0{\cdot}04 \text{ Å}$$

$$B—H_{outer} = 1{\cdot}23 \pm 0{\cdot}03 \text{ Å} \qquad H\hat{B}H_{outer} = 125° \pm 8°$$

$$B—H_{inner} = 1{\cdot}33 \pm 0{\cdot}03 \text{ Å} \qquad H\hat{B}H_{inner} = 95° \pm 5°$$

The structure being represented diagrammatically by *XIV* :

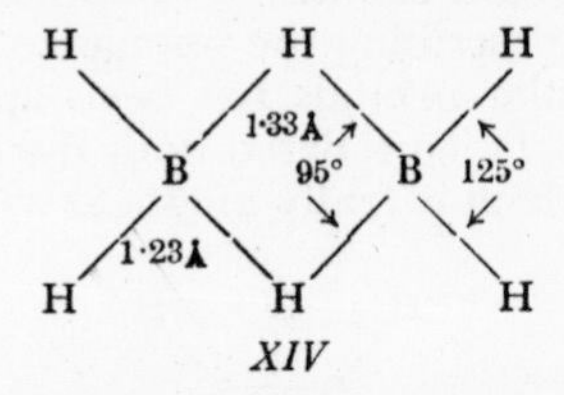

XIV

The B—H_{outer} distance corresponds to that in the molecule BH (1·216 Å) so that it may be considered that this bond in diborane is a normal, single covalent bond. The B—H_{inner} distance is greater than the B—H_{outer} distance and the bond is therefore weaker.

Such thermodynamic properties as specific heats are determined by the dimensions and modes of motion of the molecules. The only experimental data for diborane is that of STITT[14] who carried out specific heat measurements from 100° to 300° K, and concluded that the hindrance of rotation was considerably greater than in ethane, the rotational energy barrier being 4 to 6 kcals in B_2H_6 and 3 kcals in C_2H_6. This conclusion, if interpreted on the basis of an ethane structure, is particularly surprising since the distance between the hydrogen atoms of different methyl groups in ethane is 2·26 Å, whereas in diborane, assuming the ethane model of Bauer, the value is greater, being 2·70 Å. The ethane structure must thus be rejected. Rotation cannot occur in either the bridge or the ionic structures. For the bridge molecule, rotation is replaced by a torsional oscillation and the vibrational frequency has been calculated approximately by BELL and LONGUET-HIGGINS[15] and the vibrational specific heat obtained. The results are found to agree with the experimental values at all but the highest temperatures.

The Raman spectrum of liquid diborane has been investigated by ANDERSON and BURG[16] and the infra-red spectrum of the gas by STITT[17] and PRICE[18]. The interpretation of these data has been attempted by WAGNER[19] and by Bell and Longuet-Higgins[15]. The Raman spectrum has two intensive lines at 2,102 cm^{-1} and 2,523 cm^{-1} which must both be attributed to symmetrical stretching vibrations, although the ethane model permits only one such frequency. Furthermore, the infra-red spectrum contains eight bands all of which appear to be fundamentals compared with the five predicted for the ethane molecule. Attempts by Stitt and by Anderson and Burg to explain these facts by resonance splitting necessitate the introduction of various assumptions. The difficulties of interpreting the spectra of diborane are considerably lessened if the ethane model is rejected and the bridge model employed in its stead. The molecule now more closely resembles ethylene rather than ethane and the spectra is in many respects similar to that of ethylene. The most important feature is that there are now two types of B—H bond (see structure *XIV*) to which may be assigned the two Raman frequencies.

Further confirmation of the bridge type of structure comes from the methylation of diborane. It is found possible to replace only four of the hydrogen atoms with methyl groups and on further methylation instead of $B_2(CH_3)_3$, two molecules of $B(CH_3)_3$ are produced. The molecule $BH(CH_3)_2$ does not exist as the monomer, but like BH_3, dimerizes immediately on formation. These results have been discussed by SCHLESINGER and BURG[20] in terms of the bridge structure.

THE HIGHER BORON HYDRIDES

The concepts discussed above, permit proposals to be made concerning the structure of other boron hydrides which have not been subjected to such an extensive experimental investigation as has diborane. The proposed formulae fall into two groups, that favouring the resonance of structures analogous to those represented schematically for diborane in *IV* to *VIII* (SYRKIN and DYATKINA[4]) and that employing the concept of the protonated double bond (PITZER[7]).

B_4H_{10}— This molecule is represented by SYRKIN and DYATKINA[4] as a resonance hybrid of the following structures :

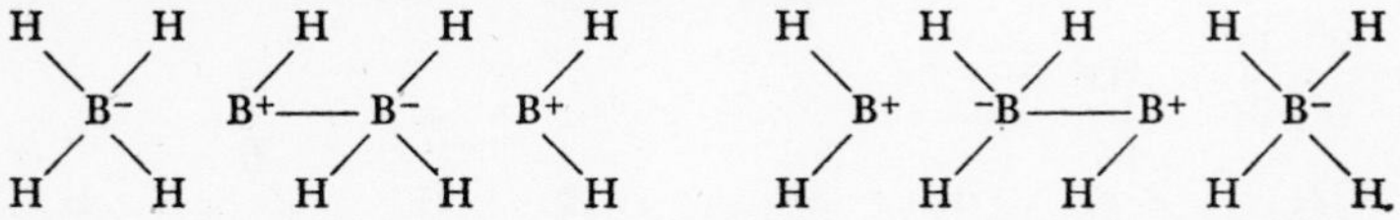

```
H    H   H    H    H          H    H    H    H    H
 \  /     \  /     /           \    \  /     /   \  /
  B-    B+---B-   B+            B+  -B-----B+     B-
 /  \     /  \     \           /    /     /      /  \
H    H   H    H    H          H    H    H    H    H
```

As pointed out above, it is doubtful whether resonance alone would be able to link the two outer boron atoms to the central group, although the ready dissociation of this molecule is explained by the looseness of this bond. A more fundamental objection is the small value of the B^-B^+H and B^+B^-H angles in the central group of atoms. The protonated double bond structure is :

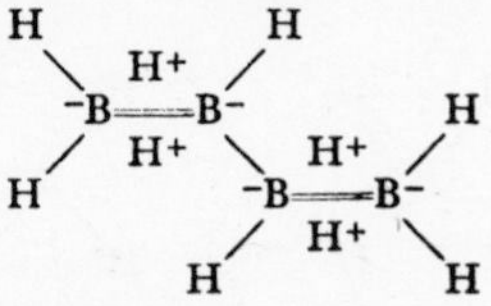

```
   H         H
    \  H+   /
    -B===B-         H
    /  H+   \  H+  /
   H         -B===B-
             /  H+  \
            H        H
```

The main objection to these formulae would appear to be the full negative charge existing on each boron atom.

B_5H_9— The proposed structures are :

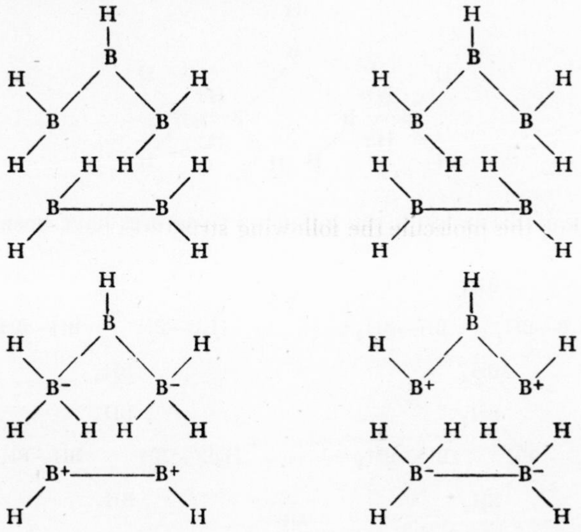

```
          H                           H
          |                           |
          B                           B
 H      /   \      H         H      /   \      H
  \   /       \   /           \   /       \   /
    B           B               B           B
  /           /                   \           \
 H      H   H      H         H      H   H      H
      /          /             \          \
    B-----------B                B-----------B
  /              \                            \
 H                H          H                H

          H                           H
          |                           |
          B                           B
 H      /   \      H         H      /   \      H
  \   /       \   /           \   /       \   /
    B-          B-              B+          B+
  /   \       /   \
 H      H   H      H         H      H   H      H
                               \  /       \  /
    B+----------B+               B-----------B-
  /              \             /              \
 H                H          H                H
```

and

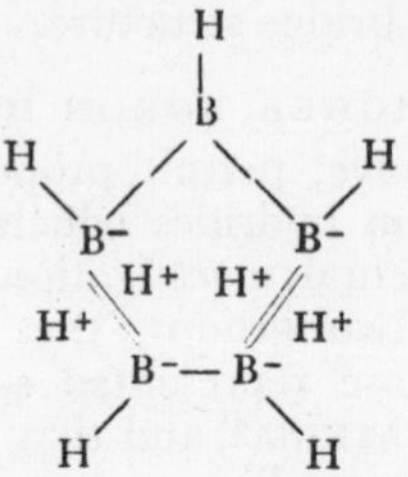

```
                H
                |
                B
         H    /   \    H
          \  /     \  /
           B-       B-
          \ H+  H+ //
       H+  \       //  H+
            B- — B-
           /       \
          H         H
```

B_5H_{11} — In this compound the structure may be represented as a resonance hybrid of the following forms :

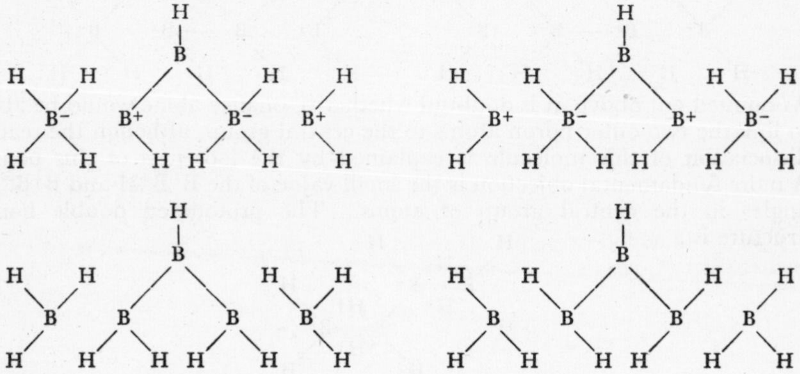

```
                  H                                              H
                  |                                              |
                  B                                              B
 H     H        /   \        H     H          H     H          /   \          H     H
  \   /        /     \        \   /            \   /          /     \          \   /
   B-     B+              B-     B+             B+      B-              B+       B-
  /   \  /  \            /  \   /  \           /  \    /  \            /  \     /  \
 H     H   H  H         H    H     H           H    H  H   H          H   H    H    H

                  H                                              H
                  |                                              |
                  B                                              B
 H     H        /   \        H     H          H     H          /   \          H     H
  \   /        /     \        \   /            \   /          /     \          \   /
   B       B              B       B             B       B              B        B
  /   \   /  \          /  \    /  \           /  \    /  \            /  \     /  \
 H     H    H  H        H    H     H           H    H  H   H          H   H    H    H
```

or by the protonated double bond structure :

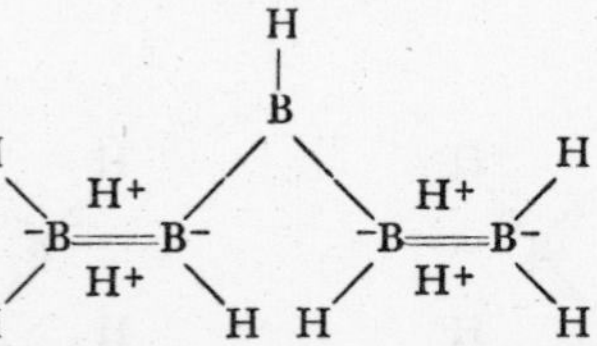

```
                  H
                  |
                  B
      H         /   \          H
       \  H+   /     \   H+   /
       -B=====B-      -B=====B-
       /  H+   \     /   H+   \
      H          H  H          H
```

B_6H_{10} — For this molecule the following structures have been proposed :

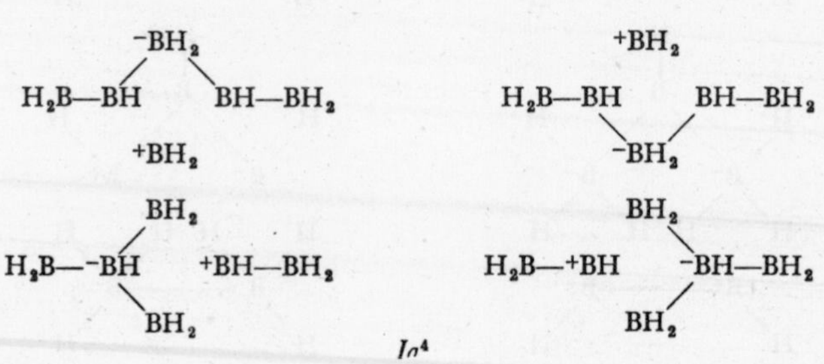

```
            -BH2                                   +BH2
           /    \
   H2B—BH        BH—BH2                  H2B—BH          BH—BH2
                                                \       /
            +BH2                                  -BH2

            BH2                                    BH2
           /                                          \
   H2B—-BH       +BH—BH2                  H2B—+BH      -BH—BH2
           \                                          /
            BH2                                    BH2
```

In[4]

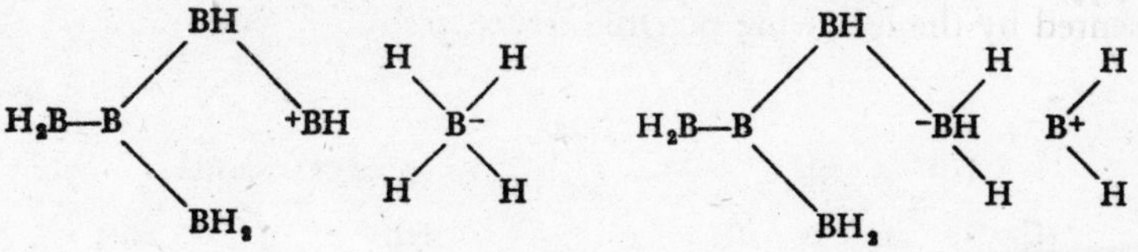

BH BH H H H H H_2B—B +BH B⁻ H_2B—B ⁻BH B+ H H H H BH_2 BH_2

Ib[4]

H H H B⁻ H+ ‖ H+ B H H B⁻ H H B B⁻ B⁻ H+ H+ ‖ H+ H+ ‖ H+ ⁻B═B⁻ B⁻ B⁻ H+ H H H H B

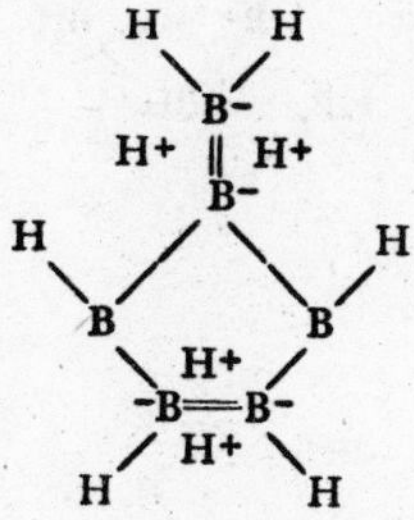

II[7] 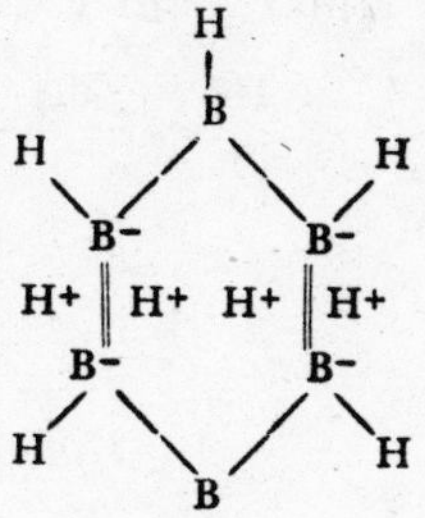 *III*[7]

B_6H_{12}— The following structures have been proposed for this compound : a chain structure,

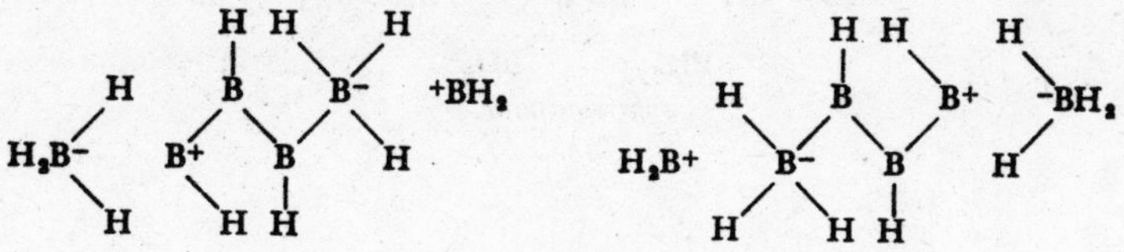

H H H H H H H B B⁻ +BH_2 H B B+ ⁻BH_2 H_2B⁻ B+ B H H_2B+ B⁻ B H H H H H H H

I[4]

and the cyclic structure,

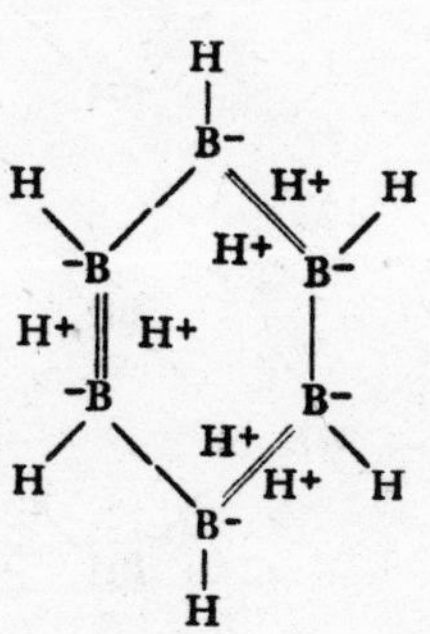

H B⁻ H H+ H ⁻B H+ B⁻ H+ ‖ H+ ⁻B B⁻ H+ H H+ H B⁻ H

II[7]

$B_{10}H_{14}$ — According to SYRKIN and DYATKINA[4] this molecule may be represented by the following possible structures :

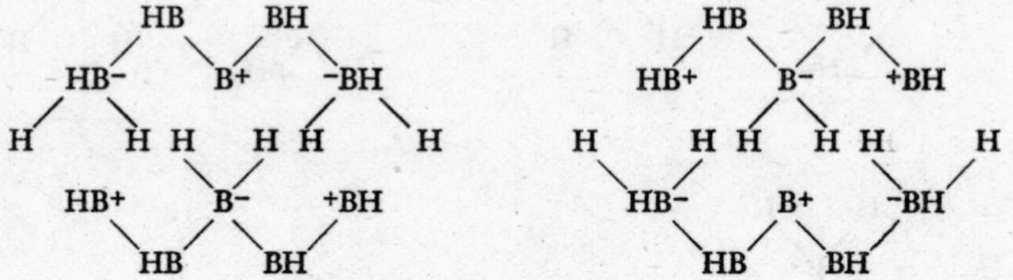

```
      HB      BH                          HB      BH
    /    \  /    \                       /   \   /   \
 HB-      B+      -BH              HB+       B-      +BH
 /   \           /   \                      /  \
H     H H    H H      H          H      H H    H H       H
        \   /                      \   /          \     /
 HB+      B-      +BH               HB-       B+      -BH
    \   /    \  /                      \    /    \  /
      HB      BH                         HB      BH
                          Ia
```

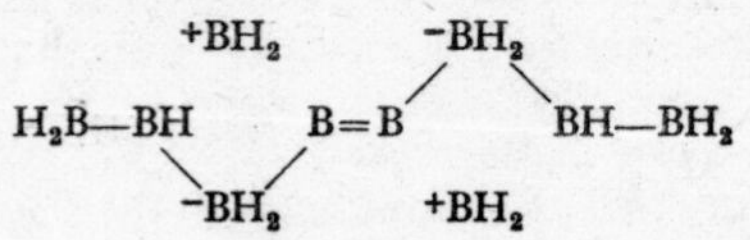

```
          +BH2          -BH2
                       /     \
 H2B—BH          B=B          BH—BH2
         \      /
          -BH2          +BH2
              four structures
```

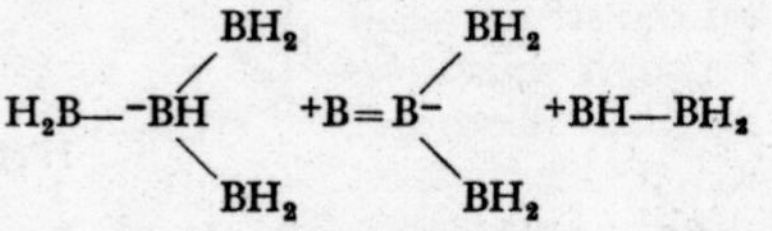

```
          BH2           BH2
         /             /
 H2B—-BH        +B=B-         +BH—BH2
         \             \
          BH2           BH2
              four structures
                    Ib
```

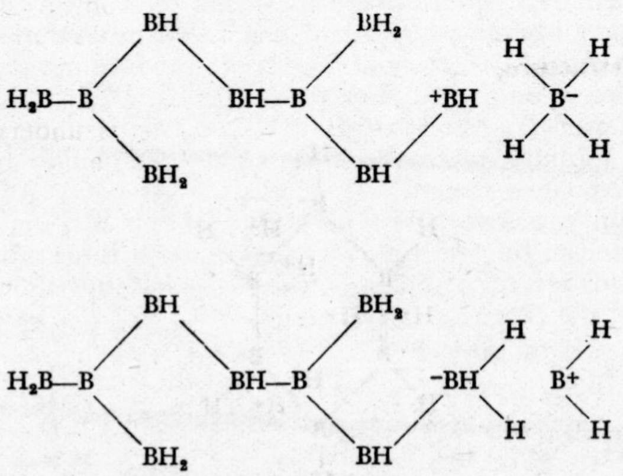

```
        BH                BH2
      /    \             /             H     H
 H2B—B       BH—B                +BH     \ /
      \           \      /                B-
        BH2          BH                  / \
                                        H   H

        BH                BH2
      /    \             /            H      H
 H2B—B       BH—B               -BH         /
      \           \      /          \      B+
        BH2          BH              H      \
                                             H
                    Ic
```

NEKRASSOV[3] has suggested a naphthalene-like structure for this molecule which has been modified on the basis of the idea of the protonated double bond to give the formula[7] :

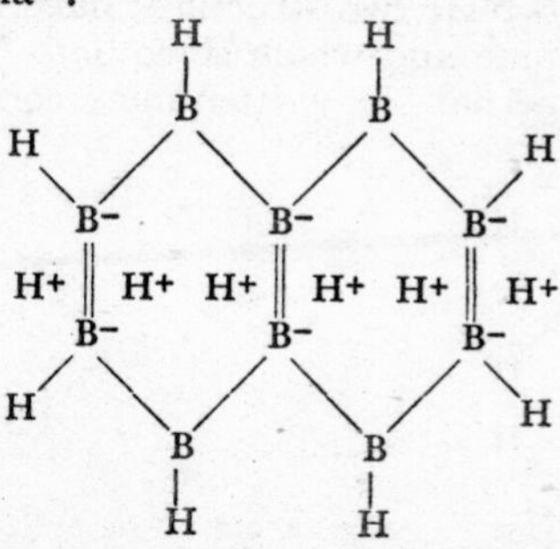

An investigation of the structure of decaborane has been recently carried out by KASPER, LUCHT and HARKER[21] by single crystal x-ray diffraction methods and the results would appear to indicate that none of the above formulae are correct, since the location of the boron atoms is as follows : No suggestion has yet been made, however, as to the nature of the bonds linking the atoms in this structure.

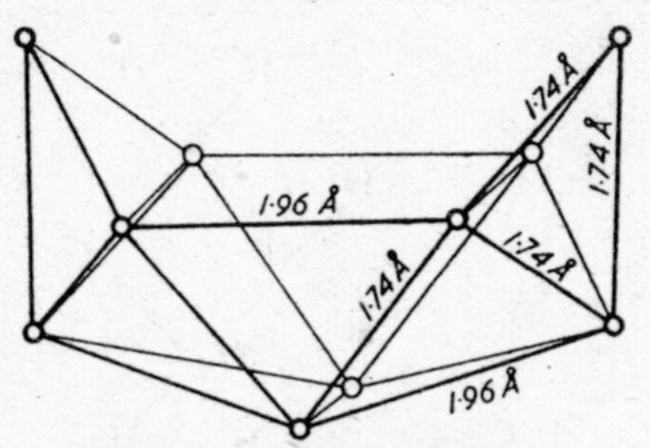

Figure 74. Structure of decaborane

It will be clear from a consideration of the structures given above that it is no longer necessary to assume a single electron bond to explain the structure of the boron hydrides. The main objections to the two groups of possible structures given are that in the forms proposed by Syrkin and Dyatkina the resonance energy of the molecule is regarded as sufficient to bond the separate parts of the molecule together and although calculation appears to show[4] that the energy thus obtained is sufficient to produce a stable molecule, the method has been criticized[5] on the grounds that the assumptions made in the calculation are not valid. The objection to the Pitzer formulae are that all boron atoms taking part in the protonated double bond bear a negative charge which would appear to produce instability.

The properties of the hydrides show that B_5H_9, B_6H_{10} and $B_{10}H_{14}$ are more stable than B_4H_{10}, B_5H_{11} and B_6H_{12}. This is understandable on both proposed formulae since the more stable compounds are shown to possess more resonance structures and more B—B bonds, or a cyclic in place of a chain structure. The instability of the B_6H_{12} ring structure may be attributed to the fact that each boron atom is negatively charged.

Diborane forms several compounds in which decomposition to BH_3 has occurred during the course of the reaction, *e.g.*

$$B_2H_6 + 2CO = 2[H_3B^{-}—C{\equiv}O^{+}]$$
$$B_2H_6 + 2N(CH_3)_3 = 2[H_3B^{-}—N^{+}(CH_3)_3]$$

The product of the reaction of diborane with ammonia is generally written in the form $B_2H_4\,(NH_4)_2$ in which it would appear that the ion $(B_2H_4)^{2-}$ occurs, but since B_2H_6 does not show acidic properties, it would be more correct to give the structure as

$$[^{-}BH_3—^{+}NH_2—^{-}BH_3] \quad ^{+}NH_4$$

which is in agreement with the behaviour of this compound in liquid ammonia[20] and further evidence for this structure is shown by the existence of a B—N—B system in $B_3N_3H_6$ and B_2NH_7[22].

For the structure of B_2NH_7 two structures have been proposed: *I* which is similar to dimethylamine and which since both N—B bonds are donor-acceptor bonds, should perhaps be written more correctly as *Ia*

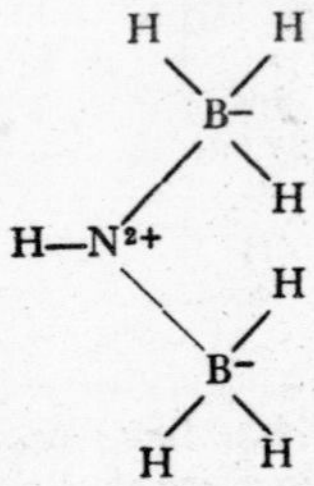

I 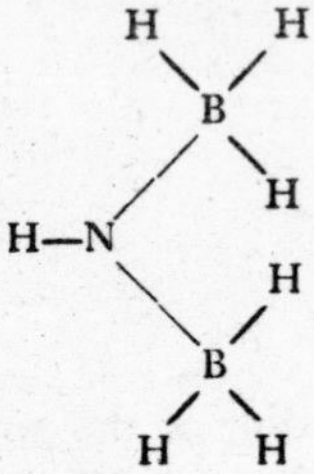 *Ia*

II which involves resonance between the structures

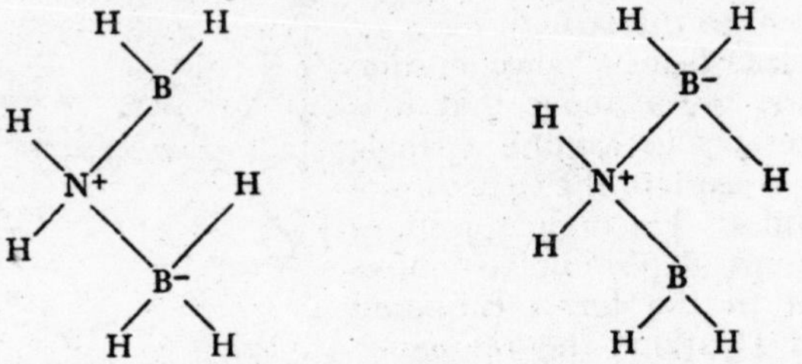

II

The electron diffraction data do not permit a choice to be made between the two formulae, but the chemical evidence indicates that the second formula is probably correct.

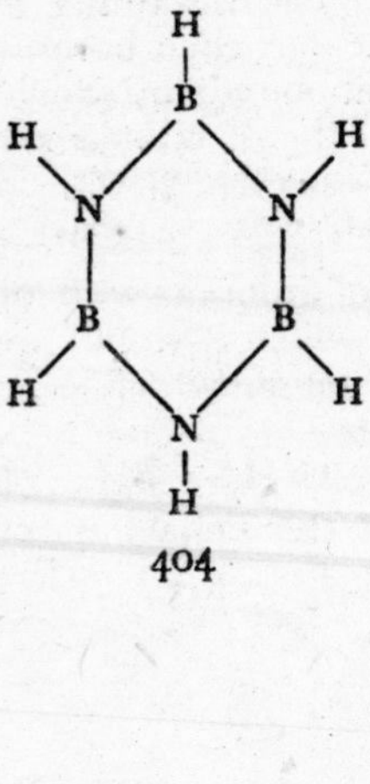

The structure of triborane triamine (borazole), $B_3N_3H_6$ appears to be analogous with benzene[23]. The analogy, however, is not complete since in triborane triamine the greatest contribution to the molecular resonance will be given by the single bond structure

and the double bonded configurations

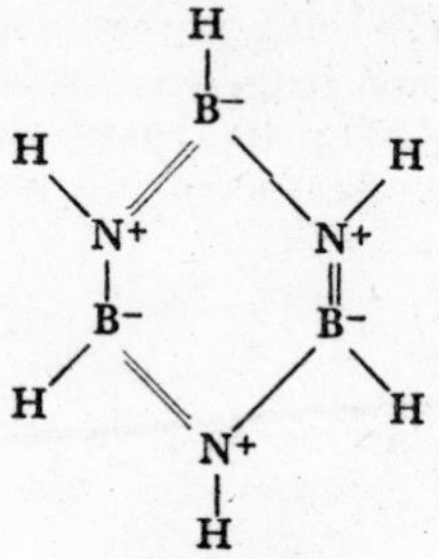

```
            H                                   H
            |                                   |
            B−                                  B−
    H     //  \      H                  H     /  |  \      H
     \   //    \    /                    \   /   |   \    /
      N+        N+                        N      |      N
      |         ||                        |      |      |
      B−        B−                        B      |      B
     /   \\    /  \                      /   \   |   /   \
    H     \\  /    H                    H     \  |  /     H
            N+                                 +N
            |                                   |
            H                                   H
```

two structures 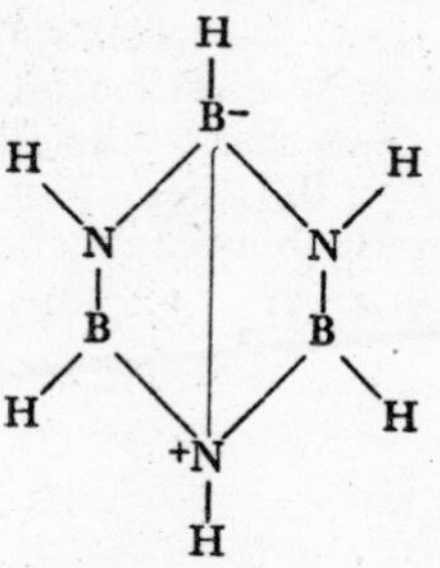 *three structures*

will play a lesser rôle, owing to the fact that the charge distribution so introduced is contrary to the relative electronegativities of the boron and nitrogen atoms. As a consequence the B—N distance is only 0·06 Å shorter than in a single bond.

The product of the addition of four molecules of ammonia to B_4H_{10} is generally written $(B_4H_6)(NH_4)_4$, but such a formula, suggesting the existence of a $(B_4H_6)^{4-}$ ion, is unlikely in view of the instability of B_4H_{10} and the lack of acid properties of B_2H_6. The structure is more probably represented by

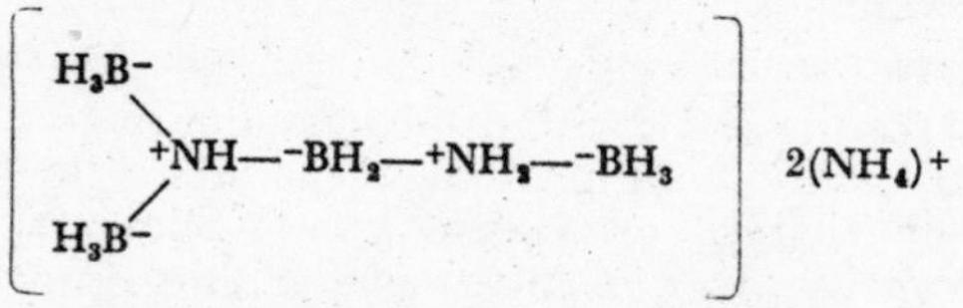

```
⎡ H3B−                          ⎤
⎢     \                         ⎥
⎢      +NH—−BH2—+NH2—−BH3       ⎥   2(NH4)+
⎢     /                         ⎥
⎣ H3B−                          ⎦
```

One of the most important reactions of diborane is its interaction with amalgams of highly active metals, *e.g.* sodium and potassium, to give compounds such as $K_2B_2H_6$, which are sometimes referred to as salts of diborane. These compounds are non-volatile, insoluble in liquid ammonia and common organic solvents and react with water. Consequently their formulae have been determined from magnetic measurements and not from molecular weight determinations. The addition of two electrons to the electronically unsaturated diborane,

$$B_2H_6 + 2e \rightarrow (B_2H_6)^{2-}$$

leads to the formation of an ion analogous to ethane and therefore expected to be stable; in fact the diborane salts are more stable than diborane[20]. It would appear therefore that the structure of these salts is represented by the formula

$$2K^+ [H_3B^- — {}^-BH_3]$$

In connection with the marked increase of stability of these compounds it is interesting to notice that whereas B_4H_8 does not exist, the corresponding salt $K_2B_4H_8$ is known; evidently it possesses the structure

$$[H_3B^- — BH — BH — {}^-BH_3] \quad 2K^+$$

Schlesinger and Burg[20] describe many metallo borohydrides which are metal-boron-hydrogen compounds containing unusually large amounts of hydrogen, prepared by the action of diborane on the metal alkyl compounds.

Lithium borohydride is a salt-like substance to which the formula $^{+}Li^{-}BH_4$ may be ascribed. The structure $Li—^{-}BH_3H^{+}$ is less probable and evidently for this reason lithium borohydride does not react with trimethylamine. On the other hand $Be(BH_4)_2$ is unlikely to have the structure $^{-}BH_4$ Be^{2+} $^{-}BH_4$ since it is volatile and possesses few salt like properties. The structure is therefore formulated as

$$H^{+}\ \ ^{-}BH_3—Be—^{-}BH_3\ \ H^{+} \qquad H^{+}\ \ ^{-}BH_3—Be^{+}\ \ ^{-}BH_4$$

sixteen structures *eight structures* .

Beryllium borohydride reacts with triethylamine to give the compound $Be(BH_4)_2N(CH_3)_3$. The structure of this compound is not fully understood, but may be represented by

$$^{-}BH_4\ \ ^{+}Be—^{-}BH_2\ \ ^{+}NH(CH_3)_3$$

or

$$H^{+}\ \ ^{-}BH_3—Be—^{-}BH_3\ \ ^{+}NH(CH_3)_3$$

Aluminium borohydride AlB_3H_{12} possesses no salt like properties and its structure may be represented by

```
H+ H3B-                              H+ H3B-
       \                                    \
        Al—-BH3  H+        and               Al+  -BH4
       /                                    /
H+ H3B-                              H+ H3B-
```

sixty four structures *forty eight structures*

This compound readily reacts with trimethylamine to give $AlB_2H_9N(CH_3)_3$.

An important feature of all the above structures is the presence of boron in the negatively charged tetravalent state. Similarity with the boron hydrides is shown by other members of the third group of the periodic table. Thus gallium forms a hydride[24] having the formula Ga_2H_6 and the structures of Al_2Cl_6, Al_2Br_6, Al_2I_6, $Al_2(CH_3)_4Cl_2$, $Al_2(CH_3)_4Br_2$ have a similar configuration[25] to that occurring in B_2H_6. The structure of $Al_2(CH_3)_6$ is not completely understood, the electron diffraction data indicating an ethane structure and the Raman spectra[26] an ethylene type of structure.

REFERENCES

1 Bell, R. P. and Emeleus, H. J. *Quart. Rev.* 2 (1948) 132
2 Dilthey, W. *Z. angew. Chem.* 34 (1921) 596
3 Nekrassov, B. V. *J. gen. Chem. Moscow* 10 (1940) 1021, 1156
4 Syrkin, J. K. and Dyatkina, M. E. *Acta Physicochem. U.R.S.S.* 14 (1941) 547
— *J. phys. Chem. U.R.S.S.* 15 (1941) 459
5 Longuet-Higgins, H. C. and Bell, R. P. *J. chem. Soc.* (1943) 250
6 Seel, F. *Z. Naturforsch.* 1 (1941) 146
7 Pitzer, K. S. *J. Amer. chem. Soc.* 67 (1945) 1126
8 Walsh, A. D. *J. chem. Soc.* (1947) 89
9 Mullikan, R. S. *Chem. Rev.* 41 (1947) 207
10 Mark, H. and Pohland, E. *Z. Krystallogr.* 62 (1925) 103
11 Bauer, S. H. *J. Amer. chem. Soc.* 59 (1937) 1096
12 — *Chem. Rev.* 35 (1942) 180
13 Dyatkina, M. E. and Syrkin, J. K. *J. phys. Chem. U.R.S.S.* 17 (1943) 20
— *C. R. Acad. Sci. U.R.S.S.* 35 (1942) 180
14 Stitt, F. *J. chem. Phys.* 8 (1940) 981
15 Bell, R. P. and Longuet-Higgins, H. C. *Proc. roy. Soc. A* 183 (1945) 357

[16] ANDERSON, T. F. and BURG, A. B. *J. chem. Phys.* 6 (1938) 586
[17] STITT, F. *ibid* 9 (1941) 780
[18] PRICE, W. C. *ibid* 15 (1947) 614
[19] WAGNER, J. *Z. phys. Chem.* *B* 53 (1943) 85
[20] SCHLESINGER, A. I. and BURG, A. B. *Chem. Rev.* 31 (1942) 1
[21] KASPER, J. S., LUCHT, C. M. and HARKER, D. *J. Amer. chem. Soc.* 70 (1948) 881
[22] BAUER, S. H. *ibid.* 60 (1938) 524
[23] — *Chem. Rev.* 31 (1942) 43
[24] WIBERG, E. and JOHANSEN, T. *Z. angew Chem.* 55 (1942) 38
— and STECHER, O. *ibid* 52 (1939) 372
— — *Ber.* 75 (1942) 2003
[25] PALMER, K. J. and ELLIOTT, N. *J. Amer. chem. Soc.* 60 (1938) 1852
BROCKWAY, L. O. and DAVIDSON, N. R. *ibid* 63 (1941) 3287
[26] KOHLRAUSCH, K. W. F. and WAGNER, J. *Z. phys. Chem.* *B* 52 (1942) 185
GERDING, H. and SMIT, E. *ibid* 50 (1941) 171 ; 51 (1942) 217

16

THE SOLUTION OF THE THREE ELECTRON PROBLEM USING SLATER'S METHOD

THE REACTION OF ATOMS WITH MOLECULES

IN THE HYDROGEN molecule, the valencies of both atoms are fully saturated and it is not possible to form a third bond to give the molecule H_3, since such a molecule is thermodynamically unstable by comparison with the system $H_2 + H$. The molecule of hydrogen may therefore only enter into reactions of the substitution type,

$$ab + c = a + bc$$

for which the reaction between a hydrogen molecule and deuterium may serve as an example :

$$\text{H—H} + \text{D} = \text{H} + \text{H—D}$$

When the atom c is a considerable distance from the molecule ab, the distribution of the electrons may be considered to be,

$$\underset{1}{a\uparrow}\ \underset{2}{\downarrow b} \qquad\qquad \underset{3}{\uparrow c}$$

I

The electrons 1 and 2 are transferred (exchanged) between the atoms a and b thereby forming the covalent bond in the molecule ab ; electron 3 at this distance takes little part in the exchange phenomenon. As atom c approaches ab, owing to the non-localization of the electrons the possibility of an electron transfer between the molecule ab and the atom c increases. Let us consider first the possibilities of transfer when the bond between a and b is maintained ; this can only occur when electrons 1 and 3 are exchanged since the transfer of electrons 2 and 3 is prohibited by Pauli's principle. The bond in the molecule ab is now formed by electrons 2 and 3, electron 1 having been transferred to the atom c. Such a transfer of electrons with parallel spins leads to an increase in the potential energy of the system (see Chapter 3) and the approaching atom is therefore repelled. Thus, in order that an atom may approach a molecule, its translational energy must be such as to overcome this energy of repulsion.

However, owing to the delocalization of the electron, the electron 2 may transfer from its original position to a position between the nuclei b and c, *i.e.* it transfers from an ab molecular orbital to a bc molecular orbital and the system now consists of an atom a and a molecule bc, *i.e.*

$$\underset{1}{a\uparrow} \qquad b \qquad \underset{2}{\downarrow}\ \underset{3}{\uparrow c}$$

II

Since the distance between the atoms b and c is greater than that between a and b, the new bond is considerably weaker than the original. Nevertheless the state *II* is superimposed on the state *I* if the atom c approaches sufficiently near to ab. Owing to the fact that electron 2 is now not always taking part in the formation of the bond between a and b, but also participates in the bond between b and c, the bond a—b is weakened. Thus an approach of the atom *c* to the molecule *ab* produces a stretching of the bond *a*—*b*.

The repulsion of *c* from *ab* (owing to the transfer of electrons 1 and 3) increases as *c* approaches *ab*. Simultaneously the state *a*—*bc* becomes more probable and resonance between the states *a*—*bc* and *ab*—*c* somewhat decreases the energy of repulsion. Thus, although it is necessary to expend energy as translational energy in order to bring atom *c* up to the molecule *ab*, there may ultimately be attained a state[1] in which *b* is equally joined to both *a* and *c*. This active complex or transitional state may be represented as

$$a\cdots\cdots b\cdots\cdots c$$

It does not represent a stable state and corresponds to the atomic configuration at the highest point of the potential energy curve. The energy expended in bringing the system from the state *I* to this configuration represents the energy of activation for the substitution reaction.

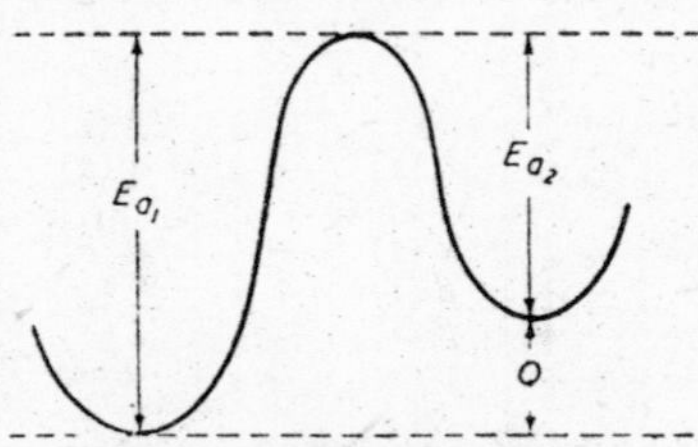

Figure 75. Energy of activation for forward and reverse reactions

The energy changes during the reaction are represented in *Figure 75*. As explained above the energy at first increases, passes through a maximum and then falls to the energy of the final state. E_{a_1} represents the magnitude of the activation energy of the forward reaction

$$ab + c \rightarrow a + bc$$

and E_{a_2} represents the activation energy of the reverse reaction

$$a + bc \rightarrow ab + c$$

The difference $E_{a_2} - E_{a_1} = \Delta H$, is the change in the heat content for the reaction.

SLATER'S METHOD

We shall now consider the system of three atoms quantitatively using the method described by SLATER[2]. We shall refer to the three atoms by the letters *a*, *b* and *c*. At great interatomic distances the electron of each atom is found only in the field of its own nucleus. We shall call the electron of atom *a*, 1; of atom *b*, 2; and of atom *c*, 3. The state of the first electron is described by the wave function $\psi_a(1)$, of the second by $\psi_b(2)$ and of the third by $\psi_c(3)$. If we now assume that the movement of the electrons in the atomic orbitals is not affected by the presence of the other atoms (see Chapter 3), we have

$$\psi_1 = \psi_a(1)\psi_b(2)\psi_c(3) \qquad \ldots.(16.1)$$

In order to simplify the symbols, we shall represent ψ_a by *a*, ψ_b by *b* and ψ_c by *c* and we shall always place the function describing the first electron first, followed by the function for the second and third electrons. Thus the expression $\psi_1 = abc$ indicates that the electron 1 is located at *a*, electron 2 at *b*, and electron 3 at *c*, *i.e.*

$$\psi_1 = abc = \psi_a(1)\psi_b(2)\psi_c(3)$$

Similarly the function $\psi_2 = bca$ indicates that the electron 1 is at b, electron 2 at c and electron 3 at a, *i.e.*

$$\psi_2 = bca = \psi_b(1)\psi_c(2)\psi_a(3)$$

For the complete description of an electronic state it is also necessary to indicate the direction of spin. Each electron may have a positive or negative projection of the spin angular momentum, s, and therefore in a system of three electrons, $2^3 = 8$ different combinations are possible. These eight states are given in *Table CLXXI* where the values of s for each electron are given, together with the value of Σs, being the total value for all the electrons.

Table CLXXI. Spin States for a Three Electron System

	First electron		Second electron		Third electron		
	s	spin function	s	spin function	s	spin function	Σs
1	$+\frac{1}{2}$	$\alpha(1)$	$+\frac{1}{2}$	$\alpha(2)$	$+\frac{1}{2}$	$\alpha(3)$	$+\frac{3}{2}$
2	$+\frac{1}{2}$	$\alpha(1)$	$+\frac{1}{2}$	$\alpha(2)$	$-\frac{1}{2}$	$\beta(3)$	$+\frac{1}{2}$
3	$+\frac{1}{2}$	$\alpha(1)$	$-\frac{1}{2}$	$\beta(2)$	$+\frac{1}{2}$	$\alpha(3)$	$+\frac{1}{2}$
4	$-\frac{1}{2}$	$\beta(1)$	$+\frac{1}{2}$	$\alpha(2)$	$+\frac{1}{2}$	$\alpha(3)$	$+\frac{1}{2}$
5	$+\frac{1}{2}$	$\alpha(1)$	$-\frac{1}{2}$	$\beta(2)$	$-\frac{1}{2}$	$\beta(3)$	$-\frac{1}{2}$
6	$-\frac{1}{2}$	$\beta(1)$	$+\frac{1}{2}$	$\alpha(2)$	$-\frac{1}{2}$	$\beta(3)$	$-\frac{1}{2}$
7	$-\frac{1}{2}$	$\beta(1)$	$-\frac{1}{2}$	$\beta(2)$	$+\frac{1}{2}$	$\alpha(3)$	$-\frac{1}{2}$
8	$-\frac{1}{2}$	$\beta(1)$	$-\frac{1}{2}$	$\beta(2)$	$-\frac{1}{2}$	$\beta(3)$	$-\frac{3}{2}$

There thus exist eight states of a system of three electrons for a given arrangement of the nuclei in space. The first state corresponds to the function :

$$\alpha(1)\alpha(2)\alpha(3)$$

and the total wave function of the system is

$$\phi_1 = \psi_a(1)\alpha(1)\psi_b(2)\alpha(2)\psi_c(3)\alpha(3) \quad \ldots.(16.2)$$

or using the simplified nomenclature

$$\phi_1 = a\alpha b\alpha c\alpha \quad \ldots.(16.3)$$

The first term $a\alpha$, *i.e.* $\psi_a(1)\alpha(1)$, represents the complete wave function of the first electron which is a product of its space function $\psi_a(1)$ and its spin function $\alpha(1)$. Similarly $b\alpha$ and $c\alpha$ are the complete wave functions of the second and third electrons. Thus the eight states are characterized by the following functions :

$$\begin{aligned} \phi_1 &= a\alpha b\alpha c\alpha & \phi_5 &= a\alpha b\beta c\beta \\ \phi_2 &= a\alpha b\alpha c\beta & \phi_6 &= a\beta b\alpha c\beta \\ \phi_3 &= a\alpha b\beta c\alpha & \phi_7 &= a\beta b\beta c\alpha \\ \phi_4 &= a\beta b\alpha c\alpha & \phi_8 &= a\beta b\beta c\beta \end{aligned} \quad \ldots.(16.3)$$

As the atoms approach each other, the electrons may exchange places and the number of possible variations of the three electrons between the three nuclei is $3! = 6$. These are given in *Table CLXXII*. The total number of wave functions describing the possible states of the system consequently is equal to $6 \times 8 = 48$. In order to satisfy Pauli's principle it is necessary to obtain the antisymmetric linear combinations of these functions (see Chapter 3). Let us consider, for example, the function :

$$\phi_3 = a\alpha b\beta c\alpha$$

and obtain the appropriate antisymmetric combination. For this purpose we need not consider the linear combination of all the forty-eight functions, but only of the six which are obtained from ϕ_3 on rearrangement of the electrons. We shall denote the rearrangement by P_{ik}, where the subscript indicates the electrons that have been exchanged. Thus $P\phi_3$ indicates that in the function ϕ_3, a rearrangement of the electrons has occurred. In the first case we have the rearrangement which is identical with the original so that no change is noticeable; this we shall denote by P_E so that

Table CLXXII. Arrangement of Three Electrons Between Three Nuclei

Function	First electron on nucleus	Second electron on nucleus	Third electron on nucleus
$\psi_1 = abc$	a	b	c
$\psi_2 = acb$	a	c	b
$\psi_3 = bac$	b	a	c
$\psi_4 = cba$	c	b	a
$\psi_5 = bca$	b	c	a
$\psi_6 = cab$	c	a	b

$$P_E\phi_3 = \phi_3 = a\alpha b\beta c\alpha \qquad \text{....(61.4)}$$

The exchange of electrons 1 and 2 gives,

$$P_{12}\phi_3 = P_{12}a\alpha b\beta c\alpha = b\beta a\alpha c\alpha \qquad \text{....(16.5)}$$

The exchange of electrons 1 and 3 gives,

$$P_{13}\phi_3 = P_{13}a\alpha b\beta c\alpha = c\alpha b\beta a\alpha \qquad \text{....(16.6)}$$

The exchange of electrons 2 and 3 gives,

$$P_{23}\phi_3 = P_{23}a\alpha b\beta c\alpha = a\alpha c\alpha b\beta \qquad \text{....(16.7)}$$

The exchange of electron 1 with 2 and 2 with 3 gives,

$$P_{123}\phi_3 = P_{123}a\alpha b\beta c\alpha = b\beta c\alpha a\alpha \qquad \text{....(16.8)}$$

and finally the rearrangement of electron 1 with 3 and 3 with 2 gives,

$$P_{132}\phi_3 = P_{132}a\alpha b\beta c\alpha = c\alpha a\alpha b\beta \qquad \text{....(16.9)}$$

The six rearrangements of the three electrons may be divided into two classes according to the number of pairs of electrons that have been exchanged. Thus on the exchange of one pair of electrons, the rearrangements are P_{12}, P_{13} and P_{23} and are termed odd. The remaining rearrangements P_E, P_{123} and P_{132} are even, since the number of pairs of electrons exchanged is zero or two. In order that the linear combination of the functions be antisymmetric, it is necessary to take the functions corresponding to even rearrangements with a positive sign and those with an odd rearrangement with a negative sign. The following wave function is then obtained:

$$\Phi_3 = a\alpha b\beta c\alpha + b\beta c\alpha a\alpha + c\alpha a\alpha b\beta - b\beta a\alpha c\alpha - c\alpha b\beta a\alpha - a\alpha c\alpha b\beta \qquad \text{....(16.10)}$$

This expression may be written as

$$\Phi_3 = \sum_P (-1)^P P a\alpha b\beta c\alpha \qquad \text{....(16.11)}$$

where $Pa\alpha b\beta c\alpha$ gives the particular rearrangement of electrons between $a\alpha$, $b\beta$ and $c\alpha$ and the term $(-1)^P$ gives the sign of the function during a given rearrangement. If the rearrangement is even, then P is even, and $(-1)^P = +1$, and when P is odd, $(-1)^P = -1$.

The function 16.10 is antisymmetric, as shown by exchanging electrons 1 and 2 when we obtain,

$$\Phi_3' = b\beta a\alpha c\alpha + c\alpha b\beta a\alpha + a\alpha c\alpha b\beta - a\alpha b\beta c\alpha - b\beta c\alpha a\alpha - c\alpha a\alpha b\beta \qquad \text{....(16.12)}$$

which is identical with 16.10 apart from the reversal of the sign throughout. Rearrangement of electrons 1 and 3 or 2 and 3 leads to the same result.

We have so far considered only the formation of the antisymmetric function Φ_3 from the function ϕ_3, but there will be in all eight such functions, corresponding to the eight possible spin combinations (*Table CLXXI*). These are :

one with $\Sigma s = + 3/2$

$$\Phi_1 = \sum_P (-1)^p P a\alpha b\alpha c\alpha$$

three with $\Sigma s = + 1/2$

$$\Phi_2 = \sum_P (-1)^p P a\alpha b\alpha c\beta$$

$$\Phi_3 = \sum_P (-1)^p P a\alpha b\beta c\alpha$$

$$\Phi_4 = \sum_P (-1)^p P a\beta b\alpha c\alpha$$

three with $\Sigma s = - 1/2$ ....(16.13)

$$\Phi_5 = \sum_P (-1)^p P a\alpha b\beta c\beta$$

$$\Phi_6 = \sum_P (-1)^p P a\beta b\alpha c\beta$$

$$\Phi_7 = \sum_P (-1)^p P a\beta b\beta c\alpha$$

and one with $\Sigma s = - 3/2$

$$\Phi_8 = \sum_P (-1)^p P a\beta b\beta c\beta$$

In order to obtain the possible energy levels of the system of three atoms, it is necessary to take the linear combination of the eight functions in equation 16.13 with arbitrary coefficients and determine the values of the coefficients when the energy has a maximum value. The procedure is analogous to that given previously for two atoms of hydrogen, but in place of two similar equations for c_1 and c_2, we obtain an expression with eight unknown coefficients. The secular equation will consist of eight rows and columns. The roots of this equation, eight in number, will give the possible values of the energy of the system. The equation is of the following form,

$$\begin{vmatrix} \mathcal{H}_{11}-E & \mathcal{H}_{12}-ES_{12} & \mathcal{H}_{13}-ES_{13} \cdots\cdots \mathcal{H}_{18}-ES_{18} \\ \mathcal{H}_{12}-ES_{12} & \mathcal{H}_{22}-E & \mathcal{H}_{23}-ES_{23} \cdots\cdots \mathcal{H}_{28}-ES_{28} \\ \mathcal{H}_{13}-ES_{13} & \mathcal{H}_{23}-ES_{23} & \mathcal{H}_{33}-E \quad \cdots\cdots \mathcal{H}_{38}-ES_{38} \\ \cdots & \cdots & \cdots \\ \mathcal{H}_{18}-ES_{18} & \mathcal{H}_{28}-ES_{28} & \mathcal{H}_{38}-ES_{38} \cdots\cdots \mathcal{H}_{88}-E \end{vmatrix} = 0 \qquad \text{....(16.14)}$$

where E is the energy of the system, $\mathcal{H}$ is the Hamiltonian operator and

$$\mathcal{H}_{11} = \int \Phi_1 \mathcal{H} \Phi_1 d\tau \qquad \mathcal{H}_{12} = \int \Phi_1 \mathcal{H} \Phi_2 d\tau \qquad S_{12} = \int \Phi_1 \Phi_2 d\tau \quad etc$$

Let us now consider the evaluation of the integrals entering into this equation. The functions of equation 16.13 must be normalized *i.e.* it is necessary to determine the coefficient of Φ_i such that $\int \Phi_i^2 d\tau = 1$. However, we shall carry out the evaluation of the integrals $\int \Phi_i^2 d\tau$ first without the normalization coefficients; let us consider the particular case of $\int \Phi_2^2 d\tau$. The function Φ_2 is given by:

$$\Phi_2 = \sum_P (-1)^p P a\alpha b\alpha c\beta$$
$$= a\alpha b\alpha c\beta + b\alpha c\beta a\alpha + c\beta a\alpha b\alpha - b\alpha a\alpha c\beta - c\beta b\alpha a\alpha - a\alpha c\beta b\alpha \qquad \ldots.(16.15)$$

The square of this expression will contain twenty-one terms, six being squares of the individual terms in equation 16.15, *i.e.* of the form $(a\alpha b\alpha c\beta)^2$ and fifteen being products of the form $2(a\alpha b\alpha c\beta)(b\alpha c\beta a\alpha)$. It is therefore necessary to evaluate the six integrals of the general form,

$$\int (a\alpha b\alpha c\beta)\,(a\alpha b\alpha c\beta) d\tau \qquad \ldots.(16.16)$$

and the fifteen integrals of the general form,

$$2\int (a\alpha b\alpha c\beta)\,(b\alpha c\beta a\alpha) d\tau \qquad \ldots.(16.17)$$

The independence of the spatial and spin functions from each other permits us to carry out two separate integrations, one involving space coordinates and the other the coordinates of spin. Thus

$$\int (a\alpha b\alpha c\beta)\,(a\alpha b\alpha c\beta) d\tau \qquad \ldots.(16.18)$$

becomes

$$\int (abc)\,(abc) dx_1 dy_1 dz_1 dx_2 dy_2 dz_2 dx_3 dy_3 dz_3 \int (\alpha\alpha\beta)\,(\alpha\alpha\beta) d\omega_1 d\omega_2 d\omega_3 \qquad \ldots.(16.19)$$

In this expression the coordinates of space and spin are independent of the electron and the integration may therefore be derived separately for each electron. Thus equation 16.19 becomes:

$$\int a^2(1) d\tau_1 \int b^2(2) d\tau_2 \int c^2(3) d\tau_3 \int \alpha^2(1) d\omega_1 \int \alpha^2(2) d\omega_2 \int \beta^2(3) d\omega_3 \qquad \ldots.(16.20)$$

where $d\tau_1$ is the element of volume in space equal to $dx_1 dy_1 dz_1$ of the first electron and $d\omega_1$ is the spin coordinate for the first electron; $d\tau_2$ and $d\omega_2$ are the respective elements for the second electron and $d\tau_3$ and $d\omega_3$ those for the third electron.

Since only two values of the spin quantum number are possible, the integration may be replaced by a summation of the two possible values, *viz* $+\frac{1}{2}$ and $-\frac{1}{2}$, hence we have:

$$\int \alpha^2 d\omega = \alpha^2(+\tfrac{1}{2}) + \alpha^2(-\tfrac{1}{2})$$
$$\int \beta^2 d\omega = \beta^2(+\tfrac{1}{2}) + \beta^2(-\tfrac{1}{2}) \qquad \ldots.(16.21$$
$$\int \alpha\beta d\omega = \alpha(+\tfrac{1}{2})\beta(+\tfrac{1}{2}) + \alpha(-\tfrac{1}{2})\beta(-\tfrac{1}{2})$$

But according to the definition of the function a and β (see equation 3.101) we have :

$$a^2(+\tfrac{1}{2}) = 1 \qquad a^2(-\tfrac{1}{2}) = 0 \qquad \beta^2(+\tfrac{1}{2}) = 0 \qquad \beta^2(-\tfrac{1}{2}) = 1 \qquad \ldots(16.22)$$

Hence it follows that,

$$\int a^2 d\omega = 1 \quad \int \beta^2 d\omega = 1 \quad \int a\beta d\omega = 0 \qquad \ldots(16.23)$$

and the spin functions are normalized and orthogonal. From equation 16.23 it follows that,

$$\int a^2(1)d\omega_1 \int a^2(2)d\omega_2 \int \beta^2(3)d\omega_3 = 1 \qquad \ldots(16.24)$$

so that

$$\int (aabac\beta)^2 d\tau = \int a^2(1)d\tau_1 \int b^2(2)d\tau_2 \int c^2(3)d\tau_3 \qquad \ldots(16.25)$$

The space functions are also normalized to unity so that,

$$\int a^2 d\tau = 1 \quad \int b^2 d\tau = 1 \quad \int c^2 d\tau = 1 \qquad \ldots(16.26)$$

and consequently each member of the term $\int (aabac\beta)^2 d\tau$ will be equal to unity ; there are six such terms.

Let us now consider the integrals of the type :

$$\int (aabac\beta)\ (bac\beta aa) d\tau$$

which may be rewritten as follows :

$$\int a(1)b(1)d\tau_1 \int b(2)c(2)d\tau_2 \int c(3)a(3)d\tau_3 \int a^2(1)d\omega_1 \int a(2)\beta(2)d\omega_2 \int a(3)\beta(3)d\omega_3 \qquad \ldots(16.27)$$

It is evident that this expression must equal zero on account of the term $\int a\beta d\omega$, (see expression 16.23 above). Therefore, in all expressions that contain the integral of two wave functions involving a different arrangement of spin functions in the spin terms, *e.g.* $aa\beta$ and $a\beta a$, the resulting occurrence of the $\int a\beta d\omega$ term will make the term equal zero. Thus of the fifteen products in $\int \Phi_2{}^2 d\tau$, the following integrals equal zero :

$$\left.\begin{array}{ll}
\int (aabac\beta)(bac\beta aa)d\tau & \int (bac\beta aa)(c\beta baaa)d\tau \\
\int (aabac\beta)(c\beta baaa)d\tau & \int (c\beta aaba)(baaac\beta)d\tau \\
\int (aabac\beta)(c\beta aaba)d\tau & \int (c\beta aaba)(aac\beta ba)d\tau \\
\int (aabac\beta)(aac\beta ba)d\tau & \int (baaac\beta)(c\beta baaa)d\tau \\
\int (bac\beta aa)(c\beta aaba)d\tau & \int (baaac\beta)(aac\beta ba)d\tau \\
\int (bac\beta aa)(baaac\beta)d\tau & \int (c\beta baaa)(aac\beta ba)d\tau
\end{array}\right\} \qquad \ldots(16.28)$$

There remain three products with identical arrangements of spin functions :

$$\left.\begin{aligned} &2\int (a\alpha b\alpha c\beta)(b\alpha a\alpha c\beta)d\tau \\ &2\int (b\alpha c\beta a\alpha)(a\alpha c\beta b\alpha)d\tau \\ &2\int (c\beta a\alpha b\alpha)(c\beta b\alpha a\alpha)d\tau \end{aligned}\right\} \qquad \ldots .(16.29)$$

The first of these integrals, $\int (a\alpha b\alpha c\beta)(b\alpha a\alpha c\beta)d\tau$ is equal to :

$$\int a(1)b(1)d\tau_1 \int b(2)a(2)d\tau_2 \int c^2(3)d\tau_3 \int \alpha^2(1)d\omega_1 \int \alpha^2(2)d\omega_2 \int \beta^2(3)d\omega_3 \qquad \ldots .(16.30)$$

Owing to the normalization of the spin functions and the function $\int c^2(3)d\tau_3$, equation 16.30 simplifies to :

$$\int a(1)b(1)d\tau_1 \int b(2)a(2)d\tau_2 \qquad \ldots .(16.31)$$

In Chapter 3 we have denoted the integral $\int \psi_a\psi_b d\tau$ by S, so that

$$\int a(1)b(1)d\tau_1 \int b(2)a(2)d\tau_2 = S^2 \qquad \ldots .(16.32)$$

In just the same way the integrals $\int \psi_a\psi_c d\tau$ and $\int \psi_b\psi_c d\tau$ are also equal to S. When the integrals are not orthogonal, they have a value which is always less than unity and in Slater's method it is assumed that the values are sufficiently small to enable the square of the functions to be neglected. This assumption is only justifiable at large distances between the nuclei and the disregard of the non-orthogonality of these functions at distances of the order of 10^{-8} cm is a considerable approximation. On neglecting the square of the non-orthogonal integral S, the Heitler-London equation for the energy of the hydrogen molecule (equations 3.91 and 3.92) becomes $C + A$ instead of $(C + A)/(1 + S^2)$. For the case of the hydrogen molecule in which the hydrogen atoms are at the equilibrium distance, $S = 0{\cdot}75$ and $S^2 = 0{\cdot}56$, thus the neglecting of S^2 introduces an error of approximately 30 per cent, but the attempt at calculation taking the non-orthogonality into account involves considerable mathematical difficulties.

If S^2 is approximately equal to zero, then the integral

$$\int (a\alpha b\alpha c\beta)(b\alpha a\alpha c\beta)d\tau$$

and the remaining integrals of equation 16.29 are zero and hence in the integral $\int \Phi_2{}^2 d\tau$ there remains only the six terms of the type $\int (a\alpha b\alpha c\beta)^2 d\tau$ each of which is equal to unity. Thus

$$\int \Phi_2{}^2 d\tau = 3\,! = 6 \qquad \ldots .(16.33)$$

In the general case, with n electrons, the total number of such integrals will be $n\,!$

Let us now introduce into the function Φ_2 the factor $1/\sqrt{n}\,! = 1/\sqrt{3}\,!$, so that

$$\int \Phi_2{}^2 d\tau = 1 \qquad \ldots .(16.34)$$

and the function Φ_2 is normalized. The same normalizing factor $1/\sqrt{6}$ will apply to all the remaining functions in equation 16.13. To show that this is so, let us evaluate the integral :

$$\int \Phi_1{}^2 d\tau = \int \sum_P (-1)^p Paabaca . \sum_{P'} (-1)^{p'} P'aabacad\tau \qquad \ldots.(16.35)$$

This function will also consist of twenty one terms, six of which will be of the form $\int (aabaca)^2 d\tau$ and equal to unity, the remaining fifteen terms are of the form :

$$\int (aabaca)(baaaca)d\tau = \int a(1)b(1)d\tau_1 \int b(2)a(2)d\tau_2 \int c^2(3)d\tau_3 \times$$
$$\times \int \alpha^2(1)d\omega_1 \int \alpha^2(2)d\omega_2 \int \alpha^2(3)d\omega_3 \qquad \ldots.(16.36)$$

which correspond to the rearrangement of the first and second electrons. In this case the spin functions are the same, being $(\alpha\alpha\alpha)$ $(\alpha\alpha\alpha)$, but the terms become zero since each will contain S^2.

Thus on normalization and assuming $S^2 = 0$, the eight functions of equation 16.13 may be written :

$$\left.\begin{aligned}
\Phi_1 &= \frac{1}{\sqrt{3!}} \sum_P (-1)^p Paabaca & \Phi_5 &= \frac{1}{\sqrt{3!}} \sum_P (-1)^p Paab\beta c\beta \\
\Phi_2 &= \frac{1}{\sqrt{3!}} \sum_P (-1)^p Paabac\beta & \Phi_6 &= \frac{1}{\sqrt{3!}} \sum_P (-1)^p Pa\beta bac\beta \\
\Phi_3 &= \frac{1}{\sqrt{3!}} \sum_P (-1)^p Paab\beta ca & \Phi_7 &= \frac{1}{\sqrt{3!}} \sum_P (-1)^p Pa\beta b\beta ca \\
\Phi_4 &= \frac{1}{\sqrt{3!}} \sum_P (-1)^p Pa\beta baca & \Phi_8 &= \frac{1}{\sqrt{3!}} \sum_P (-1)^p Pa\beta b\beta c\beta
\end{aligned}\right\} \qquad \ldots.(16.37)$$

Let us now obtain the non-orthogonal integral of two such functions, or example S_{23}. This is

$$S_{23} = \frac{1}{3!} \int \sum_P (-1)^p Paabac\beta \sum_{P'} (-1)^{p'} P'aab\beta cad\tau \qquad \ldots.(16.38)$$

and will consist of thirty six terms. It was shown above, however, that only those terms in which the same rearrangement is produced in both the first and second parts are not equal to zero (otherwise the term will contain S^2 and therefore be zero). But if, for example, in both parts of the term an identical rearrangement is made *viz*

$$\int (aabac\beta)(aab\beta ca)d\tau = \int a^2(1)d\tau_1 \int b^2(2)d\tau_2 \int c^2(3)d\tau_3 \times$$
$$\times \int \alpha^2(1)d\omega_1 \int \alpha(2)\beta(2)d\omega_2 \int \alpha(3)\beta(3)d\omega_3 \qquad \ldots.(16.39)$$

the integral becomes equal to zero on account of the $\int \alpha(2)\beta(2)d\omega_2$ term. In any other rearrangement the spin function of the first and second multipliers is different and consequently

$$S_{23} = 0 \qquad \ldots .(16.40)$$

In exactly the same manner all the remaining non-orthogonal integrals equal zero and it is therefore possible to rewrite the secular equation 16.14 in the form :

$$\begin{vmatrix} \mathscr{H}_{11}-E & \mathscr{H}_{12} & \mathscr{H}_{13} & \mathscr{H}_{14} & \mathscr{H}_{15} & \mathscr{H}_{16} & \mathscr{H}_{17} & \mathscr{H}_{18} \\ \mathscr{H}_{12} & \mathscr{H}_{22}-E & \mathscr{H}_{23} & \mathscr{H}_{24} & \mathscr{H}_{25} & \mathscr{H}_{26} & \mathscr{H}_{27} & \mathscr{H}_{28} \\ \mathscr{H}_{13} & \mathscr{H}_{23} & \mathscr{H}_{33}-E & \mathscr{H}_{34} & \mathscr{H}_{35} & \mathscr{H}_{36} & \mathscr{H}_{37} & \mathscr{H}_{38} \\ \mathscr{H}_{14} & \mathscr{H}_{24} & \mathscr{H}_{34} & \mathscr{H}_{44}-E & \mathscr{H}_{45} & \mathscr{H}_{46} & \mathscr{H}_{47} & \mathscr{H}_{48} \\ \mathscr{H}_{15} & \mathscr{H}_{25} & \mathscr{H}_{35} & \mathscr{H}_{45} & \mathscr{H}_{55}-E & \mathscr{H}_{56} & \mathscr{H}_{57} & \mathscr{H}_{58} \\ \mathscr{H}_{16} & \mathscr{H}_{26} & \mathscr{H}_{36} & \mathscr{H}_{46} & \mathscr{H}_{56} & \mathscr{H}_{66}-E & \mathscr{H}_{67} & \mathscr{H}_{68} \\ \mathscr{H}_{17} & \mathscr{H}_{27} & \mathscr{H}_{37} & \mathscr{H}_{47} & \mathscr{H}_{57} & \mathscr{H}_{67} & \mathscr{H}_{77}-E & \mathscr{H}_{78} \\ \mathscr{H}_{18} & \mathscr{H}_{28} & \mathscr{H}_{38} & \mathscr{H}_{48} & \mathscr{H}_{58} & \mathscr{H}_{68} & \mathscr{H}_{78} & \mathscr{H}_{88}-E \end{vmatrix} = 0$$

$$\ldots .(16.41)$$

Equation 16.41 may be considerably simplified by dividing it into several equations of lower order corresponding to different values of Σs. This is due to the fact that the functions Φ for different values of Σs are combined with each other. If i and k refer to functions having different values of Σs, *e.g.* $i = 1$ ($\Sigma s = +3/2$), and $k = 2$ ($\Sigma s = +\frac{1}{2}$), then it is possible to show that all the $\mathscr{H}_{ik}$ integrals are equal to zero. Let us take $\mathscr{H}_{12}$ as an example.

$$\mathscr{H}_{12} = \int \Phi_1 \mathscr{H} \Phi_2 d\tau$$

$$= \frac{1}{3!}\int \sum_P (-1)^P Pa\alpha b\alpha c\alpha \, \mathscr{H} \sum_{P'} (-1)^{P'} P'a\alpha b\alpha c\beta d\tau \qquad \ldots .(16.42)$$

The operator $\mathscr{H}$ is not dependent on spin and hence the integration of the spin terms may be considered separately. The terms of equation 16.42 on expansion give,

$$\int a(1)b(2)c(3)\alpha(1)\alpha(2)\alpha(3)\mathscr{H}a(1)b(2)c(3)\alpha(1)\alpha(2)\beta(3)d\tau$$

$$\ldots .(16.43)$$

and this expression may be rewritten in the form

$$\int a(1)b(2)c(3)\mathcal{H}a(1)b(2)c(3)d\tau_1 d\tau_2 d\tau_3 \int \alpha^2(1)d\omega_1 \int \alpha^2(2)d\omega_2 \int \alpha(3)\beta(3)d\omega_3 \quad \ldots.(16.44)$$

Clearly it becomes zero as a result of the orthogonality of the spin functions. In the group of terms before the operator in equation 16·43 we have the spin terms $\alpha\alpha\alpha$ and in the group after the operator $\alpha\alpha\beta$ so that in any rearrangement of electrons the term $\int \alpha\beta d\omega$ must be introduced and

$$\mathcal{H}_{12} = 0 \quad \ldots.(16.45)$$

The integrals $\mathcal{H}_{ik}$ are not equal to zero in those cases when integrals of the form

$$\int abc\mathcal{H}abcd\tau \int \alpha^2(1)\alpha^2(2)\alpha^2(3)d\omega_1 d\omega_2 d\omega_3 \quad \ldots.(16.46)$$

or

$$\int abc\mathcal{H}abcd\tau \int \alpha^2(1)\alpha^2(2)\beta^2(3)d\omega_1 d\omega_2 d\omega_3 \quad \ldots.(16.47)$$

in which only the square of the spin functions and not their product enter into the resulting expression. In order for this to be so it is essential that the total value of the spin quantum number s, is the same in both functions Φ_i and Φ_k Evidently the state Φ_1 ($\Sigma s = +3/2$, three α spin functions) does not combine with any one of the remaining states of the system. This will also be the case for Φ_8, when $\Sigma s = -3/2$ and all spin functions equal β. The three states Φ_2, Φ_3 and Φ_4 correspond to $\Sigma s = +\frac{1}{2}$ (two α functions and one β). Among the thirty six terms of each product $\Phi_2\Phi_3$, $\Phi_2\Phi_4$ and $\Phi_3\Phi_4$, there is the same arrangement of electrons and hence these three states may combine amongst themselves, but not with others. In the same way Φ_5, Φ_6 and Φ_7, corresponding to $\Sigma s = -\frac{1}{2}$ (two β functions and one α), may combine only with each other.

Thus the integrals :

$\mathcal{H}_{12}$, $\mathcal{H}_{13}$, $\mathcal{H}_{14}$, $\mathcal{H}_{15}$, $\mathcal{H}_{16}$, $\mathcal{H}_{17}$, $\mathcal{H}_{18}$,

$\mathcal{H}_{25}$, $\mathcal{H}_{26}$, $\mathcal{H}_{27}$, $\mathcal{H}_{28}$,

$\mathcal{H}_{35}$, $\mathcal{H}_{36}$, $\mathcal{H}_{37}$, $\mathcal{H}_{38}$,

$\mathcal{H}_{45}$, $\mathcal{H}_{46}$, $\mathcal{H}_{47}$, $\mathcal{H}_{48}$,

$\mathcal{H}_{58}$, $\mathcal{H}_{68}$, and $\mathcal{H}_{78}$,

equal zero and the integrals :

$\mathcal{H}_{11}$, $\mathcal{H}_{22}$, $\mathcal{H}_{33}$, $\mathcal{H}_{44}$, $\mathcal{H}_{55}$, $\mathcal{H}_{66}$, $\mathcal{H}_{77}$, $\mathcal{H}_{88}$,

$\mathcal{H}_{23}$, $\mathcal{H}_{24}$, $\mathcal{H}_{34}$, $\mathcal{H}_{56}$, $\mathcal{H}_{57}$, and $\mathcal{H}_{67}$

are not equal to zero. Substituting these data in equation 16.41 we have :

$$\begin{vmatrix} \mathscr{H}_{11}-E & 0 & 0 & 0 & 0 & 0 & 0 & 0 \\ 0 & \mathscr{H}_{22}-E & \mathscr{H}_{23} & \mathscr{H}_{24} & 0 & 0 & 0 & 0 \\ 0 & \mathscr{H}_{23} & \mathscr{H}_{33}-E & \mathscr{H}_{34} & 0 & 0 & 0 & 0 \\ 0 & \mathscr{H}_{24} & \mathscr{H}_{34} & \mathscr{H}_{44}-E & 0 & 0 & 0 & 0 \\ 0 & 0 & 0 & 0 & \mathscr{H}_{55}-E & \mathscr{H}_{56} & \mathscr{H}_{57} & 0 \\ 0 & 0 & 0 & 0 & \mathscr{H}_{56} & \mathscr{H}_{66}-E & \mathscr{H}_{67} & 0 \\ 0 & 0 & 0 & 0 & \mathscr{H}_{57} & \mathscr{H}_{67} & \mathscr{H}_{77}-E & 0 \\ 0 & 0 & 0 & 0 & 0 & 0 & 0 & \mathscr{H}_{88}-E \end{vmatrix} = 0 \qquad \ldots .(16.48)$$

which may be rewritten in the form of a product

$$(\mathscr{H}_{11}-E)(\mathscr{H}_{88}-E)\begin{vmatrix} \mathscr{H}_{22}-E & \mathscr{H}_{23} & \mathscr{H}_{24} \\ \mathscr{H}_{23} & \mathscr{H}_{33}-E & \mathscr{H}_{34} \\ \mathscr{H}_{24} & \mathscr{H}_{34} & \mathscr{H}_{44}-E \end{vmatrix}\begin{vmatrix} \mathscr{H}_{55}-E & \mathscr{H}_{56} & \mathscr{H}_{57} \\ \mathscr{H}_{56} & \mathscr{H}_{66}-E & \mathscr{H}_{67} \\ \mathscr{H}_{57} & \mathscr{H}_{67} & \mathscr{H}_{77}-E \end{vmatrix} = 0 \qquad \ldots .(16.49)$$

The equation of the eighth degree is thus reduced to two of the first degree and two cubic equations. It follows that one solution is

$$\mathscr{H}_{11} - E = 0$$

and

$$\mathscr{H}_{11} = E$$

This solution corresponds to a state of the system of three electrons in which all electrons have parallel spins; all three atoms are therefore repelled from each other and this is the most unfavourable energy state of the system.

Let us now calculate the values of the integrals $\mathscr{H}_{11}$, $\mathscr{H}_{22}$, $\mathscr{H}_{23}$ *etc.* We shall consider first the integral $\mathscr{H}_{11}$.

$$\mathscr{H}_{11} = \int \Phi_1 \mathscr{H} \Phi_1 d\tau = \frac{1}{3!}\int \sum_P (-1)^P Paab\alpha c\alpha \; \mathscr{H} \; \sum_{P'} (-1)^{P'} P' aab\alpha c\alpha d\tau \qquad \ldots .(16.50)$$

All the thirty six terms will contain

$$\int \alpha^2(1)\alpha^2(2)\alpha^2(3) d\omega_1 d\omega_2 d\omega_3 = \left[\int \alpha^2 d\omega\right]^3 \qquad \ldots .(16.51)$$

which, being normalized, is equal to unity. It is therefore only necessary to consider the function of coordinate space of Φ and hence

$$\mathscr{H}_{11} = \frac{1}{6}\int \Sigma\ (-1)^P Pabc \mathscr{H} \sum_{P'} (-1)^{P'} P' abcd\tau \qquad \ldots .(16.52)$$

$\Sigma(-1)^{P}Pabc$ refers to the six terms :

$$\begin{array}{ll} abc & -\,cba \\ bca & -\,acb \\ cab & -\,bac \end{array}$$

so that $\mathscr{H}_{11}$ is the sum of the thirty six integrals :

$$\begin{aligned}
\mathscr{H}_{11} = \frac{1}{6}\Big[& \int abc\,\mathscr{H}\,abc\,d\tau + \int bca\,\mathscr{H}\,bca\,d\tau + \int cab\,\mathscr{H}\,cab\,d\tau \\
& + \int cba\,\mathscr{H}\,cba\,d\tau + \int acb\,\mathscr{H}\,acb\,d\tau + \int bac\,\mathscr{H}\,bac\,d\tau \Big] \\
+ \frac{1}{6}\Big[& -\int abc\,\mathscr{H}\,bac\,d\tau - \int bca\,\mathscr{H}\,acb\,d\tau - \int cab\,\mathscr{H}\,cba\,d\tau \\
& - \int cba\,\mathscr{H}\,cab\,d\tau - \int acb\,\mathscr{H}\,bca\,d\tau - \int bac\,\mathscr{H}\,abc\,d\tau \Big] \\
+ \frac{1}{6}\Big[& -\int abc\,\mathscr{H}\,acb\,d\tau - \int bca\,\mathscr{H}\,cba\,d\tau - \int cab\,\mathscr{H}\,bac\,d\tau \\
& - \int cba\,\mathscr{H}\,bca\,d\tau - \int acb\,\mathscr{H}\,abc\,d\tau - \int bac\,\mathscr{H}\,cab\,d\tau \Big] \\
+ \frac{1}{6}\Big[& -\int abc\,\mathscr{H}\,cba\,d\tau - \int bca\,\mathscr{H}\,bac\,d\tau - \int cab\,\mathscr{H}\,acb\,d\tau \\
& - \int cba\,\mathscr{H}\,abc\,d\tau - \int acb\,\mathscr{H}\,cab\,d\tau - \int bac\,\mathscr{H}\,bca\,d\tau \Big] \\
+ \frac{1}{6}\Big[& +\int abc\,\mathscr{H}\,bca\,d\tau + \int bca\,\mathscr{H}\,cab\,d\tau + \int cab\,\mathscr{H}\,abc\,d\tau \\
& + \int cba\,\mathscr{H}\,bac\,d\tau + \int acb\,\mathscr{H}\,cba\,d\tau + \int bac\,\mathscr{H}\,acb\,d\tau \Big] \\
+ \frac{1}{6}\Big[& +\int abc\,\mathscr{H}\,cab\,d\tau + \int bca\,\mathscr{H}\,abc\,d\tau + \int cab\,\mathscr{H}\,bca\,d\tau \\
& + \int cba\,\mathscr{H}\,acb\,d\tau + \int acb\,\mathscr{H}\,bac\,d\tau + \int bac\,\mathscr{H}\,cba\,d\tau \Big]
\end{aligned} \quad \ldots.(16.53)$$

In this expression we have separated the terms into six groups, each containing six integrals. In all the members of the first group, the function to the right of the operator is the same as that to the left. In the second group, the function to the right of the operator is reproduced on the left with the rearrangement P_{ab}, *i.e.* the electrons of atoms a and b have been exchanged. In a similar manner the third group corresponds to the rearrangement P_{bc}, the fourth to the rearrangement P_{ac}, the fifth to P_{abc} and the sixth to P_{acb}. Since with the terms of the first group there is no exchange of electrons, these must refer to a Coulomb type integral, the remaining integrals are all exchange or resonance integrals.

We shall now prove that all the members of one group are equal among themselves. The Hamiltonian operator will contain terms for all the interaction of the electrons with the nuclei, for the electrons amongst themselves and of the nuclei amongst themselves. Thus

$$\mathcal{H} = -\frac{\nabla_1^2}{2} - \frac{\nabla_2^2}{2} - \frac{\nabla_3^2}{2} - \frac{1}{r_{a_1}} - \frac{1}{r_{a_2}} - \frac{1}{r_{a_3}} - \frac{1}{r_{b_1}} - \frac{1}{r_{b_2}} - \frac{1}{r_{b3}}$$
$$- \frac{1}{r_{c_1}} - \frac{1}{r_{c_2}} - \frac{1}{r_{c_3}} + \frac{1}{r_{12}} + \frac{1}{r_{13}} + \frac{1}{r_{23}} + \frac{1}{R_{ab}} + \frac{1}{R_{ca}} + \frac{1}{R_{bc}} \qquad (16.54)$$

(r_{a_1}, r_{b_1} *etc* refer to the distance between electrons and nuclei, r_{12} *etc* to the distance between electrons and R_{ab} *etc* to the distance between nuclei). From equation 16.54 we obtain :

$$\int abc\,\mathcal{H}\,abcd\tau = \int \psi_a\psi_b\psi_c\Big(-\frac{\nabla_1^2}{2} - \frac{\nabla_2^2}{2} - \frac{\nabla_3^2}{2} - \frac{1}{r_{a_1}} - \frac{1}{r_{a_2}} - \frac{1}{r_{a_3}} - \frac{1}{r_{b_1}} - \frac{1}{r_{b_2}}$$
$$- \frac{1}{r_{b_3}} - \frac{1}{r_{c_1}} - \frac{1}{r_{c_2}} - \frac{1}{r_{c_3}} + \frac{1}{r_{12}} + \frac{1}{r_{13}} + \frac{1}{r_{23}}$$
$$+ \frac{1}{R_{ab}} + \frac{1}{R_{ac}} + \frac{1}{R_{bc}}\Big)\,\psi_a\psi_b\psi_c d\tau \qquad \ldots(16.55)$$

The functions ψ_a, ψ and ψ_c satisfy equations of the type

$$\Big(-\frac{\nabla_1^2}{2} - \frac{1}{r_{a_1}}\Big)\,\psi_a(1) = E_o\,\psi_a\,(1) \qquad \ldots(3.4)$$

where E_o is the energy of an atom of hydrogen. From equations 16.55 and 3.4 it follows that

$$\int abc\,\mathcal{H}\,abcd\tau = \int \psi_a(1)E_o\psi_a(1)d\tau_1 \int \psi_b{}^2(2)d\tau_2 \int \psi_c{}^2(3)d\tau_3$$
$$+ \int \psi_a{}^2(1)d\tau_1 \int \psi_b(2)E_o\psi_b(2)d\tau_2 \int \psi_c{}^2(3)d\tau_3$$
$$+ \int \psi_a{}^2(1)d\tau_1 \int \psi_b{}^2(2)d\tau_2 \int \psi_c(3)E_o\psi_c(3)d\tau_3$$
$$+ \int \psi_a\psi_b\psi_c\Big[-\frac{1}{r_{a_2}} - \frac{1}{r_{a_3}} - \frac{1}{r_{b_1}} - \frac{1}{r_{b_3}} - \frac{1}{r_{c_1}} - \frac{1}{r_{c2}} +$$
$$+ \frac{1}{r_{12}} + \frac{1}{r_{13}} + \frac{1}{r_{23}} + \frac{1}{R_{ab}} + \frac{1}{R_{ac}} + \frac{1}{R_{bc}}\Big]\psi_a\psi_b\psi_c d\tau = 3E_o + C \qquad \ldots(16.56)$$

Using the normalized functions ψ_a, ψ_b and ψ_c, we shall now divide the last integral (C) of equation 16.56 into its components :

$$\int abc\,\mathcal{H}\,abcd\tau = 3E_o - \int\frac{\psi_a{}^2(1)}{r_{b_1}}d\tau_1 - \int\frac{\psi_a{}^2(1)}{r_{c_1}}d\tau_1 - \int\frac{\psi_b{}^2(2)}{r_{a_2}}d\tau_2 - \int\frac{\psi_b{}^2(2)}{r_{c2}}d\tau_2 -$$
$$- \int\frac{\psi_c{}^2(3)}{r_{a_3}}d\tau_3 - \int\frac{\psi_c{}^2(3)}{r_{b_3}}d\tau_3 + \frac{1}{R_{ab}} + \frac{1}{R_{bc}} + \frac{1}{R_{ac}} +$$
$$+ \int\frac{\psi_a{}^2(1)\psi_b{}^2(2)}{r_{12}}\,d\tau_1 d\tau_2 + \int\frac{\psi_a{}^2(1)\psi_c{}^2(3)}{r_{13}}d\tau_1 d\tau_3 +$$
$$+ \int\frac{\psi_b{}^2(2)\psi_c{}^2(3)}{r_{23}}\,d\tau_2\,d\tau_3 \qquad \ldots(16.57)$$

The integral $\int\frac{\psi_a{}^2}{r_b}d\tau$ gives the Coulombic energy of the interaction of the electron, described by the function ψ_a, with the nucleus b, similarly the integral $\int \frac{\psi_b^2}{r_a} d\tau$ gives the interaction energy of the electron described by the function ψ_b with the nucleus a. The term $\int \frac{\psi_a^2(1)\psi_b^2(2)}{r_{12}} d\tau_1 d\tau_2$ represents the mutual interaction energy of the electrons described by the functions ψ_a and ψ_b. Adding to these three terms the energy of repulsion of the nuclei $\frac{1}{R_{ab}}$, we obtain the total Coulombic interaction energy of atoms a and b. This quantity we shall call C_{ab} :

$$C_{ab} = -\int \frac{\psi_a^2}{r_b} d\tau - \int \frac{\psi_b^2}{r_a} d\tau + \int \frac{\psi_a^2 \psi_b^2}{r_{12}} d\tau_1 d\tau_2 + \frac{1}{R_{ab}} \qquad \ldots (16.58)$$

In just the same way we may also obtain,

$$C_{ac} = -\int \frac{\psi_a^2}{r_c} d\tau - \int \frac{\psi_c^2}{r_a} d\tau + \int \frac{\psi_a^2 \psi_c^2}{r_{13}} d\tau_1 d\tau_3 + \frac{1}{R_{ac}} \qquad \ldots (16.59)$$

and

$$C_{bc} = -\int \frac{\psi_b^2}{r_c} d\tau - \int \frac{\psi_c^2}{r_b} d\tau + \int \frac{\psi_b^2 \psi_c^2}{r_{23}} d\tau_2 d\tau_3 + \frac{1}{R_{bc}} \qquad \ldots (16.60)$$

Thus

$$C = C_{ab} + C_{ac} + C_{bc} \qquad \ldots (16.61)$$

and we may write equation (16.56) in the form :

$$\int abc\,\mathcal{H}\,abc\,d\tau = 3E_o + C_{ab} + C_{ac} + C_{bc} \qquad \ldots (16.62)$$

or more briefly

$$\int abc\,\mathcal{H}\,abc\,d\tau = 3E_o + C \qquad \ldots (16.63)$$

If we consider any other Coulomb integral of equation 16.53, then it may be shown that it equals $\int abc\,\mathcal{H}\,abc\,d\tau$. For example

$$\int bca\,\mathcal{H}\,bca\,d\tau = \int \psi_b\psi_c\psi_a \left(-\frac{\nabla_1^2}{2} - \frac{\nabla_2^2}{2} - \frac{\nabla_3^2}{2} - \frac{1}{r_{a_1}} - \frac{1}{r_{a_2}} - \frac{1}{r_{a_1}} - \right.$$

$$- \frac{1}{r_{a_1}} - \frac{1}{r_{b_2}} - \frac{1}{r_{b_3}} - \frac{1}{r_{c_1}} - \frac{1}{r_{2}} - \frac{1}{r_{a_1}} +$$

$$\left. + \frac{1}{r_{12}} + \frac{1}{r_{13}} + \frac{1}{r_{23}} + \frac{1}{R_{ab}} + \frac{1}{R_{ac}} + \frac{1}{R_{bc}} \right) \psi_b\psi_c\psi_a d\tau$$

$$= 3E_o - \int \frac{\psi_b^2(1)}{r_{c_1}} d\tau_1 - \int \frac{\psi_b^2(1)}{r_{c_1}} d\tau_1 - \int \frac{\psi_c^2(2)}{r_{a_2}} d\tau_2 - \int \frac{\psi_c^2(2)}{r_{b_2}} d\tau_2 -$$

$$- \int \frac{\psi_a^2(3)}{r_{b_3}} d\tau_3 - \int \frac{\psi_a^2(3)}{r_{c_3}} d\tau_3 + \frac{1}{R_{ab}} + \frac{1}{R_{ac}} + \frac{1}{R_{bc}} +$$

$$+ \int \frac{\psi_b^2(1)\psi_c^2(2)}{r_{12}} d\tau_1 d\tau_2 + \int \frac{\psi_b^2(1)\,\psi_a^2(3)}{r_{13}} d\tau_1 d\tau_3$$

$$+ \int \frac{\psi_c^2(2)\psi_a^2(3)}{r_{23}} d\tau_2 d\tau_3 \qquad \ldots (16.64)$$

i.e. it also equals $3E_o + C_{ab} + C_{ac} + C_{bc}$. This is due to the fact that the operator $\mathcal{H}$ is symmetrical with respect to all three electrons and on any rearrangement of the electrons, the form of the operator is not changed. In the same way the remaining members of the first group of terms in equation 16.53 are equal to $\int abc\mathcal{H}abcd\tau$. There are in all six such members, but owing to the presence of the factor 1/6 in front of the bracket, the first group of terms in equation 16.53 is equal to $3E_o + C$.

The exchange integral $\int abc\mathcal{H}bacd\tau$ is given by

$$\int abc\mathcal{H}bacd\tau = \int \psi_a\psi_b\psi_c\Big(-\frac{\nabla_1^2}{2}-\frac{\nabla_2^2}{2}-\frac{\nabla_3^2}{2}-\frac{1}{r_{a_1}}-\frac{1}{r_{a_2}}-\frac{1}{r_{a_3}}-\frac{1}{r_{b_1}}-$$
$$-\frac{1}{r_{b_2}}-\frac{1}{r_{b_3}}-\frac{1}{r_{c_1}}-\frac{1}{r_{c_2}}-\frac{1}{r_{c_3}}+\frac{1}{r_{12}}+\frac{1}{r_{13}}+$$
$$+\frac{1}{r_{23}}+\frac{1}{R_{ab}}+\frac{1}{R_{ac}}+\frac{1}{R_{bc}}\Big)\psi_b\psi_a\psi_c d\tau \qquad \ldots.(16.65)$$

in which the terms involving

$$-\frac{\nabla_1^2}{2},\ -\frac{\nabla_2^2}{2},\ -\frac{\nabla_3^2}{2},\ -\frac{1}{r_{a_2}},\ -\frac{1}{r_{a3}}-,\ \frac{1}{r_{b1}},\ -\frac{1}{r_{b_3}},$$
$$-\frac{1}{r_{c_1}},\ -\frac{1}{r_{c_2}},\ -\frac{1}{r_{c_3}},\ \frac{1}{R_{ac}},\ \frac{1}{R_{bc}},\ \frac{1}{r_{23}},\ \frac{1}{r_{13}},$$ on our

approximation will be zero. Thus there remains only the expression

$$\int \psi_a\psi_b\Big(-\frac{1}{r_{a_1}}-\frac{1}{r_{b_2}}+\frac{1}{r_{12}}+\frac{1}{R_{ab}}\Big)\psi_b\psi_a d\tau_1 d\tau_2 \qquad \ldots.(16.66)$$

which represents the exchange integral of the electrons of the two atoms a and b. We shall represent this term by A_{ab}. Thus

$$\int abc\mathcal{H}bacd\tau = A_{ab} \qquad \ldots.(16.67)$$

In the same way all the remaining integrals of this group corresponding to the rearrangement P_{ab}, reduce to the expression 16.66. The sum of the integrals of the second group is thus $6A_{ab}$. Similarly, the integral, $\int abc\mathcal{H}acbd\tau$ represents the exchange integral of the electrons of atoms b and c; this we shall term A_{bc}, and all the remaining integrals of the third group of integrals in the expression 16.53 corresponding to the P_{bc} rearrangement, will equal this quantity. In the same way each of the integrals in the fourth group will be equal to A_{ac}. In the fifth and sixth groups we have integrals of the type $\int abc\mathcal{H}bcad\tau$ and $\int abc\mathcal{H}cabd\tau$ corresponding to the simultaneous rearrangement of all three electrons. However, since the term S^2 will appear in each case, they may be neglected. To show that this is correct let us take the integral $\int abc\mathcal{H}bcad\tau$.

$$\int abc\,\mathcal{H}\,bcad\tau=\int\psi_a\psi_b\psi_c\Big(-\frac{\nabla_1^2}{2}-\frac{\nabla_2^2}{2}-\frac{\nabla_3^2}{2}-\frac{1}{r_{a_1}}-\frac{1}{r_{a_2}}-\frac{1}{r_{a_3}}-$$
$$-\frac{1}{r_{b_1}}-\frac{1}{r_{b_2}}-\frac{1}{r_{b_3}}-\frac{1}{r_{c_1}}-\frac{1}{r_{c_2}}-\frac{1}{r_{c_3}}+\frac{1}{R_{ab}}+\frac{1}{R_{ac}}+\frac{1}{R_{bc}}+$$
$$+\frac{1}{r_{12}}+\frac{1}{r_{13}}+\frac{1}{r_{23}}\Big)\,\psi_b\psi_c\psi_a d\tau$$
$$=\int\psi_a(1)E_o\psi_b(1)d\tau_1\int\psi_b(2)\psi_c(2)d\tau_2\int\psi_c(3)\psi_a(3)d\tau_3+\cdots\cdots\cdots$$
$$+\int\frac{\psi_a(1)\psi_b(1)}{r_{a_1}}d\tau_1\int\psi_b(2)\psi_c(2)d\tau_2\int\psi_c(3)\psi_a(3)d\tau_3+\cdots\cdots\cdots \quad \ldots.(16.68)$$

Thus all members of the fifth and sixth groups in equation 16.53 are zero and this equation reduces to

$$\mathcal{H}_{11}=3E_o+C-A_{ab}-A_{bc}-A_{ac} \quad \ldots.(16.69)$$

Calculation of the value of the integral $\mathcal{H}_{11}$ shows, in agreement with the statement made earlier, that three atoms with the electron state $\Sigma s=+3/2$, *i.e.* with parallel spins, are repelled. The energy of interaction in this case is given by

$$\mathcal{H}_{11}-3E_o=C_{ab}+C_{bc}+C_{ac}-A_{ab}-A_{bc}-A_{ac} \quad \ldots.(16.70)$$

The exchange integrals with a negative sign indicate repulsion and although the Coulomb integrals are positive, the Coulomb energy is not great, only comprising about 10 per cent of the exchange energy.

Let us pass now to a calculation of the integrals of the cubic equation :

$$\begin{vmatrix}\mathcal{H}_{22}-E & \mathcal{H}_{23} & \mathcal{H}_{24}\\ \mathcal{H}_{23} & \mathcal{H}_{33}-E & \mathcal{H}_{34}\\ \mathcal{H}_{24} & \mathcal{H}_{34} & \mathcal{H}_{44}-E\end{vmatrix}=0 \quad \ldots.(16.71)$$

We shall consider first the integral $\mathcal{H}_{22}$:

$$\mathcal{H}_{22}=\int\Phi_2\,\mathcal{H}\,\Phi_2 d\tau=\frac{1}{3\,!}\int\sum_P(-1)^P Paabac\beta\;\mathcal{H}\sum_{P'}(-1)^{P'}P'aabac\beta d\tau \quad \ldots.(16.72)$$

In this case we cannot discard the spin functions immediately since the arrangement of the electrons according to the spin functions does not remain unchanged, and during the electronic rearrangements there arises the following combinations of spin :

P_E	$\alpha\alpha\beta$
P_{ab}	$\alpha\alpha\beta$
P_{ac}	$\beta\alpha\alpha$
P_{bc}	$\alpha\beta\alpha$
P_{abc}	$\alpha\beta\alpha$
P_{acb}	$\beta\alpha\alpha$

The expression corresponding to P_E possesses the function $aabac\beta$ on the left of the operator and the spin terms have the form $\alpha\alpha\beta$. This indicates that the first and second electrons have positive spin projections and the third electron a negative spin projection. Only those terms in which the function on the right of the operator is identical with that on the left will not be equal to zero. This occurs only in the case of the rearrangements P_E and P_{ab}. These are given by :

$$\int aabac\beta\mathcal{H}aabac\beta d\tau = \int abc\mathcal{H}abcd\tau\int \alpha^2(1)d\omega_1\int \alpha^2(2)d\omega_2\int \beta^2(3)d\omega_3$$

$$= \int abc\mathcal{H}abcd\tau = 3E_o + C \qquad \ldots.(16.73)$$

$$\int aabac\beta\mathcal{H}baaac\beta d\tau = \int abc\mathcal{H}bacd\tau\int \alpha^2(1)d\omega_1\int \alpha^2(2)d\omega_2\int \beta^2(3)d\omega_3$$

$$= \int abc\mathcal{H}bacd\tau = A_{ab} \qquad \ldots.(16.74)$$

All the remaining members of the expression will contain the expression $\int \alpha\beta d\omega$ and will be equal to zero. Thus, for example, on making the rearrangement P_{ac} in the function to the right of the operator in equation 16.72 we obtain,

$$\int aabac\beta\mathcal{H}c\beta baaad\tau$$

$$= \int abc\mathcal{H}cbad\tau\int \alpha(1)\beta(1)d\omega_1\int \alpha^2(2)d\omega_2\int \beta(3)\alpha(3)d\omega_3 = 0 \qquad \ldots.(16.75)$$

In the first summation term of equation 16.72, let us make the rearrangement P_{ab} ; the function before the operator will now be $baaac\beta$. Again, on rearrangement of the term after the operator we obtain only two expressions which are not equal to zero, one corresponding to the rearrangement P_{ab} and the other to P_E. These are :

$$\int baaac\beta\mathcal{H}baaac\beta d\tau = \int bac\mathcal{H}bacd\tau = 3E_o + C \qquad \ldots.(16.76)$$

$$\int baaac\beta\mathcal{H}aabac\beta d\tau = \int bac\mathcal{H}abcd\tau = A_{ab} \qquad \ldots.(16.77)$$

These two expressions again refer to the Coulomb integral $3E_o + C$ and the exchange integral A_{ab}. On making the rearrangement P_{ac} in the first term of equation 16.72 and in the second term also, we obtain

$$\int c\beta baaa\mathcal{H}c\beta baaad\tau = 3E_o + C \qquad \ldots.(16.78)$$

and the rearrangement P_{acb} :

$$\int c\beta baaa\mathcal{H}c\beta aabad\tau = A_{ab} \qquad \ldots.(16.79)$$

It may also be shown by the use of the above methods that the remaining rearrangements of the first term lead to the same integrals $3E_o + C$ and A_{ab}, *i.e.*

$$\mathcal{H}_{22} = \frac{1}{6}\left[6\int abc\mathcal{H}abcd\tau - 6\int abc\mathcal{H}bacd\tau\right] = 3E_o + C - A_{ab} \qquad \ldots.(16.80)$$

Thus the integral $\mathcal{H}_{22}$ consists of the Coulomb integral $\int abc\mathcal{H}abcd\tau$ and one exchange integral $\int abc\mathcal{H}bacd\tau$.

The remaining integrals entering into the cubic equation may similarly be shown to be :

$$\mathscr{H}_{33} = \int abc\mathscr{H}abcd\tau \; - \int abc\mathscr{H}cbad\tau = 3E_o + C - A_{ac}$$

$$\mathscr{H}_{44} = \int abc\mathscr{H}abcd\tau \; - \int abc\mathscr{H}acbd\tau = 3E_o + C - A_{bc}$$

$$\mathscr{H}_{23} = \; - \int abc\mathscr{H}acbd\tau = - A_{bc} \qquad \ldots(16.81)$$

$$\mathscr{H}_{34} = \; - \int abc\mathscr{H}bacd\tau = - A_{ab}$$

$$\mathscr{H}_{24} = \; - \int abc\mathscr{H}cbad\tau = - A_{ac}$$

Introducing into equation 16.71 the values of the integrals given by 16.80 and 16.81 we obtain

$$\begin{vmatrix} 3E_o + C - A_{ab} - E & - A_{bc} & - A_{ab} \\ - A_{bc} & 3E_o + C - A_{ac} - E & - A_{ac} \\ - A_{ab} & - A_{ac} & 3E_o + C - A_{bc} - E \end{vmatrix} = 0 \qquad \ldots(16.82)$$

For the solution of this equation, we shall proceed as follows. Instead of the functions Φ_2, Φ_3 and Φ_4, let us introduce their linear combinations :

$$\left.\begin{aligned} \Phi_{\mathrm{II}} &= \frac{1}{\sqrt{2}}(\Phi_3 - \Phi_4) \\ \Phi_{\mathrm{III}} &= \frac{1}{\sqrt{2}}(\Phi_2 - \Phi_3) \\ \Phi_{\mathrm{IV}} &= \frac{1}{\sqrt{3}}(\Phi_2 + \Phi_3 + \Phi_4) \end{aligned}\right\} \qquad \ldots(16.83)$$

The mathemetical basis of introducing these new functions lies in the fact that the cubic equation formed with these functions in a similar manner to equation 16.71 *i.e.*

$$\begin{vmatrix} \mathscr{H}_{\mathrm{II\,II}} - ES_{\mathrm{II\,II}} & \mathscr{H}_{\mathrm{II\,III}} - ES_{\mathrm{II\,III}} & \mathscr{H}_{\mathrm{II\,IV}} - ES_{\mathrm{II\,IV}} \\ \mathscr{H}_{\mathrm{II\,III}} - ES_{\mathrm{II\,III}} & \mathscr{H}_{\mathrm{III\,III}} - ES_{\mathrm{III\,III}} & \mathscr{H}_{\mathrm{III\,IV}} - ES_{\mathrm{III\,IV}} \\ \mathscr{H}_{\mathrm{II\,IV}} - ES_{\mathrm{II\,IV}} & \mathscr{H}_{\mathrm{III\,IV}} - ES_{\mathrm{III\,IV}} & \mathscr{H}_{\mathrm{IV\,IV}} - ES_{\mathrm{IV\,IV}} \end{vmatrix} = 0 \qquad \ldots(16.84)$$

may be easily reduced to a linear and a quadratic equation. We shall now evaluate the integrals entering into equation 16.84. These are :

$$\mathscr{H}_{\mathrm{II\,II}} = \tfrac{1}{2}\int(\Phi_3 - \Phi_4)\;\mathscr{H}\;(\Phi_3 - \Phi_4)d\tau = \tfrac{1}{2}\,\mathscr{H}_{33} + \tfrac{1}{2}\,\mathscr{H}_{44} - \mathscr{H}_{34}$$

$$= 3E_o + C - \frac{A_{ac}}{2} - \frac{A_{bc}}{2} + A_{ab} \qquad \ldots(16.85)$$

Similarly

$$\mathscr{H}_{\text{III III}} = 3E_o + C - \frac{A_{ab}}{2} - \frac{A_{ac}}{2} + A_{bc}$$

$$\mathscr{H}_{\text{IV IV}} = 3E_o + C - A_{ab} - A_{ac} - A_{bc}$$

$$\mathscr{H}_{\text{II III}} = -\frac{3E_o + C}{2} + A_{ac} - \frac{A_{ab}}{2} - \frac{A_{bc}}{2}$$

$$\mathscr{H}_{\text{II IV}} = 0 \qquad \mathscr{H}_{\text{III IV}} = 0$$

$$S_{\text{II II}} = \tfrac{1}{2}\int(\Phi_3 - \Phi_4)^2 d\tau = \tfrac{1}{2}(S_{33} + S_{44} - 2S_{34}) = 1 \qquad \ldots.(16.86)$$

$$S_{\text{III III}} = 1 \quad S_{\text{IV IV}} = 1 \quad S_{\text{II III}} = 0 \quad S_{\text{II IV}} = 0 \quad S_{\text{III IV}} = 0$$

And hence in place of equation 16.84, we obtain

$$\begin{vmatrix} \mathscr{H}_{\text{II II}} - E & \mathscr{H}_{\text{II III}} & 0 \\ \mathscr{H}_{\text{II III}} & \mathscr{H}_{\text{III III}} - E & 0 \\ 0 & 0 & \mathscr{H}_{\text{IV IV}} - E \end{vmatrix} = 0 \qquad \ldots.(16.87)$$

or

$$\begin{vmatrix} \mathscr{H}_{\text{II II}} - E & \mathscr{H}_{\text{II III}} \\ \mathscr{H}_{\text{II III}} & \mathscr{H}_{\text{III III}} - E \end{vmatrix} = 0$$

$$\mathscr{H}_{\text{IV IV}} - E = 0$$

Substituting into these equations the values for the integrals from equation 16.86 we obtain :

$$3E_o + C - A_{ab} - A_{ac} - A_{bc} - E = 0 \qquad \ldots.(16.88)$$

$$\begin{vmatrix} 3E_o + C - \frac{A_{ac}}{2} - \frac{A_{bc}}{2} + A_{ab} - E & -\frac{3E_o + C}{2} + A_{ac} - \frac{A_{ab}}{2} - \frac{A_{bc}}{2} \\ -\frac{3E_o + C}{2} + A_{ac} - \frac{A_{ab}}{2} - \frac{A_{bc}}{2} & 3E_o + C - \frac{A_{ab}}{2} - \frac{A_{ac}}{2} + A_{bc} - E \end{vmatrix} = 0$$

$$\ldots.(16.89)$$

Thus the problem has been reduced to that of solving a quadratic equation. Apart from this, however, the introduction of the new functions also has another advantage since it permits a more comprehensive presentation of the physical meaning of the results. Let us consider the spin terms of the new functions. The function Φ_3 arose from the antisymmetric nature of the function $aab\beta c\alpha$ in which the spin terms are $\alpha\beta\alpha$ and Φ_4 from the antisymmetric nature of $a\beta ba c\alpha$ in which the spin function is $\beta\alpha\alpha$. Consequently :

$$\Phi_{\text{II}} = \frac{1}{\sqrt{2}}(\Phi_3 - \Phi_4) = \frac{1}{\sqrt{2}} \sum_P (-1)^p P\left\{a\alpha b\beta c\alpha - a\beta b\alpha c\alpha\right\}$$

$$\ldots.(16.90)$$

i.e. the function Φ_{II} contains the term $abc(\alpha\beta\alpha - \beta\alpha\alpha)$ in which the spin term,

$$\alpha\beta\alpha - \beta\alpha\alpha = \big(\alpha(1)\beta(2) - \beta(1)\alpha(2)\big)\alpha(3) \qquad \ldots.(16.91)$$

contains the factor

$$\big(\alpha(1)\beta(2) - \beta(1)\alpha(2) \big) \qquad \ldots.(16.92)$$

This expression is identical with that given by the spin function for the case of a bond between two atoms (see equation 3.112). Whenever the spin electronic state of two electrons is described by the function $(\alpha\beta - \beta\alpha)$, it is possible to state that a bond is formed by those electrons. In the present case the electrons 1 and 2, belonging originally to atoms *a* and *b* produce the bond. The function thus describes the state of the system when the atom *c* is at infinity and does not participate in bond formation. For this state $S = \frac{1}{2}$ and $\Sigma s = +\frac{1}{2}$.

The energy of the system *a—bc* is given by

$$\mathscr{H}_{\text{II II}} = 3E_o + C + A_{ab} - \frac{A_{ac}}{2} - \frac{A_{bc}}{2} \qquad \ldots.(16.93)$$

If the atom *c* is located a long way from the molecule *a—b*, then the energy is,

$$E = 3E_o + C_{ab} + A_{ab}$$

$$|\, C_{bc} = 0 \;\; ; \;\; C_{ac} = 0 \;\; ; \;\; A_{ac} = 0 \;\; ; \;\; A_{bc} = 0 \,| \qquad \ldots.(16.94)$$

When, however, the atom *C* is close to *a—b*, the interaction of the three electrons and of the three nuclei enter into the Coulomb energy and

$$C = C_{ab} + C_{bc} + C_{ac}$$

in which each term will include the attraction of the electrons by the nuclei and the mutual repulsion of the electrons and nuclei. The attraction energy, however, outweighs the repulsion energies and hence the introduction of the additional terms lowers the potential energy of the molecule. In addition to the exchange energy of the bond, *a—b* which is equal to A_{ab}, the additional terms $-\frac{A_{ac}}{2}$ and $-\frac{A_{bc}}{2}$ are introduced, which represent the exchange of two pairs of non-bonding electrons. The exchange integrals enter into equation 16.93 with the coefficient 1/2 and a negative sign, so that the electron exchange leads to an increase of the energy and the non-bonding electrons repel each other (the equation 16.93 should be compared with 4.4).

Owing to the electron exchange phenomena, the structure *II* (page 408), in which *b* and *c* are bonded and *a* is a free atom, is possible, and is described by the function Φ_3, in which spin term is

$$\alpha(1)\big(\alpha(2)\beta(3) - \beta(2)\alpha(3)\big) \qquad \ldots.(16.95)$$

and the energy is given by

$$E = 3E_o + C + A_{bc} - A_{ac}/2 - A_{ab}/2 \qquad \ldots.(16.96)$$

In this case also $S = \frac{1}{2}$ and $\Sigma s = +\frac{1}{2}$. It would appear possible that we could write still a third function,

$$\Phi = \frac{1}{\sqrt{2}}(\Phi_2 - \Phi_4) \qquad \ldots.(16.97)$$

describing the state where there is a bond *a—c* and a free atom *b*. This function, however, is not independent of the other two, as is shown by the following expression :

$$\Phi = \frac{1}{\sqrt{2}}(\Phi_2 - \Phi_4) = \frac{1}{\sqrt{2}}(\Phi_2 - \Phi_3 + \Phi_3 - \Phi_4) = \Phi_{\text{III}} + \Phi_{\text{II}} \qquad \ldots.(16.98)$$

Let us consider the spin term of the last function Φ_{IV} :

$$\Phi_{IV} = \frac{1}{\sqrt{3!}}(\Phi_2 + \Phi_3 + \Phi_4) = \frac{1}{\sqrt{3!}} \sum_P (-1)^p Pabc(\alpha\alpha\beta + \alpha\beta\alpha + \beta\alpha\alpha) \quad \ldots(16.99)$$

In this case $S = 3/2$ and $\Sigma s = 1/2$. The solution of the secular equation of the eighth degree has thus been divided into two stages. First, we obtained the functions corresponding to each value of the sum of the spin projections and by so doing, the equation was reduced to two equations of the first order and one cubic equation. This cubic equation was due to the presence of three functions corresponding to $\Sigma s = +\frac{1}{2}$ and $-\frac{1}{2}$. These values correspond in one case to $S = +3/2$ and in the other two to $S = \frac{1}{2}$. Secondly, having obtained the functions corresponding to the various values of S, the cubic equation was reduced to the quadratic equation of 16.89, and the equation of the first order 16.88. The equation of the first order gives

$$E = 3E_o + C - A_{ab} - A_{bc} - A_{ac} \quad \ldots(16.100)$$

and its solution, is identical with $\mathcal{H}_{11}$. This is understandable since the functions Φ_I and Φ_{IV} are related to one and the same value of the resultant spin.

The energy of the lowest energy state may be obtained on solution of the quadratic equation, which has two roots :

$$E = 3E_o + C_{ab} + C_{ac} + C_{bc} \pm \pm (A^2_{ab} + A^2_{ac} + A^2_{bc} - A_{ab}A_{ac} - A_{ab}A_{bc} - A_{ac}A_{bc})^{\frac{1}{2}} \quad \ldots(16.101)$$

The positive sign before the square root term gives the lowest energy state. The energy of the system of three atoms is therefore :

$$E = 3E_o + C_{ab} + C_{ac} + C_{bc} + + (A^2_{ab} + A^2_{ac} + A^2_{bc} - A_{ab}A_{ac} - A_{ab}A_{bc} - A_{ac}A_{bc})^{\frac{1}{2}} \quad \ldots(16.102)$$

where E = total energy of the system
E_o = energy of one atom
C_{ab} = Coulomb energy of interaction of atoms a and b
C_{ac} = Coulomb energy of interaction of atoms a and c
C_{bc} = Coulomb energy of interaction of atoms b and c
A_{ab} = exchange energy of atoms a and b
A_{ac} = exchange energy of atoms a and c
A_{bc} = exchange energy of atoms b and c

This expression was first derived by LONDON[1].

ENERGY OF ACTIVATION

Using equation 16.102 it is possible to obtain an approximate value of the energy of activation of the reaction between the three atoms. London considered the special case where the configuration of the three atoms was linear, when the energy of activation is a minimum.

Initially atom c is a considerable distance from atoms a and b and there is no interaction, if weak van der Waal's forces are ignored, between a and b on the one hand and c on the other. Hence we may state

$$C_{ac} = 0, \quad A_{ac} = 0 \quad \text{for large values of } R_{ac}$$
$$C_{bc} = 0, \quad A_{bc} = 0 \quad \text{for large values of } R_{bc}$$

These terms can in fact be neglected when R_{ac} or R_{bc} exceeds 3 or 4 Å. In these circumstances the expression 16.102 becomes

$$E = 3E_o + C_{ab} + A_{ab} \quad \ldots.(16.103)$$

This equation is identical with that deduced by Heitler and London for the hydrogen molecule with the addition of the energy of the third atom E_o, S^2 being neglected. On the approach of c to ab, the distances R_{ac} and R_{bc} decrease and it is no longer possible to neglect the interaction of the electron of atom c with the electrons of atoms a and b. Thus the integrals A_{bc} and A_{ac} can no longer be considered as equal to zero although they will still have values less than A_{ab}. If the atom c approaches the molecule ab so that it is nearer to atom b, *i.e.* in the linear arrangement a—b c, interaction with b occurs before the interaction with a becomes significant. Thus R_{bc} is greater than R_{ab}, although of the same order of magnitude, and R_{ac} is considerably greater than R_{ab}. Under these circumstances C_{ac} and A_{ac} may be considered equal to zero, but since the terms C_{bc} and A_{bc} cannot now be neglected, equation 16.103 becomes

$$E = 3E_o + C_{ab} + C_{bc} + (A_{ab}{}^2 + A_{bc}{}^2 - A_{ab}A_{bc})^{\frac{1}{2}} \quad \ldots.(16.104)$$

The additional Coulomb energy C_{bc} causes attraction between the atoms b and c and therefore lowers the energy of the system ; this effect, however, is not great and the energy of the system is determined mainly by the exchange energies. Since $R_{bc} > R_{ab}$, then $A_{bc} < A_{ab}$ and consequently $A_{bc}{}^2 < A_{ab}A_{bc}$ and the expression in the bracket in equation 16.104 is less than $A_{ab}{}^2$. Hence the energy of the system is greater than when c is located at infinity and c is therefore repelled by a—b.

In order to simplify the mathematical treatment, London assumes that the distance between a and b in the molecule a—b remains unchanged on the approach of the atom c, and only the interaction with c is taken into consideration. Thus the value of A_{ab} remains constant and the variation of the energy depends only on A_{bc}, *i.e.* on the distance between b and c. The value of A_{bc} increases with decrease of the distance between b and c until this distance is identical with the a—b distance. The energy of the system is then a maximum, which can be determined by taking the differential coefficient of E with respect to A_{bc} and equating to zero, *viz*

$$\left(\frac{\partial E}{\partial A_{bc}}\right)_{A_{ab}} = \frac{2A_{bc} - A_{ab}}{2(A^2{}_{ab} + A^2{}_{bc} - A_{ab}A_{bc})^{\frac{1}{2}}} \quad \ldots.(16.105)$$

On solution of equation 16.105 we find that the energy has a maximum value when $A_{bc} = A_{ab}/2$. Substituting this expression in equation 16.104, we find that at the transitional state the energy is given by

$$E = 3E_o + C + \frac{A_{ab}\sqrt{3}}{2} = 3E_o + C + 0{\cdot}86A_{ab} \quad \ldots.(16.106)$$

The energy is thus greater than in the initial state, by 0·14 A_{ab} and this quantity is an approximate evaluation of the energy of activation. In the final state there is a molecule b—c and a free atom a. The energy of such a system is given by

$$E = 3E_o + C_{bc} + A_{bc} \quad \ldots.(16.107)$$

The variation of the energy as the atom c approaches the molecule a—b, in which the distance R_{ab} remains constant, is shown in *Figure 76*. Each contour line corresponds to a definite energy value. The variation of the

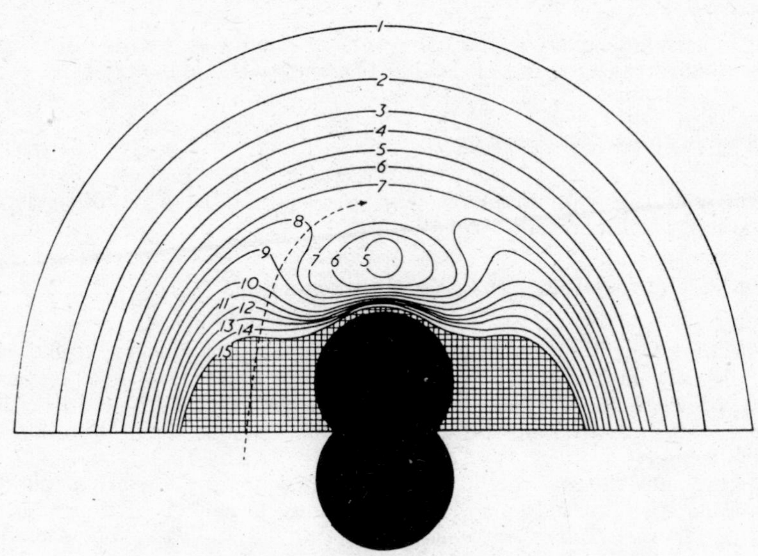

Figure 76. Variation of energy of interaction as an atom approaches a rigid molecule along line of centres

energy with the distance between b and c is calculated in the following manner. From experimental data the curve is constructed giving the energy of the molecule as a function of the distance between the atoms, *i.e.* the potential energy curve obtained from spectroscopic data. It is assumed that the Coulomb energy always comprises a definite and constant proportion of the total energy, in the given example, 20 per cent, and by calculating this quantity from the total energy it is possible to obtain the exchange energy at various distances. From the diagram (*Figure 76*) it follows that the approach along the line of centres is most favourable. In order that c may approach ab, energy of translation is necessary to overcome the repulsion. The transition state corresponds to an energy value 7·5 kcals above the initial value and further approach is accompanied by a decrease of energy owing to the formation of the molecule bc.

The above treatment is approximate since the presence of the third electron will cause an increase of the distance R_{ab} and the assumption that this remains constant produces an incorrect result. For the case when

$$A_{ab} = A_{bc} \qquad \ldots.(16.108)$$

which corresponds to the configuration when both the distances R_{ab} and R_{bc} are equal, substitution of equation 16.108 in equation 16.104 gives

$$E = 3E_o + C + (A^2_{ab} + A^2_{bc} - A_{ab}A_{bc})^{\frac{1}{2}} = 3E_o + C + A_{ab} \qquad \ldots.(16.109)$$

i.e. the energy of the system

$$a\cdots b\cdots c \qquad \text{when} \qquad R_{ab} = R_{bc}$$

is identical with the energy of the system

$$a\text{—}b \quad c$$

at the commencement of the reaction. This is clearly incorrect.

If the exchange energy A_{ac} is taken into consideration, *i.e.* the interaction of the atoms a and c, equation 16.102 becomes, when $A_{ab} = A_{bc}$:

$$E = 3E_o + C + A_{ab} - A_{ac} \qquad \ldots .(16.110)$$

This result shows that the state

$$a \cdots\cdot b \cdots\cdot c$$

is less favourable from an energy point of view than $a—b\ \ c$. Nevertheless in the linear configuration

$$a \quad b \quad c$$

a is located farther from c than b and consequently

$$A_{ac} < A_{bc}$$

The reason for the error in the above calculation is due to the fact that the increase in the $a—b$ distance as c approaches, has been ignored. Thus although the expression 16.102 is correct for $a \cdots\cdot b \cdots\cdot c$ the value of A_{ab} to be inserted in this expression, is different from that for the molecule $a—b$.

EYRING and POLANYI have used the data from the above calculations to construct a potential energy surface giving the energy of the system of the three atoms a, b and c at various values of R_{ab} and R_{ac}. The exchange energies were obtained from the experimental potential energy curve of the hydrogen molecule and they took into consideration the fact that both distances R_{ab} and R_{bc} change during the reaction. From the values of A_{ab}, A_{bc} and A_{ac} for various values of R_{ab} and R_{bc}, they obtained by means of formula 16.102 the energies of the various configurations of the system. From these data it was possible to construct a contour map (*Figure 77*) in which the values of R_{ab} and R_{bc} are given along the axes and the contour lines connect points of equal energy. The point A represents the initial state of the system when atoms a and b form the molecule $a—b$ and the atom c is at infinity; the energy of the system will be $3E_o + C_{ab} + A_{ab}$. The point B corresponds to the final state of the reaction, *i.e.* to a molecule $b—c$ and a separate atom a; the energy of this system being $3E_o + C_{bc} + A_{bc}$.

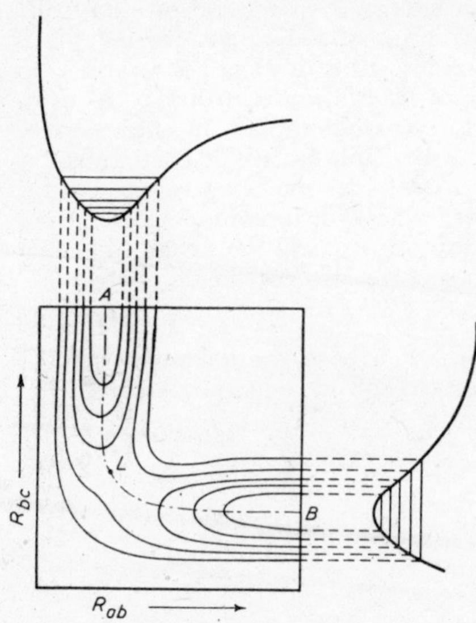

Figure 77. Potential energy surface for the reaction $H + H_2 = H_2 + H$

The path AL lies in a valley between two regions of higher energy. The shift of the system from the equilibrium position at A is repelled by either the repulsion between a and b or by the attraction between a and b according to the direction of the shift, *i.e.* as shown in *Figure 77* the cross-section through the diagram at A gives the potential energy curve of the molecule $a—b$. The height from the bottom of the valley to the plateau on the right of the diagram requires an energy equal to 103·2 kcals, *i.e.* the dissociation energy of the hydrogen molecule.

Although we refer here to the 'bottom of the valley' this actually means the lowest possible vibrational state of the molecule and will be a distance above the minimum, equal to the zero-point energy.

The passage of the system from A to L corresponds to the approach of the atom *c* to the molecule *ab* and since *c* is repelled by *ab* this change involves an increase in energy. As indicated by the diagram, the passage of the system from A to L involves not only a decrease of R_{bc} but also an increase of R_{ab}. The most favourable path for the reaction is that shown by the dotted line, the height of the energy barrier which has to be surmounted is 13 kcals above the original state at A. The value of 13 kcals for the energy of activation is obtained on the assumption that the Coulomb energy is 14 per cent and the exchange energy 86 per cent of the total energy. EYRING and POLANYI[1] found that at the summit of the energy barrier for the reaction $H_2 + H$ there existed a shallow minimum whose depth was 1·5 kcals below the barrier. This indicates the existence of the intermediate complex H_3 as a separate entity. This has not been confirmed by experiment. A similar depression is observed in the potential surface for the reaction[3] $Cl_2 + Cl$.

The method of calculating the energy of activation described above is obviously approximate and it has been pointed out[4] that the assumptions concerning non-orthogonality in the London equation may lead to considerable errors. Nevertheless in spite of the approximate nature of the calculations, this treatment is of considerable importance, adding materially to our knowledge of the mechanism of chemical reactions and explaining the origin of the energy of activation.

REFERENCES

1 LONDON, F. *Z. Elektrochem.*. 35 (1929) 552
EYRING, H. and POLANYI, M. *Z. phys. Chem. B* 13 (1931) 275
EVANS, M. G. and POLANYI, M. *Trans. Faraday Soc.* 31 (1935) 875
GLASSTONE, S., LAIDLER, K. H. and EYRING, H. *The Theory of Rate Processes* New York, 1941
2 SLATER, J. C. *Phys. Rev.* 38 (1931) 1109
3 GLASSTONE, S., LAIDLER, K. J. and EYRING, H. *ibid*
4 JAMES, H. M. and COOLIDGE, A. S. *J. chem. Phys.* 2 (1934) 811
SCHUCHOWITZKY, A. *Acta Physicochim. U.R.S.S.* 1 (1935) 901

17

THE POLYELECTRON PROBLEM AND RESONANCE ENERGY

THE FOUR ELECTRON PROBLEM

SLATER'S METHOD which has been described in Chapter 16 for the problem of three electrons may be applied to systems with any number of electrons. Each electron may exist in the field of any of the nuclei, and resonance among the different states, representing different electronic distributions,. will occur. With four atoms having four valency electrons, $4! = 24$ different arrangements of the electrons between the nuclei are possible, with $2^4 = 16$ different spin states. In all there will therefore be $24 \times 16 = 384$ different complete wave functions. But as we have already seen, states with different values of the spin quantum number do not interact with one another. This permits a considerable reduction in the number of states to be considered. We are only concerned with stable configurations in which all the electrons in pairs neutralize their spin by the formation of a covalent bond, *i.e.* $S=0$ and $\Sigma s=0$.

With four electrons, we have three possible ways of pairing the electrons, *i.e.* 1 with 2 and 3 with 4; 1 with 3 and 2 with 4; 1 with 4 and 2 with 3. If as before we attach electron 1 to atom *a*, electron 2 to atom *b*, electron 3 to atom *c* and electron 4 to atom *d*, the three methods of neutralizing the electron spins denote the formation of bonds between the atoms, as shown below:

I ab and *cd*

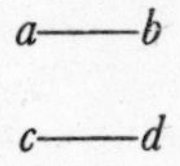

II ac and *bd*

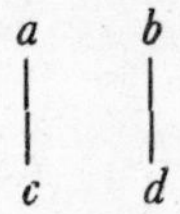

III ad and *bc*

It would appear that for a description of the four electron system it would be necessary to consider the superposition of the three given structures with different localizations of the valency bonds. However, it is still possible to make a further simplification. In the problem of three electrons, three structures also were possible: with the bond between *a* and *b* and with a free atom *c* (spin function $\alpha\beta\alpha - \beta\alpha\alpha$); with a bond between atoms *b* and *c* and a free atom *a* (spin function $\alpha\alpha\beta - \alpha\beta\alpha$); with the bond between atoms *a* and *c* and a free atom *b* (spin function $\alpha\alpha\beta - \beta\alpha\alpha$). But we pointed out that these three functions were not independent, the third being a linear combination of the other two. Let us write down the appropriate functions for the four electron problems describing the states *I*, *II* and *III*. The space coordinate part of any wave function of four electrons will have the form

$$\psi_1 = \sum_P (-1)^p Pabcd \qquad \ldots .(17.1)$$

i.e. it will be a linear combination of the function *abcd* and of all functions which are obtained from that function by a rearrangement of the electrons.

In the structure *I*, electrons 1 and 2 mutually neutralize their spins, therefore the projection of the spin angular momentum of one is $+\frac{1}{2}$ (spin function α) and of the other $-\frac{1}{2}$ (spin function β). The spin function of the two electrons in the case of the bond will be, as we have seen,

$$\alpha(1)\beta(2) - \beta(1)\alpha(2) \qquad \text{....(17.2)}$$

A similar function will also describe the spin function of the second pair of bonded electrons, 3 and 4,

$$\alpha(3)\beta(4) - \beta(3)\alpha(4) \qquad \text{....(17.3)}$$

so that the complete spin function of structure *I* will be

$$\begin{aligned}\sigma &= [\alpha(1)\beta(2) - \beta(1)\alpha(2)][\alpha(3)\beta(4) - \beta(3)\alpha(4)] \\ &= \alpha\beta\alpha\beta - \beta\alpha\alpha\beta - \alpha\beta\beta\alpha + \beta\alpha\beta\alpha \qquad \text{....(17.4)}\end{aligned}$$

The complete wave function of the structure *I* will therefore be

$$\Phi_{\mathrm{I}} = \sum_P (-1)^P Pabcd\{\alpha\beta\alpha\beta - \beta\alpha\alpha\beta - \alpha\beta\beta\alpha + \beta\alpha\beta\alpha\} \qquad \text{....(17.5)}$$

In the structure *II*, the bonds are formed by electrons 1 and 3, and 2 and 4. The spin functions of these pairs will be respectively,

$$\alpha(1)\beta(3) - \beta(1)\alpha(3) \qquad \text{....(17.6)}$$

$$\alpha(2)\beta(4) - \beta(2)\alpha(4) \qquad \text{....(17.7)}$$

The complete spin function of structure *II* will therefore be

$$\begin{aligned}\sigma &= [\alpha(1)\beta(3) - \beta(1)\alpha(3)][\alpha(2)\beta(4) - \beta(2)\alpha(4)] \\ &= \alpha\alpha\beta\beta - \beta\alpha\alpha\beta - \alpha\beta\beta\alpha + \beta\beta\alpha\alpha \qquad \text{....(17.8)}\end{aligned}$$

and the complete wave function is

$$\Phi_{\mathrm{II}} = \sum_P (-1)^P Pabcd\{\alpha\alpha\beta\beta - \beta\alpha\alpha\beta - \alpha\beta\beta\alpha + \beta\beta\alpha\alpha\} \qquad \text{....(17.9)}$$

For the third structure the bonds are formed by electrons 1 with 4 and 2 with 3 and the appropriate spin functions are

$$\alpha(1)\beta(4) - \beta(1)\alpha(4) \qquad \text{....(17.10)}$$

$$\alpha(2)\beta(3) - \beta(2)\alpha(3) \qquad \text{....(17.11)}$$

and the complete spin function is

$$\begin{aligned}\sigma &= [\alpha(1)\beta(4) - \beta(1)\alpha(4)][\alpha(2)\beta(3) - \beta(2)\alpha(3)] \\ &= \alpha\alpha\beta\beta - \beta\alpha\beta\alpha - \alpha\beta\alpha\beta + \beta\beta\alpha\alpha \qquad \text{....(17.12)}\end{aligned}$$

and the complete wave function is

$$\Phi_{\mathrm{III}} = \sum_P (-1)^P Pabcd\{\alpha\alpha\beta\beta - \beta\alpha\beta\alpha - \alpha\beta\alpha\beta + \beta\beta\alpha\alpha\} \qquad \text{....(17.13)}$$

It is clearly seen that Φ_{III} is a linear combination of Φ_{I} and Φ_{II} since

$$\begin{aligned}\Phi_{\mathrm{III}} = \Phi_{\mathrm{II}} - \Phi_{\mathrm{I}} &= \sum_P (-1)^P Pabcd\{\alpha\alpha\beta\beta - \beta\alpha\alpha\beta - \alpha\beta\beta\alpha + \beta\beta\alpha\alpha\} \\ &\quad - \sum_P (-1)^P Pabcd\{\alpha\beta\alpha\beta - \beta\alpha\alpha\beta - \alpha\beta\beta\alpha + \beta\alpha\beta\alpha\} \\ &= \sum_P (-1)^P Pabcd\{\alpha\alpha\beta\beta - \alpha\beta\alpha\beta - \beta\alpha\beta\alpha + \beta\beta\alpha\alpha\} \qquad \text{....(17.14)}\end{aligned}$$

This means that the structure *III* is not an independent form but is a superposition of the first two structures.

RUMER's theory (Chapter 5), gives a method of obtaining the number of canonical structures for any particular number of electrons. Rumer's equation is $\dfrac{n!}{\left(\frac{n}{2}\right)!\left(\frac{n}{2}+1\right)}!$ which, when $n = 4$ becomes $4!/2!3! = 2$.

These two forms are evidently structures *I* and *II*.

The function of the system of four electrons when $\Sigma s = 0$ may be regarded as a linear combination of the complete wave functions of structures *I* and *II*, *viz*

$$\Phi = c_1\Phi_{\mathrm{I}} + c_2\Phi_{\mathrm{II}} \qquad \ldots.(17.15)$$

The secular equation of the second order is obtained in the manner described previously :

$$\begin{vmatrix} \mathscr{H}_{\mathrm{I\,I}} - E & \mathscr{H}_{\mathrm{I\,II}} - ES_{\mathrm{I\,II}} \\ \mathscr{H}_{\mathrm{I\,II}} - ES_{\mathrm{I\,II}} & \mathscr{H}_{\mathrm{II\,II}} - E \end{vmatrix} = 0 \qquad \ldots.(17.16)$$

where E is the energy of the system over and above that of the energy of the four atoms, and

$$\left.\begin{aligned} \mathscr{H}_{\mathrm{I\,I}} &= \int \Phi_{\mathrm{I}}\mathscr{H}\Phi_{\mathrm{I}}d\tau \\ \mathscr{H}_{\mathrm{I\,II}} &= \int \Phi_{\mathrm{I}}\,\mathscr{H}\Phi_{\mathrm{II}}d\tau \\ \mathscr{H}_{\mathrm{II\,II}} &= \int \Phi_{\mathrm{II}}\mathscr{H}\Phi_{\mathrm{II}}d\tau \\ S_{\mathrm{I\,II}} &= \int \Phi_{\mathrm{I}}\Phi_{\mathrm{II}}d\tau \end{aligned}\right\} \qquad \ldots.(17.17)$$

EVALUATION OF INTEGRALS OF SECULAR EQUATION

We shall now consider the evaluation of the integrals $\mathscr{H}_{\mathrm{I\,I}}$, $\mathscr{H}_{\mathrm{I\,II}}$ and $\mathscr{H}_{\mathrm{II\,II}}$. If the deviation from orthogonality is neglected the integrals may be considered as the sum of the Coulomb (C) and exchange (A) integrals for different pairs of atoms, *ab*, *ac*, *bc*, *bd* and *cd*. The method employed may follow that used in the case of three electrons but involves certain difficulties and PAULING suggested a simpler method[1].

The structures *I* and *II* are represented by the following

$$\begin{matrix} a - b \\ \\ c - d \end{matrix}\quad I \qquad \begin{matrix} a & & b \\ | & & | \\ c & & d \end{matrix}\quad II$$

For the calculation of $\mathscr{H}_{\mathrm{I\,II}}$ we arrange the atoms in the same way but introduce all the bonds of the structures *I* and *II viz*

$$\mathscr{H}_{\mathrm{I\,II}} \quad \begin{matrix} a & - & b \\ | & & | \\ c & - & d \end{matrix}$$

The corresponding structure for $\mathscr{H}_{\mathrm{I\,I}}$ is obtained if structure *I* is superposed upon itself giving,

$$\mathscr{H}_{\mathrm{I\,I}} \quad \begin{matrix} a = b \\ \\ c = d \end{matrix}$$

In a similar manner we have $\mathcal{H}_{\text{II II}}$ given by,

$$\mathcal{H}_{\text{II II}} \quad \begin{matrix} a & & b \\ \| & & \| \\ c & & d \end{matrix}$$

According to Pauling each such arrangement consists of 'islands', and each isolated part of the structure not united to other parts by a bond represents a separate island. In the structure for $\mathcal{H}_{\text{I II}}$, there is only one island and in $\mathcal{H}_{\text{I I}}$ and $\mathcal{H}_{\text{II II}}$ there are two in each. If the total number of islands is i and the number of electrons n, then the coefficient of the Coulomb integral is $1/2^{\left(\frac{n}{2}-i\right)}$ Thus, when $n = 4$, the coefficient of the Coulomb integral in $\mathcal{H}_{\text{I I}}$ is, since $i = 2$:

$$1/2^{\left(\frac{n}{2}-i\right)} = 1/2^{(2-2)} = 1$$

in $\mathcal{H}_{\text{II II}}$ $(i = 2)$

$$1/2^{\left(\frac{n}{2}-i\right)} = 1/2^{(2-2)} = 1$$

and in $\mathcal{H}_{\text{I II}}$ $(i = 1)$

$$1/2^{\left(\frac{n}{2}-i\right)} = 1/2^{(2-1)} = \tfrac{1}{2}$$

In addition, exchange integrals will enter into $\mathcal{H}_{\text{I I}}$ $\mathcal{H}_{\text{II II}}$ and $\mathcal{H}_{\text{I II}}$; these will be :

a and b	A_{ab}
a and c	A_{ac}
a and d	A_{ad}
b and c	A_{bc}
b and d	A_{bd}
c and d	A_{cd}

The coefficient of each of these integrals is

$$f(p).1/2^{\left(\frac{n}{2}-i\right)} \qquad \ldots .(17.18)$$

If the atoms concerned in a given structure belong to different islands, then p is equal to zero and $f(p) = -\tfrac{1}{2}$. This refers, for example, to atoms a and c in the structure $\mathcal{H}_{\text{I I}}$. If the atoms are located in the same island, p is equal to the number of steps necessary to pass from one atom to another; thus, for example, in the structure $\mathcal{H}_{\text{I II}}$,

$$\mathcal{H}_{\text{I II}} \quad \begin{matrix} a & — & b \\ | & & | \\ c & — & d \end{matrix}$$

p is equal to one for atoms a and b or a and c, but to two for atoms a and d. If $p = 1, 3, 5, \ldots$, $f(p) = +1$, and if $p = 2, 4, 6, \ldots$, $f(p) = -2$.

Let us determine the coefficient for the integrals in $\mathcal{H}_{\text{I I}}$:

$$\mathcal{H}_{\text{I I}} \quad \begin{matrix} a & = & b \\ \\ c & = & d \end{matrix}$$

Here

$$1/2^{\left(\frac{n}{2}-i\right)} = 1$$

For atoms a and b, $p = 1$ and $f(p) = +1$ and the coefficient of A_{ab} is $+1$.
For atoms a and c, $p = 0$ and $f(p) = -\tfrac{1}{2}$ and the coefficient of A_{ac} is $-\tfrac{1}{2}$.

The same applies to the pairs of atoms a and d, b and c and b and d. Finally for atoms c and d, which are located in the same island, $p = 1$ and $f(p) = +1$ and the coefficient of $A_{cd} = +1$. Hence

$$\mathscr{H}_{\mathrm{I\,I}} = C + A_{ab} + A_{cd} - \tfrac{1}{2}A_{ac} - \tfrac{1}{2}A_{bc} - \tfrac{1}{2}A_{ad} - \tfrac{1}{2}A_{bd} \quad \ldots.(17.19)$$

In the structure $\mathscr{H}_{\mathrm{II\,II}}$, *viz*

$$\begin{array}{cc} a & b \\ \| & \| \\ c & d \end{array}$$

the pairs of atoms ab, ad, bc and cd are on different islands and for these pairs $p = 0$ and $f(p) = -\tfrac{1}{2}$. The atoms a and c, and b and d are in the same island and $p = 1$ and $f(p) = +1$. Thus

$$\mathscr{H}_{\mathrm{II\,II}} = C + A_{ac} + A_{bd} - \tfrac{1}{2}A_{ab} - \tfrac{1}{2}A_{ad} - \tfrac{1}{2}A_{bc} - \tfrac{1}{2}A_{cd} \quad \ldots.(17.20)$$

For the structure $\mathscr{H}_{\mathrm{I\,II}}$, *viz*

$$\begin{array}{ccc} a & - & b \\ | & & | \\ c & - & d \end{array}$$

we have

$$1/2^{\left(\frac{n}{2}-i\right)} = 1/2^{(2-1)} = 1/2$$

and all the atoms are in the same island. In order to transfer from a to b it is necessary to pass either one or three groups (a—c, c—d, d—b) consequently $f(p) = 1$ and the coefficient of the integral A_{ab} is

$$f(p).1/2^{\left(\frac{n}{2}-i\right)} = 1/2$$

This applies also to the pairs of atoms a and c, b and d, and c and d and the corresponding exchange integrals. In order to transfer from a to d, two groups have to be passed (a—c and c—d) so that in this case $p = 2$ and $f(p) = -2$, and the coefficient of exchange integral A_{ad} is

$$f(p).\,1/2^{\left(\frac{n}{2}-i\right)} = -2\,.\,1/2 = -1$$

This also applies to the pair of atoms b and c. Thus we obtain,

$$\mathscr{H}_{\mathrm{I\,II}} = \tfrac{1}{2}C + \tfrac{1}{2}A_{ab} + \tfrac{1}{2}A_{ac} + \tfrac{1}{2}A_{bd} + \tfrac{1}{2}A_{cd} - A_{ab} - A_{bc} \quad \ldots.(17.21)$$

In addition to the integrals $\mathscr{H}_{\mathrm{I\,I}}$, $\mathscr{H}_{\mathrm{II\,II}}$ and $\mathscr{H}_{\mathrm{I\,II}}$ the secular equation 17.16 contains the non-orthogonal integral

$$S_{\mathrm{I\,II}} = \int \Phi_{\mathrm{I}}\Phi_{\mathrm{II}}d\tau$$

The integral $S_{\mathrm{I\,II}}$ will be reduced to integrals of two types :

$$\int (aabac\beta d\beta)^2 d\tau \quad \text{and} \quad \int (aabac\beta d\beta)(c\beta baaad\beta)\,d\tau$$

All integrals of the second type will be equal to zero on account of the orthogonality of the spin functions and integrals of the first type, corresponding to a Coulomb integral will be equal to unity, since the space coordinate and spin functions are normalized. In $S_{\mathrm{I\,II}}$ the coefficient will be the same as the Coulomb integral in $\mathscr{H}_{\mathrm{I\,II}}$ and thus

$$S_{\mathrm{I\,II}} = \tfrac{1}{2} \quad \ldots.(17.22)$$

We are now in a position to set out in its general form the secular equation for the four electron problem. This will take the following form :

$$\begin{vmatrix} \mathscr{H}_{\mathrm{I\,I}}-E & \mathscr{H}_{\mathrm{I\,II}}-ES_{\mathrm{I\,II}} \\ \mathscr{H}_{\mathrm{I\,II}}-ES_{\mathrm{I\,II}} & \mathscr{H}_{\mathrm{II\,II}}-E \end{vmatrix} =$$

$$\begin{vmatrix} C+A_{ab}+A_{cd}-\frac{A_{ac}}{2}-\frac{A_{ad}}{2}-\frac{A_{bc}}{2}-\frac{A_{bd}}{2}-E & \frac{C}{2}+\frac{A_{ab}}{2}+\frac{A_{ac}}{2}+\frac{A_{bd}}{2}+\frac{A_{cd}}{2}-A_{ad}-A_{bc}-\frac{E}{2} \\ \frac{C}{2}+\frac{A_{ab}}{2}+\frac{A_{ac}}{2}+\frac{A_{bd}}{2}+\frac{A_{cd}}{2}-A_{ad}-A_{bc}-\frac{E}{2} & C+A_{ac}+A_{bd}-\frac{A_{ab}}{2}-\frac{A_{ad}}{2}-\frac{A_{bc}}{2}-\frac{A_{cd}}{2}-E \end{vmatrix}$$

$$=0 \qquad \ldots.(17.23)$$

The same result is obtained if the integrals are calculated as in the three electron problem, but Pauling's method is shorter.

CALCULATION OF ENERGIES FOR MOLECULES OF BUTADIENE, BENZENE AND FULVENE

Consider the four π electrons of the butadiene molecule. There are two possible bond localizations given by the canonical structures :

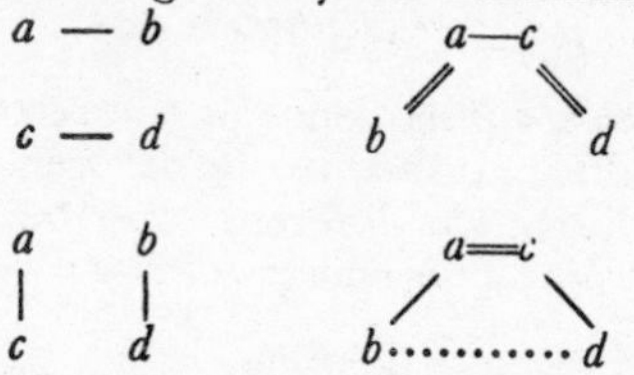

```
a — b          a—c
              /   \        I
c — d        b     d

a   b          a═c
|   |         /   \        II
c   d        b.........d
```

In the first formula the double bonds occur between the outer pairs of carbon atoms, as in the normal formula of butadiene, whereas in the second case the double bond is located between the middle pair of carbon atoms and there is an elongated bond between the outer carbon atoms. Here the integrals A_{ab}, A_{ac} and A_{cd}, which are the exchange integrals for the bonds *ab*, *ac* and *cd*, are approximately equal and will be denoted by α ; thus

$$A_{ab}=A_{ac}=A_{cd}=\alpha \qquad \ldots.(17.24)$$

All the remaining integrals refer to the exchange between non-adjacent atoms, located at comparatively large distances from each other. The value of these integrals is small and consequently may be neglected *i.e.*

$$A_{bc}=A_{ad}=A_{bd}=0 \qquad \ldots.(17.25)$$

Combining equations 17.24 and 17.25 with 17.19 we obtain,

$$\mathscr{H}_{\mathrm{I\,I}}=C+3\alpha/2 \qquad \ldots.(17.26)$$

This would represent the energy of the molecule if only structure *I* were present. In this formula we have taken into consideration the Coulomb energy C, the exchange energy of two bonds, 2α, and the repulsion of the non-bonding electrons of atoms a and c ($-\alpha/2$). In addition, however, we must consider the alternative structure *II*. Its energy is easily seen from equations 17.20, 17.24 and 17.25 to be given by

$$\mathscr{H}_{\mathrm{II\,II}}=C \qquad \ldots.(17.27)$$

In this structure there is, in fact, only one bond, that between a and c.

The second bond ($b \cdots\cdots d$) in which the interatomic distance is 2·8 Å contributes nothing to the energy of the molecule. The exchange energy of the bond a—c is compensated by repulsion energy of the non-bonding electrons of a and b, and c and d ($-\ 2 \times \alpha/2$). The energy of structure *II* is thus less than *I*, but the superposition of the two structures leads to an additional stabilization of the system.

From equations 17.21, 17.24 and 17.25 we obtain

$$\mathcal{H}_{\mathrm{I\,II}} = C/2 + 3\alpha/2 \qquad \ldots.(17.28)$$

and the secular equation for the π electrons of butadiene now becomes

$$\begin{vmatrix} C + \frac{3}{2}\alpha - E & \frac{C}{2} + \frac{3}{2}\alpha - \frac{E}{2} \\ \frac{C}{2} + \frac{3}{2}\alpha - \frac{E}{2} & C - E \end{vmatrix} = 0 \qquad \ldots.(17.29)$$

Hence we obtain

$$E = C \pm \alpha\sqrt{3} = C \pm 1{\cdot}73\alpha \qquad \ldots.(17.30)$$

i.e. there are two solutions for E:

$$E_1 = C + 1{\cdot}73\alpha \qquad \ldots.(17{\cdot}31)$$

$$E_2 = C - 1{\cdot}73\alpha \qquad \ldots.(17{\cdot}32)$$

This result means that as a consequence of the resonance, two states of the system arise, which are distinguished by the different coefficients c_1 and c_2 in equation 17.15, thus indicating a different contribution to the resonance from the structures *I* and *II*. The energy of the lower state is given by equation 17.31, *viz*

$$E_1 = C + 1{\cdot}73\alpha$$

If we compare this with the energy of the isolated structure *I*, as given by equation 17.26:

$$E = C + 1{\cdot}5\alpha$$

we see that the stabilization energy due to resonance is equal to 0·23α. This is the value of the resonance energy of butadiene. By such methods it is possible to obtain the secular equation for any even number of electrons.

In benzene there are six π electrons and the number of independent canonical structures is five. If we denote the carbon atoms by the letters a, b, c, d, e and f, these structures will be represented as follows:

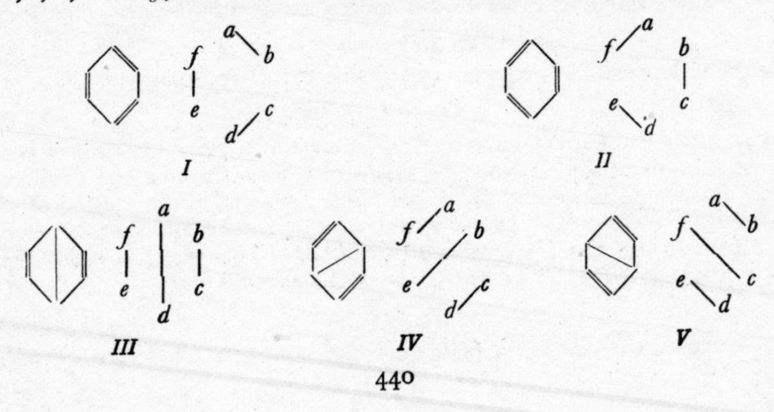

The secular equation for the five resonance structures will be

$$\begin{vmatrix} \mathcal{H}_{\mathrm{I\,I}}-E & \mathcal{H}_{\mathrm{I\,II}}-ES_{\mathrm{I\,II}} & \mathcal{H}_{\mathrm{I\,III}}-ES_{\mathrm{I\,III}} & \mathcal{H}_{\mathrm{I\,IV}}-ES_{\mathrm{I\,IV}} & \mathcal{H}_{\mathrm{I\,V}}-ES_{\mathrm{I\,V}} \\ \mathcal{H}_{\mathrm{I\,II}}-ES_{\mathrm{I\,II}} & \mathcal{H}_{\mathrm{II\,II}}-E & \mathcal{H}_{\mathrm{II\,III}}-ES_{\mathrm{II\,III}} & \mathcal{H}_{\mathrm{II\,IV}}-ES_{\mathrm{II\,IV}} & \mathcal{H}_{\mathrm{II\,V}}-ES_{\mathrm{II\,V}} \\ \mathcal{H}_{\mathrm{I\,III}}-ES_{\mathrm{I\,III}} & \mathcal{H}_{\mathrm{II\,III}}-ES_{\mathrm{II\,III}} & \mathcal{H}_{\mathrm{III\,III}}-E & \mathcal{H}_{\mathrm{III\,IV}}-ES_{\mathrm{III\,IV}} & \mathcal{H}_{\mathrm{III\,V}}-ES_{\mathrm{III\,V}} \\ \mathcal{H}_{\mathrm{I\,IV}}-ES_{\mathrm{I\,IV}} & \mathcal{H}_{\mathrm{II\,IV}}-ES_{\mathrm{II\,IV}} & \mathcal{H}_{\mathrm{III\,IV}}-ES_{\mathrm{III\,IV}} & \mathcal{H}_{\mathrm{IV\,IV}}-E & \mathcal{H}_{\mathrm{IV\,V}}-ES_{\mathrm{IV\,V}} \\ \mathcal{H}_{\mathrm{I\,V}}-ES_{\mathrm{I\,V}} & \mathcal{H}_{\mathrm{II\,V}}-ES_{\mathrm{II\,V}} & \mathcal{H}_{\mathrm{III\,V}}-ES_{\mathrm{III\,V}} & \mathcal{H}_{\mathrm{IV\,V}}-ES_{\mathrm{IV\,V}} & \mathcal{H}_{\mathrm{V\,V}}-E \end{vmatrix} = 0 \qquad \ldots.(17.33)$$

We shall now calculate using Pauling's method, the integrals in equations 17.33. For this purpose we shall take into account only the exchanges between adjacent atoms, *i.e.*

a—b
b—c
c— d
d e
e f
a–f

All the corresponding exchange integrals will be equal to each other *i.e.*

$$A_{ab} = A_{bc} = A_{cd} = A_{de} = A_{ef} = A_{af} = \alpha \qquad \ldots.(17.34)$$

The remaining exchange integrals between non-adjacent atoms as stated above will be assumed to be equal to zero :

$$A_{ac} = A_{ad} = A_{ae} = A_{bd} = A_{be} = A_{bf} = A_{ce} = A_{cf} = A_{df} = 0 \qquad \ldots.(17.35)$$

The integral $\mathcal{H}_{\mathrm{I\,I}}$ will correspond to the structure

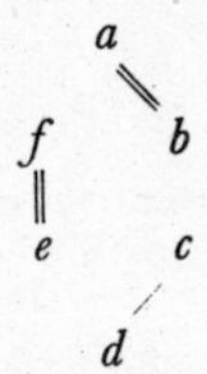

in which there are three islands, so that $i = 3$; $n/2 = 3$ and $1/2^{\left(\frac{n}{2}-i\right)} = 1$. Thus the coefficient of the Coulomb integral is 1. Now let us consider the coefficients of the exchange integrals of equation 17.34. Each pair of atoms, a—b, c—d, e—f, constitute a single island for which $f(p) = 1$ and consequently the coefficients $f(p).1/2^{\left(\frac{n}{2}-i\right)}$ for the integrals A_{ab}, A_{cd} and A_{ef} are equal to unity. The pairs of atoms b—c, d—e, a—f are in different islands and hence $p = 0$, $f(p) = -\frac{1}{2}$ and the coefficients for the integrals A_{bc}, A_{de} and A_{af} are equal to $-\frac{1}{2}$.

Thus

$$\mathcal{H}_{\mathrm{I\,I}} = C + A_{ab} + A_{cd} + A_{ef} - \tfrac{1}{2}A_{bc} - \tfrac{1}{2}A_{de} - \tfrac{1}{2}A_{af}$$
$$= C + 3\alpha - 3\alpha/2 = C + 3\alpha/2. \qquad \ldots.(17.36)$$

In the same way in $\mathcal{H}_{\mathrm{II\,II}}$

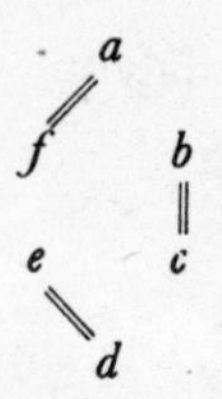

$i = 3$; $n/2 = 3$; $1/2^{\left(\frac{n}{2}-i\right)} = 1$, and thus for A_{af}, A_{bc} and A_{de}, $p = 1$ and the coefficient of the integrals is 1. For A_{ab}, A_{cd} and A_{ef}, $p = 0$ and the coefficient is $-\frac{1}{2}$. Hence

$$\mathcal{H}_{\mathrm{II\,II}} = C + A_{af} + A_{bc} + A_{de} - \tfrac{1}{2}A_{ab} - \tfrac{1}{2}A_{cd} - \tfrac{1}{2}A_{ef}$$
$$= C + 3\alpha/2 \qquad \ldots.(17.37)$$

Thus both Kekulé structures with three normal π bonds have the same energy. Now let us consider the energy of the Dewar structures. For $\mathcal{H}_{\mathrm{III\,III}}$ we have the structure,

Here $i = 3$; $n/2 = 3$; $1/2^{\left(\frac{n}{2}-i\right)} = 1$. For A_{bc} and A_{ef}, $p = 1$ and the integral coefficient is 1. For A_{ab}, A_{cd}, A_{de} and A_{af}, $p = 0$ and the coefficient is $-\frac{1}{2}$, so that

$$\mathcal{H}_{\mathrm{III\,III}} = C + A_{bc} + A_{ef} - \tfrac{1}{2}(A_{ab} + A_{cd} + A_{de} + A_{af})$$
$$= C + 2\alpha - \frac{4}{2}\alpha = C \qquad \ldots.(17.38)$$

In exactly the same way

$$\mathcal{H}_{\mathrm{IV\,IV}} = \mathcal{H}_{\mathrm{V\,V}} = C \qquad \ldots.(17.39)$$

The energy of the Dewar structures is less than that of the Kekulé structures since there is virtually no third π bond on account of the great distance.

For the structure $\mathcal{H}_{\mathrm{I\,II}}$ we have the structure

It consists of a single island, hence $i = 1$ and $1/2^{\left(\frac{n}{2}-i\right)} = 1/2^{(3-1)} = 1/4$. For all pairs of atoms which shall be considered here $p = 1$; $f(p) = 1$ and the coefficient of the exchange integrals is $f(p) . 1/4. = 1/4$ Hence

$$\mathcal{H}_{\mathrm{I\,II}} = \tfrac{1}{4}(C + 6\alpha) = C/4 + 3\alpha/2 \qquad \ldots.(17.40)$$

The structure for $\mathcal{H}_{\text{I III}}$ has the form

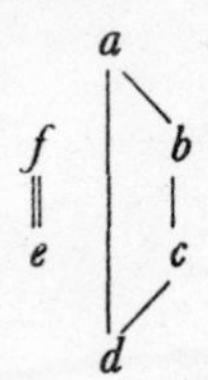

The number of islands is 2, $i = 2$ and $1/2^{(\frac{n}{2}-i)} = 1/2^{(3-2)} = 1/2$. For A_{ab}, A_{bc}, A_{cd} and A_{ef}, $p = 1$ and $f(p) = 1$. The atom groups $a—f$ and $d—e$ are located in different islands and for these cases $p = 0$, $f(p) = -\frac{1}{2}$. Hence it follows that

$$\mathcal{H}_{\text{I III}} = \tfrac{1}{2}(C + 4\alpha - 2\alpha/2) = C/2 + 3\alpha/2 \qquad \text{....(17.41)}$$

For the structures

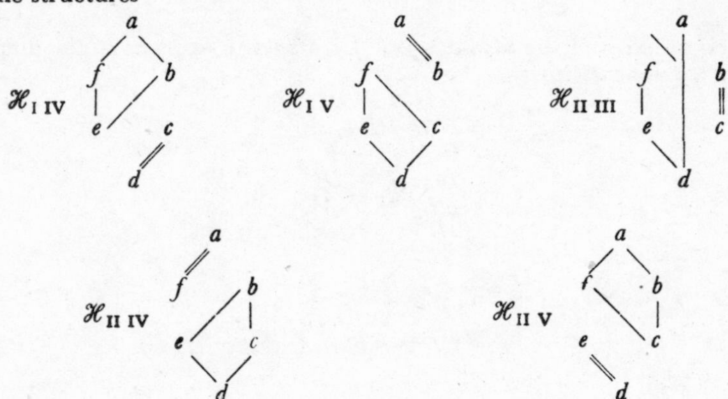

we find that

$$\mathcal{H}_{\text{I IV}} = \mathcal{H}_{\text{I V}} = \mathcal{H}_{\text{II III}} = \mathcal{H}_{\text{II IV}} = \mathcal{H}_{\text{II V}} = C/2 + 3\alpha/2 \qquad \text{....(17.42)}$$

In the structure for $\mathcal{H}_{\text{III IV}}$

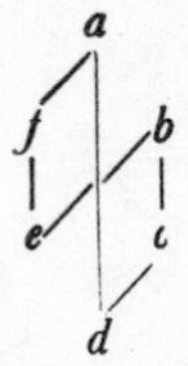

there is only one island $a—f—e—b—c—d—a$ and $i = 1$. From a it is possible to transfer to f passing only one space, $p = 1$, and the same applies to the pairs $b—c$, $c—d$, $e—f$. In order to transfer from a to b, it is necessary to pass from a to d, d to c and c to b. Thus for integrals A_{ab} and A_{de}, $p = 3$ and $f(p) = 1$. The coefficients of the Coulomb and all transfer integrals will be $1/4$ and hence

$$\mathcal{H}_{\text{III IV}} = \tfrac{1}{4}(C + 6\alpha) = C/4 + 3\alpha/2 \qquad \text{....(17.43)}$$

Similarly

$$\mathcal{H}_{\text{III V}} = \mathcal{H}_{\text{IV V}} = C/4 + 3\alpha/2 \qquad \text{....(17.44)}$$

From the equations 17.36 to 17.44 we obtain the following secular equation for benzene

$$\begin{vmatrix} C+\frac{3}{2}a-E & \frac{1}{4}C+\frac{3}{2}a-\frac{1}{4}E & \frac{1}{2}C+\frac{3}{2}a-\frac{1}{2}E & \frac{1}{2}C+\frac{3}{2}a-\frac{1}{2}E & \frac{1}{2}C+\frac{3}{2}a-\frac{1}{2}E \\ \frac{1}{4}C+\frac{3}{2}a-\frac{1}{4}E & C+\frac{3}{2}a-E & \frac{1}{2}C+\frac{3}{2}a-\frac{1}{2}E & \frac{1}{2}C+\frac{3}{2}a-\frac{1}{2}E & \frac{1}{2}C+\frac{3}{2}a-\frac{1}{2}E \\ \frac{1}{2}C+\frac{3}{2}a-\frac{1}{2}E & \frac{1}{2}C+\frac{3}{2}a-\frac{1}{2}E & C-E & \frac{1}{4}C+\frac{3}{2}a-\frac{1}{4}E & \frac{1}{4}C+\frac{3}{2}a-\frac{1}{4}E \\ \frac{1}{2}C+\frac{3}{2}a-\frac{1}{2}E & \frac{1}{2}C+\frac{3}{2}a-\frac{1}{2}E & \frac{1}{4}C+\frac{3}{2}a-\frac{1}{4}E & C-E & \frac{1}{4}C+\frac{3}{2}a-\frac{1}{4}E \\ \frac{1}{2}C+\frac{3}{2}a-\frac{1}{2}E & \frac{1}{2}C+\frac{3}{2}a-\frac{1}{2}E & \frac{1}{4}C+\frac{3}{2}a-\frac{1}{4}E & \frac{1}{4}C+\frac{3}{2}a-\frac{1}{4}E & C-E \end{vmatrix} = 0 \qquad \ldots\ldots(17.45)$$

This equation is of the fifth degree. Let us write in place of the functions I–V new ones such that

$$\begin{aligned} A &= I + II \\ B &= III + IV + V \\ C &= II - I \\ D &= V - III \\ E &= IV - V \end{aligned} \qquad \ldots\ldots(17.46)$$

Then

$$\left.\begin{aligned} \mathscr{H}_{AA} &= \mathscr{H}_{I\,I} + \mathscr{H}_{II\,II} + 2\mathscr{H}_{I\,II} = 2C + 3a + \tfrac{1}{2}C + 3a = \tfrac{5}{2}C + 6a \\ \mathscr{H}_{AB} &= \mathscr{H}_{I\,III} + \mathscr{H}_{I\,IV} + \mathscr{H}_{I\,V} + \mathscr{H}_{II\,III} + \mathscr{H}_{II\,IV} + \mathscr{H}_{II\,V} = 3C + 9a \\ \mathscr{H}_{AC} &= \mathscr{H}_{I\,II} + \mathscr{H}_{II\,II} - \mathscr{H}_{I\,I} - \mathscr{H}_{I\,II} = 0 \text{ etc} \end{aligned}\right\} \qquad \ldots\ldots(17.47)$$

and the secular equation has the form

$$\begin{vmatrix} \frac{5}{2}C+6a+\frac{5}{2}E & \frac{3}{2}C+9a-3E & 0 & 0 & 0 \\ 3C+9a-3E & \frac{9}{2}C+9a-\frac{9}{2}E & 0 & 0 & 0 \\ 0 & 0 & C\frac{3}{2}-\frac{3}{2}E & 0 & 0 \\ 0 & 0 & 0 & \frac{3}{2}C-3a-\frac{3}{2}E & 0 \\ 0 & 0 & 0 & 0 & \frac{3}{2}C-3a-\frac{3}{2}E \end{vmatrix} = 0 \qquad \ldots\ldots(17.48)$$

This equation may be reduced to a quadratic and three linear equations :

$$\begin{vmatrix} \frac{5}{2}C+6a-\frac{5}{2}E & 3C+9a-3E \\ 3C+9a-3E & \frac{9}{2}C+9a-\frac{9}{2}E \end{vmatrix} = 0 \qquad \ldots\ldots(17.49)$$

$$C - E = 0 \qquad \ldots.(17.50)$$

$$C - 2\alpha - E = 0 \qquad \ldots.(17.51)$$

$$C - 2\alpha - E = 0 \qquad \ldots.(17.52)$$

From these equations we find all the solutions of E:

$$E_1 = C + \alpha(\sqrt{13} - 1) = C + 2{\cdot}6\alpha \qquad \ldots.(17.53)$$

$$E_2 = C \qquad \ldots.(17.54)$$

$$E_3 = E_4 = C - 2\alpha \qquad \ldots.(17.55)$$

$$E_5 = C - \alpha(\sqrt{13} + 1) = C - 4{\cdot}6\alpha \qquad \ldots.(17.56)$$

As a result of the resonance of the valence bond structures five states arise, the energy of the lowest state, *i.e.* the most stable being $C + 2{\cdot}6\alpha$. The energy of one Kekulé structure is $C + 1{\cdot}5\alpha$ (see equation 17.36). The resonance energy of benzene is thus $1{\cdot}1\alpha$.

As a second example of the six electron problem we shall consider fulvene, which is of particular interest as it is the simplest coloured hydrocarbon. Its chemical structure is

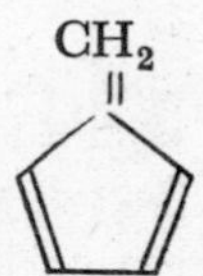

As in benzene there will be five canonical structures

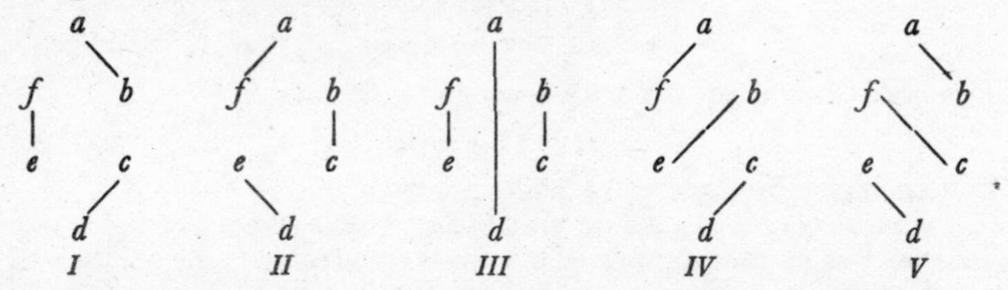

Indicating the carbon atoms of fulvene in the following manner

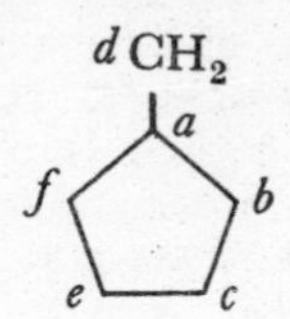

it follows that the canonical structures correspond to the following valence bond structures

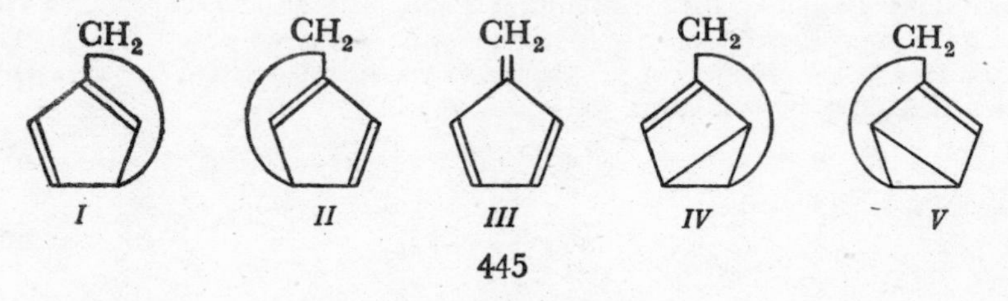

Although the same formula for the calculation of the integrals has been preserved, there is an essential difference introduced by the different arrangement of atoms in space, in that the integrals between adjacent atoms A_{ad}, A_{ab}, A_{af}, A_{bc}, A_{ce} and A_{ef} will not be equal to zero whereas the integrals A_{ac}, A_{ae}, *etc* will be equal to zero.

In the structure for $\mathscr{H}_{II}$

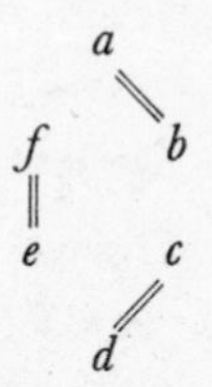

$p = 1$ for the pairs a—b and e—f, and hence the coefficient of the integrals A_{ab} and A_{ef} is unity. For the remaining pairs (a—d, a—f, b—c and c—e), $p = 0$ and the coefficient of the integrals A_{ad}, A_{af}, A_{bc} and A_{ce} is $-\frac{1}{2}$. Thus

$$\mathscr{H}_{II} = C + A_{ab} + A_{ef} - \tfrac{1}{2}A_{ad} - \tfrac{1}{2}A_{af} - \tfrac{1}{2}A_{bc} - \tfrac{1}{2}A_{ce} \quad \ldots.(17.57)$$

The remaining integrals and the solution of the secular equation is obtained as in the case of benzene and we obtain for the energy of fulvene :

$$\begin{aligned} E_1 &= C + 2a \\ E_2 &= C + 0{\cdot}24a \\ E_3 &= C - a \\ E_4 &= C - 3a \\ E_5 &= C - 4{\cdot}24a \end{aligned} \quad \ldots.(17.58)$$

The energy of structure *III* with localized π bonds is

$$E = C + 1{\cdot}5a \quad \ldots.(17.59)$$

so that the resonance energy of fulvene is $0{\cdot}5a$.

In the same way it is possible to calculate the resonance energies of other molecules, but as the number of electrons is increased, the solution of the equations in spite of the various simplifications which have been introduced, is difficult. For eight electrons a secular equation of the fourteen stages is obtained, for ten electrons one of forty two stages, corresponding to the possible number of canonical structures. It is true that these equations, as in the case of benzene, can be divided into several more simple equations. But such methods, which are to some extent limited in application, require additional special methods which are generally not particularly effective. Thus in the case of naphthalene, with ten π electrons, it is necessary to solve an equation of sixteen stages. However, certain assumptions may be made which simplify the calculation; in order to illustrate the nature of these assumptions we shall apply them to the case of benzene. In this case we have two Kekulé structures with equal energies, $E = C + \frac{3}{2}a$ and three Dewar structures $E = C$. Owing to the equality of the energy values, both Kekulé structures enter the equation :

$$\Phi = c_1\Phi_{I} + c_2\Phi_{II} + c_3\Phi_{III} + c_4\Phi_{IV} + c_5\Phi_{V} \quad \ldots.(17.60)$$

with equal coefficients

$$c_1 = c_2 = a \quad \ldots.(17.61)$$

and applying the same argument to the case of the Dewar structures, we have

$$c_3 = c_4 = c_5 = b \qquad \ldots.(17.62)$$

Substituting equations 17.61 and 17.62 in 17.60 we obtain

$$\Phi = a(\Phi_{I} + \Phi_{II}) + b(\Phi_{III} + \Phi_{IV} + \Phi_{V}) = a\Phi_a + b\Phi_b \qquad \ldots.(17.63)$$

Thus the resonance of only two states corresponding to Φ_a and Φ_b has to be considered. We then have the secular equation

$$\begin{vmatrix} \mathcal{H}_{aa} - E & \mathcal{H}_{ab} - ES_{ab} \\ \mathcal{H}_{ab} - ES_{ab} & \mathcal{H}_{bb} - E \end{vmatrix} = 0 \qquad \ldots.(17.64)$$

The integrals of equation 17.64 are easily obtained from the canonical structures and the final secular equation will be

$$\begin{vmatrix} \frac{5}{2}C + 6\alpha - \frac{5}{2}E & 3C + 9\alpha - 3E \\ 3C + 9\alpha - 3E & \frac{9}{2}C + 9\alpha - \frac{9}{2}E \end{vmatrix} = 0 \qquad \ldots.(17.49)$$

with the roots

$$E = C + \alpha(-1 \pm \sqrt{13}) \qquad \ldots.(17.65)$$

i.e. not all energy levels are obtained but only the lowest and one of the higher levels.

An alternative method of simplification of the secular equation consists in rejecting the less probable structures. If in benzene, for example, only the Kekulé structures are considered,

$$\Phi = c_1\Phi_1 + c_2\Phi_2 \qquad \ldots.(17.66)$$

then from equations 17.36, 17.37 and 17.40 we obtain the following secular equation :

$$\begin{vmatrix} C + \frac{3}{2}\alpha - E & \frac{1}{4}C + \frac{3}{2}\alpha - \frac{1}{4}E \\ \frac{1}{4}C + \frac{3}{2}\alpha - \frac{1}{4}E & C + \frac{3}{2}\alpha - E \end{vmatrix} = 0 \qquad \ldots.(17.67)$$

with the solutions

$$E_1 = C + 2{\cdot}4\alpha \qquad \ldots.(17.68)$$

and

$$E_2 = C \qquad \ldots.(17.69)$$

By this approximate method the resonance energy becomes

$$E_{res.} = (C + 2{\cdot}4\alpha) - (C + 1{\cdot}5\alpha) = 0{\cdot}9\alpha \qquad \ldots.(17.70)$$

Thus it follows that the resonance energy is determined mainly by the superposition of the Kekulé structures. The Dewar structures giving the comparatively insignificant additional stabilization of $0{\cdot}2\alpha$.

CALCULATION OF RESONANCE ENERGY BY THE MOLECULAR ORBITAL METHOD

When two electrons form a bond between two atoms, each electron is located in a bonding molecular orbital :

$$\psi = c\psi_1 + b\psi_2 \qquad \ldots.(17.71)$$

where ψ_1 and ψ_2 are atomic orbitals of the electrons of the two atoms. The energy of the electron in such an orbital will be

$$E = C + \beta \qquad \ldots.(17.72)$$

where C is the Coulomb energy of interaction of the electron with both nuclei and the second electron, and β is the exchange integral. The exchange energy being caused by the exchange of the electron between the two atomic orbitals ψ_1 and ψ_2. The exchange integral is

$$\beta = \int \psi_1 \mathscr{H} \psi_2 d\tau \qquad \text{....(17.73)}$$

which must not be confused with the exchange integral of two electrons

$$\alpha = \int \psi_a(1)\psi_b(2) \mathscr{H} \psi_b(1)\psi_a(2) d\tau \qquad \text{....(17.74)}$$

In each molecular orbital two electrons may be located and in the present treatment it is considered that the motions of the two electrons are independent of each other. The wave function of the bond will therefore be the product of the two wave functions of the first and second electrons and the energy will be the sum of the two electronic energies, *i.e.*

$$E = 2C + 2\beta \qquad \text{....(17.75)}$$

The energy of a single π bond will thus be given by this expression and therefore if the three π bonds in benzene are localized, then the energy will be

$$E = 6C + 6\beta \qquad \text{....(17.76)}$$

Actually, each of the six π electrons is located in the field of six nuclei, *i.e.* in the molecular orbital :

$$\psi = c_1\psi_1 + c_2\psi_2 + c_3\psi_3 + c_4\psi_4 + c_5\psi_5 + c_6\psi_6 \qquad \text{....(17.77)}$$

If the values of the coefficients for which the energy is a maximum is obtained, for example, by the variation method, it is then possible to obtain the most probable orbitals for the electrons in the field of six nuclei and to obtain the energies of these orbitals. Starting from the equation 17.77, we obtain the following secular equation :

$$\begin{vmatrix} \mathscr{H}_{11}-E & \mathscr{H}_{12}-ES_{12} & \mathscr{H}_{13}-ES_{13} & \mathscr{H}_{14}-ES_{14} & \mathscr{H}_{15}-ES_{15} & \mathscr{H}_{16}-ES_{16} \\ \mathscr{H}_{12}-ES_{12} & \mathscr{H}_{22}-E & \mathscr{H}_{23}-ES_{23} & \mathscr{H}_{24}-ES_{24} & \mathscr{H}_{25}-ES_{25} & \mathscr{H}_{26}-ES_{26} \\ \mathscr{H}_{13}-ES_{13} & \mathscr{H}_{23}-ES_{23} & \mathscr{H}_{33}-E & \mathscr{H}_{34}-ES_{34} & \mathscr{H}_{35}-ES_{35} & \mathscr{H}_{36}-ES_{36} \\ \mathscr{H}_{14}-ES_{14} & \mathscr{H}_{24}-ES_{24} & \mathscr{H}_{34}-ES_{34} & \mathscr{H}_{44}-E & \mathscr{H}_{45}-ES_{45} & \mathscr{H}_{46}-ES_{46} \\ \mathscr{H}_{15}-ES_{15} & \mathscr{H}_{25}-ES_{25} & \mathscr{H}_{35}-ES_{35} & \mathscr{H}_{45}-ES_{45} & \mathscr{H}_{55}-E & \mathscr{H}_{56}-ES_{56} \\ \mathscr{H}_{16}-ES_{16} & \mathscr{H}_{26}-ES_{26} & \mathscr{H}_{36}-ES_{36} & \mathscr{H}_{46}-ES_{46} & \mathscr{H}_{56}-ES_{56} & \mathscr{H}_{66}-E \end{vmatrix} = 0 \qquad \text{....(17.78)}$$

Let us now evaluate the integrals. Integrals of the type $\mathscr{H}_{ii}$ are given by

$$\mathscr{H}_{ii} = \int \psi_i \mathscr{H} \psi_i d\tau \qquad \text{....(17.79)}$$

As is clearly seen, these integrals denote the energy of Coulomb interaction of the electron of atom i (in orbital ψ_i) with all the remaining nuclei and electrons. Let us denote these integrals throughout by C. The integral $\mathscr{H}_{12}$ equals

$$\mathscr{H}_{12} = \int \psi_1 \mathscr{H} \psi_2 d\tau \qquad \text{....(17.80)}$$

and represents the exchange of the electron between two adjacent atoms 1 and 2. We shall call this integral β (see equation 17.73) and since in benzene all the nuclei are identical, the remaining integrals between adjacent atoms, $\mathscr{H}_{23}$, $\mathscr{H}_{34}$, $\mathscr{H}_{45}$, $\mathscr{H}_{56}$ and $\mathscr{H}_{16}$ are equal to β. The exchange integrals between non-adjacent atoms are small and may be neglected. Non-orthogonal integrals of different atoms, *e.g.*

$$S_{12} = \int \psi_1 \psi_2 d\tau \qquad \ldots.(17.81)$$

may also be taken as equal to zero. With these modifications the secular equation 17.78 becomes :

$$\begin{vmatrix} C-E & \beta & 0 & 0 & 0 & \beta \\ \beta & C-E & \beta & 0 & 0 & 0 \\ 0 & \beta & C-E & \beta & 0 & 0 \\ 0 & 0 & \beta & C-E & \beta & 0 \\ 0 & 0 & 0 & \beta & C-E & \beta \\ \beta & 0 & 0 & 0 & \beta & C-E \end{vmatrix} = 0 \qquad \ldots.(17.82)$$

The solution of this equation may be obtained in the usual way and the roots are :

$$\begin{aligned} E_1 &= C + 2\beta \\ E_2 &= C + \beta \\ E_3 &= C + \beta \\ E_4 &= C - \beta \\ E_5 &= C - \beta \\ E_6 &= C - 2\beta \end{aligned} \qquad \ldots.(17.83)$$

Consequently there are six orbitals for the electrons, the most favourable being the first, with energy $C + 2\beta$, and in it will be located two electrons. The remaining four electrons will occupy the following two orbitals, both with energy $C + \beta$. It is not difficult to see that the remaining orbitals are non-bonding orbitals since the energy in orbitals 4, 5 and 6 is greater than in the atomic orbital $E = C$. The stability of the system is due to the fact that all the electrons may be located in bonding orbitals and the energy of the six electrons will be equal to the sum of the energies of the different orbitals occupied by the electrons *i.e.*

$$2(C + 2\beta) + 2(C + \beta) + 2(C + \beta) = 6C + 8\beta$$

With six isolated π bonds the energy would be only $6C + 6\beta$ and hence the transfer of the six electrons to the field of all the nuclei gives a gain of 2β. This represents the value of the resonance energy, expressed in different terms than in the Slater-Pauling method.

COMPARISON OF CALCULATED AND EXPERIMENTAL VALUES OF RESONANCE ENERGY

The resonance energies of a number of molecules are given in *Table CLXXIII.* In the second column the resonance energy calculated by the Slater-Pauling method is given in terms of the exchange integral α ; in the third column the same quantity, calculated by the molecular orbital method is given, expressed in terms of the exchange integral β. Comparison of the two methods is made by obtaining the ratio β/α (column four) which should be a constant, and is found to be so for the aromatic hydrocarbons. In the fifth column are given the esperimental values of the resonance energy calculated according to the methods given in Chapter 11. From these values it is possible to obtain values for α and β which are given in columns six and seven respectively. As is to be expected both series of values are approximately constant. The low value of α for butadiene is due to the fact that we have assumed that all the exchange integrals between adjacent atoms are equal. This is correct in benzene but in butadiene, the actual distances between the atoms in the bonds *a—b* and *c—d* are equal to 1·35 Å and the interatomic distance in *a—c* is 1·46 Å. The true value of A_{ac} is therefore less than A_{ab}. Thus since in the calculation of the resonance energy, we assumed that both forms contributed equally to the resonance, the contribution of the structure with the double bond between the central atoms was overestimated and that with the double bonds between the outer carbon atoms underestimated.

Table CLXXIII. Calculated and Experimental Values of Resonance Energy

Molecule	*Resonance energy calculated by method of*		$\frac{\beta}{\alpha}$	*Experimental value of resonance energy kcals*	$\alpha = \frac{E_{exp.}}{E_{calc.}}$ kcals	$\beta = \frac{E_{exp.}}{E_{calc.}}$ kcals
	Slater-Pauling	*Molecular orbital*				
Butadiene	0·23α	0·47β	0·49	4·1	18	—
Hexatriene	0·48α	0·99β	0·48	—	—	—
Octatriene	0·73α	1·52β	0·48	—	—	—
2-Vinylbutadiene	0·44α	0·90β	0·49	—	—	—
Benzene	1·1α	2β	0·55	34·4	31	17
Diphenyl	2·37α	4·38β	0·54	75·6	32	17
Naphthalene	2·04α	3·68β	0·55	63·4	31	17
Styrol	1·31α	2·42β	0·54	38·2	29	16
Stilbene	2·59α	4·88β	0·53	79·0	30·5	16
Anthracene	—	5·32β	—	86·2	—	16
Phenanthrene	—	5·42β	—	93·0	—	17

COLOUR OF CHEMICAL COMPOUNDS

We have seen that owing to the resonance of valence bond structures there arises several energy levels of the molecule. The lowest of these is the ground state of the molecule and the higher levels represent excited states. If the difference in energy between these levels is not great, then the transfer of energy $E_1 \rightarrow E_2$ may be brought about by the absorption of a quantum of light radiation $h\nu$ in the ultraviolet or visible region of the spectrum[2]. If the light quantum absorbed corresponds to a frequency in the visible part of the spectrum, the compound will be coloured. The method of Slater and Pauling described in this chapter gives the different energy states of the molecules. In benzene the difference in energy of the ground and the first excited state is 2·6α, or when only the Kekulé structures are considered 2·4α. The calculated energy differences of the ground and excited states of a number of molecules are given in the second column of *Table CLXXIV*, and since for the higher aromatic hydrocarbons, only the Kekulé structures have been considered, the value of 2·4α is taken for benzene. In the third column are given the experimental wave lengths of the absorbed radiation and by equating $E_1 - E_2 = h\nu = hc/\lambda$ it is possible to determine α (fourth column). For aromatic hydrocarbons α varies from 37 to 43 kcals. The deviations in the case of butadiene and hexatriene are due to the same reason that has been discussed above. From resonance energies, the value obtained for α varies from 29 to 31 kcals and taking into consideration the very approximate nature of the calculation better agreement is hardly to be expected. The fact that the widely differing methods of thermochemistry and spectroscopy lead to values of the same order of magnitude, may be regarded as support for the quantum mechanical treatment. The theory correctly predicts the existence of a close series of energy levels which explains the absorption in the long wave ultra violet and in the visible part of the spectrum.

Table CLXXIV. Difference of Energy Levels and Positions of Light Absorption Maximum

Molecule	*Difference of energy levels* E_1–E_2	*Position of maximum absorption Å*	α *kcals*
Benzene ..	2·4α	2,550	42
Naphthalene	1·97α	2,750	37
Anthracene	1·60α	3,700	41
Naphthacene	1·31α	4,000	41
Pentacene ..	1·08α	5,800	43
Phenanthrene	1·94α	2,950	39
Pyrene ..	1·70α	3,300	39
Fulvene ..	1·76α	3,600*	43
Azulene ..	3·42α	2,170	51
Butadiene ..	2·71α	2,650†	49
Hexatriene ..	1·04α	7,000	50

* According to measurements on ω, ω–dimethylfulvene.
† According to measurements on $C_6H_5(CH{=}CH)_3CH_2COOH$.

The relationship between resonance and the colour of chemical compounds has proved to be of great assistance in explaining the observed empirical laws of relationship between colour and chemical constitution.

REFERENCES

[1] PAULING, L. C. *J. chem. Phys.* 1 (1933) 280
[2] SKLAR, A. L. *ibid* 5 (1937) 669

18

MATHEMATICAL APPENDIX

SOLUTION OF THE SCHRÖDINGER EQUATION FOR THE HYDROGEN ATOM

THE detailed solution of the equation

$$\frac{\partial^2\psi}{\partial x^2}+\frac{\partial^2\psi}{\partial y^2}+\frac{\partial^2\psi}{\partial z^2}+\frac{8\pi^2 m}{h^2}\left(E+\frac{e^2}{r}\right)\psi=0 \qquad \ldots.(18.1)$$

has been given in several monographs[1] and it will be sufficient for our purpose here if we show how the discrete energy levels and the quantum numbers arise as a natural consequence of the method. It is necessary first to express equation 18.1 in terms of the spherical coordinates r, θ and ϕ. The relationship between the cartesian and spherical coordinates is given by the following expressions :

$$\left.\begin{aligned} x&=r\sin\theta\cos\phi & r&=\sqrt{x^2+y^2+z^2}\\ y&=r\sin\theta\cos\phi & \cos\theta&=\frac{z}{\sqrt{x^2+y^2+z^2}}\\ z&=r\cos\theta & \tan\phi&=\frac{y}{x} \end{aligned}\right\} \qquad \ldots.(18.2)$$

Substituting the values of x, y and z given in equation 18.2 into 18.1 we obtain :

$$\frac{1}{r^2}\frac{\partial}{\partial r}\left(r^2\frac{\partial\psi}{\partial r}\right)+\frac{1}{r^2\sin^2\theta}\frac{\partial^2\psi}{\partial\phi^2}+\frac{1}{r^2\sin\theta}\frac{\partial}{\partial\theta}\left(\sin\theta\frac{\partial\psi}{\partial\theta}\right)+\frac{8\pi^2 m}{h^2}\left(E+\frac{e^2}{r}\right)\psi=0 \qquad \ldots.(18.3)$$

This equation may be divided into three more simple equations. We shall seek a solution ψ, which is dependent on the three variables r, θ and ϕ and which is the product of three functions, $R(r)$ dependent only on r, Θ dependent on θ and Φ dependent on ϕ. Thus,

$$\psi(r,\theta,\phi)=R(r)\,\Theta(\theta)\,\Phi(\phi) \qquad \ldots.(18.4)$$

Substituting equation 18.4 in 18.3 and dividing the equation obtained by $\dfrac{\psi}{r^2\sin^2\theta}$ we obtain :

$$\frac{\sin^2\theta}{R}\frac{d}{dr}\left(r^2\frac{dR}{dr}\right)+\frac{1}{\Phi}\frac{d^2\Phi}{d\phi^2}+\frac{\sin\theta}{\Theta}\frac{d}{d\theta}\left(\sin\theta\frac{d\Theta}{d\theta}\right)+\frac{8\pi^2 mr^2\sin^2\theta}{h^2}\left(E+\frac{e^2}{r}\right)=0 \qquad \ldots.(18.5)$$

in which ϕ occurs only in the term $\dfrac{1}{\Phi}\dfrac{d^2\Phi}{d\phi^2}$. Rearranging, we obtain :

$$\frac{\sin^2\theta}{R}\frac{d}{dr}\left(r^2\frac{dR}{dr}\right)+\frac{\sin\theta}{\Theta}\frac{d}{d\theta}\left(\sin\theta\frac{d\Theta}{d\theta}\right)+\frac{8\pi^2 mr^2\sin^2\theta}{h^2}\left(E+\frac{e^2}{r}\right)= =-\frac{1}{\Phi}\frac{d^2\Phi}{d\phi^2} \qquad \ldots.(18.6)$$

The left hand side of equation 18.6 contains only the variables r and θ and is independent of ϕ, whereas the right hand side is a function only of the independent variable ϕ and since the expression $-\frac{1}{\Phi}\frac{d^2\Phi}{d\phi^2}$ is seen to be equal to terms independent of ϕ we may put it equal to a constant, which we shall call $\bar{m}^2$*.

We then have

$$\frac{1}{\Phi}\frac{d^2\Phi}{d\phi^2} = -\bar{m}^2 \qquad \ldots.(18.7)$$

or

$$\frac{d^2\Phi}{d\phi^2} = -\bar{m}^2\Phi \qquad \ldots.(18.8)$$

The solution of this equation will be

$$\Phi(\phi) = A \exp(i\bar{m}\phi) \qquad \ldots.(18.9)$$

As is clear from *Figure 2*, ϕ may vary only from 0 to 2π, the function having identical values at ϕ and $\phi + 2\pi$, consequently in order for the function to be single-valued, $\bar{m}$ must be equal to an integer. Thus the solution of equation 18.9 is only possible when $\bar{m} = 0, \pm 1, \pm 2$ *etc.* The parameter $\bar{m}$ occurred in the old quantum theory as the magnetic quantum number. In the above treatment it arises directly in the solution of the Schrödinger equation, in contrast to the old quantum theory in which it was introduced as a separate postulate.

The constant A may be obtained by normalization. For this, it is necessary to integrate the expression $\Phi_{\bar{m}}(\phi)\,\Phi^*_{\bar{m}}(\phi)$, where $\Phi^*_{\bar{m}}(\phi)$ is the complex conjugate of $\Phi_{\bar{m}}(\phi)$ through the range of variation of ϕ, *i.e.* from 0 to 2π, and to equate to unity:

$$\left.\begin{aligned} &\int_0^{2\pi} \Phi_{\bar{m}}(\phi)\Phi^*_{\bar{m}}(\phi)d\phi = 1 \\ \text{where} \quad &\Phi^*_{\bar{m}}(\phi) = A\exp(-i\bar{m}\phi) \end{aligned}\right\} \qquad \ldots.(18.10)$$

This gives

$$A^2\int_0^{2\pi} \exp(i\bar{m}\phi)\exp(-i\bar{m}\phi)d\phi = A^2\, 2\pi = 1 \qquad \ldots.(18.11)$$

and hence

$$A = 1/\sqrt{2\pi} \qquad \ldots.(18.12)$$

Thus the normalized function $\Phi_{\bar{m}}(\phi)$ is given by:

$$\Phi_{\bar{m}}(\phi) = [\exp(i\bar{m}\phi)]/\sqrt{2\pi} \qquad \ldots.(18.13)$$

Equation 18.8 is satisfied by the functions $\exp(i\bar{m}\phi)$ and $\exp(-i\bar{m}\phi)$ and also by $\cos\bar{m}\phi$ and $\sin\bar{m}\phi$. In certain cases it is more convenient to use the real in the place of the complex functions. The values of the function

* This constant designated by $\bar{m}$ must not be confused with the symbol for mass

$\Phi_{\bar{m}}(\phi)$ in real and complex forms are given below for the various values of $\bar{m}$ (0, ± 1, ± 2 etc) :

Function $\Phi_{\bar{m}}(\phi)$

$$\left.\begin{array}{llll}
\Phi_0(\phi) = \dfrac{1}{\sqrt{2\pi}} & & & \\
\Phi_1(\phi) = \dfrac{1}{\sqrt{2\pi}} \exp(i\phi) & \text{or} & \Phi_{1\,cos}(\phi) = \dfrac{1}{\sqrt{\pi}} \cos\phi \\
\Phi_{-1}(\phi) = \dfrac{1}{\sqrt{2\pi}} \exp(-i\phi) & \text{or} & \Phi_{1\,sin}(\phi) = \dfrac{1}{\sqrt{\pi}} \sin\phi \\
\Phi_2(\phi) = \dfrac{1}{\sqrt{2\pi}} \exp(2i\phi) & \text{or} & \Phi_{2\,cos}(\phi) = \dfrac{1}{\sqrt{\pi}} \cos 2\phi \\
\Phi_{-2}(\phi) = \dfrac{1}{\sqrt{2\pi}} \exp(-2i\phi) & \text{or} & \Phi_{2\,sin}(\phi) = \dfrac{1}{\sqrt{\pi}} \sin 2\phi
\end{array}\right\} \quad \ldots.(18.14)$$

Substituting the value of $\bar{m}^2$ given by equation 18.7 into 18.6 gives :

$$\frac{\sin^2\theta}{R}\frac{d}{dr}\left(r^2\frac{dR}{dr}\right) - \bar{m}^2 + \frac{\sin\theta}{\Theta}\frac{d}{d\theta}\left(\sin\theta\frac{d\Theta}{d\theta}\right) + \frac{8\pi^2mr^2\sin^2\theta}{h^2}\left(E+\frac{e^2}{r}\right) = 0 \quad \ldots.(18.15)$$

or dividing by $\sin^2\theta$:

$$\frac{1}{R}\frac{d}{dr}\left(r^2\frac{dR}{dr}\right) - \frac{\bar{m}^2}{\sin^2\theta} + \frac{1}{\Theta\sin\theta}\frac{d}{d\theta}\left(\sin\theta\frac{d\Theta}{d\theta}\right) + \frac{8\pi^2mr^2}{h^2}\left(E+\frac{e^2}{r}\right) = 0 \quad \ldots.(18.16)$$

which on rearranging gives

$$\frac{1}{R}\frac{d}{dr}\left(r^2\frac{dR}{dr}\right) + \frac{8\pi^2mr^2}{h^2}\left(E+\frac{e^2}{r}\right) = \frac{\bar{m}^2}{\sin^2\theta} - \frac{1}{\Theta\sin\theta}\frac{d}{d\theta}\left(\sin\theta\frac{d\Theta}{d\theta}\right) \quad \ldots.(18.17)$$

In this expression, r does not occur in the right hand side and θ does not occur in the left hand side, consequently each part may be equated to a constant. Let us call this constant β and after multiplication of the r terms by $\frac{R}{r^2}$ and the θ terms by Θ we obtain :

$$\frac{1}{\sin\theta}\frac{d}{d\theta}\left(\sin\theta\frac{d\Theta}{d\theta}\right) - \frac{\bar{m}^2\Theta}{\sin^2\theta} + \beta\Theta = 0 \quad \ldots.(18.18)$$

$$\frac{1}{r^2}\frac{d}{dr}\left(r^2\frac{dR}{dr}\right) - \frac{\beta R}{r^2} + \frac{8\pi^2m}{h^2}\left(E+\frac{e^2}{r}\right)R = 0 \quad \ldots.(18.19)$$

We shall now seek a solution of equation 18.18 in the form of a series. The principles of this method are as follows :

Let us substitute $\cos\theta$ by z, then

$$\Theta(\theta) = P(z) \quad \ldots.(18.20)$$

$$\frac{d\Theta}{d\theta} = \frac{dP}{dz}\frac{dz}{d\theta} = -\frac{dP}{dz}\sin\theta \quad ; \quad \sin^2\theta = 1 - z^2 \quad \ldots.(18.21)$$

and equation 18.18 assumes the form :

$$\frac{d}{dz}\left\{(1-z^2)\frac{dP(z)}{dz}\right\}+\left\{\beta-\frac{\bar{m}^2}{1-z^2}\right\}P(z)=0 \quad \ldots.(18.22)$$

If we now make the substitution

$$P(z)=(1-z^2)^{|\bar{m}|/2}G(z) \quad \ldots.(18.23)$$

where $|\bar{m}|$ is the absolute value of $\bar{m}$, we obtain:

$$(1-z^2)\frac{d^2G}{dz^2}-2(|\bar{m}|+1)z\frac{dG}{dz}+\Big\}\beta-|\bar{m}|(|\bar{m}|+1)\Big\}G=0 \quad \ldots.(18.24)$$

This should now be directly soluble by a power series.

Let $G=a_0+a_1z+a_2z^2+a_3z^3+\cdots\cdots=\sum_{v=0}^{\infty}a_vz^v$ ....(18.25)

which on differentiation gives,

$$\frac{dG}{dz}=a_1+2a_2z+3a_3z^2+\cdots\cdots=\sum_{v=0}^{\infty}va_vz^{v-1} \quad \ldots.(18.26)$$

$$\frac{d^2G}{dz^2}=2a_2+3.2a_3z+4.3a_4z^2+\cdots\cdots=\sum_{v=0}^{\infty}a_vv(v-1)z^{v-2} \quad \ldots.(18.27)$$

The substitution of (18.25), (18.26) and (18.27) into (18.24) gives

$$\begin{gathered}1.2a_2+2.3a_3z+3.4a_4z^2+4.5a_5z^3+\cdots\cdots\cdots\quad-\\-1.2a_2z^2-2.3a_3z^3-3.4a_4z^4-4.5a_5z^5-\cdots\cdots\cdots\quad-\\-2(|\bar{m}|+1)a_1z-2.2(|\bar{m}|+1)a_2z^2-2.3(|\bar{m}|+1)a_3z^3-\cdots\cdots\cdots+\\+\{\beta-|\bar{m}|(|\bar{m}|+1)\}a_0+\{\beta-|\bar{m}|(|\bar{m}|+1)\}a_1z+\\+\{\beta-|\bar{m}|(|\bar{m}|+1)\}a_2z^2+\{\beta-|\bar{m}|(|\bar{m}|+1)\}a_3z^3+\cdots\cdots\cdots=0\end{gathered} \quad \ldots.(18.28)$$

In order that this is true for all values of z, the coefficients of z and the higher powers of z must be equal to zero. Hence,

$$\left.\begin{array}{ll}z^0 & 1.2a_2+\{\beta-|\bar{m}|(|\bar{m}|+1)\}a_0=0\\ z^1 & 2.3a_3+[\{\beta-|\bar{m}|(|\bar{m}|+1)\}-2(|\bar{m}|+1)]a_1=0\\ z^2 & 3.4a_4+[\{\beta-|\bar{m}|(|\bar{m}|+1)\}-2.2(|\bar{m}|+1)-1.2]a_2=0\\ z^3 & 4.5a_5+[\{\beta-|\bar{m}|(|\bar{m}|+1)\}-2.3(|\bar{m}|+1)-2.3]a_3=0\\ \cdots & \cdots\cdots\cdots\cdots\cdots\cdots\cdots\cdots\\ z^v & (v+1)(v+2)a_{v+2}+[\{\beta-|\bar{m}|(|\bar{m}|+1)\}-2.v(|\bar{m}|+1)-v(v-1)]a_v=0\end{array}\right\} \quad \ldots.(18.29)$$

or

$$a_{v+2}=\frac{(v+|\bar{m}|)(v+|\bar{m}|+1)-\beta}{(v+1)(v+2)}a \quad \ldots.(18.30)$$

A detailed investigation of the series obtained shows that it does not have a finite sum when $|z|=1$, which corresponds to the values for θ of 0 and π. But since $\Theta(\theta)$ is a parameter of the wave function ψ, which is finite at all points in space, $\Theta(\theta)$ must also always be finite, even when $\theta=0$ or π. These conditions are only possible when the series contains a finite number of terms and the series may be broken off at the term in z^v by putting

$$\beta=(v+|\bar{m}|)(v+|\bar{m}|+1) \quad \ldots.(18.31)$$

This makes the numerator of equation 18.30 equal to zero, so that at any value, a_v, all the coefficients a_{v+1}, a_{v+2} *etc* will be equal to zero and instead of an infinite series, a polynomial is obtained. Thus, owing to the condition that the function ψ must be finite, the function β may only assume certain definite values.

It will be convenient to introduce a new quantum number l, given by

$$l = v + |\bar{m}| \qquad \ldots.(18.32)$$

which may have the value zero, or any real number. From equations 18.31 and 18.32, we have

$$\beta = l(l+1) \qquad \ldots.(18.33)$$

The substitution of equation 18.33 in 18.18 gives the equation for θ. The functions $\Theta(\theta)$ are known as associated Legendre functions. We shall not derive the general solution of the equation but shall give the solutions which may be shown to be correct by substitution in equation 18.18 (for full details of the method see PAULING and WILSON[1] page 125 *et seq*).

The solutions of equation 18.18 are dependent on two quantum numbers and $\bar{m}$. As we have shown above, l may have the values 0, 1, 2, 3 *etc* and is the analogue of the azimuthal quantum number of the Bohr-Sommerfeld treatment. From that fact that $l \geqslant |\bar{m}|$, it follows that for each value of l there corresponds $2l + 1$ values of $\bar{m}$ which may have the values $-l, -l+1, \cdots -3, -2, -1, 0, +1, +2, +3, \cdots l-1, l$. The values of the function Θ_{ml} are given below :

Function Θ_{ml}

$$\left.\begin{array}{lll}
l=0 \quad \bar{m}=0 & \Theta_{00}(\theta) & = \dfrac{\sqrt{2}}{2} \\[2ex]
l=1 \quad \bar{m}=0 & \Theta_{10}(\theta) & = \dfrac{\sqrt{6}}{2}\cos\theta \\[2ex]
l=1 \quad \bar{m}=\pm 1 & \Theta_{1\pm 1}(\theta) & = \dfrac{\sqrt{3}}{2}\sin\theta \\[2ex]
l=2 \quad \bar{m}=0 & \Theta_{20}(\theta) & = \dfrac{\sqrt{10}}{4}(3\cos^2\theta - 1) \\[2ex]
l=2 \quad \bar{m}=\pm 1 & \Theta_{2\pm 1}(\theta) & = \dfrac{\sqrt{15}}{2}\sin\theta\cos\theta \\[2ex]
l=2 \quad \bar{m}=\pm 2 & \Theta_{2\pm 2}(\theta) & = \dfrac{\sqrt{15}}{4}\sin^2\theta
\end{array}\right\} \quad (18.34)$$

It now remains to solve the equation for the radial function 18.19, *viz*

$$\frac{1}{r^2}\frac{d}{dr}\left(r^2\frac{dR}{dr}\right) - \frac{\beta R}{r^2} + \frac{8\pi^2 m}{h^2}\left(E + \frac{e^2}{r}\right)R = 0 \qquad \ldots.(18.19)$$

or putting $R(r) = rv(r)$

$$\frac{d^2}{dr^2}\{rv(r)\} - \frac{l(l+1)}{r}v(r) + \frac{8\pi^2 m}{h^2}\left(E + \frac{e^2}{r}\right)rv(r) \qquad \ldots.(18.35)$$

This equation contains the term E, the energy of the atom. When the electron is at an infinite distance from the nucleus, the energy will be zero and since, as the electron is brought up to the nucleus a negative amount of work is performed, the energy will have a negative sign. Since we are interested here only in the non-ionized atom we shall solve the equation for negative values of E. For large values of r the terms containing $\frac{l(l+1)}{r}$ and $\frac{8\pi^2me^2}{h^2r}$ will be very small and may be neglected. Equation 18.35 then becomes

$$\frac{d^2}{dr^2}\{rv(r)\} + \left(-\frac{8\pi^2mE}{h^2}\right) rv(r) = 0 \qquad \ldots.(18.36)$$

which may be rewritten as,

$$\frac{d^2}{dr^2}(rv(r)) + a^2rv(r) = 0 \qquad \ldots.(18.37)$$

where

$$a = (-8\pi^2mE/h^2)^{\frac{1}{2}} \qquad \ldots.(18.38)$$

The solutions of equation 18.37 are,

$$rv(r) = C \exp(ar) \qquad \ldots.(18.39)$$

$$rv(r) = C \exp(-ar) \qquad \ldots.(18.40)$$

Only the second of these solutions satisfies the condition that equation 18.37 approaches zero as r tends to infinity. We shall now obtain a general solution in the form of a product of the above solution, obtained for large values of r, with a function $f(r)$, which must first be evaluated :

$$rv(r) = f(r) \exp(-ar) \qquad \ldots.(18.41)$$

Substituting this expression in equation 18.35, we obtain the following equation for $f(r)$:

$$\frac{d^2f}{dr^2} - 2a\frac{df}{dr} + \left(\frac{8\pi^2me^2}{h^2r} - \frac{l(l+1)}{r^2}\right)f = 0 \qquad \ldots.(18.42)$$

The solution of this equation will again be a power series

$$f(r) = \sum_{v=0}^{\infty} b_v r^v \qquad \ldots.(18.43)$$

whence

$$\frac{df}{dr} = \sum_{v=1}^{\infty} v b_v r^{v-1} \qquad \frac{d^2f}{dr^2} = \sum_{v=2}^{\infty} b_v . v(v-1)r^{v-2} \qquad \ldots.(18.44)$$

Substitution of the derivatives in (18.42) leads to the following equation involving the coefficients of (18.43) :

$$\left[v(v+1) - l(l+1)\right]b_{v+1} = b_v\left[2v\left(\frac{-8\pi^2mE}{h^2}\right)^{\frac{1}{2}} - \frac{8\pi^2me^2}{h^2}\right] \qquad \ldots.(18.45)$$

When $v = l$ it is evident that the left hand side of equation 18.45 will be equal to zero. Consequently values of b_v with $v \leqslant l$ equal zero and the series will begin with the term $b_{l+1}r^{l+1}$

Investigation by the usual methods shows that the summation of this series for arbitrary values of E, tends to infinity as $r \to \infty$ and hence the product of the series with [exp $(-ar)$], *i.e.* the radial part of the wave function, does not tend to zero as $r \to \infty$, which is necessary. This restriction places a limitation on the values that E may assume and finite solutions exist only for such values of E, when commencing with $v = n$, the series breaks off. This will occur if the coefficient of b_v on the right hand side of equation 18.45 is equal to zero :

$$2v\left(-\frac{8\pi^2 mE}{h^2}\right)^{\frac{1}{2}} - \frac{8\pi^2 me^2}{h^2} = 0 \qquad \ldots.(18.46)$$

which leads to the following solution for E (putting $v = n$) :

$$E = -\frac{2\pi^2 me^4}{n^2h^2} \qquad \ldots.(18.47)$$

where n is an integer and $l \leqslant n - 1$. Substitution in equation 18.19 and solution of the resulting equation leads to the following functions, generally known as the Laguerre functions :

$$\left.\begin{array}{llll}
n=1 & l=0 & 1s & R_{10}(r) = \frac{1}{a^{\frac{3}{2}}}\, 2 \exp\left(-\frac{r}{a}\right) \quad \text{where } a = \frac{h^2}{4\pi^2 me^2} \\
n=2 & l=0 & 2s & R_{20}(r) = \frac{1}{2\sqrt{2a^3}}\left(2 - \frac{r}{a}\right) \exp\left(-\frac{r}{2a}\right) \\
n=2 & l=1 & 2p & R_{21}(r) = \frac{1}{2\sqrt{6a}}\frac{r}{a} \exp\left(-\frac{r}{2a}\right) \\
n=3 & l=0 & 3s & R_{30}(r) = \frac{1}{9\sqrt{3a^3}}\left(6 - 4\frac{r}{a} + \frac{4}{9}\frac{r^2}{a^2}\right) \exp\left(-\frac{r}{3a}\right) \\
n=3 & l=1 & 3p & R_{31}(r) = \frac{1}{9\sqrt{6a^3}}\left(4 - \frac{2}{3}\frac{r}{a}\right)\frac{2}{3}\frac{r}{a} \exp\left(-\frac{r}{3a}\right) \\
n=3 & l=2 & 3d & R_{32}(r) = \frac{1}{9\sqrt{30a^3}}\frac{4}{9}\frac{r^2}{a^2} \exp\left(-\frac{r}{3a}\right)
\end{array}\right\} \qquad \ldots.(18{\cdot}48)$$

The product of the functions Φ, Θ and R (equation 18.4) gives the full solutions of the Schrödinger equation which have been given in *Table IV*.

The functions ψ, corresponding to various atomic states, are orthogonal. This means that the integral $\int \psi_i \psi_k d\tau = 0$. The proof of the orthogonality of the wave functions is given by PAULING and WILSON[1] page 441 and will not be discussed further here.

DIRECTIONAL COVALENCY

We wish to show first that the electron clouds of the three p electrons, possessing a shape similar to a figure eight, are directed along the cartesian coordinates. If $f(r)$ represents the radial part of the wave function, we obtain from equation 18.14 and 18.34 the following expressions for the three p states :

$$\left.\begin{array}{ll}
\bar{m} = \pm 1 & \left\{\begin{array}{l} \psi_{p_x} = \frac{\sqrt{3}}{2\sqrt{\pi}} f(r) \sin\theta \cos\phi \\ \psi_{p_y} = \frac{\sqrt{3}}{2\sqrt{\pi}} f(r) \sin\theta \sin\phi \end{array}\right. \\
\bar{m} = 0 & \psi_{p_z} = \frac{\sqrt{3}}{2\sqrt{\pi}} f(r) \cos\theta
\end{array}\right\} \qquad \ldots.(18.49)$$

From equation 18.2, it follows that

$$\left.\begin{aligned} \sin\theta\cos\phi &= x/r \\ \sin\theta\sin\phi &= y/r \\ \cos\theta &= z/r \end{aligned}\right\} \qquad \ldots.(18.50)$$

and hence,

$$\begin{aligned} \psi_{p_x} &= \frac{\sqrt{3}}{2\sqrt{\pi}} f(r)\frac{x}{r} = f_1(r)x \\ \psi_{py} &= \frac{\sqrt{3}}{2\sqrt{\pi}} f(r)\frac{y}{r} = f_1(r)y \\ \psi_{p_z} &= \frac{\sqrt{3}}{2\sqrt{\pi}} f(r)\frac{z}{r} = f_1(r)z \end{aligned} \qquad \ldots.(18.51)$$

where $f_1(r) = \dfrac{\sqrt{3}}{2\sqrt{\pi}}\dfrac{f(r)}{r}$ Thus the function ψ_{p_x} is directed along the x axis, function ψ_{p_y} along the y axis and ψ_{p_z} along the z axis.

Let us consider an atom a with two valency p electrons and let these electrons be described by the functions ψ_{p_x} and ψ_{p_y}; let the p_x electron be termed electron 1 and the p_y electron as electron 2. On the approach of an atom b, its electron (3) will exchange with both the electrons of a, with one of them, for example 1, it will form a covalent bond whilst it will be repulsed by the second. The energy of the molecule ab according to equation 4.6 is

$$E = C + A_{ik} - \tfrac{1}{2}A'_{ik} = C_{13} + C_{23} + A_{13} - \tfrac{1}{2}A'_{23} \qquad \ldots.(18.52)$$

where C_{13} and C_{23} are the Coulomb integrals, A is the exchange integral between the electrons of 1 and 3 and A'_{23} represents the exchange integral between the non-bonded electrons of a and b, *i.e.*

$$\begin{aligned} C_{13} &= \int \psi^2_{p_x}(1)\,\mathscr{H}\,\psi^2_b(3)\,d\tau & A_{13} &= \int \psi_{p_x}(1)\psi_b(3)\,\mathscr{H}\,\psi_{p_x}(3)\psi_b(1)\,d\tau \\ C_{23} &= \int \psi^2_{p_y}(2)\,\mathscr{H}\,\psi^2_b(3)\,d\tau & A'_{23} &= \int \psi_{p_y}(2)\psi_b(3)\,\mathscr{H}\,\psi_{p_y}(3)\psi_b(2)\,d\tau \end{aligned} \qquad \ldots.(18.53)$$

Let the atom b approach atom a along a line making an angle α with the axis x along which the electron cloud of the p_x electron is concentrated. If the x and y axes are now rotated through the angle α (*Figure 78*) to form the axes x' and y', the atom b will approach a along x'. The new coordinates will be related by the formulae

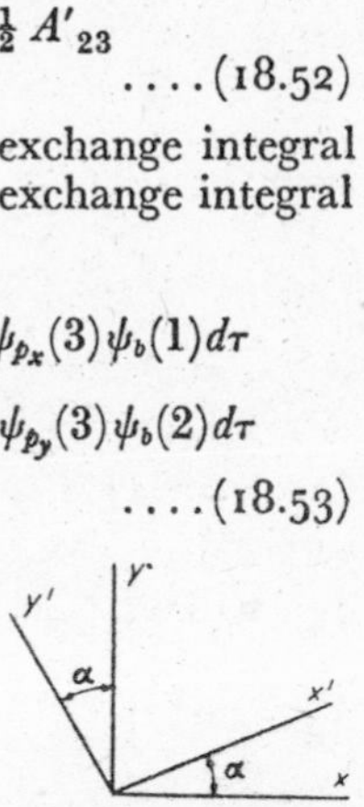

Figure 78. Rotation of axes through an angle α

$$\begin{aligned} x &= x'\cos\alpha - y'\sin\alpha \\ y &= x'\sin\alpha + y'\cos\alpha \end{aligned} \qquad \ldots.(18.54)$$

and the functions ψ_{p_x} and ψ_{p_y} become on the new system of coordinates

$$\begin{aligned} \psi_{p_x} &= f_1(r)x = f_1(r)[x'\cos\alpha - y'\sin\alpha] = \psi'_{p_x}\cos\alpha - \psi'_{p_y}\sin\alpha \\ \psi_{p_y} &= f_1(r)y = f_1(r)[x'\sin\alpha + y'\cos\alpha] = \psi'_{p_x}\sin\alpha + \psi'_{p_y}\cos\alpha \end{aligned} \qquad \ldots.(18.55)$$

Substituting these values in equation 18.53 we obtain :

$$\left.\begin{aligned} C_{13} &= \int(\psi'_{p_x}\cos a - \psi'_{p_y}\sin a)^2(1)\mathscr{H}\psi^2{}_b(3)d\tau \\ &= \cos^2 a\int\psi'^2{}_{p_x}(1)\mathscr{H}\psi^2{}_b(3)d\tau + \sin^2 a\int\psi'^2{}_{p_y}(1)\mathscr{H}\psi^2{}_b(3)d\tau - \\ &\quad - 2\sin a\cos a\int\psi'_{p_x}(1)\psi'_{p_y}(1)\mathscr{H}\psi^2{}_b(3)d\tau \\ C_{23} &= \sin^2 a\int\psi'^2{}_{p_x}(2)\mathscr{H}\psi^2{}_b(3)d\tau + \cos^2 a\int\psi'^2{}_{p_y}(2)\mathscr{H}\psi^2{}_b(3)d\tau + \\ &\quad + 2\sin a\cos a\int\psi'_{p_x}(2)\psi'_{p_y}(2)\mathscr{H}\psi^2{}_b(3)d\tau \end{aligned}\right\} \quad \ldots.(18.56)$$

Similarly from equations 18.53 and 18.55 it follows that

$$\left.\begin{aligned} A_{13} &= \int(\psi'_{p_x}(1)\cos a - \psi'_{p_y}(1)\sin a)\psi_b(3)\mathscr{H}\psi_b(1)(\psi'_{p_x}(3)\cos a - \psi'_{p_y}(3)\sin a)d\tau \\ &= \cos^2 a\int\psi'_{p_x}(1)\psi_b(3)\mathscr{H}\psi_b(1)\psi'_{p_x}(3)d\tau + \sin^2 a\int\psi'_{p_y}(1)\psi_b(3)\mathscr{H}\psi_b(1(\psi'_{p_y}(3)d\tau - \\ &\qquad - 2\sin a\cos a\int\psi'_{p_y}(1)\psi_b(3)\mathscr{H}\psi_b(1)\psi'_{p_x}(3)d\tau \\ A'_{23} &= \sin^2 a\int\psi'_{p_x}(2)\psi_b(3)\mathscr{H}\psi_b(2)\psi'_{p_x}(3)d\tau + \\ &\qquad + \cos^2 a\int\psi'_{p_y}(2)\psi_b(3)\mathscr{H}\psi_b(2)\psi'_{p_y}(3)d\tau + \\ &\qquad + 2\sin a\cos a\int\psi'_{p_y}(2)\psi_b(3)\mathscr{H}\psi_b(2)\psi'_{p_x}(3)d\tau \end{aligned}\right\} \quad \ldots.(18.57)$$

It is possible to show that the integrals $\int\psi'_{p_x}(1)\psi'_{p_y}(1)\mathscr{H}\psi^2{}_b(3)d\tau$ and $\psi'_{p_x}(1)\psi_b(3)\mathscr{H}\psi_b(1)\psi'_{p_y}(3)d\tau$ are equal to zero and hence

$$\begin{aligned} C_{13} &= \cos^2 a\int\psi'^2{}_{p_x}(1)\mathscr{H}\psi^2{}_b(3)d\tau + \sin^2 a\int\psi'^2{}_{p_y}(1)\mathscr{H}\psi^2{}_b(3)d\tau \\ C_{23} &= \sin^2 a\int\psi'^2{}_{p_y}(2)\mathscr{H}\psi^2{}_b(3)d\tau + \cos^2 a\int\psi'^2{}_{p_y}(2)\mathscr{H}\psi^2{}_b(3)d\tau \\ A_{13} &= \cos^2 a\int\psi'_{p_x}(1)\psi_b(3)\mathscr{H}\psi_b(1)\psi'_{p_x}(3)d\tau + \sin^2 a\int\psi'_{p_y}(1)\psi_b(3)\mathscr{H}\psi_b(1)\psi'_{p_y}(3)d\tau \\ A'_{23} &= \sin^2 a\int\psi'_{p_x}(2)\psi_b(3)\mathscr{H}\psi_b(2)\psi'_{p_x}(3)d\tau + \cos^2 a\int\psi'_{p_y}(2)\psi_b(3)\mathscr{H}\psi_b(2)\psi'_{p_y}(3)d\tau \end{aligned} \quad \ldots.(18.58)$$

whence it follows that

$$C = C_{13} + C_{23} = \int\psi'^2{}_{p_x}\mathscr{H}\psi^2{}_b d\tau + \int\psi'^2{}_{p_y}\mathscr{H}\psi^2{}_b d\tau \quad \ldots.(18.59)$$

Thus the total Coulombic energy does not depend on the angle of approach of the atom *b*. On a change in the value of *a*, the energy of interaction of the electron of atom *b* with each of the electrons of *a* changes, but the sum of the interaction energies remains constant.

The exchange energy, on the other hand, is given by :

$$A = A_{13} + \tfrac{1}{2} A'_{23} = (\cos^2 a - \tfrac{1}{2}\sin^2 a)\int \psi'_{p_x}\psi_b \mathcal{H} \psi_b \psi'_{p_x} d\tau +$$
$$+ (\sin^2 a - \tfrac{1}{2}\cos^2 a)\int \psi'_{p_y}\psi_b \mathcal{H} \psi_b \psi'_{p_y} d\tau$$
$$= \{(3\cos^2 a - 1)/2\}\{\int \psi'_{p_x}\psi_b \mathcal{H} \psi_b \psi'_{p_x} d\tau - \int \psi'_{p_y}\psi_b \mathcal{H} \psi_b \psi'_{p_y} d\tau\} +$$
$$+ \tfrac{1}{2}\int \psi'_{p_y}\psi_b \mathcal{H} \psi_b \psi'_{p_y} d\tau \qquad \ldots.(18.60)$$

and as is evident, A is dependent on the angle a. The relative positions of a and b in the molecule will be such that the energy of the system is at a minimum and the exchange energy is a maximum. This position may be obtained by differentiating 18.60 with respect to a :

$$dA/da = 3\{\int \psi'_{p_x}\psi_b \mathcal{H} \psi_b \psi'_{p_x} d\tau - \int \psi'_{p_y}\psi_b \mathcal{H} \psi_b \psi'_{p_y} d\tau\}\sin a \cos a \qquad \ldots.(18.61)$$

and it is evident that $dA/da = 0$ when $a = 0°$ or $90°$. The bond is thus formed in the direction of the x axis where the overlapping of the electron orbitals is at a maximum and the repulsion energy due to the p_y electron is at a minimum.

HYBRID ELECTRON FUNCTIONS

In order to derive the tetrahedral hybrid electron functions we shall follow the method of PAULING[2] and show that the linear combination of one s and three p wave functions give maximum stability of the bond. The linear combination has the form :

$$\psi_i = a\psi_s + b\psi_{p_z} + c\psi_{p_y} + d\psi_{p_x}$$

We shall attempt to determine the values of the coefficients a, b, c, and d which permit the greatest possible overlap of the resulting orbitals with the orbital of another atom. Let us suppose that the bond is formed in the direction of the z axis, so that the linear combination of the orbitals may be limited to

$$\psi_1 = a\psi_s + b\psi_{p_z} \qquad \ldots.(18.62)$$

This function must be normalized, *i.e.*

$$\int \psi_1^2 d\tau = a^2\int \psi_s^2 d\tau + 2ab\int \psi_s\psi_{p_z} d\tau + b^2\int \psi^2_{p_z} d\tau = 1 \quad \ldots.(18.63)$$

The wave functions ψ_s and ψ_{p_z} are also normalized and mutually orthogonal :

$$\int \psi_s^2 d\tau = 1 \qquad \int \psi^2_{p_z} d\tau = 1 \qquad \int \psi_s\psi_{p_z} d\tau = 0 \quad \ldots.(18.64)$$

and it therefore follows in view of equation 18.64, that 18.63 becomes

$$a^2 + b^2 = 1 \qquad \ldots.(18.65)$$

and therefore equation 18.62 may be written,

$$\psi_1 = a\psi_s + (1 - a^2)^{\frac{1}{2}}\psi_{p_z} \qquad \ldots.(18.66)$$

we have that :

$$\psi_s = \frac{1}{2\sqrt{\pi}} f(r)$$

$$\psi_{p_x} = \frac{\sqrt{3}}{\sqrt{\pi}} f(r) \sin \theta \cos \phi \qquad \ldots.(18.67)$$

$$\psi_{p_y} = \frac{\sqrt{3}}{2\sqrt{\pi}} f(r) \sin \theta \sin \phi$$

$$\psi_{p_z} = \frac{\sqrt{3}}{2\sqrt{\pi}} f(r) \cos \theta$$

We are concerned here only with the angular dependence of the wave function and we may assume that the radial parts of the wave functions are so closely similar that their differences can be neglected. If we then regard $1/2\sqrt{\pi}$ as part of the normalization constant and put $f(r) = 1$ we obtain :

$$\begin{aligned} \psi_s &= 1 \\ \psi_{p_x} &= \sqrt{3} \sin \theta \cos \phi \\ \psi_{p_y} &= \sqrt{3} \sin \theta \sin \phi \\ \psi_{p_z} &= \sqrt{3} \cos \theta \end{aligned} \qquad \ldots.(18.68)$$

For the particular case of the direction along the z axis (*i.e.* when $\theta = 0$)

$$\begin{aligned} \psi_s &= 1 \\ \psi_{p_z} &= \sqrt{3} \end{aligned} \qquad \ldots.(18.69)$$

which on substitution into equation 18.66 gives

$$\psi_{1(\theta = 0)} = a + \sqrt{3(1 - a^2)} \qquad \ldots.(18.70)$$

In order to determine the value of a corresponding to the greatest value for ψ in a given direction, it is necessary to differentiate equation 18.70 with respect to a and equate to zero :

$$\frac{d\psi_1}{da} = 1 - \frac{3.2a}{2\sqrt{3(1 - a^2)}} = 0 \qquad \ldots.(18.71)$$

and

$$a = 1/2 \qquad \ldots.(18.72)$$

and consequently

$$\psi_1 = \frac{1}{2} \psi_s + \sqrt{3}\, \psi_{p_z}/2 \qquad \ldots.(18.73)$$

In the same way it is possible to find the hybrid orbital of the second electron. Let the second bond occur in the plane xz. For this orbital it is necessary to consider only the linear combinations of the functions ψ_s, ψ_{p_x} and ψ_{p_z} :

$$\psi_2 = a_2\psi_s + b_2\psi_{p_z} + d_2\psi_{p_x} \qquad \ldots.(18.74)$$

and, as in equation 18.63, the normalization of the wave functions leads to

$$a_2^2 + b_2^2 + d_2^2 = 1 \qquad \ldots.(18.75)$$

The functions ψ_1 and ψ_2 must be orthogonal and hence since $d_1 = 0$,

$$\int \psi_1 \psi_2 d\tau = \int (\tfrac{1}{2}\psi_s + \sqrt{3}.\psi_{p_z}/2)\,(a_2\psi_s + b_2\psi_{p_z} + d_2\psi_{p_x})d\tau = a_2/2 + \sqrt{3}\,.\,b_2/2 = 0 \quad \ldots.(18.76)$$

and hence

$$a_2 = -\,b_2\sqrt{3} \quad \ldots.(18.77)$$

From equations 18.75 and 18.77 it follows that

$$4a_2^{\,2}/3 + d_2^{\,2} = 1 \quad ; \quad d_2 = (1 - 4a_2^{\,2}/3)^{\frac{1}{2}} \quad \ldots.(18.78)$$

i.e.

$$\psi_2 = a_2\psi_s - a_2\psi_{p_z}\sqrt{3}/3 + (1 - 4a_2^{\,2}/3)^{\frac{1}{2}}\psi_{px} \quad \ldots.(18.79)$$

In the plane xz, the angle $\phi = 0$, so that

$$\begin{aligned} \psi_{px} &= \sqrt{3}\sin\theta \\ \psi_{py} &= 0 \\ \psi_{p_z} &= \sqrt{3}\cos\theta \end{aligned} \quad \ldots.(18.80)$$

Substitution of equation 18.80 into 18.79 gives, since $\psi_s = 1$,

$$\psi_2 = a_2 - a_2\cos\theta + (1 - 4a_2^{\,2}/3)^{\frac{1}{2}}.\sqrt{3}\sin\theta \quad \ldots.(18.81)$$

and the values of a_2 and θ at which ψ_2 has a maximum value will be obtained by differentiation :

$$\left.\begin{aligned} \frac{\partial\psi_2}{\partial a_2} &= 1 - \cos\theta - \frac{\dfrac{4a_2}{3}}{\sqrt{1 - \dfrac{4a_2^{\,2}}{3}}}\,.\sqrt{3}\sin\theta = 0 \\ \frac{\partial\psi_2}{\partial\theta} &= a_2\sin\theta + \sqrt{1 - \frac{4a_2^{\,2}}{3}}\,.\,\sqrt{3}\cos\theta = 0 \end{aligned}\right\} \quad \ldots(18.82)$$

and these equations are satisfied if

$$\cos\theta = -\,1/3 \quad ; \quad a_2 = 1/2 \quad \ldots.(18.83)$$

and consequently

$$b_2 = -\,1/2\sqrt{3} \quad ; \quad d_2 = \sqrt{2/3} \quad \ldots.(18.84)$$

and substitution of these values in 18.74 gives

$$\psi_2 = \frac{1}{2}\psi_s + \frac{\sqrt{2}}{\sqrt{3}}\psi_{px} - \frac{1}{2\sqrt{3}}\psi_{p_z} \quad \ldots.(18.85)$$

Since $\cos\theta = -\,1/3$, the function ψ_2 is directed along an axis making an angle of 109° 28′ with the z axis. In a similar manner we find for the third and fourth electrons :

$$\left.\begin{aligned} \psi_3 &= \frac{1}{2}\psi_s - \frac{1}{2\sqrt{3}}\psi_{p_z} - \frac{1}{\sqrt{6}}\psi_{px} + \frac{1}{\sqrt{2}}\psi_{p_y} \\ \psi_4 &= \frac{1}{2}\psi_s - \frac{1}{2\sqrt{3}}\psi_{p_z} - \frac{1}{\sqrt{6}}\psi_{px} - \frac{1}{\sqrt{2}}\psi_{p_y} \end{aligned}\right\} \quad \ldots.(18.86)$$

the angle between any two axes being the tetrahedral angle.

Another series of tetrahedral orbitals may be obtained starting from the assumption that each hybrid orbital consists of one quarter of each of the s, p_x, p_y p_z electrons (*i.e.*, $a_1^2 = a_2^2 = a_3^2 = a_4^2 = \frac{1}{4}$). On this basis the coefficients of ψ_s, ψ_{p_x}, ψ_{p_y}, ψ_{p_z} in the combined function will be $\pm\frac{1}{2}$. The four orbitals will thus differ in the different arrangement of the + and − signs of the wave functions :

$$\begin{aligned} \psi_1 &= \tfrac{1}{2}(\psi_s + \psi_{p_x} + \psi_{p_y} + \psi_{p_z}) \\ \psi_2 &= \tfrac{1}{2}(\psi_s - \psi_{p_x} - \psi_{p_y} + \psi_{p_z}) \\ \psi_3 &= \tfrac{1}{2}(\psi_s - \psi_{p_x} + \psi_{p_y} - \psi_{p_z}) \\ \psi_4 &= \tfrac{1}{2}(\psi_s + \psi_{p_x} - \psi_{p_y} - \psi_{p_z}) \end{aligned} \qquad \ldots .(18.87)$$

These functions are exactly equivalent to those given above, their advantage lies in the fact that the identity of the four orbitals is more apparent.

For the hybridization of one s and two p electrons, the s function is divided equally amongst the three resulting hybrid functions, so that into each hybrid electron orbital there enters one third of the s cloud (*i.e.* $a^2 = 1/3$). The first orbital may therefore be represented by

$$\psi_1 = \sqrt{1/3}.\psi_s + \sqrt{2/3}.\psi_{p_x} \qquad \ldots .(18.88)$$

and is directed along the x axis. The remaining orbitals will be

$$\begin{aligned} \psi_2 &= a_2\psi_s + b_2\psi_{p_x} + c_2\psi_{p_y} \\ \psi_3 &= a_3\psi_s + b_3\psi_{p_x} + c_3\psi_{p_y} \end{aligned} \qquad \ldots .(18.89)$$

From the normalization conditions it follows that

$$\begin{aligned} a_2^2 + b_2^2 + c_2^2 &= 1 \\ a_3^2 + b_3^2 + c_3^2 &= 1 \end{aligned} \qquad \ldots .(18.90)$$

and since

$$a_2 = a_3 = \sqrt{1/3} \qquad \ldots .(18.91)$$

then

$$\begin{aligned} b_2^2 + c_2^2 &= 2/3 \\ b_3^2 + c_3^2 &= 2/3 \end{aligned} \qquad \ldots .(18.92)$$

From the orthogonality of the wave functions it follows that

$$\int (\sqrt{1/3}\,\psi_s + \sqrt{2/3}\,\psi_{p_x})(\sqrt{1/3}\,\psi_s + b_2\psi_{p_z} + c_2\psi_{p_y})d\tau = 1/3 + \sqrt{2/3}\,b_2 = 0 \qquad \ldots .(18.93)$$

Hence from equations 18.92 and 18.93 it follows that :

$$\left.\begin{aligned} b_2 &= -\sqrt{1/6} \\ c_2 &= \sqrt{1/2} \end{aligned}\right\} \qquad \ldots .(18.94)$$

and similarly :

$$\left.\begin{aligned} b_3 &= -\sqrt{1/6} \\ c_3 &= -\sqrt{1/2} \end{aligned}\right\} \qquad \ldots .(18.95)$$

Finally we have

$$\left.\begin{aligned}\psi_1 &= \frac{1}{\sqrt{3}}\psi_s + \sqrt{\frac{2}{3}}\psi_{px} \\ \psi_2 &= \frac{1}{\sqrt{3}}\psi_s - \frac{1}{\sqrt{6}}\psi_{p_x} + \frac{1}{\sqrt{2}}\psi_{p_y} \\ \psi_3 &= \frac{1}{\sqrt{3}}\psi_s - \frac{1}{\sqrt{6}}\psi_{p_x} - \frac{1}{\sqrt{2}}\psi_{p_y}\end{aligned}\right\} \quad \ldots.(18\ 96)$$

The hybrid wave functions of one *s* and *p* electron will be

$$\left.\begin{aligned}\psi_1 &= \frac{1}{\sqrt{2}}\psi_s + \frac{1}{\sqrt{2}}\psi_{p_x} \\ \psi_2 &= \frac{1}{\sqrt{2}}\psi_s - \frac{1}{\sqrt{2}}\psi_{p_x}\end{aligned}\right\} \quad \ldots.(18.97)$$

Five hydrogen like *d* orbitals are :

$$\begin{aligned}d_z &= \sqrt{\frac{5}{4}}f(r)\ (3\cos^2\theta - 1) \\ d_{y+z} &= \sqrt{15}f(r)\sin\theta\cos\theta\cos\phi \\ d_{x+z} &= \sqrt{15}f(r)\sin\theta\cos\theta\sin\phi \\ d_{x+y} &= \sqrt{\frac{15}{4}}f(r)\sin^2\theta\sin 2\phi \\ d_{xy} &= \sqrt{\frac{15}{4}}f(r)\sin^2\theta\cos 2\phi\end{aligned} \quad \ldots.(18.98)$$

where $f(r)$ is the radial part of the wave function which need not concern us, as we are primarily concerned with the angular dependence of the wave functions.

For six hybrid d^2sp^3 orbitals we obtain :

$$\begin{aligned}\psi_1 &= \frac{1}{\sqrt{6}}\psi_s + \frac{1}{\sqrt{2}}\psi_{p_z} + \frac{1}{\sqrt{3}}\psi_{d_z} \\ \psi_2 &= \frac{1}{\sqrt{6}}\psi_s - \frac{1}{\sqrt{2}}\psi_{p_z} + \frac{1}{\sqrt{3}}\psi_{d_z} \\ \psi_3 &= \frac{1}{\sqrt{6}}\psi_s + \frac{1}{\sqrt{12}}\psi_{d_z} + \tfrac{1}{2}\psi_{d_{xy}} + \frac{1}{\sqrt{2}}\psi_{p_x} \\ \psi_4 &= \frac{1}{\sqrt{6}}\psi_s + \frac{1}{\sqrt{12}}\psi_{d_z} + \tfrac{1}{2}\psi_{d_{xy}} - \frac{1}{\sqrt{2}}\psi_{px} \\ \psi_5 &= \frac{1}{\sqrt{6}}\psi_s + \frac{1}{\sqrt{12}}\psi_{d_z} - \tfrac{1}{2}\psi_{d_{xy}} + \frac{1}{\sqrt{2}}\psi_{p_y} \\ \psi_6 &= \frac{1}{\sqrt{6}}\psi_s + \frac{1}{\sqrt{12}}\psi_{d_z} - \tfrac{1}{2}\psi_{d_{xy}} - \frac{1}{\sqrt{2}}\psi_{p_y}\end{aligned} \quad \ldots.(18.99)$$

and for the formation of four dsp^2 hybrid orbitals we obtain by the same methods :

$$\psi_1 = \tfrac{1}{2}\psi_s + \tfrac{1}{2}\psi_{d_{xy}} + \frac{1}{\sqrt{2}}\psi_{p_x}$$

$$\psi_2 = \tfrac{1}{2}\psi_s + \tfrac{1}{2}\psi_{d_{xy}} - \frac{1}{\sqrt{2}}\psi_{p_x} \qquad \ldots.(18.100)$$

$$\psi_3 = \tfrac{1}{2}\psi_s - \tfrac{1}{2}\psi_{d_{xy}} + \frac{1}{\sqrt{2}}\psi_{p_y}$$

$$\psi_4 = \tfrac{1}{2}\psi_s - \tfrac{1}{2}\psi_{d_{xy}} - \frac{1}{\sqrt{2}}\psi_{p_y}$$

VIBRATIONAL AND ROTATIONAL STATES

In order to determine the vibrational and rotational states of molecules, we shall consider the case of the diatomic molecule. To a first approximation we shall assume that the vibrations are harmonic (see Chapter 1 equations 1.12 *et seq*). We have

$$F = -kx = m(d^2x/dt^2) \qquad \ldots.(18.101)$$

where x is the displacement due to the force F and k is the proportionality constant. The angular velocity ω is given by

$$\omega = \sqrt{k/m} \qquad \ldots.(18.102)$$

and since

$$\omega = 2\pi\nu \qquad \ldots.(18.103)$$

where ν is the frequency of vibration hence

$$\nu = (1/2\pi)\sqrt{k/m} \qquad \ldots.(18.104)$$

In a diatomic molecule, if both atoms are vibrating, the masses are m_1 and m_2 and the equilibrium distances from the centre of gravity of the molecule are r_1 and r_2, then

$$m_1r_1 = m_2r_2 \qquad \ldots.(18.105)$$

Let the nuclei be displaced through distances x_1 and x_2, the centre of gravity will remain in the same position and hence

$$m_1(r_1 + x_1) = m_2(r_2 + x_2) \qquad \ldots.(18.106)$$

or

$$m_1x_1 = m_2x_2 \qquad \ldots.(18.107)$$

Thus we have $x_1 = m_2x_2/m_1$ and $x_2 = m_1x_1/m_2$. The total displacement is $(x_1 + x_2)$ and consequently

$$F = -k(x_1 + x_2) \qquad \ldots.(18.108)$$

substituting for x_1 and x_2 we obtain

$$F = -k\left(\frac{m_2 + m_1}{m_1}\right)x_2 = -k\left(\frac{m_1 + m_2}{m_2}\right)x_1 \qquad \ldots.(18.109)$$

The corresponding equations of motion, will be :

$$m_1\frac{d^2x_1}{dt^2} = -k\left(\frac{m_1 + m_2}{m_2}\right)x_1 \text{ and } m_2\frac{d^2x_2}{dt^2} = -k\left(\frac{m_1 + m_2}{m_1}\right)x_2 \qquad \ldots.(18.110)$$

Multiplying the first equation by $m_2/(m_1+m_2)$ and the second by $m_1/(m_1+m_2)$ and adding, we obtain

$$\left(\frac{m_1 m_2}{m_1 + m_2}\right)\left(\frac{d^2x_1}{dt^2} + \frac{d^2x_2}{dt^2}\right) = -k(x_1 + x_2) \qquad \ldots(18.111)$$

Replacing $(x_1 + x_2)$ by x, we obtain

$$\frac{m_1 m_2}{m_1 + m_2}\frac{d^2x}{dt^2} = -kx \qquad \ldots(18.112)$$

This represents the vibration of a particle of mass m where

$$m = m_1 m_2/(m_1 + m_2) \qquad \ldots(18.113)$$

Thus, the vibration of two atoms about two equilibrium positions may be replaced by a single oscillator with a reduced mass m. The frequency of the oscillator will be

$$\nu = (1/2\pi)\sqrt{k/m} = (1/2\pi)\sqrt{k(m_1 + m_2)/m_1 m_2} \qquad \ldots(18.114)$$

The work done in displacing the oscillator from the equilibrium position to a distance x is

$$\int_0^x kx\,dx = kx^2/2 \qquad \ldots(18.115)$$

This quantity is numerically equal to the potential energy V. Since $x = A \cos 2\pi\nu t$ (where A is the amplitude) then

$$V = kx^2/2 = 2\pi^2\nu^2 m x^2 = 2\pi^2\nu^2 m A^2 \cos^2 2\pi\nu t \qquad \ldots(18.116)$$

The kinetic energy T is given by,

$$T = mv^2/2 = \frac{m}{2}\left(\frac{dx}{dt}\right)^2 = 2\pi^2\nu^2 m A^2 \sin^2 2\pi\nu t \qquad \ldots(18.117)$$

Thus the total energy of the oscillator is :

$$E = 2\pi^2\nu^2 m A^2(\cos^2 2\pi\nu t + \sin^2 2\pi\nu t) = 2\pi^2\nu^2 m A^2 \qquad \ldots(18.118)$$

In the old quantum theory it was assumed that the oscillator may only have certain energy values defined by :

$$E = nh\nu \qquad \ldots(18.119)$$

where n is an integer. The oscillator can absorb energy only in quanta, and the energy changes from $E_n = nh\nu$ to $E_{n+1} = (n + 1)h\nu$. From equation 18.118 we have

$$E_n = nh\nu = A_n^2 2\pi^2\nu^2 m \qquad \ldots(18.120)$$

$$E_{n+1} = (n + 1)h\nu = A^2_{n+1} \cdot 2\pi^2\nu^2 m \qquad \ldots(18.121)$$

During the absorption of energy, the frequency remains the same, only the amplitude changing. Thus in contrast to the classical treatment the amplitude cannot possess any values but only certain values A, $A\sqrt{2}$, $A\sqrt{3}$, *etc* and

$$\frac{A_{n+1}}{A_n} = \frac{\sqrt{n+1}}{\sqrt{n}} \qquad \ldots(18.122)$$

In the same way that the application of quantum mechanics has modified the original quantum treatment of the hydrogen atom, the above equations have to be modified. The Schrödinger equation for a linear oscillator is

$$\frac{d^2\psi}{dx^2} + \frac{8\pi^2 m}{h^2}(E - 2\pi^2\nu^2 m x^2)\psi = 0 \qquad \ldots(18.123)$$

For convenience in the following treatment we shall put

$$\frac{8\pi^2 mE}{h^2} = a \qquad \text{and} \qquad \frac{4\pi^2 m\nu}{h} = b \qquad \ldots.(18.124)$$

and

$$a/b = 2E/h\nu \qquad \ldots.(18.125)$$

In place of the coordinate x, we shall employ a coordinate q which is related to x by

$$q = x\sqrt{b} \qquad \ldots.(18.126)$$

Then

$$\frac{d^2\psi}{dx^2} = b\,\frac{d^2\psi}{dq^2} \qquad \ldots.(18.127)$$

Substituting equations 18.125 and 18.127 in 18.123 we obtain :

$$\frac{d^2\psi}{dq^2} + \left(\frac{a}{b} - q^2\right)\psi = 0 \qquad \ldots.(18.128)$$

On solution of this equation it appears that a/b may assume only the values 1, 3, 5, 7 *etc*, or in general $2n + 1$, where n is an integer. It is clear, for example, that

$$\psi = \exp(-\,q^2/2) \qquad \ldots.(18.129)$$

is a solution. The second differential coefficient of equation 18.129 gives

$$\frac{d^2\psi}{dq^2} + (1 - q^2)\psi = 0 \qquad \ldots.(18.130)$$

i.e.

$$a/b = 1 = 2E/h\nu \qquad \text{or} \qquad E = h\nu/2 \qquad \ldots.(18.131)$$

also

$$\psi = 2q\exp(-\,q^2/2) \qquad \ldots.(18.132)$$

may be a solution ; on differentiation we obtain

$$\frac{d^2\psi}{dq^2} + (3 - q^2)\psi = 0 \qquad \ldots.(18.133)$$

and

$$a/b = 3 \qquad \text{or} \qquad E = 3h\nu/2 \qquad \ldots.(18.134)$$

Other solutions will be

$$\psi = (4q^2 - 2)\exp(-\,q^2/2) \qquad E = 5h\nu/2 \qquad \ldots.(18.135)$$

$$\psi = (8q^3 - 12q)\exp(-\,q^2/2) \qquad E = 7h\nu/2 \qquad \ldots.(18.136)$$

$$\psi = (16q^4 - 48q^2 + 12)\exp(-\,q^2/2) \qquad E = 9h\nu/2 \qquad \ldots.(18.137)$$

From the above solutions we see that in general the energy of the oscillator (harmonic) may be expressed by

$$E = (n + \tfrac{1}{2})h\nu \qquad \ldots.(18.138)$$

and the energy may only assume certain values and is never zero, the lowest value (*i.e.* the zero point energy) being $\frac{1}{2}h\nu$.

Let us now consider the possible rotational states of the diatomic molecule. The rotational energy of a diatomic molecule is given by

$$E = m_1 v_1^2/2 + m_2 v_2^2/2 \qquad \ldots.(18.139)$$

where v_1 and v_2 represent the velocities of the two atoms. If the number of rotations in unit time is ν then

$$v_1 = 2\pi r_1 \nu \qquad \ldots(18.140)$$

$$v_2 = 2\pi r_2 \nu \qquad \ldots(18.141)$$

and

$$E = 4\pi^2\nu^2/2(m_1r_1^2 + m_2r_2^2) \qquad \ldots(18.142)$$

We have, $2\pi\nu = \omega$, where ω is the angular velocity and $(m_1r_1^2 + m_2r_2^2) = I$ where I is the moment of inertia of the molecule. Equation 18.142 thus becomes

$$E = I\omega^2/2 \qquad \ldots(18.143)$$

On the basis of the old quantum theory the angular momentum mvr was quantized in units of $Jh/2\pi$ where J was an integer. Applying the same hypothesis to the case of the rotating molecule we have

$$m_1v_1r_1 + m_2v_2r_2 = Jh/2\pi \qquad \ldots(18.144)$$

and substituting equations 18.140 and 18.141 we have

$$2\pi\nu(m_1r_1^2 + m_2r_2^2) = I\omega = Jh/2\pi \qquad \ldots(18.145)$$

From equations 18.145 and 18.143 we obtain

$$E = J^2h^2/8\pi^2I \qquad \ldots(18.146)$$

i.e. the energy of the rotator is proportional to J^2. The introduction of quantum mechanical methods leads to a similar solution. In the case of the rigid rotator, r is a constant and it may readily be seen that in this case, treatment by the methods given in equations 18.15 to 18.19 gives

$$\beta = 8\pi^2IE/h^2$$

and since $\beta = l(l + 1)$ where l is an integer we have in place of equation 18.146

$$E = J(J + 1)h^2/8\pi^2I \qquad \ldots(18.147)$$

It may readily be shown that the moment of inertia is related to the interatomic distance. Since $r = r_1 + r_2$, from 18.105 we have:

$$m_1r_1 = m_2r_2 \quad \text{and} \quad m_1r_1 = m_2(r - r_1) \qquad \ldots(18.148)$$

or

$$r_1 = r\frac{m_2}{m_1 + m_2} \qquad \ldots(18.149)$$

and

$$r_2 = r\frac{m_1}{m_1 + m_2} \qquad \ldots(18.150)$$

and substitution in the expression for the moment of inertia gives,

$$I = m_1r_1^2 + m_2r_2^2 = \frac{m_1m_2}{m_1 + m_2}r^2 = mr^2 \qquad \ldots(18.151)$$

THE CLAUSIUS-MOSOTTI EQUATION

Consider a plane condenser with two infinite plates located at a definite distance from each other. The condenser is charged and the surface charge densities are $+\sigma$ and $-\sigma$. We have to calculate the force acting on a unit charge situated at a point O in the space between the plates (*Figure 79*). Let us draw OA perpendicular to the plate and construct two concentric circles with A as centre and with radii s and $s + ds$ (AB and AC). The area of the annular ring between the two circumferences is $2\pi s ds$ and as is seen from *Figure 79*,

$$AB = s = OB \sin\beta \qquad \ldots.(18.152)$$

$ds = BC$, the angle $C\hat{B}D = \beta$ and the side BD is given by

$$BD = OB \sin d\beta \qquad \ldots.(18.153)$$

In view of the small value of the angle $d\beta$, we may write

$$BD = OB\, d\beta \qquad \ldots.(18.154)$$

and

$$BC = ds = \frac{BD}{\cos\beta} = \frac{OB\, d\beta}{\cos\beta} \qquad \ldots.(18.155)$$

The area of the annular ring is then given by :

$$2\pi s ds = \frac{2\pi(OB)^2 \sin\beta d\beta}{\cos\beta} \qquad \ldots.(18.156)$$

Its charge, therefore, is

$$\sigma' = \frac{2\pi\,(OB)^2\,\sigma \sin\beta d\beta}{\cos\beta} \qquad \ldots.(18.157)$$

The force acting on the point charge O due to the charged ring will be

$$\frac{\sigma' \cos\beta}{(OB)^2} = 2\pi\sigma \sin\beta d\beta \qquad \ldots.(18.158)$$

In order to obtain the field due to the whole of the charged plate, (18.158) must be integrated over the range 0 to 90°. This gives $2\pi\sigma$. The unit negative charge, however, is attracted to the positive plate and repelled to an equal extent by the negative plate. The total force acting on the point charge will therefore be $4\pi\sigma$.

If we now fill the space between the plates with a dielectric, *e.g.* benzene, the molecules will be polarized, the positive nuclei being displaced in the

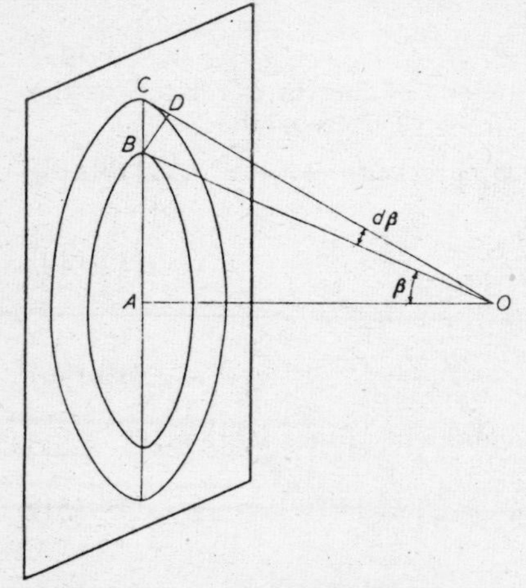

Figure 79. Forces acting on unit charge at a point O between plates of a plane condenser

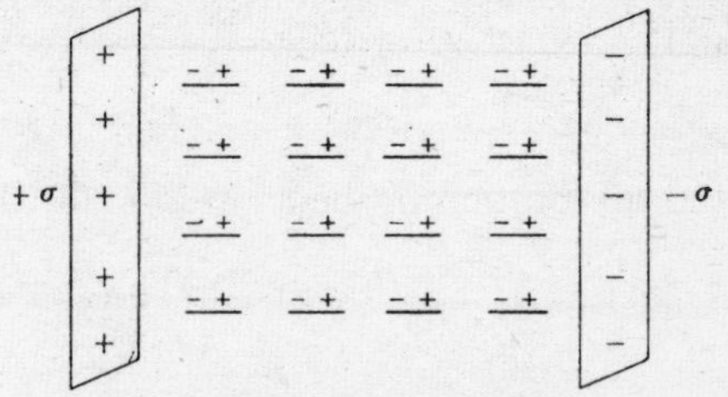

Figure 80. Representation of induced dipoles in dielectric of a plane condenser

direction of the negative plate and the negatively charged electrons displaced towards the positive plate (*Figure 80*). The induced dipole moment will be de, where d is the displacement and e the charge. If the dielectric consisted of a substance with a permanent dipole moment, the molecules would be oriented in the field due to the charged plates. It is thus possible to regard the space between the plates as filled with dipolar molecules arranged end to end as is depicted schematically in *Figure 80*. It is clear that the force acting on the unit charge is now not the same as in the absence of the dielectric. All the dipoles within the dielectric will be compensated, but there will exist a layer of negative charges close to the positive plate, and a layer of positive charges adjacent to the negative plate. These layers of charges may be regarded as a second inner condenser and if the surface charge density is I, since the field due to the inner condenser will act in the opposite direction to that due to the outer, the resultant force acting on the point charge is not $4\pi\sigma$ but $4\pi\sigma - 4\pi I$. We then write

$$\frac{4\pi\sigma}{4\pi\sigma - 4\pi I} = \frac{\sigma}{\sigma - I} = \epsilon \qquad \ldots.(18.159)$$

where ϵ is the dielectric constant.

It will be clear that I is dependent both on the number of dipoles and on the magnitude of the moment, whether induced or induced and permanent, thus

$$I = nm \qquad \ldots.(18.160)$$

where n is the number of molecules per cc and m is the dipole moment in the direction of the field.

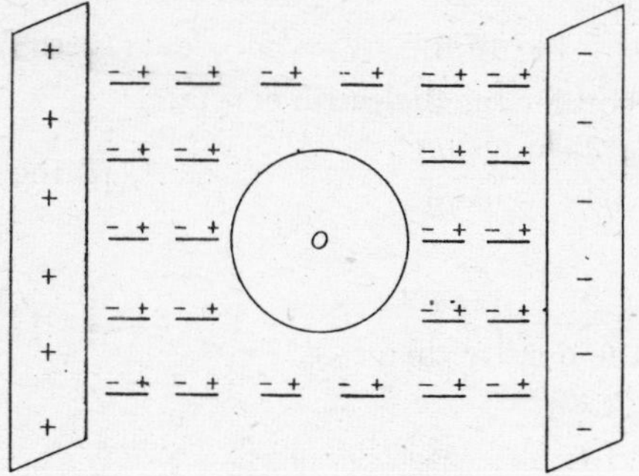

Figure 81. Representation of unit charge within dielectric medium of condenser

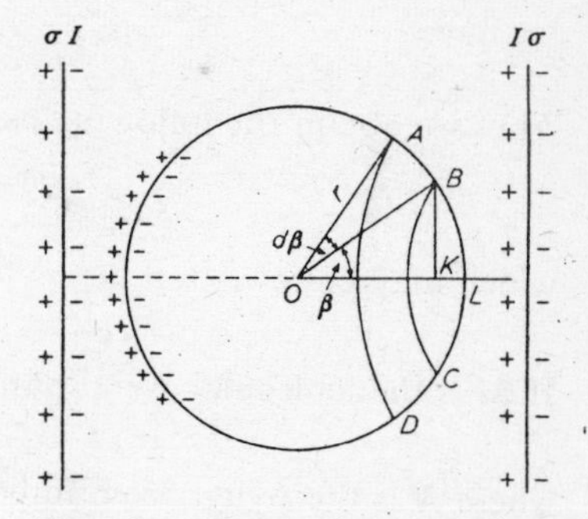

Figure 82. Forces acting on unit charge within plane condenser filled with a dielectric

We now wish to determine the effective field acting on a molecule situated in the dielectric. To do this, a spherical cavity is constructed around a point charge (*Figure 81*). The force acting on the charge may be divided into three parts: that due to the charge on the condenser, $4\pi\sigma$; the force F_2 determined by the polarization of the molecules surrounding the cavity; and the force F_3 due to the molecules within the cavity. Thus

$$F = 4\pi\sigma + F_2 + F_3 \qquad \ldots.(18.161)$$

In order to evaluate F_2, we shall consider a ring $ABCD$ (*Figure 82*) of surface area:

$$2\pi(BK)(AB) = 2\pi\,(r\sin\beta)(r\,d\beta) = 2\pi r^2 \sin\beta\, d\beta \qquad \ldots.(18.162)$$

where r is the radius of the sphere. The surface charge density of the sphere is $I\cos\beta$ since the charge I of an area s, perpendicular to OL when transferred to the sphere will occupy an area $s/\cos\beta$. Thus the total charge on the ring will be :

$$I' = 2\pi I r^2 \sin\beta \cos\beta d\beta \qquad \ldots.(18.163)$$

At the centre of the sphere, the field acting on the point charge will be,

$$I' \cos\beta/r^2 = 2\pi I \sin\beta \cos^2\beta d\beta \qquad \ldots.(18.164)$$

On integrating equation 18.164 from 0° to 180° we obtain $4\pi I/3$ which represents the charge on the sphere. The direction of this field, as is clear from *Figure 82* is the same as that of the outer, *i.e.* original field, hence

$$F_2 = -4\pi I + 4\pi I/3 = -8\pi I/3 \qquad \ldots.(18.165)$$

The calculation of F_3 produced by the molecules within the cavity presents the greatest difficulty since it is necessary to know the arrangement of the molecules within the cavity ; LORENTZ[3] has shown, however, that when the dielectric possesses a sodium chloride type lattice, or when the molecular distribution is completely random, $F_3 = 0$.

Thus the total force, F, acting on the point charge is :

$$F = 4\pi\sigma - 8\pi I/3 = 4\pi\sigma - 8\pi nm/3 \qquad \ldots.(18.166)$$

The moment of the molecule in the direction of the field, is to a first approximation, proportional to the field,

$$m = aF \qquad \ldots.(18.167)$$

where a is the polarizability. Substituting equation 18.167 in 18.166 we have

$$F = 4\pi\sigma - 8\pi naF/3 \qquad \ldots.(18.168)$$

Thus we obtain the following expression for the dielectric constant :

$$\epsilon = \frac{\sigma}{\sigma - I} = \frac{1/4\pi + 2na/3}{1/4\pi - na/3} \qquad \ldots.(18.169)$$

which may be rewritten in the form

$$(\epsilon - 1)/(\epsilon + 2) = 4\pi na/3 \qquad \ldots.(18.170)$$

If M is the molecular weight and d the density then

$$n = Nd/M$$

where N is the Avagadro number and

$$(\epsilon - 1)/(\epsilon + 2) \, . \, M/d = 4\pi Na/3 \qquad \ldots.(18.171)$$

THE LANGEVIN-DEBYE EQUATION

If a polar molecule of moment μ forms an angle β with the field, the component moment in the direction of the field is $\mu \cos\beta$. This is the quantity which enters into the experimentally determined polarization. Each dipole will be oriented at an angle to the field and hence the sum of all component moments is

$$\mu\cos\beta_1 + \mu\cos\beta_2 \cdot \cdot \cdot \cdot + \mu\cos\beta_N$$

and in order to determine the average value, it is necessary to divide the sum of the component moments by the number of molecules.

We shall first consider the probability of a free molecule, in the absence of an applied field, making an angle between β and $\beta + d\beta$ with an arbitrary direction, if all directions are equally probable. Let us imagine that the molecules are rearranged, without change of orientation, so that one end of each molecule is located at the point O (*Figure 82*). We shall draw a sphere with this point as centre and let OL be the given arbitrary direction. We mark out on the surface of the sphere a ring $ABCD$ whose area will be $2\pi r^2 \sin \beta d\beta$ (equation 18.162). The probability of a molecule making an angle between β and $\beta + d\beta$ with OL, will be equal to the ratio of the surface of the ring to the surface of the sphere :

$$dW = \frac{2\pi r^2 \sin \beta d\beta}{4\pi r^2} = \tfrac{1}{2} \sin \beta d\beta \qquad \ldots (18.172)$$

When the molecule is located in an applied field, the distribution will be determined by the Maxwell—Boltzmann law. Thus if the probability of a particular state in the absence of a field is a, then in the presence of a field the probability will be $a \exp(-V/kT)$ where V is the potential energy of the molecule in the field, k is Boltzmann's constant and T the absolute temperature. Thus the probability of a molecule forming an angle β with the direction of the field will be, $\frac{1}{2} \sin \beta\, [\exp(-V/kT)] d\beta$. We have now to obtain an expression for the potential energy of the dipole in the field. In order to do this we must calculate the work done in rotating the dipole from a position AB, perpendicular to the field, to a position CD where it forms an angle β with the direction of the field (*Figure 83*). If the end of the dipole has moved through the distance AC, the work done is

$$Fe(CK) = Fe(OC) \cos \beta \qquad \ldots (18.173)$$

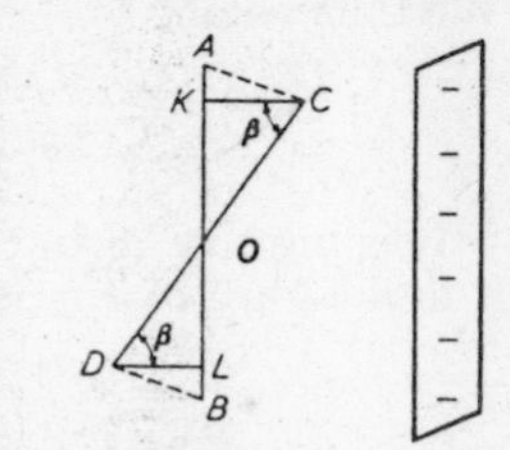

Figure 83. Determination of potential energy of dipole in the field of a condenser

where F is the applied field numerically equal to the force acting on a unit charge, e is the positive charge on the dipole and CK is the displacement in the field. The opposite end of the dipole moves through the distance BD and the work done is

$$Fe(DL) = Fe(DO) \cos \beta \qquad \ldots (18.174)$$

The total work done is therefore

$$Fe \cos \beta\, (DO + OC) = Fel \cos \beta \qquad \ldots (18.175)$$

where l is the length of the dipole.
Since

$$el = \mu \qquad \ldots (18.176)$$

the potential energy of the dipole in the field will be

$$V = -F\mu \cos \beta \qquad \ldots (18.177)$$

As is evident, the potential energy is at a maximum when $\beta = 0$. Thus the probability of the dipole forming an angle between β and $\beta + d\beta$ with the field is :

$$dW = \tfrac{1}{2} \sin \beta \left(\exp \frac{F\mu \cos \beta}{kT}\right) d\beta \qquad \ldots (18.178)$$

In order to find the number of molecules forming an angle β with the field it is necessary to multiply dW by the total number of molecules, N. Each of these molecules will possess a dipole moment μ and a component moment in the direction of the field of $\mu \cos \beta$. The sum of all the component moments is therefore $NdW\mu \cos \beta$. Integrating this expression through all possible angles from 0° to 180°, we obtain the sum of the component moments for all the molecules. Dividing this value by N, we obtain the average value of the moment in the direction of the field :

$$\bar{m} = \int_0^\pi \tfrac{1}{2}\mu \sin \beta \cos \beta \left(\exp \frac{F\mu \cos \beta}{kT} \right) d\beta \qquad \ldots .(18.179)$$

Under the experimental conditions $\frac{F\mu \cos \beta}{kT}$ is always considerably less than unity. For example, a dipole with $\mu = 1\text{D} = 1 \times 10^{-18}$ e.s.u situated in a field of 300 v/cm possesses a potential energy 4×10^{-4} times the thermal energy. Consequently in place of $\exp\left(\frac{F\mu \cos \beta}{kT}\right)$ we use the first two terms of the series *i.e.* we assume

$$\exp\left(\frac{F\mu \cos \beta}{kT}\right) = 1 + \frac{F\mu \cos \beta}{kT} \qquad \ldots .(18.180)$$

We thus obtain

$$\bar{m} = \frac{\mu}{2} \int_0^\pi \sin \beta \cos \beta \left(1 + \frac{F\mu \cos \beta}{kT}\right) d\beta = \frac{\mu^2 F}{3kT} \qquad \ldots .(18.181)$$

It is possible to integrate the expression 18.179 directly without putting it in the form of a series. We then obtain

$$\frac{\bar{m}}{\mu} = \frac{\exp(a) + \exp(-a)}{\exp(a) - \exp(-a)} - \frac{1}{a} = L(a), \text{ where } a = \frac{F\mu}{kT}$$

At small values of a this reduces to the expression given in equation 18.181.

A more exact quantum-mechanical treatment of orientation polarization leads to the same expression if the temperature is not too low. At low temperatures, corrections have to be introduced. Generally, however, dipole moments are measured at temperatures where equation 18.181 may be used.

The moment in the direction of the field is proportional to the strength of the field, *i.e.*

$$\bar{m} = a_{or.} F \qquad \ldots .(18.182)$$

and hence we obtain,

$$a_{or.} = \frac{\mu^2}{3kT} \qquad \ldots .(18.183)$$

DIPOLE MOMENTS OF BONDS

Let us consider the origin of the electrical dipole moment of a single molecule. In a diatomic molecule containing a single covalent bond, each nucleus together with the nonvalency electron shells may be regarded as a point charge of $+e$, the electrical centre of gravity of two such charges will be located midway between them. The two negatively charged electrons, one to each atom may be conceived, on the basis of quantum mechanics, as an electron cloud which surrounds the nuclei. In the hydrogen atom the electron cloud of the 1*s* electron possesses spherical symmetry and its centre of gravity is located at the centre of the sphere which coincides with the nucleus.

If the electron be described by the function ψ, the average value of its coordinate, x, is given by the following expression :

$$\bar{x} = \frac{\int \psi x \psi d\tau}{\int \psi^2 d\tau} \qquad \ldots.(18.184)$$

which will represent the mean value of the coordinate of the electron cloud in the state represented by the function ψ. This expression is obtained in the following way. It will be remembered that in classical mechanics, the average value of any dimension x is $\bar{x} = \dfrac{\int f(x)xdx}{\int f(x)dx}$ where $f(x)dx$ is the probability that x has a value between x and $x + dx$. Let us consider a particular example. If the distribution of velocity of gas molecule obeys Maxwell's law, the probability that a molecule has a velocity between v and $v + dv$ equals $A\left(\exp\dfrac{-mv^2}{2kT}\right) v^2dv$, where A is a constant. If this expression be integrated through all values of v we obtain :

$$A\int \exp\,(-\,mv^2/2kT)v^2dv = 1$$

or

$$A = 1\Big/\int \exp\,(-\,mv^2/2kT)v^2dv$$

If the total number of molecules is N, the number of molecules with a velocity between v and $v + dv$ is :

$$NA \exp\,(-\,mv^2/2kT)v^2dv$$

The sum of the velocities of these molecules is

$$NvA \exp\,(-\,mv^2/2kT)v^2dv$$

The sum of the velocities of all the molecules is therefore

$$\int NvA \exp\,(-\,mv^2/2kT)v^2dv$$

and the mean velocity

$$\bar{v} = \int vA \exp\,(-\,mv^2/2kT)v^2dv$$

Substituting for A we obtain :

$$\bar{v} = \frac{\int v \exp\,(-\,mv^2/2kT)v^2dv}{\int \exp\,(-\,mv^2/2kT)v^2dv} = \frac{\int vf(v)dv}{\int f(v)dv}$$

where $f(v)$ is the probability that the value of the velocity lies between v and $v + dv$. In quantum mechanics where the probability is given by $\psi^2 d\tau$ or more exactly by $\psi^* \psi d\tau$ we have the analogous formula

$$\bar{x} = \frac{\int \psi^* x \psi d\tau}{\int \psi^* \psi d\tau}$$

Following equation 18.184, for several electrons the average value of the coordinate will be

$$\overline{\sum_i x_i} = \frac{\int \psi \sum_i x_i \psi d\tau}{\int \psi^2 d\tau} \quad \ldots .(18.185)$$

where $i = 1, 2, 3 \ldots\ldots n$ and n is the number of electrons.

In a diatomic molecule the electronic centre of gravity will be found on the line of centres which may be taken as the x axis. If the origin of the system of coordinates is located at the centre of gravity of the positive charges, the distance $\sum_i x_i$, determined by equation 18.185, will give the average distance between the electrical centres of gravity. The dipole moment will therefore be

$$\mu = \frac{e\int \psi \sum_i x_i \psi d\tau}{\int \psi^2 d\tau} \quad \ldots .(18.186)$$

In the case of two electrons the above expression becomes

$$\mu = \frac{e\int \psi (x_1 + x_2) \psi d\tau}{\int \psi^2 d\tau} \quad \ldots .(18.187)$$

If the bond in the molecule is entirely covalent then its moment may be obtained by substituting into this expression, equation 3.95, for the homopolar bond :

$$\mu_{hom.} = \frac{e\int \{\psi_a(1)\psi_b(2) + \psi_b(1)\psi_a(2)\}^2 (x_1 + x_2) d\tau}{2 + 2S^2} \quad \ldots .(18.188)$$

which on rearrangement becomes

$$\mu_{hom.} = \frac{e\int \psi_a^2(1)\psi_b^2(2)(x_1 + x_2) d\tau}{2 + 2S^2} + \frac{e\int \psi_b^2(1)\psi_a^2(2)(x_1 + x_2) d\tau}{2 + 2S^2} + $$
$$+ \frac{2e\int \psi_a(1)\psi_b(1)\psi_a(2)\psi_b(2)(x_1 + x_2) d\tau}{2 + 2S^2} \quad \ldots .(18.189)$$

From this expression it is clear that the moment of the homopolar bond consists of the moments of the structures $\psi_a^2(1)\psi_b^2(2)$ and $\psi_b^2(1)\psi_a^2(2)$ corresponding to the location of the electrons on atoms a and b, and the moment of the transitional structure $\psi_a(1)\psi_b(2)\psi_a(2)\psi_b(1)$:

$$\mu_1 = \frac{e\int \psi_a^2(1)\psi_b^2(2)(x_1 + x_2) d\tau}{2 + 2S^2} = \frac{e(A + B)}{2 + 2S^2} \quad \ldots .(18.190)$$

$$\mu_2 = \frac{e\int \psi_b^2(1)\psi_a^2(2)(x_1 + x_2) d\tau}{2 + 2S^2} = \frac{e(B + A)}{2 + 2S^2} \quad \ldots .(18.191)$$

$$\mu_{per.} = \frac{2e\int \psi_a(1)\psi_b(1)\psi_a(2)\psi_b(2)(x_1 + x_2)d\tau}{2 + 2S^2} = \frac{4eTS}{2 + 2S^2} \quad \ldots.(18.192)$$

where

$$A = \int \psi_a{}^2 x d\tau \quad B = \int \psi_b{}^2 x d\tau \quad T = \int \psi_a\psi_b x d\tau \quad \ldots.(18.193)$$

Let us place the origin of the system of coordinates midway between the atoms, then

$$A = r/2 \quad \ldots.(18.194)$$

$$B = -r/2 \quad \ldots.(18.195)$$

where r is the interatomic distance. It is then clear that $\mu_1 = \mu_2 = 0$ and for bonds between identical atoms the integral T and hence $\mu_{hom.}$ become zero and the molecule, as is to be expected, is nonpolar.

In the case of covalent bonds formed between different atoms, the electron cloud due to the transitional structure is almost certain to be asymmetric. Although we have considered the motion of a pair of electrons in the field of two identical positive charges, it is nevertheless necessary to take into consideration the fact that the wave functions of the electrons taking part in bond formation may be different (for example, one may be an *s* electron and the other a *p* electron as in HF). Consequently it is not clear *a priori* whether or not the transitional structure possesses a moment. The calculation has been made for the bond in hydrogen fluoride, where the asymmetry of the electron cloud might be considered to be significant owing to the considerable difference in the electronegativity of the hydrogen and fluorine atoms. It is found[4] that the moment is less than 0·1 D and we may therefore conclude that the moment of a homopolar bond is in general negligible.

The ionic state of the bond is described by the function $\psi_a(1)\psi_a(2)$, we then obtain,

$$\mu_i = e\int \psi_a{}^2(1)\psi_a{}^2(2)(x_1 + x_2)d\tau = 2eA = er \quad \ldots.(18.196)$$

in accordance with the usual expression.

In bonds between different atoms the dipole moment may have intermediate values owing to the superposition of covalent and ionic states. In such cases the bond is described by the function

$$\psi = c_1\{\psi_a(1)\psi_b(2) + \psi_b(1)\psi_a(2)\} + c_2\psi_a(1)\psi_a(2) \quad \ldots.(18.197)$$

Substituting this expression into equation 18.187 we obtain,

$$\mu = e\frac{c_1{}^2[2(A+B)+4TS]+2c_2{}^2A+4c_1c_2(AS+T)}{c_1{}^2(2+2S^2)+c_2{}^2+4c_1c_2S} = \frac{e(c_2{}^2r+2c_1c_2TS)}{c_1{}^2(2+2S^2)+c_2{}^2+4c_1c_2S} \quad \ldots.(18.198)$$

The bond moment is thus composed of the moment of the homopolar structure

$$\mu_{hom.} = e\frac{2A + 2B + 4TS}{N} \approx 0 \quad \ldots.(18.199)$$

where N is the normalization constant.

The moment of the ionic structure will be :

$$\mu_i = e \, . \, 2A/\text{N} = er/\text{N} \text{ with coefficient } c_2^2 \qquad \ldots . (18.200)$$

and the moment of the transitional structure is,

$$\mu_{per.} = e\frac{2AS + \text{T.}}{\text{N}} \cong e\frac{2AS}{\text{N}} = \frac{erS}{\text{N}} \text{ with coefficient } 2c_1c_2 \qquad \ldots (18.201)$$

Equation 18.198 may be used to calculate c_1 and c_2 and by this means the weights of the different valence bond structures may be determined.

DEFORMATION, ORIENTATION AND DISPERSION EFFECTS

Let us now calculate the field due to a dipole. The potential due to the dipole *AD* at the point *O* (*Figure 84*) will be $e/r_1 - e/r_2 = e(r_2 - r_1)/r_1r_2$ where r_1 and r_2 are the distances of the point *O* from the positive and negative ends of the dipole. If *O* is a sufficiently large distance from *AD*, we may substitute r^2 for r_1r_2, where r is the distance from *O* to the centre of the dipole and it will be possible to regard the angles $O\hat{A}D$ and $O\hat{C}D$ as equal.

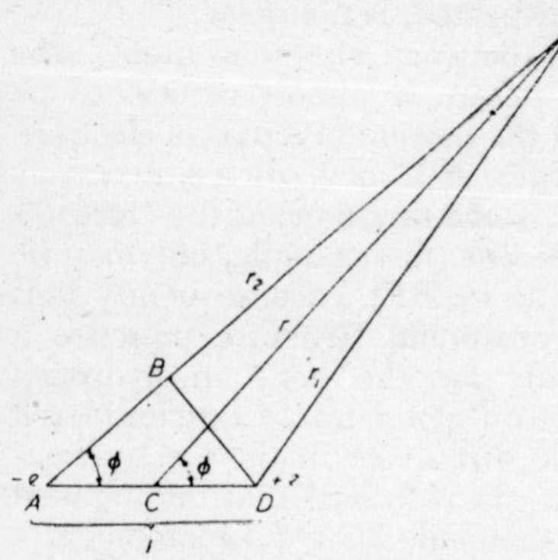

Figure 84. Field due to a dipole

From the figure, we see that

$$r_2 - r_1 = AB = l \cos \phi \qquad \ldots . (18.202)$$

where l is the length of the dipole and ϕ is the angle $O\hat{A}D$. Thus the potential energy V is given by :

$$V = (el \cos \phi)/r^2 = (\mu \cos \phi)/r^2 \qquad \ldots . (18.203)$$

The field component in the direction of r, will be

$$-\partial V/\partial r = (2\mu \cos \phi)/r^3 \qquad \ldots . (18.204)$$

and in the direction perpendicular to this,

$$-\partial V/r\partial \phi = (\mu \sin \phi)/r^3 \qquad \ldots . (18.205)$$

From equations 18.204 and 18.205 we obtain the following expression for the resulting field

$$F = \left\{ \left(\frac{2\mu \cos \phi}{r^3}\right)^2 + \left(\frac{\mu \sin \phi}{r^3}\right)^2 \right\}^{\frac{1}{2}} = \frac{\mu}{r^3}\left\{ 4 \cos^2\phi + \sin^2\phi \right\}^{\frac{1}{2}}$$

$$= \frac{\mu}{r^3}\left\{ 3 \cos^2\phi + 1 \right\}^{\frac{1}{2}} \qquad \ldots . (18.206)$$

The mean value of $\cos^2\phi$ is equal to 1/3 since the probability that an angle lies between ϕ and $\phi + d\phi$ is $\frac{1}{2} \sin \phi d\phi$; the average value of $\cos^2\phi$ is therefore

$$\int_0^\pi \tfrac{1}{2} \cos^2\phi \sin \phi d\phi = 1/3$$

Consequently the mean value of F becomes:

$$F = \mu\sqrt{2}/r^3 \qquad \ldots.(18.207)$$

We shall now obtain an expression for the deformation interaction of two molecules. The action of the field F_1 of the first molecule is to induce into the second molecule a moment given by,

$$m_2 = ex = a_2F_1 \qquad \ldots.(18.208)$$

where x is the displacement and a_2 is the polarizability of the second molecule.

The force acting on the charge e is F_1e. On the displacement of this charge through a distance x by the field, the work done is $\int_0^x F_1edx$ and since from equation 18.208 we have:

$$eF_1 = e^2x/a_2$$

consequently

$$\int_0^x F_1edx = \int_0^x \frac{e^2x}{a_2}\,dx = \frac{e^2x^2}{2a_2} = \frac{a_2F_1^{\,2}}{2} \qquad \ldots.(18.209)$$

The potential energy of the induced dipole of the second molecule in the field due to the first molecule is $-F_1m_2\cos\beta$ (see equation 18.177) which in the present instance will be $-F_1m_2$. Thus combining with equation 18.208,

$$F_1m_2 = -F_1a_2F_1 = -a_2F_1^{\,2} \qquad \ldots.(18.210)$$

Consequently from equations 18.209 and 18.210 the total potential energy of the induced dipole in the field of the first molecule is

$$-a_2F_1^{\,2} + a_2F_1^{\,2}/2 = -a_2F_1^{\,2}/2 \qquad \ldots.(18.211)$$

If the second molecule has a dipole moment of μ_2 and the polarizability of the first molecule is a_1, a moment is induced into the first molecule equal to $m_1 = a_1F_2$ and the potential energy of the first molecule in the field of the second is $-a_1F_2^{\,2}/2$. The total energy of the two molecules is therefore

$$-a_2F_1^{\,2}/2 - a_1F_2^{\,2}/2 \qquad \ldots.(18.212)$$

For two identical molecules,

$$a_1 = a_2 \quad \text{and} \quad \mu_1 = \mu_2$$

so that

$$E = -aF^2 \qquad \ldots.(18.213)$$

and substituting for F from equation 18.207 we have

$$E_{def.} = -2\mu^2a/r^6 \qquad \ldots.(18.214)$$

The equation 18.214 expresses the deformation energy of interaction of two dipoles and forces of this type do not depend to a first approximation on the temperature. For the calculation of the energy of orientation interaction it is possible to proceed in the same manner as in the deduction of the Debye equation (see above) but it is also possible to proceed directly from equation 18.214.

If a molecule possesses a permanent dipole moment μ, it is equivalent to the existence of an effective polarization of $\mu^2/3kT$ (equation 18.183) and substitution into equation 18.214 leads to

$$E_{or.} = -2\mu^4/3r^6kT \qquad \ldots(18.215)$$

This expression will only be valid at high temperatures, since in the deduction of the Debye equation we restricted ourselves to the case when $V \ll kT$. At low temperatures it may be shown that the interaction energy is given by

$$\underset{\text{Lim. } T=0}{E_{or.}} = -2\mu^2/r^3 \qquad \ldots(18.216)$$

For the calculation of the dispersion effect we shall consider the interaction of two dipolar linear oscillators. Let each of these consist of a positive and negative charge. The frequency of oscillation ν_0 of each oscillator is related to the force constant k by the equation

$$(\nu_0 = 1/2\pi)\sqrt{k/m} \qquad \ldots(18.104)$$

The force due to the field F on the charge will be

$$eF = kx \qquad \ldots(18.217)$$

where x is the displacement. From equation 18.208 it follows that

$$a = ex/F \qquad \ldots(18.218)$$

which with equation 18.217 gives

$$a = e^2/k \qquad \ldots(18.219)$$

and hence

$$\nu_0 = \frac{1}{2\pi}\sqrt{\frac{e^2}{ma}} \qquad \ldots(18.220)$$

The potential energy of the first oscillator is

$$V = kx_1{}^2/2 \qquad \ldots(18.221)$$

and the kinetic energy is

$$T = mv_1{}^2/2 = p_1{}^2/2m \qquad \ldots(18.222)$$

where $p_1 = mv_1$ is the momentum.
The total energy of the first oscillator is therefore

$$E_1 = p_1{}^2/2m + kx_1{}^2/2 \qquad \ldots(18.223)$$

and similarly for the second oscillator

$$E_2 = p_2{}^2/2m + kx_2{}^2/2 \qquad \ldots(18.224)$$

Let us now consider the interaction of linear oscillators separated from each other by a distance r. From Coulomb's law there is an electrostatic energy (*Figure 85*) :

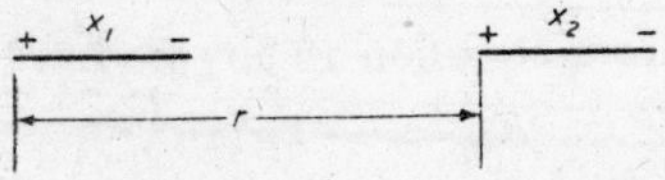

Figure 85. Interaction of linear oscillators

$$U = e^2\left\{\frac{1}{r + x_2 - x_1} - \frac{1}{r + x_2} - \frac{1}{r - x_1} + \frac{1}{r}\right\} = -\frac{2e^2x_1x_2}{r^3} + \ldots \qquad \ldots(18.225)$$

The first member of the series gives the interaction of the dipoles, the second of dipole with quadrupole, the third quadrupole with quadrupole *etc.*

We shall only consider here the dipole-dipole interaction. The total energy will thus be

$$E = (p_1^2 + p_2^2)/2m + k(x_1^2 + x_2^2)/2 - 2e^2x_1x_2/r^3 \quad \ldots.(18.226)$$

In order to solve this equation we shall introduce new coordinates u_1 and u_2, such that

$$u_1 = (x_1 + x_2)/\sqrt{2} \quad \text{and} \quad u_2 = (x_1 - x_2)/\sqrt{2} \quad \ldots.(18.227)$$

then

$$x_1 = (u_1 + u_2)/\sqrt{2} \quad \text{and} \quad x_2 = (u_1 - u_2)/\sqrt{2} \quad \ldots.(18.228)$$

Substituting the new coordinates in place of x_1 and x_2 we obtain in place of equation 18.226 :

$$E = \left[\frac{1}{2m}p_1^2 + \tfrac{1}{2}\left(k - \frac{2e^2}{r^3}\right)x_1^2\right] + \left[\frac{1}{2m}p_2^2 + \tfrac{1}{2}\left(k + \frac{2e^2}{r^3}\right)x_2^2\right] \quad \ldots.(18.229)$$

This expression corresponds to the energy of two oscillators with frequencies :

$$\nu_1 = \frac{1}{2\pi}\sqrt{\frac{1}{m}\left(k - \frac{2e^2}{r^3}\right)} \quad \ldots.(18.230)$$

$$\nu_2 = \frac{1}{2\pi}\sqrt{\frac{1}{m}\left(k + \frac{2e^2}{r^3}\right)} \quad \ldots.(18.231)$$

or from equation 18.104,

$$\nu_1 = \frac{1}{2\pi}\sqrt{\frac{k}{m}\left(1 - \frac{2e^2}{kr^3}\right)} = \nu_0\sqrt{1 - \frac{2e^2}{kr^3}} \quad \ldots.(18.232)$$

$$\nu_2 = \frac{1}{2\pi}\sqrt{\frac{k}{m}\left(1 + \frac{2e^2}{kr^3}\right)} = \nu_0\sqrt{1 + \frac{2e^2}{kr^3}} \quad \ldots.(18.233)$$

The physical meaning of this result is that if before interaction both oscillators vibrate with a frequency ν_0, owing to the interaction the oscillators now vibrate with different frequencies, one greater and the other less than the original.

If the zero point energy were originally given by

$$E = h\nu_0/2 + h\nu_0/2 = h\nu_0 \quad \ldots.(18.234)$$

now in accordance with equations 18.232 and 18.233 it will be given by :

$$E' = \frac{h\nu_0}{2}\left(1 - \frac{2e^2}{kr^3}\right)^{\frac{1}{2}} + \frac{h\nu_0}{2}\left(1 + \frac{2e^2}{kr^3}\right)^{\frac{1}{2}} \quad \ldots.(18.235)$$

From the series formulae :

$$(1 - a)^{\frac{1}{2}} = 1 - a/2 - a^2/8 - a^3/16 - \cdots\cdots \quad \ldots.(18.236)$$

and

$$(1 + a)^{\frac{1}{2}} = 1 + a/2 - a^2/8 + a^3/16 - \cdots\cdots \quad \ldots.(18.237)$$

we obtain from equation 18.235

$$E' = h\nu_0\left(1 - \frac{e^4}{2k^2r^6}\right) \quad \ldots.(18.238)$$

Thus owing to the interaction, the potential energy has decreased and the system is more stable. On combining equation 18.238 with 18.219 the energy of attraction will be given by

$$\Delta E = h\nu_0\alpha^2/2r^6 \quad \ldots.(18.239)$$

If the oscillators are not linear, the oscillations must be considered in terms of the component along the x, y and z axes and equation 18.225 becomes :

$$u = e^2(x_1x_2 + y_1y_2 - 2z_1z_2)/r^3 \qquad \ldots.(18.240)$$

and

$$E = -3\alpha^2 h\nu_0/4r^6 \qquad \ldots.(18.241)$$

SLATER and KIRKWOOD[5] obtained an expression for the dispersion energy in terms of the polarizability and the number of electrons in the outer shell N :

$$E = -\frac{3eh}{8\pi r^6}\sqrt{\frac{N\alpha^3}{m}} \qquad \ldots.(18.242)$$

This expression may be obtained by inserting the value of ν_0 from equation 18.220 in 18.241.

ENERGY STATES OF AN ELECTRON GAS

We wish to calculate the energy of an electron gas in a cubic box of side L when over the whole space of the box the potential is zero whilst at the surface of the box it becomes infinite, remaining so everywhere outside the box.

Let us consider first the simplest case of an electron moving in one dimension, along the x axis. The Schrödinger equation is :

$$\frac{d^2\psi}{dx^2} + \frac{8\pi^2 m}{h^2} E\psi = 0 \qquad \ldots.(18.243)$$

and its solution is given by

$$\psi = \sin\,(8\pi^2 mE/h^2)^{\frac{1}{2}} \,.\, x \qquad \ldots.(18.244)$$

In the particular case under consideration, it is necessary to impose certain conditions on the wave function ψ since the electron is enclosed in the box and may not pass outside it. The wave function must therefore become zero at the surface of the box, and such functions must therefore have an integral number of nodes in the length L. Hence,

$$(8\pi^2 mE/h^2)^{\frac{1}{2}} = n\pi/L \qquad \ldots.(18.245)$$

where $n = 1, 2, 3, \ldots$

Then

$$\psi = \sqrt{2/L}\,.\,\sin\,(n\pi x/L) \qquad \ldots.(18.246)$$

where $\sqrt{2/L}$ is the normalization coefficient,

and

$$E = n^2h^2/8mL^2 \qquad \ldots.(18.247)$$

For the general case of three dimensions, the Schrödinger equation has the form :

$$\frac{\partial^2\psi}{\partial x^2} + \frac{\partial^2\psi}{\partial y^2} + \frac{\partial^2\psi}{\partial z^2} + \frac{8\pi^2 m}{h^2} E\psi = 0 \qquad \ldots.(18.248)$$

with the boundary conditions that $\psi = 0$ when $x = 0$, $x = L$, $y = 0$, $y = L$, $z = 0$, $z = L$.

The solution of the equation is

$$\psi = \sqrt{\frac{8}{L^3}}\,.\,\sin\frac{\pi n_1 x}{L}\,.\,\sin\frac{\pi n_2 y}{L}\,.\,\sin\frac{\pi n_3 z}{L} \qquad \ldots.(18.249)$$

where n_1, n_2 and n_3 are quantum numbers.

The energy may have the values

$$E = (n_1^2 + n_2^2 + n_3^2)\, h^2/8mL^2 \qquad \ldots.(18.250)$$

or since $L^3 = V$

$$E = (n_1^2 + n_2^2 + n_3^2)\, h^2/8mV^{2/3} \qquad \ldots.(18.251)$$

In each state corresponding to a particular set of values for the three quantum numbers, a maximum of two electrons may be accommodated according to the Pauli principle. Since there are three quantum numbers it is possible to have different states with the same energy value, *i.e.* the states are degenerate. Thus $n_1^2 + n_2^2 + n_3^2 = 6$ when

$n_1 = 2$	$n_2 = 1$	$n_3 = 1$
$n_1 = 1$	$n_2 = 2$	$n_3 = 1$
$n_1 = 1$	$n_2 = 1$	$n_3 = 2$

The various energy levels for the electron in a box are given in *Figure 86*; along the ordinate the values of $(n_1^2 + n_2^2 + n_3^2)$ are shown and p gives the degeneracy. We now wish to calculate the maximum energy that any electron may have *i.e.* the energy of the highest occupied state and the total energy of all the electrons. Let us consider a lattice in which the distance between the points is unity (*Figure 87*); all the lattice points will thus have whole number coordinates. If the coordinates are n_1, n_2 and n_3, the energy of the state is

$$E = \frac{h^2}{8mL^2}(n_1^2 + n_2^2 + n_3^2)$$

All states of equal energy E will lie on a sphere of radius

$$(n_1^2 + n_2^2 + n_3^2)^{\frac{1}{2}} = (8mL^2E/h^2)^{\frac{1}{2}} \qquad \ldots.(18.252)$$

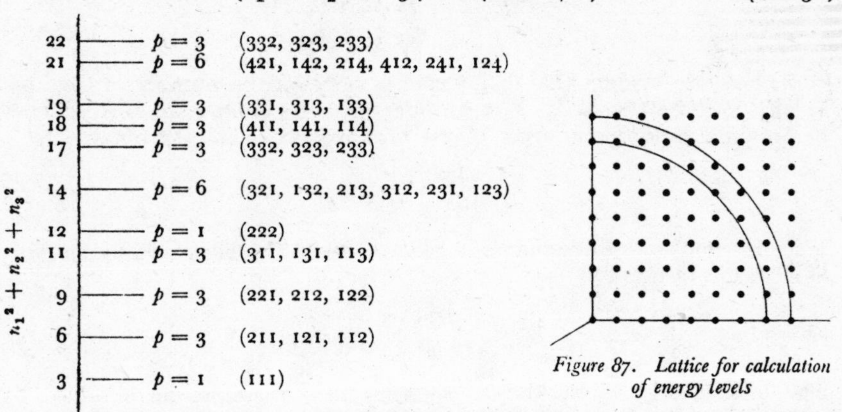

Figure 87. Lattice for calculation of energy levels

Figure 86. Energy levels of an electron in a box

We shall now find the number of states with an energy less than a certain value E and which will all lie within the sphere of radius given by equation 18.252. As the distance between adjacent points is unity and the number of points within a sphere is equal to its volume, the density of the points will be unity. We are, however, not interested in all the points but only those for which all three quantum numbers n_1, n_2 and n_3 are positive, since only such points express the quantum states. It is evident that all such points will lie in an octant and that the number of such points will be 1/8 of the volume of the sphere of radius $(8mL^2E/h^2)^{\frac{1}{2}}$. Hence we find that the number of quantum states with energies less than E is :

$$n = \frac{1}{8}\frac{4}{3}\pi\left(\frac{8mL^2E}{h^2}\right)^{\frac{3}{2}} = \frac{\pi}{6}\left(\frac{8mL^2E}{h^2}\right)^{\frac{3}{2}} \qquad \ldots.(18.253)$$

and since

$$L^3 = V$$

we may rewrite this as

$$n = \frac{\pi V}{6}\left(\frac{8mE}{h^2}\right)^{\frac{3}{2}} \qquad \ldots.(18.254)$$

If E_{max} represents the maximum possible energy of the electron *i.e.* the energy of the highest of the occupied states, the number of states with energy less than E_{max} is given by :

$$\frac{\pi V}{6}\left(\frac{8mE_{max}}{h^2}\right)^{\frac{3}{2}}$$

We wish to obtain the minimum value of the energy of N electrons, *i.e.* the state when $N/2$ lowest levels are occupied by pairs of electrons ; by doing this we can then compare the number of occupied states $N/2$ with the number of states with energy less than E_{max},

$$\frac{N}{2} = \frac{\pi V}{6}\left(\frac{8mE_{max}}{h^2}\right)^{\frac{3}{2}} \qquad \ldots.(18.255)$$

and hence

$$E_{max} = \frac{h^2}{8m}\left(\frac{3N}{\pi V}\right)^{\frac{2}{3}} \qquad \ldots.(18.256)$$

It is therefore evident that E_{max} depends only on the number of electrons in unit volume *i.e.* N/V. The number of states from E to $E + dE$ may be obtained by differentiating 18.254 with respect to E. We obtain :

$$\frac{\pi V}{4}\left(\frac{8m}{h^2}\right)^{\frac{3}{2}}\sqrt{E}\,.\,dE \qquad \ldots.(18.257)$$

Since in each state there may be accommodated two electrons, the number of electrons in these states is

$$2\,.\,\frac{\pi V}{4}\left(\frac{8m}{h^2}\right)^{\frac{3}{2}}\sqrt{E}\,.\,dE \qquad \ldots.(18.258)$$

The total energy of all the N electrons may therefore be obtained by multiplying 18.258 by E and integrating from 0 to E_{max} :

$$E = \int_0^{E_{max}} \frac{\pi V}{2}\left(\frac{8m}{h^2}\right)^{\frac{3}{2}} E\sqrt{E}\,.\,dE = \frac{3}{5}NE_{max} \qquad \ldots.(18.259)$$

and hence the total energy of an electronic cloud in its ground state is

$$E = \frac{3Nh^2}{40m}\left(\frac{3N}{\pi V}\right)^{\frac{2}{3}} \qquad \ldots.(18.260)$$

REFERENCES

[1] PAULING, L. C. and WILSON, E. R. *Introduction to Quantum Mechanics* New York, 1935
DUSHMAN, S. *The Elements of Quantum Mechanics* New York, 1938
[2] PAULING, L. C. *J. Amer. chem. Soc.* 53 (1931) 1367
[3] LORENTZ, H. A. *The Theory of Electrons* Leipzig, 1909
[4] DYATKINA, M. E. *J. phys. Chem. U.R.S.S.* 14 (1940) 1589
[5] SLATER, J. C. and KIRKWOOD, J. G. *Phys. Rev.* 31 (1931) 682
KIRKWOOD, J. G. *Phys. Z.* 33 (1932) 57

AUTHOR INDEX

Where the author's name does not appear in the text but only in the bibliography, the page number in parentheses refers to the text reference.

ABELSON, P. H. 31
ADAMS, R. M. 292 (272)
ANDERSON, T. F. 359, 398
ASTON, J. G. 292 (288), 293 (288)

BACHER, R. F. 42 (24)
BAEYER, J. F. W. A. VON 80
BAMBERG, E. 94
BARNETT, S. J. 352
BAUER, S. H. 128 (118), 292 (270), 397, 398, 407 (403, 404)
BEACH, J. W. 128 (118), 292 (288), 293 (290)
BECKMANN, E. 277
BELL, R. P. 396, 398, 406 (395)
BENOIT, F. 328
BERGMANN, E. 362
BERNAL, J. D. 310
BERZELIUS, J. J. 43
BETHE, H. 341 (302)
BOERSCH, H. 183
BOHR, N. 1
BONHOEFFER, K. K. 158
BORN, M. 162 (144), 198, 318, 319
BOWEN, E. J. 162 (148)
BRAGG, W. L. 335, 342 (340)
BRANCH, G. E. K. 292 (283)
BRAUNE, H. 357
BRIDGMAN, P. W. 341 (302)
BRILL, R. 335, 341 (303)
BROCKWAY, L. O. 80 (75), 99 (94), 192 (181), 236 (217), 292 (273), 407 (406)
BROWN, H. C. 292 (272)
BRUCK-WILLSTÄTER, M. 342 (309)
BUCHDAHL, R. 42 (40)
BUCKLES, R. E. 293 (291)
BUERGER, M. J. 332
BURG, A. B. 398, 405, 407 (403)
BURRAU, Ø. 67 (55)

CALVIN, M. 42 (40), 293 (291)
CARRUTHERS, W. H. 236 (214)
CARTWRIGHT, C. H. 196
CHADWICK, J. 1
CHICHIBABIN, A. E. 98
CLAUSEN, E. 292 (272)
CLEVELAND, F. F. 192 (172), 388
CLOWE, A. 393 (350)
COFFMAN, D. D. 236 (214)
COLE, A. G. 83
COLLIE, J. N. 111
COOLIDGE, A. S. 66, 433 (433)
COOP, I. E. 196, 236 (217)
COOPER, G. R. 393 (355)
COULSON, C. A. 129, 139, 140, 142 (136)
CRAWFORD, B. L. 292 (288)
CRUICKSHANK, J. H. 350
CURRAN, B. C. 292 (270)

DAVIDSON, N. R. 407 (406)
DAVIES, M. M. 275
DAVISSON, J. W. 3
DE BROGLIE, L. 3, 6
DEBYE, P. 105, 194, 196, 268, 312
DEITZ, V. 342 (309)
DEMING, L. S. 342 (331)
DENNISON, D. M., 161, 162 (158), 292 (288)
DHAR, J. 99 (94)
DICKINSON, B. N. 67 (55)
DILTHEY, W. 395
DIRAC, P. A. M. 6, 18
DOESCHER, R. N. 292 (288)
DOTY, P. M. 292 (288)
DUKELSKI, V. M. 40
DUSHMAN, S. 485 (456, 458)
DYATKINA, M. E. 99 (90), 128 (127), 205, 236 (210, 213, 230), 395, 399, 402, 403, 406 (397), 485 (477)

EDSALL, J. T. 192 (174)
EGLOFF, G. 204
EIDINOFF, M. L. 292 (288)
ELLIOTT, N. 407 (406)
EMELÉUS, H. J. 396, 406 (395)
ENGEL, L. 362
ERHARDT, C. H. 342 (331)
ERLENMEYER, E. 94
ERRERA, J. 196
ESTERMAN, I. 4
EUCKEN, A. 158, 206
EVANS, K. M. C. 305
EVANS, M. G. 433 (409)
EWENS, V. G. 357, 362, 365
EYRING, H. 99 (83, 87), 289, 432, 433 (409), 433

FAJANS, K. 104, 198
FANKUCHEN, I. 99 (86)
FARKAS, A. 158
FERMI, E. 26
FERNELIUS, W. C. 394 (377)

FINKELSTEIN, B. N. 67 (55)
FINLAY, G. R. 270
FORSTER, W. S. 292 (288)
FRANCK, J. 1
FREIDLINA, R. K. 389
FRENKEL, J. 316
FRIEDEL, C. 111
FRISCHMUTH, G. 393 (355)
FUCHS, O. 224

GANTMACHER, A. R. 128 (112)
GARNER, C. S. 292 (288)
GASSELL, — 342 (339)
GAYDON, A. G. 149, 150, 237
GEIGER, H. 1
GERDING, H. 407 (406)
GERMER, L. H. 3
GIGUÈRE, P. A. 188, 236 (211)
GLADYSHEV, A. I. 292 (276)
GLASSTONE, S. 433 (409), 433
GLOCKLER, G. 42 (40)
GOLDENBERG, N. 374
GOLDING, D. R. V. 292 (288)
GOLDSCHMIDT, V. M. 324
GOMBAS, P. 128 (105)
GOMBERG, M. 95
GORDY, W. 192 (184, 187)
GORIN, E. 289
GOUDSMIT, S. 17, 42 (24)
GRAFFUNDER, W. 362
GRAY, F. W. 350
GRIGNARD, V. 393 (349)
GUILLEMIN, V. 67 (55)
GUNTZ, A. 328
GURGANOWA, E. W. 236 (221)
GWINN, W. D. 292 (288)

HAAYMANN, P. W. 99 (83)
HALFORD, J. O. 292 (288)
HAMPSON, G. C. 186, 342 (331)
HANNAY, N. B. 236 (214)
HARKER, D. 403
HARRIES, C. 94
HARTECK, P. 158
HARTREE, D. R. 46
HEISENBERG, W. 6, 158, 198, 393 (357)
HEITLER, W. 55, 66, 129, 134, 139, 430
HELLER, H. A. 270
HELMANN, H. 42 (40)
HELMHOLZ, L. 334, 342 (318)
HENDRICKS, S. B. 192 (191), 332, 342 (331)
HERMANN, C. 335, 341 (303)
HERTZ, H. R. 1
HERZBERG, G. 80 (69), 129, 149, 150, 162 (148), 237, 260
HEYMANN, E. 362
HIBBEN, J. H. 171
HILLER, K. Z. 158
HIPPLE, J. A. 265
HOROWITZ, G. E. 67 (55)
HÜCKEL, E. 140
HUGHES, E. W. 236 (211)
HUME-ROTHERY, W. 301, 305, 306, 341 (302)
HUND, F. 24, 129, 158
HUNTER, J. S. 188, 210
HUNTER, L. 292 (277)
HYLLERAAS, E. A. 42 (40), 55, 329

IONOV, N. I. 40

JACOBI, H. 292 (272), 394 (363)
JACOBS, R. B. 342 (324)
JAFFÉ, G. 55
JAMES, H. M. 66, 342 (331), 433 (433)
JANKELEVICH, Z. A. 292 (270)
JOHANSEN, T. 407 (406)
JOHNSON, V. A. 342 (331)
JOHNSON, W. H. 99 (86)
JONES, H. 307, 341 (302)
JONES, R. N. 99 (95)
JOOS, G. 198

KADESCH, R.G. 192 (173)
KARLE, I. L. 99 (94), 192 (181), 292 (273)
KASPER, J. S. 403
KASSEL, L. S. 292 (288)
KAUFMAN, H. S. 99 (86)
KAZARNOVSKI, J. 42 (40)
KAZARNOVSKY, Y. S. 156
KENNEDY, J. W. 42 (31)
KENNEDY, R. M. 292 (288), 293 (288)
KIMBALL, G. E. 99 (83, 87), 347, 371, 377
KIRKWOOD, J. G. 128 (105), 268, 482
KISTIAKOWSKI, G. B. 237, 239, 292 (288)
KLEMM, W. 292 (272), 393 (349, 355), 394 (363)
KOEHLER, J. S. 292 (288)
KOHLRAUSCH, K. W. F. 407 (406)
KOSSEL, W. 44, 207
KRISCHNAMURTI, P. 171
KRISHNAN, R. S. 163
KRONIG, R. DE L. 162 (148)

LACHER, J. R. 292 (288)
LAIDLER, K. H. 433 (409), 433 (433)
LANDÉ, A. 342 (321)

LANDSBERG, G. S. 163
LANDSHOFF, R. 319
LANE, T. J. 292 (270)
LANGEVIN, A. 196, 350
LANGMUIR, I. 44
LARK-HOROWITZ, K. 342 (331)
LAUBENGAYER, A. W. 270
LE BEL, J. A. 43
LENNARD-JONES, J. E. 129, 142 (130, 140)
LEVEDAHL, B. H. 292 (288)
LEVINE, A. A. 83
LEVY, R. B. 324, 328
LEWIS, G. L. 292 (288)
LEWIS, G. N. 44, 76, 104, 395
LIPSON, H. 299
LISTER, M. W. 189, 357, 365
LONDON, F. 55, 66, 129, 134, 139, 266, 308, 309, 429, 430, 433 (409)
LONG, L. H. 137
LONGUET-HIGGINS, H. C. 396, 398
LORENTZ, H. A. 472
LOWE, J. 342 (331)
LU, C. S. 236 (211)
LUCHT, C. M. 403

MABBOTT, G. W. 305
MCCALLUM, K. J. 42 (40)
MCCUSKER, P. A. 292 (270)
MCMILLAN, E. M. 31
MCREYNOLDS, J. P. 394 (377)
MAGNUS, A. 324
MALTBIE, M. 330
MAMOTENKO, M. 42 (40)
MANDELSTAM, — 163
MARCHI, L. E. 394 (377)
MARK, H. 99 (86), 406 (397)
MARKOVNIKOV, V. V. 212
MARSDEN, E. 1
MAXWELL, J. C. 194
MAXWELL, L. R. 192 (188, 191), 342 (331)
MAY, A. 342 (324)
MAYER, J. E. 40, 236 (198), 318, 319, 324, 328, 330
MAYER, M. G. 236 (198)
MECKE, R. 158
MEISENHEIMER, J. 115
MENDELÉEFF, D. I. 16, 30
MEYER, L. 206
MOORE, W. J. 342 (332)
MORSE, P. M. 149
MOSELEY, H. G. 1, 16
MOSELEY, V. M. 192 (188, 191)
MOTT, N. F. 307, 341 (302)
MULLIKAN, R. S. 41, 129, 133, 136, 142 (131), 397
MURRAY, M. J. 192 (172), 388

NEKRASSOV, B. V. 395, 402
NESMEYANOV, A. N. 389
NEUGEBAUER, T. 128 (105)
NEWTON, I. 3
NICKLE, A. G. 292 (288)
NIELSEN, L. E. 188
NIESSEN, K. F. 2
NIEUWLAND, J. A. 236 (214)
NIKITIN, B. A. 292 (269)

OESPER, P. F. 236 (234)
ONSAGER, L. 268
OPPENHEIMER, R. 162 (144)
OSBORNE, D. W. 292 (288)

PALMER, K. J. 292 (288), 293 (290), 407 (406)
PARTO, A. 236 (196)
PASCAL, P. 349
PAULI, W. 2, 61
PAULING, L. C. 71, 72, 81, 99 (83, 87), 100, 105, 129, 134, 138, 142 (130), 162 (152), 187, 190, 192 (184, 187), 198, 205, 245, 250, 258, 292 (282), 302, 320, 321, 325, 342 (317, 332), 347, 370, 386, 395, 436, 456, 458, 461
PAWLOW, G. 261 (247)
PECHERER, B. 292 (288)
PÉLIGOT, E. M. 16
PENIN, N. A. 134
PENNEY, W. G. 80 (69), 150, 236, (211), 237
PETERS, C. 335
PFEIFFER, W. 282
PFLAUM, D. I. 236 (217)
PHILLIPS, G. M. 188, 210
PIEKARA, A. 268
PINNOW, R. 357
PITZER, K. S. 243, 289, 292 (288), 396, 399, 406 (403)
PLANCK, M. 1
PLOTNIKOV, V. A. 292 (270)
POHLAND, E. 406 (397)
POLANYI, M. 432, 433
PÖSCHL, G. 149
POWELL, H. M. 362
PRICE, W. C. 265, 298
PRILEZHAEVA, N. A. 192 (175)
PROSEN, E. J. 99 (86)
PSHEZHETSKY, S. Y. 128 (105)

RACAH, G. 394 (377)
RAMAN, C. V. 163

Ramsey, N. 16
Ransom, W. W. 292 (288)
Rayleigh, Lord 16
Redlich, O. 188
Rice, W. W. 292 (288)
Robertson, J. M. 186, 192 (181, 185), 211
Rogers, M. J. 334
Rosen, N. 66, 149
Rossini, F. D. 99 (86), 237, 239
Rubin, T. R. 292 (288)
Rumer, Y. 99 (83, 87), 436
Russell, C. D. 393 (355)
Russell, H. 292 (288)
Rutherford, E. 1

Saunders, R. H. 192 (172)
Saylor, J. H. 192 (187)
Scherrer, P. 94
Schlesinger, A. I. 405, 407 (403)
Schomaker, V. 188, 190
Schrödinger, E. 6, 9
Schuchowitzky, A. 433 (433)
Schumann, S. C. 292 (288)
Schuth, W. 393 (355)
Seaborg, G. T. 42 (31)
Seel, F. 406 (395)
Seitz, F. 341 (302)
Selwood, P. W. 393 (349)
Seward, R. P. 40
Shand, W. 188
Sheka, I. A. 292 (270)
Shialowski, — 292 (269)
Shott-Lvova, E. A. 236 (196, 231)
Shugam, E. A. 394 (369)
Sidgwick, N. V. 104, 395
Sigiura, V. 67
Simon, J. H. 40
Skinner, H. A. 192 (187)
Sklar, A. L. 451 (450)
Slater, J. C. 71, 81, 129, 134, 139, 408, 409, 415, 482
Slovokhotova, N. A. 192 (173)
Smit, E. 407 (406)
Smyth, C. P. 236 (221, 234), 292 (288)
Sommerfeld, A. 2, 341 (302)
Sponer, H. 342 (309)
Spurr, R. A. 188
Srivastava, B. N. 342 (318)
Stecher, O. 407 (406)
Steinberg, H. 393 (355)
Stern, O. 4
Stevenson, D. P. 190, 265, 293 (290)
Stitt, F. 293 (288), 398
Stokes, A. R. 299
Stoner, E. C. 393 (352)
Stosick, A. J. 342 (331)
Sucksmith, W. 352
Sugden, S. 391
Sugden, T. M. 265
Sutherland, G. B. B. M. 236 (211), 275
Sutton, L. E. 188, 189, 192 (187), 196, 210
Sutton, P. P. 42 (40)
Swift, E. 99 (97)
Syrkin, J. K. 99 (90), 128 (112, 127), 192 (173, 175), 236, (196, 221, 229, 230, 231), 268, 292 (269, 276), 395, 399, 402, 403, 406 (397)

Tandon, A. N. 342 (318)
Taufen, H. J. 388
Taylor, H. S. 247
Teller, E. 67 (55), 149
Terenin, — 162 (148)
Thiele, J. 85
Thomson, G. P. 3
Tickle, C. 111
Tilk, J. 394 (363)
Turkevitch, J. 236 (234), 293 (290)

Ufford, C. W. 80 (74)
Uhlenbeck, G. E. 17

Van den Broek, A. 1
Van der Mullen, D. A. 270
Van't Hoff, J. H. 43, 72, 287
Van Vleck, J. H. 142 (129, 139), 370, 393 (349, 352)
Vasiliev, W. G. 236 (204, 229, 231)
Vier, D. T. 40
Von Auwers, K. 277, 282
Vosburgh, W. C. 393 (355)

Wagner, J. 398, 407 (406)
Wahl, A. C. 42 (31)
Walsh, A. D. 137, 265, 396
Walter, J. 99 (83, 87), 289
Wang, S. C. 66
Wasastjerna, J. A. 321
Weghofer, H. 342 (309)
Weinbaum, S. 66
Weiss, J. 156
Weller, S. W. 192 (173)
Wenzke, H. H. 236 (217)
Werner, A. 43, 343
West, J. 335

WHELAND, G. W. 236 (223), 292 (282)
WHITE, H. E. 15 (13), 42 (24)
WIBAUT, J. L. 99 (83)
WIBERG, E. 407 (406)
WIGNER, E. 161
WILLSTÄTER, R. W. 94
WILSON, A. H. 341 (302)
WILSON, E. B. 456, 458
WOLKENSTEIN, M. V. 128 (112), 192 (173, 175)
WOODWARD, I. 192 (186)
WU, T. 42 (40)
YABROFF, D. L. 292 (283)
YEARIAN, H. J. 342 (331)
YOST, D. M. 292 (288), 293 (288)
ZAHN, E. T. 236 (225)
ZELINSKI, N. 261 (247)
ZENER, C. 67 (55)
ZHDANOV, G. S. 394 (369)

SUBJECT INDEX

ACETIC ACID, heat of dimerization 275
Acetoacetic acid 178
— ester 284
Acetone, atom polarization 196
— diamagnetic susceptibility 350
Acetophenone, carbonyl group frequency 172
Acetylacetone 254, 285
Acetyl chloride 251
— durene 172
— mesitylene 172
Acetylene 179, 245
— arrangement of bonds 77
— dicarboxylic acid, bromination of 79
— electron affinity 213
Acrolein, dipole moment 218
Actinons 31
Activation energy 288, 409, 429
Active complex 409
Alkaline earth metals, electron affinity 40
Alkyl iodides, heat of combustion 241
Allene 79, 179
Alloys, structure 305
— ratio of valency electrons to atoms 306
Alternating polarity 126
Aluminium, crystal structure 302
— borohydride 406
— triacetylacetonate 391
Americium 31
Amines, heat of neutralization 249
— resonance structures 114
Amino acids 235
Aminoacetic acid, copper salt 389
p-Aminoazobenzene, heat of neutralization 249
p-Aminodiphenyl, dipole moment 222
Amino-oxyhydrates 115
o-Aminophenol, heat of neutralization 249
α-Aminopyridine 233
Ammino compounds 383
Ammonia, heat of vaporization 262
— proton affinity 326
Ammonium chloride, crystal structure 319
— iodide, crystal structure 319
Amphiboles 337
Angular distribution functions for H atom 14
Anharmonicity constant 148, 149
Aniline, dipole moment 278
— heat of neutralization 249
— heat of vaporization 262
— resonance structures 121, 221, 248
Anthracene 179
— hydrogenation 92
— resonance energy 246
— resonance structures 91
Antibonding orbital 130, 132
Antimony, crystal structure 300
Anti-Stokes lines 164, 165
Antisymmetric wave function 62, 159
Arsenic 39
— crystal structure 300
Arsenolite, crystal structure 331
Association in gaseous phase 262
— liquid phase 262
— solution 262, 277
Atom polarization 193, 194, 196, 197, 296
Atomic number 1
— orbitals, stability sequence 18
— refraction, additivity 201
Azimuthal quantum number 2, 10
Azobenzene 186
Azomethane 188, 189

BARIUM 27, 38, 346
Benitoite 337
Benzaldehyde, resonance structures 220
Benzanthrone, resonance structures 231
Benzene 204, 247, 354
— atom polarization 196
— canonical structures 83
— ozonolysis 83
— resonance structures 81
— resonance energy 246, 445
Benzene sulphonic acid 128
Benzoic acid, heat of dimerization 275
Benzonitrile, resonance structures 220
Benzophenone 179
p-Benzoquinone 196
Beryl 337
Beryllium 22, 39, 343
— borohydride 406
— valency states 109
Betaine 173

Biradicals 98
Bismuth, crystal structure 300
Body centred cubic lattice 295
Bohr orbit 13
— magneton 351
— theory of atomic structure 8
Bond, dative 113
— distance in hydroxides 333
— energy 54, 65, 67
— — additivity 239
— — alkali halides 102
— — calculation of 238
— — deviations from additivity 243
— — halogen compounds 260
— — heteropolar bonds 250
— — hydrides 260
— — inorganic compounds 255
— — ionic molecules 101
— — organic compounds 237, 240
— homopolar (covalent) 43, 102, 241
— ionic character 100
— length, dependence on multiplicity 181
— localized 68, 72
— multiplicity 181
— refractions 201
— semipolar 113
Bonding and antibonding orbitals, relative strength 135
— orbital 130, 132
— orbitals, relative strength 152
π-Bonds 76, 77
σ-Bonds 76, 77
Bonds, intermediate type 104
Boric acid, esters of 110
Born-Haber cycle 40, 318, 329, 330, 339
Boron 22, 343
— hydrides 154, 395
— nitride 299
— valency states 109
Branched chain hydrocarbons, heat of formation 243
Butadiene 85
— resonance energy 440
Butane, heat of formation 243
2-Butene 181
Butyl bromide 179
Butylene 213, 244

CADMIUM 346
— crystal structure 302
— iodide lattice 314
Caesium 27
— chloride lattice 312
— crystal structure 302
Calcium 27, 38, 346
— carbide 305
— ion, ionic radius 321
Canonical structures, benzene 83
— — naphthalene 87, 88
Carbon 22, 24, 343
— amorphous 300
— crystal structure 301
— dioxide, arrangement of bonds 79
— — structure 113
— — vibrations 166
Carbon disulphide, atom polarization 196
— halogen bond 187
— monofluoride 300
— monoxide 137
— — structure 112
— suboxide, structure 114
— tetrabromide, crystal structure 310
— tetraiodide, crystal structure 310
— valency states 112
Carbonate ion 182
Carbonic acid, resonance structures 249
Carbonyls, metallic 358
Carboxylate ion 182
Carboxylic acids, resonance structures 170
Chargeability of ions 108
Chichibabin's hydrocarbon, dissociation 98
Chlorine, valency structures 125
Chloroacetone 350
Chlorobenzene, resonance structures 119, 219
— dipole moment 223
o-Chlorobenzoic acid 283
p-Chlorobenzonitrile, dipole moment 224
p-Chlorotoluene, dipole moment 223
Chromium 26, 27, 355
— electronic configuration 26
Chrysene 179
— resonance energy 246
Clausius-Mosotti equation 193, 469
Clausius-Mosotti-Debye equation 196
Close packed spheres, volume of 296
Closepacking of equivalent spheres 294
Cobalt 27, 344, 346, 356
— acetylacetonate 391
Colour of chemical compounds 450
Combustion, heat of 241
Complex compounds 343
Compton effect 3
Conjugated double bond, delocalization of π-electrons 84
Coordination lattice 312
— number 298, 323, 330
Coordinate bond 44, 113
Copper, complex of β-diketones 392
— electron affinity 40
— group 31
Coulomb integral 53, 59, 424
Coulombic energy 71, 422, 424
Coumarone, dipole moment 231
Covalent bond 43, 102
— radii 189
— — of elements 190
— radius, hydrogen 190
Covelline 340
Crystal lattice 310
— — ionic 102
— structure of elements 294, 297
— — of non-metals 296
Crystals, chemical bond in 294
Cubic close packing 294, 295
Cuprite lattice 313
Curium 36
*Cyclo*butadiene 86
*Cyclo*butane 253
*Cyclo*heptadiene 204
*Cyclo*heptane 253
*Cyclo*hexane 179, 253

*Cyclo*hexane dehydrogenation 247
*Cyclo*octadiene 204
*Cyclo*octatetrene 86
*Cyclo*pentadiene 204, 214, 249
*Cyclo*pentane 179, 253
*Cyclo*propane 179, 253
Cyanides 369

DATIVE BOND 113
DE Broglie equation 3, 6
Decaborane, x-ray study 403
n-Decane 200
— heat of formation 243
Deformation energy 478
— oscillation 163
cis-Dekalin 253
trans-Dekalin 253
Delocalization energy 140
— of electron 46, 84, 408
Deuterium 157
Deuteronitric acid, Raman spectra 188
Dewar structures of benzene 82
Diacetylene 179
Diamagnetic susceptibility 349, 350
Diamagnetism 349
Diamond 179
— heat of formation 299
— lattice 295, 296
— — electron density 298
Diazomethane 183, 188
2,3,6,7-Dibenzanthrene, hydrogenation 93
Dibenzyl 179
— dissociation 95
Diborane 395, 397
— action on metal alkyls 405
— electron diffraction 397
— Raman spectrum 398
— specific heat 398
— x-ray study 397
Dibromacetylene 179
Dibromofumaric acid 79
Dibromomaleic acid 79
Dicyandiamide 184
Dicyanogen 183
— heat of formation 252
Dielectric constant 193
— — variation with concentration 278
— polarization 193
Diethyl ether, atom polarization 196
Diffraction of electrons 3
— α-particles 4
Dihydrobenzene 204
1,2-Dihydrobenzene, resonance energy 247
2,6-Dihydroxybenzoic acid 283
Di-iodoacetylene 179
β-Diketones, complexes of 390, 392
Dimerization, heat of 275
Dimethyl acetylene 245
2,3-Dimethyl butadiene, resonance energy 245
Dimethyl nitrosamine 178
2,2-Dimethyl pentane, heat of formation 243
2,3-Dimethyl pentane, heat of formation 243
3,3-Dimethyl pentane, heat of formation 243
2,4-Dimethyl pentane, heat of formation 243
Dioxan, atom polarization 196
— effect 278
Diphenyl, resonance structures 94
— resonance energy 246
Diphenyl acetylene, resonance energy 246
Diphenylaminotetramethylammonium 115
Diphenyl methane, resonance energy 246
Diphenyl nitric oxide, resonance structures 116
Diphenyl nitrogen 97
α,α'-Diphenyl-β-picrylhydrazine 233
α,α'-Diphenyl-β-picrylhydrazyl 234
Diphenylene oxide, dipole moment 231
Dipole moment 165, 166, 193, 206–212, 215, 217–219, 222–224, 226, 229, 231, 278
— aliphatic aldehydes 217, 218
— aliphatic molecules 214, 215
— aliphatic nitriles 219
— and molecular structure 235
— and relative weight of valence bond structures 206–210, 217
— aromatic molecules 219
— bonds 474
— comparison for aliphatic and aromatic compounds 219
— disubstituted derivatives of benzene 224, 225
— hydrocarbons 211, 212
— hydrogen halides 206
— influence on boiling point 267
— ionic molecules 103
— liquids 268
— magnitude of 104
— measurement by molecular beam method 197
— measurement in solution 197
— molecular compounds 270
— organic halogen compounds 215, 217
— permanent 193
— relation to bond type 103
— sign and direction 223
— temperature variation 290
— valency angles from 224
Dipole-dipole interaction 263
Dipole-quadrupole interaction 266
Directional covalency 72, 347, 458
Dispersion energy 265, 478
— forces 266
Dissociation energy 151, 153, 155, 156, 261
— alkali metals 70
— diatomic molecules 156
— dibenzyl 95
— hydrogen 69
— hydrocarbons into free radicals 96
Distortion of bond angles 253
Divinylacetylene 213
n-Dodecane 200
Durene 181, 227

Eigen function 9
— value 9

Electrical conductivity of fused halides 327, 328
Electron affinity, acetylene 213
— — elements 40
— — oxygen 156
— bridge 298
— cloud density 130
— clouds of hydrogen atom 13, 14
— delocalization of 46, 84, 408
— density, diamond lattice 298
— — magnesium 303
— — potassium ion 322
— diffraction 3, 397
— distribution function 54, 61
— — in atoms 19
— — in hydrogen-like atoms 20
— gas, energy states 482
— in box, energy levels 483
— octet 44
— pair method, comparison with molecular orbital method 141
— polarization 193–195
— spin 17
Electronegativity 40
— values of elements 41
Electronic configuration of atoms 28, 29, 30
— spectra 145
— state of atoms 356
— states of hydrogen atom 10
Electrostatic bond 43
— interaction 262
Enclase 336
Energy, activation 409, 429
— — for internal rotation 288
— barrier 288
— benzene 440
— bond, 54, 65, 67, 101, 102, 239, 240, 243, 250, 255, 260
— butadiene 439
— coulomb 71, 422, 424
— deformation 478
— delocalization 140
— different electronic states 344, 346
— dispersion 265, 478
— dissociation 69, 70, 151, 153, 155, 156, 261
— exchange 71, 424
— excitation 23
— fulvene 445
— lattice 316, 317, 319, 325, 328, 329, 332
— levels of diatomic molecules 144
— orientation 478
— resonance 83, 245–247, 252, 253, 434, 440, 445, 446
— rotational 144, 145, 162
— single and double bonds 256
— vibrational 146
— zero point 147, 330
Ethane 179
— crystal structure 310
— rotation in 287
cis-2,3-Ethoxybutane 179
trans-2,3-Ethoxybutane 179
Ethyl acetate 350
— alcohol, atom polarization 196
— — heat of vaporization 262
— benzene, resonance energy 246
Ethyl chloroacetate 350
3-Ethyl pentane, heat of formation 243
Ethylene 179, 291
— arrangement of bonds 76, 77
— heat of chlorination 241
Ethylenic hydrocarbons, heat of formation 244
Europium 354
Exchange energy 71, 424
— integral 53, 59
Excitation energy 23

FACE centred cubic lattice 295
Felspar 338
Ferromagnetism 349
Ferrous chloride 353
Fluorene, dipole moment 278
— resonance structures 214
Fluorine 22
— molecule, molecular orbitals 135
— valency states of 118
Fluorite lattice 313
Formaldehyde, resonance structures 218
Formanilide, association in solution 277
Formic acid, dimerization 273
— heat of dimerization 275
Four electron problem 434
Free radicals 95, 353
— stabilization of 96
Fulvene, energy 445
— resonance energy 446
Fumaric acid 291
Furan, resonance structures 119, 231, 249

GALLIUM 27, 38
— crystal structure 302
Gerade molecular orbitals 130
Germanium 39
— oxide 338
Glass 339
Gold, electron affinity 40
Granite 338
Graphite, heat of formation 299
— lattice 298
Graphitic oxide 299
Gyromagnetic effect 352, 354

HALIDES, electrical conductivity of fused 328
— melting points and electrical conductivity 327
Halogen compounds 324
Hamiltonian operator 48
Harmonic vibration 146
— wave 5
Heat of chlorination 241
— combustion 241
— dimerization 275
— dissociation 241
— formation 111, 237–239, 243, 244, 252, 257, 258, 269, 277, 299
— neutralization 249

Heat of sublimation 262, 264, 302, 303, 308, 309
— vaporization 262
Heisenberg's uncertainty principle 8
Heitler-London theory 55, 81
Helium 20, 22, 30
— heat of vaporization 262
— valency state 108
n-Heptane 200
— heat of formation 243
Heterocyclic compounds 247
— — dipole moments of 231, 232
Heteronuclear diatomic molecules, electron distribution 136
Heteropolar bond 100
Hexachlorbenzene 179
Hexagonal close packing 294
Hexamethyl benzene 181
Hexamethyl ethane 243
Hexamethylene tetramine 332
n-Hexane 200
— atom polarization 196
Hexa-*p*-nitrophenyl ethane 234
Hindered rotation 289
Homonuclear diatomic molecules, electron distribution 133
— — — dissociation energy 151
— — — internuclear distance 151
— — — vibrational frequency 151
Homopolar bond 43, 102
— double bond 241
Hume-Rothery rule 300, 301
Hund's law 24, 41, 343
Hybrid bonds, special arrangement 348
— electron functions 461
— orbitals 347
— — *sp* 75
— — sp^2 75
— — sp^3 74
— — — directional character 75
Hybridization of bond orbitals 74
Hydrazine 189
— heat of dissociation 241
— — — formation 257
Hydrazoic acid, resonance structures 116
Hydrides 152
— crystal structure 329
— dissociation energy 153
— internuclear distance 153
— vibrational frequency 153
Hydrindene 204
Hydrogen 20, 22, 30, 199
— atom, electronic states 10
— —, structure 1
— bond 273
— — and properties of liquids 279
— — formation 275
— — in hydroxide lattices 333
— — — ice 273, 311
— — — salt hydrates 387
— — intramolecular 282
— — length of 273
— — nature of forces 275
— chloride, molecular orbitals 136
— fluoride, hydrogen bonding 275
— heat of vaporization 262
— molecule 55, 308
Hydrogen molecular bond energy 65, 67
— — complete wave function 11
— — interatomic distance 65, 67, 69
— — ion 45, 133
— — molecular orbitals 133
— — — bond energy 54
— peroxide 256
— — structure 211
— sulphide structure 122
— valency states, 108
Hydroxides, bond distances 333
— crystal structure 329
o-Hydroxybenzaldehyde 282

Ice, hydrogen bond in 273, 311
Indium 38
— crystal structure 302
Induced dipole interaction 263
— polarization 263
Inert gases, molecular compounds 269
— — refractions 199
Inner coordination compounds 389
— pressure 267
Interatomic distance 4, 179
— — alkali halides 191
— — — metals 69
— — carbon compounds 191
— — CC bond 178, 180
— — CCl and CF bonds 187
— — CN bond 184
— — C–O bond 182
— — C=O bond 182
— — hydrogen molecule 69
— — metals 4
— — polyatomic molecules 163
Interionic distance in AgBr, AgCl, AgI 190
— — — crystals 319
— — — CsCl lattice 323
Intermolecular attraction 262
Internal rotation 286
— — energy of activation 288
— — inhibition by hydrogen bond 291
— — variation of potential energy during 287, 290
Internuclear distance 65, 67, 151, 153, 155, 156
— — single and multiple bonds 257
Interstitial solid solutions 305
Intramolecular hydrogen bond 282
Iodic acid 334
Ion, chargeability 108
— polarization of 198
Ionic bond 100, 102
Ionic character of bonds 100
— crystals 315
— — energy of 316
— molecules 102
— — bond energy of 101
— radii 320, 321
— — additivity 320
— — ratio 320, 323
— — table of 322
— radius 189, 321
Ion-induced dipole forces 270
Ionization potential, elements 36, 37, 39

Ionization potential, molecules 265
Iron 27, 344, 346
— acetylacetonate 391
— electronic structure 356
Isobutane 179
— heat of formation 243
Isobutylene 213, 244
Isoelectronic molecules 137
Isomeric change, change in heat content 243
Isopentane, heat of formation 243
Isoprene, resonance energy 245
Isoquinoline, dipole moment 229
Isotopic molecules 157

KEKULÉ structures of benzene 82
Kerr effect 195
Ketene 179
Keto-enol tautomerism 178, 253, 254, 284
Krypton 27
— heat of vaporization 262

LAGUERRE functions 458
Landé splitting factor 352, 354
Langevin-Debye equation 472
Lanthanons 27, 30
Lanthanum 27
Lattice energy 316, 317, 319
— — hydroxides 329
— — oxides 332
— — silver and copper halides 325
— — thallium halides 328
Lead, crystal structure 302
— monoxide 332
Legendre functions 456
Linear combination of atomic orbitals 129
Lithium 20
— borohydride 406
— electron affinity 40
— molecule, molecular orbitals 134
— valency states 108
Localized bonds 68, 72
— molecular orbitals 139
— pairs, method of 71
Lorentz-Lorenz equation 105

MADELUNG's constant 316
Magnesium, electron density map 303
Magnetic criterion of bond type 349
— moment, lanthanon sulphates 353
— — salts of transition elements 354
— quantum number 10
— susceptibility 349
Maleic acid 291
Manganese 27, 344, 346
— crystal structure 302
Markovnikov rule 212
Mendeléeff periodic table 30
Mercury 346
— crystal structure 302
— electron affinity 40
Mesitylaldehyde 173
Mesitylene 181, 227
Metal hydroxides, crystal structure 333
Metaldehyde 179
Metals, electrical properties 303
— interatomic distances in 4
— structure 301
Metallic carbonyls 358
Methane 211
— crystal lattice 310
9-Methoxy-10-phenanthroxy radical 97
Methylacetylene 212, 213, 245
Methyl alcohol, atom polarization 196
1-Methylbutadiene, resonance structures 214
— resonance energy 245
2-Methylbutadiene 214
Methyl cyanide 183, 220
4-Methylglyoxaline, dipole moment 278
2-Methyl hexane, heat of formation 243
3-Methyl hexane, heat of formation 243
Methyl isocyanide 183, 184
— — resonance energy 253
2-Methyl nonane, heat of formation 243
5-Methyl nonane, heat of formation 243
Methyl radical, formation 97
Mica 338
Molecular beam 197
— compounds 269
— — heat of formation 269
— crystals 308
— — heat of sublimation 308, 309
— ions 155
— lattice 103
— orbital treatment 129
— — — comparison with electron 129
— pair method 141
Molecular orbitals diatomic molecules 129
— — homonuclear molecules 133
— — localized 139
— — Mullikan's notation 133
— — non-localized 140
— — polyatomic molecules 139
Molecular refraction 194
— — additivity 200
— — exaltation 202–204
— resonance 120
— spectra 143
Morse equation 149
Mullikan's notation of molecular orbitals 133
Multiplet splitting 30
Mutual suppression of ionic structures 216

NAPHTHACENE, resonance structures 92
Naphthalene 179
— bond inequality 87
— canonical structures 87, 88
— hydrogenation 86, 90
— resonance energy 246
— substitution in 87
β-Naphthylamine, dipole moment 278
— heat of neutralization 249
α-Naphthylamine, heat of neutralization 249
Neon 22
Neptunium 31

Neutralization, heat of 249
Nickel 27, 344, 346
o-Nitraniline, heat of neutralization 249
p-Nitraniline, dipole moment 278
— heat of neutralization 249
— resonance structures of 248
Nitrate ion, structure of 116, 189, 259
Nitric acid, anhydrous 188
— — Raman spectra 188
— — structure of 259
Nitric oxide 353
— — molecular orbitals 138
Nitrides, dissociation energy 155
— internuclear distances 155
— vibrational frequency 155
Nitriles 177
4-Nitro-4′-aminodiphenyl 227
Nitro compounds 366
Nitro group 116
Nitrobenzene, atom polarization 196
— dipole moment 278
— resonance structures 121, 128, 220
m-Nitrobenzonitrile, dipole moment 226
o-Nitrobenzonitrile, dipole moment 226
p-Nitrobenzonitrile, dipole moment 226
p-Nitrochlorobenzene, dipole moment 223, 226
m-Nitrodiphenyl, dipole moment 222
p-Nitrodiphenyl, dipole moment 222
Nitrogen 22, 252, 301, 343
— heat of vaporization 262
— trifluoride 210
— valency states of 114
Nitromethane, dipole moment 220
1-Nitro-2-naphthylamine 229
2-Nitro-1-naphthylamine 229
3-Nitro-1-naphthylamine 229
4-Nitro-2-naphthylamine 229
4-Nitro-1-naphthylamine 229
5-Nitro-1-naphthylamine 229
m-Nitrophenol 282
o-Nitrophenol 282, 283
p-Nitrophenol 282
2-Nitroresorcinol 282
Nitrosyl compounds 366
N-methylacridone 233
N-methylketopeperidene 233
Nonacosane 179
n-Nonane 200
Non-localized molecular orbitals 140
Non-orthogonal integral 53
Normalization 9

OCTAHEDRAL holes 305
n-Octane 200
— heat of formation 243
Operators 48
Orbital, angular momentum 131
— antibonding 130, 132, 135
— bonding 130, 132, 135
p-Orbitals, directional character 72, 74
Orbitals, hybrid 74, 75, 347
— overlap 72
s-Orbitals, spherical symmetry 72, 74
Orientation energy 478

Orientation polarization 193, 194
Ortho effect 226
— hydrogen 158
Orthosilicates 336
Overlap of bonding orbitals 72
Oxanthrene, structure 235
Oxides 154
— crystal structure 329
— dissociation energy 153
— internuclear distance 153
— of nitrogen, heat of formation 258
— vibrational frequency 153
Oxyacids, crystal structure 329
o-Oxybenzophenol 285
Oxygen 22, 24, 200, 301, 343, 353
— coordination number 330
— dissociation energy 156
— electron affinity 40, 156
— heat of vaporization 262
— molecule, molecular orbitals of 135
— valency states 110
α-Oxypyridine 233
— dipole moment 278
Ozone 210
Ozonolysis of benzene 83
— — o-xylene 84

PALLADIUM 27
— oxide, crystal lattice 332
Parahydrogen 158
— percentage in hydrogen 161
Paraldehyde 178
Paramagnetism 349
Paramagnetic susceptibility 350
Partial valency 85
Pauli exclusion principle 17, 18, 31, 61, 131, 159, 304, 408
Pauling's method of islands 437
n-Pentane 179, 200
Pentane, heat of formation 243
1-Pentene 239
Periodic classification of the elements 16
— law 16
— table 30
— — expanded form 31, 34, 35
— — Mendeléeff form 32, 33
Periodicity of properties of elements 36
Peroxides 201
Perturbation 47
Perylene, resonance energy 246
Phenanthraquinone, resonance structures 230
Phenanthrene, hydrogenation 93
— resonance energy 246
— resonance structures 93
Phenol 254
— resonance structures 121, 221
Phenyl iodochloride 221
Phosgene 187
— carbonyl group frequency 171
Phosphorus, crystal structure 300
— valency states 124
Photoelectric effect 3
Phthalocyanine, structure 185

α-Picoline, atom polarization 196
— resonance energy 247
β-Picoline, atom polarization 196
— resonance energy 247
Planck's constant 1
Plutonium 31
Polarity of bonds 210
Polarizability 167
— atoms 197
— ions 198
Polarization 193, 194, 197, 296
— atom 196
— dielectric 193
— electron 193, 194, 195
— induced 263
— orientation 193, 194
Polyelectron problem 434
Potassium 27
Potential energy curve 146
— — — diatomic molecule 146, 147
— — — harmonic oscillator 146
— — — hydrogen molecule 148
— — surface 432
Primary solid solutions 305
Principal quantum number 2, 10
Principle of superposition 5
Propagation of light, theory of 3
Propane 179
Propargyl chloride 187
Proton affinity of ammonia 326
Protonated double bond 396, 399
Propylene 212
Pyrazine 179
Pyrazole, dipole moment 278
Pyridine 179
— atom polarization 196
— dipole moment 229
— resonance energy 247
Pyrites 340
Pyroxenes 337
Pyrrole 179
— dipole moment 278

QUADRUPOLE 263
— interaction 264, 266
Quantum number 2, 10, 18
Quenching of orbital magnetic moment 354, 355
Quinoline, dipole moment 229
— resonance energy 247
Quinone 179

RAMAN EFFECT 163
— — applications of 178
— spectra 188
— frequencies of acetoacetic ester 178
— — — C=C, C≡C and C=O bonds 176
— — — nitriles 177
Rare earths 27
Ratio of valency electrons to atoms in alloys 306
Rayleigh scattering 164, 165
Refraction, atomic 201
— bond 201
— bonds involving hydrogen 199
— — — oxygen 200
— inert gases 199
— inorganic molecules 197
— molecular 194, 199, 200, 202, 203, 204
— — organic molecules 200
— — peroxides 201
Relative strength of bonding and anti-bonding orbitals 135
Relaxation time 194
Resonance energy 83, 245–247, 252, 253, 434, 440, 445, 446
— benzene derivatives 247
— calculation 447
— comparison of calculated values 449, 450
— covalent and ionic structures 100, 105–107
— heterocyclic compounds 247
— nitrogen compounds 252
— molecular 120
— of valency structures 81
Rhenium 31
Rhodium 27
Rhombic sulphur 300
Rotational energy 144, 145
— — hydrogen 162
— — orthohydrogen 160
— — parahydrogen 160
Rotational spectra 145
— states 460
Rubidium 27
Rumer's theory 436
Russell-Saunders coupling 352
Rutherford-Bohr theory of atomic structure 1
Rutile lattice 313
Rydberg constant 2, 9

SALICYLALDEHYDE 285
Salicylic acid 283
Salt hydrates 383
— — hydrogen bond in 387
— — stability 388
Samarium 354
Scandium 344, 346
— electronic structure 26
Schrödinger wave equation 6, 7, 46
— — for hydrogen 7, 9
— — solution for H atom 452
Screening constant 321
Selanthrene, structure 235
Selenium 39
— crystal structure 300
Semipolar bond 113
Senarmonite, crystal structure 331
Silica, crystal structure 314
Silicates 334
Sillimanite 338
Silver 27
— electron affinity 40
— fluoride, crystal structure 324
— iodide, crystal structure 325

Slater's method for three electrons 409
Sodium 27
— bromide, interionic distance 190
— chloride, electron density map 315
— — interionic distance 190
— — lattice 312
— iodide, interionic distance 190
Solid solutions, factors governing formation 305
Spectra, diatomic molecules 143
— electronic 145
— molecular 143
— Raman 188
— rotational 145
— vibrational-rotational 145, 163
Spherical coordinates 12
Spin of electron 17
— quantum number 18
— wave function 61
s-States 10
p-States 10
d-States 10
f-States 10
Stilbene 179, 181
— resonance energy 246
Stokes lines 164
Strontium 27, 38
Styrene, resonance energy 246
Subhalides of alkaline earth metals 328
Subhalogen compounds, dissociation energy 261
Sublimation, heat of 262, 264, 302, 303, 308, 309
Sulphamide, polymerization of 126
— structure 126
Sulphides, crystal structure 339
Sulphite ion, structure 123
Sulphur dioxide, structure 123
— electron affinity 40
— hexafluoride 124
— trioxide, structure 123
— valency states 122
Symmetric wave function 62, 159
Synthesis of new elements 31

TALCUM 338
Tautomerism 82
— keto-enol 178, 253, 254, 284
Tetrachloro-*p*-quinone 196
Tetrahedral holes 305
— lattice 295
Tetrahydrofuran 179
Tetralin 86, 204
Tetramethylammonium iodide 114
Tetramethylbenzene 179
Tetramethylethylene 181
Tetramethylmethane, heat of formation 243
Tetraphenylhydrazine, dissociation of 97
Thallium 38, 328
— crystal structure 302
Thianthrene 235
Thiele's theory of partial valency 85
Thioethers, resonance structures 122
Thiophene 179
Three electron bond 138, 258
— — problem 408
— — system, spin states 411
Tin, crystal structure 301
— monoxide, crystal structure 332
Titanium 344, 346
Toluene 212
— atom polarization 196
— resonance energy 246
p-Toluidine, heat of neutralization 249
Transition elements 31
— — magnetic moment of salts 354
Transitional electron cloud 106, 107
— structure 55
Transuranium elements 31
Triacetylacetone derivatives 391
Trialkyl phosphines, oxidation 125
Triboranetriamine 404
Trichlorbenzene 350
Trimethylamine 189
— oxide, dipole moment 278
2,2,4-Trimethyl pentane, heat of formation 243
1,3,5-Trinitrobenzene 196
Triphenyl methane, dipole moment 278
— resonance energy 246
Triphenylmethyl 95
Trouton's rule 237

UNCERTAINTY principle 8
n-Undecane 200
Ungerade molecular orbitals 130
United atom viewpoint 131
Uranium 31
Urea 182
— carbonyl group frequency 171
— crystal structure 311
— molecular and bond resonance 120

VALENCE bond structures, weights of 205
Valence states of second period elements 121
Valency angles 224
— — distortion of 396
— — from electron diffraction measurements 183
— — in carbon compounds 75, 78
— definition of 108
— oscillation 163
— range of values 361
— states of atoms involving *d* electrons 343, 345
— structure of elements 107
— — values 73
Valentinite, structure 332
Vanadium 344
— electronic configuration of 26
Van der Waals' forces 262, 266, 296
— radius 264, 267
Vaporization, heat of 262
Variation method 47
Vector addition of bond moments 206
Vibration, harmonic 144
— modes of 163

Vibrational energy 144
— frequency 151, 153, 155, 156, 172
— — amino acids 174
— — carbonyl group 169, 171
— — carboxylic acids 171
— — ethylenic compounds 174, 175
— — multiple bonds 168
— — polyatomic molecules 163
— states 466
— -rotational spectra 145, 163
Vinylacetylene 213

WATER, atom polarization 196
— heat of formation 111
— heat of vaporization 262
— structure 311
Wave equation 4
— — Shrödinger 6, 7, 9, 46, 452
— function, antisymmetric and symmetric 62, 159
— functions for hydrogen atom 11
Wavelengths of particles from de Broglie equation 4
Weight of structure 55
Weight relative of valence bond structures 207–209, 217
Wurtzite lattice 312, 313

XENON 27
— heat of vaporization 262
x-ray spectra of elements 1
o-Xylene, ozonolysis 84
— resonance energy 246

YTTERBIUM 346
Yttrium 27

ZEOLITE 338
Zero point energy 147, 330
Zinc 27, 346
— blende lattice 295, 296, 312
— chloride 353
— crystal structure 302
— group 31
— sulphide 340
Zirconium 340

FORMULA INDEX

Ag 38, 40, 303
Ag_3Al 306
Ag_5Al_3 306
Ag_9Al_4 306
$AgBr$ 324, 325
$AgCd$ 306
$AgCd_3$ 306
$AgCl$ 324, 325
$Ag(CN)_2^-$ 369
AgF 324, 325
AgH 153
AgI 324, 325
$AgMg$ 306
$[Ag(NH_3)_2]^+$ 384
AgO 153
Ag_2O 330
$Ag_{31}Sn_8$ 306
$AgZn$ 306
$AgZn_3$ 306
Ag_5Zn_8 306
Al 25, 37, 40, 303
$AlAs$ 340
$AlB_2H_9N(CH_3)_3$ 406
AlB_3H_{12} 406
Al_2Br_6 406
$AlBr_3 \cdot (C_2H_5)_2O$ 270
$AlBr_3 \cdot C_6H_5NO_2$ 270
$AlBr_3 \cdot H_2S$ 270
$Al(C_5H_7O_2)_3$ 392
$Al_2(CH_3)_4Br_2$ 406
$Al_2(CH_3)_4Cl_2$ 406
$Al_2(CH_3)_6$ 406
$AlCl$ 261
$AlCl_3$ 327
$AlCl_3 \cdot C_2H_4$ 272, 273
$AlCl_3 \cdot C_2H_5NH_2$ 270
$AlCl_3 \cdot (C_2H_5)_2O$ 270
$AlCl_3 \cdot (C_6H_5)_2CO$ 270
$AlCl_3 \cdot C_6H_5NO_2$ 270
$AlCl_3 \cdot C_6H_5OCH_3$ 270
$AlCl_3 \cdot ClC_6H_4NO_2$ 270
$AlCl_3 \cdot H_2S$ 272
$AlCl_3 \cdot NH_3$ 272
$AlCl_3 \cdot NO_2C_6H_4CH_3$ 270
Al_2Cl_6 406
AlF_3 327
AlH 153
Al_2I_6 406
AlN 340
AlO 153
Al_2O_3 330, 331, 341
$Al(OH)_3$ 333
AlP 340
$AlSb$ 340
Al_2SiO_5 338
Am^{241} 31
Ar 25, 40, 197, 199, 309
As 73, 190, 256
As_2 151, 155, 340
As_2^+ 155
As_4 257
$AsBr_3$ 73, 209
$As(CH_3)_3$ 73
$AsCl_3$ 73, 209
AsF_3 209
AsH_3 209
AsI_3 73, 209
AsN 155
AsO 153
As_2O_3 331
As_4O_6 331, 332
AsS 340

AsS_4^{3-} 334
Au 38, 40, 303
Au_5Al_3 306
$AuCd_3$ 306
$AuCl_2^-$ 379, 380
$AuCl_3$ 385
$AuCl_4$ 356
$AuCl_4^-$ 379, 380, 381
AuH 153
$AuHg_3$ 306
$Au(NH_3)_4Cl_3$ 384, 385
$[Au(NH_3)_4]^{3+}$ 384
$AuZn$ 306
$AuZn_3$ 306
Au_5Zn_8 306

B 22, 23, 37, 40
B^+ 107
B^- 107
B_2 151
BBr 261
$B(CH_3)_3$ 75, 397, 398
$B_2(CH_3)_3$ 398
BCl 261
BCl_3 109, 327
$BCl_3 \cdot CH_3CN$ 270
$BCl_3 \cdot C_2H_5CN$ 270
$BCl_3 \cdot (C_2H_5)_2O$ 270
BF_3 272, 327, 397
$BF_3 \cdot (CH_3)_2O$ 270, 271
$BF_3 \cdot (C_2H_5)_2O$ 270, 272
$BF_3 \cdot C_2H_5OCH_3$ 270
$BF_3 \cdot C_4H_8O$ 272
$BF_3 \cdot NH_3$ 383
BF_4^- 110, 334
BH 153, 154
BH_3 395, 396, 397, 398, 403
BH_4 396
BH_4^- 115
$BH(CH_3)_2$ 398
BH_3CO 182, 183
$B_2H_4(NH_4)_2$ 403
$(B_2H_4)^{2-}$ 403
B_2H_6 288, 395–398, 403, 405, 406
$(B_2H_6)^{2-}$ 405
$(B_4H_6)(NH_4)_4$ 405
$(B_4H_6)^{4-}$ 405
B_4H_8 405
B_4H_{10} 399, 403, 405
B_5H_9 399, 403
B_5H_{11} 400, 403
B_6H_{10} 400, 403
B_6H_{12} 401, 403
$B_{10}H_{14}$ 402, 403
BN 155
B_2NH_7 404
$B_3N_3H_6$ 117
$B_3N_3H_6$ 404
BO 153
BO_3^{3-} 334
B_2O_3 339
$B_3O_3(CH_3)_3$ 118
$B(OH)_3$ 333
$B(OC_2H_5)_3$ 110
$B(OC_2H_5)_4^-$ 110

Ba 23, 37, 38
Ba^{2+} 198
Ba_2 152
$BaCl$ 328
$BaCl_2$ 327, 328
BaH 153
BaO 153, 330
BaS 339
BaS_3 73
$BaTiSi_3O_9$ 337
Be 22, 23, 37, 40
Be^{2+} 105, 198
Be_2 152
$BeAlSiO_4(OH)$ 336
$Be_3Al_2Si_6O_{18}$ 337
$Be(BH_4)_2$ 406
$Be(BH_4)_2N(CH_3)_3$ 406
$BeBr_2 \cdot 2(C_2H_5)_2O$ 270
$BeCl$ 261
$BeCl_2$ 109, 261, 327
$BeCl_2 \cdot 2(C_2H_5)_2O$ 270
BeF_2 327
BeF_4^{2-} 334
BeH 153, 155
BeH^+ 155
BeO 153, 330
$Be_4O(CH_3COO)_6$ 182
BeS 340
$BeSe$ 340
$BeTe$ 340
Bi 73
Bi_2 151
BiH 153
BiO 153
Br 40, 41, 190
Br^- 198, 199
Br_2 100, 150, 151, 189, 205
Br_2^{79} 162
$BrCl$ 100
BrO_3^- 334

C 22, 23, 40, 190
C^+ 107
C^- 107
C_2 151
CBr_4 350
C_2Br_2 179
C_2Br_6 350
CCl_2F_2 187
CCl_3F 187
CCl_4 43, 112, 187, 211
C_2Cl_4 187
C_2Cl_6 350
C_6Cl_6 187
CD 157
CF_4 187, 327
C_2I_2 179
CH 149, 153–155, 157
CH^+ 155
CH_3 95, 168
CH_4 43, 75, 76, 181, 199, 211, 239, 242, 244, 309, 310
C_2H_2 163, 168, 181
C_2H_4 96, 168, 181
C_2H_5 168

C_2H_6 70, 75, 95, 168, 219, 239, 288, 310
C_3H_4 79, 176, 180, 212, 213, 245, 265
C_3H_6 174, 212, 265, 288
C_3H_7 168, 265
C_3H_8 75, 239, 288
C_4H_2 180, 246, 265
C_4H_4 175, 213, 246
C_4H_6 85, 176, 180, 202, 212, 245, 246, 288
C_4H_7 181
C_4H_8 78, 174, 212–214, 244, 265, 288
C_4H_9 168
C_4H_{10} 75, 239, 288, 289
C_5H_3 289
C_5H_5 180, 250
C_5H_6 180, 212, 214
C_5H_8 176, 202, 212, 214, 245
C_5H_{10} 174, 244
C_5H_{11} 168
C_5H_{12} 75, 239, 288
C_5H_{14} 238
C_6H_6 81, 84, 180, 202, 213, 246, 247, 265, 445
C_6H_8 86, 246, 247
C_6H_{10} 176, 202, 203, 212, 245–247
C_6H_{12} 78, 174, 246, 247
C_6H_{14} 239, 266
C_7H_7 95, 96
C_7H_8 212, 214, 219, 224, 265, 268
C_7H_{12} 176, 202, 212
C_7H_{14} 174
C_7H_{16} 239
C_8H_6 212, 224, 231
C_8H_8 86, 175, 202
C_8H_{10} 84, 212, 265
C_8H_{14} 174, 176
C_8H_{16} 174
C_8H_{18} 239
C_9H_8 176, 212
C_9H_{10} 175, 202, 212
C_9H_{12} 176
C_9H_{18} 174
C_9H_{20} 239
$C_{10}H_8$ 86, 91, 203
$C_{10}H_{10}$ 86, 91, 202–204, 212
$C_{10}H_{12}$ 91, 202, 212
$C_{10}H_{14}$ 212
$C_{10}H_{22}$ 239
$C_{11}H_{10}$ 175, 203
$C_{11}H_{12}$ 202, 212
$C_{11}H_{14}$ 202
$C_{11}H_{24}$ 239
$C_{12}H_8$ 180
$C_{12}H_{10}$ 203, 265
$C_{12}H_{12}$ 203
$C_{12}H_{14}$ 202
$C_{12}H_{16}$ 203
$C_{12}H_{26}$ 239
$C_{13}H_{10}$ 203, 212, 214
$C_{13}H_{16}$ 202
$C_{14}H_{10}$ 91, 93, 180, 203
$C_{14}H_{12}$ 92, 93, 180, 202, 203, 212
$C_{14}H_{14}$ 93–95, 203
$C_{14}H_{18}$ 94, 202
$C_{15}H_{12}$ 203
$C_{15}H_{14}$ 202
$C_{16}H_{10}$ 203
$C_{16}H_{14}$ 202
$C_{19}H_{16}$ 212
$C_{22}H_{14}$ 93
$C_{22}H_{16}$ 93
$C_{28}H_{18}$ 94
$C_{34}H_{22}$ 94
$C_{38}H_{28}$ 98
$C_{44}H_{32}$ 99
$C_{74}H_{60}$ 96
$CHBr_3$ 75, 350
CH_2Br_2 75, 350
C_2HBr 217
C_2H_3Br 175
$C_2H_2Br_2$ 217
$C_2H_4Br_2$ 288, 290
C_2H_5Br 75, 268
$C_4H_6Br_2$ 85
C_3H_5Br 175
C_3H_7Br 75
C_4H_7Br 175
C_4H_9Br 75
C_6H_5Br 225
C_7H_7Br 225
$C_9H_{11}Br$ 228
$C_{10}H_9Br$ 268
$C_{10}H_{13}Br$ 228
C_2H_4BrCl 288, 290
$CHCl_3$ 75, 112, 187, 350
CH_2Cl_2 75, 187, 216, 350
CH_3Cl 187, 215, 216
$CHCl_2F$ 187
$CHClF_2$ 187
CH_2ClF 75, 187
C_2HCl 217
C_2HCl_3 187
$C_2H_2Cl_2$ 187, 217, 265
C_2H_3Cl 119, 175, 187, 265
$C_2H_3Cl_3$ 75, 216, 288
$C_2H_4Cl_2$ 216, 288–290
C_2H_5Cl 215, 216
$C_3H_2Cl_2$ 187
C_3H_3Cl 187
CH_3Cl 383
C_3H_5Cl 175, 215
$C_3H_6Cl_2$ 216
C_3H_7Cl 75, 215
C_4H_9Cl 75, 215
$C_6H_2Cl_4$ 187
$C_6H_3Cl_3$ 187
$C_6H_4Cl_2$ 187
C_6H_5Cl 119, 187, 219, 220, 223, 225, 247
C_6H_7Cl 213
$C_6H_{11}Cl$ 215
C_7H_7Cl 223, 225
C_8H_5Cl 225, 226
$C_{38}H_{24}Cl_4$ 99
$C_4H_6D_2O_4$ 273
CH_2F_2 75, 187
CH_3F 187
$C_2H_3F_3$ 216, 288
CH_2I_2 350
CH_3I 268
C_2H_3I 175
C_7H_7I 225
$C_6H_4ICl_3$ 225
$C_6H_5ICl_2$ 221
CH_3Li 112
CH_2N_2 184

CH_5N 168, 208, 219, 288
CH_6N 265
C_2H_3N 177, 183, 184, 219, 251, 267
$C_2H_4N_4$ 186
$C_2H_6N_2$ 184
C_2H_7N 209, 265, 288
C_3H_3N 175, 202, 219
C_3H_5N 219, 267, 268
C_3H_9N 73, 184, 206, 209, 265, 383
$C_4H_4N_2$ 184, 288, 290
C_4H_5N 180, 183, 184, 202, 219
C_4H_7N 219, 267
C_5H_5N 183, 184, 247, 277
$C_5H_6N_2$ 232, 233
C_5H_9N 219
C_6H_7N 121, 219, 221, 225, 247, 248
$C_6H_{12}N_4$ 75, 184, 332
C_7H_5N 177, 219, 220, 224–226, 247
C_7H_9N 225, 240
C_8H_7N 177, 225
C_9H_7N 229, 268
$C_9H_{13}N$ 228
$C_9H_{14}N^+$ 127
$C_{10}H_{15}N$ 228
$C_{12}H_{10}N$ 97
$C_{12}H_{10}N_2$ 186
$C_{12}H_{11}N$ 222
$C_{12}H_{12}N_2$ 247
$C_{16}H_{22}N_2$ 115
$C_{18}H_{15}N$ 247
$C_{24}H_{20}N_2$ 97
$C_{32}H_{18}N_8$ 185
C_6H_6NBr 228
$C_{10}H_{14}NBr$ 228
C_7H_4NCl 224, 225
$C_8H_{20}NI$ 114
CH_3NO_2 168, 184, 215, 219, 220, 267, 383
CH_4N_2O 120, 171, 182–184, 252, 253, 273, 310
CH_5NO 188
C_2H_5NO 168
$C_2H_5NO_2$ 78, 174, 182, 215, 267, 273
$C_2H_6N_2O$ 178
$C_3H_7NO_2$ 174, 215, 267
C_3H_9NO 189
$C_4H_2N_2O_4$ 252
$C_4H_6N_4O_3$ 252
$C_4H_9NO_2$ 174, 215
$C_5H_4N_3O$ 252
$C_5H_4N_4O_3$ 252
C_5H_5NO 232, 233
$C_5H_5N_4O$ 252
$C_5H_9NO_2$ 252
$C_5H_{11}NO_2$ 173
$C_6H_4N_4O_6$ 227
$C_6H_5NO_2$ 121, 128, 177, 219, 220, 224–226, 247, 268
$C_6H_5NO_3$ 228, 282
$C_6H_5NO_4$ 282
C_6H_6NO 232
$C_6H_6N_2O_2$ 225, 226, 228, 248
C_6H_7NO 233, 248
$C_6H_{11}NO_2$ 252
C_7H_5NO 286
C_7H_7NO 252, 277
$C_7H_7NO_2$ 225, 285
$C_7H_7NO_3$ 228
$C_8H_5NO_2$ 252
$C_8H_9NO_3$ 228
$C_8H_{10}N_2O_2$ 228
$C_9H_{11}NO$ 228, 252
$C_9H_{11}NO_2$ 228
$C_{10}H_8N_2O_2$ 229
$C_{10}H_{13}NO_2$ 228
$C_{10}N_{13}NO_3$ 228
$C_{10}H_{14}NO_2$ 228
$C_{11}H_{13}NO$ 228
$C_{12}H_9NO_2$ 222
$C_{12}H_{10}NO$ 116
$C_{12}H_{10}N_2O_2$ 227, 228
$C_{12}H_{15}NO$ 228
$C_{12}H_{17}NO_3$ 228
$C_{12}H_{18}N_2O_2$ 228
$C_{13}H_{11}NO$ 252, 285
$C_{13}H_{11}N_3O_3$ 228
$C_{13}H_{12}N_2O$ 252
$C_{14}H_{11}NO$ 232, 233
$C_{14}H_{11}NO_2$ 252
$C_{14}H_{14}N_4O_2$ 228
$C_{14}H_{17}NO$ 228
$C_{15}H_{13}NO_3$ 228, 286
$C_{16}H_{16}N_2O_2$ 228
$C_{17}H_{20}N_2O$ 228
$C_{18}H_{12}N_5O_6$ 234
$C_{18}H_{13}N_5O_6$ 233
$C_{21}H_{15}NO_3$ 252
$C_{38}H_{24}N_6O_{12}$ 234
$C_6H_4NO_2Br$ 225, 228
$C_{10}H_{12}NO_2Br$ 228
CH_2NOCl 172
$C_2H_6NO_2Cl$ 174
$C_3H_8NO_2Cl$ 174
$C_4H_{10}NO_2Cl$ 174
$C_6H_4NO_2Cl$ 223, 225, 226
$C_6H_4NO_2I$ 225
CH_4N_2S 183, 184, 253
C_2H_3NS 253
$C_{14}H_{11}NS$ 232
C_2H_5Na 112
CHO_2^- 171
CH_2O 182, 217, 218, 265
CH_2O_2 78, 171, 182, 241
CH_4O 168, 206, 207, 215, 219, 239, 265, 266, 288
CH_4O_2 171, 201
C_2H_2O 79, 182
$C_2H_2O_2$ 84
$C_2H_2O_4$ 78, 273
$C_2H_3O_2^-$ 171
C_2H_4O 78, 182, 217–219, 265
$C_2H_4O_2$ 171
$C_2H_4O_4$ 273, 274
C_2H_6O 73, 110, 206, 207, 215, 219, 239, 265, 266, 288
$C_2H_6O_2$ 201
$C_2H_7O^+$ 110
C_3H_4O 176, 202, 218, 265
C_3H_6O 174, 178, 215, 217, 253, 254, 265, 288
$C_3H_6O_2$ 241, 268
C_3H_8O 215, 239, 265, 288
$C_3H_8O_2$ 201
$C_4H_2O_4$ 79
C_4H_4O 73, 119, 120, 180, 231, 249

$C_4H_4O_4$ 291
C_4H_6O 176, 202, 217, 219, 265
$C_4H_6O_2$ 84, 250
$C_4H_6O_3$ 249
C_4H_8O 174, 175, 217
$C_4H_8O_2$ 73, 178, 278
$C_4H_8O_4$ 273
$C_4H_{10}O$ 215, 239, 265, 272
C_5H_6O 175
C_5H_8O 175, 176
$C_5H_8O_2$ 175, 254, 285
$C_5H_8O_3$ 178
$C_5H_{10}O_2$ 113
$C_5H_{12}O$ 215, 239, 273
$C_6H_4O_2$ 179
C_6H_6O 121, 219, 221, 225, 247, 254
$C_6H_6O_2$ 273
$C_6H_{10}O_3$ 178
$C_6H_{14}O$ 215, 239, 272
$C_7H_5O_2$ 283, 284
$C_7H_5O_4$ 283
C_7H_6O 219, 221, 247
$C_7H_6O_2$ 247, 282
C_7H_8O 219, 225, 268
$C_7H_8O_2$ 231, 232
$C_7H_{10}O_2$ 251
$C_7H_{12}O_3$ 178
$C_7H_{16}O$ 239
$C_8H_4O_3$ 247
C_8H_8O 172, 247
$C_8H_{10}O$ 247
$C_8H_{14}O$ 176
$C_8H_{18}O$ 239
$C_9H_6O_2$ 232
$C_9H_{20}O$ 239
$C_{10}H_{12}O$ 173, 228
$C_{10}H_{18}O$ 176
$C_{10}H_{22}O$ 239
$C_{11}H_{14}O$ 173, 228
$C_{12}H_8O$ 231
$C_{12}H_8O_2$ 235
$C_{12}H_{10}O$ 219
$C_{12}H_{16}O$ 172, 228
$C_{13}H_8O_2$ 232
$C_{13}H_{10}O_2$ 285
$C_{14}H_8O_2$ 230
$C_{15}H_{11}O_2$ 97, 98
$C_{15}H_{24}O$ 176
$C_{17}H_{10}O$ 231
$C_{17}H_{12}O_2$ 232
$C_{22}H_{34}O$ 176
C_2HOCl_3 187
C_2H_3OCl 251, 268
C_2H_7OCl 111, 276
C_3H_3OCl 176
C_3H_5OBr 218
$C_3H_7OCl_3$ 276
C_4H_3OCl 183
$C_4H_7OCl_3$ 276
$C_7H_{11}OCl$ 228
$C_{11}H_{13}OCl$ 228
$C_4H_2O_4F_6$ 273
CHO_2Na 78, 182
$C_{13}H_8OS$ 232
$C_{17}H_{12}OS$ 232
C_2H_6S 265, 288
C_4H_4S 73
$C_4H_{10}S$ 122, 265
C_6H_4S 180
C_6H_6S 219
$C_6H_{14}S$ 265
$C_{12}H_8S_2$ 235
$C_{12}H_{10}S$ 219
$C_6H_6SO_3$ 128
$C_{12}H_8Se_2$ 235
CN 137, 155
C_2N_2 180, 183, 184, 200, 252
CO 27, 44, 112, 136, 137, 153–155, 168, 182, 200, 266, 309
CO^+ 137, 155
CO_2 79, 113, 163, 182, 200, 249, 263, 335, 336
CO_3^{2-} 182, 200, 334
C_3O_2 114, 182
$COCl_2$ 78, 172
COS 182
$CSCl_2$ 78
Ca 23, 37, 38
Ca^{2+} 198
Ca_2 152
$Ca_3Al_2Si_3O_{12}$ 338
CaB_2O_4 338, 339
$CaCO_3$ 182
$CaCl_2$ 327, 328
CaF 261
CaF_2 261, 313, 314
CaH 153
CaO 153, 330
$Ca(OH)_2$ 333
CaS 339
Cd 37, 38
Cd_2 151
$CdCl_2$ 329
$Cd(CN)_2$ 369
CdH 153
CdI_2 315, 329
$Cd(NH_3)_4Cl_2$ 384
$[Cd(NH_3)_2]^{2+}$ 384
CdO 330
$Cd(OH)_2$ 333
CdSe 340
CdTe 340
Cl 25, 40, 41, 190, 433
Cl_2^+ 155, 156
Cl^- 103, 107, 198, 199
Cl_2 100, 102, 103, 150, 151, 155, 156, 189, 205, 296, 309, 432
Cl_2^{35} 162
ClO 138
ClO_2 25, 138
ClO_2^- 125, 334
ClO_3^- 125, 334
ClO_4^- 125, 334
Cl_2O 25, 73
Cl_2O_3 25
Cm^{242} 36
$Co(CO)_4^-$ 365
$Co_2(CO)_8$ 359, 365
$Co_4(CO)_{12}$ 359
$Co(CO)_4H$ 365, 366
$Co(CO)_3NO$ 366
$CoCl_2$ 329, 355, 356, 386
$CoCl_3$ 356, 385
$[Co(CN)_6]^{3-}$ 378

$[Co(CN)_6]^{4-}$ 378
CoH 153
$Co(NH_2)_3H_2O_2$ 273
$[Co_2NH_2(NH_3)_{10}]^{5+}$ 386
$Co(NH_3)_3(NO_2)_3$ 386, 387
$[Co(NH_3)_6]^{2+}$ 386
$Co(NH_3)_6Cl_2$ 355, 386
$[Co(NH_3)_6]^{3+}$ 386
$Co(NH_3)_6Cl_3$ 385, 386
$Co(N_2H_4)_2(CH_3COO)_2$ 355
$Co(N_2H_4)_2Cl_2$ 355
$Co(N_2H_4)_2SO_3H_2O$ 355
$Co(NO_2)_6{}^{3-}$ 368
CoO 330
$Co(OH)_2$ 333
Cr 26, 27
$CrCl_3$ 356, 385
$[Cr(CN)_6]^{3-}$ 375
$Cr(CO)_6$ 359, 364
$Cr(NH_3)_6Cl_3$ 384, 385
CrO 153
$CrO_4{}^{2-}$ 334, 355, 357
Cr_2O_3 331
Cs 37, 38, 197, 303
Cs^+ 198
Cs_2 69, 151
$CsAuCl_3$ 379
$CsBr$ 102, 318, 320, 323
$CsCl$ 102, 103, 314, 315, 318, 320, 323, 327
CsF 318
CsH 152, 153, 154, 329
CsI 102, 103, 318, 320, 323
Cu 27, 38, 40, 303
Cu_3Al 306
Cu_9Al_4 306
$CuBe$ 306
$CuBe_3$ 306
$CuBr$ 325
$CuCd_3$ 306
Cu_5Cd_8 306
$CuCl$ 325, 328, 356
$CuCl_2$ 356, 385
Cu_9Ga_4 306
Cu_3Ge 306
CuH 153
CuI 325
$Cu(NH_2CH_2COO)_2$ 389, 390
$Cu(NH_3)_4Cl$ 386
$Cu(NH_3)_4Cl_2$ 385
CuO 153
Cu_2O 313, 330
CuS 340
$CuSO_4$ 356
$CuSO_45H_2O$ 388
Cu_3Sn 306
Cu_5Sn 306
$Cu_{31}Sn_8$ 306
$CuZn$ 306
$CuZn_3$ 306
Cu_5Zn_8 306

D_2 157, 158, 162
DCl 157
DI 157

F 22, 23, 40, 41, 190
F^- 105, 198, 199
F_2 135, 151, 296
Fe 27
$FeAs_2$ 340
$FeAsS$ 340
$FeCl_2$ 329, 353, 356, 370, 372, 373, 386
$FeCl_3$ 356
$Fe(CN)_2$ 370
$[Fe(CN)_6]^{3-}$ 378
$[Fe(CN)_6]^{4-}$ 343, 378
$Fe(Co)_2(NO)_2$ 367
$Fe(CO)_4{}^{2-}$ 365
$Fe(CO)_4H_2$ 364
$Fe(CO)_5$ 359, 361, 362
$Fe_2(CO)_9$ 359, 362
$Fe_3(CO)_{12}$ 359, 364
FeF_3 357
FeH 153
$Fe(H_2O)_6Cl_2$ 386
$Fe(NH_3)_6Cl_2$ 386
$Fe(NO)_4$ 366
FeO 330
Fe_2O_3 331
$Fe(OH)_2$ 333
FeS_2 340
$FeSbS$ 340
Fe_2SiO_4 336
Fe_5Zn_{21} 306

Ga 37, 38
$GaAs$ 340
$GaCl_3$ 327
Ga_2H_6 406
GaO 153
Ga_2O_3 331
GaP 340
$GaSb$ 340
Ge 190
GeO 153
GeO_2 330

H 20, 40, 41, 68, 190, 197, 432
H^+ 108
H^- 107, 108, 198
H_2 44, 45, 69, 76, 102, 103, 133, 151, 155, 157, 205, 263, 432
$H_2{}^+$ 45, 133, 155
H_4 70
HBF_4 110
HBr 104, 153, 199, 206, 264, 266, 309
HCl 76, 104, 133, 153, 155, 157, 199, 206, 264, 266, 309, 327
HCl^+ 155
HCN 219
H_2CN_2 183
HD 157
HF 104, 153, 154, 199, 206, 276
HI 104, 153, 154, 157, 199, 206, 264, 266, 309
HIO_3 273
HN_3 116
HNO_3 188, 258, 259

H_2O 72, 73, 74, 76, 111, 199, 206, 207, 265, 266, 361
H_2O_2 201
H_3O^+ 103, 111, 199
H_3PO_2 124
H_3PO_3 124
H_3PO_4 124, 125
H_2S 73, 74, 122, 199, 206, 210, 265
H_2S_2 256
H_2Se 73, 74
He 20, 40, 68, 197
He_2 134
He_2^+ 134, 142
HeH 68
Hg 37, 38, 40
Hg_2 151
HgBr 261
$HgBr_2$ 261
$Hg(CH_3)_2$ 346
HgCl 261
$HgCl_2$ 261
$Hg(CN)_2$ 369
HgH 153
$HgHal_2$ 211
HgI 261
HgI_2 261
HgS 340
HgSe 340
HgTe 340
Hf 30

I 40, 41, 190, 197
I^- 198, 199
I_2 100, 150, 151, 205
IBr 100, 102
ICl 100
ICl_4^- 381
IO_4^- 334
IO_6 334
In 37
InCl 328
$InCl_3$ 327, 328
InH 153
InO 153
$Ir(CO)_4H$ 365
IrO_2 330

K 37, 38, 190, 197, 303
K^+ 198
K_2 69, 100, 151
$K_2B_2H_6$ 405
$K_2B_4H_8$ 405
$K_3B_3O_6$ 338, 339
KBr 100, 102, 103, 318, 320
KCl 102, 103, 318, 320, 321, 327
$KCo(CO)_4$ 366
$K_3CO(CN)_6$ 378
$K_4Co(CN)_6$ 378
K_2CrO_4 356
$K_3Cr(CN)_6$ 375, 376
$K_4Cr(CN)_6$ 376
KF 318
$K_3Fe(CN)_6$ 370, 373, 376, 382
$K_4Fe(CN)_6$ 343, 370–373, 376
$K_2Fe(CO)_4$ 366
KH 153, 329
KHF_2 273
KI 102, 103, 318, 320
$KICl_4$ 381
$KMg_3(OH)_2(AlSi_3O_{10})$ 338
$KMn(CN)_3$ 373
$K_3Mn(CN)_6$ 373, 375
$K_4Mn(CN)_6$ 373, 374
$K_5Mn(CN)_6$ 374
$KMnO_4$ 350, 355, 356
K_2MnO_4 355, 356
$K_3Mn(CN)_8$ 377
$K_4Mo(CN)_8$ 369, 376
$K_2NaCo(NO_2)_6$ 368
$K_2Ni(CN)_4$ 378
$K_4Ni(CN)_4$ 379
KO_2 156
K_2O 330
$K(OSO_3N)$ 379
K_2PtCl_4 381
K_2PtCl_6 381
$K_2S_3O_8$ 73
$K_4W(CN)_8$ 376
Kr 27, 197, 199, 309

La 27
LaO 153
Li 22, 23, 37, 40, 41, 190, 197
Li^+ 105, 198
Li_2 69, 76, 134, 151
$LiBH_4$ 406
LiBr 318, 320
LiCl 102, 318, 322, 327
LiD 157
LiF 100, 318, 327
LiH 152, 153, 157, 329
LiI 318, 320
Li_2O 330
LiOH 333

Mg 23, 25, 37, 40, 303
Mg^{2+} 105, 198
Mg_2 152
$MgCl_2$ 327, 329
MgF_2 327
MgH 153
MgO 153, 330, 339
$Mg(OH)_2$ 333
$Mg_3(OH)_2(Si_4O_{10})$ 338
MgS 339
Mg_2SiO_4 336
MgTl 340
Mn 27
$MnCl_2$ 329, 356, 374
$MnCl_3$ 356
$MnCl_4$ 358
$Mn(NH_3)_6Br_2$ 386
MnO 330
MnO_2 330
MnO_4^- 334
$Mn(OH)_2$ 333

$MnSO_4$ 386
$MoCl_4$ 355
$MoCl_5$ 355, 357
$[Mo(CN)_8]^{3-}$ 377
$Mo(CO)_6$ 359
MoF_5 356
MoF_6 355, 356, 357
MoO_2 330
MoO_4^{2-} 334

$Ni(CO)_4$ 182, 359–361, 365
NiH 153
$[Ni(NH_3)_4]SO_4$ 379
NiO 330
$Ni(OH)_2$ 333
Ni_5Zn_{21} 306
Np^{237} 31
Np^{238} 31
Np^{239} 31

N 22, 23, 40, 190
N^- 107
N_2 44, 76, 102, 103, 134, 136, 137, 151, 155, 156, 162, 205, 296, 309
N_2^+ 137, 155, 156
NF_3 210, 327
NH 149, 153, 154
NH_2OH 168
NH_3 72–74, 76, 114, 115, 199, 206–209, 265, 266, 361, 383
NH_4^+ 114, 115, 199
NH_4Br 326
NH_4Cl 319, 326
NH_4F 273
$(NH_4)_3FeF_6$ 370, 382
NH_4HF_2 273
NH_4I 326
NH_4N_3 273
N_2H_4 257
NO 44, 137, 138, 142, 153, 155, 168, 224, 258, 309
NO^+ 155, 156
NO_2 258
NO_2^- 334
NO_3 258, 259
NO_3^- 116, 189, 259, 334
N_2O 257, 258
N_2O_2 257, 258
N_2O_3 258
N_2O_4 258
N_2O_5 211, 258, 259
NOCl 44
Na 25, 37, 40, 190, 303
Na^+ 105, 198, 388
Na_2 69, 100, 102, 151, 189
$NaAlSi_2O_6$ 338
$NaAlSi_3O_8$ 338
NaBr 102, 318, 320
NaCl 100, 102, 150, 314, 315, 318, 320, 327
NaD 157
NaF 44, 318, 327
NaH 153, 157, 329
$NaHCO_3$ 273
$NaHF_2$ 273
NaI 102, 318, 320, 322
NaK 100, 102
Na_2O 330
$Na_2SO_4 10H_2O$ 388
NbO_2 330
Ne 22, 23, 40, 197, 199, 309
Ne_2 135
Ni 27
$NiCl_2$ 329, 356
$[Ni(CN)_4]^{2-}$ 378

O 22, 23, 40, 190
O^- 107
O^{2-} 105, 198, 199
O_2 44, 135, 138, 142, 151, 153, 155, 156, 205, 256, 296, 309
O_2^+ 137, 155, 156
O_3 188, 210
O_4 256
OD 157
OF_2 73, 327
OH 153, 154, 157
OH^- 199
$OsCl_8$ 357
$Os(CO)_4H_2$ 365
$Os(CO)_5$ 359
$Os_2(CO)_9$ 359
OsF_8 356, 357
OsO_2 330
OsO_4 356

P 25, 40, 73, 190, 256
P_2 151, 340
P_4 257, 300
PBr_3 73, 74, 209
$P(CH_3)_3$ 73
PCl_3 73, 74, 261
PCl_5 261
PF_3 73, 74, 327
$PFCl_2$ 73
PH 153
PH_3 73, 74, 199, 209
PH_3AlHal_3 272
PH_3CuHal 272
PI_3 73, 74
PN 155
PO 153
PO_4^{3-} 124, 334
P_4O_6 332
P_4O_{10} 332
$P_4O_6S_4$ 332
Pb_2 151
$PbCl_2$ 328
$PbCl_4$ 328
PbH 153
PbI_2 329
PbO 153, 330, 332
PbO_2 330
PbS 340
PbSe 340
PbTe 340
Pd 27
PdO 330, 332
$PtAs_2$ 340

$Pt(CH_3)_3Cl$ 381
$PtCl_2$ 353
$PtCl_4$ 356, 381
$[PtCl_4]^{2-}$ 381
$[PtCl_6]^{2-}$ 381
PtO 330, 332
PtP_2 340
$PtSb_2$ 340
Pt_5Zn_{21} 306
Pu^{238}_{94} 31
Pu^{241} 31
Pu^{239} 36

Rb 37, 38, 303
Rb^+ 198
Rb_2 69, 151
$RbBr$ 102, 103, 318, 320
$RbCl$ 102, 318, 320, 327
RbF 318
RbH 153, 329
RbI 102, 318, 320, 323
$Re_2(CO)_{10}$ 359
ReO_4^- 334
$[Rh(CO)_3]_n$ 359
$Rh_2(CO)_8$ 359
$[Ru(CO)_4]_n$ 359
$Ru(CO)_5$ 359
RuO_2 330
$Ru_2(CO)_9$ 359

S 25, 40, 190, 256
S^{2-} 107, 198
S_2 151, 340
S_8 73, 300
SCl_2 73
S_2Cl_2 210, 260
SF_6 124
SH^- 199
SN 155
$S_4N_5H_7O_8$ 126
SO 153
SO_2 122, 200, 210, 260
SO_3 123, 200, 210, 260
SO_3^{2-} 122, 334
SO_4^- 387, 388
SO_4^{2-} 124, 334
$SOCl_2$ 123, 260
SO_2Cl_2 124, 260
$S_2O_5Cl_2$ 260
$SO_2(NH_2)_2$ 126
$SO_2(NHAg)_2$ 126
Sb 73, 190
Sb_2 151
$SbBr_3$ 73, 209
$SbCl_3$ 73
SbI_3 73
SbN 155
SbO 153
Sb_2O_3 331, 332
Sb_4O_6 331, 332
SbS 340
ScO 153
Se 73, 190, 256
Se^{2-} 198
Se_2 151
Se_2Cl_2 210
SeO 153
SeO_4^{2-} 334
Si 25, 40, 190
$Si(CH_3)_4$ 288, 289
$SiCl_4$ 211
SiF_4 327
SiH 153
SiH_4 199, 211
Si_2H_6 288, 289
$SiHBr_3$ 75
$SiHCl_3$ 75, 216
SiH_2Cl_2 216
SiH_3Cl 216
SiN 155
SiO 153, 154, 330
SiO_2 200, 314, 315, 330, 335, 336, 339, 341
$(SiO_3)^{2-}$ 337
$(SiO_4)^{4-}$ 334, 337
$(Si_2O_7)^{6-}$ 337
$(Si_3O_9)^{6-}$ 337
$(Si_4O_{12})^{8-}$ 337
$(Si_6O_{18})^{12-}$ 337
SiS_2 341
Sn 190
$SnBr_4$ 179
$SnBrCl_3$ 179
$SnBr_2Cl_2$ 179
$SnBr_3Cl$ 179
$SnCl_2$ 328
$SnCl_4$ 179, 198, 328
$SnCl_4 \cdot (CH_3)_2O$ 272
$SnCl_4 \cdot 2(CH_3)_2CO$ 270
$SnCl_4 \cdot (C_2H_5)_2O$ 270
$SnCl_4 \cdot 2C_6H_5CHO$ 270
$SnCl_4 \cdot C_6H_5CN$ 270
$SnCl_4 \cdot 2C_6H_5COCH_3$ 270
SnH 153
SnO 153, 330, 332
SnO_2 330
SnS_4^{4-} 334
Sr 23, 37, 38
Sr_2 152
Sr^{2+} 198
$SrCl$ 328
$SrCl_2$ 327, 328
SrH 153
SrO 153, 330
SrS 339

Te 73, 190
Te^{2-} 198
Te_2 151
TeO 153
TeO_2 330
TiO 153
TiO_2 313, 315, 330
Ti_2O_3 331
$TiCl_4 \cdot C_2H_5CN$ 270
$TiCl_4 \cdot C_6H_5CN$ 270
Tl 37
$TlBr$ 328
$TlCl$ 328

$TlCl_3$ 327, 328
TlH 153
TlI 328

U^{237} 31
U^{238} 31, 36
U^{239} 31
UO_3 16
U_2O_3 16

V 26
VO 153
VO_2 330
V_2O_3 331
VS_4^{3-} 334

WBr_5 355
WCl_6 355, 357
$W(CO)_6$ 359
WF_6 357
WI_4 355
WO_2 330
WO_4^{2-} 334

Xe 197, 199

YO 153

Zn 37, 38
$ZnCl_2$ 329
$Zn(CN)_2$ 369
ZnH 153
ZnO 312, 330
$Zn(OH)_2$ 333
ZnS 315, 340
ZnSe 340
ZnTe 340
ZrO 153